FRESH-WATER BIOLOGY

BY

HENRY BALDWIN WARD

Emeritus Professor of Zoology in the University of Illinois, Special
Investigator for the United States Bureau of Fisheries, Etc.

AND

The Late GEORGE CHANDLER WHIPPLE

Formerly Professor of Sanitary Engineering in Harvard University and
the Massachusetts Institute of Technology

WITH THE COLLABORATION OF A STAFF
OF SPECIALISTS

NEW YORK
JOHN WILEY & SONS, Inc.
London: CHAPMAN & HALL, Limited

Printed in U. S. A.

Stanhope Press

F. H. GILSON COMPANY
BOSTON, U.S.A.

3-36

COLLABORATORS

EDWARD ASAHEL BIRGE, Dean of the College of Letters and Science in the University of Wisconsin

NATHAN AUGUSTUS COBB, United States Department of Agriculture

WESLEY ROSWELL COE, Professor of Biology in the Sheffield Scientific School of Yale University

HERBERT WILLIAM CONN, Late Professor of Biology, Wesleyan University

CHARLES BENEDICT DAVENPORT, Director of the Station for Experimental Evolution, Cold Spring Harbor, Long Island, N. Y.

CHARLES HOWARD EDMONDSON, Assistant Professor of Zoology in the University of Oregon

CARL H. EIGENMANN, Professor of Zoology in Indiana University

HERBERT SPENCER JENNINGS, Professor of Zoology in Johns Hopkins University

EDWIN OAKES JORDAN, Professor of Bacteriology in the University of Chicago

CHARLES DWIGHT MARSH, United States Department of Agriculture

JOHN PERCY MOORE, Professor of Zoology in the University of Pennsylvania

JAMES GEORGE NEEDHAM, Professor of Limnology in Cornell University

EDGAR WILLIAM OLIVE, Curator of the Brooklyn Botanic Garden

ARNOLD EDWARD ORTMANN, Curator of Invertebrate Zoology in the Carnegie Museum, Pittsburgh

ARTHUR SPERRY PEARSE, Associate Professor of Zoology in the University of Wisconsin

RAYMOND HAINES POND, Late Professor of Botany in the Texas Agricultural College

EDWARD POTTS, Late of Media, Pa.

JACOB ELLSWORTH REIGHARD, Professor of Zoology in the University of Michigan

RICHARD WORTHY SHARPE, Instructor in Biology in the Dewitt Clinton High School, New York City

VICTOR ERNEST SHELFORD, Assistant Professor of Zoology in the University of Illinois

FRANK SMITH, Professor of Zoology in the University of Illinois

JULIA WARNER SNOW, Associate Professor of Botany in Smith College

CAROLINE EFFIE STRINGER, Head of the Department of Biology in the Omaha High School

BRYANT WALKER, Detroit, Mich.

ROBERT HENRY WOLCOTT, Professor of Zoology in the University of Nebraska.

PREFACE

For the ordinary student and teacher on this continent fresh-water life has a significance heretofore greatly underestimated. In most parts of the country it lies at one's very door, readily accessible, and is indeed the only type of aquatic existence which can be studied living and at work. This fact gives to fresh-water life, once the student has been introduced into its domain, an appealing interest that fetters his attention and stimulates his desire to know something more of it. Among the most remarkable of early works that followed hard upon the first use of the microscope are some great classics which represent work in this very field.

Various European countries possess elaborate monographs on fresh-water organisms as a whole and on single groups, but no attempt has been made heretofore to deal with North American fresh-water life in its entirety, and few treatises have essayed to cover completely any group of fresh-water organisms. American workers in general have accordingly avoided this field and the few who have attempted to engage in its study have found their problems very difficult to solve.

The preparation of the present work was undertaken many years ago with the purpose of stimulating the study of the material so easily obtainable and of aiding workers of all grades to acquire some definite and precise knowledge of the organisms met in such study. Each chapter has been handled by a specialist on the group and the results achieved by this method have a significance that could not have been attained in any other way. Conditions entirely unavoidable led to the completion of the different parts of the work at somewhat different dates. It is believed that this will not, in fact, impair the value of the work as a whole and will find an excuse in the magnitude of the task. Individual chapters represent a survey of the group treated that is complete

v

for this continent up to the time at which the chapter was closed.

The first few chapters are devoted to a discussion of general biological factors. Evident space limits prevented extended discussion of many most interesting biological topics, which are at best only outlined here. The exact citation of sources at the close of these chapters will aid the reader to pursue such topics further if desired. Not all discussions on general questions have been confined to the introductory chapters. The chapter on Rotifera, by Jennings, presents an admirable description of life processes, which, altho written specifically for that group, applies with appropriate modifications to all groups of many-celled organisms. In the chapter on Copepoda, Marsh has treated with some detail the general question of distribution as illustrated by this group; yet the very factors which he shows to be operative in it are those that lie at the basis of the distribution of most if not all other groups. The discussion of the aquatic vertebrates by Eigenmann is purely biological and the systematic outline is omitted entirely, since that of itself would demand an entire book for its adequate presentation. The same is true of the chapter on Bacteria, by Jordan, and of that on the higher aquatic plants which are treated by Pond in the physiological (chemico-physical) aspect primarily.

Apart from those just mentioned all chapters conform to the same general plan. Each is devoted to a single group of organisms and opens with a general account of the occurrence and history of the group. The description of the anatomy of the forms treated is very brief and deals chiefly with such features as are of special value in the key. Similarly the life history is given in condensed form. More attention is devoted to the biological relations which at this point are discussed with reference to the entire group, whereas individual features are left for later record under individual species except as they are needed for illustrations of general questions. Care has been exercised to include descriptions of special methods for collecting, preserving, and studying the organisms of each particular group.

Special details both biological and morphological regarding genera and species are included under a synoptic key which comes at the close of each chapter except as noted above; in some cases it is carried to species but in others only to genera. The form utilized for the keys has been in constant use for many years at the University of Illinois, having been applied to many aquatic types by Professor S. A. Forbes and his associates. The introductory number of each key line is followed by an alternative number printed in parentheses and on reaching a decision that this line is not acceptable, the student proceeds at once to the line introduced by the alternative number; in case a given alternative is accepted the further course of the inquiry is indicated by a number at the close of the line.

In order to achieve maximum ease in use and perspicacity in grasping the facts presented, all the information on a given form, viz., the illustration, the description, and the biological features with the frequence, range, and other special data, are included between the key line which introduces the name and the key line next following. The total information on a single type forms thus a solid panel and appeals promptly and as a whole to the eye and mind of the student. Each chapter closes with a brief list of the most essential references to the topic. No textbooks are cited and only such works are noted as may be considered indispensable for present-day study of North American forms. The student is cautioned not to regard any such list as in any sense a bibliography of the subject.

To encompass such a mass of material within the limits of a single volume, even tho it be generous in size, has necessitated brevity of treatment at every point. Technical terms are defined or discussed only once and no glossary is introduced. The index includes important terms and all of the scientific names used in the keys so that the reader can find every item promptly.

A serious effort was made to attain uniformity in the use of names thruout the entire work but the worker will find that this end was not fully achieved. The most conspicuous failure in this particular obtains in the citation of host names for various parasitic species. In all such cases that name is employed which was used by the authority from which the record is cited. It was felt that in the absence of monographic revisions of the species of parasites noted any other method would have been indefensible in a brief treatise.

Abundant use has been made of figures to illustrate the forms described. Most of the illustrations are new and many of them drawn by the author of the chapter especially for this work.

In chapter II certain figures and tables are taken with modifications from Shelford's Animal Communities in Temperate America by courtesy of the Geographic Society of Chicago and the University of Chicago Press.

It would be impossible to acknowledge all of the aid which has been extended during the progress of the work. Valuable suggestions from many sources have been freely extended us and as freely utilized.

To all of our colleagues who, in spite of multitudinous difficulties and seemingly interminable delays, have worked so generously to perfect their individual chapters the sincerest thanks of the editors are due. Especial mention should be made of the numerous helpful suggestions and criticisms given outside their own chapters during the preparation of the work by Professors E. A. Birge and Frank Smith. Grateful acknowledgement is also due E. C. Faust and H. G. May for aid in reading and checking proof.

Finally, it is a pleasure as well as a duty to express our appreciation of the work of the publishers. Their forbearance and continued kindly assistance during the long and difficult period of preparation has made possible the completion of the work and its presentation to the scientific worker in attractive form.

CONTENTS

ix

CHAPTER I

INTRODUCTION

By HENRY B. WARD

Professor of Zoology in the University of Illinois

ON the surface of the globe, water and life are intimately associated. As water grows scantier life becomes more restricted until with the total failure of water life also disappears. In regions where water is very scarce the few organisms that exist have learned to store water or to discharge vital functions with a minimum supply and thus to meet the natural defects of the situation.

The hydrosphere, or the total water mass on the globe, forms the subject of study for hydrography which is readily subdivided into (1) oceanography, that deals with the vast continuous mass of salt water in the ocean, and (2) limnology, which treats of the various fresh-water units. The term limnology is sometimes restricted in its application to the more stable bodies such as lakes and ponds, in which case rheology is used to cover various types of flowing waters. All fresh water is distributed over the surface of the land and variably grouped into separate series of systems connected with each other only through the ocean to which each system is joined. The rare desert systems, such as terminate in the Carson Sink or the Dead Sea, are exceptional in having no present connection with the ocean.

Fresh water is deposited on the land in the form chiefly of rain or snow, and tends ultimately to reach the sea, though first and last a considerable part is taken up by evaporation and goes back directly into the atmosphere. Much of the precipitation soaks into the ground to reappear elsewhere in springs or by seepage to feed ponds and streams. Activity or rate of movement distinguishes two classes of water bodies: the flowing water of streams and the temporarily quiet water of lakes. The latter almost always form parts of stream systems and have thereby an intimate connection with the ocean that is of fundamental importance in determining the origin of fresh-water organisms.

The more or less actively flowing waters appear in the form of springs or rivulets, then increase and unite to make brooks, creeks, and rivers. The transition is ordinarily gradual and size has only a secondary influence on the biological character of the stream. The rate of flow, and the physical and chemical character of the soil over and through which water drains into a stream and by which its banks and beds are formed are the chief factors in determining its life.

From the tiniest rivulet to the mightiest river one may find every possible intermediate stage, and between the swiftest mountain torrent and the most sluggish lowland stream there exists every intermediate gradation. Biologically considered, the torrent imposes on the development of life within its waters evident mechanical limitations which are not present in the slow-flowing streams. Ordinarily the biological wealth of a stream varies inversely with its rate of flow, and anything which stops or checks the flow makes conditions more favorable for the development of life. Flowing waters are thinly inhabited and also present considerable difficulties to the student; hence they are relatively unexplored territory.

Waters of the static type, characterized by lack of flow, form an equally continuous series from the great lakes or inland seas progressing by insensible gradations through lake, pond, and pool to the morass or swamp. In the first group size permits more wind action; it also provides greater stability in level as well as in thermal and chemical conditions. Possessing only limited communication with the ocean these bodies of water constitute biological units of great definiteness. The lake is a microcosm; a minute replica of the ocean, it responds more quickly to changes in its environment, is simpler to grasp and easier to study. Yet it is withal the most complicated of inland environments (Shelford).

The distinction between water bodies of different size is often indefinite. Puddle, pond, and lake form in fact a continuous series. Yet in a strict sense lakes are characterized by a central region deep enough to exceed the limits of growth of the flora in the shore zone. Ponds are shallow lakes, usually insignificant in area, yet still of relative permanence. They constitute distinct.

units of environment. These more nearly stable units, the lakes and ponds, are often rich in life. They are exceptionally favorable for study and have been extensively investigated both in Europe and in this country.

The temporary water body, a puddle or pool, whatever its area, affords only conditions for transient existence that are sometimes irregular in their recurrence and sometimes present themselves with considerable regularity. They are fitted for organisms that reproduce very rapidly during the favorable season and also have special means of tiding the species over the unfavorable period. Purely temporary water bodies, such as pools that form in hollows after a heavy rain or in a wet season, develop little if any life. Such places on poor soil are most barren of all; the aquatic life increases with the fertility of the soil, the age of the water body, and the consequent accumulation of organic debris. Residual ponds, water bodies in which the drying out is more gradual and often incomplete and in which a central area may be protected from complete desiccation by vegetation or proximity to the general water level, afford conditions at the opposite extreme. The wide stretches of lowland subject to periodic overflow from great inland rivers like the Illinois, Missouri, and Danube in certain regions, develop a rich flora and fauna which equals or exceeds·in abundance that found under other circumstances (Antipa, Forbes). Similarly among ponds adjacent to a lake basin the permanent are poorer than those which dry out for a time (Shelford).

The smaller water body presents nearly uniform conditions throughout and therewith also a single series of inhabiting organisms. The entire area falls within the shore or shallow water zone which is limited to such parts as support fixed plants. In this general region are readily distinguished two zones, (a) that of the emergent vegetation where the larger plants reach conspicuously above the water level and constitute the dominant feature to the eye, and (2) that of submerged vegetation in which the plants rarely project at all above the surface and in consequence the water itself dominates the view. Both of these regions may be subdivided on the basis of the particular form of vegetation which is common in a given portion. In a swamp these regions are often the only ones that are present. But in a pond one can usually determine the existence of a third zone in which the fixed vegetation is lacking.

With increase of the water body in size or more especially in depth, new conditions are presented. The littoral region passes over insensibly into a deeper bottom region with its own biological series and to a free open-water area known as the limnetic region. The corresponding region in the ocean is designated the pelagic and this term is also used by some for the fresh-water area. The plants and animals in this region are characteristic; they constitute what is called the plankton, the floating life of the water. Such organisms remain suspended in water during their entire existence; they live and die "on the wing." In the larger lakes the shore zone loses in prominence whereas the pelagic and bottom regions gain in distinctness and relative importance.

Lakes vary widely in character and abundance in different regions. They are infrequent in areas that are physiographically old and most abundant in glaciated territory, where they occur in eroded rock basins, in partially filled rock valleys, in hollows over the moraine, and more rarely at the margin of the ice sheet. Sometimes lakes are found in old volcanic craters, in the depressions of a lava-covered area, or behind a lava flow dam. They occur regularly in streams as mere expansions in the course or are formed by the inflowing delta of a lateral tributary or when the stream breaks through a narrow neck and leaves an ox bow or cut-off lake at the side. One finds them often on low coastal plains some distance from the shore, more commonly close to the sea and even on the same level with it. Old lakes without an outlet become strongly alkaline or saline and develop aquatic life of a type peculiar to each. Most lakes, however, are fresh and shelter organisms of the same general type.

Taken together lakes compose one-half the fresh water on the surface of the globe. They present an infinite variety of physical features in rocky, sandy, swampy margins, in steep and shallow shores, in regular and broken contours with no islands or many, with shallow water or depths that carry the bottom far below the level of the sea.

They vary in the chemical character of the soil in the lake basin as well as in their banks and bed, in the degree of exposure to wind and sunshine, in the relative inflow and outflow in ratio to their volume, in their altitude as well as in geographic location. All of these and many other factors modify and control the types of living things and their abundance in the waters. Lake, pond, and swamp are successive stages in change from the water-filled hollow to the terrestrial plain that ultimately occupies the same location. Along the margin of the lake, especially at the points where tributary streams empty into it, the inflowing water brings detritus of all sorts that builds out the shore and forms a shelf on which the littoral vegetation gains a foothold. As the lake grows old this region increases at the expense of the pelagic and bottom areas, until the latter disappears and the former persists only in reduced amount. Finally the entire area is conquered by deposits of silt and growth of vegetation. The swamp comes and is made over into dry land traversed in winding channels by the stream system that is responsible for these changes. In other cases the outflowing stream cuts down the level and ultimately drains the lake.

Lakes are thus in a geologic sense only temporary features of the river system to which they belong. Similar influences direct the evolution of the stream from the violent instability of its youth to the sluggish stability of its age. During this process of evolution the life in the waters undergoes parallel changes. At first the fauna is scanty but increases in numbers and variety as new habitats are created. Unstable and intermittent conditions indicate paucity of life; but when the aquatic environment becomes more permanent organisms more easily invade the territory successfully and its life grows increasingly complex as time goes on.

Lakes influence noticeably the life of a stream system in that they act as filters or settling basins for inflowing waters and also regulate the volume of the discharge; thus the outflowing stream is free from sediment and approaches constancy in level. This greater permanence militates against the development of certain types of life but favors others. The continued dilution of the stream by the addition of water free from life and the removal of such organisms as are produced at a given point by the constant flow of the water make the river plankton scanty in amount, but many fresh-water lakes produce an immense number of plankton organisms. These have been much studied in recent years and about them alike in ocean and fresh water has grown up a new study, Plank-tology, the Planktonkunde of the Germans.

Among the forms of the open water are some, primarily the fishes, which manifest individual power of movement adequate to make them independent of water movements, storms, and distances. They can thus determine their own distribution in an active fashion and stand in marked contrast with the plankton, for the latter is unable to regulate effectively its location, and is dependent upon the winds and waves for its dispersal. Typical plankton organisms, in fresh water known together as the limnoplankton, are found only in water bodies of some size, whereas in small lakes or ponds the circumscribed open-water area contains life which consists of migrants from shore and shallow water regions. Whereas on the land higher forms, especially domestic animals, depend on the higher fixed plants for food, in the water the higher types depend upon the smaller floating plant and animal organisms which transform inorganic materials and organic debris into available food substances.

The floating organisms which taken together constitute the plankton are grouped into two purely artificial classes according to methods used in collecting. The constant use of fine nets (cf. p. 74) for collecting plankton organisms led to a conception of this type of life that unconsciously assigned a minimum limit in size. Thus the organisms taken in the plankton net are all that the older authors included under the term plankton, an assemblage which should be termed more correctly the net plankton. It is well known through the work of many investigators during recent years and includes a great variety of Crustacea and Rotifera with many Protozoa and Protophyta, and less regularly some other types.

Within very recent times there has been obtained by more precise methods of collecting what has been termed by Lohmann the nannoplankton (dwarf plankton) with a size limit he set arbitrarily at 25μ. It consists of the most minute organisms only, those that (Fig. 1) pass through the meshes of the finest silk gauze, Swiss bolting cloth No. 25,* having meshes that measure 0.04 to 0.05 mm. square. The nannoplankton is composed chiefly of flagellates and algæ; although bacteria are constantly present they apparently form but a minor constituent in bulk and weight. The number and variety of these organisms is truly astonishing even in the clear waters of Alpine lakes where according to Ruttner they stand to the organisms of the net plankton numerically in the ratio of 160 : 3 and at least two-thirds of them are still undescribed and difficult to include in known genera. The maximum number of nannoplanktonts thus far recorded is from Lake Mendota, Wis., where Cyclotella has been found to the number of over 30,000,000 per liter of water.

FIG. 1. A piece of bolting cloth No. 20 with plankton organisms drawn between the meshes to show relative size. Above, *Rhizosolenia alata.* Upper row, left mesh: *Gymnodinium*, beneath *Amphidinium rotundatum* and *Exuviaella baltica*, right *Pouchetia parva*; middle mesh: *Prorocentrum micans* and *Rhynchomonas marina*; right mesh: *Nitschia sigmatella, Achradina pulchra, Halteria rubra, Nitschia closterium.* Middle row, left mesh: *Tintinnopsis nana, Tintinnus steenstrupi, Oxyrrhis phaeocysticola*; middle mesh: chain of small *Chaetoceras* species, above it on the left *Thalassiosira nana* and *saturni*, on the right *Carteria*; right mesh: chain of large *Chaetoceras* species (*Chaet. didymum*), *Tintinnopsis beroidea.* Lower row, left mesh: *Rhodomonas baltica, Distephanus speculum*; middle mesh: *Strombidium caudatum* (?), *Meringosphaera mediterranea, Amoeba*; right mesh: *Coccolithophora wallichi*, beneath on the left *Pontosphaera huxleyi*, on the right *Coccolithophora leptopora*, above on the right Chrysomonadine without shell, at the very bottom *Rhabdosphaera claviger.* × 110. (After Lohmann.)

Ruttner also calculates the volume of the nannoplankton in the Lunzer lakes as three times that of net plankton. According to Birge and Juday the weight of its dry organic matter varies in three Wisconsin lakes from slightly less (rarely) to 15 or 20 times more than that of the net plankton and is ordinarily 5 to 6 times as great. This amount is unquestionably of marked importance both scientifically and practically, and the character of the organisms indicates even more clearly their fundamental importance in the problems of aquatic biology.

Plankton organisms are characterized by transparency, delicate colors, and above all by their power of floating due to buoyancy and

* New No. 25 is identical with No. 20 of older authors (Lohmann).

form resistance in contrast with related organisms. The buoyancy is achieved by oil droplets and gas bubbles formed in the cells whereas heavy cell walls and skeletal structures are wanting. Flotation-apparatus in the shape of lateral wings, bristles, spines, or a body form like a parachute, a spiral thread, or a gelatinous cover — provides against rapid sinking. Ostwald has determined that the rate of sinking is equal to the excess weight of the organism above that of an equal water volume divided by the product of the form resistance and the viscosity of the fluid.

Generally speaking great depth in a water body and large inflow in proportion to volume are unfavorable to the abundant development of the plankton organisms whereas minimal depth and scanty inflow favor the production of plankton.

When water is first deposited on the earth it is almost absolutely pure, containing only the minute amount of materials which it has leached out of the atmosphere. From the ground over which it flows or the soil through which it percolates come substances organic or inorganic, in solution and suspension, here of one type and there of another, that serve to enrich it and make of it an environment capable of supporting life. "The aquatic population of a lake or stream is thus sustained by the wastes of the land, materials which would otherwise be carried down practically unaltered to the sea; and rivers and lakes may be looked upon as a huge apparatus for the arrest, appropriation, digestion, and assimilation of certain raw materials about to pass from our control" (Forbes).

For the determination of physical data on the character of bodies of water, methods and apparatus of considerable complexity have been devised, largely by students of oceanography, and adapted later to fresh-water conditions. By such means the investigator is enabled to measure in a comparative way, and sometimes in absolute fashion, and to record environmental conditions such as the depth, temperature, turbidity, and other physical features of the water body. Some of these determinations are simple and require only limited apparatus; others are complex and beyond the powers of the ordinary student of aquatic biology. The application of such data to biologic problems is discussed in part in the following chapter. An adequate consideration of methods and apparatus demands more space than is available here and for further information the student is referred to manuals dealing with that phase of aquatic investigation. General methods of collecting and photographing aquatic organisms form the subject of a separate chapter while such methods as are applicable to the study of each special group are discussed in the chapter on that group.

The environment of water organisms as of all others is a complex of many elements. The physical factors are determined by the materials held in suspension or in solution in the water, by its temperature, depth, movement, illumination, shore and bottom. Chemical factors are found in the acidity or alkalinity of the water and in the gases, salts, and other materials in it. The organisms themselves make the biological environment. Living or dead, as food or feeder, parasite or host, friend, enemy, or neutral, each living thing contributes to the sum total of the biological complex by which each living unit is surrounded. It is the problem of science to unravel this tangle and to determine the relation of each constituent, living or non-living, to the others. The conditions of existence to which organisms are subject in different aquatic environments and the influence which these environments exert on organisms in general are discussed in the following chapter. In subsequent chapters an attempt has been made to present these relations as illustrated by each group of organisms. To become thoroughly acquainted with a single group involves a knowledge of the relations its members bear to every other organism in the community.

No climate is too rigorous for fresh-water life. It exists in fresh-water lakes at 77° N. L., hardly if ever free from ice, often only slightly melted and with a maximum temperature of less than 2° C. at the bottom. The Shackleton expedition described an extensive microfauna at 77° 30′ S. L. from Antarctic lakes that are frozen solid for many months, often for several years. At the other extreme of temperature evidence is less complete but Cypris is recorded from hot springs at 50° C., ciliates and rotifers from waters at 65° C., Oscillaria and nostocs from places that are recorded at 70° to 93° C.

The aquatic life of a permanent fresh-water body is variable within certain limits of time and space. Each season witnesses the coming and going of certain types which are active only in definite periods and by resting spores, gemmules, or eggs bridge over the intervening time. This known seasonal succession is so definite that it gives the life of fresh water a changing character as clear if not as conspicuous to the eye as that on land. One may readily confuse with seasonal succession (1) the numerical variation of a species or group due to favorable or unfavorable conditions, and (2) the migrations which alter vertically or horizontally through various water levels the distribution of a given organism.

One can demonstrate also a stratification of aquatic organisms of at least two types: vertical, as when different species are found to occur within definite limits of depth, and horizontal, as when species are confined to particular regions of streams or lakes. Such relations are discussed fully elsewhere.

Peculiar types of aquatic environment, such as elevated lakes, saline lakes, and underground waters, have each special types of living organisms. Some of these special environments have been made the objects of extended study which has shown the clear relation of their life to that of other fresh-water bodies of the region while demonstrating at the same time that they present a distinct character of their own (cf. Zschokke, Banta).

The life of fresh water is probably not original but derived. It came from the sea, by migration through brackish waters or swamps or up into stream systems, by the gradual freshening of marine basins cut off from the sea and converted into fresh-water bodies, by direct transport from one body of water into another through the agency of the wind, on the feet of birds or other wandering animals, and finally by invasion from the land direct. Perhaps the bottom forms came first, as conditions there were first established. Certainly the plankton forms found no opportunity for existence in the violent instability of a young stream. At present the shore forms are the most abundant and the most varied.

In some deep lakes has been found a peculiar bottom fauna, designated as the fauna relicta, which is composed of types unlike other fresh-water forms and closely related to marine animals. This fauna is often regarded as the survival from a period when connections with the ocean were more immediate, or when climatic conditions were different as during a glacial epoch.

The poverty of fresh-water life in variety and number of types in comparison with that of the sea has often been emphasized. Experimental data show it can hardly be due to lack of opportunity for marine organisms to adapt themselves to fresh water for in some geologic periods conditions have been very favorable though in others distinctly the opposite. The severity of the fresh-water climate, the obstacle of an ever outflowing current and the relative newness of fresh-water bodies are evident difficulties. Furthermore marine animals have generally free-swimming embryos, distributed by water movements and sure therefore to be eliminated gradually from the fresh-water environment even if the adults were introduced successfully. Fresh-water animals rarely have free-swimming larval stages and manifest what is known as an accelerated or abbreviated development in which the young on emerging from the egg is at a well-advanced stage.

Man has been a powerful agent in modifying fresh-water life. By hunting and fishing he has exterminated many forms directly. Through modifications of streams or shore for commercial purposes he has indirectly eliminated many more and finally by polluting the waters with sewage and waste he has rendered extensive water areas almost devoid of aquatic life except bacteria and even incapable of supporting any other forms. Streams below great cities and in mining and manufacturing districts are aquatic deserts.

Fresh-water biology is relatively a new field of study. Its earliest records on this continent are hardly more than half a century old. Among individual investigators in this field mention should first be made of S. A. Forbes, whose pioneer work on the Great Lakes has been followed by important work on the Illinois river system. The work of Birge on Wisconsin lakes, of Reighard on Lakes Erie and St. Clair, and of Kofoid on the Illinois river, warrant also especial notice. Many others whose names and work are recorded in the following chapters have made valuable contributions to the general and special problems of fresh-water biology.

Fresh-water biological stations have aided by organized effort the conquest of the field. The activities of the Illinois State Laboratory of Natural History on the Illinois river, of the Wisconsin Geological and Natural History Survey on the lakes in that state, of the U. S. Bureau of Fisheries on the Mississippi, of Ohio State University on Lake Erie, of the University of Montana Biological Station on Flathead Lake in the Rocky Mountains, show the variety and scope of these interests. Unfortunately only the first three are active all the year through. Other universities, notably Michigan, Indiana, Iowa, Colorado, North Dakota, and Cornell, have participated in the study of fresh-water life during part of the year or for a short series of years, and much emphasis has been laid upon the lake biological station as a factor in teaching biology. Few of these enterprises have had continuous existence or permanent support. Such institutions are slowly but surely gaining ground; their future development will aid both the investigations of pure science and the application of such discoveries to the solution of practical problems. The significance for man of the problems outlined in this chapter and their bearing upon the progress of social development have been discussed in the final chapter of the book.

Save insects which moreover are primarily terrestrial forms, no type of fresh-water life has developed to the diversity and complexity attained by the same type in the ocean. Yet each type has achieved a variety well illustrated in the subsequent chapters. Only a few of those that occur in the ocean are unrepresented in fresh water and even strictly terrestrial groups like the mammals and flowering plants or aerial forms like birds have their aquatic representatives. In subsequent chapters each of these groups is discussed from the biological standpoint and in its especial relations to fresh-water life as well as with regard to its relative importance as a factor in the fresh-water flora and fauna.

The records of science contain only scanty references to the types of fresh-water life and their distribution on the North American continent, and regarding all other continents save one the records are even more fragmentary. Of Europe alone is the information adequate to outline a picture of the life in fresh water. A comparison of the records shows conspicuously the uniformity of fresh-water life on the surface of the globe, especially among plankton organisms. Many of the forms discussed on later pages are identical with those that occur in Europe and many more are closely related species. The uniformity noted is not confined to Europe and North America, but extends, within the limits of records already made, to other continents also and even to the islands of the sea. It is most striking perhaps among the lowest groups as was emphasized by Schewiakoff for Protozoa.

This uniformity is due in part at least to the ease of dispersal that the lower forms in the fresh-water fauna and flora enjoy. They uniformly have hard-shelled resting spores, gemmules, or eggs which are very resistant to adverse conditions, and are produced in enormous numbers. These structures are carried from point to point on the feet of birds and other migrating animals and are blown about in the dust until suitable conditions, *e.g.*, temperature and moisture, incite development and the beginning of a new life cycle.

Fresh-water life includes both plant and animal organisms of various types. The number of groups represented among the plants is not so great as the animals furnish. For details on individual groups the student is referred to the appropriate chapter. The following plant groups are found in fresh water:

Schizomycetes or Bacteria
Lowest type of plant life in the water; either saprophytic or parasitic in habit; found in great variety in different sorts of aquatic environment.

For a general discussion of their relations to fresh water consult Chapter IV, page 90.

Algae
Characteristic and abundant aquatic plants, nearly all free-living, found in all kinds of water bodies; represented by a great variety of genera and species.

For Cyanophyceae or Blue-Green Algae, see Chapter V, page 100.

For other classes of Algae see Chapter VI, page 115.

Higher Plants   Among these plants which are more typically land organisms, a few species of various sorts have become a part of the fresh-water flora. In this change they have undergone important modifications adapting them to an aquatic existence. No synoptic treatment of these forms has been attempted.

For general biological relations involved see Chapter VII, page 178.

Animals are represented in fresh water by many more types and varieties than are plants. A brief outline of the various animal groups indicates in general the part played by each in aquatic life and will serve to correlate the various chapters dealing with individual groups. Zoologists are not agreed as to the number and rank of the subdivisions of the animal kingdom which should be recognized; and other texts will show some variations from the system used here. The student should bear in mind that the order in the printed text does not express the relationship between higher and lower groups and no arrangement in a linear series can show that relationship. The phyla are indicated by full-faced type.

Protozoa or Single-celled Animals   Characteristic water-living forms with numerous parasitic types; represented in fresh water by many species frequently found in great abundance; in all regions and in all types of water bodies. The following four sub-phyla are usually recognized.

SARCODINA   The amoeboid Protozoa furnish both free-living and parasitic species.

For the former see Chapter VIII, page 210.

MASTIGOPHORA   Flagellate Protozoa include both free-living and parasitic species; forms of the first type are treated in Chapter IX, page 238.

INFUSORIA   Ciliate Protozoa include both free and parasitic species.

For the former see Chapter IX, page 271.

SPOROZOA   Exclusively parasitic forms; certain types are abundant in fresh-water animals everywhere. North American forms almost unknown. Group not treated in this book.

Porifera or Sponges	Preëminently marine; fresh-water bodies shelter a considerable number of characteristic siliceous forms all embraced in a single family, Spongillidae.

These are described in Chapter X, page 301.

Coelenterata	A group manifesting great variety and abundance in the sea, represented in fresh water by a very few widely scattered types, both polyps and medusae, all belonging to one class, the Hydrozoa; other classes confined to the sea.

For Hydrozoa see Chapter XI, page 316.

Echinodermata	Includes crinoids, brittle-stars, starfish, sea-urchins, and sea-cucumbers; not represented in fresh water by a single known species.
Platyhelminthes or Flatworms	Four classes are recognized, all of which furnish important representatives to the fresh-water fauna.
Turbellaria or Free-living Flatworms	Common in salt and fresh waters; species found in the latter generally insignificant in size. A few are terrestrial in moist environments.

See Chapter XII, page 323.

Trematoda or Flukes	All species parasitic; many in or on fresh-water animals; with developmental stages, embryos (miracidia) and larvæ (cercariae) that occur free-swimming in fresh water.

See Chapter XIII, page 369.

Cestoda or Tapeworms	Exclusively parasitic forms. Adults common in fresh-water vertebrates; developmental stages in various aquatic animals, mostly invertebrates; rarely with a free-swimming embryonic stage.

See Chapter XIII, page 424.

Nemertina	Mostly marine; a very few species of small size and simple organization widely distributed in fresh water.

See Chapter XIV, page 454.

Nemathelminthes or Round-worms	A confused group of three classes showing little similarity in structure and associated in a single phylum largely as a matter of convenience. All are well represented in the fresh-water fauna.

NEMATODA OR TRUE ROUND-WORMS	Both free and parasitic forms common in all sorts of environments; free-living species most abundant in fresh waters and in moist soils; parasitic species common in fresh-water hosts.

For free-living Nematoda, see Chapter XV, page 459.

For parasitic Nematoda, see Chapter XVI, page 510.

GORDIACEA OR HAIR SNAKES — Parasitic in young life in insects; adult stage free-living in fresh water.

See Chapter XVI, page 535.

ACANTHOCEPHALA OR THORNY-HEADED WORMS — Exclusively parasitic, without trace of alimentary system. In many fresh-water hosts. Adults in vertebrates; larval forms imperfectly known, parasitize invertebrates.

See Chapter XVI, page 542.

Trochelminthes or Trochal Worms — Among the most characteristic of aquatic organisms. Favorite objects of study with the early microscopists.

ROTATORIA OR WHEEL ANIMALCULES — Microscopic free-living forms, very rarely parasitic. Abundant in fresh-water bodies of all sorts; rare in the sea.

See Chapter XVII, page 553.

GASTROTRICHA — Minute free-living forms. Abundant in fresh water to which the group is limited. Imperfectly known.

See Chapter XVIII, page 621.

Coelhelminthes (Annelida) or Segmented Worms — Two classes in fresh water both well represented; other classes exclusively marine.

CHAETOPODA OR BRISTLE WORMS — One sub-class (Polychaeta) confined to the sea save for rare types in fresh-water bodies near the ocean; the other sub-class (Oligochaeta) found mostly in fresh water and on land.

See Chapter XIX, page 632.

HIRUDINEA OR LEECHES — Both free-living and parasitic species, the former mostly in fresh water with a few species also on land in moist regions; rarely marine, as ectoparasites of fishes.

See Chapter XX, page 646.

Arthropoda Three of the five classes usually recognized are found in fresh water.

CRUSTACEA Only one sub-class, Cirripedia or Barnacles furnishes no fresh-water representatives. The others are well represented in the fresh-water fauna. With few exceptions free-living forms.

For Phyllopoda see Chapter XXI, page 661.

For Cladocera see Chapter XXII, page 676.

For Copepoda see Chapter XXIII, page 741.

For Ostracoda see Chapter XXIV, page 790.

For Malacostraca see Chapter XXV, page 828.

ARACHNIDA Chiefly terrestrial with some parasitic forms. One or two spiders have secondarily invaded fresh water. Among the mites one sub-order, the Hydracarina, is exclusively aquatic. Nearly all species inhabit fresh water.

For Hydracarina, or Water Mites, see Chapter XXVI, page 851.

Two aberrant groups often attached to this class are the following:

Linguatulida, exclusively parasitic, occur rarely in fresh-water hosts.

Tardigrada, minute free-living forms known as water bears; a few species not uncommon in fresh water.

INSECTA Typically land animals which in some cases (especially for developmental stages) have gone into fresh water and manifest secondary adaptations to aquatic life.

See Chapter XXVII, page 876.

Tentaculata Of two classes, one, the Brachiopoda, is exclusively marine. The other follows:

BRYOZOA OR MOSS ANIMALCULES Sessile animals, nearly always colonial; exclusively free-living; chiefly marine but with some fresh-water forms widely distributed.

See Chapter XXVIII, page 947.

Mollusca

Of the five classes commonly recognized, three which are relatively small are not represented in fresh water. Two main classes Lamellibranchia (bivalves) and Gastropoda (univalves) common in fresh waters, widely distributed.

See Chapter XXIX, page 957.

Chordata

Three of the four sub-phyla are exclusively marine in distribution; but the fourth, the Vertebrata, which is also the largest and best known, plays an important part in the fresh-water fauna. No attempt has been made to give a synopsis of fresh-water vertebrates.

For a discussion of biological relations of the Vertebrata to aquatic existence see Chapter XXX, page 1021.

IMPORTANT GENERAL REFERENCES

The literature on the subject is so extensive that only the most important and essential items are listed below. Many general papers of marked value had to be omitted for lack of space. All contributions bearing on a special phase of the subject have been listed at the end of the chapter on that topic. Longer bibliographies appear in Steuer, Wesenberg-Lund, Needham, and others. In general only the latest or most general paper of a given author is listed here.

ANTIPA, GR. 1912. Das Ueberschwemmungsgebiet der unteren Donau. Bukarest. 496 pp., 3 charts, 23 pl.

APSTEIN, C. 1896. Das Süsswasserplankton. Methode und Resultate der quantitativen Untersuchungen. Kiel und Leipzig. 200 pp., 5 pl.

BANTA, A. M. 1907. The Fauna of Mayfield's Cave. Carnegie Inst., Washn., Pub. 67; 114 pp.

BIRGE, E. A. 1895–6. Plankton Studies on Lake Mendota. I, II. Trans. Wis. Acad., 10: 421–484, 4 pl.; 11: 274–448, 28 pl.

BIRGE, E. A. and JUDAY, C. 1911–14. The Inland Lakes of Wisconsin. Bull. Wis. Geol. Nat. Hist. Surv., 22, 27.

1914. A Limnological Study of the Finger Lakes of New York. Bull. U. S. Bur. Fish., 23: 525–609.

BLOCHMANN, F. 1895. Die mikroskopische Tierwelt des Süsswassers. Hamburg. 2 Aufl.

BRAUER, A. 1909. Die Süsswasserfauna Deutschlands. Jena. (19 parts by 32 authors.)

EKMAN, S. 1915. Die Bodenfauna des Vättern qualitativ und quantitativ untersucht. Int. Rev. ges. Hydrobiol., 7: 146–204, 275–425, 8 pl.

EYFERTH, B. 1900. Einfachste Lebensformen des Tier- und Pflanzenreiches. Braunschweig. 3 Aufl., 584 pp., 16 pl.

FORBES, S. A. 1914. Fresh Water Fishes and their Ecology. Urbana, Ill. 19 pp., 31 pl.

FOREL, F. A. 1892-1904. Le Léman, monographie limnologique. 3 vol. Lausanne.

1901. Handbuch der Seenkunde. Allgemeine Limnologie. Stuttgart. 249 pp., 1 pl., 16 figs.

FRIČ, A. und VÁVRA, V. 1894-1902. Untersuchungen über die Fauna der Gewässer Böhmens. Prag.

FURNEAUX, W. 1896. Life in Ponds and Streams. London and New York. 406 pp. 8 pl. 311 text figs.

HENSEN, V. 1887. Ueber die Bestimmung des Planktons oder des im Meere treibenden Materials an Pflangen und Tieren. Komn. wiss. Untersuch. d. Deutschen Meere zu Kiel. V. Bericht, 107 pp., 6 pl.

KNAUTHE, K. 1907. Das Süsswasser. Neudamm. 663 pp., 194 figs.

KOFOID, C. A. 1903. Plankton of the Illinois River, 1894-1899. I, II. Bull. Ill. State Lab. Nat. Hist., 6: 95-629, 50 pl.; 8: 1-360, 5 pl.

LAMPERT, KURT. 1910. Das Leben der Binnengewässer. Leipzig. II Ed. 856 pp., 17 pl., 279 figs.

LOHMANN, H. 1911. Ueber das Nannoplankton und die Zentrifugierung kleinster Wasserproben zur Gewinnung desselben in lebendem Zustande. Int. Rev. ges. Hydrobiol., 4: 1-38, 5 pl.

MURRAY, SIR JOHN and PULLAR, L. 1910. Bathymetrical Survey of the Scottish Freshwater Lochs. Edinburgh. 6 vols.

NEEDHAM, J. G. and LLOYD, J. T. 1915. The Life of Inland Waters. Ithaca. 438 pp., 244 figs.

OSTWALD, W. 1903. Theoretische Planktonstudien. Zool. Jahrb., Syst., 18: 1-62.

1903. Zur Theorie der Schwebevorgänge sowie der specifischen Gewichtsbestimmungen schwebender Organismen. Arch. ges. Physiol., 94: 251-272.

PASCHER, A. 1913. Die Süsswasserflora Deutschlands, Österreichs und der Schweiz. Jena. (16 parts by various authors.)

PÜTTER, A. 1909. Die Ernährung der Wassertiere und der Stoffhaushalt der Gewässer. Jena. 168 pp.

REGNARD, P. 1891. La vie dans les eaux. Paris.

REIGHARD, J. E. 1894. A Biological Examination of Lake St. Clair. Bull. Mich. Fish Com., No. 4; 60 pp., 1 chart.

RUSSELL, I. C. 1895. Lakes of North America. Boston. 125 pp., 23 pl. 1898. Rivers of North America. New York. 327 pp., 17 pl.

SCHEWIAKOFF, W. 1893. Ueber die geographische Verbreitung der Süsswasser-Protozoen. Mém. Acad. Sci. St. Petersbourg, 41, No. 8; 201 pp., 4 pl.

SHELFORD, V. E. 1913. Animal Communities in Temperate America. Chicago. 362 pp., 306 figs.

STEUER, H. 1910. Planktonkunde. Leipzig and Berlin, 723 pp., 365 figs., 1 pl.
1910 a. Leitfaden der Planktonkunde. 382 pp., 279 figs., 1 pl.

STOKES, A. C. 1896. Aquatic Microscopy for Beginners. 3d Ed. Trenton. 326 pp.

WARD, H. B. 1896. A Biological Examination of Lake Michigan in the Traverse Bay Region. Bull. Mich. Fish Com., No. 6; 100 pp., 5 pl.
1898. The Freshwater Biological Stations of the World. Rept. Smith. Inst., 1898: 499-513, 3 pl.

WESENBERG-LUND, C. 1908. Plankton Investigations of the Danish Lakes. Copenhagen. Dan. Freshwater Biol. Lab. Op. 5; 389 pp., 46 pl.
1910. Grundzüge der Biologie und Geographie des Süsswasserplanktons, nebst Bemerkungen über Hauptprobleme zu künftiger limnologischer Forschung. Int. Rev. ges. Hydrobiol., 3. 1-44. (Biol. Suppl., Heft 1.)

WHIPPLE, G. C. 1914. Microscopy of Drinking Water. 3d Ed. New York. 409 pp., 19 pl.

ZACHARIAS, O. 1891. Die Tier- und Pflanzenwelt des Süsswassers. Leipzig. 2 vols.
1909. Das Plankton. Leipzig. 213 pp.

ZSCHOKKE, F. 1900. Die Tierwelt der Hochgebirgsseen. Denkschr. Schweiz. naturf. Ges., 37; 400 pp., 4 charts, 8 pl.
1911. Die Tiefseefauna der Seen Mitteleuropas. Eine geographisch-faunistische Studie. Leipzig. 246 pp., 2 pl.

Contributions to Canadian Biology. Fasc. II. Freshwater Fish and Lake Biology. (Various authors.) Sessional Paper No. 396. 1915. Ottawa. 222 pp., 21 pl.

JOURNALS

American Naturalist. Especially Synopses of North American Invertebrates (older volumes), edited by W. M. Woodworth.

Annales de biologie lacustre. E. Rousseau. Brussels since 1906.

Archiv für Hydrobiologie und Planktonkunde. Stuttgart since 1905. (Continuation of Forschungsberichte aus der Biologischen Station zu Plön; 10 parts, 1893–1903.)

Internationale Revue der gesammten Hydrobiologie und Hydrographie. R. Woltereck. Leipzig since 1908.

Transactions of the American Microscopical Society. T. W. Galloway, Ripon, Wis. Since 1880.

CHAPTER II

CONDITIONS OF EXISTENCE

By VICTOR E. SHELFORD

Assistant Professor of Zoology, University of Illinois. Biologist Illinois State Laboratory of Natural History

CONDITIONS of existence are of importance only in so far as they affect the life and death processes of organisms. The present knowledge of such effects is far from complete and there is justification for noting in detail only those conditions which observation and experiment have shown to be important. Nevertheless if no scientific observations or experiments had ever been made upon organisms, water and its properties would occupy an important place in a discussion of conditions of existence of aquatic life.

Water possesses certain thermal properties and certain characteristic relations to other substances which put it in a class quite apart from the vast majority of chemical substances (Henderson). The thermal properties of water are such as to make it a very fit condition of existence for organisms. In raising the temperature of water one degree centigrade, several times as much heat is absorbed as in the case of various other common substances, except living matter itself. This property moderates both winter and summer temperatures to which aquatic organisms are subjected (Birge). Ice melts at fully a hundred degrees lower than the fusing point of other common environmental substances and the latent heat of melting ice is proportionately high. Thus in melting, ice absorbs large quantities of heat and in freezing water gives off this heat again. This further modifies the aquatic climate as compared with one that might be afforded by some other substance. The latent heat of evaporation of water is also relatively high and this tends to prevent the evaporation of all the water from the surface of the land.

The expansion of water on freezing is one of its most important properties. If water contracted on freezing ice formed at the surface would sink to the bottom, more would be formed and accumulate at the bottom in winter. Here it would thaw very slowly or not at all in summer and the entire surface of the earth would thus quickly become refrigerated. The expansion of water on heating is also very important as it is responsible for the setting up of currents which ventilate the aquatic environment.

Water is by far the most general solvent for other substances. No other liquid will dissolve so many common substances. Though it is one of the most stable and inert compounds, like salts in solution, it dissociates into parts or *ions* and a very small proportion of pure water is in the form of H^+ (the cation bearing a positive electric charge) and OH^- (the anion bearing a negative electric charge). These ions are known respectively as hydrogen and hydroxyl ions. At 25° C. 1000 grams of pure water contain 0.000,000,1 gram of ionized hydrogen and 0.000,001,7 gram of ionized hydroxyl. Salts in solution in water are ionized. For example common salt, NaCl, exists chiefly as Na^+ and Cl^-. Henderson states that solutions in water are the best source of ions. The variety and complexity of the environment of aquatic organisms and the number and variety of chemical reactions are increased by the presence of ions.

As compared with air, water is much denser, being 773 times as heavy. Gases and other solutes are presented to organisms in solution and gases need not be taken into solution by surfaces moistened by body fluids as in the case of land organisms. The diffusion of gases is less rapid in water than in air. Some food substances are in solution in water; many food organisms float in it on account of its great density. This enables some aquatic animals to rest in one position and secure food without effort.

PHYSICAL AND CHEMICAL CONDITIONS

Physical conditions can be separated from chemical conditions only arbitrarily. Combinations of the various physical conditions in water may be included under the term physiography. Physiography in the broad sense includes topography of the land associated with aquatic environments, size and texture of surface materials, direction of prevailing winds, etc.

In streams the strength of the current is a function of volume of water and slope of stream bed. The amount of sediment carried and the size of the sediment particles is determined by the strength of the current and by the character of the materials eroded. The character of the stream floor, the ventilation of the environment, and hence its gaseous content as well as turbidity, are determined by the same factors. All these factors combined comprise important conditions of existence which while they influence organisms are often so difficult to analyze into constituent controlling factors that for ordinary purposes it is better to lump them together under the head of physiographic conditions in streams. Fishes and mollusks migrate upstream during floods and downstream during drought periods. Thus different species of fishes in a number of streams about equally accessible to Lake Michigan but differing in size and age as shown in Fig. 2 are very definitely related to the longitudinal conditions in the various streams, each fish species penetrating up stream to a point characterized by certain physiographic conditions, regardless of the size of the stream as a whole (compare Table I with Fig. 2). An analysis of the physical factors to which the fishes respond and which thus determine the locality they occupy would be a very intricate task but by a simple method of physiographic analysis the differences in their ecological constitution is clearly brought out. Thus important features of conditions of existence may be determined by physiographic analysis and the classification of streams should be determined by physiographic age and physiographic conditions.

Conditions of existence in lakes and ponds are markedly influenced by physiographic conditions. High surrounding country broken into hills and valleys influences the action of winds on the surface. Wind is important in determining circulation. The surrounding topography determines the carrying power of streams and thus the amount of sediment carried into lakes. The amount of sediment determines the depth of light penetration.

The depth of lakes and ponds is definitely related to physiographic conditions. Coastal lakes are usually shallow with sandy or muddy bottom. Morainic lakes are usually relatively deep with clay bottoms and sides. Solution lakes and ponds of limestone regions usually have abrupt rocky sides.

TABLE I

SHOWING THE DISTRIBUTION OF FISH (NOMENCLATURE AFTER FORBES AND RICHARDSON) IN THREE ILLINOIS STREAMS AT THE TIMES INDICATED

(The observations on Pettibone Creek were repeated in four succeeding years with the same results. Stars indicate presence; numbers refer to Fig. 2)

Name of stream and common name of fish	Date and scientific name	1	2	3	4	5	6	7
Glencoe Brook..........	August, 1907							
Horned dace..........	Semotilus atromaculatus..	*						
County Line Creek......	1907–8.................							
Horned dace..........	Semotilus atromaculatus..	*	*	*	*			
Black-nosed dace.....	Rhinichthys atronasus....			*	*			
Johnny darter........	Boleosoma nigrum.......			*	*			
Blackhead minnow....	Pimephales promelas.....				*			
Blunt-nosed minnow....	Pimephales notatus......				*			
Common sucker.......	Catostomus commersonii..				*			
Pettibone Creek[1]........	September, 1909, and April, 1910							
Horned dace..........	Semotilus atromaculatus..	?	*	*	*			
Red-bellied dace......	Chrosomus erythrogaster..		*	*	*			
Black-nosed dace.....	Rhinichthys atronasus....			*	*			
Johnny darter........	Boleosoma nigrum.......			*	*			
Common sucker.......	Catostomus commersonii..				*			
Bull Creek–Dead River.	September, 1909							
Horned dace..........	Semotilus atromaculatus..	*	*	*	*	*		
Red-bellied dace......	Chrosomus erythrogaster..		*	*	*			
Black-nosed dace.....	Rhinichthys atronasus....			*	*			
Common sucker......	Catostomus commersonii..				*	*		
Blunt-nosed minnow..	Pimephales notatus......					*	*	
Little pickerel........	Esox vermiculatus........					*	*	*
Bluegill..............	Lepomis pallidus........						*	*
Large-mouthed black bass................	Micropterus salmoides....						*	*
Pike..................	Esox lucius.............							*
Crappie..............	Pomoxis annularis.......							*
Red-horse............	Moxostoma aureolum.....							*
Chub-sucker..........	Erimyzon sucetta.......							*
Golden shiner........	Abramis crysoleucas.....							*
Common shiner.......	Notropis cornutus........							*
Cayuga minnow......	Notropis cayuga.........							*
Tadpole cat..........	Schilbeodes gyrinus......							*

[1] The lower part of Pettibone Creek has been destroyed by the United States Naval School, otherwise the table would include the records for a point 5 and perhaps a point 6, but probably not 7.

Physical factors include bottom, currents, light, temperature, density, pressure, viscosity, etc.

The size of bottom materials is an important condition of existence. In streams the current sorts the materials, leaving the coarsest in the swiftest current and the finest in the most sluggish current. In the curves of streams the current is usually swiftest on the outside and most sluggish on the inside. Different animals

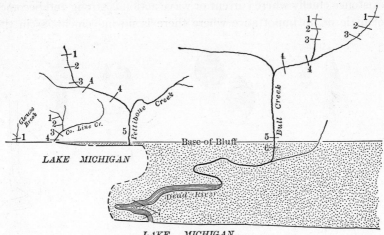

FIG. 2.

Diagrammatic arrangement of four streams flowing into Lake Michigan. The streams are mapped to a scale of one mile to the inch, and the maps are placed as closely together as possible in the diagram. The intermediate shore lines are shown in broken lines which bear no relation to the shore lines which exist in nature. Toward the top of the diagram is west. Each number on the diagram refers to the pool nearest the source of the stream which contains fish, as follows: 1, horned dace (*Semotilus atromaculatus*); 2, red-bellied dace (*Chrosomus erythrogaster*); 3, black-nosed dace (*Rhinichthys atronasus*); 4, the suckers and minnows; 5, the pickerel and blunt-nosed minnow; 6, sunfish and bass; 7, pike, chub sucker, etc. The bluff referred to is about 60 feet high. The stippled area is a plain just above the level of the lake. (After Shelford.)

tend to occupy the different kinds of bottom materials (Fig. 3). Thus the differentiation of bottom constitutes an important differentiation of conditions of existence.

The bottom of a swift stream eroding sandy soil is very unstable and the fauna very sparse. Such streams are essentially aquatic deserts and only a few burrowers are able to live in them. Sandy bottomed streams with sluggish current have a luxuriant fauna of burrowers and flora of rooted vegetation. Rocky and stony streams have rich faunas of clinging and hiding animals.

In lakes and ponds the importance of bottom is determined by the strength of wave action and the amount of current. The fine bottom materials around the margin of a large lake are constantly moved about; the particles grind upon one another making the presence of bottom organisms impossible. Thus the sandy shores of the Great Lakes down to a depth of eight feet or more are usually almost entirely without bottom organisms.

The character of *terrigenous* bottom is an important condition of existence chiefly where current or wave action is strong and becomes of little or no importance where there is no movement, as in the

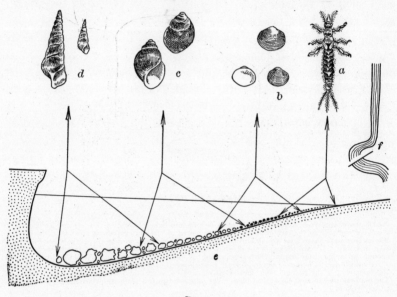

FIG. 3.

The form of bottom and size of bottom materials in a cross section of the North Branch of the Chicago River with distribution of animals. *a* to *d* natural size. *a*, burrowing may-fly nymph (*Hexagenia* sp.); *b*, small bivalve (*Sphærium stamineum*), two individuals, two views; *c*, viviparous snail (*Campeloma integrum*), seen from two sides; *d*, the long river snail, young and full grown (*Pleurocera elevatum*); *e*, cross section of the stream with reference to a curve (*f*). (Original.)

bottom of one of the Great Lakes. However, bottoms of soft *muck* containing putrescible organic matter occur in the absence of current and constitute a condition of existence sharply differentiated from terrigenous bottoms because they can support only certain types of organisms, mainly anaërobes, and but few of these. Many aquatic animals use the bottom materials in the construction of their cases, nests, etc. Thus the caddis worms (certain species of *Mollana* and *Geora*) build cases of sand grains weighted at the sides by small pebbles. The horned dace and several other fishes associated with it use pebbles to build their nests. The pebbles must be of a certain average size. Many animals form associations (memory) with reference to certain stones or pebbles under or near which they live (*e.g.*, mayfly nymphs) and thus work out simple homing paths.

As has been stated, in streams the rate of flow is determined by volume of water and slope of stream bed. In a comparatively straight stream the current is swiftest in the center at the top and least swift at the sides near the bottom; the center of the stream bed has a current intermediate between the two. Thus sluggish portions of streams like the Fox River (Illinois) may be swift enough at the bottom of the center to support some swift stream animals such as *Hydropsyche* and Heptageninæ. There are back eddies about stones and other obstructions so that currents in streams are somewhat irregular.

In lakes circulation is determined by wind and differences in temperature. A lake which is equal in temperature throughout has a complete circulation (Fig. 4 *A*). The wind indicated by the arrow (*W*) tends to pile the water up on one side. To compensate

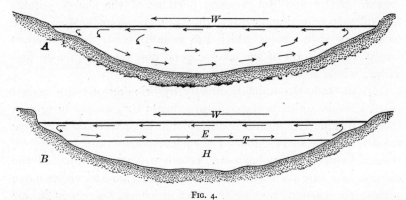

FIG. 4.

The circulation of the water (*A*) in a lake of equal temperature; (*B*) in a lake of unequal temperature. *W* represents the direction of the wind; *E*, epilimnion; *T*, thermocline; *H*, hypolimnion. (After Birge.)

for this currents are started downward along the shore and a circulation across the bottom and upward on the other side is initiated. Very shallow lakes and deeper lakes in the cold months of the year have a complete circulation. Lakes of unequal temperature are very different. For example a deep lake has a uniform temperature for a time in the spring just after the ice melts, complete circulation takes place and the bottom waters are aërated. As the

sun warms the surface waters they become so much lighter than
the deeper colder waters that the currents set up to compensate
for the piling up of the water by the wind can no longer flow to
the bottom and a superficial circulation is accordingly set up
(Fig. 4 B). A distinct thermocline (T) is thus established. The
epilimnion (E) is warm and constantly aërated by circulation and
the hypolimnion (H) is stagnant. In the autumn as the water
gradually cools the thermocline gradually migrates to the bottom
and the earlier, complete circulation (Fig. 4 A) is again established.

In addition to the general circulation, waves and their action
must be considered. As was noted in connection with bottom, the
shifting of fine bottom materials eliminates most animals from
sandy shores. On rocky shores in large lakes are representatives
of some of the same animal species found in swift streams. The
alternating current does not appear to exclude many such species.
In small lakes and ponds the small wave action removes decaying
organic matter and thus renders portions of the shores suitable
for animals requiring or preferring a terrigenous bottom. The
location of such shores which are usually sandy is determined
largely by the form of the lake or pond and the direction of prevailing winds and inflow of water.

Currents influence animals directly by bringing pressure against
parts. Sessile animals respond to currents by changes in growth
form. But few fresh water sessile animals have been studied in this
respect, and the exact character of such responses cannot be stated,
though sponges and polyzoa are known to vary greatly. Motile
animals as a rule turn with their heads upstream and either move
against the current, making progress upstream, or remain in one
position by swimming enough to maintain themselves. Fishes
under experimental conditions will often swim against a current
which is stronger than their optimum until they are exhausted.
Many fishes orient themselves by visual impressions of the bottom
as they float downstream. Others appear to orient by differences
in pressure on the two sides of the body or by rubbing against the
bottom as they float down. Sight is probably ineffective during
floods on account of sediment. Current is essential to the spinning
of the characteristic cocoons and cases of some insects living in

rapids. They make a shapeless mass without it. A few animals require very complete aëration or they die very quickly. Suckers appear to die from lack of oxygen while the rainbow darter adds something to the water in which it lives which is not removed by artificial aëration and which kills the fish unless the number of fishes is small or the water changed often.

Light penetrates clear water to great depths. During the cruise of the Michel Sars the penetration of sufficient light to markedly affect the most sensitive photographic plates in 80 min. was found at a depth of 1000 meters (latitude 31° 20', June 5–6. Sun nearly over head; for methods see Murray and Hjort). No effect was obtained at 1700 meters with an exposure of two hours. Light sufficient to affect the plates in 2 hours lies somewhere between 1000 and 1700 meters. There were many rays of all kinds at 100 meters but least of the red. Though penetration is rarely as great in fresh water as in the sea, light may possibly penetrate to the bottom of Lake Baikal which is the deepest fresh water lake known (1300 to 1700 meters are reported).

In temperate latitudes light does not penetrate so far vertically because it enters the water obliquely. The depth of penetration can easily be calculated for any latitude or season from the angle of declination of the sun, when the penetration in similar water is known for other latitudes and seasons.

The most important factor limiting the penetration of light into fresh water is turbidity. Forel found the light penetration in Lake Geneva (Switzerland) greatest when the lake contained least sediment. Table II gives the depth of light penetration in Lake Geneva in March when it is clearest. Forel used much less sensitive plates than were used on the Michel Sars, the sun was much lower in the horizon and the locality 15 degrees farther north. Thus Forel's records show that light did not diminish notably in the first 25 meters, fell off gradually in the second 25 meters and then dropped off rapidly to zero for his plates at 110 meters. Fol and Sarasin with more sensitive silver salts than were used by Forel found that light reached 200 meters in winter. It is altogether probable that the plates and apparatus of the Michel Sars would show much light at three or four times the depth given by Forel.

FRESH-WATER BIOLOGY

TABLE II

SHOWING DEPTH OF LIGHT PENETRATION IN LAKE GENEVA (SWITZERLAND) AND
CONDITIONS AFFECTING THE SAME IN BOTH LAKE GENEVA (AFTER
FOREL) AND LAKE MICHIGAN

In the eighth column the relative results are given in seconds, in terms
of the effect on the photographic plate, of exposures to the sun.

Lake Michigan				Month	Lake Geneva, Switzerland			
Rainfall		Velocity of wind at noon			Rainfall and light		Light and depth	
Inches	Centimeters	Miles per hour	Meters per second		Prec. in cm.	Light limit at depth in meters	Intensity of light (March) at depth in next column	Depth in meters
2.0	5.1	17.8	8.0	.....January.......	4.87	....	500 sec.	0.0
2.3	5.2	20.0	9.0	.....February......	3.65	....	500 sec.	19.6
2.5	6.4	20.4	9.1	.....March.........	4.72	110	500 sec.	25.2
2.7	6.9	19.4	8.7	.....April.........	5.68	....	400 sec.	45.5
3.5	8.9	18.3	8.2	.....May:..........	7.91	75	360 sec.	55.5
3.7	9.4	14.4	6.5	.....June..........	7.59	....	120 sec.	65.6
3.6	9.2	14.6	6.6	.....July..........	7.08	45	60 sec.	75.6
2.8	7.2	13.4	6.0	.....August........	8.04	....	25 sec.	85.7
3.0	7.7	16.7	7.5	.....September.....	9.42	50	10 sec.	95.8
2.6	6.6	17.6	7.9	.....October.......	10.10	....	2 sec.	105.4
2.6	6.6	19.0	8.5	.....November.....	7.4	85	0 sec.	115.6
2.1	5.3	19.9	8.9	.....December.....	5.11	....	....	....

Little work on the depth of light penetration has been undertaken in the North American waters. In Table II the rainfall and wind velocity over Lake Michigan are shown and the rainfall for Lake Geneva (Switzerland). The greatest light penetration in Lake Geneva comes when the rainfall is low and when the mountains are still frozen. The Lake Michigan water commission found in a brief period of study that the greatest turbidity fell in January, February, March, and April. The table indicates that this is in months with high wind velocity. The great rainfall of the spring and early summer months tends to keep Lake Michigan turbid, so the greatest light penetration may be predicted for August which has least rain and least wind.

Various streams are normally so muddy that light cannot be expected to penetrate more than a few feet and the fauna accordingly lives in very faint light. Others, as for example streams and lakes in some of the western mountains, are very clear and one can see to depths of 5 to 15 meters. Depth at which objects may be seen is measured by lowering a white disc 20 cm. in diameter known as the disc of Secchi.

When light penetrates water the red rays are most rapidly absorbed, then orange, yellow, etc. In the Michel Sars measurements there were scarcely any red rays at 500 meters, one-half the depth at which light was measured. Fol found off Nice that when down in 30 meters of water he could see a stone 7–8 meters away and a bright object at a distance of 25 meters. Red animals looked black, while green and blue green algæ looked quite bright.

In water there is no dawn or twilight. The surface of the water reflects practically all the light when the rays come to it very obliquely. Fol found that in 10 meters of water solar light disappeared quite suddenly long before sunset. In Funchal Harbor (Madeira) the Prince of Monaco used Regnard's apparatus in which a film is moved before an opening by clockwork, and found that at 20 meters in March the day lasted 9 hours whereas at 40 meters the film showed the effects of light for only about 15 minutes at 2 P.M.

Light profoundly influences the migrations and distribution of animals probably largely because it has a marked effect on life processes. Unfortunately, however, with the exception of ultra-violet light which penetrates the atmosphere into low altitudes in minimal amount, very little is known of the actual physiological effects of light. Under experimental conditions animals usually avoid or select the blue end of the spectrum. Red usually acts as darkness or very faint light. Thus animals living in very strong light usually accumulate in blue or violet when exposed to spectrum colors. Animals living in darkness collect in the red. Animals living in moderate light usually wander about throughout the spectrum but a majority congregate in the blue. Probably animals are affected through photo-chemical reactions which are brought about most often by the blue end of the spectrum. Daphnias select the brightest part of the spectrum which is the green or the yellow for most organisms, brightness being determined by some specific effect of particular wave lengths upon the light recipient organs. Yellow is brightest to the human retina. In addition to color animals react to direction and to intensity of light. Probably the majority of fresh-water animals react more strongly to direction than to intensity. *Hydropsyche* and *Argia* do not react to intensity at all but react to direction very sharply. Experimental conditions in which direction away from source accompanies a sharp decrease in intensity gives sharpest reactions with most aquatic animals.

Animals react to intensity with reference to an optimum. The optimum usually corresponds to the usual light in their natural environments. The organism may often be modified by changes in the chemical character of the water, or even by rough handling (*Daphnia, Ranatra*), so that it selects a different optimum, or reverses its reaction to direction of rays.

Many animals react to shadows or small areas of illumination. Thus frogs will hop to a shadow in the middle of a sunny field and Amblystoma will follow a person along a sunny road. This type of behavior is doubtless an important thing under water but has been but little investigated.

One of the topics which has absorbed much of the attention of limnologists is the daily depth migrations of certain crustacea. They usually accumulate near the surface at night and in deeper water during the day. The causes of these migrations are very complex and light is an important factor. Dice has recently discussed the matter in full. Light is probably important in confining certain animals in deep water, in turbid streams, under stones and logs and in caves, ground water, etc.

The early invention of the thermometer has led to quite complete investigation of temperature and an over-estimation of its importance in the direct control of the distribution of life in water. The tendency of modern investigation is to weaken the belief in its direct importance.

Stream temperatures are probably about the same at the various points in any cross-section, except the shallow sluggish margin on warm summer days. The extent to which daily, seasonal, and weather fluctuations in atmospheric temperature affect a lake is determined by the depth and size. Small lakes with incomplete circulation in summer are cold at the bottom, being heated at the surface only (Fig. 4 B). Lake Michigan is a large deep lake and none of the seasonal temperature changes extend to the deepest parts (Table III). In summer the water of the surface is warmed, but if the vertical circulation is complete all the heat in the waters flowing downward at the leeward side (Fig. 4 B) must be absorbed above 110 meters (Table III) when the temperature of maximum density is recorded. These are chiefly bottom records and do not therefore represent the temperatures at the same level in the open water, especially in the shallower situations where the sun's energy is distributed through a thinner layer of water.[1]

TABLE III

TEMPERATURE OF LAKE MICHIGAN (AFTER WARD)

Temperature at depth in next column		Depth		Date	Hour P.M. unless stated	Sky	Temperature of air	Temperature at surface
° C.	° F.	Meters	Feet				° C.	° C.
18.3	64.9	5.66	18.6	Aug. 16	4:05	Clear	16.7	18.3
16.7	62.0	11.32	37.1	Aug. 18	9:00 A.M.	Cloudy	18.9	17.2
7.2	44.9	22.63	74.1	Aug. 18	12:25	Clearing	16.7	17.5
7.5	45.5	32.06	105.2	Aug. 16	5:10	Clear	16.7	18.3
7.2	44.9	43.38	142.3	Aug. 25	3:25	....	20.0	19.4
5.2	41.3	55.93	183.5	Aug. 16	12:05	Clear	15.6	18.3
5.1	41.1	108.22	355.0	Aug. 11	10:30 A.M.	Hazy	....	18.9
4.2	39.5	112.00	367.5	Aug. 16	1:50	Clear	16.7	18.3
4.2	39.5	132.66	436.0	Aug. 18	4:30	Scattered clouds	18.9	18.3

Most fresh-water animals are poikilothermic or cold-blooded and their temperature varies with the surrounding temperature. Mammals and birds with the exception of the manatee and rare fresh-water dolphins and seals are not truly aquatic. Truly aquatic warm-blooded animals usually have a thick covering of fat which is a poor conductor of heat. A few fishes maintain 10° C. or more above the surrounding medium, but for most fresh-water animals 0.1° to 5.0° C. are reported. Rogers recently reported only very minute difference for goldfish. This heat is due to metabolism.

[1] Temperatures below the surface may be taken with a thermometer in a two-gallon bottle filled at the desired level or better with a Negretti-Zambra reversing thermometer. For devices making continuous records of temperature, the thermophone of Whipple or Friez's soil and water thermograph may be used.

Cold increases the metabolism of warm-blooded animals and decreases that of cold-blooded animals. In the cold-blooded animals a rise of 10° C. within limits reasonably compatible with life increases the rate of metabolism, or rate of development of young, by two or three times. This is taken as evidence that life is a chemical process because similar changes in temperature have corresponding changes in rate of chemical reaction.

Thus animals aquatic in their developmental stages and which happen to be in very shallow temporary water are automatically accelerated in development as the sun warms the water, evaporates it and decreases its volume at the same time increasing its temperature.

Animals react to temperature with considerable precision. Both marine and fresh-water animals can recognize differences of 0.2° C. and will turn back when such slight differences are encountered under experimental conditions.

Pressure in water increases with depth. The results given by Forel are shown in Table IV.

TABLE IV

Pressure in atmospheres......	1	2	3	5	8	10	20
Depth in meters.............	10.328	20.6	30.9	51.5	82.4	103.27	206.49

There is a little less than one atmosphere increase in pressure for each 10 meters of depth. According to this, animals in the deepest parts of a lake like Lake Michigan are living under a pressure of about 375 pounds to the square inch.

The effect of pressure on organisms was studied by Regnard. Contrary to the popular idea he found that gelatine, agar, and various plants and animals and excised parts of animals take up water, swell and increase in weight under high pressure. This is true even of terrestrial insects. At 400 to 600 atmospheres Paramecia become swollen and immobile, including the cilia. They recover from ten minutes' exposure. Carp become listless at 200 atmospheres, die at 300 and become swollen and rigid at 400 atmospheres. Salmon ova are destroyed at 400 atmospheres but chlorophyll bodies of green algæ continue to work at 600 atmospheres and cress seeds have germinated after an exposure to 1000 atmospheres.

Table V shows the conditions and distribution of life in Lake Michigan. The greatest pressure is 27 atmospheres which on the basis of the work of Regnard would seem trivial. Animals may react to pressure differences but this is not known as no pressure gradient can be established without involving gravity also. Pressure would appear to play a relatively insignificant rôle.

TABLE V

CONDITIONS IN LAKE MICHIGAN

Approximate physical conditions	Depth		Vegetation and animals
	Meters	Feet	
Strong wave action	0–1.5	0–5	Bottom organisms wanting on sandy shores, abundant on rocky shores
Limit of sand-moving waves	8	26	Organisms abundant
Limit of daily temperature fluctuations; limit of wave action; beginning of light decrease; pressure about 2½ atmospheres	25	82	Lowest record of *Chara* and *Cladophora*. Lower limit of Mollusks except Sphæridæ
Pressure 4 atmospheres, light reduced to ⅛	39	128	Scanty filamentous algæ
Seasonal temperature fluctuations less than 1° C.; light reduced to ¾; pressure 5⅗ atmospheres	54	177	Lower limit of most shallow water animals. Nostoc and diatoms
Light ⅛; pressure 7 atmospheres	70	230	No bottom plants recorded
Probably dark as night; pressure 11 atmospheres; little change in temperature; nearly uniform conditions	115	377	No plants recorded
Greatest depth in lake; pressure 27 atmospheres	274	900	No plants recorded

With a rise of temperature both the density and viscosity of water decrease. This tends to cause such organisms as behave like small inanimate particles to sink. Ostwald suggested that these differences are responsible for the depth migrations of plankton organisms. He considered that a decrease in viscosity causes them to sink.   The diffusion currents bring them up again (Johnstone).   This is no doubt a matter deserving investigation. Turbidity is important largely through its relation to light.   Most aquatic animals will tolerate much sediment, at least under experimental conditions.

Chemical factors are not directly or clearly separable from factors that may be regarded as physical or biological.   Under this heading are considered dissolved gases, inorganic salts, acidity, alkalinity, and neutrality.

In order to support animals and plants continuously water must contain certain minerals and gases in solution.   Salts (carbonates, sulphates, and chlorides) of magnesium, calcium, potassium, and sodium, and salts of iron and silicon are practically always in solution in water and their presence in definite proportions is believed to be essential to the life of organisms.   Pure distilled water has been shown to be harmless to certain animals for comparatively short periods but it is doubtful if it will sustain life indefinitely.   Dissolved gases in definite proportions are essential.

The occurrence of gases and their solubility under experimental conditions are shown in Table VI.   A standard method of expressing quantity of gas in solution is in cubic centimeters per liter at 0° C. and 760 mm. of mercury.   Values are commonly given in these terms.

Nitrogen is the most inert and least important of the dissolved gases.   It rarely has any direct effect on animals and plants and this apparently only when present in considerable excess of saturation.   Under such conditions it accumulates in the blood vessels and tissues of fishes, crayfishes, insects, etc.   In the organs of circulation it may thus stop the blood flow and the animals die of asphyxia.   Birge and Juday state that in lakes in the region of the thermocline and below an excess of 12 to 38 per cent of saturation occurs, but under the conditions of pressure there this would have no effect.   It is probable that in nature this condition of excess is not commonly great enough and does not often occur for a time long enough to cause any fatal results.   Several hours or days, depending upon the excess, are required.   Excess nitrogen is a great source of difficulty in aquaria.

TABLE VI

SHOWING THE SOLUBILITY AND DISTRIBUTION OF ATMOSPHERIC GASES

Gas	Composition of air in percentages	Gas values in cubic centimeters per liter at 0° C. and 760 mm. mercury			Kind of water having gas content given in preceding column
		At. temp. 20° C. 760 mm.		Maximum amounts found in natural fish waters, springs excepted	
		Water absorbs from air	Water absorbs pure gas		
Nitrogen, argon, etc............	79.02	12.32	15.00	19.00	Lakes
Oxygen............	20.95	6.28	28.38	24.00	Streams, lakes in winter, or with green algæ
Carbon dioxide....	0.03	0.27	901.00	30.00	Ponds
Ammonia..........	Small traces locally	....	Very large quantities	14.00	Sewage contaminated
Methane...........	"	....	34.00	10.00	Bottom of lake
Hydrogen sulphide.	"	....	2900.00	0.55	Lakes, and sewage contaminated

The oxygen content of water varies from 0 cc. per liter to 25 cc. in the presence of green algæ on sunny days. The bottoms of lakes and ponds where much putrescible matter occurs are usually without oxygen. The hypolimnion of lakes with a thermocline is in part without oxygen in summer. Probably free oxygen is usually necessary to most organisms except anaërobic bacteria. Most animals that have been studied in behavior experiments select water with some oxygen. While some species of fishes such as suckers, small mouthed black bass, and some cyprinids appear to be affected by a considerable decrease from saturation at ordinary temperatures, this appears to be the exception rather than the rule. Increase to 25 cc. per liter under experimental conditions does not appear to have any marked effect upon fishes so far as life and death are concerned. Allee working on isopods found that an increase in oxygen increases size, vigor, and amount of positive response to current as well as efficiency of response to current. His results have been confirmed by several students who have repeated the experiments using different forms.

Juday has shown that a long list of common protozoa, worms,

insects, etc., can live for a long time without free oxygen, and in fact occur in the putrescible organic muds of the bottoms of lakes and ponds and the hypolimnion of thermocline lakes in summer. They evidently obtain oxygen from some chemical compounds. Carbohydrates are present in the sea in solution in minute quantity and there is every reason to believe them present in fresh water.   Packard found that marine Fundulus embryos live in lack of oxygen from 73 to 141 per cent longer in the presence of glucose, maltose, levulose, and cane sugar, the amount of increase in resistance differing with the different sugars.   Lactose has no such effect, probably because it cannot be absorbed or digested.

According to Mathews' depolarization theory oxygen is obtained from the water in a manner analogous to the oxidation of alcohol to acetic acid.   In the presence of O_2 the reaction is as follows:

$$C_2H_5OH + O_2 = CH_3COOH + H_2O.$$

In the absence of oxygen and the presence of levulose

$$C_2H_5OH + H_2O = CH_3COOH + 2\,H_2$$
$$2\,H_2 + 2\,C_6H_{12}O_6 = 2\,C_6H_{14}O_6.$$

The levulose unites with the hydrogen and thus permits the protoplasm to use the oxygen.   The protoplasm is thus a strong reducing agent.

High respiratory quotients of various animals are further evidence of anaërobic respiration.   The respiratory quotient is $\dfrac{\text{Vol. } CO_2 \text{ given off}}{\text{Vol. } O_2 \text{ absorbed}}$.   In aërobic animals this value is less than 1 because oxides other than CO_2 are given off and CO_2 does not represent all the oxygen used.   Thus when the quotient is more than 1 it indicates that oxygen is obtained from some source other than free oxygen.   The respiratory quotient of the medical leech is usually near or a little more than 1 while that of a sea cucumber (*Cucumaria*) and a sea sponge (*Suberites*) is over 2.5 (Pütter).   A large number of aquatic animals are probably able to secure oxygen from compounds containing it and they are therefore facultative anaërobes to a considerable degree.

Distribution of organisms in water is not clearly correlated with oxygen content.   The minimum for most animals is comparatively low as, for example, in fishes insufficient oxygen acts on the respiratory center through the development of organic acid in the blood due to incomplete oxidation, and causes the respiratory movements to be increased. There is some evidence that respiratory activity is increased through direct reflex action through the gills and opercles. This increased respiratory activity supplies plenty of oxygen.

Ammonia occurs in minimal quantities in natural waters but may be present in some quantity in sewage or gas works wastes. Ammonia like the other gases (CO, SO_2, and C_2H_4) introduced into streams by gas works is not only extremely poisonous, but fishes do not turn back from it when they encounter it and are often overcome without giving the avoiding reactions which protect fishes from excesses of other substances normal to fish environments.

Methane is a saturated hydrocarbon and has minor effects upon organisms though it may be present in the hypolimnion of lakes in considerable quantity. Traces of carbon monoxide occur also.

Hydrogen sulphide is usually present in very small quantities in the bottoms of lakes and sewage contaminated streams. It is very abundant in salt lakes and arms of the sea. It results from putrefactions and from the reduction of sulphates through the action of the bacteria which prey upon organic sulphur (Lederer). Though very poisonous it is not ordinarily present in sufficient quantity to injure fishes (Shelford and Powers) though its absorption of oxygen [1] reduces the amount of this gas very materially.

Carbon dioxide is the most important gas in fresh water. In small quantities it is essential rather than detrimental to aquatic

---

[1] Samples of water without oxygen must be handled with utmost caution as an appreciable amount of oxygen will be absorbed through the surface exposed by the narrow neck of a 250 cc. bottle in a few seconds. Biologists are very likely to attempt great accuracy in putting up solutions and to exercise insufficient care in taking and titrating samples. For ordinary work, in making up solutions it is sufficient to weigh to one decimal place; chemicals must be carefully selected; especially, KI. The normal solutions used will not be correct if made by an unskilled person; a correcting factor must be used which may as well be 0.876 as 0.989. Skill in titrating and standardizing with solutions made by a chemist should be acquired. For methods see Birge and Juday, and Sutton. Routine sanitary analyses include several items of unknown or doubtful value to living organisms and do not include some of the most important determinations such as acidity, alkalinity, hydrogen sulphide, and carbonaceous materials that might be absorbed as food. Determinations are often not made at once, and samples are commonly not collected from important animal habitats within the body of water.

animals. In large quantities it is rapidly fatal acting as a narcotic. It is particularly injurious in the absence of oxygen which absence is usually associated with it. Abundant oxygen decreases its toxicity because blood has greater affinity for oxygen than for carbon dioxide and the latter is crowded out of combination. On account of the fact that it is usually accompanied by lack of oxygen, putrescible muck bottom, etc., its presence in quantities greater than 6 to 7 cc. per liter if accompanied by a bottom entirely of such muck would indicate that the water was unsuitable for trout, basses, sunfishes, and crappies.

One of the most important characteristics of a water is its acidity or alkalinity. Protoplasm must maintain essential neutrality or it will die. It possesses a very effective physico-chemical mechanism based upon the presence in excess of very weak acids (carbonic and phosphoric) and alkalies in the form of carbonates and phosphates. Since protoplasm must remain nearly neutral the acidity or alkalinity of the surrounding medium cannot be great. Thus Wells found that fishes do not live well in alkaline water but become sluggish and inactive. Neutrality is likewise toxic to some fresh-water fishes. They require a certain amount of acid. The optimum acidity for the different species differs. The optimum for the bluegill (*Lepomis pallidus* Mit.) is 1 to 3 cc. of carbon dioxide per liter and for crappies (*Pomoxis annularis* Raf.) 4 to 6 cc. per liter. Wells showed by using various other acids that the hydrogen ions are the important factor. In other words fishes require a certain concentration of hydrogen ion. Neutrality is avoided by fishes. In the absence of acidity they select alkaline in preference to neutral water. Fishes and various crustaceans will live in distilled water if it is slightly acid, while it is rapidly fatal if neutral and more rapidly fatal if alkaline. The toxicity of much ordinary distilled water is due to colloidal copper or other metal from coolers, in suspension in it.

Wells made a rearrangement of some of the data of Birge and Juday which showed that various plankton organisms are distributed with reference to alkalinity, neutrality, and acidity,[1] a few

[1] In the determination of alkalinity and acidity great care should be exercised in the making of collections so as to prevent the escape of CO_2. The choice of indi-

species showing a distinct avoidance of neutrality. In a number of species the number of individuals on either side of neutrality was greater than at the neutral region (Table VII).

TABLE VII

SHOWING CORRELATION BETWEEN DISTRIBUTION AND ALKALINITY AND ACIDITY
TO PHENOLPHTHALEIN (AFTER WELLS)

(Figures show numbers of individuals in a cubic meter of water)

Name of animal	Alkalinity in cc. per liter of CO_2 to make neutral			Neutrality	Acidity in cc. of CO_2 per liter			
	3–2	1.5–1	0.5–0.25	0	0.25–0.5	0.75–1	1–1.5
Pleosoma..........R...	3,925	0	0	0	0	0	0
Asplanchna.........R...	11,320	400	0	0	0	0	0
Diaphanosoma......C...	2,885	2,750	n. c.	260	0	0	0
Diaptomus........Co...	7,850	6,660	17,350	2,220	1,440	390	100
Anuraea...........P...	4,000	1,250	200	30	20	20	20
Cyclops...........Co...	13,775	7,620	7,620	25	30	0	5
Notholca..........R...	625	685	65	0	65	0	0
Daphnia...........C...	1,260	650	400	130	1,145	25	0
Ceratium..........P...	52,330	104,500	85,160	2,025	11,760	5,750	1,670
Polyarthra........R...	12,350	1,620	2,350	160	1,190	1,240	40
Triarthra.........R...	0	n. c.	0	n. c.	1,050	1,110	2,425

R = Rotifer, C = Cladoceran, P = Protozoan, Co = Copepod, n. c. = no collection.

The amount of salt in parts per million which ranges from 50–500 in water occupied by numerous fresh-water species is of comparatively little significance to animals but of much importance to plants. The effect of most salts upon organisms is due to the character of the ions, valence, electrical charges, etc. The effect of any combination of salts is due to their combined action. For example, marine animals will not live in NaCl alone even when the osmotic pressure is the same as in sea water; it is very toxic. They will not live in NaCl and KCl or NaCl and CaCl₂; all three

cators is also very important. Methyl orange is unaffected by CO_2 and other organic acids because of their small ionization. Thus Marsh's conclusion, based upon methyl orange, that if water becomes acid it kills fishes is incorrect for this reason and because it turns red at $\dfrac{H^+ \, 10^{-4}\,N}{OH^- \, 10^{-10}\,N}$ and remains yellow at $\dfrac{H^+ \, 10^{-5}\,N}{OH^- \, 10^{-9}\,N}$. Phenolphthalein is faint pink at $\dfrac{H^+ \, 10^{-8}\,N}{OH^- \, 10^{-6}\,N}$ and turns red at $\dfrac{H^+ \, 10^{-9}\,N}{OH^- \, 10^{-5}\,N}$. Rosalic acid is rose at $\dfrac{H^+ \, 10^{-7}\,N}{OH^- \, 10^{-7}\,N}$ which is true neutrality. In the table above true neutrality probably falls in the first column to the right of the center. CO_2 production may be sufficient to neutralize this slight alkalinity in the layer of water next to the animal. The terms alkalinity and acidity are used in this chapter with reference to phenolphthalein 'neutrality' (PH 8.0).

are necessary. This is believed to be due to the neutralization of the toxicity of the NaCl by the other salts; this is known as antagonism. The effects are due to the cations, one anion being sufficient though some are more favorable than others.

Salts present in excess, or without the proper antagonistic salts or ions, and salts not commonly present in quantity in fresh water are toxic to fresh-water animals. The toxicity varies for different salts and according to the concentration of hydrogen or hydroxyl ions which accompany it. Ammonia salts are poisonous to fishes if present in company with carbonates. Carbonates are not essential to the life of fishes as sulphates may be substituted entirely, at least for short periods. Carbonates alone are fatal to fishes because of their alkalinity. In the presence of CO_2, however, carbonates are converted into bicarbonates which are normally present in all natural fish waters. Bicarbonates accompanied by a small excess of CO_2 are not harmful. Of the salts of potassium, the sulphate is most poisonous; sodium salts are less injurious than those of potassium. The presence of an excess of calcium causes the tail fins of the rock bass to degenerate and this fact was probably responsible for the tailless trout found in certain waters of the British Isles where the water was contaminated with waste from paper mills. There is much evidence that calcium tends to lower the metabolic activity of organisms.

As shown by Wells fishes react to salts in solution. They are usually negative to nitrates, more or less positive to chlorides (markedly so to NaCl) but are decidedly negative to $CaCl_2$ and $MgCl_2$. They are positive to ammonium chloride and are usually very negative to sulphates. The reaction of the fishes to the salts was shown to have a distinct relation to the acidity of the water, as fishes that were decidedly negative to Na_2SO_4 for instance in slightly acid water were made positive to this salt by running the experiment in strongly acid water (*i.e.*, 20 cc. CO_2 per liter). A part of the effect of ions lies in their effect on permeability. Alkalies increase permeability of protoplasm. Acids first decrease and later increase it.

In animals and plants there are various rhythms of activity constituting parts of their physiological life histories or recurring functions lying within them. These often coincide with rhythms of conditions. The principal environmental rhythms are daily, seasonal, weather, and lunar, and, in the sea, tidal.

Rhythms of fresh-water organisms have been but little studied. From the seasonal standpoint it has been observed that some organisms tend to do certain things even though the external conditions which usually accompany them are delayed, thus showing that the environmental rhythms have been impressed upon the organism. The best examples of this have to do with the tide and thus do not belong to fresh water. Bohn found that there are rhythms of activity related to tide. The green flatworm (*Convoluta roscoffensis*) comes to the surface of the sand at low tide and descends as the tide comes in. The worm continues to ascend and descend at tide time for several days after having been removed from the sea and kept in an aquarium.

One of the best known rhythmic movements in fresh water is the daily depth migration of crustacea. Whether they show any tendency to make such movements when placed under uniform conditions is not known. Lunar rhythms likewise appear to have been little investigated among fresh-water organisms though Kofoid noted rhythmic monthly increases of Illinois River plankton. The best examples of these are found among the marine worms. The Atlantic palolo swarms within three days of the last day of the last quarter of the June 29 to July 28 moon (Mayer), the swarming taking place under the influence of the light of the moon.

Various single factors have been regarded as of prime importance in the control of organisms. Thus many writers emphasize food, others temperature, etc. Merriam has maintained for years that the total of temperature above an arbitrary minimum during the growing season controls the distribution of life in North America. Sanderson has shown that for some insects and some horticultural plants winter temperatures are more important, just as may be the case with organisms like fresh-water sponges and bryozoans having winter bodies, and aquatic plants with seeds and spores. Marine workers emphasize salinity and density. Birge and Juday emphasize oxygen. All these ideas have important bearings on questions of aquatic biology but no one of them is adequate.

Dormancy sometimes makes otherwise insignificant conditions

important. It is a common characteristic of the eggs of rotifers, of crustacea, insects, and other arthropods, and also of the spores and seeds of plants. Many crustaceans deposit eggs in the autumn which require freezing before they will hatch. Some, as for example those of the fairy shrimp (*Eubranchipus*), require both summer drying and winter freezing. The statoblasts of the fresh-water Bryozoa germinate better after freezing or drying. Thus some simple condition such as the rupture of the egg shell or covering may be a requirement for growth as it is in some seeds.

Any scheme that fails to consider the complete physiological life history in relation to complete annual cycles is inadequate. Still, because of the complexity of the problems involved simple indices must be sought which will indicate the condition of waters with reference to as many important factors as possible. These indices must be selected with two facts in mind: First, that there is in each annual cycle of the life of an individual or a species a period of maximum sensitiveness; this falls at or near the breeding period or at the time of appearance of young. Second, adequate measure of hydrographic conditions are to be found in the peculiar character of the annual rhythm rather than in the totals of this or that factor for the year or a particular period.

Many organisms, especially food fishes, deposit their eggs on the bottom. It is to the bottom that the dead bodies of organisms sink and at the bottom that they decompose and produce poisonous substances in greatest quantity. Decomposition of the bodies of plants and animals results finally in gases such as ammonia, carbon dioxide, hydrogen sulphide, methane, etc. The presence or absence of fishes and their animal food is controlled by (a) their ability to recognize the presence of strange or detrimental substances and to turn back when such are encountered, and (b) by their survival or death in situations where they cannot escape the deleterious conditions. Their ability to recognize common injurious substances has been shown to be very marked and precise. The difference between different species is one of degree and special habits. The effects of the various decomposition products are the same in a wide range of species with only slight differences in degree. The less sensitive fishes are usually of less food value. Food fishes usually live associated with organisms which, like themselves, are very sensitive to decomposition products, and usually disappear with the fishes.

Indices are of three types, (1) results of the inspection of the bottom, (2) results of chemical tests of the water for decomposition products, and (3) for fishes the presence or absence of index organisms of a semi-stationary character, such as snails, etc., see p. 52. Here the first two types only will be considered.

If a body of water is to support desirable game fishes it should have an area of terrigenous bottom covered with from 6 inches to 2 feet of water for breeding grounds and an area of submerged (Chara, etc.) and of emerging vegetation to supply food. It is probable that for the best results these three should be about equal. The terrigenous bottom should be comparatively free from putrescible material. Humus which does not contain putrescible material or even the roots of plants may be used by a few game fishes for breeding. The amount of terrigenous (non-putrescible) bottom up to one third that occupied by vegetation and muck is a rough index of the suitability of an ordinary pond or lake (see Fig. 7, p. 58) for game fishes and associated organisms. In river bottom lakes and bayous floods may remove putrescible material and leave bottoms composed chiefly of silt upon which luxuriant vegetation springs up. Forbes has shown that productivity of carp, and fishes generally, bears some direct relation to the area fairly well supplied with submerged vegetation. The second index must be applied to such waters.

The second index is essential but must accord with the first. The chemical character of the water must be such that the fishes will not suffer from it or leave on account of it. Carbon dioxide results from the decomposition of organic matter. In the process oxygen is consumed so that the presence of any large quantity of carbon dioxide nearly always indicates lack of oxygen. While exact figures cannot be given it is probable that the carbon dioxide content of water over breeding grounds (terrigenous bottom) should not average more than three cubic centimeters per liter, nor exceed six cubic centimeters during the summer months. Such amounts are not usually accompanied by lack of oxygen. *Thus the amount of carbon dioxide may be taken as an index of the suitability of the water.* Excessive acidity due to carbon dioxide probably favors the germination of the Saprolegnias, fungi which are very destructive of fish eggs and fishes.

FOOD AND BIOLOGICAL CONDITIONS

Nitrates are necessary for the growth of aquatic plants and an insufficient quantity is secured from mineral soil. Nitrogen can be fixed only by nitrogen fixing bacteria, such as *Clostridium*, an anaërobe, and *Azotobacter*, an aërobe. These bacteria occur on plants and animals in the mud of the bottom of bodies of water. Plants and animals provide carbon compounds for the bacteria; bacteria provide nitrates or nitrites.

Ammonia results from the decomposition of the dead bodies of plants and animals. The bacteria (*Nitrosomonas, Nitrobacter, Nitrococcus*) oxidize it to nitrous acid; nitrous acid, to nitric acid. These acids unite with bases to form nitrates and nitrites. Working against these two sources of nitrate and nitrite are various denitrifying bacteria (*e.g., Bacterium actinopelte*), which reduce nitrogen compounds to free nitrogen. Their work is greatly influenced by temperature. Baur placed nitrate inoculated with *Bacterium actinopelte* at several temperatures with results as follows:

a. Temperature, 25° C.: Denitrification initiated 24 hours after inoculation; in 7 to 11 days later without nitrate.

b. Temperature, 15° C.: Denitrification initiated 4 days after inoculation; in 27 days the solution was without nitrate.

c. Temperature, 4 to 5° C.: Denitrification began 20 days after inoculation; denitrification incomplete 112 days after.

d. Temperature, 0° C.: Denitrification not initiated.

The quantity of life in water is believed to be in proportion to the available nitrogen compounds. The greatest quantity of plankton in the sea is in the polar regions in the summer. It has been suggested that the greater retarding effect of low temperature on the denitrifying organisms as compared with the nitrate producers is a cause of the greater quantity of life in the colder waters. Loeb holds the theory that the greater quantity is due to the longer life of the organism in cold water. Dissolved nitrogen is important for the work of nitrogen fixing bacteria. Oxygen is necessary for the production of CO_2. Carbon dioxide is necessary for the starch building of chlorophyll-containing plants and animals. These green organisms form the chief food basis of all other organisms. Proteids or other complex foodstuffs are necessary for all animals. It is only animals which contain chlorophyll in the form of algæ living symbiotically in their bodies, that can survive without taking in complex foodstuffs. Proteids are made only when starch, nitrates, and several other inorganic foods are present. Because of their proteid and starch demands light is indirectly necessary to animals which can live in darkness.

According to Pütter and Raben, who confirmed his determinations using better methods, sea water, and probably fresh water as well, contains amino-acids, oils, and carbohydrates. Pütter has shown that many aquatic animals absorb nutrition from solution which renders them only in part dependent upon plankton.

Plants are commonly covered with a coating of small organisms, so that animals such as snails may rasp the surface and secure food without eating the plant tissues themselves. One could probably remove all the larger plants and substitute glass structures of the same form and surface texture without greatly affecting the immediate food relations. Aquatic plants are of particular use to animals as clinging, hiding, and nesting-places.

The quantity of plankton has been much studied. Quantity is usually expressed as number of organisms per liter or cubic meter of water, determined by counting a part of a collection; or in cubic centimeters per cubic meter of water. Ward found an average of 11.5 cc. per cubic meter in water from the surface 2 m.; from 2 to 25 m., 3.9 cc.; 25 m. to bottom, 0.4 to 1.5 cc., in Lake Michigan (August). Pine Lake, a small lake adjoining, contained relatively less plankton than Lake Michigan, the surface stratum containing more and the deeper strata much less. Lake Michigan contains twice as much plankton as Lake St. Clair. A small European lake (Dobersdorfer See) contains about ten times as much plankton as Lake Michigan. Kofoid found the average for the year to be 2.71 cc. per cubic meter for the Illinois River and

71.36 cc. per cubic meter the maximum; 684 cc. per cubic meter (Turkey Lake, Ind.) is the largest amount recorded by Juday.

Small streams and lakes with large inflow and outflow have little plankton. Large amount of plankton is usually associated with much CO_2, little oxygen, and a large amount of dissolved carbonate.

The amount of plankton fluctuates from season to season. The maximum for the Illinois River is from April to June. It gradually decreases until December and January, when the minimum is reached. The light of the moon may increase photosynthesis and thus the amount of phyto-plankton (Kofoid). The maximum of Entomostraca was found by Marsh to fall in July, August, and September, differing in different years. In small bodies of water an abundance of plankton is usually, though not invariably, associated with a large quantity of larger animals and rooted plants. Large lakes like the Great Lakes are exceptions to this because of the absence of shallow water vegetation.

Liebig's Law of Minimum has been applied to plankton by Johnstone who states it as follows: "A plant requires a certain number of foodstuffs if it is to continue and grow, and each of these food substances must be present in a certain proportion. If one of them is absent the plant will die; if one is present in a minimal proportion, the growth will also be minimal. This will be the case no matter how abundant the other foodstuffs may be. Thus the growth of a plant is dependent upon the amount of that foodstuff which is presented to it in minimal quantity." The amount of plankton probably follows the same law. All food substances must be present in correct proportions. The amount of plankton may be determined by a deficiency in the amount of one substance.

The quantity of plant and animal life probably increases with the age of bodies of water with small outlet (see Fig. 7, p. 58). This is because foodstuffs are washed in with inflowing water, and because rooted plants absorb food from soil in which they grow, and when they die and decay these foodstuffs are added to the water and made available to plankton and to animals in general. Accordingly, the older the pond and the longer rooted vegetation has grown, the greater the quantity of life up to the time the pond becomes intermittent. This principle is illustrated by an age series of ponds at the south end of Lake Michigan. These are similar in size and age increases in order back from the lake.

TABLE VIII

SHOWING THE NUMBER OF ENTOMOSTRACA IN APPROXIMATELY 90 LITERS OF WATER (AFTER SHELFORD)

Body of water	September 3, 4, 1909	April 30, 1910	Average number of collections in parentheses	Relative age of ponds
Wolf Lake..............	213	2,900	1,556 (3)	1
Prairie Pond I..........	232	9,333	4,781 (3)	6
Prairie Pond II.........	4,115	19,866	11,991 (3)	28
		Aug. 28, 1912		
Pond I.................	556	104	874 (6)	2
Pond VII...............	539	....	927 (6)	14
Pond XIV..............	2,773	133	2,680 (6)	28
Pond XXIX............	1,039	....	....	60*
Pond LII...............	351	2,600	....	104*
Pond LXXXIX.........	2,870	11,400	....	178*
Pond CXV.............	....	2,480	....	190*

Here the number of Entomostraca is greater in the older ponds though some irregularities occur, related to the amount of rainfall. In rainy seasons the increase with age appears almost throughout the series.

*Intermittent ponds which show irregularities.

TABLE IX

SHOWING RATIO OF NUMBER OR QUANTITY OF DIFFERENT ORGANISMS WHEN THE MAXIMUM IS 100 (AFTER SHELFORD)

	Relative age of ponds		
	2	14	28
Rooted vegetation..................	20	60	100
Entomostraca......................	32	35	100
Midge larvae	80	80	100
Sphaeridae	0	50	100
Gilled snails.......................	20	50	100
Lunged snails......................	10	50	100
Amphipoda........................	50	90	100
Crayfishes.........................	10	50	100
Insects............................	40	90	100
Fish...............................	100	87	87

The Entomostraca are rated on the basis of actual count of six collections. The other figures are estimates.

In passing from younger to older ponds an increase is noted in the number of animals, excepting fish. These appear to decrease, probably because of the increasing unsuitability of the ponds as fish breeding places. The oxygen content decreases, particularly on the bottom. The distribution of the fish present in these ponds, in so far as breeding habits were known, was found to be correlated with the distribution of the bottom upon which they breed. This becomes less and less in amount as the ponds grow older.

TABLE X

SHOWING QUANTITATIVE RESULTS OF EXAMINATION OF FACTORS RELATED TO QUANTITY OF PLANKTON

	Pond numbers — age-series			No. of collections
	2	14	28	
Total carbonates in parts per million.	138.800	160.200	160.300	1
CO_2, cc. per liter at bottom..........	0.0	3.4	2.7	2
Oxygen, cc. per liter at bottom.......	6.28	3.47	2.78	4
Bacteria per cc...................	779	2450	3550	2

On the whole the carbonates, CO_2, and bacteria are greater in quantity according to age. Oxygen on the whole is less.

The increase in quantity of animals with increase of soil fertility supports Knauthe's contention that with fishes productivity of water is directly correlated with the richness of the soil. The weak place in Knauthe's ideas lies in the fact that as quantity increases quality decreases. The game basses and sunfishes give way to the more inferior types and these are gradually succeeded by bullheads, mud-minnows and dogfish. This is due to the destruction of breeding bottom for the desirable fishes by putrescible organic matter which results in much carbon dioxide, hydrogen sulphide, ammonia, and lack of oxygen. The German carp comes into such a series rather late and thus productivity in carp is no doubt correlated with a fertile substratum.

The amount and kind of rooted vegetation are very important to animals. Of all the aquatic situations which present themselves the largest lakes have fewest attached plants, and these are all algæ. *Cladophora, Chara* and filamentous algæ are the most common. These do not appear to have been recorded below about 25 meters; some of them require solid bodies for attachment and are probably most abundant on the rock outcrops of shallow water.

The vegetation of young streams consists largely of holdfast algæ similar to those among the rocky shores of a lake. These are of importance to animals. Sluggish streams have rooted aquatic vegetation.

The vegetation is used as breeding places. Eggs are stuck into plant tissues by the predaceous diving beetles (Dytiscidæ) and by the water scorpions (*Ranatra*). Eggs are attached to plants by the electric light bug (Belostomidæ), back swimmers, may-flies, caddis-flies, water scavengers (Hydrophilidæ), long horned leaf beetles (*Donacia*), snails, and many fishes (*Umbra*, and probably *Abramis*). Young animals are often dependent upon plants for shelter, to escape from enemies, etc. Many insects must come to the surface for oxygen. The most important of these are the Dytiscidæ (adults and larvæ), the Hydrophilidæ (adults and larvæ), the back swimmers, *Zaitha*, *Belostoma*, *Donacia*, snails, *Ranatra*, and Haliplidæ. Some, for example *Zaitha* and dragon-fly nymphs, lie in the vegetation and wait for their prey.

Different kinds of vegetation have different values for animals. The bulrush is barren for the following reasons: (1) hardness makes it a bad place for eggs; (2) there are no clinging places; (3) there is little shade; (4) it gives a high temperature in summer; (5) there is no great addition of oxygen by vegetation; (6) it does not afford a suitable place for securing food. *Equisetum* is unfavorable for similar reasons. *Elodea* is excellent; *Myriophyllum*, good; water-lilies and *Chara*, only fair.

ANIMAL COMMUNITIES

Plants and animals select their habitats through physiological characters. Sessile plants and animals have disseminules which usually come to rest in a great variety of conditions and grow to maturity only in those conditions that are suitable to stimulate development. The physiological character of the reproductive bodies and external conditions are responsible for the distribution.

Animals select their environments by one of three methods: (1) by wide dissemination of reproductive bodies and selective survival, (2) by turning back when the environment in which they move about is found to change, and (3) by selection after trial in connection with migration.

Numbers of animals select the same environment because of physiological similarity. All the animals occupying a relatively uniform habitat constitute an animal community. A physiological agreement exists among the animals of a community. The rapids community of a large creek is in a *general agreement* in reactions to certain factors, and *disagreement in respect* to factors differing in intensity vertically. In Fig. 5 is shown a noteworthy agreement in reaction to bottom and current under experimental condi-

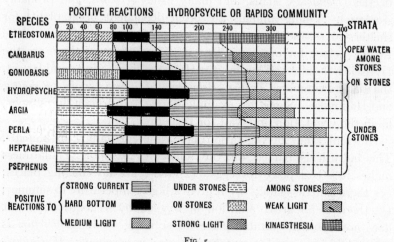

FIG. 5.

To show the agreement and disagreement of the reactions of the animals of the rapids community. Note agreement of reaction to bottom and current and disagreement in two other reactions related to the level at which the animals live. These results were obtained by placing the animals under experimental conditions in which they had a choice between different kinds of bottom, different strengths of light, and in which their behavior in a water current was noted. In the case of water current the percentage of animals headed upstream is given. When headed upstream animals are said to be positive to current. In the case of the other stimuli the percentage of animals in the kind of conditions available was noted and the animals are said to be positive to the conditions in which the greatest number are found. Thus note that the darter (*Etheostoma*) was 80 per cent among the stones and is said to be positive to this kind of situation. It will be noted that if the animals had been 100 per cent positive to the various stimuli the entire 400 units would be occupied in the diagram. This could be true only if there were no other factors entering into the reactions of the animals. The common names of the animals are as follows: *Etheostoma*, darter, *Cambarus*, crayfish; *Goniobasis*, snail; *Hydropsyche*, caddice worm; *Argia*, damsel fly; *Perla*, stone fly; *Heptageninæ*, may-fly sub-family; *Psephenus*, water penny.

tions. The preference for hard bottom in these experiments means the avoidance of sand as only sand and hard bottom were present in the experiments. Animals living under stones were under stones in darkness in the experiments. The snail (*Goniobasis*) which lives on stones was found on stones in the experiments. The darter (*Etheostoma*) and the crayfish (*Cambarus*) which live among stones were found among stones in the experiments. Thus the different animals differ in their relations to bottom and are in disagreement with reference to their vertical distribution in nature. Turning to reactions to light one finds a comparable difference. Animals living beneath stones show a preference for weak light; those living on stones, medium light; those among stones, strong light. If one were to study the community in full one would find that reactions to many other factors are of importance. Associative memory no doubt plays a rôle. Thus there is agreement in reaction to factors of prime importance in the community habitat as a whole and disagreement in respect to factors differing strikingly in the levels in which the animals live within the community habitat. These

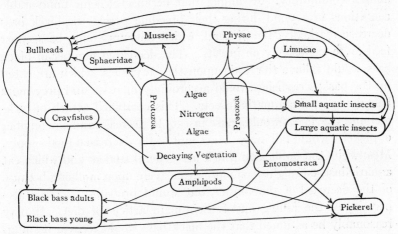

Fig. 6.

Food relations of aquatic animals. Arrows point to animal doing the eating. For explanation see text.

levels are called strata. The pool community shows a striking difference from the rapids community in the presence of a strong preference for sand bottom and in the presence of the burrowing habit, both of which are wanting among the animals of the rapids community. The non-burrowing pool species are positive to current but the burrowing species do not respond within ordinary lengths of time.

Forbes has devised a method by which the frequency of association may be determined for any two or more species. Data regarding such frequency may be obtained from collections made so as to cover several animal communities. The association which would result from an indiscriminate distribution is first eliminated. Then from the total number of collections, the number of collections containing each species, and the number of collections containing both species, he derives a *coefficient of association* by very simple calculations.

Each animal prefers certain food. The food relations of pond animals are shown in Fig. 6. For purposes of illustration one may suppose the existence of a community composed of the species named only.

Any marked change of conditions will disturb the balance in an animal community. Assuming that because of some unfavorable conditions in a pond during their breeding period the black bass decrease markedly, the pickerel, which devours young bass, must feed more exclusively on insects. The decreased number of black bass would relieve the drain upon the crayfishes, which are eaten by the bass; crayfishes would accordingly increase and prey more heavily upon the aquatic insects. This combined attack of pickerel and crayfishes would cause insects to decrease and the number of pickerel would fall away on account of the decreased food supply. Meanwhile the bullheads, which are general feeders and which eat aquatic insects, might feed more extensively upon mollusks because of the decrease of the former, but would probably decrease also because of the falling off of their main article of diet. It may reasonably be assumed that the black bass would recover its numbers because of the decrease of pickerel and bullheads, the enemies of its young. A further study of the diagram shows that a balance between the numbers of the various groups of the community might soon result. Under certain circumstances, such as the extinction of the black bass, the resulting condition would be entirely different from the original one, but a balance between supply and demand would nevertheless finally be established. The community is said to have *equilibrated* when such a condition is reached; that is, a new equilibrium is established, which *may or may not be like the old*.

The causes of fluctuations of numbers of organisms are numerous. Cold winters often destroy aquatic vertebrates. Large rainfall dilutes the plankton and in streams carries it away. Too little sunshine causes a poor production of the chlorophyll bearing organisms which are a food basis of others. Open winters favor denitrification and may be unfavorable to certain lower invertebrates.

Animals fed upon certain kinds of food supply enzymes digesting that kind of food in the proper quantity. The proportion of the different kinds of enzymes changes with changes in diet. Under proper experimental conditions anti-pepsin, anti-trypsin, etc., are developed by organisms. Organisms may develop immunity to toxins introduced into the alimentary canal with food, but the process is a slow one. The introduction of toxins, or bacteria reproducing them, directly into the blood is doubtless a common thing among aquatic animals which are probably as subject to injury and disease as are land animals (see Hill or Rosenau). Various aquatic organisms must possess natural immunity for the various decomposition products of fresh water (see under bacteria, p. 94). Acclimatization must often involve the development of immunity. As knowledge along these lines is increased the conviction that enzymes, toxins, immunity and related phenomena play a very important rôle in the life of fresh-water animals grows proportionately. Lillie has recently found that comparable phenomena are of great significance in connection with the fertilization of the eggs of marine animals and future investigation along these lines will doubtless be of much importance.

Ecological classification must be based upon community of physiological make up, behavior, and mode of life and similarity of habitat. Those natural groups of animals which possess likenesses are the communities which must be recognized. One community ends and another begins where a general more or less striking difference in the larger physiological characters of the organisms concerned occurs. These communities generally occupy relatively uniform environments. For any given organisms the other organisms of the community are a part of the conditions of existence. There is general agreement in the recognition of *strata*, of *associations* as communities based upon minor differences in habitats, and *formations* based upon larger major differences in habitats and considerable agreement in the use of *consocies* and *mores*.

Communities of different orders are given below with taxonomic divisions of corresponding magnitude opposite for comparison. With the exception of the first, these taxonomic groupings do not bear the slightest relation to the ecological groupings, but are added to indicate magnitude.

Ecological Groups	Taxonomic Groups
(Mos) Mores	Form (forms) (species)
Consocies	Genus
Stratum or story	Family
Association or society	Orde:
Formation	Class
Extensive formation	Phylum
(Aquatic and terrestrial)	(Vertebrates and invertebrates)

Mores[1] are groups of organisms in full agreement as to physiological life histories as shown by the details of habitat preference, time of reproduction, reaction to physical factors of the environment, etc. The organisms constituting a mores usually belong to a single species but may include more than one species or one species may occupy two or more habitats and be made of several mores (Shelford; Allee).

Consocies are groups of mores usually dominated by one or two of the mores concerned and in agreement as to the main features of habitat preference, reaction to physical factors, time of reproduction, etc.

Strata are groups of consocies and organisms not so grouped, occupying the recognizable vertical divisions of a uniform area. Strata are in agreement as to material for abode and general physical conditions but in less detail than the consocies which constitute them; for example, the understone stratum of a rapid brook (see Fig. 5, p. 52).

[1] Mores (latin singular mos), "behavior," "habits," "customs"; admissible here because behavior is a good index of physiological conditions and constitutes the dominant phenomenon of a physiological life history and of community relations. This term is used just as form and forms are used in biology, in one sense to apply to the general ecological attributes of motile organisms, in another sense to animals or groups of animals possessing peculiar attributes. When applied in this latter sense to single animals or a single group of animals the plural is used in a singular construction. This seems preferable to using the singular form *mos* which has a different meaning and introduces a second word. The organism is viewed as a complex of activities and processes and *mores* is therefore a plural conception.

A given animal is classified primarily with the stratum in which it breeds, as being most important to it, and secondarily with the stratum in which it feeds and lives, as in many cases most important to other animals. The migration of animals from one stratum to another makes the division line difficult to draw in some cases. Still, the recognition of strata is essential even though a rigid classification is undesirable.

Associations are groups of strata uniform over a considerable area. The majority of *mores, consocies,* and *strata* are different in different associations. A minority of strata may be similar. The term is applied in particular to stages of formation development of this ranking. The unity of association is dependent upon the migration of the same individual and the same *mores* from one stratum to another at different times of day or at different periods of their life histories. Such migration is far more frequent than from one association to another.

Formations are groups of associations. Formations differ from one another in all strata, no two being closely similar. The number of species common to two formations is usually small (*e.g.,* 5 per cent). Migrations of individuals from one formation to another are relatively rare.

The following is a list of the commoner fresh-water communities:

I. Communities of ice, snow, and glacier pools (Moore).

They live at 0° C. or below throughout the year (worms, insects, and crustaceans).

II. Stream Communities (Shelford).

1. Communities of snow and ice fed streams. They live at a little above the freezing point most of the year. Insects are the chief inhabitants.
2. Intermittent Stream Communities
    a. Intermittent rapids — variable conditions and fauna
    b. Intermittent pool — variable conditions and fauna
    c. Permanent pool — variable aquatic conditions and hardy animals
3. Permanent Stream Communities
    a. Spring dominated stages
        (1) Spring *consocies* — often few or no animals on account of water conditions
        (2) Spring brook associations

4. Creek and River Communities
   a. Pelagic sub-formations, independent of bottom and shores
   b. Riffle formation (turbulent water formation)
   c. Sand or gravel bottom formations
   d. Sandy bottomed stream sub-formation, shifting bottom sub-formation, aquatic desert
   e. Silt or sluggish stream communities
      (1) Sluggish-stream sub-formations
      (2) Pelagic formations
      (3) Bare bottom formations
      (4) Vegetation formations

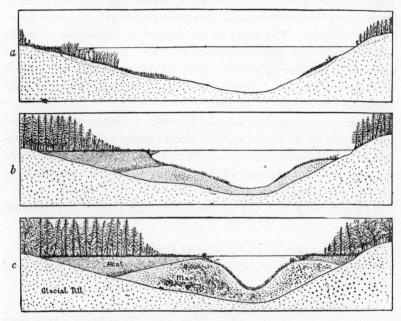

FIG. 7.

Three stages in the history of a glacial lake. *A,* An early stage showing bare bottom, and submerged and emerging vegetation; *B* and *C,* successive stages in the deposition of peat and marl and the migration of the submerged vegetation toward the center; Erosion and bare bottom are indicated near the shore at the right in *A* and *B* but are absent in *C.* The area inside the emerging vegetation is the plankton region. (After Trauseau.)

III. Large Lake Communities (Shelford; Whipple).

1. Pelagic formations
2. Eroding rocky shore sub-formations (turbulent water formations)
3. Depositing, shifting-bottom sub-formations
4. Lower shore formations
5. Deep water formations

IV. Lake-Pond Communities (see Figs. 7 and 8) (Shelford).

1. Pelagic sub-formations
2. Terrigenous bottom formations
3. Vegetation formations
    a. Submerged vegetation associations
    b. Emerging vegetation associations
4. Temporary pond formations (Shelford)

Conditions of existence in fresh water at any given point are changing in a definite direction. This change involves every item of the environment which has been enumerated on the preceding pages. Streams wear down their beds, wear their valleys wider, reduce the speed of their current, grind their coarse bottom materials into the finest silt. The waves of lakes cut away the shores, grind up the rocks they break off in this process, and deposit the silt thus produced in the bottom. Streams lower the outlets of lakes and carry detritus into them.

Ponds and small lakes support vegetation which decays, filling their bottoms with putrescible material which is gradually transformed to humus with a lowering of oxygen and the development of poisonous decomposition products. The ponds and lakes are thus filled as well as drained and all become swamp and finally dry land.

Streams gradually erode their way down to sea level and become meandering base level streams with fine silt bottom, sluggish

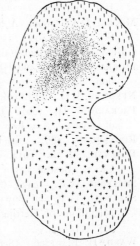

FIG. 8.

Diagrammatic representation of a lake in surface view. Horizontal dashes mark the region of erosion and sandy bottom. Vertical dashes indicate the region of emerging vegetation. Crosses indicate the region of submerged vegetation. Stippling indicates the region of deep water or the hypolimnion. The region of plankton occupies the entire lake except the area of emerging vegetation and that immediately above the bottom. (Original.)

current and an abundance of vegetation. The base level streams and dry land are the ultimate fates of all bodies of fresh water. With the changes enumerated, there is always almost complete change of animal and plant life. The physiological requirements of the life of the first stages of the process are entirely different from those of the last.

IMPORTANT REFERENCES

ADAMS, CHAS. C.   1913.   Guide to the Study of Animal Ecology.   New York.

BIRGE, E. A. and JUDAY, C.   1914.   (See list in Chapter I.)

FORBES, S. A.   1877.   The Lake as a Microcosm.   Peoria Science Assoc.

FOREL, F. A.   1892–1904.   (See list in Chapter I.)

HENDERSON, L. J.   1913.   The Fitness of the Environment.   New York.

HILL, L., MOORE, B., MACLEOD, J. J. R., PEMBREY, M. S., and BEDDARD, A. P.   1908.   Recent Advances in Physiology and Biochemistry.   London.

JOHNSTONE, JAMES.   1908.   Conditions of Life in the Sea.   Cambridge.

MAYER, A. G.   1908.   The Swarming of the Atlantic Palolo.   Carnegie Inst. Pub. 102.

MOORE, J. P.   1899.   A Snow Inhabiting Enchytraeid.   Proc. Acad. Nat. Sci., Phila., 1899 : 125–149.
  Bibliography and general remarks on snow-inhabiting animals.

MURRAY, SIR JOHN and HJORT, J.   1912.   The Depths of the Ocean.   London.

NEEDHAM, J. G. and Lloyd, J. T.   1915.   (See list in Chapter I.)

PACKARD, W. H.   1907.   The Effect of Carbohydrates on Resistance to Lack of Oxygen.   Am. Jour. Physiol., 18 : 164–180.

REGNARD, P.   1891.   (See list in Chapter I.)

ROSENAU, M. L.   1914.   Preventative Medicine and Hygiene.   Sec. II, Ch. 1.   Boston.

SHELFORD, V. E.   1913.   (See list in Chapter I.)

SHELFORD, V. E. and POWERS, E. B.   1915.   An Experimental Study of the Migrations of Herring and other Salt Water Fishes.   Biol. Bull., 28 : 315–334.

WARD, H. B.   1896.   (See list in Chapter I.)

WELLS, M. M.   1915.   The Reaction and Resistance of Fishes in their Natural Environment to Acidity, Alkalinity and Neutrality.   Biol. Bull., 29 : 221–257.

  1915a.   The Resistance and Reactions of Fishes in their Natural Environments to Salts.   Jour. Exp. Zool., 19 : 243–283.

WHIPPLE, G. C.   1898.   Classification of Lakes According to Temperature.   Am. Nat., 32 : 25–53.

CHAPTER III

METHODS OF COLLECTING AND PHOTOGRAPHING

By JACOB REIGHARD

Professor of Zoology in the University of Michigan; Formerly Director of the Lake Laboratory of the U. S. Bureau of Fisheries, at Put-in-Bay, Ohio

METHODS OF COLLECTING

I. VERTEBRATES

1. FISH must be collected under the state laws which usually forbid the use in inland waters of any apparatus except hook and line or dip or lift nets held in the hand. In most states licenses to use nets for scientific purposes may be obtained either from the state fish commission or from the game and fish warden.

(*a*) *Seines* are long nets with a weighted lead line attached to the lower edge and a cork line attached to the upper edge so that the nets remain upright in the water. When the net is so stretched that it forms rectangular meshes "square mesh" is the length in inches of one side of a single square. For use in brooks or for collecting small shore fishes, seines twelve or twenty-four feet long and four or five feet in depth are suitable. The former should be of one-quarter inch square mesh, while the latter may be of one-half inch square mesh.

For larger fish, seines of fifty and one hundred feet in length, five to nine feet deep and of inch mesh should be used, but larger seines are not easily handled by two persons. The longer seines should be of the twine ordinarily used for such purposes and knotted at every crossing. For the shorter lengths the excellent and cheaper "common-sense" minnow seines which are woven to resemble coarse burlap may be used. Very serviceable seines may be made of a good quality of heavy bobbinet which may be had of dealers in dry goods. All seines are much more efficient if provided with a bag at the center, as is the Baird col-

lecting seine, but seines of this form are expensive and not absolutely necessary.

Seines can be used only where the bottom is free from large
stones or deadwood and the water not much obstructed by vegetation. A brail, or stout pole, is fastened by a double half-hitch to
both cork and lead lines at each end of the seine so as to extend
from the cork line to the lead line and keep the seine stretched
between the two lines. The seine is then operated by two persons
each of whom holds a brail in such a way that the lead line is kept
close to the bottom which it sweeps, while the seine forms an arc
of a circle between the two brails. At the end of the haul the
seine is best landed on a gently sloping bank by seizing the lead
line and drawing it in first to the bank. Where the bank does
not afford a suitable landing place a short seine may be "tripped"
in any depth of water by quickly pulling up the lead line until it
lies in the same horizontal plane as the cork line. The seine sag-
ging between the two lines retains the fish. A short seine may be
thrown or cast from a boat in deep water and immediately drawn
in and tripped. Small surface-swimming fishes are caught in this
way. Where a long seine is to be used in water too deep to wade,
a heavy weight is attached to the lower end of one brail so as
to keep it upright in the water. To the same brail a short rope
is so fastened that it extends loosely from one end of the brail
to the other. To the middle of this short rope, or bridle, is
attached a long hauling rope. The end of the seine is then
carried out into deep water by means of a boat and the free
end of the hauling rope brought back to shore, from which the
seine is hauled in by means of the rope. If a hauling rope and
weight are attached to each brail the seine may be set in the water
at any convenient distance from shore and parallel to it and may
then be hauled to shore by means of the ropes.

(b) *Trammel nets* consist of one web of fine twine of about one
inch mesh between two webs of coarse twine of about six inches
mesh. A length of one hundred feet and a depth of six or eight
feet is convenient. The fine-meshed web is much deeper than
the coarser ones and all three are attached between a single
cork line and a single lead line. The net is "laid" in a boat

(see below under gill nets) and is set by stretching it along the seaward edge of vegetation or other shelter in which fish lurk and from which they cannot be taken with other nets. The net may be fastened to stakes or allowed to float in water of about its own depth, where it stands upright like a fence. The fish are then driven from their shelter toward the net, which they strike with such force as to carry the nearly invisible, fine web through the meshes of the coarser webs, so as to form pockets in which the fish are held. The trammel net is easily transported and very effective, especially in slightly turbid water or at night.

(c) *Fyke Nets.* A fyke net is made like a seine, but at its middle is left a circular opening bordered by a hoop of wood or iron. To the hoop is attached the pot, a series of truncated cones of netting open at both ends. The smaller end of the first cone leads into the larger end of the second cone and this often into a third. The last cone of the pot is closed at its smaller end by a draw string. Both ends of the lead and cork lines should be tied into loops and the net should be "laid" in a boat (see below under gill nets) and taken to the place of setting together with two stout poles of suitable length, a rope and a heavy stone or other anchor. The loops at one end are slid over a pole which is then thrust or driven into the bottom. The net is then paid out from the boat rowed in the direction in which it is desired to set it. When the pot is reached it is thrown overboard. When the other end of the net is reached it is fastened to a pole set in the bottom in the manner already described, but the net is left quite slack between the two poles. The pot is then picked up, the rope attached to the terminal funnel and the whole pulled usually toward the shore.[1] The pull causes the net to bend into a V the wings of which stretch from the pot to the poles. The anchor is now attached to the end of the rope and thrown overboard. If the water is deep a small cord with a float at one end is attached by its opposite end to the anchor line and serves to pull up the anchor line when the pot is to be lifted. The anchor line may be tied back to a

---

[1] The larger fish usually taken in a fyke are caught as they go from the vegetation zone or beyond it into shoal water. They might be caught as they *leave* the shoal water by setting the net the other way about.

stake and the anchor dispensed with. Fykes are usually set across
the mouth of a small bay or inlet but may be placed anywhere.
In running water the net may face either up or down stream. It
may be necessary to set a row of stakes across the stream above
the net to catch drift wood. When fish attempt to enter the bay
or inlet across which the net is set, they follow the wings of the
fyke and enter the pot from which they are unable to escape.
The net may be left set for a long time and the fish taken from it
at intervals by lifting the pot and loosening the draw string. The
wings of a fyke may be from fifteen to fifty feet long according to
its location, but for brook use fykes are made without wings.

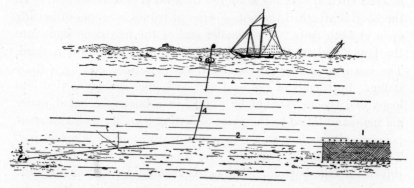

FIG. 9   Showing one end of a gill net as set when used in the cod fishery on the Massachusetts Coast.
1, end of the net.   2, anchor line.   3, anchor.   4, buoy line.   5, buoy.   (After Goode.)

The fyke is an excellent net for catching turtles, but should then
be modified as indicated in the section on turtles (p. 66).

(d) *Gill nets* are made of very fine cotton or linen twine and of
various meshes. Inch or two-inch square mesh and a length of
one hundred or one hundred and fifty feet are useful for collecting.
The nets are intended to be left out for days, at least, on the
bottom in deep water. They stand upright in the water (Fig. 9)
and the fish strike them usually at night and become entangled in
the meshes, so that they are commonly dead when the nets are
lifted.

A small rope of at least the length of the net is attached to one
end of the cork line and a stone or other heavy weight to serve as
an anchor is made fast to the other end of the rope. The anchor

is placed in the boat and the rope carefully coiled near it. The net is then carefully "laid" by folding it back and forth after the manner of a folding fan. It is not necessary to keep the net stretched to its full width between the cork and lead lines. When the opposite end of the net is reached a second and equal anchor line with anchor attached is made fast to the cork line. A number of gill nets may be fastened together end to end and used as a single net, with a single pair of anchor lines and anchors. It is convenient to lay the net on a "setting board" four or five feet long and as wide. The board may be made like a batten door of smooth boards and placed across the stern of the boat, where the net is to be set. The net should be set where it is thought fish will run, as across a narrow neck connecting two parts of a lake or across the mouth of a bay. If the net is set down the wind it may be handled by a single person. The upper anchor is thrown out and, as the boat drifts with the wind, first the anchor line and then the net are paid out, and care is taken that the net is not fouled in going over the side of the boat. When the second anchor line has been paid out to near its middle a small rope, long enough to reach to the surface of the water is made fast to it and to the free end of this is fastened a piece of wood to serve as a float. When the end of the second anchor line is reached, the net is pulled taut, and the second anchor thrown over. The fish may be removed from the net by pulling up the float line until the anchor line is recovered and by then running along this and the cork line of the net, hand over hand, allowing the part of the net that has been examined to fall back into the water.

(e) *Traps.* A cylinder is formed of wire netting of one-fourth or one-half inch mesh. Into one end of this is fitted a cone of the same material with its apex directed inward. The apex is truncated so as to leave an opening two or more inches in diameter. A similar cone may be fitted over the other end of the cylinder or this may be closed by a flat cover of netting. One end of the cylinder must be removable to permit baiting and removal of the fish. The cylinder may be two or three feet long and a foot in diameter and the cone eight inches deep — but larger sizes may be used to advantage. The trap is baited with fish or meat hung near its middle by a wire and is lowered to the bottom at any depth by a cord supported by a float. It is used chiefly for smaller fish, crayfish, or Necturus. It may be set anywhere but is especially useful where water is obstructed by vegetation, rocks, or fallen trees so that nets cannot be drawn.

(f) *Care of nets*. Both fyke nets and gill nets should be taken from the water at intervals, washed, dried, and mended before they are again used. For mending it is necessary to have a supply of twine of which the nets are made and several wooden shuttles or needles such as fishermen use; it is also necessary to learn the knot used in making nets by hand. All nets when taken from the water should be washed and carefully dried before being put away. If left with the twine clogged with accumulated organic matter they rapidly decay and this decay is the more rapid if the nets are damp. They may be stored by hanging them loosely in some dry loft or they may be packed in bags and hung from the ceiling by cords. If left accessible to rats or mice they may be ruined by being utilized as nest material.

In laying a net for storage or transportation the lead and cork lines should each be folded back and forth on itself. The lead line should be so folded that the leads are brought together and they should then be securely tied together. If this precaution is not taken the loose leads, carrying the lead line with them, become woven back and forth through the net and the whole is almost inextricably tangled together.

2. *Turtles*. Turtles are best taken in a turtle net which is a form of fyke net. It should be of heavy twine and coarse mesh and, if it is desired to keep the turtles alive, should be modified as follows: The terminal section of the pot is made cylindrical or the whole pot may be made with square hoops. A circular opening is cut in the upper side of the terminal section of the pot and to this is attached the lower end of a cylinder of netting which extends to the water's surface. The upper end of this cylinder is attached to an opening cut in one side of a wooden box provided on the opposite side with a hinged lid fastened with a hasp. The box is supported at the surface of the water on poles set in the bottom. When turtles reach the terminal section of the pot they are able

to enter the box through the cylinder of netting and are thereby saved from drowning which would ensue if they could not reach the air. They may be removed through the lid at the convenience of the collector.

II. INVERTEBRATES

Invertebrates are to be collected in three situations: in the aquatic vegetation bordering the shore, in the open water, beyond this vegetation-zone, and on the bottom, so that the apparatus suitable to each of these situations may be separately considered.

It is convenient to consider first those methods designed for qualitative work, for finding out what organisms are present, and second those methods by which the number or quantity of organisms present in a unit volume of water or under a unit area of surface may be determined.

A. Collecting in Littoral Vegetation

1. *By dip nets.* The dip net (Fig. 10) is here of greatest use. It consists of a conical netted bag about one foot in diameter and eighteen inches deep attached to a stout ring of brass or iron, firmly fixed to a stiff, wooden handle seven or eight feet long. The lower third of the net may often be advantageously lined with thin, cotton cloth to retain smaller organisms. A form of this net adapted to scraping flat surfaces, such as logs, flat stones, banks, etc., is also shown (Fig. 10). It has a semi-circular rim and a shallow bag of canvas with

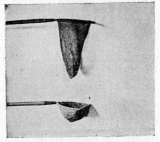

FIG. 10. Two forms of dip net. For description see text. (From photographs by the writer.)

a bottom of No. 6 or 8 bolting cloth. The handles used on dip nets are rake handles. The iron rings may be made by any blacksmith. The bags are sold as minnow dip nets by dealers in fishing tackle or by mail-order houses.

2. *By collecting larger aquatic plants.* With such nets many forms visible to the naked eye may be collected directly, or the

aquatic vegetation may be obtained and searched for smaller organisms. Many forms that are detected with difficulty in the field appear in abundance in the water of small dishes containing aquatic plants, when allowed to stand undisturbed for some days (annelids, flat worms, rotifers, hydras, protozoa, etc.). Submerged vegetation which grows in deeper water and cannot be reached by other means may be obtained by dragging behind a boat the grapple (Fig. 11) described as follows by Pieters (1901): "This is made by passing four or five bent steel wires through a piece of $1\frac{1}{2}$-inch pipe and bending back the free ends to make hooks. The pipe was filled with lead to make it heavier and a rope fastened through the loops of the wires."

FIG. 11. Pieters' plant grapple. (After Pieters.)

3. *The cone dredge.* Many organisms are too small to be readily collected with dip nets and many escape when aquatic vegetation is gathered. These may be readily obtained by this ingenious device of Professor E. A. Birge, which may be run among aquatic plants where the townet cannot be used.

The cone dredge (Fig. 12) now used by Professor Birge consists of four parts.

A. The *body* is a cylinder of sheet copper three inches in diameter and one inch deep, wired at its lower edge to form a lip on the outside. A brass wire bent into a V with an eye at its apex is soldered by its free ends inside the body while its apex extends upward like the bail of a pail.

B. A *cone* of brass wire netting of about twenty meshes to the inch fits over the bail. Its base is soldered to the body and its apex to the eye of the bail which projects through it. Two flat loops of wire soldered to the outside of the body serve for the attachment of cords.

C. The *net* is a conical bag of cheesecloth eighteen to twenty-

FIG. 12. Cone dredge. At bottom funnel-filter for use with the dredge. (Original photograph from apparatus loaned by Professor Birge.)

two inches long and may, by altering the dimensions, be cut out according to the directions given for the townet. It should be faced with strong muslin for two or three inches at each end. It is tied by its upper end over the flange on the body.

D. The *screw tip* consists of the screw top of a kerosene oil can, extended by soldering to the male screw a copper cylinder an inch and a quarter long. The cylinder is wired at its top to form a projecting flange over which the tip of the net is tied. The cap is weighted by soldering to it a lead ring of about two ounces. Two loops of wire soldered to the outside of the screw tip serve for the attachment of cords from the loops on the body and these support the weight of the screw tip and take the strain off the net.

This net may be readily dragged behind a boat among dense water plants by means of a cord attached to the eye. The cone fends off the water plants and lessens the amount of debris entering the net and clogging it. The net may also be thrown from shore to a distance of thirty or forty feet and safely hauled back through thick vegetation. It may also be run at some depth or along the bottom by attaching a suitable weight to the line, two or three feet in front of the cone.

When a haul has been made the screw cap is removed so that the contents of the net fall into a cup or jar of water. Several successive hauls may be united. When the foreign matter which always enters the net has settled to the bottom of the jar, the clear water containing the entomostraca is poured into a metal funnel with a long neck made of brass wire gauze of about forty meshes to the inch (Fig. 12). The neck, which serves as a filter, terminates in a tin ring which is corked. When the entomostraca have been filtered from the water, the cork is removed and the catch washed into an eight-dram homeopathic vial, short form, in which it is preserved.

When many catches from different localities are to be kept separate, Professor Birge uses flat bags, one by three inches, made by stitching together on the sewing machine pieces of India linen. Before going into the field the bags are numbered and strung on a thread so that they may be pulled off in order. The catch is poured through an ordinary tin funnel into the bags, which are then tied and placed in the preservative.

An "improved" form of cone dredge has been described by Wolcott (1901), who has worked out a standard type of holder for cone dredge, dip net, sieve, and scoop. A folding-cone dredge is sold under the name simplex plankton net. Its cone is made of cloth.

The plankton pump may also be used for collecting free swimming forms among aquatic vegetation.

In making collections along the margin of a pond or stream, or in the puddles of a bog or half-dried ditch, it is advantageous to use a dipper with a cane or short bamboo handle. One may fasten to such a handle a wide-mouth bottle, a dipper with fine metal gauze bottom, a pruning hook or other apparatus for securing samples of the plant or animal life in such places as are somewhat inaccessible. A shallow glass dish or white soup plate is very useful in examining immediately refuse obtained from the margin or bottom of such pools. By some such means the heavier particles of sand and silt may be separated from the collection before it is preserved.

B. Bottom Collecting

The dredge that is commonly used in deep-sea work is of little value in fresh water owing to the relative barrenness of lake bottoms. The larger bottom vegetation may be obtained at any depth by the use of Pieters' grapple already described. For the smaller organisms that live in the superficial ooze of the bottom, the cone dredge or the townet may be used. A weight heavy enough to bring the line to the bottom is attached to the towline two or three feet in front of the net. The cone dredge when attached to a weighted line may be made to run along the bottom by weighting the screw tip, but in that case it is well to fasten a band of cloth about the base of the wire cone so as to leave only the upper part free. The net, while admitting water through the tip of the wire cone, then glides over the bottom without scraping up mud. A townet mounted on runners, as shown here (Fig. 13), has been found very useful by the writer for taking organisms just above soft bottom. From the iron ring which supports the mouth of the net four pieces of half-inch band iron extend radially for about three inches and then turn and run parallel to one another for some distance beyond the tip of the net. Here they are bent inward and riveted at the center.

To collect organisms that live in the bottom it is necessary to use some form of dredge that will bring up the bottom material. To bring up the superficial ooze the weight attached to the townet line or cone dredge line may have the form of a rake, or be otherwise irregular, so that it stirs up the ooze and drives animals from it to be caught in the net. For

FIG. 13. Townet on runners, designed by the writer. For description see text. (From an original photograph.)

FIG. 14. Triangle dredge as used by the writer. For description see text. (From an original photograph.)

animals that cannot be thus dislodged the writer has used a triangle dredge (Fig. 14). This consists of a bag of one-fourth-inch square mesh netting, or burlap, or other coarse material, lined at the bottom with muslin and hung from a wrought-iron frame which may be made by any blacksmith. The frame consists of an equilateral triangle, twelve to fifteen inches on each side, of heavy band iron, and of three stout iron rods, one extending from each angle of the triangle at right angles to its surface, to a distance of about three feet. The edge of the triangle is formed into large saw-teeth bent slightly outward so that they tend to dig into the bottom. An eye at each corner serves to attach a rope which extends to the hauling line. The rods serve to keep the triangle upright when the net is drawn along the bottom, so that the mouth of the bag is open and the teeth plow into the bottom.

Another useful type of dredge has the form of a triangular or quadrangular pyramid, whose side and slant height are each about six inches. A number of stout steel wires, about six on each side, are soldered together so as to form the apex of the pyramid, while their opposite ends are bent slightly outward beyond its base, so that they project like the teeth of a comb. The framework thus formed is covered with wire cloth and the apex of the pyramid is filled with lead to the depth of an inch and a half. An eye at each angle serves to attach a cord. This dredge is very effective in collecting bottom mollusca.

C. Open Water Collecting — Qualitative Methods

1. *The townet* is the simplest device for collecting the plankton organisms which abound in the open water. The following direc-tions for making a townet are modified from Kofoid (1898). The completed net (Fig. 15) consists of a conical bag of India linen or better of silk bolting cloth hung from a ring which is sup-ported by three cords. The bolting cloth may be number 12, 16 or 20 and is to be had from dealers in mill supplies, but discarded cloth may often be obtained from flour mills. Before cut-ting the cloth should be shrunk by boiling in soapsuds and then pressed. A pattern for cutting two nets twelve inches in diameter from a yard of forty-inch wide bolting cloth is given (Fig. 16). The cloth has been doubled lengthwise (with the warp) and is shown with the fold at the right and the two free edges at the left. With a radius equal to the length of the cloth two arcs are struck from the points a and b as centers. These arcs, which form the tops of the completed nets, must be equal in length to one-half the circumference of the net hoop and these lengths may be most readily determined by rolling the net ring along the arcs. An additional width must be allowed on the piece d, since this is in two parts and has two seams. This is accomplished by cutting the two pieces apart along the line ab a quarter of an inch to the right of the diagonal. The pieces are then formed into cones and closed by a French seam along the side and by the seam across the apex. The top of the net is finished by sewing on a band made of a doubled strip of butcher's linen, cut bias and provided with a heavy cord sewed into its upper margin. The net is attached to the ring by over-cast stitches of heavy thread. The ring r (Fig. 15) of

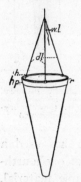

Fig. 15. Simple townet without bucket. *h*, wire rings for draw lines. *dl*, draw lines. *hp*, head piece sewn to top of net. *r*, net ring. *wl*, weight line. (Modified from Kofoid.)

No. 5 spring brass wire, standard American gage, has three pairs
of wire rings *h* soldered on it at equal distances to hold the
drawlines *dl* in place.   To the drawlines at
their junction a short cord *wl* may be attached
for the support of a weight.

If the net is used in this form the catch
must be removed from it by turning it inside
out and sousing the tip in a bottle of water.
It is more convenient to cut off the tip of
the net along the line *ij* and tie into it a
screw tip like that described above for the
cone dredge, but without the weight.   A short
glass tube closed by a rubber stopper or a
bucket like that of the plankton net may be
used in place of the screw tip.   Provided with
a bucket the net is identical with the plankton
net except that it lacks the canvas cone.

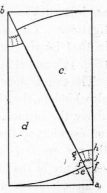

Fig. 16. Showing method of
laying out a pattern for cutting two townets from a
yard of cloth forty inches
wide. *a-b*, line along which
cloth is to be cut. *c-d*, the
two net patterns. *e-f*, seam
by which the bottom of the
net is closed if no bucket is
attached (see Fig. 15). *g-h*,
line of attachment of bucket.
i-j, line along which net is
cut off when bucket is used.
(After Kofoid.)

The townet may be dragged behind a boat
either at the surface or submerged to any depth
by means of a weight attached to the weight
line.   When the haul is completed the net is
soused in the water or water is thrown on its outer surface, until
the contents are washed to the tip of the net, which is then turned
inside out and the contents obtained by rinsing the tip in a bottle
of water, or allowing them to fall into preserving fluid.   The pro-
cedure for a net provided with a bucket is described under the
plankton net and cone dredge.

2. *Plankton Cylinders.*   Various forms of apparatus have been
designed for collecting plankton from a rapidly moving boat.   These
are made with a very small opening for the entrance of water and
with a large filtering surface.   They are designed to reduce the
pressure of the water on the filtering surface.   They are described
by Steuer and others.   They are chiefly of use in the sea or in
other situations accessible only to large vessels and are little employed in fresh water.   The plankton cylinder is one form of such
apparatus in which a torpedo-shaped metal jacket admits water
through a small opening on its conical end and carries the filtering
gauze in the interior or on its other end.

D. Quantitative Methods in Open Water

1. *The Quantitative Plankton Net.* The plankton net and pump
are intended for the collection of plankton for quantitative investigations. *The plankton net* differs from the townet described
in that its rim extends upward into a truncated cone of canvas
(Fig. 17), and that it is provided with a removable bucket.

The canvas cone hinders bottom ooze from entering the net and
also hinders the slopping out of the contents as the net is drawn
above the surface. It serves further to lessen the diameter of the
net opening, so that a larger fraction of the column of water above
the net opening is filtered and less of it is pushed aside by the
resistance of the filtering gauze.

The plankton net (Fig. 17) in use at the University of Wisconsin
is here first described with the permission of Professor Birge. The
ring which supports the net is about
seven inches in diameter and from this
measurement the other dimensions of
the apparatus may be roughly measured
on the figure. The canvas cone stretches
from the net ring to an upper ring and
both rings are of one-eighth-inch spring
brass wire. Three eight-shaped pieces
of lighter wire are strung on each ring
through one opening, while the other
opening receives the eyes on the ends
of three connecting rods which hold the
two rings together. The upper supporting ring has three brass rings soldered to
it for the attachment of the draw lines.
The canvas cone and the band, which
is ordinarily sewn to the top of the net,

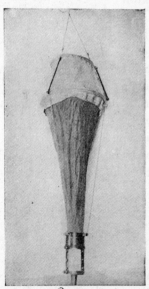

Fig. 17. Wisconsin plankton net.
(Original photograph from apparatus loaned by Professor Birge.)

are in this case cut from one piece of
shrunken canvas. This is sewn around
the upper supporting ring and is attached
to the inside of the lower ring by means of a tape sewn to its outside. The bolting cloth net (No. 16 or No. 20 cloth) is sewn to

the inside of the band, with its margin turned back over its outer surface for the fraction of an inch.   By this construction the canvas cone folds conveniently for transportation, while the inner surfaces of cone and net are continuous and smooth, so that plankton organisms do not readily lodge on them.   If convenience in transportation is not important the cone may be better made of sheet brass.

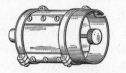

FIG. 18.   Bucket of Wisconsin plankton net. From apparatus loaned by Professor Birge.   At right is one of the writer's tubes for filtering plankton.   For descriptions see text.   (From original photographs.)

The original feature of this net is the bucket (Figs. 18 and 19), which is made of telescope tubing of two sizes.   The smaller size (two inches in internal diameter) is used to make the *headpiece* shown attached to the net in Fig. 17.   This (Fig. 19, *a*) is one and three eighths inches long and is fastened to the net by means of a brass band clamp (Fig. 19, *b*) made of two pieces, with wings at the ends through which pass clamp screws. A pin soldered into the headpiece fits a hole in each half of the clamp and prevents its turning when the bucket is twisted to remove it (seen near the upper margin of Fig. 19, *a*). Three brass rings soldered to the outside of the band clamp serve to attach cords which extend to the lower supporting ring of the canvas cone and carry the weight of the bucket.

FIG. 19.   Headpiece and bucket of the Wisconsin plankton net.   *a*, headpiece; *b*, headpiece clamp; *c*, bucket; *d, e*, lower and upper band clamps; *f*, one of the side clamps with screws; *g*, side clamp in position; *h*, semi-cylindrical rod soldered to strip between windows; *i*, stem of the plug which closes the spout seen below at left of *c*; *j*, millimeter scale.   For description see text.   (From original photograph of apparatus loaned by Professor Birge.)

The *bucket* (Fig. 18) is made of telescope tubing of a size which fits over that used for the headpiece.   Pieces are cut from the sides of this so as to form four windows separated by strips about one-half inch wide. These strips are strengthened by soldering to the inside of each a semi-cylindrical rod about one-quarter inch in diameter (Fig. 19, *h*).

The bottom of the bucket which is conical and ends in a tapering spout is shrunk into place flush with the lower edge of the windows, after heating the bucket in a jet of steam. A taper plug of brass, with a long stem (Fig. 19, *i*) which ends in a milled head, is inserted from within and closes the spout. The edge of the bucket has an L-shaped incision which receives a pin soldered to the outside of the headpiece so as to form a bayonet catch which holds the bucket in place on the headpiece. The four windows in the bucket are closed by a single piece of bolting cloth, held in place by a band clamp at top and bottom (Fig. 19 *d*, *e*) and by four side clamps *g* screwed between the windows. The holes for the screws are conveniently burned through the bolting cloth with a hot wire.

A cheaper bucket described by Kofoid (1898) is shown in section in Fig. 20. It is a cylinder of sheet copper around the top of which

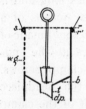

FIG. 20. Simple townet bucket as seen in section. *b*, conical bottom. *dp*, drip point. *rr'*, wire rings soldered to top of bucket. *s*, string by which tip of net is tied to the bucket between the two wire rings. *t*, tube at center of bottom for emptying bucket. *wg*, wire gauze in one of the three windows cut in sides of bucket. The rubber stopper with wire handle is seen at center of bucket. (After Kofoid.)

are soldered two light-wire rings, which serve to hold in place the string *s*, which ties the tip of the net to the bucket. In the sides of the cylinder are cut three equidistant windows, each one and one-half by one and three-quarters inches, which are closed by brass wire gauze *wg*, soldered to the edges. Gauze containing two hundred meshes per linear inch answers very well for these windows. The bottom of the bucket is a cone of copper with a central opening which continues into a short, obliquely-pointed tube *t*. The opening is closed by a rubber stopper with a wire handle which extends above the top of the bucket and is bent into a loop.

The *net* is constructed like the townet, except that the tip is cut off at the point *ij* (Fig. 16) and the silk slit along the dotted lines between *gh* and *ij* to allow for the fitting and fastening of the bucket in place.

The plankton net is drawn from the bottom to the surface, and the organisms that have been caught in it are washed into the bucket by throwing water onto the outside of the net, or by sousing it in the water. The net is then lifted above the water, the bucket removed, and the water allowed to drain from it. When only so much water remains as fills the conical bottom of the bucket, the stopper is drawn and the contents allowed to fall into a suitable container. Organisms adhering to the inside of the bucket are then rinsed into the container with a little filtered or distilled water from a wash bottle. If the contents are to be preserved they may be allowed to fall directly into a bottle which contains the preservative or fixing fluid, so concentrated that the addition of the plankton brings it to its normal constitution. Ninety-five per cent alcohol may be used and in that case the plankton may be allowed to fall from the bucket into about three times its own volume of alcohol, so that it is preserved in alcohol of about 70 per cent strength.

If it is desired to use a fixing fluid before preservation in alcohol, the stronger picrosulphuric acid may be diluted with two volumes of water and three volumes of this may be used to one of plankton, so that the latter is fixed in Kleinenberg's solution. Other fluids may be used in like manner, adapted either to the plankton as a whole, or to special groups of plankton organisms. The plankton is then best caught in a strainer made by removing the bottom of a short eight-dram homeopathic vial and tying bolting cloth over the neck (Fig. 18). The plankton may be kept in this strainer by tying bolting cloth over the bottom, and the strainer may then be passed through fixing fluids and grades of alcohol. The fluids may be made to enter the strainer by withdrawing the air by means of a pipette held against the bolting cloth (Reighard, 1894).

Plankton nets may be made closable and various devices have been used for this purpose (*e.g.*, by Marsh, 1897). Such a net may be lowered, drawn upward any desired distance, then closed and drawn to the surface. It thus filters only that part of the column of water through which it is drawn while open, and aids the investigator to determine what forms occur at various depths.

Although the plankton net may seem to filter a vertical column of water, the base of which is equal in area to the net opening, it does not in practice do this. The resistance of the net gauze causes a certain part of this column to be pushed aside. The part pushed aside not only is greater as the net moves faster but is increased as the net becomes clogged and is therefore greater toward the end of the haul than at its beginning. The filtering capacity of the net gauze is further liable to change with age, as its pores clog and its threads loosen and tend to obstruct the openings. Although elaborate methods have been devised for determining the errors of the plankton net, no one of them is satisfactory.

2. *The Plankton Pump.* The difficulties encountered in the use of the plankton net for accurate quantitative work have led to the development of the plankton pump, which is now largely used in conjunction with the ordinary plankton net and which, used in that connection, has nearly displaced the closable plankton net (Birge, 1895; Marsh, 1897) in fresh water. This may be any pump which delivers at each stroke a known and constant volume of water. The water is drawn through a hose which extends from the pump to any desired depth and may terminate in a metal cone, closed by very coarse wire netting, which serves to exclude foreign bodies from the hose. From the pump the water may be conveniently delivered through a shorter hose to some device for filtering the plankton from it. For this purpose a plankton net is used. The net may be suspended in air and the water pumped into it, but some small organisms are thus forced through the net gauze and lost, and others are doubtless injured by the impact of the stream of water and the weight of the water in the net. This is avoided if the net be held under water with only the canvas cone above the surface. The whole operation may be readily carried out by one person if the net be supported in the water by a wooden float surrounding the cone (Fig. 23) and the delivery hose be attached to the net (Kofoid, 1897). When sufficient water has been pumped, the net is taken up and the catch removed and treated in the usual way.

The end of the suction hose may be allowed to remain at any desired depth during the pumping. The pump is calibrated so that the volume of water delivered at each stroke is known. The number of strokes made during any haul is counted, so that a simple calculation gives the total volume of water pumped.

The end of the hose may also be lowered to near the bottom and may then, while pumping is in progress, be slowly drawn upward at a uniform rate. In this way is pumped a vertical column of water which extends from the bottom to the surface, and the volume of such a column may be calculated.

The following forms of plankton pump may be referred to briefly.

(a) *Fordyce pump* (Fordyce, 1898). This invention of Professors Ward and Fordyce is shown in perspective (Fig. 21) and in section (Fig. 22). It "is practically a force pump. . . . The cylinder

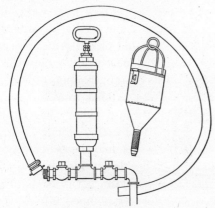

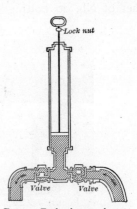

FIG. 21. Fordyce's pump and strainer. For description see text. (After Fordyce.)

FIG. 22. Fordyce's pump in sections. For description see text. (After Fordyce.)

of the pump is eleven by three and one-half inches and has a capacity $347\frac{1}{2}$ cubic inches per stroke. The stroke of the piston is definite in length and is regulated by a lock nut as shown in the plate. The valves used are finely-ground check valves, to which it is believed the accuracy of the working of the apparatus is largely due. The pump is connected with the water by a hose one and one-half inches in diameter, whose lower end is adjusted to the various vertical zones of water by means of attachment to a floating block."

For filtering the water Fordyce uses the device shown in Fig. 21, at the right of the pump. This is similar to the device already described in connection with the Wisconsin plankton net, and is used in the same way. It is provided with a rim to which a cover of wire netting may be attached to exclude foreign matter. A net of bolting cloth may be attached outside the wire gauze filter, and the whole instrument is then adapted for the various work of the ordinary net.

On account of its cheapness and portability a pump of this form is probably best adapted for work not carried on from a station especially equipped for aquatic biology.

(*b*) *The clock pump* has been used for some years at the University of Wisconsin (Juday, 1904). At Wisconsin the pump is fixed to the bottom of the boat and the water, drawn through a half-inch garden hose, is pumped into a submerged plankton net of No. 20 bolting cloth.

Fig. 23. Thresher tank-pump in use. The water reaches the pump through the hose at the left and is delivered to the net through the hose at the right. The net cone is seen supported by a rectangular wooden float. (After Kofoid.)

(*c*) *The thresher tank-pump*, a double-acting force pump with two cylinders each six by nine inches, has been used by Kofoid (1897). The mode of using the pump is shown (Fig. 23). This pump is fastened to the boat and is too heavy to be carried or to be used apart from a permanent mounting.

3. *The Water Bottle.* To obtain small samples of water for the study of the nannoplankton a water bottle may be used. Many complicated and expensive forms of these bottles have been devised (see Helland-Hansen) for use at all depths in the sea. The bottle described by Theiler appears to be the simplest and least expensive of them. For use in fresh water a Meyer's bottle (Fig. 24) serves fairly well and is easily made. A stout glass bottle of one or

two liters capacity, and with a good-sized neck is provided with a
tight rubber stopper to which is attached the draw-cord by which
the bottle is to be lowered and the stopper drawn.   Beneath the
bottle is attached a weight a little heavier than needed to sub-
merge the empty stoppered bottle.   The bottle may be lowered
to a depth of a hundred feet or less and the stopper removed
by jerking on the draw-cord.

E. Quantitative Study of the Net Plankton

If the plankton net were a perfect instrument it should catch
all the organisms contained in the vertical column of water through
which it is drawn, that is, in a column of the diameter of the net
opening and equal in height to the distance through which the
net is drawn.   But the net filters only a part of the column of
water through which it is drawn, a part which depends on the age
of the net, the rate at which it is drawn and upon
the rapidity with which it becomes clogged while
being drawn.   If the net is of the form described
above, is cleansed by throwing a stream of water on
it after each haul and is drawn at about the rate
of one meter per second, it filters about 40 per cent
of the column of water which it traverses.   Hence,
to know the total amount of plankton in the column
of water traversed by the net, we must multiply the
amount actually taken by two and one-half.   This
number is called the coefficient of the net.   The
coefficient depends on the construction of the net,
on the fineness of the gauze used, and on the rate
at which the net is drawn, and must therefore be
determined by calculation for each net for the
different rates.   Not only does the net filter but a
part of the water and a different part at different
times, but it removes from the water filtered only
a part of the organisms contained in it.   Even the
finest gauze permits a *leakage* through it of very many small
organisms.   Owing to the sources of error indicated the net
method is useful chiefly with the larger organisms, such as crus-

Fig. 24.   Meyer's
bottle.   (After
Wiley and Jones.)

tacea.   Smaller organisms escape in variable quantity and the
smallest are not caught at all.   When the pump is used a known
volume of water is drawn from a known source and all of this is
filtered, so that the source of error arising from a varying and
uncertain net coefficient is eliminated.   The leakage error remains
uncorrected so long as a net is used to separate the
plankton from the water.   The plankton obtained
by nets whether directly or by aid of the pump
may be treated quantitatively by the following
methods:

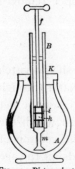

FIG. 25. Piston pipette
as designed by Hen-
sen.   A, glass vessel
which contains di-
luted plankton.   B,
strong glass tube. In-
side the tube is a pis-
ton made of alternate
layers of metal i and
cork h, held together
by screws; m, spool-
shaped metal piece at-
tached to the piston.
Its flanges fit the
glass tube accurately.
The space between its
spindle and the glass
vube is of known vol-
ume; f, piston-rod
with handle; K, cover
of vessel. (From Ap-
stein, after Hensen.)

(a) The *volume* may be obtained by allowing the
alcoholic material to stand for 24 hours in graduated tubes (carbon tubes of the chemist) until it has
settled, when the volume may be read off.   There
is thus obtained in cubic centimeters the volume of
one catch and from this may be calculated the volume per cubic meter or under one square meter of
the original water.

(b) The approximate *weight* may be obtained by
drying the sample on filter paper and weighing it.
The net weight is obtained by deducting the weight
of the filter paper, and from this the number of
grams of plankton per cubic meter of water or under
one square meter of surface may be calculated.

(c) *Chemical analyses* may be made of the dried
material and from these the quantities of the
various constituents: ash, organic material, silica, etc., may be
calculated per cubic meter of water or per square meter of
surface.

(d) The *organisms may be counted* in the Sedgwick-Rafter cell.
The ordinary plankton catch is so concentrated that it is impossible to count the organisms in it until it has been diluted.   A
measured quantity of water added to the plankton for this purpose replaces the alcohol or fixing fluid.   This water is then agitated
to distribute the organisms uniformly through it and a carefully
measured sample is taken from it with a specially constructed pipette
provided with a piston (Fig. 25).   The organisms in the sample are

then counted by transferring the sample to a glass cell under the microscope.   If the bottom of the cell is ruled in squares the contents of a certain number of these may be counted without the use of the eyepiece micrometer and the whole number present in the cell estimated.   In the case of the larger and rarer organisms it is best to count all that the cell contains.

Since the total volume of water from which the catch was made is known, the number of each sort of organism per cubic meter of water or under each square meter of surface may be easily calculated, or the numbers in the entire lake may be approximately determined.

F. Quantitative Study of the Nannoplankton*

The nannoplankton may be studied in two ways, namely, by enumerating the various organisms, or by obtaining a sufficient quantity to determine its dry weight.   In the former method the organisms may be counted directly, which is very desirable for the more abundant forms, or they may be concentrated either by filtering or by centrifuging.   The filters that are most generally used for concentration are hard surface filter paper and sand. When filter paper is used the filtered organisms are carefully washed from the paper, the volume of the wash water containing the organisms is taken, and samples of it are then used for enumeration.   It is necessary to use hard surface filter paper in order to prevent undue loss of organisms in the meshes of the paper.   Even with the best quality of hard surface paper, many individuals become embedded in the meshes so firmly that they cannot be washed out. For all counting the Sedgwick-Rafter counting cell is to be used.

The Sedgwick-Rafter sand filter as described by Whipple has been used extensively in sanitary work.   In this method also there is a considerable loss of organisms since some of them are so small that they pass between the grains of sand and since it is practically impossible to separate all of the organisms from the sand after filtration.   In all filtering methods the filters soon become clogged, which decreases the rapidity of the filtering very markedly.

* This section has been prepared by Chancey Juday of the Wisconsin Geological and Natural History Survey.

The centrifuge is the most convenient as well as the most efficient instrument for obtaining the nannoplankton. A rather high speed machine is best, one which makes 2500 or more revolutions per minute, and the electrically driven type is most satisfactory. For most fresh-water organisms the sedimentation is complete in five to eight minutes at this speed, but occasionally for some forms a second centrifuging is necessary. In bodies of fresh water the nannoplankton is usually so abundant that only a small quantity of water, not more than 15 cc., is required for a sample. Thus the standard makes of centrifuges will serve for such investigations. The glass tube which holds the sample of water should be well tapered at the bottom. This form concentrates the material on a small area from which it can be removed more conveniently as well as more completely. The material is taken up together with one cubic centimeter of water in a long pipette and is then transferred to a Sedgwick-Rafter counting cell. This cell and its use are fully described by Whipple. Sometimes it is desirable to centrifuge 50 or even 100 cc. in order to study the rarer forms. For enumeration studies a combination of the direct counting and the centrifuge methods gives the most satisfactory results.

Whenever possible, living material should be used for the counting. The samples may be preserved in formaldehyde neutralized with sodium carbonate and then centrifuged at a later time, but some of the monads are recognized with difficulty after preservation. Most of the flagellates do not move rapidly enough to offer any serious difficulty in counting them alive but the ciliates do. When the latter are present, it is best to make a special count for them. They are readily killed by placing a drop of iodine solution in the corner of the counting cell before the sample is introduced.

Material for a study of the dry weight as well as the organic matter of the nannoplankton may be obtained either by filtering a relatively small sample of water through a coarse-grained alundum cone or by passing a large sample of water through a power centrifuge that acts continuously. In the former process the sample of water, from one to five liters, is filtered through the cone and the material and cone are then thoroughly dried in an oven. The weight is taken and the cone is weighed again after having been ignited. The loss in weight represents the organic matter.

Larger samples of material are needed for more accurate quantitative work, and especially for the study of the chemical composition of the nannoplankton. For the latter purpose at least two or three grams of organic matter are required. In order to secure this amount, even from a lake which is rich in plankton, it is necessary to centrifuge one to two thousand liters of water. This process requires an apparatus that will act continuously. For this work the Wisconsin Geological and Natural History Survey is using a De Laval clarifier and filter, belt style, A size, in which the water is first centrifuged and then filtered. This machine has a maximum speed of 6000 revolutions per minute and will both centrifuge and filter from ten to twelve liters per minute. In general about ninety per cent of the material is deposited in the bowl of the centrifuge and ten per cent on the filter papers. This method requires a special laboratory and equipment (*cf.* Juday, 1916).

Very little is known of the bacterial portion of the nannoplankton. The culture methods used for the other bacteria do not seem to be well adapted to the strictly aquatic forms and only a small part of them can be obtained with a centrifuge. Recently, however, it has been found that the direct count method of Brew can be used for determining the number and distribution of aquatic bacteria, but no results have thus far been published.

G. *Special Methods for Invertebrates*

Special methods for collecting and preserving various sorts of fresh-water organisms are described in the chapters devoted to invertebrate groups. To secure the best results it is necessary to become familiar with the habits of the animals. The collection of the larvæ of aquatic insects is facilitated by the use of the ingenious apparatus made by the Simplex Net Company. The imagos of many such insects are readily collected at night by some one of the forms of traps used by entomologists in which a light serves as a lure.

UNDER-WATER PHOTOGRAPHY

If the water is clear and the surface unruffled, near objects may be seen almost as clearly in natural waters as in air. If the camera be pointed at them, the resulting picture rarely shows more than the *surface* of the water, as opaque as that of milk and with as little visible beneath it. It is as though the camera has been pointed at the blue sky. This result is due to the light of the sky and other distant objects reflected from the surface of the water into the camera. This strong light, which the eye neglects, obscures in the negative the effects of the weaker light from objects beneath the

FIG. 26. The screen shown in use for photographing objects under water. For description see text. (From an original photograph.)

surface of the water; if it be cut off by a screen these objects may be photographed.

This is shown (Fig. 26) in a photograph of the nest of a black bass in about eight inches of water. Little can be seen beneath the water, except within the reflected image of the screen. Within this image the reflected sky light is cut off, although the sun shines from the left full upon the nest of clean stones. What is clear in the photograph lies not within the shadow of the screen but within its image. A longer exposure would have given a clear picture of what lies within the narrow shadow at the bottom of the screen. In field practice a serviceable and portable screen may be made by tying a square of black, opaque cloth to two poles stuck slanting in the bottom.   Occasionally dense foliage, a bridge or building is so placed as to form a natural screen, within the image of which photography is possible.

If the surface of the water is rough the photograph may be made through the bottom of a water glass (Fig. 27).   The glass (Fig. 28) is a frame of galvanized iron with a bottom of plate glass. The bail of band iron serves to hold the screen (Fig. 27).   The glass shown here is two feet square and is supported on legs run through thimbles at the corners and held in place by set screws. That shown in Figure 28 is a foot square and is intended to float. At the left is shown a cover for the bottom of the water glass.   This protects the glass during transit.

FIG. 27. Water glass supported on legs as used in rough water of a brook. For description see text. (From an original photograph.)

The difficulties arising from the rough or reflecting surface of the water may be overcome by placing the camera beneath that surface. For this purpose a reflecting camera is to be preferred, since it permits focusing with the sensitive plate uncovered.   Any dealer in photographic goods can supply catalogues of such cameras showing their mechanism.   Here it need only be said that the ground glass is placed in the top of the camera and the operator looks at it through a hood extending from the top of the camera. He focuses the full-sized image on the ground glass and while looking exposes the plate by pressing a button at the side of the camera.   For use under water such a camera is placed in a water-tight box (Fig. 29), with a plate glass front through which the lens looks.   The hood of the camera extends into the pyramidal lid of the box and the operator looks into it through a second plate of glass.   A milled head, shown on the right of the box, is connected through a water-tight stuffing box with the focusing head of the camera, while a similar arrangement on the opposite side of the box operates the mechanism which controls the exposure. The operator wades and holds the box beneath the surface of the water with only the upper part of the hood exposed. With the right hand he focuses, with the left he makes the exposure.

FIG. 28. Floating water glass. For description see text. (From an original photograph.)

FIG. 29. Water-tight metal box with plate-glass front for enclosing a reflecting camera when used under water. For description see text. (From an original photograph.)

After each exposure the box must be opened to change the plate. For details the reader should consult the literature cited.

Means of Securing Collecting Apparatus

The various types of commercial nets described may be had of dealers in fishing nets. The Simplex Net Company of Ithaca, N.Y., supplies ingenious folding townets, plankton nets, and dip nets. The special apparatus mentioned can be constructed by any skilled mechanic under direction.

IMPORTANT REFERENCES ON APPARATUS AND METHODS

APSTEIN, C. 1896. (See list in Chapter I.)

BIRGE, E. A. 1895. (See list in Chapter I.)

FORDYCE, CHAS. 1898. A New Plankton Pump. Proc. and Coll. Neb. State Hist. Soc., 2: 293–296.

HELLAND–HANSEN, B. 1912. The Ocean Waters, an Introduction to Physical Oceanography. I. General Part (Methods). Int. Rev. ges. Hydrob. u. Hydrog., Hydrogr. Suppl., 1. ser., Heft 2.

HENSEN, V. (See list in Chapter I.)

JUDAY, CHANCEY. 1896. The Plankton of Turkey Lake. Proc. Ind. Acad. Sci., 1896. (Description of plankton net and its use.)

    1904. The Diurnal Movement of Plankton Crustacea. Trans. Wis. Acad. Sci. Arts. and Letters, 14: 534–568, 2 figs. (Clock pump and its use.)

    1916. Limnological Apparatus. Trans. Wis. Acad., 18: 566–592, 5 pl. Received too late for adequate consideration in the text.

KOFOID, C. A. 1897. Plankton Studies. I. Methods and Apparatus in Use in Plankton Investigations at the Biological Experiment Station of the University of Illinois. Bull. Ill. State Lab. Nat. Hist., 5: 1–25, 7 pl.

    1898. Hints on the Construction of a Tow Net. Jour. Appl. Micros., 1: 111–113, 5 figs.

    1903. (See list in Chapter I.)

KOLKWITZ, R. 1907. Entnahme und Beobachtungs-instrumente für biologische Wasseruntersuchungen. Mitth. Kgl. Prüfungsamt f. Wasserversorg. u. Abwasserbeseit. zu Berlin, Heft 9: 111–144, 22 figs.

MARSH, C. D. 1897. On the Limnetic Crustacea of Green Lake. Trans. Wis. Acad., 11: 179–224, 10 pl. (Description of closable net.)

NEEDHAM, JAMES G. 1903. An Outdoor Equipment for College Work in Biology. Am. Nat., 37: 867–874, 2 figs. (Description of plankton apparatus.)

REIGHARD, JACOB. 1894. (See list in Chapter I.)

    1898. Methods of Plankton Investigation in Their Relation to Practical Problems. Bull. U. S. Fish Comm., 17: 169–175.

    1908. The Photography of Aquatic Animals in their Natural Environment. Bull. U. S. Bureau Fish., 27: 41–68, 4 pl.

    1909. An Experimental Field Study of Warning Coloration in Coral Reef Fishes. Carnegie Inst., Washington, Publication 103: 257–325, 5 pl. (Contains reproductions of photographs made with camera under water.)

    1910. Methods of Studying the Habits of Fishes, with an Account of the Breeding Habits of the Horned Dace. Bull. U. S. Bureau Fish., 28: 1111–1136, 7 pl.

RUTTNER, FRANZ. 1914. Ueber einige bei der Untersuchung der Lunzer Seen verwendeten Apparate und Gerätschaften. Int. Rev. ges. Hydrob. u. Hydrog., 6: 53–62, 1 pl.

STEUER. 1910. (See list in Chapter I.)

THEILER, A. 1914. Ein neuer Wasser- und Planktonschöpfer nach Friedinger. Int. Rev. ges. Hydrob. u. Hydrog. Biol. Suppl. Band 6, Heft 4.

WARD, H. B. 1896. (See list in Chapter I.)

WARD, R. H. 1895. Improved Methods of Collecting Aquatic Micro-organisms. Amer. Mo. Micr. Jour., 16: 33–41, 1 pl.

WHIPPLE, G. C. (See list in Chapter I.)

WOLCOTT, R. H. 1901. A Modification of the Birge Collecting Net. Jour. Appl. Micros., 4: 1407–1409, 4 figs.

CHAPTER IV

BACTERIA

By EDWIN O. JORDAN

Professor of Bacteriology in the University of Chicago

BACTERIA are unicellular organisms, for the most part very small. Considerable differences in size, however, are observed. A certain large, rod-shaped species studied by Schaudinn measures from 50μ to 60μ in length and from 4μ to 5μ in width. On the other hand the bacillus of influenza averages about 0.5μ in length and 0.2μ in width. The average rod-shaped bacterium, such as is found in water and soil, measures about 2μ in length and about 0.5μ in diameter. Some microörganisms are known to exist which are so small that they will pass through the pores of the finest Berkefeld filter and remain invisible under the most powerful lenses, but it is not surely established that all these so-called ultramicroscopic organisms belong to the group of bacteria.

For the methods of studying bacteria, special laboratory manuals or guides should be consulted. A number of such guides are in existence, among which may be mentioned Heinemann (1911) and Frost (1905). In any case a proper familiarity with laboratory methods can be gained only with the assistance of a skilled laboratory instructor possessed of individuality and resource.

Bacteria are generally classed as plants rather than animals, but, as is well known, the dividing line between animals and plants is an entirely arbitrary one, and there is no general agreement among naturalists respecting what shall constitute a determinative plant or animal characteristic. It is largely considerations of convention and convenience that place them among the plants. From their lack of chlorophyl and the fact that they multiply by division or fission the bacteria are classed as *Schizomycetes* or fission fungi.

Within the group of bacteria themselves classification is, for practical purposes, especially important, but because they are so

minute in size and the observable differences in structure are so
slight, any classification grounded on morphological characters,
such as that of Migula (1897), meets with many difficulties, and
would seem at present to be premature. Because of the great practical importance of physiological qualities, bacteriologists have
come to lay great stress upon bacterial functions, and considerations of convenience have often led to groups being established on
physiological characteristics. The practice of dealing with bacteria
in related groups is growing. For the identification of specific and
group characters the Report of the Committee of the Society of
American Bacteriologists on Method of Identification of Bacterial
Species should be consulted.

The forms of bacteria are very simple. The complex and elaborate structures found among certain other groups of unicellular
organisms (diatoms, desmids, radiolaria) do not occur among bacteria. Three principal type forms are recognized: the sphere
(coccus or micrococcus), the rod (bacillus), and the spiral (spirillum

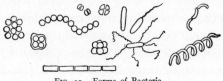

FIG. 30. Forms of Bacteria.

and spirochæte) (Fig. 30). Closely resembling these are certain
filamentous organisms known as *Trichomycetes*, which connect the
bacteria with the higher fungi or moulds.

The minute size of bacteria renders the study of their finer
structure somewhat difficult, but a few features have been clearly
determined. Most species, perhaps all, are provided with a *capsule* or outer layer of gelatinous substance originating from the
cell-membrane and seen in stained preparations surrounding the
cell like a halo. The capsule is much more prominently developed
in some species than in others. The *cell-membrane* is chiefly remarkable for its chemical composition, differing as it does from the
cell-membrane of the higher plants in not being composed of cellulose. The nature of the *cell-substance* of bacteria has been the
object of much discussion from the standpoint of its relation to the

nuclear substance of higher cells. It has been held by different
observers that a bacterial cell is to be compared either to a free
nucleus or to an unnucleated mass of cytoplasm, but these views
have now been practically abandoned. It seems to be clear from
the researches of recent investigators that the chromatin substance
instead of being gathered together in a definite nucleus, as in the
cells of most higher forms of life, is fragmented and distributed
irregularly through the body of the cell. The bacterial chromatin
is usually present in great abundance, varies in amount and in
position in different kinds of bacteria and occurs most frequently
in a finely-divided condition. Not only are particles of chromatin
scattered through the cell, but other granules that react to stains
in special ways are present in the cell substance, particularly in
certain species. The physiological significance of these so-called
metachromatic granules, as they occur for example in the diphtheria
bacillus, is unknown, but it seems probable that they are to be
looked upon as reserve food substances.

Many forms of bacteria show independent movement, distinct
from the oscillating or trembling movement exhibited by all minute
particles suspended in water and known as the Brownian movement.
The power of motility depends upon the possession of long, fragile,
filamentous appendages termed *flagella*. In the case of certain
large spirilla, flagella can be seen on the living, unstained cell, but
ordinarily special methods of staining must be applied to demonstrate their presence. The position of the flagella on the cell body
differs in different species. Some species possess a single flagellum
at one pole, as is the case with the cholera spirillum; others have a
flagellum at either pole; others have polar tufts of flagella; and
still others possess flagella attached to the sides as well as the
ends of the cell (typhoid bacillus) (Fig. 30). In certain nonmotile
bacteria, such as the anthrax bacillus, no flagella have been observed.

Under certain conditions some bacteria pass from the ordinary
or vegetative stage into a highly resistant state, known as a *spore*
or *endospore*. The spores of bacteria are approximately spherical or
oval, are stained with great difficulty with the ordinary aniline
dyes and resist destructive agencies, such as heat and chemical
disinfectants, much better than the vegetative forms from which

they spring. A single cell, as a rule, gives rise to but one spore, so that spore formation can not be looked upon as a process of multiplication. It is generally considered that the bacterial spore is a resting stage, physiologically similar to an encysted amoeba and serving to tide the species over a period of hard times. Not all bacteria are spore producing; in fact the number known to form spores is rather limited.

Great adaptability is shown by bacteria to extremes of temperature. Some species have been found multiplying in the water of polar seas at or near the freezing point, while others have been found living in the water of hot springs at a temperature of 79° C. Most of the ordinary bacteria found in pond or river water multiply abundantly at a temperature of about 20° C. When water is frozen, most of the bacteria that it contains are killed at once. A small proportion survive, but in gradually diminishing numbers, so that at the end of a few weeks clear ice is practically sterile. Bacteria contained in masses of organic matter, however, may have their life in ice considerably prolonged.

Bacteria not only adapt themselves to great extremes of temperature, but to varied sources of food supply. Many species can content themselves with relatively simple chemical compounds, such as the ammonium salts of the organic acids. Others require for their development complex nitrogenous substances. The nitrifying bacteria, so abundant in most soils and waters, obtain the energy necessary for their development altogether from inorganic compounds. On the other hand, certain bacteria are entirely dependent upon particular organic compounds present in the bodies of the higher animals, and can thrive only in the presence of blood serum or similar fluids.

Fundamental differences exist among bacteria in respect to their relative need for oxygen. Some, the *obligatory aërobes*, require free oxygen for the maintenance of their life activities, while others, the *obligatory anaërobes*, do not grow except in the almost complete absence of free oxygen. There are also some, the *facultative anaërobes*, that can multiply either in the presence or absence of free oxygen. The anaërobic bacteria, as a class, thrive best in the presence of substances capable of undergoing reduction or fermentation.

The addition of glucose or nitrate, for example, to ordinary nutrient broth will enable certain species of bacteria to grow under conditions otherwise unfavorable. The relation between anaërobic life and food supply is an intimate one. The anaërobes, in a word, are those organisms able to obtain their needed energy from the simple splitting of organic compounds without oxidation. If a microörganism is so specialized to an anaërobic mode of life that the presence of oxygen, except in minute quantities, interferes with its habitual method of attacking food substances, it is an obligatory anaërobe. In a modified form, therefore, Pasteur's conception of fermentation as "life without air" is not very far from the modern view.

Those decompositions of organic substances that are usually termed putrefactions and are characterized by the evolution of malodorous gases such as hydrogen sulphide and the production of substances like skatol, indol, mercaptan, etc., are due to the agency of anaërobic bacteria. In fact, researches indicate that the putrefactive decomposition of native proteins is wholly the work of the obligatory anaërobes. As is well known, the ooze at the bottom of ponds and streams is peculiarly the home of such anaërobic decompositions.

Bacteria are everywhere present in natural bodies of water. They are more abundant as a rule in surface waters than in ground waters. Deep well waters and spring waters in certain regions often contain very few bacteria, perhaps only five to ten per cubic centimeter, while the water of lakes and ponds usually contains several hundred, and ordinary river water contains numbers that at times rise into the thousands and tens of thousands. As a general rule, sewage-polluted waters contain more bacteria than pure waters. An excessively polluted stream, such as the Chicago River once was, may hold as many as several million bacteria per cubic centimeter.

The number of bacteria in a river water varies greatly at different seasons of the year, being generally larger in the colder months than in summer. Probably this is due in part to the winter increase in current caused by rains and melting snows which prevents sedimentation; in part to the heavy rains of winter which wash into a stream numberless germs from cultivated lands, and partly also to the lower temperature of the water in winter which favors the continuance of bacterial vitality. In highly-polluted rivers the processes of decomposition are retarded by cold weather; in consequence, bacteria together with their food substances travel for a greater distance down stream in winter than in summer. This condition has been shown to exist, for example, in the Illinois River which is heavily polluted with Chicago sewage.

Besides these important seasonal fluctuations, daily and hourly changes may be noticed, depending upon the amount of rainfall, the velocity of the current, the direction and force of the wind and perhaps the germicidal action of sunlight. For these reasons, it is necessary, in order to interpret correctly the sanitary significance of the bacterial content of any body of surface water, to make repeated examinations under a variety of circumstances and with particular attention to the effect of modifying conditions. In the case of ground waters (wells, springs, etc.), the number of bacteria is less affected by changes in external conditions, but here also great caution is necessary in drawing conclusions from a limited number of observations.

The following table gives some conception of the number of bacteria that may be found by the gelatin plate method in various bodies of water. Great variations occur and any such tabulation can have only an approximate value.

	Per cubic centimeter	
Sewages or sewage-polluted waters	100,000 to	1,500,000
Rivers not highly polluted	1,000 to	10,000
Lakes and ponds not highly polluted	100 to	1,000
Pure spring waters	5 to	50

The enormous number of bacteria which such figures show to be present in all natural bodies of water comprises many different kinds. There is no special and characteristic class of "water bacteria," but germs from the air, from the soil, from decomposing animal and plant substances and from the healthy and diseased tissues of animals and plants may at times find their way into water. The bacterial flora of a given stream or pond is therefore constantly changing, and varies from time to time not only in the number, but in the nature of the individuals composing it (Fig. 31). Little work has yet been done upon the changes in the kinds of bacteria in river or lake water due to the shifting seasons and other

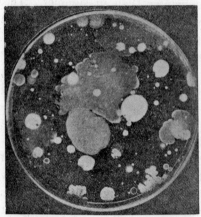

factors, but there is no doubt that important differences do exist. Many varieties of bacteria have been isolated from water. During the course of a study of the bacteria in the water of the Illinois River the writer found that out of 543 cultures, 17 well-defined groups and 41 subgroups were represented. These groups include a number of pigment-producing or chromogenic forms, some of which are

Fig. 31.—Photograph of "plate culture," showing different kinds of bacterial colonies. (Original.)

among the most common inhabitants of water, and also a number of bacteria closely related to organisms associated with the production of disease in the higher animals. Among the bacteria commonly found in natural waters may be mentioned *B. fluorescens* vars. *liquefaciens* and *non-liquefaciens* (the green water bacillus), *B. subtilis* (the hay bacillus), *B. mesentericus* (the potato bacillus), *B. proteus* and *B. cloacae* (commonly associated with the decomposition of vegetable and animal matter), *B. liquefaciens*, *B. hyalinus*, *B. violaceus*, and many chromogenic and non-chromogenic micrococci; in polluted waters, *B. coli* is usually found in large numbers and organisms of the *B. proteus* type and streptococci are more abundant than in normal waters.

It is well known that the germs of several of the principal infectious diseases of man are commonly conveyed in drinking water. Typhoid fever and Asiatic cholera are familiar examples. Both the typhoid bacillus and the cholera spirillum have been found in water, although, partly because the technical difficulties of investigation are considerable, partly because the longevity of these organisms in water is limited, positive findings have not been very frequent. Under ordinary conditions there is no reason to suppose that pathogenic bacteria multiply in water or that they retain their vitality for more than a few weeks. In polluted soil, however, they may live much longer than in water, and a river may be continuously polluted during a long period by bacteria that are washed into it from accumulations of fecal material. Other pathogenic bacteria occasionally water-borne are the dysentery bacillus and the anthrax bacillus.

Since the search for specific pathogenic bacteria in a water is hardly ever likely to be crowned with success, various indirect means for determining the purity of a water have been proposed. The most useful of these analytical methods is the test based on the determination of the relative number of *Bacillus coli*. This, the colon bacillus, is a normal inhabitant of the healthy human intestine and is found in large numbers in fresh sewage where, by appropriate methods, it is usually detected in each $\frac{1}{10000}$ c.c. examined. Since it is also present in the droppings of many of the larger domestic animals and hence occurs in garden soil and in pastures, its occasional presence in water does not necessarily indicate possible or even probable pollution with fecal matter of human origin. The researches of many investigators, however, have shown that the *relative abundance of Bacillus coli* in water is a very satisfactory criterion of the sanitary quality of such a water. If, for example, it is found uniformly present in a water in each 1 c.c. sample, the water is looked upon as distinctly suspicious. In cases, however, where it is rarely found in 1 c.c. samples and only occasionally when quantities as large as 10 c.c. or even 50 c.c. are examined, the water is usually considered potable.

The bacteria in water stand in important relations to the life of other aquatic plants and animals. It is a familiar fact that but for bacterial activity the nitrogen and carbon in complex organic compounds once bound would remain forever locked up and unavailable for the nutrition of other forms of life. As is well known also, the first steps in decomposition or the breaking down of organic substances are due to bacterial agency. Ammonia and ammoniacal compounds are among the chief nitrogenous products of this decomposition. The processes of disintegration and oxidation do not end with the production of such a relatively simple compound as ammonia. Further oxidation of the ammonia to nitrites takes place and the nitrites in turn are oxidized to nitrates. The formation of nitrites and nitrates, like the formation of ammonia, is due to bacterial activity; this process is known as *nitrification*. Special and peculiar varieties of bacteria are concerned in the process of nitrification. One species is able to oxidize ammonia to nitrite, but is unable to carry the process of oxidation any further. At this stage of decomposition a second species takes up the work and completes the process by oxidizing the nitrites to nitrates.

If we follow the fate of the nitrogen introduced into a sewage-polluted river, we find that there occurs first a breaking down of the albuminous compounds and a consequent increase in the amount of "free ammonia" in the water; further down, nitrites begin to appear and eventually nitrates are found. A river water in which the process of nitrification has occurred and which is therefore rich in nitrates affords a peculiarly favorable medium for the growth of plant life and often "blooms" with a myriad of microscopic algae. The presence of a multitude of algae influences in its turn the life conditions of aquatic protozoa and of higher animal organisms. At times when through the advent of low temperature or other unfavorable conditions the algae die off, the albuminous compounds constituting their dead bodies undergo decomposition; ammonia, nitrites, and then nitrates are again formed, and the nitrogen cycle begins anew. The food supply of the whole plankton of fresh-water streams and ponds is therefore dependent upon the activity of bacteria, and the share of these organisms in producing or modifying the conditions under which all aquatic life is possible can never be ignored.

IMPORTANT REFERENCES ON BACTERIA

CLEMESHA, W. W. 1912. The Bacteriology of Surface Waters in the Tropics. London.

HORROCKS, W. H. 1901. Introduction to the Bacteriological Examination of Water. London.

HOUSTON, A. C. 1913. Studies in Water Supply. London.

JORDAN, E. O. 1903. The Kinds of Bacteria Found in River Water. Journal of Hygiene, 3: 1.

MIGULA, W. 1900. System der Bacterien. Jena.

OHLMÜLLER and SPITTA. 1910. Wasser u. Abwasser. 3d ed., Berlin.

PRESCOTT and WINSLOW. 1913. Elements of Water Bacteriology. 3d ed., New York.

Report of the Committee on Standard Methods of Water Analysis to the Laboratory Section of the American Public Health Association.

SAVAGE, W. G. 1906. Bacteriological Examination of Water Supplies. London.

CHAPTER V

BLUE–GREEN ALGAE (CYANOPHYCEAE)

By EDGAR W. OLIVE

Curator of the Brooklyn Botanic Garden

THE blue-green algae are found principally in fresh waters, although numerous forms occur also in the sea, and are almost universally distributed over the whole earth. In moist climates they are particularly abundant, growing in almost every conceivable situation as gelatinous masses or strata on rocks, stones, the trunks of trees, damp ground, etc. Many of them occur abundantly in both marine and fresh-water plankton. The peculiar phenomenon of "water-bloom" (or "working" or "blooming" of the lakes, "breaking of the meres," "Flos aquae," "Wasserblüte") is due to the sudden appearance in lakes and ponds of a surface scum formed of vast quantities of certain plankton species of these organisms. This frothy scum, forming the so-called "water-bloom," is of common occurrence in midsummer in quiet waters, especially after a protracted period of heat. Disagreeable "pig-pen" odors and bad tastes are caused by such masses when decay sets in, due, according to Jackson and Ellms, to the decay of highly nitrogenous organic matter in which partially decomposed sulphur and phosphorous compounds play a large part. The occurrence of blue-green algae in public water supplies often thus becomes of great economic importance; and Moore has found in this connection that such algal growths in reservoirs may be readily eradicated or their growth prevented by the use of a dilute solution of copper sulphate.

In addition to their importance as polluting organisms in water reservoirs, some recent observations appear to indicate that certain plankton forms of blue-green algae are sometimes used as food by fish fry. Their indirect importance in this respect may be regarded as well established, since Birge has shown that the common plankton Crustacea, which themselves form the basis of the food of many small fishes, depend to a great extent upon *Aphanizomenon*, *Anabaena*, and other blue-green algae for their own sustenance.

Some species of Cyanophyceae have become adapted to living in hot springs; these organisms, in fact, together with certain sulphur bacteria, constituting the sole organic life of thermal springs. According to the careful observations of Setchell, the blue-green algae grow in some abundance in thermal waters up to 68° C., and scantily in springs showing a temperature as high as 75°–77° C.

The varied colors — shades of yellow, orange red, pink, blue, and blue green — shown by the siliceous deposits around certain hot springs of the Yellowstone Park, are due in great part to the presence of brilliantly colored blue-green algae within the deposit. Weed has discussed the part played by these algae in the formation of carbonaceous and siliceous rocks about hot springs.

Some of the Cyanophyceae, principally of the genera *Scytonema*, *Stigonema*, and *Nostoc*, are found associated with certain fungi to form lichens; while still others, notably *Nostoc* and *Anabaena*, occur regularly endophytically in the roots of Cycads and in the leaves of *Azolla* and other water plants.

Like the bacteria, with which these algae are supposed to show close relationship, most of the Cyanophyceae possess cell walls which become much swollen and mucilaginous in their outer layers. Thus most of the filamentous forms become invested in either a thin mucous sheath or a tough, lamellose sheathing tube. Many of the colonial forms consist of masses of cells embedded in a thick, jelly-like matrix, the external surface of which is often covered with a thin cuticle.

Much dispute has arisen in recent years as to the nature of the contents of the cells of these algae. On examination with the compound microscope, one usually notes a number of granular bodies, apparently of two kinds — numerous small granules and a few larger, clear ones. In the shorter-celled species, the smaller and more numerous granules frequently lie in regular double rows, on either side of the cross walls which separate the cells. In the longer-celled forms, such as *Nostoc* and *Tolypothrix*, the small granules generally occur abundantly in all parts of the peripheral protoplasm. These minute granules are generally regarded as the "cyanophycin granules" (Borzi), and they are probably albuminous in their nature and serve as reserve food. The few larger granules mentioned above are more hyaline and transparent than the cyanophycin granules, and they appear to lie in or near the center of the cell. These larger granules have been called by Palla "slime globules"; by Zacharias "Centralkörner." Their function is in dispute.

The cells of favorable forms of the blue-green algae, *e.g.*, *Oscillatoria*, show two more or less evident portions of the protoplasm — a peripheral layer, to which the pigment is confined and in which the cyanophycin granules lie, and a central colorless part, the so-called "central body." The majority of recent studies on the subject maintain that the central body is a nucleus, although this conclusion has been several times disputed. Carefully stained, thin sections show, however, that it is made up of both chromatic and achromatic substances. Moreover, Macallum and others find in the central body complex proteid substances containing phosphorus and "masked" iron to a marked degree, which they regard as characteristic constituents of chromatin. Fischer claims, however, to have demonstrated by means of a tannin-safranin stain that the central body is filled with certain carbohydrates, of the nature of glycogen.

The central body divides according to some, by simple amitotic division; while others believe that the division is mitotic. At any rate, the division of this nucleus, or central body, precedes the division of the cell, and, as in other lower plants, the two processes appear to take place independently of each other. Cell division is accomplished in these forms in the same manner as has been described for many other filamentous Thallophytes, by constriction: a ring-formed wall grows in from the outer wall, similarly to the closing of an iris diaphragm, and finally cuts the cell in two.

The varying shades of color shown by these organisms are caused by varying mixtures of the green chlorophyll and the reddish or bluish phycocyanin, the pigments being apparently confined to the peripheral cytoplasm. The phycocyanin may readily be extracted by killing the plant, when the plasma membrane at once allows the dissolved pigment to pass out through the cell wall. When plants are dried and pulverized, then soaked in water, a solution of the bluish coloring matter is thus readily obtained. A quicker method is to place the blue-green algae in chloroform water (made by shaking up a small quantity of chloroform in water, allowing it to settle, then decanting the water, which is then used in the experiment), or in water containing a few drops of carbon bisulphide, for a short time. Death of the plants at once ensues and the dichroic phycocyanin passes out into the surrounding water, leaving the filaments bright green from the remaining chlorophyll pigment.

Sap vacuoles occur sometimes in the cells of the Cyanophyceae, particularly in the older elongated cells of such forms as *Tolypothrix* and *Calothrix*. Another kind of vacuole, filled with gas, is said by Klebahn and others to occur in certain free-floating blue-green algae, such as *Coelosphaerium*, *Anabaena*, and *Oscillatoria*, when they rise to the surface to form water-bloom. These authors regard the so-called gas vacuoles as directly concerned with the floating capacity of the algae which possess them; their contentions have been disputed a number of times, however, and the gas vacuole theory is regarded by many as untenable.

Sexual reproduction is unknown among the blue-green algae. Asexual multiplication takes place in the simpler forms by cell division and subsequent separation of the daughter cells. In the higher, filamentous Hormogoneae, short one- to few-celled filaments, known as hormogonia, are regularly set free and these fragments form new plants. Spherical or cylindrical resting spores are formed in some species by the growth in size of the vegetative cells and by the thickening of the walls.

Heterocysts are special cells developed in some forms from ordinary vegetative cells, whose significance is not well understood. Their protoplasmic contents apparently soon die and one or two polar thickenings appear in the cell. Undoubtedly they are at times connected with the breaking up of the filaments, but in some cases they normally occur at the basal ends only of the filaments.

A few of the Cyanophyceae show remarkable oscillating, gliding, or rotating movements, the cause of which has never been satisfactorily explained. In *Oscillatoria* and *Spirulina*, these movements are particularly conspicuous.

CYANOPHYCEAE

(MYXOPHYCEAE, PHYCOCHROMOPHYCEAE, SCHIZOPHYCEAE)

Algae possessing more or less of a blue-green color; free-floating or living in gelatinous masses or strata; sexual reproduction unknown, reproducing asexually by means of cell division, the daughter cells either soon separating into more or less independent cells, or remaining adherent to form filaments or plates or solid colonies. The vegetative cells each made up of two more or less easily distinguishable parts: a colored peripheral cytoplasm, which contains the bluish or reddish phycocyanin, in addition to the chlorophyll pigment, and also generally a number of minute granular bodies — the "cyanophycin granules"; and the colorless "central body," which is the nucleus of the cell. Embedded in the central body, in addition to the chromatic and achromatic substances, there usually occur a few large, globular, transparent bodies — the so-called "slime globules." Sap vacuoles sometimes occur in the cytoplasm. Thick-walled resting spores are formed in some species; heterocysts are also found in certain forms, which are peculiar cells, whose protoplasmic contents apparently soon die and whose significance is but little understood.

1 (25)   One-celled plants, living either free or united into colonies by being embedded in a common gelatinous matrix.
                                    Order **Coccogoneae** Thuret . .   2

2 (24)   Cells generally free-floating or forming a gelatinous stratum; not differentiated into base and apex.
                                    Family CHROOCOCCACEAE . .   3

3 (8, 11) Cell division in one plane only. 4

4 (7)   With wide mucous covering. 5

5 (6)   Cells elongate, each with a special mucous coat. *Gloeothece* Nägeli.

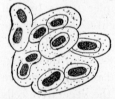

Cells oblong or cylindrical, with thick, sometimes lamellose, gelatinous membrane; single or united into microscopically small colonies, which are enclosed after the manner of *Gloeocapsa* within the gelatinous membrane of the mother cell. On wet rocks, rarely floating.

FIG. 32. *Gloeothece confluens* Nägeli. X 450. (After West.)

6 (5)   Cells little longer than broad, many adhering together to form large, irregular colonies, enclosed by a common mucous matrix. . . . . *Aphanothece* Nägeli.

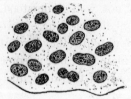

Cells oblong, dividing only at right angles to the long axis; forming irregular, gelatinous colonies which sometimes grow to be an inch or more in diameter. At margins of lakes and on wet rocks.

FIG. 33. *Aphanothece microscopica* Nägeli. X 1000. (Original.)

7 (4)   Cells with thin cell walls. . . . . *Synechococcus* Nägeli.

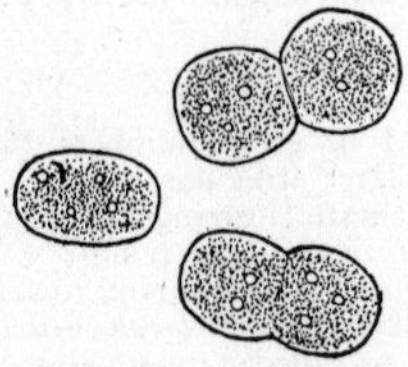

Cells comparatively large, cylindrical or ellipsoidal, living usually singly or sometimes forming small families of two to four united in a row or chain. Cell-contents blue-green, sometimes yellowish, pinkish, or pale orange. Free-floating in ponds and pools, or on rocks.

FIG. 34. *Synechococcus aeruginosus* Nägeli. × 575. (After Kirchner.)

8 (3, 11)   Cell-division in two planes. 9

9 (10)   Cells spherical or oblong, forming flat, plate-like colonies.

Merismopedia Meyen.

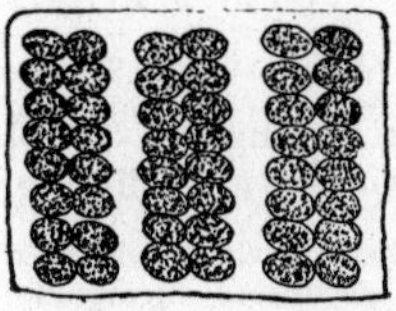

Cells usually adhering in groups of four, and arranged in regular rows to form a flat, rectangular, plate-like colony. In plankton, in ponds, and lakes.

FIG. 35. *Merismopedia elegans* A. Braun. × 450. (After West.)

10 (9)   Cells flat, quadrangular in outline, solitary, or forming small colonies. . . . . *Tetrapedia* Reinsch.

Cells with thin membrane; solitary or united into flat colonies of 2 to 16 cells.

11 (3, 8)   Cell-division in three planes. 12

12 (23)   Cells united into definite, often comparatively large colonies.   13

13 (16)   Colonies more or less regularly spherical. 14

14 (15)   Colonies hollow; cells closely and regularly arranged at the surface.

Coelosphaerium Nägeli.

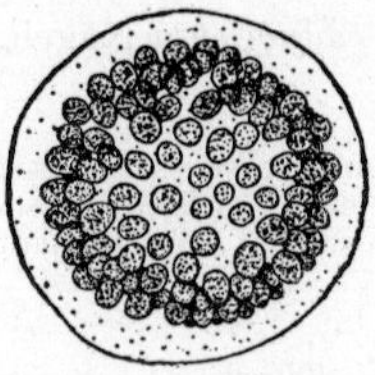

Cells globose or oblong, forming on the surface of lakes and ponds microscopically small, hollow, spherical colonies embedded in a mass of mucus; reproduction by means of single cells escaping from the colony as well as through the constriction of old colonies to form new ones. Common in fresh-water plankton.

FIG. 36. *Coelosphaerium kützingianum* Nägeli. × 465. (Original.)

15 (14)   Colonies solid; cells sparsely scattered through the jelly, pyriform in shape. . . . . *Gomphosphaeria* Kützing.

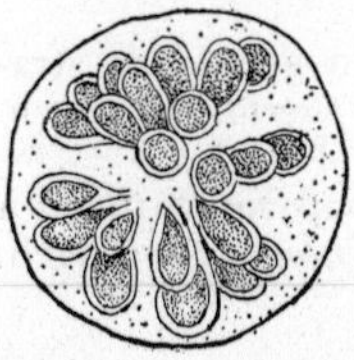

Cells enclosed by a colorless gelatinous matrix to form microscopically small, solid, globular, or ellipsoid colonies; the peripheral cells grouped in pairs and egg-shaped or pyriform, or (during division) heart-shaped. In ponds, stagnant water, etc.

FIG. 37. *Gomphosphaeria aponina* Kützing. × 465. (Original.)

16 (13)   Colonies, when old, generally not spherical. 17

17 (18, 19)   Colonies microscopically small, solid, globular, or clustered.

Microcystis Kützing.

(Probably should be united with *Clathrocystis*.) Cells spherical, or through pressure somewhat angular; uniting in great numbers to form microscopically small solid colonies. Common in ponds and ditches.

18 (17, 19) Colonies at first globular, later irregular in shape, and perforated
      or netted. . . . . *Clathrocystis* Henfrey.

Cells spherical, united in great numbers to form at first globular, later irregular colonies, which often become clathrate, forming an open meshwork. Common in lakes and ponds; *C. aeruginosa* Henfr. is often thrown upon rocks along shores to form, mixed with *Coelosphaerium kützingianum* Näg., the so-called "green paint."

FIG. 38. *Clathrocystis aeruginosa* Henfrey. X 465.
(Original.)

19 (17, 18) Colonies irregular in shape, frequently forming films. 20
20 (21, 22) Individual mucous coats clearly evident for each daughter cell of
      the colony. . . . . *Gloeocapsa* Kützing.

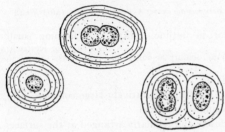

Cells spherical, with thick, often lamellose, gelatinous membrane; solitary or generally united into microscopic colonies in which the membranes of the daughter cells remain enclosed for a long time within that of the mother-cell. Forming gelatinous substrata on moist walls and wet and dripping rocks.

FIG. 39. *Gloeocapsa polydermatica*
Kützing. X 465. (Original.)

21 (20, 22) Cells enveloped in a common gelatinous matrix.
                                    Aphanocapsa Nägeli.

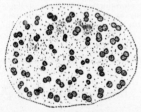

Cells globose, forming irregular colonies enclosed in a thick, homogeneous integument. Differing from *Aphanothece* only in its globose cells. In stagnant water, on wet rocks, etc.

FIG. 40. *Aphanocapsa grevillei* Rabenhorst. X 450.
(After West.)

22 (20, 21) Cells globose, reddish purple, arranged in a thin gelatinous stra-
      tum. . . . . *Porphyridium* Nägeli.
        Common on damp ground and at the base of damp walls.

23 (12)   Cells solitary or a few adhering together in a group, not forming a
      definite layer. . . . . *Chroococcus* Nägeli.

Cells globose or somewhat angular, with firm, often thick, lamellose or homogeneous membrane. Free-floating, or forming a stratum on wet rocks.

FIG. 41. *Chroococcus giganteus* West. X 300. (After West.)

24 (2)   Cells epiphytic; with a distinct base and apex.
                    Family CHAMAESIPHONACEAE.
          Only one genus. . . *Chamaesiphon* A. Braun and Grunow.

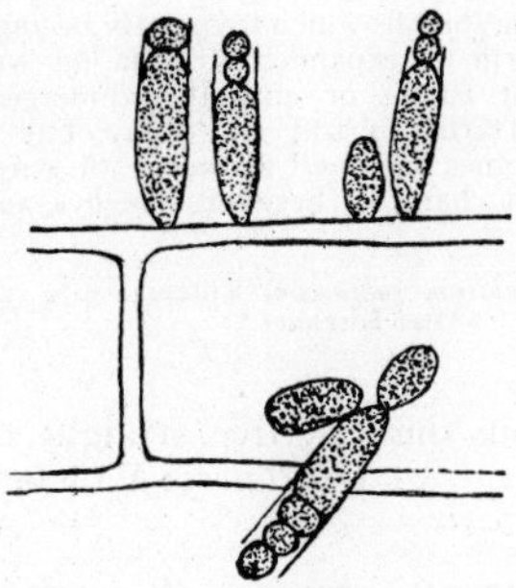

Cells small, ovoid, pyriform, or cylindrical; attached by their base and generally widening upwards to their free apex. Solitary or aggregated; sheaths present; cell walls very thin; cell contents homogeneous, blue-green, violet, or yellow; reproduction by one-celled, non-motile cells which are successively cut off from the upper portion of the plants, gradually escaping from the open apex. Common on *Oedogonium* and other algae in ponds.

FIG. 42. *Chamaesiphon incrustans* Grunow. X 800.
(After West.)

25 (1)   Plants filamentous; filaments simple or branched; consisting of
          one or more rows of cells generally enclosed within a more
          or less evident sheath. Asexual reproduction by means
          of hormogonia, and more rarely by spores.
                    Order **Hormogoneae** Thuret . . 26

26 (64)   Filaments cylindrical, sometimes narrowed at the extremities.
                    Suborder **Psilonemateae** . . 27

27 (53)   Filaments not branched. 28

28 (43)   Filaments consisting of a single row of cells, seldom (*Spirulina*)
          one-celled; not branched; heterocysts absent; sheaths vari-
          able, more or less gelatinous, and sometimes enclosing more
          than one filament. . . . Family OSCILLATORIACEAE . . 29

29 (39)   Never more than one filament within a sheath.
                    · Subfamily LYNGBYEAE . . 30

30 (31)   Filaments apparently one-celled, coiled into a regular spiral, often
          showing rapid rotatory movements. . . *Spirulina* Turpin.

Filaments very narrow, consisting of a single elongated cell, sometimes of great length, regularly spirally coiled; sometimes showing rapid oscillat-ing and rotatory movements. Common in stag-nant water.

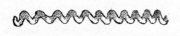

FIG. 43. *Spirulina major* Kützing. X 1000. (Orig-inal.)

31 (30)   Filaments many-celled. 32

32 (36)   Filaments simple, generally showing oscillating and gliding move-
          ments; sheaths thin, hyaline, sometimes not evident. . 33

33 (34, 35) Filaments more or less confluent by their mucous sheaths.

Phormidium Kützing.

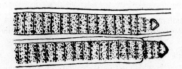

Filaments many-celled, straight or bent; enclosed in hyaline sheaths which frequently become adherent to form an expanded stratum on wet rocks or moist earth, or entirely submerged. Usually this stratum is soft and slimy, but it sometimes becomes hard and leathery. A genus intermediate in character between *Lyngbya* and *Oscillatoria*.

FIG. 44. *Phormidium subfuscum* Kützing. × 575.
(After Kirchner.)

34 (33, 35) Filaments generally without conspicuous sheaths; free, straight, or with curved extremities. . . . . . . Oscillatoria Vaucher.

A

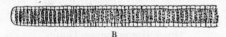

B

FIG. 45. A, *Oscillatoria prolifica* Gomont. B, *Oscillatoria limosa* Agardh. × 465. (Original.)

Filaments composed of numerous short cylindrical cells, the end cell sometimes much attenuated; without a sheath or with an almost imperceptible one; generally showing lively creeping and oscillating movements. Found in great profusion in all kinds of wet situations; sometimes free-floating at the surface of lakes and ponds, or forming filmy growths on wet soil or rocks. *O. limosa* is extremely abundant on the soil, etc., in greenhouses, while *O. prolifica* occurs in the plankton of some lakes in such quantities as to impart a reddish or purplish color to the water and occasionally to form a "water-bloom." The latter species has been found in some instances to persist even into the winter and to color the ice a reddish or pinkish color.

35 (33, 34) Filaments without sheaths, twisted into a regular spiral.

Arthrospira Stizenberger.

Filaments commonly without a sheath, differing from *Oscillatoria* in being regularly spirally coiled, and from *Spirulina* in being many-celled. Living singly or forming dark-green slimy strata in stagnant water.

FIG. 46. *Arthrospira jenneri* Stizenberger. × 500. (After Gomont.)

36 (32)   Filaments not showing oscillating movements; sheaths firm. .   37

37 (38)   Filaments free and simple, free-floating or forming an expanded stratum. . . . . Lyngbya C. Agardh.

Filaments many-celled, straight or bent, each enclosed in a firm, generally hyaline, sometimes lamellose, membrane. Free-floating, or forming densely intricate, floccose masses, or an expanded stratum. Frequently abundant in plankton.

FIG. 47. *Lyngbya major* Meneghini. × 465.
(Original.)

38 (37)   Filaments forming erect tufts, often branched. . *Symploca* Kützing.

Filaments densely interwoven to form a slimy substratum from which arise erect tufts of variable height. Sometimes more or less procumbent. False branches solitary; sheaths thin, colorless, firm or somewhat mucous; apex of the filament straight, sometimes a little tapering; outer membrane of the apical cell slightly thickened in some species. In hot springs, on damp earth, walls, or trunks of trees.

FIG. 48.   *Symploca lucifuga* Harvey. a, × 250; b, natural size.   (After Wolle.)

39 (29)   Several filaments in a common sheath which is frequently branched. . . . . Subfamily VAGINARIEAE . . 40

40 (41, 42) Sheaths often colored; lamellose; filaments few or many, loosely aggregated within the common sheath. *Schizothrix* Kützing.

Several filaments enclosed in a firm lamellose sheath which is at first colorless but later becomes yellowish, brownish, or purplish; filaments simple or variously branched. Forming cushion-like masses, erect tufts, or a flat stratum on moist substrata, rarely free-floating.

FIG. 49.   *Schizothrix rubella* Nägeli. × 430.   (After Gomont.)

41 (40, 42) Sheaths hyaline, fused with adjoining sheaths.   *Hydrocoleum* Kützing.

Filaments composed each of numberless short cells, the end cell with thickened cap-like membrane. Filaments two to many in colorless, slimy sheaths, which become fused with those of adjoining filaments. In brooks and waterfalls.

FIG. 50.   *Hydrocoleum homoeotrichum* Kützing.   × 390.   (After Gomont.)

42 (40, 41) Sheaths hyaline, not lamellose, containing a large number of filaments. . . . . *Microcoleus* Desmazières.

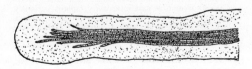

Filaments simple, consisting generally of long cells; closely aggregated in great numbers in the center of a conspicuous, hyaline, cylindrical sheath.

FIG. 51.   *Microcoleus delicatulus* W. and G. S. West.   × 350.   (After West.)

43 (28)   Filaments simple, unbranched; with heterocysts; living singly or in
           gelatinous masses, often of definite form.   Sheaths very
           delicate, mostly confluent. Cells generally torulose, in a
           single row . . . . Family NOSTOCEAE . . 44
44 (47)   Filaments enclosed within a gelatinous mass of definite form.   45
45 (46)   Forming delicate, hollow, cylindrical colonies.
                                          Wollea Bornet and Flahault.

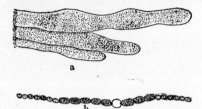

Delicate colonies; filaments straight or
slightly bent, arranged in tolerably parallel
rows, with a common gelatinous envelope;
heterocysts intercalary; spores in chains,
bordering on one or both sides of the
heterocysts. *W. saccata* Bor. and Flah.
occurs in stagnant water.

FIG. 52. *Wollea saccata* Bornet and Flahault.
a, × 250; b, natural size. (After Wolle.)

46 (45)   Colonies spherical, or of varied form; with the enclosed filament
           irregularly interwoven and contorted. . . *Nostoc* Vaucher.

Forming leathery or slimy gelatinous masses, at first spherical or oblong, later of varied form, solid or hollow, and
attached or unattached; filaments contorted and curved in
all directions; the gelatinous sheath sometimes sharply
delimited, more often fused with the enveloping jelly.
Cells globular, barrel-shaped, or cylindrical; heterocysts
intercalary, or (when young) sometimes terminal; spores
globular or oblong, formed in rows in varying number between the heterocysts. Forming free-floating or attached
masses, on damp ground, wet rocks, etc.

FIG. 53. *Nostoc commune* Vaucher. a, natural size; b, × 465.
                          (Original.)

47 (44)   Filaments more or less straight, free-floating or forming a thin
           mucous stratum. 48
48 (52)   Heterocysts and spores intercalary. 49
49 (50, 51) Filaments naked, or with a thin sheath; single, or aggregated into
           formless, flocculent masses; cells equal to or longer than
           their diameter. . . . . *Anabaena* Bory.

Filaments straight or circinate, naked or enclosed
in a thin sheath, free floating as single filaments or
united to form a thin, slimy stratum; vegetative
cells as long or somewhat longer than thick; heterocysts numerous and intercalary; spores variously
disposed, borne singly or rarely in short chains.
A. flos-aquae Bréb. and *A. circinalis* Rabenh. are
frequently abundant in fresh-water plankton.

FIG. 54. *Anabaena   flos-aquae* Brébisson.   × 465.
                      (Original.)

50 (49, 51) Filaments short, straight, densely aggregated in parallel bundles to form small, feathery, plate-like masses.

Aphanizomenon Morren.

Filaments without sheath, straight or somewhat tapering at the end; united in small, spindle - shaped or plate-like, free-floating bundles; spores much elongated, cylindrical, solitary, not bordering on the intercalary heterocyst. *A. flos-aquae*

Fig. 55. *Aphanizomenon flos-aquae* Ralfs. × 465. (Original.)

Ralfs is sometimes found floating in great abundance in the still waters of ponds and lakes.

51 (49, 50) Filaments free; cells shorter than their diameter.

Nodularia Mertens.

Filaments enclosed in a thin, often evanescent sheath; free-floating as single filaments or united into colonies of indefinite form; heterocysts intercalary, depressed; spores almost spherical, in rows, not bordering on the heterocysts.

Fig. 56. *Nodularia* sp. × 465. (Original.)

52 (48) Heterocysts terminal and the spores always contiguous to them.

Cylindrospermum Kützing.

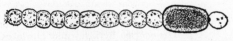

Filaments without sheath relatively short, aggregated to form an expanded film or colony of indefinite shape; vegetative cells cylindrical, longer than the diameter; heterocyst terminal; spores generally solitary, borne next to

Fig. 57. *Cylindrospermum stagnale* Bornet and Flahault. × 465. (Original.)

the heterocyst. Common on damp earth and stones.

53 (27) Filaments with true or false branches. 54

54 (60) Filaments bearing false branches; sheaths firm, of more or less equal thickness; filaments consisting of a single row of cells, with heterocysts (except *Plectonema*).

Family SCYTONEMACEAE . . 55

55 (56, 59) Without heterocysts or spores. . . . . . . *Plectonema* Thuret.

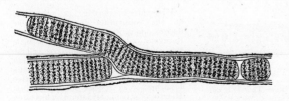

Filaments consisting only of vegetative cells, without heterocysts; falsely branched, branches single or in pairs; borne singly in a firm, colorless or yellowish sheath. *P. wollei* Farl. occurs in some abundance in ponds, attached to stones, etc.

Fig. 58. *Plectonema wollei* Farlow. × 260. (After Kirchner.)

56 (55, 59) With intercalary heterocysts. One filament in each sheath. . 57

57 (58)　　　Branches generally arising in pairs. . . . . . *Scytonema* Agardh.

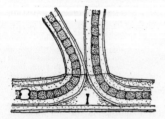

Filaments consisting of vegetative cells and heterocysts; borne singly in a sheath; sheath tough, lamellose, frequently yellowish or brownish in color; false branches borne generally in pairs between the heterocysts. Forming felt-like masses on wet rocks, etc.

FIG. 59. *Scytonema mirabile* Thuret. × 465. (Original.)

58 (57)　　　Branches arising as a rule singly. . . . . . *Tolypothrix* Kützing.

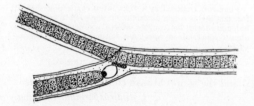

Filaments resembling closely those of *Scytonema*, but false branches arising singly as a rule instead of in pairs, as outgrowths in the region of the heterocysts; the latter 1–5 in a row; spores (in a few species) elliptical, borne singly or in rows. Occurring among various aquatic plants in ponds and lakes.

FIG. 60.　　*Tolypothrix lanata* Wartmann. × 465. (Original.)

59 (55, 56) With basal heterocysts. Two to several filaments enclosed in each sheath. . . . . *Desmonema* Berkeley and Thwaites.

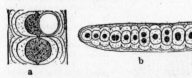

Filaments sometimes slightly branched; heterocysts always basal. On stones, in brooks, and waterfalls.

FIG. 61.　*Desmonema wrangelii* Borzi. × 200. (After Borzi.)

60 (54)　　　Filaments usually stout, bearing true branches; cells rounded, disposed generally in more than one row; heterocysts present.
　　　　　　　　　　　　　　　　　　　　Family STIGONEMACEAE . . 61

61 (62, 63) Sheaths thick; firm. . . . . *Stigonema* Agardh.

Filaments free-floating or aggregated on the substratum to form felt-like masses; filaments composed partly of two to several cell-rows, sometimes of a single row, enclosed in a thick, lamellose, yellowish or brownish sheath, which is often of irregular thickness. Hormogonia formed at the ends of the vegetative branches or in special short branches. Heterocysts commonly lateral, or less often intercalary. Vegetative cells rounded, frequently showing protoplasmic continuity. Growing generally on damp or wet rocks or moss; sometimes free-floating.

FIG. 62.　a, *Stigonema ocellatum* Thuret; b, *Stigonema minutum* Hassall. × 440. (After West.)

62 (61, 63) Sheaths thin; branches commonly unilateral. *Hapalosiphon* Nägeli.

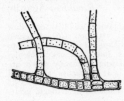

Filaments free-floating amongst other algae or subaerial. Branches long and flexuose, slightly attenuated, generally narrower than the main axis and borne unilaterally. Primary axis consisting of a single row, rarely of 2 to 3 rows of cells, enclosed in a strong sheath of uniform thickness. Spores and heterocysts intercalary. Among water weeds, in hot springs, etc.

FIG. 63. *Hapalosiphon hibernicus* W. and G. S. West. × 440. (After West.)

63 (61, 62) Sheaths thick; fused to form an irregular gelatinous mass.

Nostochopsis Wood.

Forming rounded, Nostoc-like masses, attached to water plants. Filaments composed of but one cell-row; profusely branched.

FIG. 64. *Nostochopsis lobata* Wood. × 330. (After Bornet.)

64 (26) Filaments conspicuously attenuated towards one or both extremities, which are generally piliferous.
Suborder **Trichophoreae** . . 65

Filaments sheathed, simple or branched, attenuated from the base to the apex, which is piliferous; heterocysts generally basal, rarely absent. . . . . . . Family RIVULARIACEAE . . 65

65 (68) Filaments free or forming penicillate tufts or soft velvety expansions. 66

66 (67) Branches, when present, distinct and free. . . . *Calothrix* Agardh.

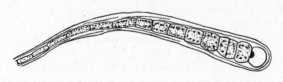

Filaments simple or slightly branched, single in a thick sheath; heterocysts basal or intercalary or, in a few species, absent. Forming tufts or soft velvety expansions on wet or submerged rocks.

FIG. 65. *Calothrix thermalis* Hansgirg. × 465. (Original.)

67 (66) Branches several (2 to 6) within a common sheath.
Dichothrix Zanardini.

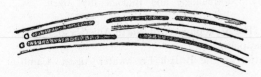

Filaments more or less dichotomously branched; heterocysts basal or intercalary. On wet rocks, etc.

FIG. 66. *Dichothrix interrupta* W. and G. S. West. × 420. (After West.)

68 (65) Filaments forming a hemispherical or globular mass, closely united by mucus. 69

69 (70)   Filaments radiately disposed in a globose or hemispherical, attached mass. Spores unknown. . . . . *Rivularia* Agardh.

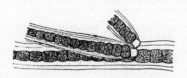

Forming hemispherical, globular, or hollow spherical colonies attached to submerged plants, such as *Chara*, *Myriophyllum*, or to stones in streams and cataracts. Colonies composed of radiating filaments which are repeatedly branched; filaments attenuated and with piliferous extremities; heterocysts basal; the whole enclosed in a tough, gelatinous matrix.

FIG. 67.   *Rivularia minutula* Bornet and Flahault. ✕ 300. (After West.)

70 (69)   Filaments radiately disposed; colony often free-floating. Spores regularly present. . . . . *Gloeotrichia* J. Agardh.

FIG. 68.   *Gloeotrichia pisum* Agardh.   ✕ 465. (Original.)

(Probably not sufficiently distinguished from *Rivularia* to justify its being made a separate genus.) Colony globose, free-floating or attached to submerged water plants; solid when young, but inflated and hollow when old; composed of radiating, branched, attenuated filaments. Spores elongated, cylindrical, borne immediately above the basal heterocyst. *G. pisum* Ag. is a common plankton form and constituent of "water-bloom."

IMPORTANT REFERENCES ON BLUE-GREEN ALGAE

FARLOW, W. G. 1877. Remarks on some algae found in the water supplies of the City of Boston. Bull. Bussey Inst., 2: 75–80.

FORTI, A. 1907. Sylloge Myxophycearum; in De Toni's Sylloge Algarum omnium, Vol. V.

GARDNER, N. L. 1906. Cytological studies in Cyanophyceae. Univ. of Calif. Pub. Bot., 2: 237–296.

HYAMS, ISABEL F., AND RICHARDS, ELLEN H. 1901, 1902, 1904. Notes on *Oscillatoria prolifica*. Tech. Quarterly, Vols. 14, 15, 17.

KIRCHNER, O. 1900. Schizophyceae; in Engler-Prantl Nat. Pflanzenfamilien.

OLIVE, EDGAR W. 1904. Mitotic division of the nuclei of the Cyanophyceae. Beihefte z. Botan. Centralb., 18: 9–44.

—— 1905. Notes on the Occurrence of *Oscillatoria prolifica* in the Ice of Pine Lake, Waukesha County, Wisconsin. Trans. Wis. Acad. Sci., 15: 124–134.

OLTMANNS, FRIEDR. 1904–05. Morphologie und Biologie der Algen. 2v. Jena.

TILDEN, JOSEPHINE. 1910. The Myxophyceae of North America and Adjacent Regions, etc. Minneapolis.

WEST, G. S. 1904. A Treatise on the British Freshwater Algae. Camb. Univ. Press.

WOLLE, F. 1887. Fresh-water Algae of the United States. Bethlehem, Pa.

CHAPTER VI

THE FRESH–WATER ALGAE

(EXCLUDING THE BLUE–GREEN ALGAE)

By JULIA W. SNOW

Associate Professor of Botany in Smith College, Northampton, Mass.

THE fresh-water algae are among the most widely distributed of plants. They are found in all natural bodies of water, whether these be rapidly-running streams, brooks, and rivers, or the more quiet bodies, such as pools, ponds, and lakes. They abound wherever there is moisture. All low-growing vegetation in moist places, the bark of trees, the earth itself, and even snow-covered mountains, bear species, although they may be invisible to the naked eye.

The forms of the fresh-water algae are most varied, and there are all gradations from the most minute cell of primitive, spherical shape to the large filamentous, richly-branched structure, or cell complex. The difference between the simple unicellular forms and many of the higher forms is less than would appear at first sight. The larger forms often instead of being complex organisms with many organs, each with its own special function, seem to be more like aggregates of unicellular individuals, each capable of performing all the life functions, and each living independently of its neighbors. This is manifested in forms where a single cell is separated from all others and continues to live and to reproduce. An example of this is seen in *Stigeoclonium* and *Chaetophora*, which under certain conditions fall apart completely, and each cell exists indefinitely as a unicellular organism undergoing division in three directions. Such a state is known as the palmella condition. Each cell in this aggregate, however, when in the right environment, has the power to reproduce again the original plant, a fact which would indicate that environment as well as heredity is a factor in the determination of form. It was formerly thought that such a polymorphism was characteristic for the majority of the higher algae, but though frequent it is by no means universal.

Certain of the genera of the unicellular algae must be closely related to certain genera of the filamentous forms, such as *Stichococcus* and *Hormidium*, *Botrydiopsis* and *Conferva*. The structure of the cell, the color, size, and shape of the chromatophores, the reproduction, the chemica substances formed by the cells of the different genera, are in each case identical, and practically the only difference is that in the one case the cells are cylindrical and united into a filament, while in the other case they may be somewhat spherical and solitary.

The resemblance is so great between the Chloromonadaceae, *Conferva*, *Botrydiopsis*, and other forms in reference to the light color, the small chromatophores, the nature of the zoospores, and several other points, that many modern writers classify them together under the head of Heterokontae, in spite of the fact that some are unicellular, some flagellate, and some filamentous forms. Though this resemblance is fully recognized by the writer, in this brief outline of the fresh-water algae the older classification of Wille will be retained.

The adult algal cell is a typical plant cell, bounded by a membrane, usually of cellulose, but in the Diatomaceae of a siliceous nature. Just within the membrane is a layer of protoplasm which encloses one or more vacuoles and in which are imbedded one or more chromatophores occupying either a parietal or a central position. The nucleus usually lies near the center. In by far the larger number of species there is a single nucleus in a cell, but in the Cladophoraceae and the non-septate Siphonales there are many nuclei. The non-septate algae are called coenocytes.

The chromatophores of the algae are large in proportion to the size of the cell, and may be disc-shaped, plate-like, star-shaped, or spiral. They may be regular or irregular, perforated, netted, or entire. Nowhere else in the plant kingdom do we find such a variety of shapes and structures among chromatophores as among the algae. Within the chromatophores of many species is a body denser in structure and albuminous in character, the pyrenoid.

This usually is surrounded by starch and is the center of reserve material.

Davis regards the pyrenoid as the center of activity of the chromatophore. Certain it is that the division of the pyrenoid is the first visible stage in the division of the chromatophore and of the entire cell, and takes place in some cases at least before the division of the nucleus.

On the basis of the color of the chromatophore of the different forms, together with the mode of reproduction, are formed the chief divisions of the algae. The different classes are as follows and each of them is treated separately in a synoptic key at the place indicated:

Chlorophyceae, color green, page 134.

Cyanophyceae, color blue-green, page 100.

Phaeophyceae, color brown, page 174.

Rhodophyceae, color red or purplish green, page 175.

Bacillariaceae, color yellow, page 125.

In all cases where the color is other than green there is in the chromatophore a coloring matter which screens the chlorophyll and gives the characteristic hue to members of the group. In the Cyanophyceae the coloring matter is phycocyan; in the Phaeophyceae, phycophaein; in the Rhodophyceae, phycoerythrin; and in the Bacillariaceae, diatomin.

Reproduction in the algae is either sexual or asexual.

Asexual reproduction may take place either by simple cell division or by the formation of some cell specially modified for that purpose. Cell division may occur in one of two ways: first, by fission, where a membrane is formed across a cell, dividing the original membrane and contents, as in *Pleurococcus;* second, by internal division, where the contents are simply divided into two, then four, and perhaps eight or more portions, as in *Dactylococcus* and *Chlorella.* The membrane remains for a time unaltered, but finally becomes ruptured when the daughter cells increase in size, thus setting free the new individuals. They germinate immediately and each produces a new plant.

Oblique divisions of cells, so frequently attributed to the algae, rarely if ever occur. They appear to take place very frequently, as in *Ankistrodesmus, Dactylococcus,* and *Chlamydomonas,* but observation proves that such divisions are always transverse or longitudinal, and that the parts in growing slip by each other and elongate, producing the diagonal line of demarcation between them.

In reproduction by internal division, the new individuals are called by Artari gonidia, by West autospores, and by Wille akinetes, with the akinete character but slightly developed. The contents of such cells may become denser, and possibly be filled with oil or starch; at the same time the membrane becomes thickened and the whole cell more resistant to unfavorable conditions, such as heat, cold, or drought. They may remain in this condition for long periods, and in this way maintain the life of the organism over conditions which would threaten the existence of an ordinary vegetative cell. Such cells or akinetes, according to Wille, may be seen in the palmella condition of *Stigeoclonium* and *Chaetophora.*

The modification of these cells may continue farther, and a rejuvenescence occur. Each cell becomes invested with a new membrane and the old membrane is cast off before germination. These structures Wille would designate as aplanospores. He also calls attention to the fact that there are many transitional stages between the vegetative cells and akinetes, and also between the akinetes and the aplanospores.

In many of the Confervales and Protococcales, instead of autospores, there are formed motile spores or zoospores. These are mostly oval in shape, without a membrane, with one, two, or four cilia, a reddish pigment spot, one or two chromatophores, and usually two contracting vacuoles in the anterior end. The zoosporangium, or cell in which they are borne, is in the greater number of cases developed from an ordinary vegetative cell, but more rarely from a cell specialized for that purpose. The zoospores originate by the repeated bipartition of the cell contents, by which 2, 4, 8, 16, 32, 64, or even 128 spores are formed, as in the production of autospores. More rarely a single spore is formed from a cell. The zoospores are set free either by the entire cell wall becoming gelatinous, or by its dissolving at a single point,

through which the spores gradually press their way. In some
instances the membrane splits and the spores are thus liberated.
If the conditions be not favorable to the liberation of the spores,
however, they may move for a time within the mother membrane,
or may never come into motion at all, but may germinate immediately without being liberated, and become invested with membranes
of their own. They soon increase in size so that the zoosporangium
wall is broken, but they often remain adhering to each other for a
long time, thus forming a cluster of cells like the parent individual.

Sexual reproduction is always preceded by fertilization. This
process consists in a union of two cells which may be either alike
or unlike, and are known as gametes If the cells are alike they
are called isogametes, but if unlike, heterogametes. The simplest
form of fertilization is seen when two isogametes unite or conjugate
to form a zygospore. These gametes may be two motile cells
resembling zoospores, as n *Protosiphon*, or they may be non-
motile cells, either distinct individuals as in the Desmids, or as
parts of filaments, as in *Spirogyra*. Frequently a slight difference
in size may be detected between these two cells, and undoubtedly
this is a beginning of sex differentiation. In all of the higher
algae this differentiation has advanced much farther and a great
difference exists between the gametes: the female cell, the oosphere
or egg cell, being large and non-motile, while the male cell, the
antherozoid or spermatozoid, is endowed with independent motion.
Only in the Florideae does the male cell, the spermatium, lack
motion, and remain dependent upon the action of the water to
transfer it to the egg cell.

The female organ which bears the egg cell is called the oogonium, the male organ which bears the antherozoid is the antheridium. The result of fertilization of an egg by an antherozoid is an
oospore, which is resistant to unfavorable conditions and is usually
dormant for a period before germination.

The female organ of the Florideae is called the procarp. It is
flask-shaped and made up of two parts, the enlarged basal portion, the carpogonium, which contains the egg cell, and a projecting
neck, the trichogyne, for conducting the spermatium to the egg.
The influence of fertilization is manifested by a rapid production

of spores from the base of the carpogonium, surrounded by sterile filaments; these together form the cystocarp.

Just as in the study of the higher plants attention has been turned largely from a purely systematic investigation to a physiological study, so among the algae the most important work is done along the line of physiology. The simplicity of their structure, the ease with which many may be cultivated, the readiness with which they respond to and adapt themselves to external conditions make them a most valuable group with which to experiment. It would seem that many of the physiological phenomena which in the higher plants are rendered obscure, due to intricacy of structure and complexity of environment, might be made plain in these lower forms which lend themselves so readily to manipulation.

Most valuable results in the physiology of reproduction have already been attained by Klebs who has taken the chief elements in the environment and studied their effect on the organism. As a result he has shown that reproduction, at least in the forms studied, instead of being a phenomenon which, without any determining cause, occurs simply as a stage of growth, is a phenomenon which is dependent upon external conditions; and that as these are altered, the one or the other form of reproduction may be originated, perfected, or altogether checked, according to the will of the investigator. He has shown most conclusively that the sexual form of reproduction does not of necessity alternate with the asexual reproduction. If the conditions be maintained, it is possible in certain cases to suppress either form of reproduction indefinitely, or if desired, to call forth the one to the entire exclusion of the other. An example of this is cited by Klebs in *Vaucheria*, *Protosiphon*, and a number of other forms. These facts would go to prove that an alternation of the sexual and asexual form of reproduction does not exist in the green algae, though West and others hold that it occurs in a large number of the Chlorophyceae. The sporophyte generation, they believe, is represented by the sexual spore which produces asexual zoospores; each of these in turn, on germinating, ushers in a gametophyte generation.

In studying the algal flora of any region and the conditions under which it exists, one notes ecological relations among the algae quite as much as among higher plants. The forms which may be found are determined very largely by the nature of their environment, and many of them cannot be transferred from one set of conditions to another. A large number of species which live submerged in water soon perish if subjected to the atmosphere, while others, such as the common *Pleurococcus vulgaris*, which normally live exposed to the air, are never found in water. A few forms, such as *Chlorella*, *Stichococcus* and *Hormidium*, may adapt themselves to either environment, and are very widely distributed under the different conditions where algae are found.

As all forms are dependent on moisture, the geological formations which determine the amount of moisture must determine the algal flora of any region. In localities where there are large tracts of level land without elevations and depressions, the algal flora is extremely meager; while in a hilly country where the water accumulates in depressions of the earth this flora is abundant, certain forms such as *Stigeoclonium*, *Draparnaldia*, and *Batrachospermum* preferring the rapidly-running water of streams, while the larger number of species choose the quieter water of ponds and lakes.

From early spring to late fall the algae are most numerous, but they are also found in winter, even in the vegetative condition, as many are not injured by freezing. In these cases the chief effect of cold upon them is simply a retarding of growth and of reproduction. But while some forms are found at all seasons, different forms predominate at different times, some species being most abundant at one period and others most abundant at another. It does not follow, however, that the same date in successive years will find the same form predominating. Within certain limits the flora of a body of water is constantly changing, due probably to changes in temperature, light, and nutrition, or possibly to other causes too obscure to detect.

Usually the littoral region supports a number of filamentous algae. *Cladophora* is one of the most frequent and is especially abundant in regions where wave action is strong and the current great. On the other hand, if the water be shallow and exposed to the direct rays of the sun, such forms as *Spirogyra, Zygnema, Oedo-*

gonium, and *Bulbochaete* are found. *Chara* and *Nitella* are found in huge beds at the bottom of lakes at a depth of from one to many feet.

Of the unicellular forms also, different species occur under different conditions. An especially favorable position for this group is among the leaves and on the surface of the higher aquatic plants. Indeed unless higher algae or phanerogams exist in certain localities but few of the minute forms are ever found. There seem to be certain preferences on the part of different species of unicellular algae as to the forms of the higher plants with which they associate. This may be simply that the shape, texture, and arrangement of parts of certain of these plants afford a better shelter and protection for the single cells than do others, but it is more probable that the plant itself exerts some chemical influence which is attractive or repulsive to these forms. For instance, enormous numbers of different species may be found growing among *Chara*, while in connection with *Ceratophyllum*, the leaves of which are very finely cut, but few species occur.

The endophytic forms, such as *Endosphaera* and *Scotinosphaera*, live principally in the tissues of *Potamogeton*, *Lemna*, and other water plants, though they may also be found outside of the tissues. The discoid forms, such as *Coleochaete* and *Ulvella*, are found on the surface of the broader-leaved types of submerged plants, especially on *Potamogeton;* and the unicellular blue-green forms occur abundantly among the Charas, though they are also numerous in most stagnant water.

In the plankton are always found many species that exist in the littoral region, but there are also many forms which are distinctively plankton types. These are characterized by a great surface in proportion to the mass of the cells, thus rendering them more buoyant. This is provided for in several ways: by the presence of long gelatinous or cellulose spines, as in *Chodatella* and *Richteriella;* by the union of cells into ribbons or bands, as in *Fragilaria;* and by the production of a homogeneous gelatinous matrix in which the cells are imbedded, as in *Kirchneriella* and *Sphaerocystis*.

In studying the life history of the algae, cultivation is absolutely essential in order that development may be traced from step to step without confusing the different phases of the form in question with other species which may be found in connection with it. Aside from this, too, cultures are useful in determining what species, especially of the unicellular forms, are present in any collection. Many of these are so minute that they could easily be overlooked unless they exist in great masses, which is rarely the case. So if all forms of a locality are desired, it is well to put a small portion of material gathered, bits of moss, earth, lichen, or washings from higher aquatic plants into a culture medium and allow it to stand 3 to 4 weeks, when it may be examined; the chances are that many forms will appear which could not be detected before-hand. Indeed this is the only way in which certain species may be obtained.

When a pure culture is desired bacteriological methods for pure cultures are most useful, but one who is skillful in working under the low power of a microscope can often, by means of a tiny capillary pipette, isolate a single cell, or a cluster of cells, which he knows to be all of one kind. If the medium in which the form was growing contained many other species, the chances are that the first time that the cell or cluster is transferred, a cell of some other minute form such as *Chlorella* or *Stichococcus*, too small to notice under that power, may be transferred with the desired form; so to prevent this impurity from being carried to the final culture, thus making the culture worthless, the better way is to transfer the cell first to a drop of distilled water on a slide, then sterilize the pipette in boiling water and, allowing it to cool, transfer the cell again to a drop of distilled water; the process should be repeated three or four times, and the cell finally transferred to the receptacle in which the culture is required.

For this purpose small low glass preparation dishes with loosely fitting covers are the best. A receptacle that will admit a little air is better than one that excludes air entirely. These small receptacles may then be placed directly on the stage of a microscope and the forms studied from time to time without disturbing the growth in the least.

The bacteriological method for obtaining pure cultures employs gelatine or agar-agar plates. These plates are prepared by spreading a thin layer of gelatine or agar-agar mixed with some good nutrient solution over the bottom of a petri dish or a small glass culture dish. This must then be sterilized before the culture is made. In preparing the culture a very minute portion of the medium containing the desired form is mixed with a large drop of distilled water and then this is scattered at intervals over the surface. The material must be diluted with enough water so that each cell will be by itself.

In the course of a few days the single cells will have increased, and then, while the culture is on the stage of a microscope, the little colony of cells may be transferred to a liquid medium by means of a sterilized needle, the tip of a fine brush, or a very fine pipette.

To a very large extent the culture medium must be adapted to the species to be cultivated. No one medium is favorable to all species of algae, and the form must be taken into consideration before a medium is prepared. If the species be a new form, various different media must often be tried before the right one is determined. If a quantity of different forms from any collection be placed in one medium and a second quantity in another, the probabilities are that in the course of three or four weeks but few of the same species will be found in both cultures. Certain forms will have died in one while perhaps those very forms have found in the other medium the substances and conditions for their development.

The media to which the greatest number of forms are adapted are Moore's solution and Knop's solution:

Moore's solution:
Ammonium nitrate............................... 0.5 gram.
Potassium phosphate............................ 0.2 gram.
Magnesium sulphate............................ 0.2 gram.
Calcium chloride................................ 0.1 gram.
Iron sulphate.................................... trace.

These amounts should be dissolved in one liter of distilled water.

Knop's solution:
Potassium nitrate................................ 1 gram.
Potassium phosphate............................ 1 gram.
Magnesium sulphate............................ 1 gram.
Calcium nitrate................................. 4 grams.
Chloride of iron................................ trace.

The first three substances are dissolved in the required amount of water to make from 1 to 5 per cent of the solution, then the calcium nitrate is added. This solution may then be diluted as needed; usually a 0.2 per cent or a 0.4 per cent solution is favorable for ordinary cultures.

It should be borne in mind that among the plankton forms there are many which will not develop in either. For these the best solution has been found to be a solution made from the organisms in the plankton itself. In this a perfectly normal development may be obtained for many forms, though even in this some fail of development. Bouillon, earth decoctions, moist, finely pulverized earth, bits of bark and cubes of sterilized peat, all form good substances for the ordinary cultivation of the unicellular algae. The filamentous algae are far more difficult to cultivate. Before satisfying one's self with the life history of any form, that form should be maintained in culture for an extended period, when observation can be made from time to time and the effect of different conditions determined.

An attempt has been made to give the principal genera of fresh-water algae found in North America, but the list is by no means complete. A very few genera of diatoms and desmids here cited have not been found by the writer and no report of their occurrence in North America could be obtained; but these groups are distributed so universally that they probably will be discovered in this territory.

KEY TO NORTH AMERICAN FRESH-WATER ALGAE

CLASS I. Bacillariaceae (Diatoms)

Color yellow; plant a single cell, sometimes united into chains; membrane silicified, with minute, definite markings.

These are unicellular algae but, by means of a gelatinous substance, are frequently held together in bands or masses. The membrane is silicified, making it hard and rigid. It is always composed of two parts, valves, which may be separated from each other and which are often compared to a box and its overlapping cover; the side where the edges overlap is spoken of as the girdle side, while the outer surface is referred to as the valve side; this and, more rarely, the girdle side also are sculptured with fine striations, dots, dotted lines, and grooves. Many have extending lengthwise a conspicuous line, the raphe, which frequently bears at its middle and both ends rounded portions called nodules.

Reproduction is by auxospores, either sexual or asexual. The asexual are formed by the contents of a cell collecting, throwing off the membrane, and forming either one or two spores. The sexual auxospores are formed by the throwing off of the membrane and the copulation of two cells in one of the following ways: (a) Two cells divide, making two pairs of daughter-cells; each individual of one pair fuses with one from the other pair, thus making two spores. (b) Two cells unite to form one auxospore. (c) Two cells come together but do not copulate; two auxospores are formed.

1 (9, 10)   Valves circular, raphe lacking, markings radial.   2

2 (5)   Cells cylindrical or ellipsoidal, united into filaments.   Valve side circular, either convex or flat. . . Family MELOSIRACEAE . .   3

3 (4)   Cells with no spines or teeth; valves either smooth or punctate, usually convex; girdle side punctate. . . . .   *Melosira* Agardh.

Melosira is very common in ponds, rivers, lakes, and reservoirs, and occurs in great quantities in the plankton. The filaments are often very long.

FIG. 69.   *Melosira varians* Agardh.   × 600.   (Original.)

4 (3)   Cells similar to those of *Melosira*, but with a circle of tooth-like projections between the valve and girdle sides.
Orthosira Thwaites.

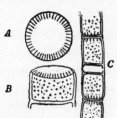

Van Heurck and West include *Orthosira* under *Melosira*, while many others make a separate genus. The *Orthosira* forms are found in the same localities as *Melosira* but are much less abundant.

FIG. 70.   *Orthosira orichalcea* W. Smith.   × 600.   (Original.)

5 (2)   Cells single, disc-shaped, not forming filaments; valves flat, convex, or undulating, mostly with radial rows of punctulations.
Family COSCINODISCACEAE . .   6

6 (7, 8)   Valves circular or nearly so, with radiating rows of dots or areolations, the disc with a distinct edge, usually bearing a circle of inconspicuous submarginal spines.
Coscinodiscus Ehrenberg.

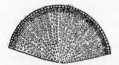

The number of species of *Coscinodiscus* is very large, mostly marine, although some occur in fresh water with other similar centric forms.

FIG. 71.   *Coscinodiscus apiculatus* Ehrenberg.   × 330.   (After Wolle.)

7 (6, 8)   Valves circular, showing a central smooth or punctate area, and an outer margin of radiating striations.   Girdle view with undulating ends. . . . .   *Cyclotella* Kützing.

The cells are disc-shaped and are distinguished from other disc-shaped forms principally by the smooth or punctate center and the undulating ends.   It is found commonly in the plankton.

FIG. 72.   *Cyclotella compta* Kützing var. *affinis* Grun.   *a*. Valve side; *b*. girdle side.   × 408.   (After Schütt and van Heurck-Grunow.)

A   B

8 (6, 7) Valves circular, with radial rows of dots, between which are clear spaces; center either punctate or hyaline; on the margin a circle of acute spines; girdle view with undulating ends.

Stephanodiscus Ehrenberg.

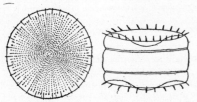

The length of the spines on the margins of the cells varies greatly; in some species they are short and acute, while in others they may exceed the diameter of the cell many times. *Stephanodiscus* occurs frequently in the plankton, but usually not in great quantities.

FIG. 73. *Stephanodiscus niagareoe* Ehrenberg. × 606. (Original.)

A   B

9 (1, 10) Valves more or less cylindrical, often in chains, ends greatly extended, usually forming long spines.

Family RHIZOSOLENIACEAE.

Only one genus. . . . . *Rhizosolenia* Ehrenberg.

FIG. 74. *Rhizosolenia eriensis* H. Smith. × 190. (After Schröter.)

10 (1, 9) Valves not circular or cylindrical, of different shapes, symmetrical in reference to a longitudinal or transverse axis; surface marked by costae or punctate lines making definite angles with a middle raphe or a median line. 11

11 (34, 38) A middle nodule present on the raphe of both valves. . . . 12

See also 40 and 65.

12 (32, 36) Girdle view symmetrical with reference to both a transverse and a longitudinal axis. 13

13 (26) Valves not arched or keeled; usually symmetrical with reference to a straight or a sigmoid raphe. Family NAVICULACEAE . . 14

Valves symmetrical with reference to a straight or curved middle line; girdle symmetrical with reference to both axes; a straight or curved raphe; a central and two end nodules present.

14 (15) Cells without inner partitions; raphe and valves straight. . . . 16

15 (14) Raphe and valves sigmoid. . . . . *Pleurosigma* W. Smith.

FIG. 75. *Pleurosigma attenuatum* W. Smith. × 300. (After Smith.)

16 (19) Cells linear, oblong, with rounded nodules, the two end ones turned toward one side, the prominent costae not punctate. . . 17

17 (18) The costae interrupted by a plain band at the center.

Stauroptera Ehrenberg.

18 (17) The costae not interrupted at the center. . *Pinnularia* Ehrenberg.

FIG. 76. *Pinnularia viridis* Smith. × 600. (Original.)

19 (16) Cells more lance-shaped, the end nodules not turned toward one side. Striations composed of lines of individual dots. . 20

20 (23, 24, 25) Central nodule small, rounded, or slightly elongated. . . . 21

21 (22) No lateral longitudinal areas of transverse septa. . . *Navicula* Bory.

> A form which grows in gelatinous tubes is regarded by some authors as a different genus *Schizonema* but others regard it as a true Navicula.
>
> FIG. 77. *Navicula rhynchocephala* Kützing. × 557. (Original.)

22 (21) Two lateral longitudinal areas of transverse septa. Mostly imbedded in a gelatinous pseudothallus. . . . *Mastogloia* Thwaites.

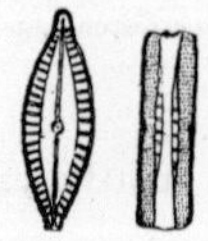

> In shape, *Mastogloia* resembles *Navicula*, but is distinguished from it by the gelatinous envelope and the presence of lateral, transverse, siliceous septa or plates which divide the lateral regions of the cells into small compartments. There are transverse striations on the valves. It is not a very common genus in America.

FIG. 78. *Mastogloia smithii* Thwaites. × about 300. (After Smith.)

A | B

23 (20, 24, 25) Central nodule broad, extending to near the margin of the valves.
Stauroneis Ehrenberg.

> *Stauroneis* occurs frequently in all bodies of water and is a constituent of the diatomaceous flora which forms large siliceous deposits at the bottom of lakes.
> FIG. 79. *Stauroneis anceps* Ehrenberg. × 600. (Original.)

24 (20, 23, 25) Central nodule elongated to a short rod. Borne on gelatinous stalks. . . . . *Brebissonia* Grun.

FIG. 80. *Brebissonia sp.* × 580. (Original.)

25 (20, 23, 24) Central and end nodules elongated, enclosed with the raphe between two longitudinal, parallel, siliceous ribs. Frustules sometimes borne in gelatinous tubes.
Vanheurckia Brébisson.

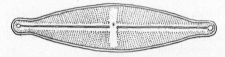

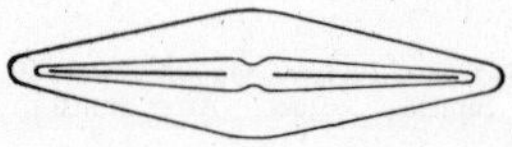

FIG. 81. *Vanheurckia rhomboides* Ehrenberg. × 370. (After West.)

26 (13) Valves asymmetrical with reference to the raphe or to a longitudinal axis; raphe arched, or nearer one margin than the other.
Family CYMBELLACEAE . . 27

27 (28) Valves greatly convex; girdle side elliptical or oval.
Amphora Ehrenberg.

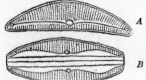

> Van Heurck regards *Amphora* as one of the most difficult genera of diatoms and notes that over 200 species have been placed in this genus. It is believed that it originated from *Cymbella*.
>
> FIG. 82. *Amphora ovalis* Kützing. a. Valve side; b. girdle side. × 600. (Original.)

28 (27) Valves flat or only slightly convex. 29

29 (30, 31) Raphe straight or bent, ending in the middle of the valve ends.
Cells free. . . . . *Cymbella* Agardh.

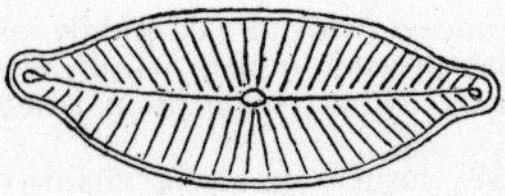

Cymbella varies in shape from that of a typical *Navicula* to one strongly arched, and they have sometimes been styled as asymmetrical *Naviculas*. Some authors include the genus *Cocconema* under *Cymbella*, but the name *Cocconema* is the older name and should be retained. Wolle reports 25 species of *Cymbella*.

FIG. 83. *Cymbella cuspidata* Kützing. × 600. (Original.)

30 (29, 31) Cells much as in *Cymbella*, but usually larger and borne on gelatinous stalks. . . . . *Cocconema* Ehrenberg.

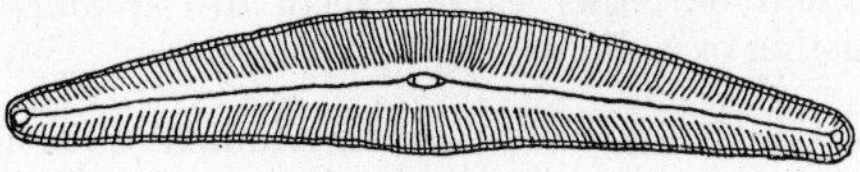

FIG. 84. *Cocconema lanceolatum* Ehrenberg. × 375. (After West.)

31 (29, 30) Raphe straight, not ending in the middle of valve ends. Cells living in gelatinous tubes. . . . . . *Encyonema* Kützing.

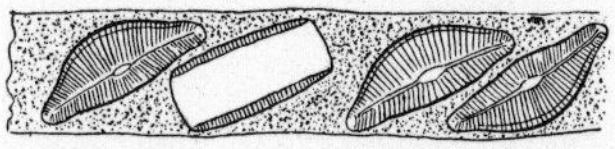

FIG. 85. *Encyonema auerwaldii* Rabenhorst. × 250. (After Wolle.)

32 (12, 36) Girdle view asymmetrical with reference to a transverse axis, the outline being wedge-shaped.
Family GOMPHONEMACEAE . . 33

33 (35) Girdle side straight. . . . . *Gomphonema* Agardh.

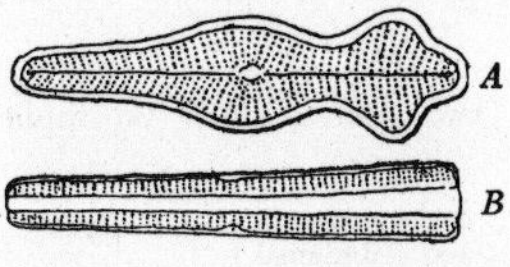

FIG. 86. *Gomphonema acuminatum* Ehrenberg. a. Valve side; b. girdle side. × 600. (Original.)

34 (11, 38) A middle nodule and a raphe present on but one valve. . . 35

35 (33) Girdle side curved; otherwise similar to *Gomphonema*.
Rhoicosphenia Grunow.

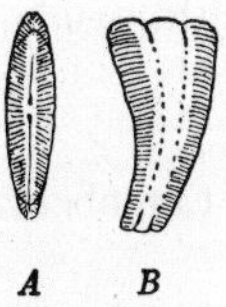

The two valves are unlike in shape and in the fact that the lower valve possesses a raphe, a central and end nodules, while the upper valve possesses only a pseudo-raphe and is without nodules.

FIG. 87. *Rhoicosphenia curvata* Grunow. a. Valve side; b. girdle side. × 380. (After Schönfeldt.)

36 (32, 37) Girdle view symmetrical with reference to a transverse, but not to a longitudinal axis, the cells being arcuate and attached to higher algae. . . . . Family COCCONEIDACEAE.
Only one genus known. . . . . *Cocconeis* Ehrenberg.

Valves oval or elliptical, symmetrical with reference to both axes; raphe straight, with middle nodules but without end nodules. Markings of faint longitudinal punctate lines; girdle and end views both curved.

FIG. 88. *Cocconeis pediculus* Ehrenberg. × 600. (Original.)

37 (36)   Girdle side geniculate. Valves straight, linear, or fusiform; frustules either free or stalked. . .   Family ACHNANTHACEAE.
Only one genus. . . . . *Achnanthes* Bory.

Cells so curved that the two valves are not alike, the one concave with raphe, middle and end nodules; the other convex, without a middle nodule, but with a pseudo-raphe. Girdle view symmetrical with reference to a transverse axis. Cells single or in bands, mostly on gelatinous stalks.

The cells may be solitary, though they usually form long, sessile chains or bands attached to the surface of green algae. The genus includes both marine and fresh-water forms.

FIG. 89. *Achnanthes exilis* Kützing. X 600. (Original.)

38 (11, 34)   No middle nodule present on either valve, except in *Ceratoneis*, or at most consisting of a slight, ring-like elevation. . .   39

39 (40, 41, 62)   Valves asymmetrical with reference to a longitudinal axis, in that on one margin there is a longitudinal row of bead-like thickenings (keel points) while on the other margin they are lacking. . . . .   Family NITZSCHIACEAE.
Only one genus. . . . . *Nitzschia* Hassall.

Valves linear, sometimes curved, keeled, with canal raphe. Cells rhomboidal in cross section.

FIG. 90. *Nitzschia linearis* Smith. X 575. (Original.)

40 (39, 62)   Valves with median, sigmoid keel, compressed, strongly arched, bearing raphe. . . . .   Family AMPHIPRORACEAE.
Only one genus. . . . .   *Amphiprora* Ehrenberg.

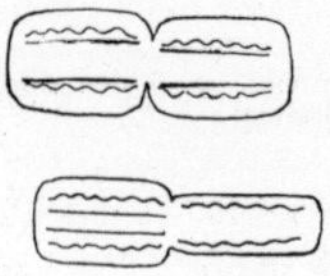

Valves fusiform, with central and two end nodules on raphe. Girdle side sharply constricted at center.

FIG. 91. *Amphiprora* sp. X 400. (Original.)

41 (39, 62)   Valves symmetrical with reference to a longitudinal axis . .   42

42 (47)   Valves each with two wing-like keels, strongly costate, with pseudoraphe but no nodules. . .   Family SURIRELLACEAE. .   43

Cells mostly large, ovate, or elliptical.

43 (44)   Cells bent in saddle shape. . . . . . .   *Campylodiscus* Ehrenberg.

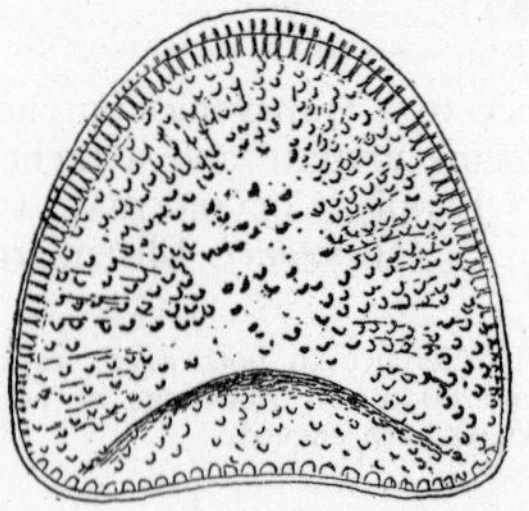

Though the shape of the cells seems more or less triangular, they are in reality circular, and their seeming angularity is due to the curvature of the frustules. It is a very large genus, some 92 species having been recorded; the species are mostly marine, though a number are found in fresh water. Their large size makes them among the most conspicuous of the diatoms.

FIG. 92. *Campylodiscus cribrosus* W. Smith. X about 300. (After Smith.)

44 (43)   Cells not bent or spirally twisted.   45

45 (46)   Valves showing a wave-like margin in girdle view.
                                        Cymatopleura W. Smith.

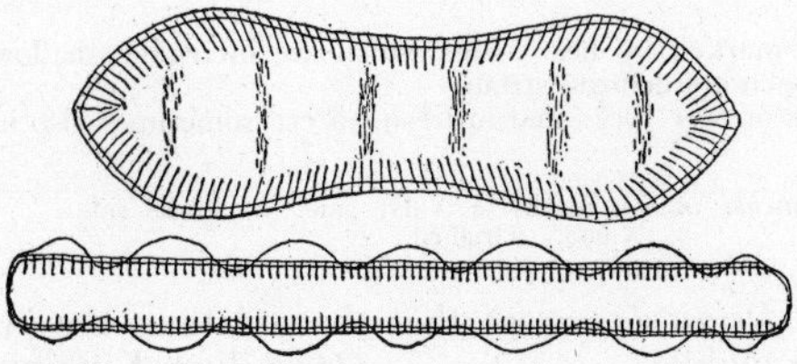

A

This is a large diatom which is easily recognized by the undulating outline of the girdle side. The genus is rather small, and Wolle reports but seven species.

B

FIG. 93.   *Cymatopleura apiculata* W. Smith. *a.* Valve side. *b.* girdle side. X 600. (Original.)

46 (45)   Girdle view without wave-like margins. . . . . . *Surirella* Turpín.

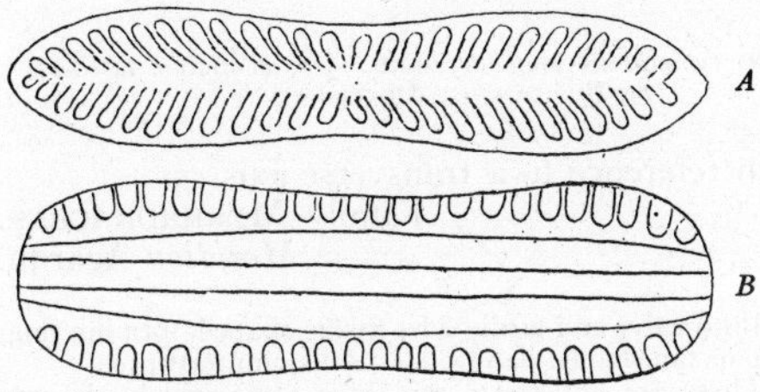

A

This genus is widely distributed and of frequent occurrence in all regions where diatoms are found. Some species are very large and conspicuous, especially in the plankton.

B

FIG. 94.   *Surirella sp.* Smith. *a.* Valve side. *b.* girdle side. X 585. (Original.)

47 (42)   Valves without keels. 48

48 (59)   Cells without deep inner partitions sometimes with imperfect septa. 49

49 (55)   Valves with transverse costae. 50

50 (54)   Valves symmetrical with reference to a transverse axis.
                                        Family DIATOMACEAE . . 51

Cells symmetrical with reference to both axes, borne in long chains; transverse striations distinct and uninterrupted except in some cases by a longitudinal plain band.

51 (52, 53)   Valve side oval or linear, transverse markings uninterrupted, girdle side rectangular, cells mostly in zig-zag chains, sometimes in short filament. . . . . . *Diatoma* de Candolle.

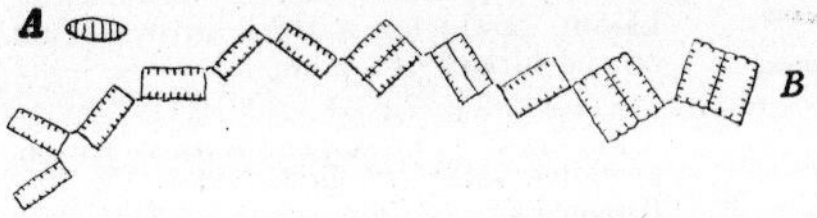

A

B   FIG. 95. *Diatoma elongatum* Agardh. *a.* Valve side. *b.* girdle side. X about 300. (After W. Smith.)

52 (51, 53) Characteristics similar to those of *Diatoma* except that the cells
are borne in ribbons. . . . . *Denticula* Kützing.

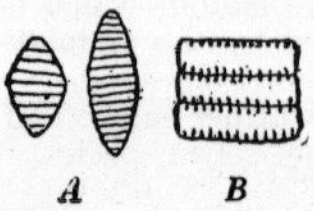

The valves are marked by heavy ribs which are in reality shallow
septa, between which are delicate striae.
Denticula occurs on wet rocks and in fresh water; sometimes also in
brackish water.

A   *B*
FIG. 96. *Denticula inflata* Smith. *a.* Valve side. *b.* girdle side.
× 600. (Original.)

53 (51, 52) Characteristics as in *Denticula* except that the striations are interrupted in the middle. . . . . . . *Odontidium* Kützing.

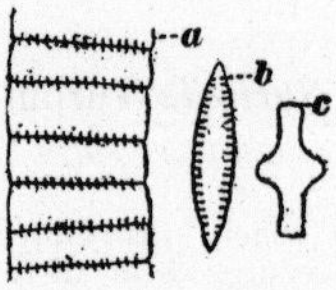

Many place the members of this genus with *Diatoma*, while
others regard the interrupted striae and the formation of short filaments instead of zig-zag chains, sufficient differences to place them
in a separate genus.

FIG. 97. *a*, *b*. *Odontidium mutabile* Smith. *c*. *Odontidium tabellaria*
Smith. × 570. (Original.)

54 (50) Valves asymmetrical with reference to a transverse axis.
Family MERIDIONACEAE.
Only one genus. . . . . *Meridion* Agardh.

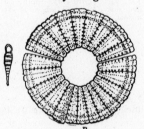

Both valve and girdle sides wedge-shaped, forming ring-
like or fan-shaped bands; striations uninterrupted.
There are imperfect transverse septa which are conspicuous on the valve side but show only laterally on
the girdle side.   Between these on the valve side are fine
punctate striae.
Van Heurck thinks this genus ought to be suppressed.
It differs from *Diatoma* only in the cuneate shape of the
valves.

FIG. 98.   *Meridion constrictum* Ralfs.   × 300.   (After
Smith.)

B

55 (49) Valves without transverse costae. . Family FRAGILARIACEAE . . 56
Cells of much the same structure as *Diatoma*. Transverse striations composed of separate
dots; with or without raphe and end nodules.

56 (57, 58) Cells very slender, not united in bands, either free or attached at
one end, forming clusters on higher algae.
Synedra Ehrenberg.

FIG. 99.   *Synedra salina* W. Smith.
× 588. (Original.)

57 (56, 58) Cells forming bands or zig-zag chains. . . *Fragilaria* Lyngbye.

A

Fragilaria is a common genus occurring in ponds, reservoirs, and lakes.
F. crotonensis has been known to occur
in such quantities as to form water
bloom, producing a thick brown scum
on the surface of a lake.

B
FIG. 100.   *Fragilaria crotonensis* Kitton.
a. Valve side. *b.* girdle side.   × 225.
(Original.)

58 (56, 57)   Cells arranged in the form of a star. . . .   *Asterionella* Hassall.

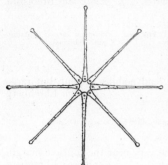

The radial arrangement of the cells is due to the presence at the inner ends of small mucous cushions which unite the cells in this manner. The cells are linear, unequally enlarged at the ends, capitate in the valve view and truncate in the girdle view. The valves are marked with delicate striations.

Asterionella is common in ponds, lakes, and water reservoirs. It is especially frequent in the plankton, probably on account of the radial arrangement of the cells, which would make it easily buoyed up by the water.

FIG. 101. *Asterionella gracillima* Heiberg. × 188.
(After Schröter.)

59 (48)   Cells with interrupted inner partitions.
Family TABELLARIACEAE . .   60

Valves linear, oblong, or elliptical, inflated at the center. Girdle side rectangular, with two or more longitudinal partitions perforated at the center.

60 (61)   Cells slender, valves with only punctate striations.
Tabellaria Ehrenberg.

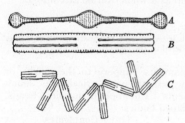

The inner partitions appear in the girdle view as distinct lines which are not always equally developed or opposite each other at the two ends of the cell. At the interruption of the partitions at the center the valve sides show an inflation.

The zig-zag chains of *Tabellaria* are conspicuous in almost all collections of algae.

FIG. 102. *Tabellaria fenestrata* Kützing. a. Valve side. b. girdle side. × 600. c. showing characteristic arrangement of cell. × about 150. (Original.)

61 (60)   Cells broader, with distinct transverse costae. . .   *Tetracyclus* Ralfs.

Aside from the interrupted inner partitions there are also transverse septa which appear on the valve sides as costae, between which are very faint striae. The septa are more numerous, and the cells more cruciform than in *Tabellaria;* they occur also in bands instead of in zig-zag chains.

FIG. 103. *Tetracyclus lacustris* Ralfs. a. Valve side. b. girdle side. × 300. (After Smith.)

62 (39, 41)   Valves asymmetrical with reference to a longitudinal axis, the cells being more or less arcuate.
Family EPITHEMIACEAE . .   63

Valves curved, usually with dotted transverse striations, sometimes also with transverse costae.

63 (64, 65)   Transverse costae coarse, converging, projecting inward, often
with lines of dots between. . .   *Epithemia* Brébisson.

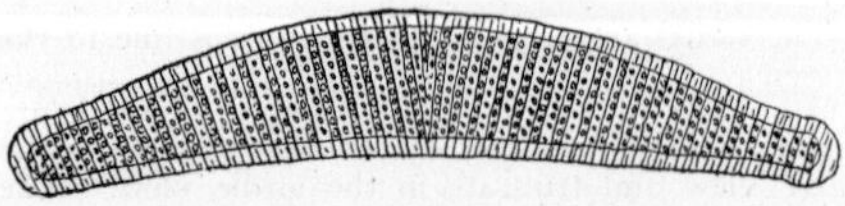

FIG. 104.   *Epithemia turgida* Kützing.
X 380.   (Original.)

64 (63, 65)   Transverse striations punctate;   end nodules present, but raphe
wanting. . . . .   *Eunotia* Ehrenberg.

FIG. 105.   *Eunotia pectinalis* Dillwyn.   X 625.   (Original.)

65 (63, 64)   Valves crescent-shaped, the raphe very near the concave margin,
with end and middle nodules.   . . .   *Ceratoneis* Ehrenberg.

There is but a single species.

FIG. 106.   *Ceratoneis arcus* Kützing.   X 600.   (Original.)

CLASS II.   Chlorophyceae

Color, a chlorophyll-green.

This group includes by far the greater number of forms of algae in fresh
water. It is so large and the characteristics of the different members so
varied that no characterization of the group as a whole will be attempted.

1 (253)   Plants fine, relatively small.   2

In regard to the *Characeae* the uncertainty of their nature and systematic position is fully
understood, but for convenience they will be considered at the end of the *Chlorophyceae*.

2 (67)   Plants of unbranched, septate filaments, slippery to the touch; or
plants of single cells of two exactly symmetrical parts, sometimes united into filaments. Chlorophyll in spiral bands,
central plates, or star-shaped bodies.

Order **Conjugales** . .   3

Filamentous or unicellular algae whose reproduction consists only in conjugation, that is
where the contents of two cells which are exactly alike, or at most differing only slightly in
reference to size, unite to form a single cell, the zygospore.

Some authors would place the *Bacillariaceae* under this group on account of the union which
takes place before the formation of the spore, but as they differ in many respects from the distinctive members of this group they have been placed in a group by themselves.

3 (59)   Plants unicellular, occasionally united into filaments; cells constricted
at the middle or not; one-half of each cell exactly symmet-
rical with the other half; 2, 4, or 8 individuals from a germinating zygospore.   . . . .   Family DESMIDIACEAE . .   4

The membrane mostly furnished with tiny protuberances and pores, both with a definite
arrangement; chromatophore radiating from or including one or more pyrenoids. Asexual
reproduction by the separation of the halves of the cell, between which two new halves are
formed, each attached to and identical with one of the older halves. In sexual reproduction
two cells come together, throw off their membranes, and their contents unite to form a
zygospore. This is usually furnished with conspicuous colorless spines.

4 (22)   Cells after division united into filaments.   5

5 (11) Cells cylindrical, with no constriction, or at most a very shallow and broad constriction, giving a slightly undulating outline.   6

6 (7, 8) Cells not longer than broad, sometimes with a very shallow, broad constriction; chromatophore central, with 6 to 10 rays about a pyrenoid. . . . . *Hyalotheca* Ehrenberg.

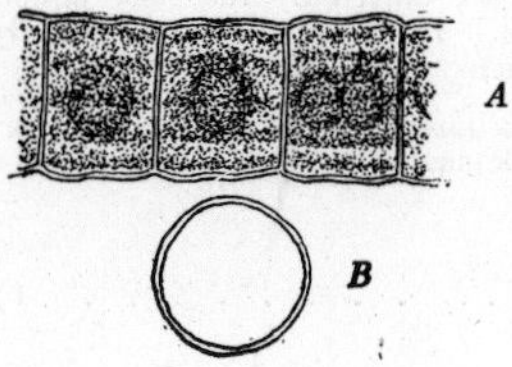

Filaments long, often twisted, and slippery to the touch. The different diameters of the cells nearly equal, varying from 20 to 35 μ. The median constriction often very slight. Chromatophore in each cell-half of radiating plates placed about a pyrenoid.

A broad gelatinous envelop is always present but it is invisible without reagents.

Hyalotheca is frequent among filamentous forms of the *Conjugales*.

Fig. 107. *Hyalotheca dissiliens* Brébisson. *a.* side view. *b.* end view. × 575. (Original.)

7 (6, 8) Cells but little longer than broad, attenuated at the end.
Leptozosma Turner.

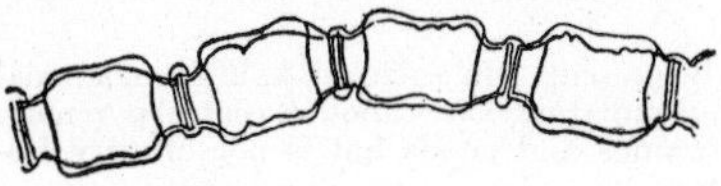

Filaments long, cateniform; not twisted, or but slightly so. Joints united by a strongly marked suture; near to *Bambuscina* Kützing, but differing therefrom in the suture.

Fig. 108. *Leptozosma catenulata* Turner. × 300. (After Turner.)

8 (6, 7) Cells much longer than broad. 9

9 (10) Chromatophore a central plate containing a row of pyrenoids.
Gonatozygon de Bary.

Fig. 109. *Gonatozygon ralfsii* de Bary.
× about 230. (After de Bary.)

Length of cells 100 to 200 μ; breadth 10 to 20 μ, much like a cell of *Mougeotia* except that the membrane is covered with minute projections; cells sometimes slightly swollen at the ends.

10 (9) Chromatophores consisting of several parietal spiral bands.
Genicularia de Bary.

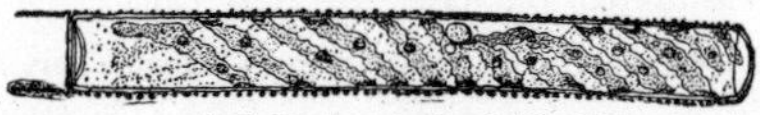

Fig. 110. *Genicularia spirotaenia* Brebisson. × 265. (After de Bary.)

Diameter of cells 17 to 22.5 μ; length 10 to 20 times as great. Membrane covered with fine projections as in *Gonatozygon*. Spiral chromatophores with many pyrenoids.

11 (5) Cells not cylindrical. 12

12 (19) End view of cells circular, oval, or elliptical, rarely triangular. . 13

13 (16) Cells not deeply constricted at the middle. 14

14 (15) Cells cask-shaped, placed end to end, with a shallow narrow constriction at the middle; end view circular, with two oppositely placed projections. . . . . *Gymnozyga.*

The membrane frequently shows longitudinal stripes. Chromatophores in each cell-half composed of a number of radially-placed plates arranged about a pyrenoid at the center.

Fig. 111. *Gymnozyga brébissonii* Nordstedt. × 568. (Original.)

15 (14)   Cells not cask-shaped, with a narrow, shallow, central constriction;
          end view elliptical or triangular, ends tapering or round.

                                                   Spondylosium Archer.

Cells 10 to 12 μ broad; 8 to 9 μ long. cells tapering towards
the ends.   Membrane smooth or with slight prominences.
A pyrenoid in each cell-half, about which radiate from 4 to 6
chlorophyll plates.
The cells of the filaments are united by the close adherence of the apices of the cells.   The filaments are frequently
twisted and enveloped in mucus.

Fig. 112.   *Spondylosium papillatum* W. and G. West.   × 600.
(Original.)

16 (13)   Cells deeply constricted in the middle.   17

17 (18)   Cell-halves acutely pointed or oval; upper and lower surface of each
          end furnished with a spine which meets a similar one on the
          adjoining cell; end view fusiform. . .   *Onychonema* Wallich.

Narrow spines frequently present.   In each cell-half a single axial
chromatophore, composed of radiating plates about a central pyrenoid.
Onychonema occurs in swamps and ponds but is not of very frequent occurrence in America.

Fig. 113.   *Onychonema loeve* Nordstedt.   × 600.   (Original.)

18 (17)   Cell-halves oval in outline, with a deep central constriction; cells
          united into filaments by small tubercles.

                                                   Sphaerozosma Archer.

Cells 22 to 33 μ broad and about half as long, end view elliptical;
membrane smooth or with tiny warts near the ends of the cells.
Sphaerozosma is distinguished from *Spondylosium* by the cells
being united by tubercles instead of by their apices directly.
S. pulchrum var. inflatum Wolle is reported by Wolle as occurring in such quantities as to color the water green.

Fig. 114.   *Sphaerozosma vertebratum* Ralfs.   × about 300.   (After de Bary.)

19 (12)   End view of cells triangular or quadrangular, seldom oval. . .   20

20 (21)   No space at the center between the transverse septa; cells slightly
          and narrowly constricted. . . . . .   *Desmidium* Agardh.

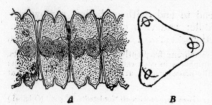

Filaments long, twisted.   Cells flat at the
ends, ⅓ to ½ as long as broad, so constricted
at the center as to give a scalloped lateral
outline to each cell.   End view with as many
pyrenoids as there are angles, from each of
which radiate two chlorophyll plates.

Fig. 115.   *Desmidium schwartzii* Agardh.   *a.* side
view.   *b.* end view.   × 550.   (Original.)

A   *B*

21 (2c) An oval opening at the center between the transverse septa.

Aptogonum Ralfs.

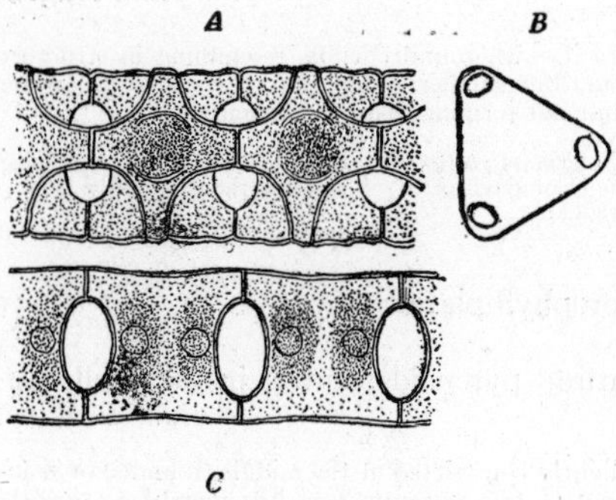

Filaments often twisted, cells slightly longer than broad, with three or four projections on each end which exactly meet others on the adjoining cells, sometimes slightly constricted. Several pyrenoids in each cell, from which radiate the plate-like chromatophores.

The genus *Aptogonum* is included by many under *Desmidium*, but the space at the center between two adjoining cells, the lack of the narrow central construction, and the greater length of the cells would seem to distinguish it from *Desmidium*.

Fig. 116. *Aptogonum baileyi* Ralfs. *a.* side view. *b.* end view. *c.* optical section. X 425. (Original.)

22 (4) Cells not united into filaments. 23

23 (33) Cells not constricted at the center, or at the most only very slightly so. 24

24 (25) Cells crescent-shaped; tapering toward both ends.

Closterium Nitzsch.

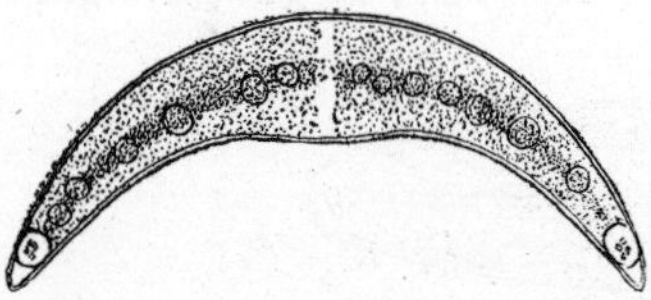

Cells varying from short, thick cells swollen in the middle to very slender cells sometimes bent in the shape of an S. Membrane smooth, or longitudinally striated, rarely with a yellow hue. Chromatophores in each cell-half of several radially-placed plates, including one or more rows of pyrenoids; at each end a large vacuole containing moving granules.

Fig. 117. *Closterium moniliferum* var. *concavum* Ehrenberg. X about 200. (Original.)

25 (24) Cells cylindrical or fusiform. 26

26 (27, 28) Chromatophore one or more parietal, spiral bands.

Spirotaenia Brébisson.

Cells straight, oblong, cylindrical, or fusiform, with rounded ends. Chromatophores one or several parietal bands with pyrenoids.

Fig. 118. *Spirotaenia minuta* Thuret. X 365. (After West.)

27 (26, 28) Chromatophore star-shaped, one in each cell-half.

Cylindrocystis de Bary.

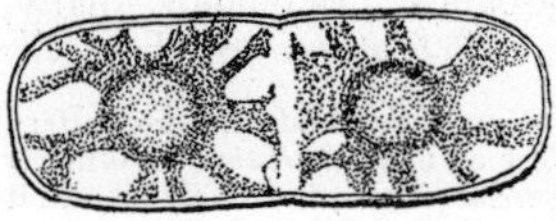

Cells with rounded ends, often oval in outline. Chromatophores two, star-shaped, many rayed, each enclosing a pyrenoid at the center.

Fig. 119. *Cylindrocystis diplospora* Lundell. X 375. (Original.)

28 (26, 27) Chromatophore straight, simple, or multiple 29

29 (30)   Chromatophore a single axial plate with one or more pyrenoids.
Mesotaenium Nägeli.

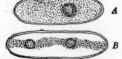

A Cells cylindrical, with rounded ends, resembling in structure cells of *Mougeotia* but smaller, sometimes adhering to each other after division but not forming distinct filaments.

B FIG. 120. *Mesotaenium endlicherianum* Nägeli. × 625. *a*. showing the surface of the chlorophyll plate. *b*. showing the edge of the chlorophyll plate. (Original.)

30 (29)   In each cell-half several chlorophyll plates. 31

31 (32)   Margins of radial plates entire; pyrenoids central in each cell-half.
Penium de Bary.

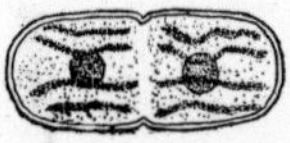

Cells sometimes slightly constricted at the middle, rounded or truncated at the ends; length 3 to 9 times the breadth; membrane smooth, punctate, or longitudinally striated; chromatophores radially placed about a large pyrenoid in each cell-half.
FIG. 121. *Penium cucurbitinum* Biss. × 295. (After West.)

32 (31)   Margins of the radial plates of the chromatophore scalloped; pyrenoids several and scattered. . . . . *Netrium* Nägeli.

Cells shaped much as in *Penium*. The scallops of the outer margin of the chromatophores conspicuous; pyrenoids not large and forming a center about which the chlorophyll plates radiate, as in *Penium*, but small and scattered.

FIG. 122. *Netrium lamellosum* Brébisson. × 200. (After Kirchner.)

33 (23)   Cells constricted at the center. 34

34 (42)   Constriction at the sides slight and usually gradual. 35

35 (38)   Length of cells usually not more than six times the breadth. . . 36

36 (37)   Central constriction very gradual and shallow; a slight incision at the ends. . . . . *Tetmemorus* Ralfs.

Cells straight, fusiform, or cylindrical, slightly and broadly constricted at the middle; ends rounded, each with a slight linear incision; length 4 to 6 times the diameter. Chromatophore axial with a single row of pyrenoids.
FIG. 123. *Tetmemorus granulatus* Ralfs. × 465. (Original.)

37 (36)   Cells short, ends truncate, constriction rather abrupt, but not deep; chromatophore of longitudinal bands; pyrenoids many, scattered. . . . . *Pleurotaeniopsis* Lundell.

This is regarded by Brébisson as a *Calocylindrus*, by de Bary as a *Pleurotaenium* and by West as a *Cosmarium*. Formerly Wille recognized the genus, *Pleuretaeniopsis*, but now includes it under *Cosmarium*.
FIG. 124. *Pleurotaeniopsis turgidus* Lund. × 130. (After de Bary.)

38 (37) Length of cells many times the breadth. 39

39 (40, 41) Cells before the middle constriction swollen, but without longitudinal flutings; chromatophore of radially-placed plates, with pyrenoids. . . . . *Pleurotaenium* Lundell.

FIG. 125. *Pleurotaenium nodulosum* Rabenhorst.
× 175. (Original.)

Cells straight, cylindrical, somewhat tapering toward the truncate ends. Membrane smooth or with small warts; at each end a colorless vacuole with dancing particles as in *Closterium*.

40 (39, 41) Cells before middle constriction swollen and with longitudinal flutings; chromatophores of longitudinal radial plates.
Docidium Lundell.

Cells tapering somewhat towards the ends; no vacuoles with moving granules; membrane either smooth or with minute protuberances and even with spines in certain regions.

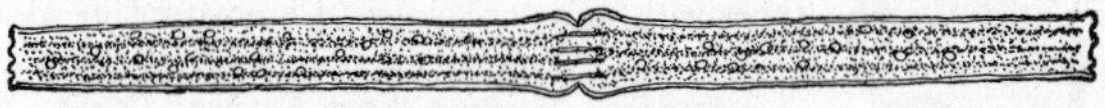

FIG. 126. *Docidium baculum* Brébisson. × 545. (Original.)

41 (39, 40) Shape of cells much as in *Pleurotaenium*, but apices broadly cleft or with bidentate processes. . . . . . *Triploceras* Bailey.

Cells large, walls covered with rings of furcate processes or small, perpendicular longitudinally-placed plates. Sometimes confused with *Docidium*.

FIG. 127. *Triploceras gracile* Bailey. One-half of a cell. (After Cushman.)

42 (34) Constrictions at the sides deep and abrupt. 43

43 (44) End views of cells 3 to several angled or rayed.
Staurastrum Lundell.

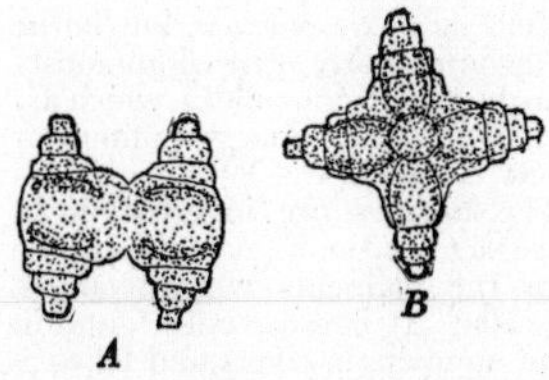

Side view hour-glass shaped; membrane smooth or with warts or spines; chromatophores in each cell-half consisting of radially-placed plates about a central pyrenoid, two plates extending into each arm or angle.

FIG. 128. *Staurastrum crenulatum* Nägeli. × 600. (Original.)

A
B

44 (43) End views of cells compressed or elliptical, often enlarged at the center. 45

45 (48) Cells at end with notches or linear incisions. 46

46 (47)   Cells disc-shaped, each cell-half with three or five lobes, the lateral ones of which are more or less deeply cut . *Micrasterias* Agardh.

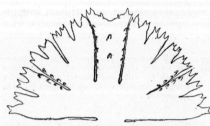

Cells broadly oval or rounded in outline. Middle constriction deep, sometimes furnished with spines; lateral lobes often one or more times dichotomously divided, the last divisions usually furnished with spines. Chromatophore the form of the cell, in which are scattered several pyrenoids.

FIG. 129. *Micrasterias papillifera* Brébisson. One half of a cell. × 365. (Original.)

47 (46)   Cells at ends with an incision or undulation, end view elliptical with one or two prominences on the sides. . . *Euastrum* Ralfs.

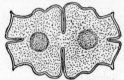

Cells oblong or elliptical, with deep, middle constriction, and variously incised, concave, or undulating margins. End view oval, with one or more rounded projections. Membrane sometimes with warts or spines. Chromatophore axial.

FIG. 130.   *Euastrum elegans* Kützing. × 588. (Original.)

48 (45)   Cells at ends without notches or linear incisions 49
49 (54)   Cells without spines 50
50 (51)   Cells free. . . . . *Cosmarium* Corda.

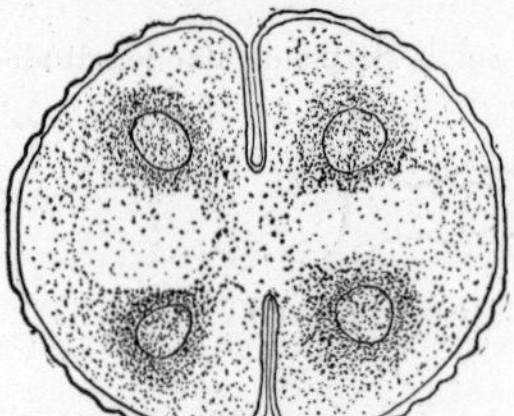

Cells elliptical or circular, sometimes with more or less undulating or tapering margins; middle constriction deep and linear; end view oval or circular, often with rounded projections. Chromatophore in each cell-half, usually of radiating plates about one or more pyrenoids; membrane often punctate or with minute warts.

FIG. 131.   *Cosmarium botrytis* Meneghini. × 575. (Original.)

51 (50)   Cells united by branched gelatinous stalks, forming colonies . .   52
52 (53)   Colonies loose, not encrusted with lime . . . *Cosmocladium* Nägeli.

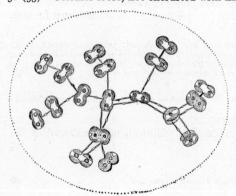

Cells as in *Cosmarium*, but borne by dichotomously or trichotomously branched gelatinous stalks, which are united to form free-swimming or sessile colonies.

The colonies are invested in an indistinct gelatinous mass, less dense than the filaments which connect the cells. It is sometimes found in large numbers in rivers and lakes.

FIG. 132.   *Cosmocladium saxonicum* de Bary. × 250. (After Schröder.)

53 (52)   Colony a compact cushion; stalks encrusted with lime.
Oocardium Nägeli.

Cells broad, middle constriction slight, chromatophores two, pyrenoid in each. Stalks closely placed so that the enveloping cylindrical lime sheaths make a honeycomb-like structure. They are sometimes branched and imbedded in the free end of each is a single cell, placed transversely. It occurs where water trickles over limestone rocks, and is also reported as being found in mountain streams.

FIG. 133.   *Oocardium stratum* Nägeli.   × 485.   Portion of figure.
(After Senn.)

54 (49)   Cells with spines   55

55 (56)   Two or four spines on each cell-half . . .   *Arthrodesmus* Ehrenberg.

General characteristics as in *Cosmarium*, except that each cell-half is furnished with two or four long spines, and the end view shows no lateral rounded prominences.

The spines in *Arthrodesmus* are all arranged in one plane, while in *Xanthidium* they may be arranged in two planes.

FIG. 134.   *Arthrodesmus convergens* Ehrenberg.   × about 250.   (Original.)

56 (55)   Two rows of strong spines on each cell-half   57

57 (58)   Spines simple . . . .   *Xanthidium* Ehrenberg.

Cells oval or nearly round, with deep, narrow, central constriction; end view elliptical, often with protruding sides; membrane with two rows of strong, horn-like spines; chromatophore parietal, more or less divided, with several pyrenoids.

As in *Arthrodesmus* the presence and the nature of the spines distinguish the genus from certain species of *Cosmarium*.

FIG. 135.   *Xanthidium fasciculatum* Ehrenberg.   × about 300.   (Original.)

58 (57)   Spines branched. . . . .   *Schizocanthum* Lundell.

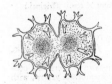

Characteristics similar to those of *Xanthidium*, except that the spines are thick, short, and branched at the ends.

West believes that *Schizocanthum* should be included under *Xanthidium* as the only difference is in the spines, and there is too much variation in these, he thinks, to make separate genera.

FIG. 136.   *Schizocanthum armatum* Lundell.   × 106.   (After Wood.)

59 (3)   Plant filamentous, cylindrical, only one individual originating from a germinating zygospore . . Family ZYGNEMACEAE . .   60

Cells cylindrical, united into filaments, usually found near the surface of the water. Chromatophores different in different genera, but all with several pyrenoids. Reproduction sexual, occurring by the conjugation of cells in two parallel filaments, ladder-like, or lateral, between two neighboring cells of the same filament. Parthenogenesis may occur.

60 (64)   In conjugating the whole of the contents of the conjugating cells passes into the zygospore.   Subfamily ZYGNEMEAE . . 61

61 (62, 63)   Chromatophores two, axial, star-shaped; a pyrenoid in the center of each. . . . . *Zygnema* de Bary.

Conjugation either ladder-like or lateral: Zygospore within one of the conjugating cells, or in the conjugating tube.   According to Collins aplanospores may take the place of zygospores, also resting akinetes with granular contents and thickened membrane may be found.

FIG. 137. *Zygnema* sp.   × 600.   (Original.)

62 (61, 63)   Chromatophore one to several parietal, spiral bands, with many pyrenoids. . . . . *Spirogyra* Link.

Conjugation ladder-like or lateral.   Zygospore in one of the conjugating cells.   Parthenospores may be formed.

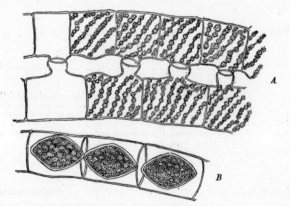

FIG. 138. *Spirogyra crassa* Kützing.   *a.* conjugation of filaments.   *b.* zygospores × 100.   (Original.)

63 (61, 62)   Chromatophore an axial plate, with several pyrenoids.
Debarya Wittrock.

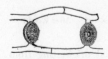

Cells long; conjugation ladder-like; zygospore between the conjugating cells; the middle layer of the spore membrane yellow, with three parallel longitudinal grooves, connected by radial striations.

FIG. 139. *Debarya glyptosperma* Wittrock, showing two zygospores.   × 95. (After de Bary.)

64 (60)   In conjugation only a portion of the contents of the conjugating cells passes into the zygospore.
Subfamily MESOCARPEAE . . 65

65 (66)   Chromatophore an axial plate, with several pyrenoids. Zygospore lens-shaped or flattened and angled, in the conjugating tube.
Mougeotia Wittrock.

Conjugation ladder-like or between two adjoining cells of the same filament. Zygospore in the inflated conjugating tube, separated from the conjugating cells by two or more transverse walls.

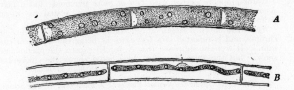

FIG. 140.   *Mougeotia* sp.   *a.* showing the surface of the chlorophyll plate.   *b.* showing the edge of the chlorophyll plate.   × about 500.   (Original.)

66 (65)   Vegetative portion as in *Mougeotia* but zygospore not known.
Gonatonema Wittrock.

Aplanospores produced between two transverse membranes near the center of an elongated cell.   Spore membrane double.

FIG. 141.   *Gonatonema ventricosum* Wittrock.   × 250.
(After West.)

67 (2)   Plants unicellular or of few cells.   Chromatophore one or more parietal bodies, rarely central. 68

68 (190, 249)   Plants unicellular, or of few cells united into minute families; frequently imbedded in gelatinous substance.
Order **Protococcales** . . 69

Each cell carries on all functions independently, and complexes may be regarded as an aggregate of individuals.
Three forms of reproduction may occur: 1, purely vegetative; 2, by asexual zoospores; 3, by isogametes.   More than one method frequently occurs in one species; the vegetative reproduction may be by simple fission or internal division.

69 (89)   Vegetative cells or colonies for a portion or the whole of their existence motile. . . . . Family VOLVOCACEAE . . 70

70 (77)   Cells single or in clusters, not forming a definite colony. 71

71 (72)   Cells spindle-shaped; chromatophores several, indefinite, with two or more pyrenoids and a pigment spot.
Chlorogonium Ehrenberg.

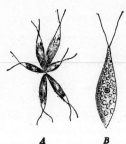

Cells with two cilia; membrane very thin, pigment spot in anterior part.   Numerous vacuoles and several pyrenoids present.   Division transverse.   Reproduction by isogametes.   Wille makes this genus a section under *Chlamydomonas*.

FIG. 142.   *Chlorogonium euchlorum* Ehrenberg.   *a.* a cluster of cells.   × about 300.   (After Ehrenberg.)   *b.* single cell.   (After Stein.)

A   *B*

72 (71)   Cells ellipsoidal or nearly spherical. 73

73 (74)   Membrane widely separated from the chromatophore but connected
with it by protoplasmic strands.   Two cilia present.
                                                Sphaerella Sommerfeldt.

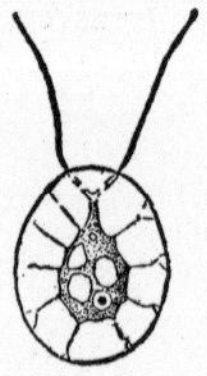

Chromatophore netted, with two or more pyrenoids and a pigment spot.
Asexual reproduction by longitudinal division, sexual by isogametes. A
palmella condition may occur.

Sphaerella often assumes a red color, due to the presence of hemato-
chrome, and is reported in a few cases as being the organism causing "red
rain." It was also supposed that *S. nivalis* caused the phenomenon of "red
snow," but the form described by Chodat shows the chloroplast as lying
close to the membrane, so this is probably a *Chlamydomonas*.

FIG. 143.   *Sphaerella pluvialis* Flotow.   X about 600.   (After Schmidle.)

74 (73)   Membrane not separated from the chromatophore. 75

75 (76)   Two cilia and a pyrenoid present.   Color rarely red.
                                                Chlamydomonas Ehrenberg.

Cells ellipsoidal or spherical; chromatophore single, hollow, parietal; a pigment
spot and two cilia at the anterior end.   Reproduction by vegetative division, also
by copulation of gametes which are either alike or slightly unlike as to size.   Zygospore green or red.   The products of the vegetative division may pass at once into
a motile state with cilia, or may be non-motile, according to conditions in the surrounding medium.

FIG. 144.   *Chlamydomonas ohioensis* Snow.   X 1000.   (Original.)

76 (75)   Structure as in *Chlamydomonas* but with 4 cilia.   Some include this
genus under *Chlamydomonas*. . . . . *Carteria* Diesing.

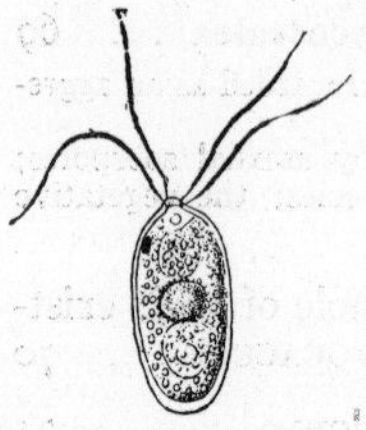

The shape of the cells in the different species differ rather more
than in *Chlamydomonas;* the structure of the cells, however, is
identical, except for the cilia.   Species also occur in much the same
localities as *Chlamydomonas* but are less frequent.

FIG. 145.   *Carteria obtusa* Dill.   X about 475.   (After Dill.)

77 (70)   Cells united to form a colony of definite shape which is constantly
in motion. 78

78 (79)   Colony not surrounded by a gelatinous envelop.
                                                Spondylomorum Ehrenberg.

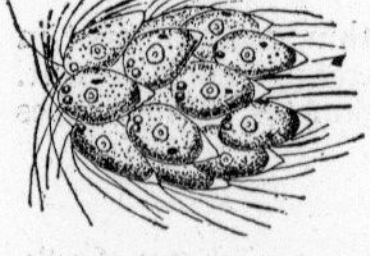

Colony of 16 cells loosely united, their anterior ends all pointing
toward one point.   The cells are obovate, with 4 cilia at their
anterior ends, a pyrenoid, and a pigment spot.   A new colony of 16
originates by successive division from a vegetative cell.

FIG. 146.   *Spondylomorum quaternarium* Ehrenberg.   (After Stein.)

79 (78)   Colony surrounded by a gelatinous envelop. 80

80 (83, 88)   Colony not spherical or spheroidal. 81

81 (82)   Colony a plate of 4 or 16 spherical cells in a single layer, each with
2 cilia. Boundary of gelatinous envelop not distinct.
Gonium Müller.

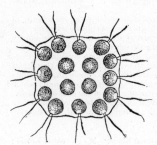

Cells oval, with two cilia and a pigment spot. Chromatophore single, parietal, hollow, with one pyrenoid. Reproduction by successive divisions of each cell, forming a
new colony; also, according to West, by isogametes.
Gonium is one of the commonest of the Volvocaceae,
occurring in almost all ponds and lakes. It is also one
of the most beautiful of the group, as the colonies are exceedingly regular and as they move they revolve, showing
first the surface and then the edge.

FIG. 147. *Gonium pectorale* Müller. × 370. (After West.)

82 (81)   Colony flattened, anterior portion rounded, posterior portion with
three wart-like projections. . . . . *Platydorina* Kofoid.

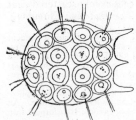

"The two faces compressed so that the cells of the two
sides intercalate; flagella upon both faces on alternate cells.
Anterior and posterior poles of major axis are differentiated
by the arrangement of the cells and by the structure of the
envelope; long and short transverse axes differentiated by
the flattening of the colony. Cells similar, bi-flagellate,
each with stigma, chromatophore, and pyrenoid. Asexual
reproduction by repeated division of all the cells, each
forming a daughter colony."

FIG. 148. *Platydorina caudata* Kofoid. × 628. (After Kofoid.)

83 (80, 88)   Colony spherical or spheroidal, but small. Cells not numerous. 84

84 (85, 86, 87)   Colony of 4 or 8 elongated cells with irregular, pseudopodia-like
processes, arranged in a zone around the center of a firm
gelatinous sphere. . . . . *Stephanosphaera* Cohn.

Cells elongated, each with cilia at the anterior pole which
penetrate the gelatinous substance. Chromatophores irregular,
with one or several pyrenoids. Each cell gives rise to a new
colony by division; isogametes are also found.

FIG. 149. *Stephanosphaera pluvialis* Cohn. × 425. (After Hieronymus.)

85 (84, 86, 87)   Colony spheroidal, or slightly elongated, of 8 or 16 cells closely
packed at the center of the indistinct gelatinous envelop.
Pandorina Bory.

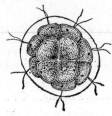

Cells heart-shaped, with two cilia at larger end, a pigment spot,
and a pyrenoid, the latter in the posterior end of the hollow
parietal chloroplast. Reproduction by successive division in
each cell whereby as many new colonies are formed as there are
cells; reproduction also by the copulation of gametes either alike
or slightly unlike as to size; zygospore red.

FIG. 150. *Pandorina morum* Müller. × about 385. (Original.)

86 (84, 85, 87) Colony spherical or ellipsoidal; cells of two types, vegetative and gonidial, which lie in the anterior and posterior parts of the colony respectively. . . . . *Pleodorina* Shaw.

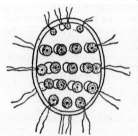

Colony consists of a spherical or elliptical coenobium of greenish, bi-flagellate cells of two types, vegetative and gonidial, in the anterior and posterior parts of the colony respectively which lie in the periphery of a hyaline gelatinous matrix and are surrounded by a common hyaline envelop. Cells each with one reddish stigma which is more prominent in the anterior part of the colony. No connecting filaments between the cells; nonsexual reproduction by gonidia which are formed by increase in size of a part of the cells of a colony. Daughters escape from parent as small colonies of bi-flagellate cells which at this stage are all similar. Sexual reproduction not known.

Fig. 151. *Pleodorina illinoisensis* Kofoid. × 335. (After Kofoid.)

87 (84, 85, 86) Colony spherical, of 8 or 16, 32 or 64 cells evenly scattered near the surface of a gelatinous sphere. . . *Eudorina* Ehrenberg.

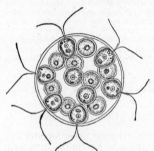

Cells spherical or oval, with two cilia and a pigment spot. Chromatophore single, parietal. Vegetative reproduction by repeated division, forming at first a plate-like daughter colony, which later becomes spherical. Sexual reproduction by a pear-shaped antherozoid and a spherical oosphere.

The cells lie at the surface of the gelatinous sphere and the cilia project at right angles to the surface. All of the vegetative cells may become transformed into oogonia and antheridia; in each of the latter 64 antherozoids are formed. The ripe oospores are brownish with a smooth external membrane. The habitats of *Eudorina* are ponds, ditches, and lakes.

Fig. 152. *Eudorina elegans* Ehrenberg. (After Stein.)

88 (80, 83) Colony a larger gelatinous sphere with a very large number of minute cells at the surface. . . . . *Volvox* Linnaeus.

Cells very small, round or pear-shaped, connected by protoplasmic filaments, each with a pair of cilia, a single chromatophore and two or more contractile vacuoles; reproduction sexual and asexual; in the latter certain cells (parthenogonidia) within the sphere enlarge and through divisions give rise to a new colony. Sexual reproduction occurs by the union of a fusiform antherozoid and oosphere; oospore spherical, with red contents and a spiny membrane.

89 (69) Colonies not motile in the vegetative condition. 90

90 (95, 131, 175) Cells in colonies, generally sessile and enclosed in a definite gelatinous envelop, or borne on gelatinous stalks. Reproduction asexual by zoospores, or sexual by isogametes. . . . Family TETRASPORACEAE . . 91

91 (94) Cells biciliate, at the surface of an inflated, attached colony. Cilia external and free. 92

92 (93) Colonies macroscopic or microscopic, expanded or intestiform, cells arranged in fours. . . . . *Tetraspora* Link.

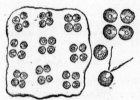

Reproduction by division in two directions; zoospores may originate directly from the vegetative cells, and by division give rise to a new colony; isogametes with two cilia may be formed, also resting spores with heavy brown walls.

FIG. 153. *Tetraspora explanata* Kützing. × 250. (After Nägeli.)

93 (92) Colonies pear-shaped, attached, cells irregularly placed near the surface. . . . . *Apiocystis* Nägeli.

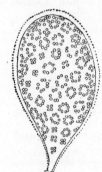

Chromatophore single, parietal with a pyrenoid. Division in three directions. A spherical zoospore with two cilia may originate from each cell and escape from the gelatinous vesicle.

FIG. 154. *Apiocystis brauniana* Nägeli. × 78. (After Nägeli.)

94 (91) Cells spindle-shaped, clustered on the ends of gelatinous stalks.
Chlorangium Stein.

Chromatophore one or two longitudinal bands; the cells may detach themselves and become zoospores with two cilia and a pigment spot. Large numbers of motile individuals may be formed in each cell, though copulation is not known.

FIG. 155. *Chlorangium stentorum* Stein. *a.* × about 200. (After Cienkowski.) *b.* (After Stein.)

A   B

95 (90, 131, 175) Cells with a thick, often indistinct gelatinous covering, uniting several together into greater or smaller free swimming, rarely attached colonies. Reproduction by fission or internal division; in a few instances by zoospores and isogametes. . . . . . . Family PALMELLACEAE . . 96

96 (102, 107) Cells embedded in more or less cylindrical and definite gelatinous tubes, strands, or stalks which are broader than the cells. 97

97 (100, 101) Cells scattered throughout a gelatinous tube or strand. . . 98

98 (99)   Cells at the ends of, or distributed along rather firm, often lamellate
gelatinous strands. . . . . *Hormotila* Borzi.

Chromatophore single, granular, without a pyrenoid. Reproduction by cell division, also by bi-ciliate zoospores, eight
of which are formed in a single zoosporangium. The zoosporangia are much larger than the vegetative cells.

FIG. 156.   *Hormotila mucigena* Borzi.   × 268.   (After West.)

99 (98)   Cells distributed throughout a structureless, cylindrical, branched
gelatinous colony. . . . . *Palmodactylon* Nägeli.

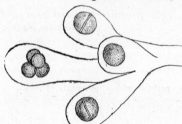

Cells spherical; gelatinous tubes branched or
unbranched, single or in clusters.   Division of
cells first in one, later in three directions.
Chromatophore parietal and often lobed.
The elongated shape of these colonies is
thought by West to be due to divisions occurring more frequently in one direction than in
others.   The plant occurs in swamps and quiet
waters.

FIG. 157.   *Palmodactylon* sp.   Portion of young
colony.   × about 600.   (Original.)

100 (97)   Cells two or four in series, at the ends of attached, dichotomously
branched stalks; chromatophores several.

Mischococcus Nägeli.

Chromatophores one to four, without pyrenoids.   Reproduction by
zoospores and isogametes which may or may not unite before germination.

FIG. 158.   *Mischococcus confervicola* Nägeli.   × about 180.   (After Rabenhorst.)

101 (97, 100)   Cells in radiating series, often branched, held together by
gelatinous strands. . . . . *Dictyocystis* Lagerheim.

Chromatophore single, central, and radial.   Reproduction probably by division.
Though *Dictyocystis* is reported by several botanists, it seems a somewhat doubtful genus.

102 (96, 107)   Cells at the surface of an invisible gelatinous mass and
borne on fine, radiating gelatinous strands. 104

103 (104, 105, 106)   Cells reniform, four on a stalk, two borne near the adjoining ends of the other two. . . *Dimorphococcus* A. Braun.

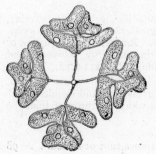

Chromatophore single and parietal, each group of
cells formed by the internal division of a single mother
cell.
The filaments which bear the cells are thought by some
to be formed from the remnants of the mother membrane,
but this needs further investigation.   Large colonies may
become fragmented into smaller colonies.   This alga is
not very frequent, and occurs in larger lakes rather than
in stagnant water.

FIG. 159.   *Dimorphococcus lunatus* A. Braun.   × 600.
(Original.)

104 (103, 105, 106) Cells single, spherical, or oval. *Dictyosphaerium* Nägeli.

Chromatophore single, parietal. Reproduction by internal division.

FIG. 160. *Dictyosphaerium pulchellum* Wood. × 570. (Original.)

105 (103, 104, 106) Colonies much as in *Dictyosphaerium* except that the cells are in clusters of four which are held together by the remnants of the mother-membrane. . . . . *Tetracoccus* West

Some regard this as a young stage in *Dictyosphaerium*.

106 (103, 104, 105) Cells clustered, grape-like, imbedded in the rather firm, often yellow gelatinous strands. . . *Botryococcus* Kützing.

West's genus *Ineffigiata* is probably a *Botryococcus* where the gelatinous envelop is somewhat contracted.
In old cultures of *Botryococcus*, and often in nature, an orange or reddish oil is produced which gives the cells that color.
The alga is found very frequently in pools, ponds, and lakes; it has been known to form the water bloom on lakes of small dimensions.

FIG. 161. *Botryococcus braunii* Kützing. × about 300. (Original.)

107 (96, 102) Cells not at the surface of a gelatinous mass but distributed through it. 108

108 (109) Colonies cylindrical, branching; gelatinous envelop somewhat rigid and often lamellate. . . . . . *Palmodictyon* Nägeli.

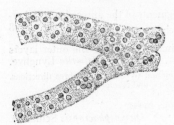

Cells in groups of two and four, the groups surrounded by gelatinous vesicles which are united to form the cylindrical colony, and give a more or less netted appearance to the gelatinous portion. Reproduction by means of resting spores with brown walls; these spores germinate and produce a new colony. West states that the outer coat often becomes very tough and of a brown color. *Palmodictyon* is a very rare alga in America, but Collins reports it from Massachusetts.

FIG. 162. *Palmodictyon viridis* Kützing. × 210.
(After West.)

109 (108) Colonies of no definite shape, of the shape of the individual cells, or more or less angled and showing a dark gelatinous layer between the cells. Cells often isolated. 110

110 (127, 128) Colonies irregular. 111

111 (120) Cells not in clusters. 112

112 (115) Gelatinous envelop containing concentric lamellae about the cells. 113

113 (114)   Cells spherical. . . . . *Gloeocystis* Nägeli.

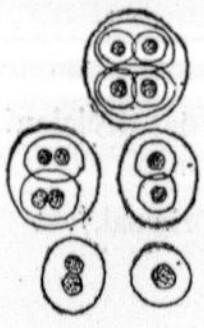

The enveloping gelatinous substance showing a concentric lamellate structure. Reproduction by repeated cell division, several generations of cells often remaining enclosed in the original mother-membrane. According to some authors reproduction also occurs by bicilliate zoospores.
The authenticity of this genus is doubtful as the non-motile stage of certain species of *Chlamydomonas* answers this description.

FIG. 163. *Gloeocystis vesiculosus* Nägeli. X 150. (After Nägeli.)

114 (113)   Cells elongated. . . . . *Dactylothece* Lagerheim.

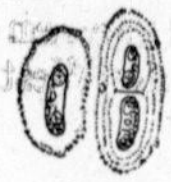

Chromatophore a parietal plate lying only on one side of the cell; no pyrenoids. Gelatinous substance often lamellate.

FIG. 164. *Dactylothece braunii* Lagerheim. X about 370. (After Lagerheim.)

115 (112)   Gelatinous envelop not containing concentric lamellae about the cells. 116

116 (117)   Gelatinous mass containing segments of the antecedent mother cell. . . . . *Schizochlamys* A. Braun.

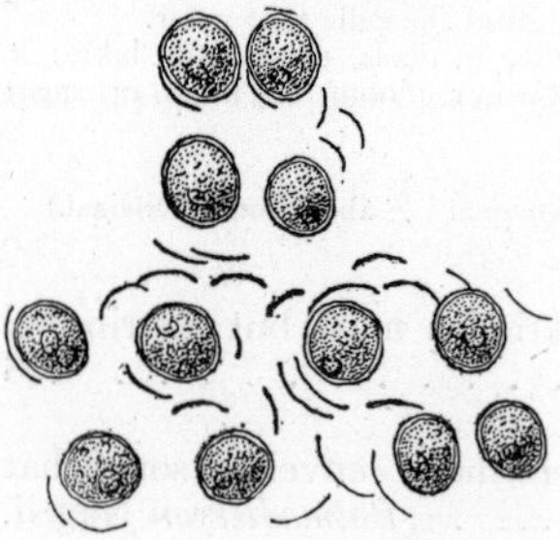

Cells spherical, scattered in a gelatinous mass together with the visible remnants of the old membranes which are split into distinct segments.
West believes that it is the formation of the large amount of gelatinous material that causes the firmer portion of the membrane to become ruptured, and that this takes place previous to the formation of the two or four daughter cells. *S. gelatinosa* is the only species reported in America, and this occurs as a pale green irregular mass either free or adhering to water plants.

FIG. 165. *Schizochlamys gelatinosa* A. Braun. X 600. (Original.)

117 (116)   Gelatinous mass not containing segments of the antecedent mother-membrane. 118

118 (119)   Cells throughout the gelatinous mass formed by the outer layers of the cell walls. . . . . *Palmella* Lyngbye.

Chromatophore parietal, with a pyrenoid. Reproduction by division in three directions. and according to Wille, by macrozoospores, microzoospores, and isogametes.

119 (118)   Cells at the surface of the gelatinous mass.
Dictyosphaeropsis Schmidle.

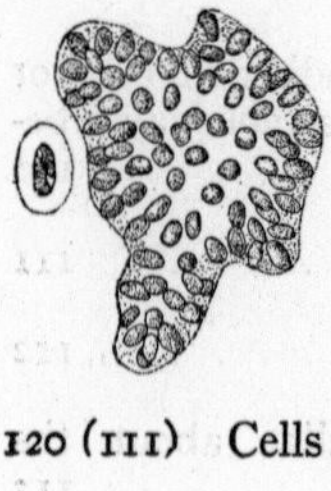

Cells free or attached, round or elongated. One or two disc-shaped parietal chromatophores present. Reproduction not well known.

FIG. 166. *Dictyosphaeropsis palatina* Schmidle. X 375. (After Schmidle.)

120 (111)   Cells in clusters, usually of eight, sometimes four or sixteen; colonies, mostly floating. 121

121 (124)   Cells spherical. 122

122 (123)   Chromatophore single. . . . .   *Sphaerocystis* Chodat.

Colonies large; clusters widely separated from each other. Gelatinous envelop invisible without reagents. Chromatophore thin, parietal, with a pyrenoid on one side and an opening on the other. Reproduction by internal division.

Sphaerocystis is almost universally found in the plankton and is one of the most conspicuous and beautiful of all the plankton forms. Sometimes the colonies are very large, consisting of many clusters.

FIG. 167. *Sphaerocystis schraeteri* Chodat. X 520.
(Original.)

123 (122)   Chromatophores many, parietal. . . . . . .   *Chlorobotrys* Bohlin.

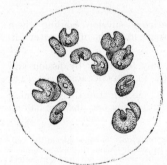

Cells spherical, in a gelatinous matrix, as in *Sphaerocystis*, but the chlorophyll in many parietal discs.

FIG. 168. *Chlorobotrys regularis* Bohlin. X 300. (After West.)

124 (121)   Cells not spherical. 125

125 (126)   Cells crescent-shaped. . . . .   *Kirchneriella* Schmidle.

Cells in clusters, as in *Sphaerocystis*, but strongly crescent-shaped.

In reproduction internal division takes place transversely and the four or eight daughter cells are set free by the breaking of the cell wall.

Several species occur in the plankton. They also occur in ponds among water plants.

FIG. 169. *Kirchneriella obesa* Schmidle. X 600.
(Original.)

126 (125)   Cells oval or bluntly pointed. . . . .   *Oocystis* Nägeli.

Cells oblong, single, or two, four, or eight in a gelatinous envelop; in some cases many clusters in a colorless gelatinous matrix. Chromatophore single, parietal, with an opening on one side, or of many small discs. Pyrenoids present in some species. Cells single or in clusters, as in *Sphaerocystis*, but ellipsoidal in shape.

Oocystis is frequently found in the plankton where it is usually in large gelatinous colonies similar to *Sphaerocystis* and *Kirchneriella*. In other localities the cells are generally solitary.

FIG. 170. *Oocystis solitaria* Wittrock. X 600. (Original.)

127 (110, 128)   Colonies somewhat cubical, showing a dark, gelatinous layer
between the cells. . . . . *Gloeotaenium* Hansgirg.

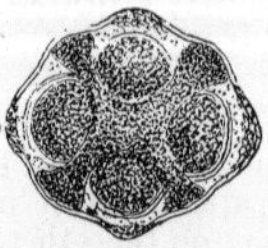

Cells globose or flattened, colonies of two, four, or eight cells, with
wide lamellate walls. Reproduction by aplanospores.

FIG. 171. *Gloeotaenium loitelsbergerianum* Hansgirg. × 220. (After Transeau.)

128 (110, 127)   Colonies the shape of the individual cells. 129

129 (130)   Cells reniform, colony of the same shape or oval.
Nephrocytium Nägeli.

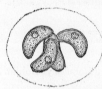

Cells single or in clusters, as in *Sphaerocystis*, but reniform in
shape.
Nephrocytium resembles *Oocystis* except that the cells are curved.
It is widely distributed but not very abundant.

FIG. 172. *Nephrocytium agardhianum* Nägeli. × 580. (Original.)

130 (129)   Cells fusiform. . . . . *Elakatothrix* Wille.

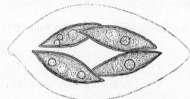

Cells elongated, fusiform, gelatinous substance dense, often lamellate.

FIG. 173. *Elakatothrix viridis* Wille. × 575.
(Original.)

131 (90, 95, 175)   Cells without a thick gelatinous envelop holding them
together; sometimes adhering to each other after di-
vision. 132

132 (137, 155, 174)   Reproduction by fission only, or rarely by fission and
internal division. . . Family PLEUROCOCCACEAE . . 133

133 (134, 135, 136)   Reproduction by fission in one direction only, forming
equal cylindrical cells, the length being one and one-half to
three times the breadth. . . . . *Stichococcus* Nägeli.

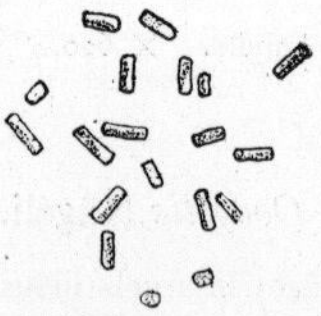

Chromatophore a parietal plate lying only on one side of the cell,
with no pyrenoid. Reproduction by simple fission, the cells sometimes
adhering to each other after the division, but not forming perfect
filaments.

FIG. 174. *Stichococcus bacillaris* Nägeli. × about 400. (Original.)

134 (133, 135, 136)   Reproduction by division in three directions. Cells
spherical or, if in small complexes, somewhat angled.
Pleurococcus Meneghini.

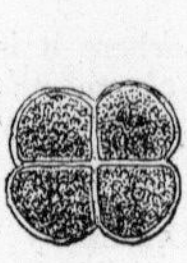

Cells either single or in small clusters of two, four, or more cells which later
fall apart. Chromatophore a thin lining to the membrane with an opening on
one side, and with or without a pyrenoid.
Pleurococcus is the chief constituent of the green coating on the bark of trees,
old wood, and stones.

FIG. 175. *Pleurococcus vulgaris* Meneghini. × 560. (Original.)

135 (133, 134, 136)   Characteristics as in *Pleurococcus*, but sometimes forming short filaments. . . . . *Pseudo-pleurococcus* Snow.

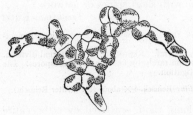

This form may remain indefinitely in either a filamentous or unicellular state according to the conditions in the environment. In the filamentous state it resembles a small form of *Stigeoclonium*, but is distinguished from it by the absence of zoospores.

Chodat regards a form similar to this as a true *Pleurococcus* and believes that short filaments are characteristic of that genus.

Fig. 176.   *Pseudo-pleurococcus vulgaris* Snow. × 600.   (Original.)

136 (133, 134, 135)   Reproduction by fission in three directions and by internal division. . . . . *Palmellococcus* Chodat.

Chromatophore a parietal plate, without a pyrenoid.   In addition to reproduction by fission and internal division, a rejuvenescence of the cell contents may occur, accompanied by a casting off of the mother-membrane.   An orange-red oil is sometimes present.

137 (132, 155, 174)   Reproduction by internal division only.

Family CHLORELLACEAE . .   138

138 (142, 151)   Cells   spherical,   ellipsoidal,   or   irregular.   Membrane smooth. 139

139 (140, 141)   Cells spherical; chromatophore a single, hollow sphere with one pyrenoid. . . . . *Chlorella* Beyerinck.

Cells spherical or somewhat elongated; chromatophore lining the membrane, open on one side, with a single pyrenoid.

The name *Zoochlorella* Brandt has been given to this same genus and antedates the name of *Chlorella* by some years, but the name *Chlorella* seems more appropriate.

Fig. 177.   *Chlorella* sp.   × 600.   (Original.)

140 (139, 141)   Cells spherical, chromatophore of many parietal discs, each with a pyrenoid. . . . . *Eremosphaera* de Bary.

Size relatively large; chromatophores many, parietal; nucleus prominent.   Reproduction by internal division.

The cells are large, spherical, and conspicuous.   The nucleus is distinct, suspended in the middle of the cell by strands of protoplasm.   Two or four daughter individuals may originate by successive division of the contents and are liberated by the rupturing of the mother membrane.   *Eremosphaera* is almost constantly found among Desmids in Sphagnum swamps.

Fig. 178.   *Eremosphaera viridis* de Bary.   × 125.   (Original.)

141 (139, 140)   Cells spherical or irregular; chromatophores many, angular, radially arranged; many pyrenoids in each.

Excentrosphaera Moore.

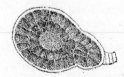

Plant consisting of a single cell, in mature condition varying in outline from spherical and elliptical to irregular and eccentric forms.   Chromatophores large, angular, usually radiately arranged, closely lining the wall.   Pyrenoids minute, numerous in each chromatophore.   Multiplication by non-motile spores (aplanospores) which escape by the dissolution of a part of the cell wall.   Reaction to all external stimuli negative.

Fig. 179.   *Excentrosphaera viridis* Moore.   × 160.   (After Moore.)

142 (138, 151)   Cells spherical or elongated, membrane with hairs, spines, or reticulate markings. 143

143 (147)   Cells spherical. 144

144 (145, 146)   Cells solitary, membrane with short spines or network.
Trochiscia Kütz.

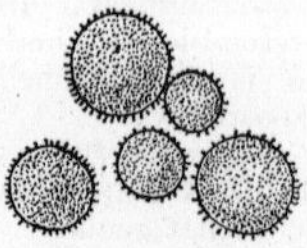

Cells perfectly spherical, the spines or reticulate markings projecting but little.
Chromatophores usually several.   Reproduction by internal division.
West also reports reproduction rarely by fission and by zoospores.   The
genus needs further investigation.

FIG. 180.   *Trochiscia vestitus* Reinsch.   X about 260.   (After Reinsch.)

145 (144, 146)   Cells solitary, bristles long, rigid, scattered over the entire
surface. . . . . *Golenkinia* Chodat.

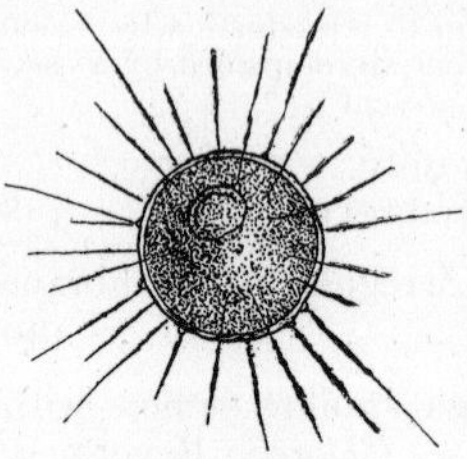

Reproduction occurs by division in one or two directions and
by autospores.   Chodat also reports the formation of zoogonidia
with four cilia.
Golenkinia has been known to occur in great quantities almost
pure in large tanks of water; it also occurs in the plankton,
though not very abundantly.   Chromatophore parietal, with one
pyrenoid.
Sir Ray Lancaster believes that his *Archerinia boltoni* described in 1885 and referred to the Protozoa is identical with
Golenkinia radiata described by Chodat in 1894, and with
Richteriella botryoides described by Lemmermann in 1898.   If
this be true the name *Archerinia* claims precedence over the
other two generic names.

FIG. 181.   *Golenkinia radiata* Chodat.   X 625.   (Original.)

146 (144, 145)   Cells in colonies of eight, sixteen, thirty-two, sixty-four, or
more cells; bristles long, only on the outer surface of a colony. . . . . *Richteriella* Lemmermann.

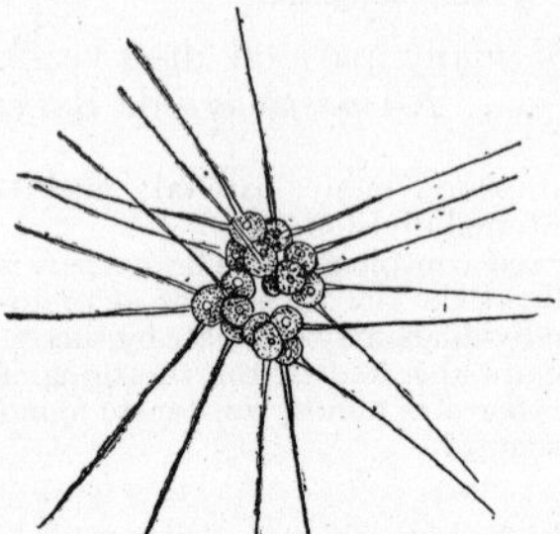

Bristles comparatively coarse and in length many
times the diameter of the cells.   Chromatophore single,
parietal, with a single pyrenoid.
The cells are usually clustered in groups of four which
are aggregated into larger colonies.   But little is known
of its reproduction except that vegetative division has
been known to occur.
It is found in the plankton of large lakes.

FIG. 182.   *Richteriella globosa* Lemmermann.   X 556.   (After
Lemmermann.)

147 (143)   Cells somewhat elongated. 148

148 (149, 150)   Bristles four, two at each end or one at each end and two at
the center, each with a basal swelling. . *Lagerheimia* Chodat.

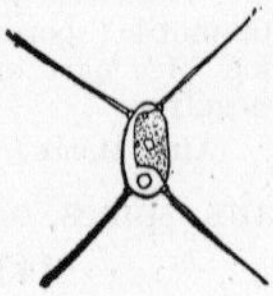

Cells ellipsoidal, with four spines on short pedicels.   Chromatophore
single, parietal, with a single pyrenoid.   Reproduction by internal
division.
Chodat and West recognize the genus *Lagerheimia* but it is very doubtful
whether the presence of only four spines with basal swellings is sufficient to
remove it from the genus *Chodatella* where the spines are more numerous
and have not the basal swellings.

FIG. 183.   *Lagerheimia genevensis* Chodat.   X 275.   (After Chodat.)

149 (148, 150) Bristles varying in number, without a basal swelling. Cells single. . . . . *Chodatella* Lemmermann.

Cells solitary, ellipsoidal; spines evenly distributed over the surface or in circles about the ends. Chromatophore parietal, with or without pyrenoids.
Chodatella is occasionally found in the plankton of larger lakes.

Fig. 184. *Chodatella citriformis* Snow. × 500. (Original.)

150 (148, 149) Bristles numerous, on the outside of the colony only. Cells usually united into a small cluster by a gelatinous substance.
Franceia Lemmermann.

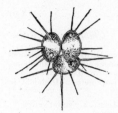

Chromatophores two, each with a pyrenoid.
This genus in its general characteristics resembles *Richteriella* but it is distinguished from it by the larger size and oval shape of the cells, the shorter spines and the two chromatophores.
Reproduction takes place by division in a single longitudinal direction.

Fig. 185. *Franceia* sp. × about 600. (Original.)

151 (138, 142) Cells of some other shape than spherical or elliptical; with points or angles. 152

152 (153, 154) Cells needle-like or fusiform, often variously curved, the length often many times the diameter. . . *Ankistrodesmus* Corda.

Ankistrodesmus is found in all ponds, lakes, and rivers. It is one of the most common and one of the hardiest of the unicellular algae.

Fig. 186. *Ankistrodesmus.* Various species. × 600. (Original.)

153 (152, 154) Cells short, fusiform, length two to four times the diameter.
Dactylococcus Nägeli.

Cells free, short, nine to eighteen μ long. Chromatophore with a pyrenoid, opposite to which there is an opening. In reproduction two to eight cells are formed by transverse internal division.

Fig. 187. *Dactylococcus infusionum* Nägeli. × 600. (Original.)

154 (152, 153) Cells distinctly three, to many-angled, angles all in one plane or not; at the ends often one or more simple or divided spines.
Tetraedron Kützing.

Chromatophore single, parietal, usually with a pyrenoid.
In this genus there is the greatest variety in regard to the shape of the cells, number of points, and size; the most common one is, however, a minute form with but few points.

Fig. 188. *Tetraedron enorme* de Bary. × 600. (Original.)

155 (132, 137, 174) Reproduction by the formation of zoospores only, or by
isogametes. . . . . . Family PROTOCOCCACEAE . . 156

156 (161, 168) Cells spherical. 157

157 (158) Chromatophores many, parietal. . . . . . . *Botrydiopsis* Borzi.

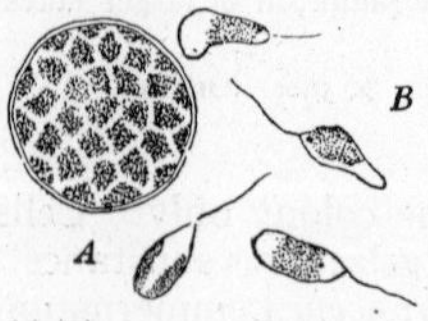

Chromatophores without pyrenoids; zoospores amoeboid, with
a single cilium, a pigment spot, and one (sometimes two) chroma-
B tophores; frequently they germinate within the mother-membrane
without a motile period.

FIG. 189. *Botrydiopsis eriensis* Snow. *a.* vegetative cell; *b.* zoospores.
× 580. (Original.)

158 (157) Chromatophore single. 159

159 (160) Chromatophore parietal. . . . . *Chlorococcum* Fries.

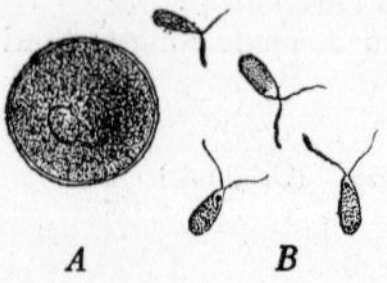

Chromatophore with a circular opening and a pyrenoid; zoospores
oval, with two cilia, a pyrenoid, and a pigment spot. Aplanospores
may form from non-liberated zoospores. An undescribed form
which greatly resembles *Chlorococcum* has isogametes. It should be
placed in a different genus.

FIG. 190. *Chlorococcum infusionum* Rabenhorst. *a.* vegetative cell.
b. zoospores. × 625. (Original.)

160 (159) Chromatophore central with radiating strands.
Radiosphaera Snow.

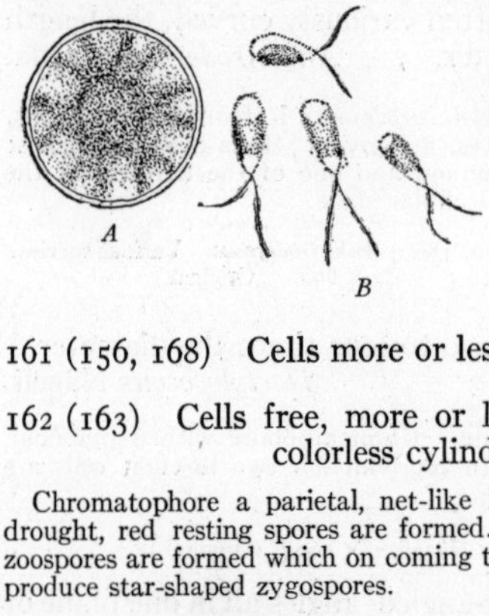

Except for the nature of the chromatophore this genus
resembles *Chlorococcum*, but at the center is a pyrenoid
from which the chromatophore radiates. Zoospores
with two cilia and a pigment spot are formed.

FIG. 191. *Radiosphaera* sp. Snow. *a.* vegetative cell;
b. zoospores. × 580. (Original.)

161 (156, 168) Cells more or less irregular, elongated, or tubular. . . . 162

162 (163) Cells free, more or less inflated or tubular, usually with a long,
colorless cylindrical portion. . . . . . *Protosiphon* Klebs.

Chromatophore a parietal, net-like layer, with pyrenoids. Under conditions threatening
drought, red resting spores are formed. In absence of light or increase of water bi-ciliated
zoospores are formed which on coming to rest produce spherical cells, or they may copulate and
produce star-shaped zygospores.

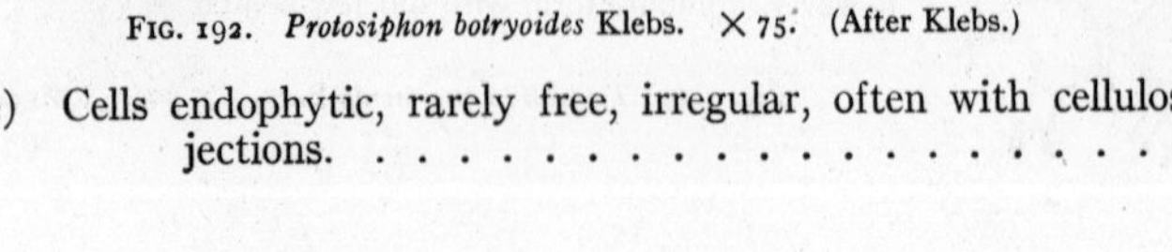

FIG. 192. *Protosiphon botryoides* Klebs. × 75. (After Klebs.)

163 (162) Cells endophytic, rarely free, irregular, often with cellulose projections. 164

164 (165) Reproduction by zoospores: chromatophore of many radially-placed rods or segments united beneath the surface.

Scotinosphaera Klebs.

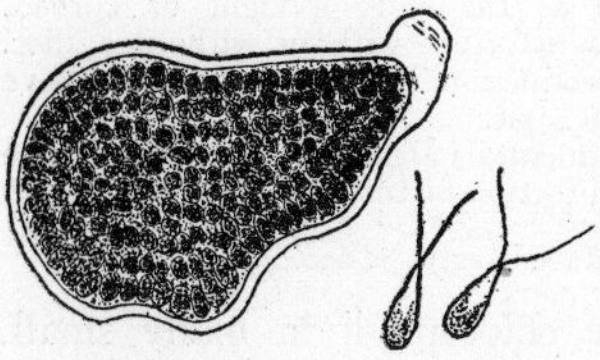

Zoospores fusiform; their production preceded by a contraction of the chromatophore to the center, about which there is a granular substance; zoospores penetrate some water plant or germinate in the water.

Resting cells occur which have one or more thickenings of the membrane.

It was first found in the dead leaves and branches of *Hypnum*, and its normal habitat is probably in the tissues of some higher water plant, but it occurs frequently in the water and may be cultivated with ease.

FIG. 193. *Scotinosphaera paradoxa* Klebs. ✕ about 265.
(After Klebs.)

165 (164) Reproduction by copulation of isogametes and in some cases by zoospores. 166

166 (167) Chromatophore a parietal layer with many pyrenoids, later showing a network. Membrane with cellulose projections.

Chlorochytrium Cohn.

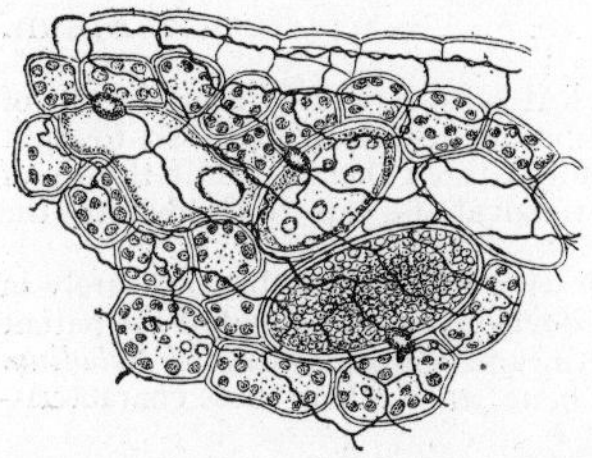

Cells spherical or slightly irregular; chromatophore with many inwardly projecting portions containing many pyrenoids. The zoospores are liberated singly; the gametes escape together while still enveloped by the inner lining to the membrane in which they copulate.

Chlorochytrium occurs in the intercellular spaces of *Lemna*. In some species a cellulose projection extends to the surface of the epidermis at the point of penetration of the zoospores, but is not found in all.

FIG. 194. *Chlorochytrium lemnae* Klebs. Cells in the tissues of *Lemna*. ✕ 500. (After Klebs.)

167 (166) Chromatophore dense, with many starch grains: membrane lamellate. . . . . *Endosphaera* Klebs.

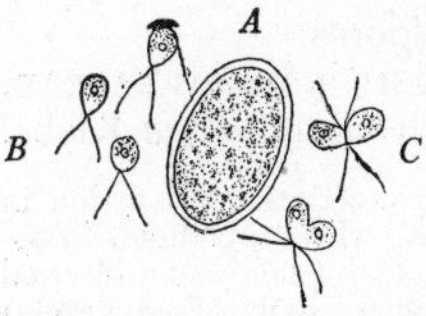

Cells spherical or irregular, found in the tissue of water plants. In reproduction internal divisions occur, giving rise to eight or sixteen oval isogametes with two cilia and a pyrenoid. The zygospore penetrates into the intercellular spaces of *Patamogeton* if it is present, but dies if it cannot be found.

In the spring time it is found as large resting cells in the tissues of the dead leaves.

FIG. 195. *Endosphaera biennis* Klebs. a. young cell; b. gametes; c. union of gametes. a. ✕ about 190; b, c. ✕ about 400. (After Klebs.)

168 (156, 161) Cells with a thin stalk-like projection on one or both ends, either free or attached. 169

169 (170) Cells free, linear, curved, or spiral, ends with a spine or stalk-like projection. . . . . *Ophiocytium* Nägeli.

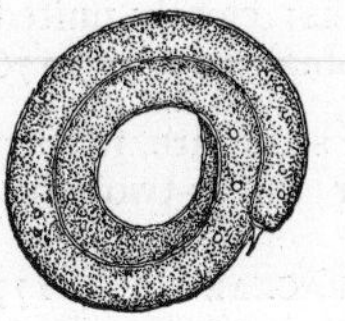

Chromatophore single, parietal, with no pyrenoid. Reproduction by means of zoospores, eight of which are formed in a single cell and are liberated by the end of the cell being thrown off like a cap.

Though the habitat of *Ophiocytium* is the same as for a number of other *Protococcaceae*, it is not so frequently found. When it does occur, however, in a body of water it may be abundant.

FIG. 196. *Ophiocytium cochleare* A. Braun. ✕ 600. (Original.)

170 (169) Cells similar, but shorter and attached. 171

171 (172, 173) Cells single, attached; oval, cylindrical, fusiform, or curved
in shape. Chromatophore single and parietal.

Characium A. Braun.

Cells oval, pointed, or rounded at the ends, straight or curved,
sessile or stalked; attached to a substratum with or without a disc.
A pyrenoid usually present. Reproduction by zoospores which have
two cilia, a pyrenoid, and a pigment spot.
Characium is very common on filamentous algae in all localities. The
shape is greatly influenced by the direction of the rays of light.

FIG. 197. Characium longipes Rabenhorst. X 600. (Original.)

172 (171, 173) Cells as in Characium, but the chlorophyll in many small,
parietal discs. . . . . Characiopsis Borzi.

The color is pale green. The zoospores are liberated by the wall of the
upper portion of the cell becoming dissolved. According to West, aplanospores may be formed, each of which becomes a gametangium and produces two or four gametes. Characiopsis is less frequent than Characium
but is found under the same conditions.

FIG. 198. Characiopsis sp. X 600. (Original.)

173 (171, 172) Cells attached, the new generation clustered at the free tip of
the empty mother cell. . . . . Sciadium A. Braun.

Thallus of six to eight cylindrical cells, radiating from the tip of
a sessile, empty, cylindrical membrane; reproduction by six to eight
zoospores with two cilia each, which attach themselves at the tip of
the mother-membrane after the removal of a cap which liberates the
spores.
Lemmermann unites Sciadium with Ophiocytium because rarely in
Ophiocytium the new generation develops from one end of the parent
cell, but the sessile characteristic and the basal disc of Sciadium
would seem to separate it from Ophiocytium where these characteristics are not found.

FIG. 199. Sciadium arbuscula A. Braun. X 600. (After Rabenhorst.)

174 (132, 137, 155) Reproduction by fission and by zoospores.

Family CHLOROSPHAERACEAE.

Only one genus known. . . . . . Chlorosphaera Klebs.

Cells usually in small cell complexes, originating by fission in
three directions. Chromatophore parietal, with a pyrenoid. Zoospores usually eight in number, originating by successive internal
divisions. These have two cilia and a pigment spot. Each vegetative cell may become a resting spore.
In its vegetative state Chlorosphaera resembles greatly Pleurococcus vulgaris, but it is aquatic, rather than aerial. It is a common
form in ponds and lakes, though rarely found in such quantities as
to be noticed, unless developed in culture.

FIG. 200. Chlorosphaera lacustris Snow. X 585. (Original.)

175 (90, 95, 131) Cells without a gelatinous envelop or stalks; closely united
to form structures of definite shape (coenobia). . . . 176

176 (187) Coenobium usually a cluster of definite shape and structure, formed
by the union of four, eight, sixteen, or thirty-two non-
motile cells arising from internal division.

Family COELASTRACEAE. . . 177

177 (182, 186) Cells radially placed or forming close clusters. 178

178 (179, 180, 181) Cells spherical. . . . . *Coelastrum* Nägeli.

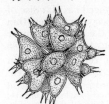

Cells spherical or slightly angled; chromatophore a hollow sphere, open at one side, with a pyrenoid opposite the opening.
Coelastrum occurs in all bodies of water, and is found in the plankton. It is very resistant to unfavorable conditions, persisting long after most other algae have perished.

FIG. 201. *Coelastrum sphaericum* Nägeli. × 620. (Original.)

179 (178, 180, 181) Cells cordate or reniform. . . . . *Sorastrum* Kützing.

Chloroplast parietal, with a single pyrenoid. Cells on short stalks radiating from a gelatinous center, but both center and stalks usually hidden by the cells. A new coenobium from each cell.
Sorastrum is of less frequent occurrence than most of the other members of the *Coelastraceae*, but is found in most localities where they are found, especially in the sediment at the bottom of ponds, and occasionally in the plankton.

FIG. 202. *Sorastrum spinulosum* Nägeli. × 600. (Original.)

180 (178, 179, 181) Cells crescent-shaped, points turned outward.
Selenastrum Reinsch.

Cells acutely pointed. Chromatophore parietal, with no pyrenoid. By many this is placed near to *Ankistrodesmus* rather than with the *Coelastraceae*.

FIG. 203. *Selenastrum gracile* Reinsch. × 565. (Original.)

181 (178, 179, 180) Cells club-shaped or elongated, forming a star.
Actinastrum Lagerheim.

Rays pointed, each ray composed of a single cell, all of which unite at the center. Chromatophore single, parietal, often not extending to the ends.

FIG. 204. *Actinastrum hantzschii* Lagerheim. × 550. (Original.)

182 (177, 186) Cells in one plane. 183

183 (184, 185) Cells four, eight, or sixteen in one or two parallel or zigzag rows. . . . . *Scenedesmus* Meyen.

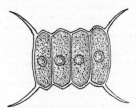

The cells oval or pointed, the membrane either smooth or furnished with distinct spines at the ends. Chromatophore single, parietal, with an opening at one side and a pyrenoid.
This is one of the most common and the best known of all of the lower algae, it being found in almost all localities where algae are ever found. Its adaptation to various environments, and to conditions unfavorable to most othe. algae, accounts for its wide distribution.

FIG. 205. *Scenedesmus quadricauda* Bréb. × 585. (Original.)

184 (183, 185) Cells grouped in fours, forming a rectangular plate of sixteen or more cells. . . . . *Crucigenia* Morren.

Cells spherical or elongated. Chromatophore thin, parietal, with a circular opening and one pyrenoid. This is regarded by Schmidle as *Staurogenia*.

FIG. 206. *Crucigenia apiculata* Chodat. × 1000. (Original.)

185 (183, 184)   Cells four together, never forming larger plates.   From two to
                 five spines on the external margin of each cell.
                                                        Tetrastrum Chodat.
Schmidle regards those forms with spines simply as different species of *Staurogenia*.

186 (182, 177)   Cells four, lying in two planes. . . . . *Tetradesmus* Smith.

This coenobium resembles a *Scenedesmus* rolled up, and in the size, shape,
and structure of the cells they are the same.

FIG. 207. *Tetradesmus wisconsiensis* Smith.   X 1500.   (After Smith.)

187 (176)   Coenobium a coarse net or a concentrically-arranged circular disc of
            cells, formed by the joining together of zoospores while within
            the mother-membrane, or still within the liberated inner
            lining of the same. . . Family HYDRODICTYACEAE . .   188

188 (189)   Coenobium a free-swimming circular plate of cells, one layer in
            thickness. . . . . *Pediastrum* Meyen.

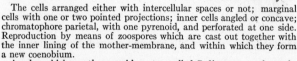

The cells arranged either with intercellular spaces or not; marginal
cells with one or two pointed projections; inner cells angled or concave;
chromatophore parietal, with one pyrenoid, and perforated at one side.
Reproduction by means of zoospores which are cast out together with
the inner lining of the mother-membrane, and within which they form
a new coenobium.

An alga which greatly resembles a two-celled *Pediastrum* was formerly
described as *Euastrum* by Schmidle, but Lagerheim places it in a new
genus *Euastropsis*. The mode of reproduction is the same as for *Pediastrum;* the zoospores, however, arrange themselves in pairs instead of
in a single plate, and form a number of new individuals which are set
free while within the inner layer of the mother-membrane.

FIG. 208. *Pediastrum boryanum* Meneghini.   X 600.   (Original.)

189 (188)   Coenobium a coarse net. . . . . *Hydrodictyon* Roth.

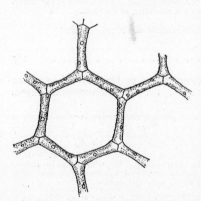

Nets large, each mesh bounded by five or six
cylindrical cells; the chromatophore reticulate,
parietal, with numerous pyrenoids; asexual reproduction by zoospores, those from each cell
forming a new net; sexual reproduction by
many isogametes. The zygospore produces
two to five large zoospores which in turn give
rise to a new net when they germinate.

In the early stages the nucleus is single, but
later divides rapidly so that the cell is multi-
nucleate. As the nets are formed within the
cylindrical mother-membrane they are cylindrical in shape for some time, but later become
torn and irregular. The nets occur as a very
thick light green scum on the surface of ponds
exposed to the direct rays of the sun. The different modes of reproduction have been proved
by Klebs to depend largely on the condition in
environment, and that by varying these conditions the different phases to development can
be produced.

FIG. 209. *Hydrodictyon reticulatum* Lagerheim.
X 100. (Original.)

190 (68, 249)   Plant of septate filaments, or of closely-arranged cells, forming
                plates or cylinders, one or more layers thick; attached or
                free-swimming. . . . . Order **Confervales** . .   191
Reproduction asexual, sexual, or both in the same species.

191 (196, 246)   Plant in adult form a macroscopic, free-swimming plate or
                 hollow cylinder of cells; in early stages often filamentous
                 and attached. . . . . Family ULVACEAE . .   192

192 (193) Plant cylindrical, flattened, or branched, of a simple layer of cells, reproduction by zoospores and isogametes.

Enteromorpha Link.

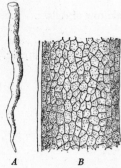

Frequently branched and variable in shape; chromatophore parietal, with one pyrenoid. Zoospores with four cilia and a pigment spot. Gametes with two cilia.
Both zoospores and gametes are formed in the vegetative cells except those at the base.
The greater number of species of *Enteromorpha* are marine, though *E. intestinalis* is found in the fresh water. Many of the salt-water forms are very variable so that the species are difficult to determine.

FIG. 210. *Enteromorpha intestinalis* L. (Link). *a.* one-half natural size. (After West.) *b.* × 360. (Original.)

A   B

193 (192) Plant in the adult stage a thin, membranaceous plate. . . . 194

194 (195) Chromatophore a thin, parietal lining to the membrane, with one pyrenoid. . . . . *Monostroma* Wittrock.

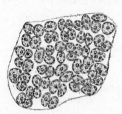

The plant in early stages a hollow sack or cylinder, becoming torn later, forming a membranaceous plate, near the base of which certain cells elongate, grow downward and form strengthening supports. Reproduction by means of zoospores with four cilia and smaller gametes with two cilia. These may germinate without copulation.
The membrane is at first very thin, but later becomes gelatinous so that the cells are more or less separated from each other. Growth is not localized but is intercalary and the cells are often clustered in groups of four.
Monostroma bullosum occurs in shallow ditches, partially submerged and partially swimming on the surface.

FIG. 211. *Monostroma bullosum* Thuret. × 350. (After Reinke.)

195 (194) Chloroplast star-shaped, radiating from the center, with one pyrenoid. . . . . *Prasiola* Meneghini.

Plant at first filamentous, but later a plate of cells grouped in small areas. Rhizoids frequent at the base. Reproduction, according to Lagerheim, in three ways: by isolated portions of the plant, akinetes, and aplanospores. No zoospores known.
Kützing has established a genus *Schizogonium* which greatly resembles *Prasiola*. The chromatophore is stellate and the filaments divide longitudinally to form two or more rows. The chief difference between this and *Prasiola* is that in the latter genus the longitudinal divisions continue, while in the former they cease after the first few times.
Wille makes *Schizogonium* a subsection under *Prasiola* and is followed in this by West.

FIG. 212. *Prasiola crispa* Meneghini. × about 50. (After Oltmann and Meneghini.)

196 (191, 246) Plant filamentous. 197

197 (219) Filaments fine, mostly unbranched. 198

198 (217, 218) Filaments generally unbranched. Chromatophore a single, parietal curved plate or cylinder, rarely axial, or of several small, distinct discs, rarely more or less united into a network.

Family ULOTHRICHACEAE . . 199

199 (211, 212, 213)   The chromatophore single, a parietal plate or cylinder. 200

200 (205)   Filaments without gelatinous envelop.   201

201 (204)   Filament always simple, composed of a single row of cells. .   202

202 (203)   Cells cylindrical. Reproduction by zoospores and in some cases
by resting spores. . . . .   *Hormidium* Kützing.

Zoospores formed singly in each cell; they have two cilia but no pigment spot. Resting spores occur with reduction of moisture.

Fɪɢ. 213. *Hormidium nitens* Meneghini. ✕ 400. (Original.)

203 (202)   Cells but little longer than broad. Reproduction by zoospores
and isogametes. . . . .   *Ulothrix* Kützing.

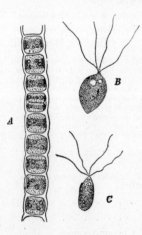

Cells relatively short; chromatophore lining the entire
membrane, or only a part, with a pyrenoid. Reproduction by zoospores and isogametes. Zoospores with four
cilia and a pigment spot; gametes smaller, with two cilia,
capable of germinating without copulation.

Ulothrix occurs frequently among other algae in ponds,
lakes, and watering troughs, though not often in great
quantities.

The resemblance to *Hormidium* is great, though the
species of the latter genus are apt to be somewhat smaller,
and the length of the cells relatively longer in proportion to
the breadth.

Ulothrix yields readily to cultivation, and different phases
of its development may be controlled by changes in the
environment.

Fɪɢ. 214. *Ulothrix zonata* Kützing; *a.* vegetative filament. ✕
225. *b.* macrozoospore. ✕ 388. *c.* microzoospore. (After Klebs.)

204 (201)   Filament at first simple, later becoming a solid mass of many cells.
Schizomeris Kützing.

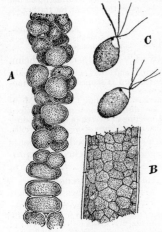

Plant in early stages like *Ulothrix*, later forming a slender, solid parenchymatous filament; reproduction by zoospores, one from each cell.

Quantities of the zoospores are liberated from a filament at a time, the walls becoming partially gelatinous, but showing a parenchymatous structure after the liberation.

By some European writers the genus is regarded as the same as *Ulothrix*, but forms such as are found in America must establish it as a separate genus. The zoospores have four cilia and a pigment spot, as in *Ulothrix*; the vegetative cells may change into resting spores.

Schizomeris has been found growing on river banks and in quiet fresh water.

Fig. 215. *Schizomeris leibleinii* Kützing. *a.* portion of filament. × about 625. *b.* portion of filament showing division in all directions. × 300. *c.* zoospores. × 625. (Original.)

205 (200) Filament with gelatinous envelop. 206
206 (209) Cells not in distinct pairs. 207
207 (208) Cells oval, gelatinous envelop homogenous.
                                                  Hormospora Brébisson.

Fig. 216. *Hormospora mutabilis* Brébisson. × about 600. (Original.)

This is regarded by many as being but a phase in the development of *Ulothrix*, but the very gelatinous membrane, the rounded ends of the cells, and the fact that this form is not known to reproduce by zoospores would indicate that it is an independent genus.

208 (207) Cells rounded. Gelatinous sheath showing radial fibrillar structure. . . . . *Radiofilum* Schmidle.

Fig. 217. *Radiofilum flavescens* West. × 300. (After West.)

Chromatophore single, parietal, with one pyrenoid. Cells spherical, ellipsoidal, or lenticular, in some species united by short necks. Filaments unbranched. Reproduction by simple division. Wille includes *Hormospora* and *Radiofilum* with *Geminella*, a genus not known to occur in America.

209 (206) Cells mostly in pairs. 210
210 (211) Cells rounded, gelatinous substance lamellate, invested by the antecedent mother-membrane. . . . *Binuclearia* Wittrock.

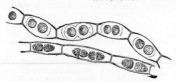

Filaments attached when young; each cell pair originates from the contents of a single cell, and is surrounded by a more or less lamellate substance, about which the original membrane is still visible. Chromatophore parietal, reproduction by division and akinetes.

Fig. 218. *Binuclearia tetrana* Wittrock. × about 450. (Original.)

211 (199, 212, 213) Chromatophore axial, with rounded clear spaces at each end. . . . . *Planktonema* Schmidle.

Filaments short, free-swimming. Cells cylindrical, rounded at the ends, mostly in pairs, each pair separated from the next by an apparently empty space. Reproduction by division within the membrane after which the parts become separated, probably by a gelatinous substance.

Planktonema resembles in many respects the form described by Wittrock as *Binuclearia* but Schmidle makes it a new genus. The two genera should be made the subject for further investigation.

FIG. 219. *Planktonema lauterbornii* Schmidle. × about 1000. (After Schmidle.)

212 (199, 211, 213) Chromatophore a parietal network. *Microspora* Lagerheim.

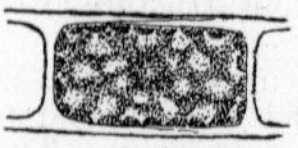

Chromatophores band-like or netted and thickened at intervals; membrane often becoming fragmented into H-shaped pieces. Reproduction by macrozoospores and microzoospores.

Filaments free, unbranched; sometimes resembling *Conferva*. Membrane thick, somewhat gelatinous, and distinctly made up of H-shaped pieces, the ends of the H either just meeting or overlapping. Reproduction by macrozoospores with four cilia, and microzoospores with two cilia.

FIG. 220. *Microspora amaena* Lagerheim. × 345. (After West.)

213 (199, 211, 212) Chromatophores many, parietal, disc-shaped. Filaments fine, unbranched, rarely (*Aeronemum*) branched. Reproduction by mono-ciliate zoospores. 214

214 (215, 216) Filaments unbranched, at first attached: no pyrenoids.
Tribonema Derbes and Solier.

Filaments light green, soft to the touch. Length of cells one to several times the breadth, sometimes slightly swollen at the middle. Chromatophores from two to many, small, parietal. Reproduction by zoospores, one or two of which are formed in a cell and liberated by the membrane falling into H-shaped pieces. Zoospores obovate, asymmetrical, with two chromatophores in the anterior part, one cilium, and no pigment spot. Resting cells may occur.

FIG. 221. *Tribonema minor* Klebs. × 800. (Original.)

215 (214, 216) Structure of cells and zoospores as in *Tribonema*; filaments composed of segments of 4 to 8 cells; each formed from the contents of a single vegetative cell, the ruptured wall of which is visible at the end of the segment. Division rarely longitudinal. . . . . *Bumilleria* Borzi.

Filaments usually short. Zoospores the same as in *Tribonema*, but liberated through a dissolved portion of the membrane, instead of through a circular split dividing the membrane into two portions. Resting cells may be formed.

FIG. 222. *Bumilleria sicula* Borzi. × about 330. (After Borzi.)

216 (214, 215) Structure of cells and zoospores as in *Tribonema*. Filaments minute, richly branched, easily passing into a unicellular condition. . . . . *Aeronemum* Snow.

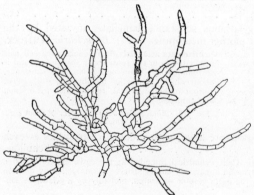

Chromatophores pale, several in a cell, without pyrenoids and closely applied to the membrane. Reproduction by zoospores which have a single cilium, a small chromatophore, and a pigment spot. They move with an amoeboid motion. This may be the same as *Monocilia* Gerneck, though the branching is much more abundant than is described in that form.

FIG. 223. *Aeronemum polymorphum* Snow. × 225. (Original.)

217 (198, 218) Plants of unbranched, free-swimming, more or less gelatinous filaments, the cells very long; chlorophyll parietal and surrounding a number of large conspicuous vacuoles which show as a row of lighter areas; pyrenoids numerous. Reproduction by heterogametes.

Family SPHAEROPLEACEAE.

Only one genus known. . . . . . . *Sphaeroplea* Agardh.

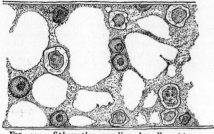

FIG. 224. *Sphaeroplea annulina* Agardh. × 1133. (After Rauwenhoff.)

Cells cylindrical, tapering; length eight to twenty times the breadth, several nuclei present. Oogonia and antheridia formed from vegetative cells, the oogonia containing many oospheres, and the antheridia a very large number of antherozoids with two cilia; these are liberated through holes in the membrane and enter the oogonia through similar holes; the oospores are red and have a thick, rough membrane. On germination each produces one to eight zoospores with a pigment spot and two cilia. Spores may be produced parthenogenetically.

218 (198, 217) Plants of unbranched, more or less gelatinous, filaments, attached in early stages; cells short, cylindrical, or swollen; chromatophore single, parietal, with one pyrenoid. Reproduction by means of zoospores with two cilia and by heterogametes. . . . . Family CYLINDROCAPSACEAE.

Only one genus known. . . . . . . *Cylindrocapsa* Reinsch.

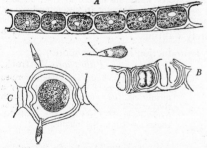

Reproduction asexual and sexual; asexual, by zoospores and akinetes; sexual, by means of oogonia, each with one oospore, and antheridia, each with two antherozoids; oospore red in color.

This is a very rare alga though it is reported by Collins as occurring in Massachusetts and by Wolle as occurring from New York to Florida.

FIG. 225. *Cylindrocapsa involuta* Reinsch. *a.* vegetative filament; *b.* formation of antherozoids; *c.* oogonium with antherozoids. × 575. (After Cienkowski.)

219 (197) Filaments coarser, mostly branched. 220

220 (233) Chromatophore with irregular, linear, or net-like perforations. 221

221 (230) Zoospores biciliate. . . . . Family CLADOPHORACEAE . . 222

Filaments mostly branched, harsh to the touch, generally attached; chromatophore parietal, with irregular, net-like perforations; contents granular; numerous pyrenoids. Nuclei many.

222 (223) Filaments never branched except at the attachment.

Chaetomorpha Kützing.

Filaments attached by a branched, rhizoid-like organ. Reproduction by means of zoospores. The species of this genus are mostly marine.

223 (222) Filaments usually branched. 224

224 (227) Branches abundant. 225

225 (226) Plants large, tufted; reproduction by zoospores. *Cladophora* Kützing.

Plant frequently very large; diameter of the filaments much greater at the base than at the ends; the length of the cells one to twenty times the diameter; reproduction by zoospores, many being formed from a vegetative cell; these with two or four cilia.

The number of species of *Cladophora* is very large, and they are found in fresh, brackish, and salt water, but probably in the greatest abundance along the shores of lakes where they are constantly washed by the waves. Some species are believed to be annual and some perennial.

FIG. 226. *Cladophora glomerata* Kützing. × 85. (Original.)

226 (225) Plant forming pulvinate coatings, cells of two kinds, one light and one dark. . . . . *Chlorotylium* Kützing.

Plant of erect, branching, parallel filaments, forming firm, dense tufts imbedded in a gelatinous mass. In each filament several cells with dense chlorophyll alternate with longer ones contain-

FIG. 227. *Chlorotylium cataractarum* Rabenhorst. × 150. (After Rabenhorst.)

ing less chlorophyll, thus giving a concentric arrangement of light and dark.

Chromatophore band-shaped, asexual reproduction by biciliate zoospores which are formed in great numbers in each zoosporagium. Akinetes are also formed.

227 (224) Branches not frequent, rarely wanting. 228

228 (229) Branches long, scattered; reproduction by resting spores.
Pithophora Wittrock.

Cells long, cylindrical; akinetes formed by the end of a cell being separated by a membrane, the contents becoming much thicker and darker, while the membrane increases in thickness and the whole becomes swollen in the middle.

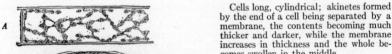

FIG. 228. *Pithophora kewensis* Wittrock. *a.* vegetative filament; *b.* formation of resting spore. × 140. (After Wittrock.)

229 (228) Branches short, attenuated, infrequent, sometimes rhizoid-like, sometimes lacking altogether. . . *Rhizoclonium* Kützing.

Filaments attached, often curved and matted, usually with short infrequent branches which consist of one or more cells, sometimes resembling rhizoids. Cell walls lamellose.

Chromatophore netted, with several pyrenoids. Nuclei several. Reproduction by biciliate zoospores and by akinetes. Sometimes occurring on damp ground.

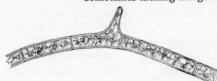

FIG. 229. *Rhizoclonium hieroglyphicum* Kützing. × 300. (Original.)

230 (221)   Zoospores with a circle of cilia near the smaller end.
                                      Family OEDOGONIACEAE . .   231

Plants of branched or unbranched filaments, attached in early stages; chromatophore with irregular, linear, or net-like perforations and several pyrenoids; membrane often with transverse striations at one end of a cell.   Reproduction by means of zoospores with a circle of cilia near the smaller end and by heterogametes.

231 (232)   **Plant not branched.** . . . . *Oedogonium* Link.

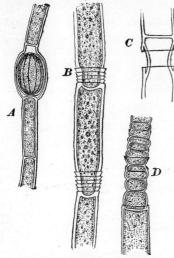

Plants either monoecious or dioecious; in the latter case the filaments bearing antheridia may be normal filaments, or tiny filaments of single cells called dwarf males, attached near the oogonia. These originate from special small zoospores called androspores.   But one oosphere in an oogonium; the spermatozoid enters through a perforation in the wall or through an opening caused by the throwing off of a cap; antheridia single or many together, each containing one or two antherozoids; oospore brown or red.   Asexual reproduction by zoospores borne singly in vegetative cells; they have a crown of cilia about a colorless spot at the anterior end.

Oedogonium occurs in almost all bodies of water and several species are usually found together.

FIG. 230.   *Oedogonium crenulato-costatum* Wittrock. *a.* oospore.   × about 600.   *b. Oedogonium* sp., vegetative filament.   *c.* division.   *d.* formation of antheridia. *b, c, d.* × about 520.   (Original.)

232 (231)   **Plant branched.** . . . . *Bulbochaete* Agardh.

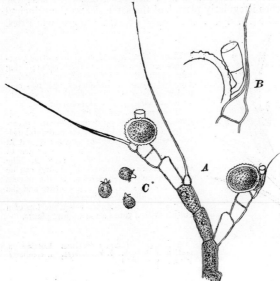

Most of the cells bearing a long colorless hair, swollen at the base. Reproduction as in *Oedogonium;* the dwarf males very frequent.

Though not so common as *Oedogonium* it is found all over the world and sometimes occurs in great quantities, completely covering submerged higher plants with a feathery coating.

Small branches which have been detached are also often found among other algae.

FIG. 231.   *Bulbochaete mirabilis* Wittrock.   *a.* Plant with oospore.   *b.* dwarf male on oospore. *c.* zoospores.   × 200. (Original.)

233 (220)   Chromatophore a single equatorial band, with one pyrenoid.   Filaments branched, attached, frequently with a gelatinous covering.   Reproduction by zoospores and isogametes.

Family CHAETOPHORACEAE . . 234

234 (242)   The zoosporangia of the same form as the vegetative cells; the larger species usually bearing long hairs.

Subfamily CHAETOPHOREAE . . 235

235 (239)   Plant attached, differentiated into base and apex. 236

236 (237, 238)   Filaments imbedded in a firm, gelatinous matrix, forming a spherical or an irregularly branched, ribbon-like thallus attached at the base. . . . . Chaetophora Shrank.

Filaments radiating from a common center, usually terminating in a colorless hair; micro-zoospores with two cilia and a pigment spot near the anterior end; macrozoospores also formed.

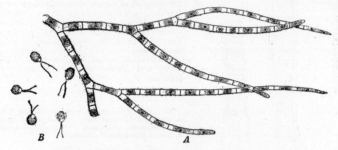

FIG. 232.   Chaetophora pisiformis Agardh.   × 100.   (Original.)

237 (236, 238)   Filaments not imbedded in a firm gelatinous matrix, the branches irregularly placed, of the same size as the principal axis. . . . . Myxonema Fries.

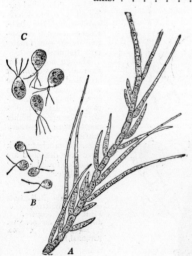

Plant either several centimeters long, attached, or very minute and free, often passing into a palmella condition.   Sexual reproduction by means of isogametes with two cilia and a pigment spot; asexual, by zoospores with four cilia, and by akinetes.

Myxonema is widely distributed, the microscopical forms occurring almost universally on mosses and liverworts in damp localities, while the larger forms are frequent in running water.   They have been known to completely cover the beds of streams.   The smaller forms are microscopical, and can be detected only after portions of the mosses and liverworts are placed in culture and the Myxonema allowed to develop.

It will then sometimes cover the top of a culture with a thin film of minute plants.

FIG. 233.   Myxonem lubricum Kützing. a. portion of branch. b. isogometes. c. zoospores. × 285.   (Original.)

238 (236, 237)   Lateral branches in whorls or tufts, smaller than the main
      axis. . . . .   *Draparnaldia* Bory.

Plant attached by a disc of cells.   Terminal cells usually ending in a long, colorless hair.
Reproduction by means of zoospores with four cilia and a pigment spot.   No fertilization
known.
In *Draparnaldia* the photosynthesis takes place principally in the tufted branches, as the
chloroplast of the principal axis is reduced to a small, equatorial band in each cell.
All forms of *Draparnaldia* are large and are found in much the same localities as the larger
forms of *Myxonema*.

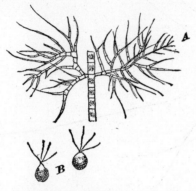

FIG. 234.   *Draparnaldia plumosa* Agardh.   × about 50.   (Original.)

239 (235)   Plant epiphytic adhering throughout to other plants.   240

240 (241)   Plant of irregularly branched filaments, setae or hairs not abundant.
                                          Herposteiron Nägeli.

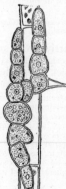

Plant small, cells with a parietal chromatophore, a
pyrenoid, and frequently a long colorless hair; reproduction by means of egg-shaped zoospores, with
four cilia and a pigment spot, two spores being formed
in a single cell.

This is of frequent occurrence on other filamentous
algae but usually occurs only as small isolated individuals.
It has long been included under the name of
Aphanochaete, but the name *Herposteiron* seems to
have priority.

FIG. 235.   *Herposteiron confervicola* Nägeli.   × 450.   (After Hazen.)

241 (240)   Individual cells flask-shaped, each with a long slender hair from
the smaller portion. . . . . . . *Chaetosphaeridium* Klebahn.

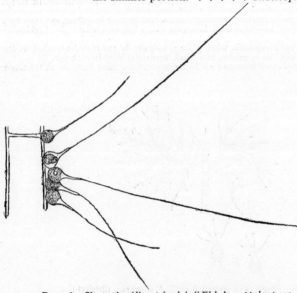

Chromatophore parietal, with one pyrenoid. Reproduction by zoospores, four of which are produced in a cell. Horizontal divisions of the cells also occurs, the lower of the daughter cells passing gradually to the side of the upper one.

Chaetosphaeridium is widely distributed in the United States though rarely occurring in quantities exceeding a few cells at a time.

These are usually attached to filamentous algae and are inconspicuous, though the long setae are usually somewhat prominent

FIG. 236. *Chaetosphaeridium pringsheimii* Klebahn.   X about 425.   (After Hazen.)

242 (234)   The zoosporangia different from the vegetative cells.
Subfamily CHROOLEPIDEAE . . 243

243 (244, 245)   Plant minute, tree-like in its branching; reproduction by
zoospores. . . . . *Microthamnion* Nägeli.

Branches from the upper end of a cell and not separated by a membrane; obtuse at the tip; color pale; chromatophore a parietal band with no pyrenoid. Zoospores formed in zoosporangia at the ends of filaments.

FIG. 237. *Microthamnion kützingianum* Nägeli.   X 600.
(Original.)

244 (243, 245)   Plant coarse, irregularly branched, partly erect and partly
creeping on stones and trees; when aerial, often colored red
by haematochrome.   Membrane thick; reproduction by
zoospores and gametes. . . . . . . *Trentepohlia* Martius.

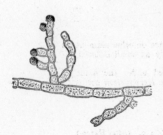

Chromatophores many, irregular discs, without pyrenoids; gametangia and zoosporangia mostly terminal; gametes and zoospores similar, being egg-shaped, with two cilia and haematochrome, but no definite pigment spot.   A palmella condition may occur.

These are sometimes referred to as the aerial algae because they exist principally in the air and form often bright-colored incrustations on the bark of trees and stones.   They are not infrequently found in connection with lichen fungi.

As the *Trentepohlias* are principally aerial, the liberation of the zoospores and gametes can occur only at the time of a rain or in the presence of a heavy dew.

FIG. 238. *Trentepohlia wainoi* Hariot.   X 125.   (After
Collins and Hariot.)

245 (243, 244) Structure as in *Trentepohlia* but many of the cells having setae. . . . . *Nylandera* Hariot.

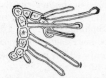

There is but one species of this genus described, and the only point of distinction between this and *Trentepohlia* is the rather coarse and unsegmented setae.

FIG. 239. *Nylandera tentaculata* Hariot. × 140. (After Hariot.)

246 (191, 196) Plant an attached disc. 247
247 (248) Plant a small, attached disc or cushion of cells, made up of radiating rows of cells either separate or grown together, bearing on the surface long sheathed hairs. Reproduction by means of zoospores and by heterogametes.

Family COLEOCHAETACEAE.
Only one genus. . . . . *Coleochaete* Brébisson.

Cells with a single, large, parietal chromatophore and a pyrenoid. Any vegetative cell may give rise to an egg-shaped zoospore. Plants either monoecious or dioecious; oogonia flask-shaped, at the end of a branch or row of cells; antheridia near the oogonia, each bearing a single anthero-zoid; a layer of cells develop about the oospore. On germination the oospore divides, producing a number of cells, in each one of which a zoospore is formed; these reproduce the parent plant.

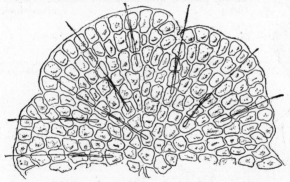

FIG. 240. *Coleochaete scutta* Brébisson. Portion of a disc. × about 215.

248 (247) Plant a disc, of one or more layers in thickness, adhering through-out to a substratum, often bearing gelatinous hairs. Repro-duction by means of zoospores, and in some instances by isogametes. . . . . Family MYCOIDEACEAE.
Only one genus recorded here. . . . . *Ulvella* Crouan.

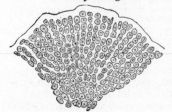

Plant a disc of radiating rows of cells, a single layer in thickness on the margin and several in the middle; chromatophore single, but thickened so as to give the appearance of many; pyrenoid single.
Appearance much as in *Coleochaete* except that mem-brane and hairs are more gelatinous and the hairs have no sheaths. Reproduction by zoospores only. These have cilia, and arise first at the center of the disc and later toward the margin. On the surface of water plants. Mr. F. S. Collins believes this to be *Chaetopeltis* but sexual reproduction characteristic for *Chaetopeltis* has not been observed in this form.

FIG. 241. *Ulvella americana* Snow (= *Pseudulvella americana* Wille). × 150. (Original.)

249 (68, 190)   Plants of non-septate, branched filaments, forming felt-like masses on water or earth; or plants minute, growing on the surface of moist earth or in the tissues of higher plants; nuclei, many. Reproduction by zoospores, isogametes, or heterogametes. . . . . Order **Siphonales** . . 250

Many marine forms; fresh water forms few, differing greatly in appearance and reproduction.

250 (251, 252)   Plant a felt-like mass of branched filaments which contain no septa except when reproductive bodies are formed.

Vaucheria de Candolle.

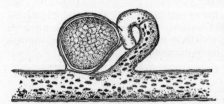

Plant branched; chromatophores numerous, parietal, disc-shaped; asexual reproduction either by zoospores or by akinetes, the former borne singly in terminal sporangia, the latter occurring as spherical cells on short, lateral branches; oogonia, each containing one oosphere, and antheridia, each with many antherozoids are borne side by side either laterally or on the ends of short branches.

FIG. 242. *Vaucheria repens* Hassall.   X 300.
(Original.)

251 (250, 252)   Plant growing on moist earth, about 1 mm. broad, erect, green, balloon-shaped, with branched, colorless rhizoids at smaller end. . . . . *Botrydium* Wallroth.

Chromatophores numerous, minute, parietal, each with a pyrenoid; reproduction by zoospores; under dry conditions resting spores may be formed in the branched rhizoid-like organ of attachment.

FIG. 243. *Botrydium granulatum* Greville.   X 15. (After Goebel and Woronin.)

252 (250, 251)   Plants growing on the tissues of higher plants.

Phyllosiphon Kuhn.

Plants parasitic in the leaves and stems of aquatic plants. The lower end is inflated, green, the upper part colorless. In the vegetative part the chromatophores are indistinct. Reproduction by internal division or aplanospores which are liberated by the rupturing of the cell wall. In these the chromatophore is distinct.

FIG. 244. *Phyllosiphon arisari* Kühn. Cells of host not shown.
X 40. (After Just.)

253 (1)   **Plant coarse,** at least several centimeters long, with a linear, cylindrical, occasionally branched axis, showing nodes and internodes; at the nodes, whorls of cylindrical leaves which in turn bear leaflets; sometimes encrusted with lime. Growth apical. . . . . Order **Charales.**
Only one family. . . . . CHARACEAE . . 254

Leaflets and internodes of both axis and leaf are each of but a single cell, the walls of which are lined with chloroplasts and in the center of which is a large sap cavity. In *Chara* the internodal cell is more or less completely covered by a layer of cortical cells of the same structure. A swamp-like odor is usually present. Reproduction sexual only; plants either dioecious or monoecious, but in the latter case the antheridia mature before the oogonia. The antheridium is spherical, its wall composed of eight "shields" which contain red chromoplasts on their inner surfaces. Attached to the middle of each shield and projecting inward is a club-shaped cell, the manubrium, which in turn bears a short cell, the capitulum. To the capitula are attached secondary capitula bearing four long, slender filaments made up of many cells, each containing an antherozoid; the antherozoids are spiral in form and have two cilia at their anterior ends; the oogonia are egg-shaped and are covered by five spiral cells, the tips of which are divided, once in *Chara* and twice in *Nitella*, to form the "crown." The term sporophydium has been suggested for the structure including the oospore, its basal cell, and enveloping cells. Below the crown cells the antherozoids penetrate to effect fertilization. Oospores are brown or yellowish; on germination they produce first a simple row of cells, the proembryo, on which the new individual arises.

254 (257) Points of the crown of the oogonium two-celled.

Subfamily NITELLEAE . . 255

255 (256) Leaflets projecting beyond the tips of the leaves, giving the appearance of forked leaves. . . . . *Nitella* Agardh.

Axis and leaves never with a cortical covering and seldom encrusted with lime. Leaves with but one whorl of leaflets, but these in turn may bear whorls of leaflets, those of the last order always projecting beyond the leaves, giving them a divided appearance. The antheridium always terminal on the middle leaf or leaflet. Oogonia either single or several together, in the place of lateral leaflets.

FIG. 245. *Nitella* sp. Natural size. (Original.)

256 (255) Leaflets not projecting beyond the tips of the leaves, or not present.
Tolypella A. Braun.

Stem and leaves never with a cortical covering. Leaves with one to three whorls of leaflets, which in turn may bear other whorls of leaflets, much smaller than the first. Antheridia single or several together, which arise from the basal or the first node of a leaf. Oogonia several, surrounding the antheridia. Plants usually monoecious.

FIG. 246. *Tolypella nidifica* v. Leonh. Three-fourths natural size. (Portion of figure after Wille.)

257 (254)   Points of the crown of the oogonium one-celled.
Subfamily CHAREAE.
Only one genus known in America. . . . . . . *Chara* A. Braun.

Plants mostly encrusted with lime. Principal axis and leaves more or less completely covered with a layer of cells forming the cortex. Leaves six to twelve in a whorl, each usually with several whorls of leaflets, mostly with stipular outgrowths. Antheridia and oogonia on the upper side of leaves. Plants either monoecious or dioecious.

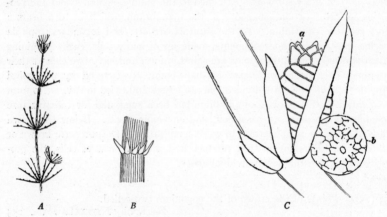

A   B   C

FIG. 247.   *Chara fragilis* Derv.   *A.* two-thirds natural size portion of figure.   (After Wille.)   *B.* portion of leaf showing cortication.   *C. Chara coronata* Ziz.   *a.* oogonium.   *b.* antheridium.

In Europe two other genera have been recognized under the *Chareae* as follows:

A. Sporophydia borne on the inferior side of the cell which carries the antheridium. . . . . *Lamprothamnus* A. Braun.

B. Sporophydia occupying the place of a leaflet on the anterior side of the leaf, situated between antheridia. . . . . *Lychnothamnus* Leonh.

CLASS III.   Phaeophyceae

Color brown; plant coarse and large; or fine, filamentous.

All species are attached and have a dark or olive green color. Many are small and resemble the Confervales while others reach an enormous size. Sexual reproduction takes place by antheridia and oogonia in the larger species, and by isogametes and zoospores in the smaller.

The members of this class, with a very few exceptions, occur in salt-water, and the classification of some fresh-water forms which are often placed in this group is doubtful.

Only one genus listed here. Plant upright, many centimeters long, differentiated into a pseudo-parenchymatous principal axis and branches, covered with short, unbranched hairs. Color an olive brown. . . . . *Thorea* Bory.

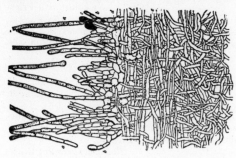

Reproduction asexual only, consisting in the formation of sporangia on the outer surface of the axis, each containing but a single spore, without cilia and without membrane. The position of this alga in the system of classification is very doubtful, but for convenience it is placed with the *Phaeophyceae*.

FIG. 248. *Thorea ramosissima* Bory. Portion of a longitudinal radial section. × about 150. (After Hedgecock & Hunter.)

CLASS IV. Rhodophyceae

Color red, or a dull, purplish green; plant sometimes complex in structure; reproduction sexual and in most cases asexual also.
Only one order. . . . . **Florideae.**

Plants mostly inhabitants of salt water, but represented in fresh water by several genera. The structure of the different fresh-water genera varies, but the sexual form of reproduction is essentially the same in all. The male reproductive organs are borne on the ends of filamentous branches, the contents of each of which produce a single spermatium. The female organ is flask-shaped, in the larger portion of which, the carpogonium, lies the oosphere; through the long neck, the trichogyne, the spermatium is conducted to the oosphere at the base, it having been previously carried by the water to the projecting tip of the trichogyne. As a result of fertilization, densely branched filaments arise from the base of the carpogonium, on the ends of which are borne carpospores; these spore-bearing branches, and the sterile branches which usually surround them, together form the cystocarp. In *Chantransia* and in many salt-water species tetraspores are also formed.

1 (8) Plant branched. 2

2 (5) Branches simple and not in whorls. 3

3 (4) Plants coarse, of simple or occasionally branched, hollow, tapering bristles with node-like swellings; brownish or dark bluish-green in color. . . . . *Lemanea* Bory.

Bristles attached to a fine, filamentous structure which is furnished with rhizoids. Bristles hollow, with a single row of cells through the center, supported at intervals by transversely placed cells. Antheridia borne in great numbers on the surface of the node-like swellings, a single spermatium in each. Carpogonia imbedded in the outer wall of the bristles, the tip of the trichogyne only projecting. Chains of carpospores project toward the center.

FIG. 249. *Lemanea torulosa* Agardh. One-half natural size. (After Kirchner.)

4 (3) Plant a steel blue, brownish or red, consisting of a single, branched row of cells, the branches of the same structure as the principal axis, irregularly placed and not in whorls.

Chantransia Fries.

Sexual reproduction resembling that of *Batrachospermum;* carpogonia on lateral branches; tetraspores resembling carpospores on the tips of cells. Plants dioecious.

FIG. 250. *Chantransia chalybea* Fries. × 190. (After Kirchner.)

5 (2) Branches in whorls. 6

6 (7) Plant purplish or bluish, beaded in appearance, due to whorls of dichotomous, accessory branches, composed of a single chain of cells on a pseudo-parenchymatous axis.

Batrachospermum Roth.

Plant several centimeters long; occasionally dioecious, the antheridia at the ends of accessory branches, the carpogonia frequently near the axis; the carpospores give rise to a protonema on which the adult form may originate as a branch. The protonema may also give rise to asexual spores which again may produce protonema.

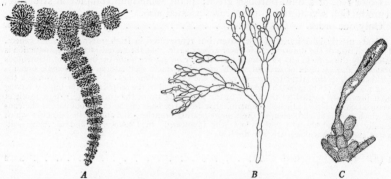

A   B   C

FIG. 251. *Batrachospermum grabussoniense* Sirodot. *A.* portion of plant. × about 25. *B.* branches. × 225. *C.* procarp. × 580. (Original.)

7 (6) Thallus erect, richly branched, several centimeters high; beaded throughout, due to whorls of branches which are so closely packed and grown together as to form a continuous outer sheath, the diameter of which is greater opposite these branches. . . . . *Tuomeya* Harvey.

Antheridia at the ends of branches, mostly at the nodes; carpogonia in the axils of branches. This genus is synonymous with *Baileya* of Kützing.

FIG. 252. *Tuomeya fluviatalis* Harvey. × 375. (After Setchell.)

8 (1)   Plant an unbranched filament of one or more rows or cells.
Bangia Lyngbye.

Structure simple, hair-like; color of different shades of red; attached at one end. Found usually in rapidly-flowing water on wood and stones.

Fig. 253.   *Bangia atro-purpurea* Agardh.   × 225.   (After Kützing.)

IMPORTANT REFERENCES ON NORTH AMERICAN FRESH-WATER ALGAE

COLLINS, F. S.   1909.   The Green Algae of North America.   Tufts College Stud., Vol. II, No. 3.   1912.   Supplement.   Tufts College Stud., Vol. III, No. 2.

CONN, H. W. and WEBSTER, L. W.   1908.   A Preliminary Report on the Algae of Fresh Water of Connecticut.   State Geol. Nat. Hist. Surv., Bull. No. 10.

DE TONI, J. B.   1887–1907.   Sylloge algarum omnium hucusque cognitarum.   Vol. I, Chlorophyceae.   Vol. II, Bacillariaceae.   Padua.

ENGLER, AD. and PRANTL, K. A. E.   1887–1909.   Die naturlichen Pflanzenfa-milien.   4v. in 17.   Leipzig.

HAZEN, T. E.   1902.   The Ulothricaceae and Chaetophorae of the United States.   Mem. Torrey Bot. Club, Vol. XI.

PASCHER, A.   1912.   (See list in Chapter I.)

SAUNDERS, D.   1894.   Protophyta-Phycophyta.   Flora of Nebraska, 1: 15–68.   Lincoln.

TILDEN, J. E.   1909.   Minnesota Algae (Schizophyceae).   Minn. Bot. Survey.

TRANSEAU, E. M.   1913.   Annotated List of the Algae of Eastern Illinois.   Ill. Acad. Sci., 6: 69–89.

VAN HEURCK, H.   1896.   A Treatise on the Diatomaceae.   London.

WEST, G. S.   1904.   (See list in Chapter V.)

WEST, W. and G. S.   1904–1912.   A Monograph of the British Desmidiaceae.   4v.   Ray Soc. Publ., Vol. 42.   London.

WOLLE, FRANCIS.   1884.   Desmids of the United States.   1887.   Fresh-water Algae of the United States.   2v.   Text and Atlas.   Bethlehem, Pa.   1890.   Diatomaceae of North America.   Bethlehem, Pa.

CHAPTER VII
THE LARGER AQUATIC VEGETATION

By RAYMOND H. POND

Late Professor of Botany, Texas Agricultural College

NEARLY all of the larger plants which have distinct roots, stems, and leaves grow attached to the muddy substratum. This habit of the larger plants to grow as attached organisms is so universal that it can hardly be regarded as an accident and it is reasonable to suppose that such attachment offers some advantage to the organism. Even the simple filamentous algae are often attached.

When a plant is floating free any portion of it may be exposed to the surface light, or to the air, because the water movements may turn its body in any direction and such a plant is better off without specialized organs which would be destroyed by exposure. It is common to see drifting plants which are dying rapidly because, among other reasons, the roots are exposed to the intense light at the surface of the water. The small, free-floating forms are simple in structure because no portion of the organism has a distinct environment of its own and changes in position are so frequent that all parts of the body are equally exposed. The common duckweed, *Lemna*, moves with the changing currents and shows a marked differentiation into an upper and a lower side. Notable, however, is the fact that its movement is always in a horizontal direction so that the upper side is uniformly up while the lower side is down, with its roots in the water, and shaded by the cap-like upper side. Thus it is that *Ceratophyllum*, which is usually regarded as a dicotyledon and which certainly occupies a much higher station in the natural system than *Lemna*, shows less differentiation in outer structure than the latter. In the case of *Ceratophyllum* attachment is purely accidental so far as special organs for the purpose are concerned. Well-developed roots have never been found on this plant although the rudiment of a root is present in the embryo. The rigid segments of the forked leaves frequently catch on the bottom so that a portion of the stem may become buried and secure the plant to the soil. Just as often, however, the plants float free in the water at the mercy of any influence that may arise to change their relative position. Examination shows the entire surface of this plant to be so uniform in structure that it makes no difference what part of the plant body is vertical or horizontal in the water.

Attachment, therefore, favors and necessitates differentiation into specialized organs.

In land plants the roots are organs of absorption as well as of attachment, but until recently the general understanding has been that the roots of aquatic plants serve for anchoring only. Investigations of the writer have proved that the roots act as organs for the absorption of mineral matter from the substratum and in this respect are perfectly analogous to the roots of land plants.

Root-hairs are present on the roots of terrestrial plants with but comparatively few exceptions. These delicate structures are unicellular with thin walls and are formed by the enlarging and protruding of the ordinary peripheral cells of the root. Their presence greatly increases the absorbing surface exposed to the soil and thus the passage of mineral matter into the plants is provided for with a minimum expenditure of tissue. Several authors have stated that root-hairs are absent in the case of submerged aquatics. This does not seem to be the case, however, as the writer has found them present on 17 out of the 20 species common in Lake Erie. Even without experimental evidence it would be reasonable to suppose that the presence of root-hairs indicates that the roots act as organs for the passage of mineral matter into the plant. Such delicate structures can hardly be regarded as lingering rudiments of more active organs present when perhaps the species was terrestrial.

Land plants have developed a highly specialized tissue system adapted to the transfer of water from the roots to stem, branches, and leaves. This conductive tissue is usually called the vascular system and the necessity for it in land plants is very apparent when the rapidity with which water passes from the plant is taken into account. That water plants likewise have conductive tissue has

been known for a long time and a great deal of attention has been
given to a study of its structure. The vascular system of aquatics
is much simpler than that of land plants and seems to represent a
degenerate type of the latter. This general fact has thus far been
interpreted uniformly as indicating that a conductive tissue is
useless in water plants. By logical inference such plants were once
terrestrial but degeneration of the vascular system has accompanied adaptation to the aquatic habit. A very different interpretation may, however, easily be made. The significant fact is,
that even those plants which live wholly submerged and are without organs of attachment show at least the rudiments of a conducting system. But why should such plants have any vascular
tissue at all? The epidermis is thin and permeable to solutions of
mineral matter, the tissues are usually only a few cells in thickness,
and in plants without roots, as *Ceratophyllum*, absorption must take
place in such a large number of the cells that a special tissue system
for the conduction of water is unnecessary.

An aquatic environment does not favor the great differentiation
of tissue characteristic of terrestrial plants. When in water plants
very simple imitations of the land plant structure are found, this
condition does not represent the extreme that has been developed
through a long succession of aquatic ancestors, but is to be regarded as indicating the tendency toward simplification made
necessary by increasing adaptation to the water life. From this
point of view the conductive tissue is becoming, rather than has
become, unnecessary. So it seems probable from anatomical study
that a simplification of the vascular system is in progress which, if
continued, will eventually lead to a suppression or total disappearance of special conductive tissue. At present, however, it may
safely be said that the majority of our larger water plants have
need of vascular tissue.

The leaves of water plants may be either floating or submerged.
Some plants have only the floating or only the submerged, while
several species have both kinds on the same plant at the same time.
The floating leaves do not show a great variety of form and tend to
be elliptical, oval, or round, while some are shield-shaped. Since
an aquatic environment is more uniform one cannot expect as

great variety in leaf form as is noticeable in land plants. The floating leaves are usually borne on a stalk which in most cases is flexible, so that the leaf blade may rise or fall with the fluctuating level of the water. The exposed surface of the floating leaf is usually waterproof. This is provided for in a variety of ways. In some cases a waxy coating renders the skin nearly impermeable. This is true with some of the *Potamo-*

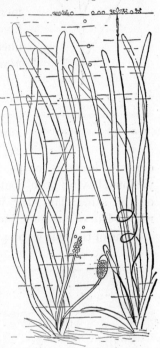

getons. In some cases a coating of very delicate hairs so abundant as to enclose an envelope of air prevents the water from actually touching the epidermis proper. This is to be ob-served in the case of *Nelumbo.* Some-times one may see drops of water standing on the surface of such leaves and when the leaf is submerged and then allowed to emerge the water rolls off leaving the leaf apparently dry.

In striking contrast to the floating leaves the submerged ones seldom have a distinct blade and stalk. This is consistent with the general tendency to uniformity of structure under a uniform environment. *Vallisneria* (Fig. 254) may be regarded as show-ing a typical ribbon form which is well adapted to life under water, because it is so flexible and is thus able to endure swiftly flowing currents or

FIG. 254. *Vallisneria spiralis.* Staminate and pistillate plants, showing the long rib-bon leaves which are all blade and have no apparent stalk. (After Kerner and Oliver.)

wave movements. In some species, as that of *Potamogeton per-foliatus*, the submerged leaves are expanded into blades but are sessile on the stem, that is, are without a leaf stalk. The latter would be of no advantage to leaves which are not intended to reach the surface. They would tend to make the plant top-heavy and easily uprooted by a sudden rush of water. Moreover, it is quite probable that a greater exposure of leaf surface is nec-essary because of the diminished light under water. Linear or thread-like leaves are very common and may be the only kind occurring on the plant, as in *Potamogeton pectinatus*, or they may occur

on the same plant together with floating leaves, as in *Potamogeton natans* (Fig. 255). It is to be noticed that most of the monocotyledons conform to some one of the types mentioned, while the dicotyledons seem to favor another habit, such as is seen in the finely dissected leaves of *Ranunculus aquatilis*, *Myriophyllum spicatum*, *Bidens beckii* (Fig. 256), and *Ceratophyllum*. Among the dicotyledons in which both floating and submerged leaves are present, as in *Ranunculus* and *Cabomba* (Fig.

FIG. 255. *Potamogeton natans.* One floating leaf and three submerged leaves, representing the thread-like form of the monocotyledonous type of submerged leaf. (After Göbel.)

257), the tendency to finely dissected leaves is conspicuous, while in the monocotyledons, having both floating and submerged leaves on the same plant, the latter tend to assume the ribbon-like or the long linear outline, as in Fig. 255.

Some of the true water plants, as *Bidens beckii* and

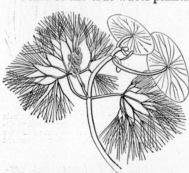

Myriophyllum spicatum, support a vertical portion of the main stem considerably above the water surface and on this emersed portion ordinary aerial leaves are borne. It is some-

FIG. 256. *Bidens beckii.* Submerged leaves finely dissected. Emersed leaves entire or slightly serrate. One whorl shows the transition stage from the submerged to the emersed form. ½ natural size. (After Göbel.)

FIG. 257. *Cabomba.* Floating leaves, entire and peltate. Submerged leaves with finely dissected blades typical of Dicotyledons. (After Göbel.)

times possible in the case of such plants to find leaves which seem to be midway in form between the finely cut submerged leaves and the bladed emersed ones, so it seems probable that the submerged leaves are to be regarded as exposed leaves which have changed in form because life under water requires such modification. Such a modification has been produced experimentally. Some plants in nature seem to be able to bring forth either floating or submerged leaves or both as the conditions imposed seem to require. If growing shoots of *Ranunculus aquatilis* are not allowed to reach the surface of the water only the segmented leaves develop. If specimens of *Potamogeton heterophyllus* are suddenly left stranded by receding water the floating leaves may persist and be succeeded by more floating leaves, thus enabling the plant to live for a considerable time, often persisting until the rising water returns. In such a case the submerged leaves soon die from exposure, but the floating leaves have, on the upper surface, stomata which, in cooperation with the thick cuticle, are able to regulate the loss of water.

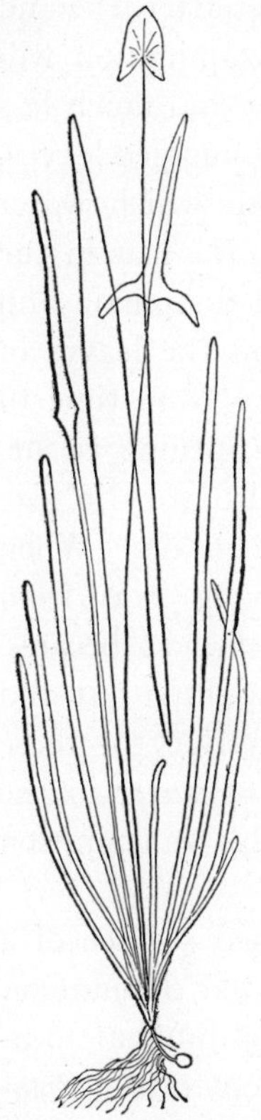

Some of the amphibious species, such as *Sagittaria natans*, are especially variable in leaf form. The early seedling leaves are bladeless and ribbon-like, while the later leaves which rise above the surface have a distinct blade and stalk (Figs. 258 and 259). From the evident plasticity of these plants it may be supposed that the form of leaf to be produced is not predetermined but depends upon conditions. Wächter has experimented with *Sagittaria natans* and finds that plants having the ribbon-like leaves may be prevented from later producing bladed leaves either by reducing the intensity of light or by partial starvation.

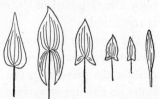

FIG. 258. *Sagittaria natans*. Transition from ribbon-like to bladed leaves. ¾ natural size. (After Wächter.)

FIG. 259. *Sagittaria chinensis*. Transition from bladed to ribbon-like leaves. The reversion has been produced by cutting off the roots repeatedly. ¾ natural size. (After Wächter.)

Plants which have already formed bladed leaves may be induced in like manner to bring forth the ribbon form. In view of such results it is not unreasonable to suppose that both the floating and the submerged leaves may easily have developed during the past from aerial leaves and that both kinds are useful to many species.

Many of the delicate submerged plants will wither rapidly when taken from the water and exposed to the air. This occurs because the outer layer of tissue or epidermis, as it is called, is thin and allows the water contained in the plant rapidly to pass into the air as vapor. If a plant which bears both floating and submerged leaves is exposed it will be noticed that the latter wilt and dry out much more rapidly than the former. Examination will show the cuticle of the floating leaves to be thicker and much less permeable to water, if at all so, than that of the submerged leaves, while special openings may be discovered through which water vapor escapes instead of passing off all over the surface as in the submerged leaves. These special openings are called stomata and are the same in structure as those which occur on the leaves of land plants. The size of these openings may vary from time to time according to the needs of the plant. Each opening is surrounded by two cells, called guard cells, which also vary in size and shape according to the amount of water they contain. When turgid they become somewhat kidney-shaped, curving away from the opening and thus making it larger. When flaccid because there is little water in the plant they tend to straighten out and thus make the opening smaller. Thus, by the activity of these stomata whose action depends upon the amount of water in the plant, the amount of water passing from the plant by transpiration is regulated.

The number of stomata occurring on the exposed surface of a floating leaf may be quite large. One author counted the number of stomata present in the area of 1 sq. mm. at five different locations on the upper surface of the floating leaves of one of the *Potamogetons*. He found a minimum of 216 and a maximum of 276 with an average of 255 per sq. mm.

It is evident that stomata are intended for leaves which must endure exposure to the air, but they do occur, though rarely, on the submerged leaves also (Fig. 260). Sometimes only one or two submerged leaves of a given plant will have them and again several specimens of the same species may be examined without finding any at all. The only explanation for the occurrence of such structures on submerged leaves is, that the ancestors of the plants bearing them were adapted to life on land or at least lived under exposure to loss of water by transpiration.

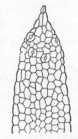

Other openings in the leaf have also been found in some species. These occur at the apex of the leaf more frequently in the submerged leaves than in the floating ones. The opening does not show any special structure, as is true of stomata, and is formed by the decay and falling away of the tissue at the apex, so that the conductive vessels in the veins of the leaf become exposed to, and in direct communication with, the water. In some cases this disintegration of tissue at the apex may go so far as to change to a marked degree the shape of the apex, making it rounded instead of pointed (Figs. 261 and 262).

Fig. 260. *Zannichellia repens.* Submerged leaf showing stomata. × about 100. (After Sauvageau.)

The formation of the opening seems to occur before the leaf matures but is seldom found on the young leaves. In addition to the

Fig. 261. *Zostera nana.* Apical portion of a mature submerged leaf, showing the change of form at the apex due to decay of apical tissue. × about 40. (After Sauvageau.)

species already known as bearing these openings the writer may mention that of *Vallisneria spiralis* on whose half-grown leaves he has observed them. Some authors have suggested that the passage of water through the conductive tissue is facilitated and that the excretion is aided. This is really a supposition and has never been proved.

The presence of an earthy coating on the leaves and stems of some water plants may be commonly observed. This mineral incrustation appears like a coating of mud on the leaf in many cases, while in others it is not so conspicuous and is only noticeable when the plant is handled. Only the submerged organs seem to bear the incrustation, even the lower surface of floating leaves being less favorable to its formation and much less frequently bearing it. *Potamogeton pectinatus* is seldom, if ever, incrusted, while other species of this genus usually are. *Chara* is

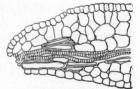

Fig. 262. *Potamogeton densus.* Leaf in longitudinal section. The decayed tissue has fallen away, leaving the vessels exposed to the surrounding water. × about 135. (After Sauvageau.)

seldom found without an incrustation, while *Vallisneria* is never found with it, although the two plants frequently grow side by side and essentially under the same conditions. The leaves of *Vallisneria* are very flexible and almost always bending with the current, hence, a deposit of solid matter is prevented. It seems probable, however, that the physiological processes going on in the plant determine largely whether or not an incrustation is to be formed. The coatings are not firmly fastened to the leaf and may be easily scaled off or loosened by bending the leaf. The presence of the coatings seems to make little difference to the plant as the tissue beneath appears of a healthy green color though frequently of more delicate tint than the unincrusted areas of the leaf.

In all cases known the substance of the incrustation has been found chemically to be the neutral carbonate of lime, which, of course, is insoluble. Microscopic examination by polarized light has revealed the presence of minute crystals in the incrustation formed on *Chara* and the same may possibly prove to be the case with plants of other families. The chemistry of the formation of this incrustation is not known. There is usually present in the water the soluble bicarbonate of lime which by loss of carbon dioxid is changed to the neutral or insoluble carbonate. Some have supposed that as the plants withdraw carbon dioxide from the water to use in the process of starch manufacture, this insoluble neutral carbonate is formed and deposited on the leaf. This process may be expressed chemically thus:

$$\overset{\text{Soluble}}{CaH_2\,(CO_3)_2} = \overset{\text{Insoluble}}{CaCO_3} + CO_2 + H_2O$$

Another explanation may be that the oxygen liberated by the plant in starch making acts catalytically upon the bicarbonate to change it to the neutral carbonate. The former process would more likely occur in water containing a larger amount of the carbonate in solution which would be precipitated except for the solvent action of the carbon dioxid in the water. The latter process would be more probable in water containing very small amounts of the bicarbonate which would remain in solution in the absence of the carbon dioxid.

Since the escape of oxygen and withdrawal of carbon dioxid are simultaneously in progress during the time the plant is making starch, both processes may operate to precipitate the neutral carbonate. If the plants secrete an alkaline carbonate this would immediately upon its escape from the plant decompose the soluble bicarbonate in the water with the formation of the neutral insoluble carbonate. It is uncertain, however, that such an alkaline carbonate is secreted by the plant and not much emphasis can be placed upon this hypothesis. The most recent explanation rests upon the discovery that a soluble calcium salt of succinic acid is present in the cell sap of *Chara*. The occurrence of this salt in the sap of other plants has not been determined, but as succinic acid is a very probable by-product in the ordinary processes of plant physiology, its wide distribution may reasonably be expected. As the calcium salt escapes from *Chara* by osmosis it is most likely decomposed with the formation of the insoluble carbonate.

Possibly the incrustation offers protection to the plant in some way, but this seems hardly probable, and at present one can only say that its formation is a consequence of processes in the plant and that its presence is of little benefit or of harm to the plant.

Various plant organs are often found to be covered with a gelatinous coating. This may occur on the lower surface of floating leaves as in species of *Nymphaea*. Young leaves and growing tips are often encased with it. In the axils of leaves arising in a rosette around a shortened stem it is likely to occur. Seed coats are often slimy and in some fruits the seeds at maturity are embedded in a mass of gelatinous substance which on swelling ruptures the ovary walls and allows the seeds an exit. Some plants, as *Brasenia peltata*, have special glands to furnish the slime, but often, as in leaf axils, there are no distinct structures for furnishing this substance. Many of the algae are embedded in a mass of slime just as the eggs of frogs are. Amphibious plants and those subject to temporary exposure, as in the case of plants which grow in tide-water, are doubtless protected from too rapid loss of water by such covering. It may also serve as a protection for young buds and leaves against devouring animals. It is quite possible that the gelatinous masses in which seeds are found embedded are of very different composition from the slime which occurs on the lower surface of a floating leaf. The occurrence of the latter may be accidental so far as the plant is concerned and have little importance in its welfare. In the algae and even with delicate parts

of higher plants such a coating may serve to retard the exchange of liquids, thus preventing plasmolysis, or in like manner it may enable the plant to maintain a cell sap of much greater density than that of the surrounding water (Fig. 263).

FIG. 263. *Brasenia peltata.* The young buds and petioles are surrounded by a gelatinous envelope of slime. (After Göbel.)

Quite a number of terrestrial species are especially adapted for retaining and digesting as food small animals which are so unfortunate as to wander into the traps borne by the plant. Few aquatic species have acquired this habit but there are some members of the genus *Utricularia* remarkable for the special organs developed to secure animal food. The bladders are generally regarded as modified leaves, and structures resembling stomata have been found on them in some cases. The bladders have small openings guarded by hairs and closed by a sort of trap-

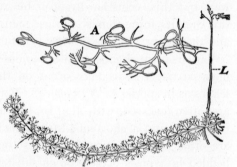

FIG. 264. *Utricularia minor.* Numerous bladders on the leaves. *A*, enlarged bladders. *L*, flower-stalk rising above the water. The main leaf axis or stem is to be imagined as horizontal in the water. (After Glück.)

door which permits small animals in the water to enter but which prevents any escape for the victims (Fig. 264).

These plants may float free, so far as roots are concerned, but, as with *Ceratophyllum*, accidental attachment or rather anchorage frequently occurs through entanglement with other plants or by being partly buried in the mud.

All of the species raise the inflorescence above the water and *Utricularia inflata* sends out whorls of leaves with inflated petioles from the flower-stalk to serve as floaters. As there are land species of *Utricularia* which also have bladders, it seems quite probable that the aquatic forms have been derived from the land species.

Some authors have suggested that, being without roots and requiring more nitrogenous food than can be obtained from substances in solution in the water, these bladders have been developed to secure animal food. It is just as probable that the aquatic forms are merely using structures that were characteristic of their ancestors, which were land plants. Why the land species have developed such structures has never been demonstrated.

Few, if any, of the flowering water plants depend upon seed reproduction. Vegetative reproduction by runners, tubers, buds, stem fragments, etc., is particularly prominent among these aquatics. Seed reproduction is, however, common and many are the contrivances utilized for securing the transfer of pollen and cross pollination. In some few cases, as *Ceratophyllum*, *Naias*, and *Zannichellia*, pollination occurs under water and the pollen is transferred by the water. The wind is an important agent in the transfer of pollen especially for many of the Potamogetons (Fig. 265).

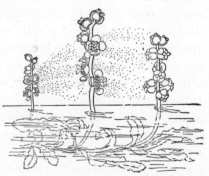

FIG. 265. *Potamogeton crispus.* Pollen distribution by the wind. (After Kerner.)

The stamens and pistils of *Potamogeton crispus* do not mature on the same plant at the same time. As the pistils mature first they must receive pollen from some other plant and by the time the stamens of their own plant are ready to shed pollen, they have been pollinated and are no longer receptive to pollen. The pollination of *Vallisneria spiralis* has become a classic illustration of the remarkable capacity for adaptation possessed by some plants. The individuals of this plant are of two kinds — one bearing stamens and the other bearing pistils only. The staminate flower cluster is enclosed in a sac which finally ruptures and the staminate flowers immediately rise to the water surface. After a short exposure to the air the flowers reflex the sepals to form a little boat which floats about with the dehiscing stamens exposed to the air, so that whenever the boat lodges by a pistillate flower some pollen is deposited upon the receptive stigma. The pistillate flower is solitary upon a long stalk, which, rising from the leaf axils, elongates very rapidly until the flower floats on the water surface, when the stigma is soon exposed to receive the pollen from the passing boats of staminate flowers (Fig. 254, page 181, and Fig. 266).

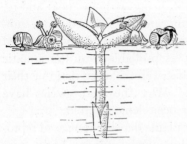

FIG. 266. *Vallisneria spiralis.*

Sometimes where *Vallisneria* is abundant the water surface is completely covered by the staminate flowers, just as *Lemna*, the duckweed, often covers certain areas. As soon as the pistillate flower is fertilized the stalk contracts to a spiral, thus drawing the flower under water to mature the fruit.

To what extent *Vallisneria* is propagated by seed is not known. It has been necessary for the writer to take hundreds of these plants from the lake for experimental purposes and a seedling has not as yet been found. The plants growing in water 2.5 to 3.5 meters deep frequently do not flower at all but readily propagate by runners.

As previously mentioned, *Zannichellia palustris* conducts its pollination under water (Fig. 267). The staminate and pistillate flowers stand in the same axil. The filament of the solitary staminate flower elongates to raise the anthers above the stigmas of the pistillate flowers. The pollen is heavy enough to slowly sink after escaping from the stamens and in still water may pollinate the flower of its own plant, but in running water is usually carried to a neighboring plant.

FIG. 267. *Zannichellia palustris.* Pollination occurs under water. Anthers are raised above the stigmas by the long filament. × about 8. (After Göbel.)

The pollen grains of aquatic plants differ in one particular from those of land forms in that they have only one coat. Perhaps this is because they are little exposed and do not need protection against a rapid loss of water.

Very few species develop a showy corolla under water, but *Heteranthera graminea* is one which has a fairly conspicuous flower under water.

Most of the attached flowering plants are perennial, and vegetative propagation is very common. *Naias flexilis* is an annual.

There is a period of rest for water plants just as for land plants and as in the latter so in the former this period occurs during the cold season. Not all of our perennial aquatics make special preparation for passing the winter, and some, as *Ranunculus aquatilis*, *Ruppia*, and *Zannichellia*, may be found in normal condition even during the winter. The drifting fragments of *Ceratophyllum* often become attached by accidental lodgment and pass the winter in the vegetative condition.

Some Potamogetons, *Ranunculus aquatilis*, and others will continue to grow uninterruptedly all winter if planted in aquaria and kept at favorable temperature in the greenhouse.

Vegetative reproduction is the conspicuous method of propagation among the larger aquatics, and although many of the species produce seed there are few which could not easily persist if seed production were to be discontinued. In some cases fruit formation has been abandoned. *Elodea* and *Potamogeton robbinsii* rarely fruit.

The rhizomes of most of the water plants are well developed and represent a considerable portion of the vegetation. In some cases, as in *Potamogeton perfoliatus*, if a plant be taken carefully from the soil fully one-half the fresh weight of the plant will be found to consist of roots and rhizomes. With the approach of cold weather the stems and leaves gradually disintegrate but the rhizomes remain alive and pass the winter buried in the mud and in the spring send up shoots from the buds previously formed (Fig. 268). *Heteranthera graminea* has long black rhizomes that are cord-like and often quite tough. The young plants seem in some cases to rise from the runners adventitiously. Among

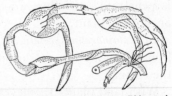

Fig. 268. *Potamogeton pectinatus.* Rhizomes in November with winter buds. (After Irmisch.)

the Nymphaeaceae large tubers are common and young plants of *Nymphaea alba* may sometimes be found floating about attached to a tuber.

The swamp plants, such as *Typha* and *Scirpus*, also have extensive rhizome systems which are important means of wintering and acquiring new territory.

Some plants have winter buds or hibernacula which form in autumn, separate from the parent plant, often drift to a new locality, and finally sink to pass the winter in a dormant condition only to commence a new generation the following spring (Fig. 269). Such winter buds are commonly formed by *Utricularia, Potamogeton crispus, P. zosterifolius, P. pusillus, P. frasii,* and possibly others. The sinking of those winter buds may be accomplished by the intercellular spaces becoming injected with water, as is the case with the autumn plants of *Lemna minor*.

Fig. 269. *Potamogeton crispus.* Winter bud germinating in the spring. A rhizome with roots and two new shoots has developed. (After Treviranus.)

Aside from special organs of propagation quite a few plants acquire new stations by means of the fragments of vegetative parts accidentally set adrift. It is common to find floating stems of *Elodea*, from the nodes of which adventitious roots have risen. These roots grow straight downward and the stem makes little growth in length while the roots are seeking the soil. A fragment of *Elodea* was found floating in Lake Erie which had an adventitious unbranched root 45 cms. in length. The roots do not branch in some species until the soil is penetrated and then a system of lateral branches develops to anchor the plant.

In *Potamogeton perfoliatus* the adventitious roots usually arise from the nodes of new rhizomes which develop in the leaf axils of the cutting.

With land plants the development of roots on the seedling is as marked as the growth of stem and leaves, but in several water plants the root development is subordinated to that of the stem and leaves, while in some species a genuine functional root is not developed. The rudiment of a root may be present as a part of the embryo in the seed, but in germination this rudiment is suppressed in its development and never gets to be a real root.

The seeds of *Ranunculus aquatilis* will germinate either on land or in water but the development of the

seedling is not alike in each case (Fig. 270). The seed leaves are similar, except that those of the land seedling are a little wider in proportion. The true leaves of

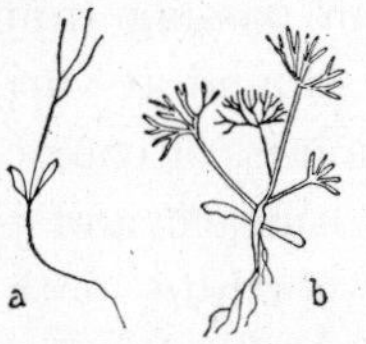

FIG. 270. *Ranunculus aquatilis*. A. Seedling germinating in water. B. Seedling germinating on land. (After Askenasy.)

the land plants have broad, segmented blades, while the water form has only a few thread-like branches with little indication of a distinct blade.

FIG. 271. *Potamogeton lucens*. Seedling with temporary primary root bearing cluster of root-hairs. (After Warming.)

Potamogeton lucens and *Naias major* send out a primary root from the seed upon which a cluster of root-hairs soon develops to help anchor the plant. But this primary root is not lasting and is soon succeeded by adventitious roots which spring from the joints of the runners which developed in the meantime (Figs. 271 and 272).

Ceratophyllum furnishes a very interesting instance of suppressed root development. There is present in the embryo of the seed a rudimentary root, but it never develops into an organ of attachment or serves for the entrance of mineral salts. When the seed germinates this rudiment of a root pushes out far enough to let the plumule rise from between the emerging cotyledons and then its growth practically stops (Fig. 273). So far as known,

FIG. 272. *Naias major*. Seedling with temporary primary root bearing cluster of root-hairs. (After Irmisch.)

adventitious roots never appear on this plant.

FIG. 273. *Ceratophyllum demersum*. Seedling with cotyledon, radicle and first leaf pair. (After Schleiden.)

In *Nuphar* and *Brasenia* the seedling escapes from the seed by pushing out a plug which before germination occupies the passage intended for the exit of the young plant.

The seeds of *Utricularia* commence to germinate in the muddy substratum, but as the embryo emerges the newly formed tissues are so buoyant that the seedling rises to the water surface often carrying with it the remains of the old seed.

By vertical distribution is understood that which exists in a plane more or less perpendicular to the earth's surface and may be illustrated by the distribution one may observe in passing from valley to mountain-top or by comparison of species found at various depths in lake or ocean. Horizontal distribution is, of course, in a plane more or less conformable to the earth's surface and is such as one notices in passing from east to west or north to south, etc. Now the factors which determine the horizontal distribution of water plants are: first, the chemical composition of the water, a factor which gives the two large divisions of fresh and salt water plants; second, temperature which gives zones of plant life such as arctic, temperate, tropical, etc.; third, competition among the plants themselves, a factor which is likewise influential in vertical distribution though perhaps to a less degree; and fourth, the nature of the substratum, which is, of course, most influential in the distribution of species which grow rooted to the bottom.

To what extent chemical composition of the water is a factor in the distribution of fresh-water plants cannot at present be stated. Sulphur springs and waters having unusual composition are not, of course, fresh water. By the latter term is understood such as occurs in the rivers and lakes and such as may be used as drink by the animals, so far as chemical composition is concerned. Such waters differ, of course, in the quantity and quality of constituents; but whether such differences are in themselves independent of other factors, sufficient to determine distribution, cannot at present be stated.

Suppose we should find that the water of some lake in Wisconsin is considerably different in chemical composition from that of a lake in New York and a species of *Potamogeton*, for example, which is abundant in the Wisconsin lake but unknown to the waters of the New York lake, be taken to the New York lake and planted there. If this plant grows well in the New York lake we would say that, other conditions being equal, the difference in chemical composition of the water in the two lakes is not a determining factor in the horizontal distribution and that the absence of the

Wisconsin species in the New York lake must be attributed to some other cause or causes. Experimental evidence is lacking for stating to what extent the chemical composition of the water becomes a determining factor in fresh water.

The important influence of temperature on distribution is at once apparent, although the influence exerted by it is much farther reaching than is at first supposed. Of course, the forms of the arctic waters would be "cooked" by the heat of the tropical waters. It has recently been ascertained that the colder waters support a more abundant plankton than the tropical waters, and one writer has explained this fact upon the basis that the colder waters are richer in nitrates and nitrites because the decomposition of organic matter proceeds much more slowly and the organisms causing decay are not so numerous and less active. Such considerations offer a glimpse of how indirectly, yet effectively, the various factors may operate to determine distribution.

The competition of species for space may be considered a factor in horizontal distribution, although it operates quite locally and does not work to modify the flora of large areas. *Chara* is infrequent on the alluvial bottoms where other species are present in abundance, but this is not because it prefers poorer soils but because it is prevented from occupying the soil of its choice by the other species.

The character of the substratum is an important factor; in fact, it is possible to predict the nature of the bottom from the species that are found growing in it. Among the islands of western Lake Erie *Potamogeton heterophyllus* is common on the reefs and pebbly shores but is not noticeable in the coves with a good soil substratum and so prominent is it in the former places that its presence may be considered characteristic of the flora.

Light cannot be counted a factor in horizontal distribution because there is always sufficient illumination within the limits established by other factors. In vertical distribution light is probably the most important factor. The amount of illuminating power lost in passing to a given depth is quite variable in different waters. Fol and Sarasin found in Lake Geneva, in September, light at 170 meters, and at 120 meters a photographic plate was darkened.

In April they were able to detect light at 250 meters. Of course the clearness of the water has much to do with the penetration of light rays. One can see deeper into the water of Lake Superior or of Lake Huron than into that of Lake Erie. The latter is shallower with much of the bottom clay, so that the water always holds minute particles in suspension which greatly interfere with the penetration of light. The red and yellow rays contained in the beams of sunlight are more readily absorbed than those of higher refrangibility, as the blue and violet, but whether this is of any importance in determining the vertical distribution cannot be stated.

Schimper gives 6 meters as the maximum depth for phanerogams, although the lower forms, such as *Chara* and *Nitella*, are said to have been found as deep as 30 meters. Temperature is of little importance because the variations are so slight within the limits established by light. This is not so much the case with the free-swimming, lower forms, but only the larger plants are considered here.

It is impracticable to attempt an elaborate classification of water plants according to their habitat or adaptation to environment. In some localities distinct zones of vegetation may be observed which are apparently determined by the depth of water. Magnin was able to distinguish four zones in the lakes of the Jura. First is the littoral, with a maximum depth of 3 meters, which may be divided into Phragmitetum with *Phragmites communis* as typical and Scirpetum with *Scirpus lacustris*, sedges, *Equisetum*, etc., as representative. A second zone, the Nupharetum, extending to 3 or 4 meters, is composed of plants with large floating leaves such as are common among the Nymphaeaceae. The third zone, the Pota-mogetonetum, in water 4 to 6 meters deep, is characterized by presence of several species of *Potamogeton*, especially *perfoliatus*, *crispus*, *lucens*, and others. The fourth zone, Characetum, occupies deep water, 8 to 12 meters, where *Chara*, *Naias*, and some mosses cover the bottom.

The flora of almost any lake may be regarded as composed of zones and even rivers and small streams show plant societies, but a grouping for one locality is frequently inapplicable to some other, and the depth of water for a species varies much according to clearness and other factors which may be incidental to a particular region.

It is possible to make a general grouping which will indicate the important conditions and varieties of environment. To some one of the groups thus established any aquatic plant may be assigned.

I. Plants without attachment.
   (a) Plankton, free swimming, microscopic.
   (b) Macroscopic, possibility of attachment by accidental lodgment, as *Lemna, Ceratophyllum*, filamentous algae common on plants in coves.

II. Plants attached to substratum.
   (a) Submerged, algae as *Chara* and *Cladophora*, and phanerogams as *Vallisneria, Elodea*.
   (b) Partially submerged, usually with floating or emersed leaves, as *Nymphaea, Bidens beckii*.

III. Swamp plants or marsh forms with roots and rhizomes under water but leaves usually emersed though able to endure inundation and temporary submersion.

Sometimes representatives of each of these three classes may be found in one small lake, especially if the water gradually deepens from a marsh or low shore as in Lake St. Clair where the wholly submerged species become so abundant as to form an aquatic meadow. *Potamogeton perfoliatus, P. foliosus, P. zosteraefolius, Vallisneria, Naias, Chara, Nitella, Elodea*, and *Myriophyllum* may be found in dense patches covering the bottom. In such formations the struggle for space must be severe and from observations during three summers on Lake Erie I should say that *Vallisneria* is a conqueror. *Naias flexilis* may be found in distinct formations in which other species are very infrequent but being an annual the creeping rootstocks of *Vallisneria* may easily invade its territory.

In many of the small inland lakes the water plants are important agents as soil collectors. The aquatic meadows tend to filter the water so that suspended matter sinks to the bottom. As the lake gradually becomes filled and the water grows more shallow a succession of plant societies occurs. The aquatic meadows yield to the

Potamogetons with floating leaves and especially the Nymphaeaceae which are followed by amphibious species until finally the
bog vegetation appears which may later support the ordinary
terrestrial plants.

It may be supposed that aquatic phanerogams have descended
from aquatic or from land species. The former supposition implies that the plants, as they are now, represent the maximum of
complexity in structure that has thus far developed. The latter
supposition implies that the simpler vascular system is not to be
considered as foreshadowing a more elaborate structure to be
evolved in the future but is a reduced form of more highly developed
structure present in the terrestrial ancestors. Perhaps some species have had land ancestors, while others have descended from
aquatic forms.

Considering the whole list of fresh-water plants, it is noteworthy
that the abundant groups are algae and phanerogams. Bryophytes
and pteridophytes do occur, but infrequently in comparison with
the former groups, the thallophytes and spermatophytes, which
include a large percentage of aquatic vegetation.

Would the great plant groups be represented in this proportion
if the evolution of aquatic forms had proceeded as in the case of
land plants? Does not a water environment insure greater uniformity of conditions and would not the evolution proceed more
slowly and the intermediate forms more likely persist in such environment? How could the great groups of monocotyledons and
dicotyledons ever become differentiated from ancestors living
wholly submerged? How could the seed habit so essentially like
that of land plants ever be acquired by the descendants of submerged forms? On the other hand if water forms have been
derived from land forms, why are not the bryophytes and pteridophytes which are frequent in moist localities better represented
in the aquatic flora? The change from aquatic structure to terrestrial must be much more difficult than from terrestrial to aquatic.
When a water plant is suddenly exposed, the loss of water by drying
is so rapid that the plant must die, while a land plant may endure
submersion for a considerable period. In one case the change of
environment causes a sudden demand for a complex vascular system

that the plant is unable to supply. In the other case the land plant may persist and gradually reduce in complexity structures already present. Thus it is that the reduction of the vascular system has proceeded in the same manner in both the dicotyledons and monocotyledons, so that the simplest stem structure is alike for members of either group. In *Ceratophyllum* the vascular system has become so simplified that its dicotyledonous relationship cannot be established by the stem structure.

How is the presence of stomata on submerged leaves to be accounted for? It can hardly be supposed that they are developing in anticipation of the time when the species is to have a transpiring surface. More likely is it that these stomata are reminders of the time when the species had an exposed surface.

In the genus *Utricularia* there are land as well as water species and the presence of bladders characterizes both varieties. It is hardly probable that submerged plants accustomed to the food supplied in solution by the surrounding water should acquire an appetite for animal food and develop such elaborate and unique organs for securing nitrogenous nourishment.

In some cases, as in *Lemna*, the ancestry is not so obvious and convincing evidence is difficult to obtain.

The pollination of *Zannichellia* under water has been previously mentioned (Fig. 267). In such cases the evolution of stamens and pistils cannot be regarded as having occurred in wholly submerged plants. Much less difficult it is to understand how land plants with stamens and pistils already developed could gradually become adapted to an aquatic habit before these organs would disappear by reduction.

It is now known that the roots of several of our genuine aquatic species bear root-hairs whose presence certainly testifies to the absorbing activity of the roots and the lingering terrestrial habits necessitating such organs.

It must be noted that the foregoing discussion is purely theoretical and the intention has been to awaken interest in the study of the aquatic flora rather than to offer a theory of origin for which any originality could be claimed.

Experimental evidence may be obtained that roots are organs

for absorption.[1]   It is possible by means of very simple apparatus
to actually measure the water which a root absorbs in a given time.
In one experiment of the writer's a small cutting 20 centimeters
long bearing a root 14 centimeters long was used and this unbranched single root absorbed 5 cubic centimeters of water in
24 hours.

Another method can be used to demonstrate that roots are
organs of absorption.   A certain substance, namely, lithium nitrate,
which is soluble in water, is offered in solution to the roots.   The
lithium in this compound burns with a rose red flame and very
small traces of this substance in plant tissue may be detected by
burning portions of the tissue and observing the color given to the
flame, and by using the spectroscope the test becomes very delicate.
In this method it is only necessary to enclose the root in a bottle
containing the lithium nitrate solution by means of a flexible
stopper made by saturating cotton in melted vaselin.   After a
time portions of the stem which could not possibly contain lithium,
unless it had passed to it from the roots, are burned and the flame
observed with the spectroscope.   Such tests have been made repeatedly and the presence of the lithium may always be traced
through the plant to whatever distance the tissue used in the
test allowed it to travel in the plant.   There can be no doubt
then but that the roots are organs for absorption and that substances absorbed by them are conducted upward into the stem and
leaves.   The distance that the lithium travels in a given tissue
probably does not represent exactly the rate of ascent of the upward current but indicates a rate of ascent which is less than that
of the water passage through the plant; that is, water travels
upward a little faster than the lithium which it holds in solution.

Mention has been made of the fact that when cuttings of *Ranunculus aquatilis* are left to drift in the water, new roots arise from
the stem at the nodes.   These roots grow directly downward and do
not branch until after penetrating the soil, when they then commence
to branch repeatedly, and as the main root pushes through the soil

---

[1] It is not strictly correct to speak of roots as organs for absorption. The structure of roots is such that solutions can pass into them. However, the term is so
commonly employed as to make it impracticable to use other phraseology here.

more branches are formed in succession. The following experiment seems to strongly indicate that light inhibits the formation of lateral branches of the roots and that the roots of drifting plants do not branch because of the exposure to the light. Five cuttings of equal length were mounted in bottles so that about 3 nodes of the stem were inside the bottle. Five similar cuttings were likewise mounted in bottles which were wrapped with black cloth so that the roots which developed from the nodes of the cutting inside the bottle were protected from the light. The darkened plants developed in all 22 roots having a total length of 1048 centimeters and bearing in all 73 branches. The plants exposed to light developed 28 roots, having a total length of 459 centimeters and bearing not one single branch. The influence of light is very evident.

There are two possible reasons why soil may be necessary for good growth. First, as a source of food and, second, as a substratum into which the roots can penetrate to anchor the plant. If the soil is not necessary as a source of food the ordinary water in which the plant grows should furnish sufficient food. If the soil is necessary only as a substratum to anchor the plant a clean washed sand substratum ought to do equally as well. Experiments along this line have been completed by the author and it has been found that soil is necessary for the good growth of every one of the plants tested. Clean washed sand cannot be substituted for soil without sacrifice of growth to the plant. It is reasonably certain that not one of our common water plants which naturally grows well rooted in a good soil bottom could live through an entire growing season if clean washed sand should be substituted for its ordinary soil substratum.

The behavior of *Ranunculus aquatilis* is interesting as indicating (figuratively speaking) an effort on the part of the plant to secure a soil attachment. This species lives wholly submerged in shallow, slowly flowing water. The leaves are finely divided and collapse when the plant is taken from the water. The stem branches freely, any branch being able to continue the growth of the plant if the main stem be removed. Roots may arise at any exposed node, except, perhaps, the terminal one. If a fragment a few internodes in length be detached and left floating, roots will spring forth from the nodes or joints of the stem in from 6 to 10 days. While the roots are lengthening toward the bottom the stem does not increase in length but quickly resumes its growth after the root has penetrated the soil. More roots then arise from the newer nodes of the stem and as they also enter the soil the plant is drawn farther down and finally becomes firmly anchored. The roots of such fragments do not branch before reaching the soil but do so very shortly after the substratum is penetrated. Numerous lateral roots then arise and form in succession as the main root advances.

The roots are well supplied with hairs; those arising from the floating fragments are often covered almost their entire length with root-hairs. In one instance a root was found to be clothed with root-hairs for a distance of 45 centimeters, which was practically its entire length. Since this plant ordinarily grows rooted in the soil whatever growth it makes under natural conditions must be regarded as the normal growth and there is no escape from the conclusion that the growth becomes abnormal when sand is substituted for soil.

How is the superior growth of plants rooted in the soil to be accounted for? Is it possible that the soil furnishes plants rooted in it with food materials that are not available to plants suspended in the water standing over it? In 1850 it was discovered that liquid manure loses its color if drained through a layer of soil sufficiently thick. Not only does the solution lose color but the organic and inorganic matter originally in it is considerably reduced after filtering through the soil. This property or capacity of soil to withdraw salts from solution is now well established although not well understood. For a time authors were not agreed as to whether the retention or fixation of salts by the soil is a chemical or a physical process. Now it is generally understood that both chemical and physical processes operate to this end. Some substances seem to be held much more firmly by the soil than others. Various investigations go to show that most soils absorb the oxids, salts of the alkalis and alkaline earths of potassium, ammonium, magnesium, sodium, and calcium in the

order given. It must be remembered, however, that this retention of dissolved substance by the soil is neither absolute nor permanent. We may suppose that in the case of a lake there are two
opposing processes operating in which the soil on the one hand
tends to withdraw salts from the water and retain them, while the
water on the other hand tends to bring salts from the soil into
solution. As a consequence of those two processes the lake water
contains certain salts in much greater proportion than others
which seem to be firmly held by the soil. Just how such conditions influence the plant is only partially known.

It seems as though the substances needed by the plant are the
ones most firmly retained by the soil, — especially the nitrogen,
phosphorous, and potassium compounds, — and yet it is hardly
possible to say that the water does not contain enough of those
substances in solution for the larger plants. While plants cannot
select certain substances and reject others they can to a certain
extent regulate the amount of a substance which they absorb.
It is evident that all of the substances absolutely necessary for
the growth of plants must be present in the water in solution
because there are so many forms which live as freely swimming
objects and depend wholly upon the water in which they live for
food. *Lemna*, the so-called duckweed, lives in the water and depends upon the water only for food (mineral), but *Lemna* has
been analyzed and found to contain substances in much greater
proportion than does the water in which it grows. One investigator found the ash of this plant to contain 13.16 per cent of potassium, and 8.73 per cent of phosphoric acid, while the mineral residue obtained by evaporating some of the water in which the *Lemna*
was growing contained those substances in the respective proportions of 3.97 per cent and 2.619 per cent. However, the fact that
Lemna can obtain all the food necessary from the water alone and
that some other plants must be rooted in the soil to thrive is no
more remarkable than the fact that some animals are herbivorous
while others are carnivorous.

Water plants may be found growing in clayey, sandy, gravelly,
or loamy soil. From field observation one would say that the
loamy soil supports the greatest variety of species. Wherever the

soil is very sandy the species may be abundant and likewise where the substratum is distinctively clay or gravel. From field observation alone it would hardly be possible to say that the quality of the soil is the determining factor, because sand and gravel are more common where other factors come in to influence growth and species selection. The loamy soil is most abundant in the coves and bayous where the water is quiet and it is in just such places that plants make good growth and wealth of species abounds. Plants which would perish in exposed situations make excellent growth in the protected coves and we cannot be certain from field observation whether the difference is to be attributed to the soil or to the more favorable locality. By direct experiment, however, it is not difficult to ascertain what quality of substratum favors growth. In such experiments it is very desirable to have conditions as nearly like those in nature as possible. Three types of soil were selected, clayey, sandy, and loamy. A large rectangular glass aquarium was used to contain a substratum of each one of the given soil types. Then the three aquaria were placed upon a submerged platform so that the aquaria themselves were also submerged. This arrangement made the aquaria similar in all conditions except as to the quality of soil, and differences in the growth of plants in each aquarium could be very easily referred to the varying quality of soil. Two types of plants were tested in this way — one was *Vallisneria*, a typical water plant of the phanerogams, and *Chara*, one of the higher algae. The latter does not have roots but simple structure called rhizoids which help to secure attachment. With both of these plants the best growth was made in the loamy soil and the poorest in the clay soil, while the sandy soil which of course contained some organic débris supported a medium growth. In the case of *Chara* an equal number of plants of equal size were planted so that the dry weight of the total growth in each aquarium might be compared. If the poorest growth in clay be taken as one, then that in sand would be about 2.06, while that in the loamy soil would be about 3.33. The total dry weight is of course a fair indication of the relative amount of growth made and there can now be no doubt but that the quality of soil is much concerned with the plant growth upon it and that of these three types of soil the loamy one is capable of supporting the best growth.

That soil is necessary for good growth has been previously mentioned and explained. The interesting question arises — why is it that plants artificially anchored but not allowed to root in the soil are unable to make a good growth? It surely must be a matter of nutrition, because the soil could hardly be so potent an influence in any other way.. When the plants are artificially anchored all other conditions are the same as with plants rooted in the soil except that the roots of the suspended plants are exposed to light and are unable to absorb nourishment from the soil. That light in some measure retards root development and thus diminishes the absorbing capacity of the plant is certain, but this factor is entirely too small to account for the stunted growth of plants denied a soil substratum.

Chemical analysis has been employed for the purpose of securing if possible some clue to the reason why these plants cannot make normal growth unless rooted in the soil. *Vallisneria spiralis*, the eel-grass, whose elaborate arrangement for pollination has been described, was selected as a typical water plant of wide distribution. The history of the material to be analyzed must, of course, be known, and in this case a large number of small plants of uniform size were carefully taken from the lake bottom and transferred to submerged boxes which were alike, except that one contained soil and the other did not. The roots of the plants artificially anchored in the box without soil were not permitted to touch the box, but dangled in the water, and thus from the water only could nourishment be taken. After a certain time the plants were gathered and carefully washed, only the living specimens, of course, being saved. In order to establish a basis for comparison the volume of each group of plants was obtained by immersion in water and measuring the displacement. The volume of the plants rooted in soil was taken to be just twice the volume of the plants artificially anchored. This material was then dried out and the dry weight taken, which, for the plants rooted in soil, was 52.7 grams and for those suspended 37.2 grams. These figures show at once that the suspended plants are relatively much heavier than the others. Further analysis discloses the reason for this. The suspended plants were found to contain relatively twice as much starch as the others. This means that the suspended plants, though dwarfed to one-half the normal size, still contained the same weight of starch that they would have contained if allowed to grow as the others did in the soil. Evidently the retarded growth cannot be because of any scarcity of starch. Since this process of starch-making is one of the very vital processes of the plant it is important to know that being artificially anchored does not disturb this fundamental function of the plant. However, as a consequence of this fact, it is evident that the suspended plants must soon become overcrowded with stored starch and this result in itself may be a reason for further disturbance of vital processes with eventually fatal consequences.

The proteid content of the suspended plants was found to be smaller, suggesting that sufficient supply of nitrogenous food was not available for them. This shows that the suspended plants must have very soon fallen into an abnormal condition in which the two very fundamental functions of starch-making and of proteid synthesis were not properly balanced.

The analysis showed further that the suspended plants contained a relatively smaller proportion of mineral matter, which of course indicates that they were unable to secure and use as much mineral food as they needed. The elements most deficient in the suspended plants were potassium and phosphorus, two of the most essential substances which are no doubt much concerned with the manufacture of food materials.

So far, then, as present knowledge is concerned we can say that the plants are dependent upon the soil for a sufficient supply of certain substances, especially nitrogen, potash, and phosphorus. When the plants are compelled to take all their nourishment from the water an abnormal condition soon arises by reason of a disproportion between proteid synthesis and starch manufacture which is manifested by a retarded growth and final death.

That such statements are not conclusively proven must not be overlooked and just why they cannot be regarded as beyond doubt would be tedious to explain here.

The natural conditions of our lakes and rivers are undoubtedly changing from decade to decade. The extensive destruction of forests that has occurred in the lake region and along tributary streams has certainly indirectly affected the plant and animal life in the lakes, although at present it cannot be stated in any detail how such influences have operated. The same may be said in regard to the vast volume of organic matter that constantly comes to the lakes and rivers as sewage from the cities. The influences which operate to regulate or determine the food supply of the water are numerous. Adequate knowledge is only possible by a thorough study of the food relations among the animals themselves, between the animals and plants and between the plants and the soil.

Cycle of matter. — Animals cannot organize food from inorganic substances but must use, as food, matter that is already organized, either as vegetable or animal substance. Plants, however, can and do organize food, using both the mineral salts occurring in the soil or water, and the gaseous carbon dioxid which occurs in the air and in the water. The dependence of the animals upon the plants is at once apparent and the dependence of the plants upon the earth and air is also apparent. The most important influence exerted by plants in fresh-water biology is undoubtedly concerned with their nutrition but they are also important in other ways.

As geological agents in the formation of marl. — The formation of lime incrustations by water plants has already been considered, so that it is only necessary to state here that considerable evidence has been brought forward to show that the large marl deposits in the marl lakes have accumulated as already described through the activity of plants, especially *Chara*.

As aerating agents. — Both animals and plants must have air to breathe, and in running water or open lakes there is usually sufficient oxygen dissolved in the water to support the respiration of the organisms present. In the still waters of coves and bayous, however, conditions are different. It is in such places that organic débris tends to accumulate, and, in decay, overcharges the water with the gases of decomposition, especially that of carbon dioxid. Of course, whatever animal life is present under such conditions still further reduces the oxygen supply and increases the carbon dioxid. The green plants on the other hand during sunlight are constantly using the carbon dioxid for making starch and giving off oxygen as a waste product of the process. In this process the volume of oxygen released equals the volume of carbon dioxid used, so that an aquatic meadow, growing vigorously in a still-water cove, would be very efficient in keeping the water well aerated and much to the advantage of all the animal life finding food and shelter there.

As affording shelter and refuge for small animals. — In these aquatic meadows many kinds of young fish spend their early life during the period when they require protection from enemies. Here, too, many of the smaller animals pursued by enemies find temporary refuge or are able to evade their pursuers.

As a base of attachment for algae. — Wherever the larger plants occur may be found also many smaller and more lowly organized forms which use the larger plants as supports. The simple forms, which are usually algae, would be unable to live as free swimming individuals, and since many of them are used as food by the animals it is important that they should be allowed to develop abundantly. The dead as well as the living larger plants may be useful in this way and only direct observation will reveal to one how much of importance the larger plants are in this one particular.

As organizers of matter and distributors of nourishment for the plankton. — If, as formerly supposed, water plants take their mineral food from the surrounding water and not from the soil at all, then it is evident that during the growing season these rooting aquatics would be continually diminishing the food supply of the free swimming plants, or the plant plankton, and this would, of course, result in a decreasing food supply for the animals dependent upon the plant plankton for nourishment. In view of the evidence now at hand it is certain that these larger plants rooting in the bottom absorb inorganic matter from the soil and organize this material into plant tissue which can be used as food by the animals and also by parasitic and saprophytic plants which can also be used as food by the animals. This, then, is perhaps the most important rôle of the larger aquatic plants, in that their life work results in an actual contribution of organic matter to the food supply of the animal life. There is no doubt but that in a body of water like Lake Erie this contribution of organic matter made from soil and air constituents that would otherwise remain unused could be measured in tons even in a single growing season.

In the marshes and shallow places immense quantities of plant débris are constantly occurring and with changing wind these masses of organic matter are carried far out into the lake, where, during the period of slow decay, they furnish food to hosts of small animals and in the decay yield valuable mineral salts, thus enriching the water to the advantage of the free swimming forms.

IMPORTANT REFERENCES ON HIGHER AQUATIC PLANTS

BRITTON, N. L., and BROWN, A.   1896–98.   Illustrated Flora of the Northern United States, Canada, and the British Possessions.   3 v.   New York.

CONARD, H. S.   1905.   The Waterlilies: a Monograph of the Genus Nymphaea.   Carnegie Inst. of Wash., Pub. No. 4.

COULTER, J. M., BARNES, C. R., and COWLES, H. C.   1911.   Textbook of Botany.   Vol. 2.   New York.

ENGLER, A.   1900+.   Das Pflanzenreich.   Leipzig.

ENGLER, A., and PRANTL, K.   1887+.   (See list in Chapter VI.)

GLÜCK, HUGO.   1905–06.   Biologische und morphologische Untersuchungen über Wasser und Sumpfgewächse.   2 v.   Jena.

KERNER, A., and OLIVER, F. W.   1895.   The Natural History of Plants, their Forms, Growth, Reproduction and Distribution.   2 v. in 4.   New York.

MORONG, THOMAS.   1886.   Studies in the Typhaceae.   Bull. Torrey Bot. Club, 15: 1–8, 73–81.

1892–93.   The Naiadaceae of North America.   Mem. Torrey Bot. Club, v. 4, No. 2; 65 pp., 55 pl.

PIETERS, A. J.   1894.   The Plants of Lake St. Clair.   Bull. Mich. Fish Com., No. 2; 10 pp.   Map.

1901.   The Plants of Western Lake Erie with Observations on their Distribution.   Bull. U. S. Fish Comm., 21: 57–79, 10 pl.

POND, R. H.   1905.   The Biological Relation of Aquatic Plants to the Substratum.   Rept. U. S. Com. of Fish and Fisheries 1903: 483–526.

WARMING, J. E. B.   1909.   Oecology of Plants; an Introduction to the Study of Plant Communities.   Oxford.

CHAPTER VIII
AMOEBOID PROTOZOA (Sarcodina)

By C. H. EDMONDSON

Assistant Professor of Zoology, University of Oregon

THE minute animals consisting of but a single cell throughout their existence are commonly called Protozoa. They are world-wide in their distribution, swarming the seas from the surface to great depths and being found abundantly under almost all conditions of moisture in fresh water as well as in the fluids and tissues of other animals where many exist as parasites.

The Protozoa may be grouped under the following subphyla:

Subphylum I. Sarcodina. — Moving by means of temporary extensions of the protoplasm, called pseudopodia.

Subphylum II. Mastigophora. — Provided with one or more whip-like processes, called flagella, as organs of locomotion or for securing food.

Subphylum III. Infusoria. — Locomotor organs in the form of fine hair-like structures, called cilia, present during the entire existence or during the embryonic stage only.

Subphylum IV. Sporozoa. — Without true organs of locomotion; usually reproducing by spores. Parasitic. No free living forms.

It will be observed that the above grouping is based upon the organs of locomotion. This basis has been found a convenient one for classification and study, little difficulty arising except in unusual cases where species are found to possess more than one kind of motile organs or where species pass through distinct phases during their life cycle. Of all the Protozoa those representing the highest degree of simplicity of structure and the greatest generalization of life processes, if not the oldest in point of time, are to be found in the group possessing pseudopodia. These form the subject of the present chapter, the flagellate and ciliate forms are considered in the next, and the parasitic Sporozoa do not properly call for attention in this work.

Previously unknown on account of their diminutive size, these organisms at once attracted the early workers with the microscope. Although Leeuwenhoek as early as 1675 initiated the study of Protozoa by his discovery of *Vorticella*, an infusorian, without doubt, Rösel's description of *Amoeba proteus* under the name "Der kleine Proteus," in 1755, represents the first recorded observation of a fresh-water protozoon of the group Sarcodina.

In 1835 Dujardin called the viscid, transparent substance composing the bodies of marine Protozoa, which he then had under observation, sarcode, but it was not until 1883 that Bütschli first employed the term Sarcodina and included under it all forms of Protozoa which move by means of protrusions of protoplasm from the body proper, called pseudopodia.

Most of the Sarcodina are very minute in size. Very few of them can be seen by the unaided eye and none can be studied with any degree of satisfaction without the aid of a compound microscope. These forms vary greatly in general appearance. Many of them are naked masses of protoplasm tending to be globular when first placed under the microscope but soon assuming variable shapes, protruding from the body, with more or less rapidity, blunt, lobe-like, or filiform pseudopodia, often branching and sometimes anastomosing. Others are provided with envelopes or shells, very diverse in form and composition, sometimes secreted by the animal itself, sometimes consisting of picked-up fragments firmly cemented together. These envelopes may be compact and rigid, or flexible, and are provided with one or more apertures through which the pseudopodia are extended. Still other forms, commonly known as the Heliozoa or "sun animalcules," are typically spherical, sometimes with shells of delicate structure and always with fine ray-like pseudopodia, usually rendered somewhat rigid by the presence of stiffened axial filaments.

Fresh-water Sarcodina may be found in very diverse habitats and within wide ranges of temperature. They occur from the level of the sea to the tops of very high mountains. Perhaps no other animals have such a vast altitudinal range as certain common species of Sarcodina. Roadside pools and also ponds, lakes and rivers are habitats of myriads of these low organisms. In most of the Sarcodina there is a marked differentiation between the endoplasm and ectoplasm, the difference consisting in the greater density and opaqueness of the inner region. This distinction between endoplasm and ectoplasm reaches a high degree in certain marine forms, the Radiolaria, where a distinct perforated membrane, the "central capsule," separates the two regions. None of the fresh-water forms possess a "central capsule." The greater density of the endoplasm is accounted for by the character of the inclusions suspended in it and by the size of the vesicles which make up its structure.

The inclusions consist of various elements: food which is to be built into body protoplasm, products which may enter into the composition of the shell, waste material on the way to the exterior, or foreign elements which have no part in the physiology of the animal. In some Sarcodina algae or bacteria are constant features of the endoplasm, this symbiotic relationship being apparently essential to the life of the protozoon.

The nucleus is confined to the endoplasm. In a few Sarcodina condensed nuclear elements have not been observed, but in these cases the chromatin is without doubt diffused throughout the cell and has the same functional value as a centralized body.

Usually a single nucleus is present, often two is the normal number, but in some forms several hundred or even several thousand have been counted in certain stages.

Commonly the nucleus is spherical, but may be modified in form, due to the shape of the body and to the flexibility of the nuclear membrane which sometimes permits considerable deformity.

In most Sarcodina the chromatin within the nuclear membrane is arranged in one or more masses, but in some of the Heliozoa it is arranged in a network not unlike that of the cell of a metazoon.

Contractile vacuoles, the function of which is the extraction of waste fluids and gases, are not found in all Sarcodina. These are absent in many of the marine forms and in some fresh-water genera. When present, the number varies from one to many. Habitually the contractile vacuole is spherical but in some species it assumes a characteristic lobed form. The position of the contractile vacuole is not always fixed but may frequently be shifted about by the flowing protoplasm. In some forms its general position is fixed and it reappears, after contraction, in the same place. As the vacuole becomes inflated by waste fluids and gases it rises toward the periphery and collapses, pouring its contents through the opening formed in the body wall. In some of the Heliozoa are seen very large contractile vacuoles which rise to the surface and push the peripheral film outward like a bubble before the collapse takes place.

Many of the shell-bearing forms are capable of raising or lowering themselves in the water. This is believed to be brought about by the presence of distinct gas vacuoles. The animals seem to be able to alter the supply of carbon dioxide in these vacuoles and thereby change their specific gravity.

The ectoplasm, when distinct from the endoplasm, usually appears as a clear hyaline zone, of greater or less width, at the periphery of the body. In most forms the vesicles of the ectoplasm are very minute but in some of the Heliozoa they exceed those of the endoplasm in size and may be arranged in a regular manner about the periphery, as in *Actinosphaerium eichhornii.*

The protrusion of the ectoplasm is the initial movement in the formation of a pseudopodium after which there may be a flow of the granular endoplasm into the axis of the finger-like extension of the ectoplasm. At times pseudopodia are but broad extensions of the ectoplasm with no appearance of endoplasm taking any part in their formation.

Great variation is seen in the pseudopodia which are characteristic features of the Sarcodina. Among the fresh-water forms several general types may be observed. The naked and many of the shell-bearing Sarcodina produce broad, blunt, finger-like, or more slender, filiform, pseudopodia; the latter may be delicate, pointed and finely branched, but neither of these fuse or anastomose when in contact. Another variety is represented by delicate thread-like pseudopodia which tend to run together and mingle, forming a great network of flowing protoplasm. This is the anastomosing type and is seen in a few fresh-water genera, but is characteristic of many marine forms.

In the Heliozoa is seen another variety. Here the ray-like

pseudopodia are usually supported by "axial filaments" which consist of stiffened protoplasmic supports forming the axes of the pseudopodia along which the soft protoplasm flows. These axial supports enter the body, the inner ends apparently resting on or near the nuclear membrane. The supports permit the flexing of the rays and at times they may become soft and be absorbed by the protoplasm of the body.

Shells, which are characteristic of many Sarcodina, may be composed of materials secreted by the protoplasm of the animal itself, such as chitin, silica, and calcium carbonate; or may be constructed of picked-up foreign materials such as sand grains, diatom shells, dirt, etc.

Shells of chitin are common among fresh-water forms. This material is deposited about the body as a membrane with one or more openings for the pseudopodia. It may or may not be applied closely to the body and is variable in thickness in different species as well as with age. In young individuals the envelop is usually thin and transparent; with age it may become thicker and more opaque. In many forms the envelop is always thin and flexible, permitting changes in shape of the body from the flowing of the enclosed protoplasm. When the deposit is in sufficient quantity a firm, rigid shell is produced. If the body does not completely fill the shell the former is united to the inner surface of the latter by protoplasmic threads and is capable of considerable amoeboid movements within the envelop. Some chitinous shells are very delicate, transparent and apparently without separate elements, while others are composed of distinct plates arranged with more or less regularity.

Species of *Difflugia* and other related forms are provided with shells composed of foreign materials including grains of sand, diatom shells, and particles of dirt. These materials are attached to a thin chitinous layer and cemented together into a compact, rigid shell with one aperture through which the pseudopodia extend.

Shells may be composed primarily of silica. In many fresh-water forms these siliceous elements are laid down in the form of regular plates which build up a firm shell. Others, as some fresh-water Heliozoa and the marine Radiolaria, secrete spicules which may be loosely connected, forming an envelop, or cemented together, building up skeletons of most delicate and beautiful designs. Sometimes spicules are developed for temporary purposes as the formation of envelopes during encystment. Calcium carbonate is the chief constituent of the shells of marine Foraminifera but is not an element of importance in the shells of fresh-water Sarcodina.

In a one-celled animal the vital processes of the body, though not different, except in degree, from those of a metazoon, must necessarily be simpler. Here all of the life-forces have their origin and all of the metabolic changes take place within the confines of a single cell.

The entrance of food into the body in the Sarcodina is a simple process. No mouth being present, material may, in general, enter at any point on the surface. In naked forms of the *Amoeba* type the pseudopodia flow around the particle to be ingested and in this way it is enclosed. The pseudopodia of shell-bearing forms draw in the food through the apertures of the shells where it is engulfed by the protoplasm.

Most of the Sarcodina are herbivorous, their chief food being unicellular plants, as bacteria, diatoms, algae, etc. The plant cells are usually entirely ingested and the soft parts absorbed, after which the indigestible parts are excreted from the body. However, in case of *Vampyrella*, the parasite penetrates the cells of algae and absorbs their contents.

Some Sarcodina are known to be carnivorous, feeding upon closely related species. Penard believes that species of *Nebela* may make use of the plates of *Quadrulella, Euglypha, Trinema*, etc., upon which they feed, in building up their own shells.

Digestion in all of the Protozoa is intracellular. After the material enters the body surrounded by a film of water forming a food vacuole, digestive fluids and enzymes act upon it converting it into suitable elements for the life of the cell. Excretion in the Sarcodina consists, as elsewhere, in the release of waste products. Waste solids may leave the body at any point of the surface. The process is the reverse of ingestion, often consisting in the mere flowing away from the material to be discarded.

Waste fluids resulting from the metabolism of the cell are collected in contractile vacuoles in most of the fresh-water Sarcodina and thereby removed. Surplus water which has been ingested is eliminated at the same time and possibly carbon dioxid may also be extracted by the contractile vacuole. In those forms, however, which do not possess contractile vacuoles, the waste fluids and gases escape from the general surface of the body.

, Respiration in the Sarcodina is performed by an interchange of gases through the body wall. Oxygen is received from the surrounding water and carbon dioxid transmitted to it by osmosis. The symbiotic relationship between algae and some forms of Sarcodina, without doubt, has an important respiratory as well as nutritive function, the plants furnishing oxygen and carbohydrates to the animals, while the latter supply carbon dioxid and nitrogenous waste for the algae.

Reproduction in the Sarcodina takes place either by the division of the body into two parts, a process commonly called fission; by the separation from the parent of one or more small masses of protoplasm known as buds; or by the production of swarm spores.

In fission, or simple cell division, which is common among freshwater forms, the nucleus divides first and this is followed by the separation of the cytoplasm into two parts, each of which encloses a portion of the original nucleus. Growth proceeds until maturity is reached, when the process of division is repeated.

When an envelop is present the enclosed body may divide by fission after which one portion creeps out at the aperture and constructs a new shell about itself. If the envelop be chitin and without distinct elements it is gradually developed at the periphery of the newly separated individual, but if it be of regular chitinous or siliceous plates, these elements, in some cases at least, are developed in the cytoplasm of the parent and pushed out to form the new envelop of the separating bud.

That the nucleus is concerned with cell division has long been known. Recent observations, however, have thrown light upon the presence of extranuclear material scattered throughout the cytoplasm in many Sarcodina as well as other protozoa. This material has the form of minute granules termed "idiochromidia" and results from the transfusion of part of the chromatin through the nuclear membrane or from the breaking up of the nucleus into small granular bodies which become diffused through the cytoplasm.

In some Sarcodina a number of buds may separate from the parent, each enclosing a quantity of idiochromidia which is built into a nucleus. This extranuclear material apparently has a functional value in reproduction and may be compared to the micronuclei of Infusoria. During the quiescent state of encystment the bodies of many Sarcodina break into swarm spores. These are minute organisms each with a portion of the parent nucleus and provided with flagella or pseudopodia as motile organs. The swarm spores may fuse with each other and develop into an adult form or, in some cases, they may develop without fusion.

Conjugation, in the form of a temporary union or a permanent fusion of the bodies of two individuals of the same species, has been observed in some Sarcodina. After temporary union and separation, in a few cases, swarm spores have been observed to be developed from both conjugants.

In most of the instances of permanent conjugation reported there is no clear evidence that the fusion resulted in a union of the nuclei of the individuals, as is the case in true conjugation. Actual fusion of the nuclei, however, has been observed in the common "sun animalcule," *Actinophrys sol*. Here two individuals come together, fuse, and become encysted. Nuclear changes take place which follow in a general way the processes of maturation and fertilization after which mitotic division results in the formation of daughter cells.

Many kinds of Sarcodina are exceedingly abundant and collecting them is not a difficult matter. Other forms are rare and only occasionally obtained. Everywhere among wet mosses and in sphagnous swamps many fine examples of shell-bearing species will be found, some inhabiting no other localities. Some prefer clear, fresh water, while others thrive in stagnant ponds and ditches.

By carefully collecting submerged decaying vegetation from shallow water and allowing it to stand in the laboratory for a few days many of the *Amoeba* and *Difflugia* types are usually found.

The ooze at the bottom of ponds or lakes is the habitat of numerous shell-bearing as well as naked forms. Others, like the Heliozoa, are commonly found among algae, diatoms, or mosses and may be collected with these plants. Inactive or encysted forms gathered during cold seasons of the year will become active on being placed in a warm laboratory. Shallow aquaria are best adapted for preserving quantities of living Sarcodina. For those species which require it, the water may be kept fresh by algae or other aquatic plants, but for many forms the water may be allowed to become stagnant, replenishing it only as evaporation takes place. The Sarcodina may be studied with a considerable degree of satisfaction, as it is possible to keep them under observation for an indefinite time, owing to their slow movements. For detailed study a good compound microscope including an oil immersion lens is necessary. Concave microscopic slides on which living forms may be isolated and retained for extended observation are useful. Methylenblue, used as an *intravitam* stain, is successful in rendering the nuclear elements visible, especially in species without shells or with transparent envelopes.

When permanent mounts are desired the following method, recommended by Benedict in the Journal of Applied Microscopy, Vol. VI, p. 2647, may be employed: "Smear a glass slide with albumen fixative, as in preparing for the mounting of paraffin sections. Then place on the surface of the film of fixative a drop or two of water containing the forms which it is desired to stain. Let nearly all the water evaporate by exposure to the air of the room until only the film of fixative remains moist. The slide can now be immersed in Gilson's or any other fixing reagent and then passed through the alcohols, stains, etc., in the same way that mounted sections are handled."

The above method is recommended for other Protozoa as well as for Sarcodina. As a rapid fixing agent, the fumes of osmic acid have been found satisfactory. By careful manipulation of fine dissecting needles under the microscope, the shells of many forms may be isolated, arranged as desired and, when dried on the slide, permanently mounted in balsam.

KEY TO NORTH AMERICAN FRESH-WATER SARCODINA

1 (161) Pseudopodia without axial filaments. . . . Class **Rhizopoda** . . 2

2 (144) Pseudopodia lobose, sometimes pointed but never anastomosing.
Subclass **Amoebea** . . 3

3 (21) Without shells. . . . . Order **Gymnamoebida** . . 4

4 One family recognized. Characteristics of the order.
Family AMOEBIDAE . . 5

5 (6) Body and pseudopodia bristling with minute spicules.
Dinamoeba Leidy.
Representative species. . . . . . . *Dinamoeba mirabilis* Leidy 1874.

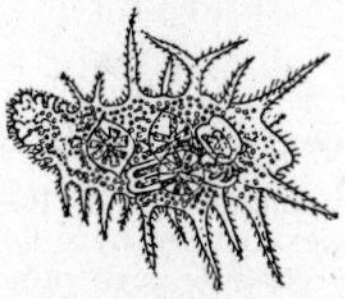

Very changeable in shape with many tapering pseudopodia. Papillae-like projections often appearing at the posterior extremity. Entire body sometimes surrounded by a jelly-like envelop. A contractile vacuole and two nuclei present. Habitat standing water. Size may reach 200 μ, including pseudopodia.

FIG. 274. *Dinamoeba mirabilis.* × 100. (After Leidy.)

6 (5) Body smooth, without spicules. 7

7 (8) Body usually enclosing symbiotic bacteria. Large size. Nuclei many.
Pelomyxa Greeff.
Representative species. . . . . . . *Pelomyxa palustris* Greeff 1870.

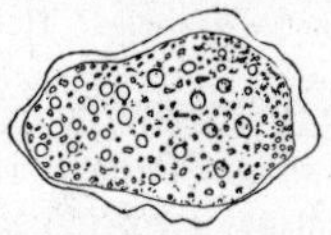

A very large form moving slowly by broad extensions of the ectoplasm. Endoplasm enclosing sand, brilliant corpuscles and bacteria; with numerous vacuoles in the ectoplasm. Nuclei may number 1000 or more. Habitat ooze of ponds and sphagnous swamps. Maximum length 2000 μ. *P. carolinensis* Wilson, described in American Naturalist, Vol. 34, p. 535, is apparently without symbiotic bacteria.

FIG. 275. *Pelomyxa palustris.* × 25. (After Penard.)

8 (7) Body not enclosing symbiotic bacteria. 9

9 (10) Ectoplasmic membranes produced between the pseudopodia.
Hyalodiscus Hertwig and Lesser.
Representative species. . . . *Hyalodiscus rubicundus* H. and L. 1874.

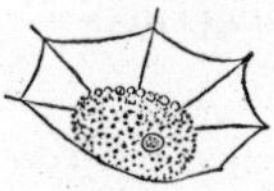

Body discoidal, moving by extending thin sheets of ectoplasm which are penetrated by ray-like pseudopodia. Endoplasm reddish-yellow in color enclosing numerous vacuoles and one or more nuclei. Habitat ooze of ponds, not common. Size 40 to 60 μ.

FIG. 276. *Hyalodiscus rubicundus.* × 315. (After Penard.)

10 (9) Ectoplasmic membranes not produced between the pseudopodia.
Amoeba Ehrenberg . . 11

11 (14) Pseudopodia sharply distinguished from the body. 12

12 (13) Pseudopodia lobe-like. . . . . *Amoeba proteus* Leidy 1878.

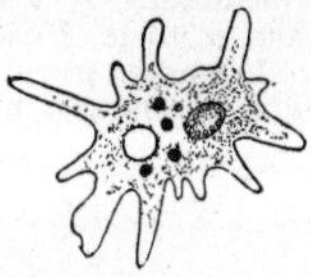

Very changeable in form, usually with numerous pseudopodia. The nucleus is always single, oval and of large size. Contractile vacuoles one or more. Habitat both stagnant and clear water. Size, one of the largest species of the genus; may reach 300 μ or more when extended.

FIG. 277. *Amoeba proteus.* × 100. (Original from a preparation.)

13 (12)   Pseudopodia ray-like. . . . . . . *Amoeba radiosa* Ehrenberg 1830.

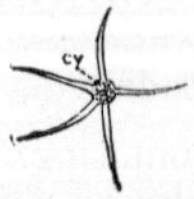

Body spherical. with pseudopodia more or less rigid. not withdrawn and reformed rapidly.   Nucleus spherical.   Habitat, very common among algae; widely distributed.   Size, usually less than 100 μ with pseudopodia extended.

FIG. 278. *Amoeba radiosa.   cv,* contractile vacuole.   × 100.   (After Leidy.)

14 (11)   Pseudopodia not sharply distinguished from the body.   15

15 (20)   Contractile vacuole spherical.   16

16 (17)   Posterior extremity villous. . . . . . *Amoeba limax* Dujardin 1841.

Slug-like, usually moving with the broad end forward.   Endoplasm filled with brilliant granules.   Contractile vacuole usually single.   Nucleus changeable in form.   Habitat ooze of ponds.   Size, large individuals usually less than 100 μ.

FIG. 279. *Amoeba limax.*   × 225.   (After Penard.)

17 (16)   Posterior extremity not villous.   19

18 (19)   Surface wrinkled, large size.   . . *Amoeba verrucosa* Ehrenberg 1838.

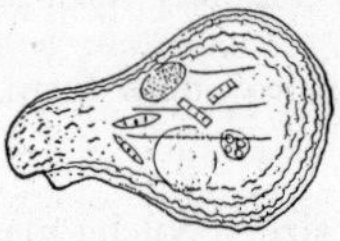

A sluggish species, moving by a slow rolling motion.   Pseudopodia short, broad lobes.   Body proper enclosed by a delicate membrane.   Surface marked by lines crossing each other resulting in a wrinkled appearance.   Habitat sphagnous swamps.   Large individuals may reach 300 μ in length when extended.

FIG. 280. *Amoeba verrucosa.*   × 100   (After Leidy.)

19 (18)   Surface not wrinkled, small size.   . . *Amoeba guttula* Dujardin 1841.

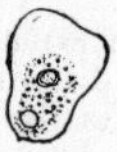

Body usually oval in outline, moving with the broad end forward.   Pseudopodia short, broad lobes produced by sudden expansions of the protoplasm.   Nucleus single and one large contractile vacuole.   Habitat stagnant water.   Size 30 μ.

FIG. 281. *Amoeba guttula.*   × 400.   (After Penard.)

20 (15)   Contractile vacuole not spherical.   . . . *Amoeba striata* Penard 1890.

Moving rapidly by broad extensions of ectoplasm but not changing form rapidly.   Usually from two to four longitudinal lines on the surface.   Two contractile vacuoles often present, the anterior one changeable in shape.   Habitat among algae; not abundant.   Size, from 30 to 60 μ.

FIG. 282. *Amoeba striata.*   × 250.   (After Penard.)

21 (3)   With shells. . . . . Order **Testacea** . .   22

22 (103)   Pseudopodia thick, finger-like, rarely filiform.

Family ARCELLIDAE . .   23

23 (96)   Pseudopodia thick, sometimes pointed.   24

24 (35)   Shell membranous, more or less flexible.   25

25 (32)   Membrane covered with organic or foreign particles.   26

26 (29)   Shell membrane double. . . . .   *Diplochlamys* Greeff. .   27

27 (28)   Hemispherical to cup-shaped, loosely coated with organic and siliceous particles. . . . . . .   *Diplochlamys fragilis* Penard 1909.

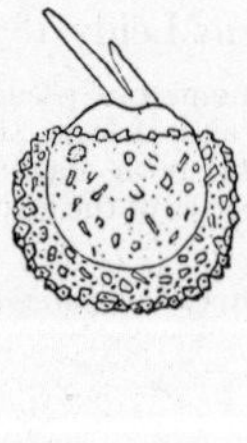

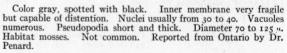

Color gray, spotted with black.   Inner membrane very fragile but capable of distention.   Nuclei usually from 30 to 40.   Vacuoles numerous.   Pseudopodia short and thick.   Diameter 70 to 125 μ.   Habitat mosses.   Not common.   Reported from Ontario by Dr. Penard.

FIG. 283. *Diplochlamys fragilis.*   × 150.   (After Penard.)

28 (27) Hemispherical to cup-shaped, densely coated with organic particles.
Diplochlamys timida Penard 1909.

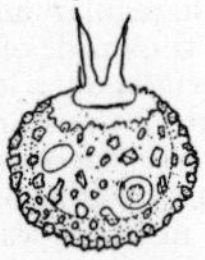

Yellowish-gray or brown. Inner membrane very delicate, flexible but resistant. Nucleus single. Vacuoles numerous. Pseudopodia large at the base, pointed, rarely extended. Diameter 45 μ. Habitat mosses. Reported from Ontario by Dr. Penard.

Fig. 284. *Diplochlamys timida.* × 275. (After Penard.)

29 (26) Shell membrane single. 30

30 (31) Hemispherical; slightly or not at all flexible. . . *Parmulina* Penard.
Representative species. . . . . . *Parmulina cyathus* Penard 1902.

In this species the shell is rigid but in *P. obtecta* Gruber it is flexible about the aperture. Shell is coated with fine particles of sand, dirt. etc. Pseudopodia are broad, rounded lobes extending from the aperture. Nucleus and contractile vacuole each single. Habitat among mosses. Diameter 45 μ.

Fig. 285. *Parmulina cyathus.* × 275. (After Penard.)

31 (30) Commonly ovoid or hemispherical, but very changeable.
Corycia Dujardin.
Representative species. . . . . *Corycia flava* Greeff 1866.

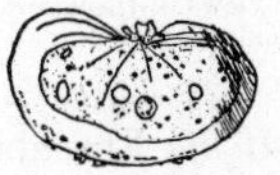

The membranous covering is dome-shaped but very changeable in form. Pseudopodia very short and thick. Vacuoles numerous. Nucleus single, usually concealed by the granules of the endoplasm. Habitat among mosses. Diameter 80 to 100 μ.

Fig. 286. *Corycia flava.* × 210. (After Penard.)

32 (25) Membrane without foreign particles; regularly punctate. . . . 33

33 (34) Patelliform; slightly flexible. . . . . *Microchlamys* Cockerell.
Representative species.
Microchlamys patella Claparède and Lachmann 1860.

Shell circular from dorsal or ventral view; convex above with a very large aperture beneath. Pseudopodium single. Contractile vacuoles numerous. Nucleus single. Habitat among mosses in swamps. Diameter 40 μ.

Fig. 287. *Microchlamys patella.* × 310. (After Penard.)

34 (33) Commonly dome-shaped, but exceedingly flexible and changeable.
Cochliopodium Hertwig and Lesser.
Representative species. . *Cochliopodium bilimbosum* Auerbach 1856.

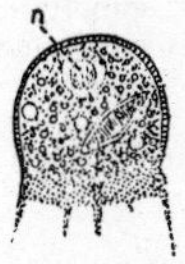

The membranous covering is capable of great expansion, especially at the aperture. Pseudopodia pointed, usually numerous. Nucleus and contractile vacuole each single and large. Common among algae. Diameter of envelop 25 to 50 μ.

Fig. 288. *Cochliopodium bilimbosum.* n, nucleus. × 300. (After Leidy.)

35 (24) Shell membranous, rigid. 36

36 (45) Shell discoidal. 37

37 (44) Shell with regular markings more or less distinct. No foreign particles attached. Aperture central. 38

38 (43) Shell with regular, distinct punctae. Aperture small.
Arcella Ehrenberg . . 39

39 (42) Periphery of shell without projecting points. 40

40 (41) Shell strongly convex. . . . . . . *Arcella vulgaris* Ehrenberg 1830.

Shell may be smooth or with regular undulations. Protoplasm united to the inside of the shell by delicate threads. Pseudopodia long, straight and very transparent. Contractile vacuoles numerous. Nuclei two, opposite in position. This species shows great variation in size and form. Very common in pond water. Diameter 80 to 140 μ.

FIG. 289. *Arcella vulgaris.* Lateral and inferior views of the same individual. × 150. (After Leidy.)

41 (40) Shell very flat. . . . . *Arcella discoides* Ehrenberg 1843.

Shell smooth, regularly punctate, with a large circular aperture. It is a shy species, the pseudopodia seldom being observed. Contractile vacuoles numerous. Nuclei two. Common in pond water. Diameter from 72 to 264 μ.

FIG. 290. *Arcella discoides.* × 175. (After Penard.)

42 (39) Shell periphery with projecting points.

Arcella dentata Ehrenberg 1830.

When viewed laterally the shell has the appearance of a crown, the teeth-like points being produced from the base of the low dome. Nuclei two; contractile vacuoles numerous. Habitat bogs and swamps. A rare species. Diameter 132 to 184 μ.

FIG. 291. *Arcella dentata.* Lateral and inferior views of the same individual. × 100. (After Leidy.)

43 (38) Shell with punctae sometimes indistinct. Aperture very wide.

Pyxidicula Ehrenberg.

Representative species. . . . . *Pyxidicula cymbalum* Penard 1902.

FIG. 292. *Pyxidicula cymbalum.* × 210. (After Penard.)

Shell patelliform, brown in color, with distinct punctae. Aperture round, nearly as wide as the diameter of the shell, bordered by a narrow rim. Contractile vacuole single. Nuclei probably two. Pseudopodia not observed in this species. Identified by Penard in material from Summit Lake, Colorado. The only species of the genus thus far reported from North America. Diameter 85 to 90 μ. Habitat mosses.

44 (37) Shell without regular markings, but with foreign particles attached. Aperture eccentric. . . . . *Centropyxis* Stein.
Representative species. . . . . *Centropyxis aculeata* Stein 1857.

Shell compressed laterally, resulting in both mouth and fundus being eccentric. Color some shade of brown. Slender spines usually developed from the fundus. Nucleus single; contractile vacuoles two or more. The species is very shy, sometimes extending a single large pseudopodium. A common species among algae. Diameter 88 to 260 μ.

FIG. 293. *Centropyxis aculeata.* × 150. (After Leidy.)

45 (36) Shell not discoidal. 46

46 (51) Shell spiral, compressed, largely composed of minute, curved, rod-like plates. . . . . . *Lecquereusia* Schlumberger . . 47

47 (48) Shell primarily of sand grains, few plates.
Lecquereusia modesta Rhumbler 1845.

This species has a short, broad neck, slightly turned to one side. Nucleus single. Pseudopodia few, large and long. Found among mosses in swamps. Length from 125 to 150 μ.

FIG. 294. *Lecquereusia modesta.* × 125. (After Penard.)

48 (47)   Shell of rod-like plates. 49

49 (50)   Plates slender, elongate.   . . *Lecquereusia spiralis* Ehrenberg 1840.

> The neck in this species is prominent and turned sharply to one side.   The siliceous plates are cemented very closely together, forming the shell.   Sand and diatoms may sometimes be incorporated with the plates.   Pseudopodia few, long and large.   Habitat sphagnous swamps.   Length 125 to 140 μ.

FIG. 295. *Lecquereusia spiralis.*   × 125.   (After Penard.)

50 (49)   Plates thick, short. . . . . *Lecquereusia epistomium* Penard 1893.

> In this species the neck is very sharply distinguished from the rounded shell and very abruptly turned to one side.   The shell is clear, without foreign particles attached.   Habitat sphagnous swamps.   Length 125 μ.

FIG. 296. *Lecquereusia epistomium.*   × 150.   (After Penard.)

51 (46)   Shell not spiral. 52

52 (57)   Shell chitinous, transparent, structureless, with no foreign particles or formed elements attached. . . *Hyalosphenia* Stein . . 53

53 (54)   Surface of shell with undulations. . *Hyalosphenia elegans* Leidy 1874.

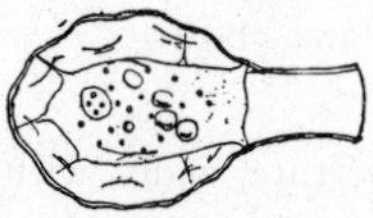

> The shell is flask-shaped, compressed, brownish in color, transparent.   Two minute pores, opposite each other, are in the base of the neck.   Protoplasm colorless.   Nucleus single.   Pseudopodia few.   Common in sphagnous swamps.   Length from 90 to 100 μ.

FIG. 297. *Hyalosphenia elegans.*   × 250.   (After Penard.)

54 (53)   Surface of shell without undulations. 55

55 (56)   With pores through the fundus. . *Hyalosphenia papilio* Leidy 1875.

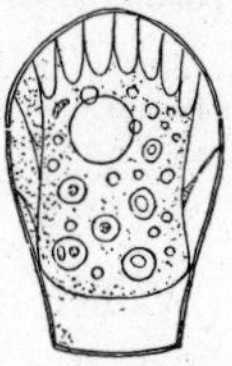

> Shell ovoid or pyriform, compressed, yellowish in color.   Slight variation in size, shape and constitution shown in this species.   Protoplasm not filling the shell but attached to the inner surface by protoplasmic processes.   Endoplasm always containing chlorophyl.   Pseudopodia often numerous.   From two to six small pores about the border of the fundus.   Common in sphagnous swamps.   Length from 110 to 140 μ.

FIG. 298. *Hyalosphenia papilio.*   × 200.   (After Leidy.)

56 (55)   Without pores through the fundus. . *Hyalosphenia cuneata* Stein 1857.

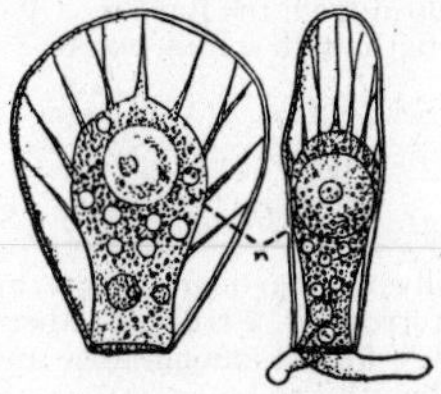

> Shell exceedingly transparent and greatly compressed.   Pseudopodia few in number, often but one.   Habitat is reported to be clear water.   A rare species.   Length from 60 to 75 μ.

FIG. 299. *Hyalosphenia cuneata.*   Broad and narrow lateral views. *n*, nucleus.   × 300.   (After Leidy.)

57 (52)   Shell chitinous, more or less densely covered with foreign particles or formed elements. 58

58 (75)   Shell primarily of foreign particles. 59

59 (72)   Shell without internal partition or diaphragm.
Difflugia Leclerc . . 60

60 (61)   Aperture not central. . . . . Difflugia constricta Ehrenberg 1841.

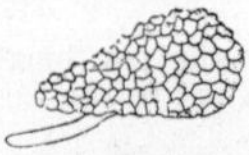

Shells of various forms from nearly spherical to oval and elongate. Aperture always eccentric. Pseudopodium single, rarely observed. Spines sometimes developed from the fundus. This species is closely related to Centropyxis aculeata. A common species, widely distributed. Large forms may reach 200 μ in length. Most individuals are very much smaller.

FIG. 300. Difflugia constricta.
× 110. (After Leidy.)

61 (60)   Aperture central. 62

62 (69)   Shell typically spherical. 63

63 (66)   Margin of aperture smooth. 64

64 (65)   Neck deeply constricted; aperture small, with margin always recurved. . . . . Difflugia urceolata Carter 1864.

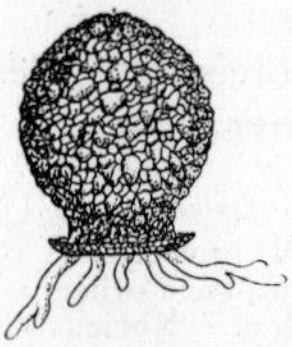

This species is without spines, but a variety, D. urceolata var. olla, may possess a few short stubby spines developed from the fundus. The protoplasm does not fill the shell. Pseudopodia numerous; nuclei many. Found in the ooze of pond water. Large forms reach a length of 350 μ.

FIG. 301. Difflugia urceolata. × 75. (After Leidy.)

65 (64)   Neck, when present, not deeply constricted; aperture wide, with margin seldom recurved. . . . Difflugia lebes Penard 1893.

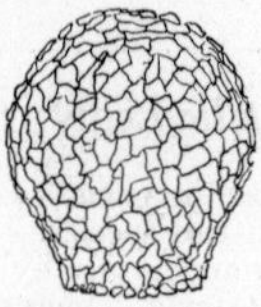

In many respects this species resembles the preceding one. The thin, recurved collar is sometimes present but the aperture is much larger. The shell is very fragile. Nuclei sometimes more than 100. Found in ooze at the bottom of ponds, lakes, etc. Very large, some reaching 400 μ in length.

FIG. 302. Difflugia lebes. × 60. (After Penard.)

66 (63)   Margin of aperture not smooth. 67

67 (68)   Margin with numerous teeth. . . . Difflugia corona Wallich 1864.

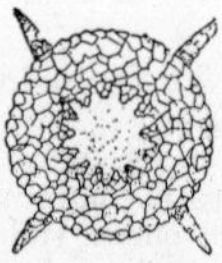

Shell composed of large sand grains but very smooth and regular in outline. Teeth usually more than twelve in number, very evenly arranged. Nucleus single. Pseudopodia numerous and large. From six to nine spines usually developed from the fundus. A very common species in ooze of ponds. Length, with spines, 200 to 250 μ.

FIG. 303. Difflugia corona. Oral view. × 90. (After Leidy.)

68 (67)   Margin with few blunt lobes. . . . Difflugia lobostoma Leidy 1874.

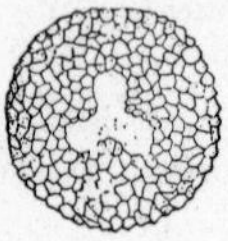

Shell ovoid or nearly spherical, usually with a quadrilobate aperture. However, the lobes are somewhat irregular, a trilobate aperture sometimes appearing. Pseudopodia few. Found among algae and in the ooze of ponds; common. Average length 150 μ.

FIG. 304. Difflugia lobostoma. Oral view. × 105. (After Edmondson.)

69 (62)   Shell never spherical. 70

70 (71) Pyriform, with posterior border usually rounded.
Difflugia pyriformis Perty 1852.

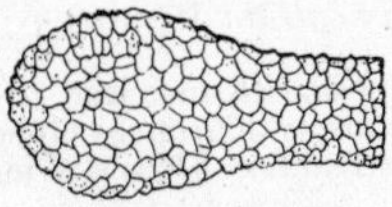

This very common species is exceedingly variable in form and size. Penard recognizes six varieties, var. *claviformis* sometimes reaching a length of 450 μ. The posterior border is usually rounded but some forms may approach the acuminate type. Found everywhere in the ooze of ponds and lakes.

FIG. 305. *Difflugia pyriformis.*
× 60. (After Leidy.)

71 (70) Elongate, cylindrical, with posterior border acuminate.
Difflugia acuminata Ehrenberg 1830.

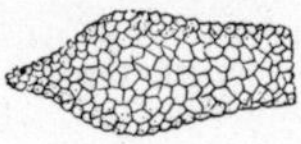

Shell cylindrical, the slightly broader posterior extremity tapering to an acute point ending in a knob-like process. Very widely distributed with other species of the genus. Large forms may reach a length of 275 μ.

FIG. 306. *Difflugia acuminata.* × 125. (After Leidy.)

72 (59) Shell with internal partition or diaphragm. 73

73 (74) Shell with deeply constricted neck and transverse, perforated partition at the point of constriction. . *Pontigulasia* Rhumbler.
Representative species. . . . *Pontigulasia spectabilis* Penard 1902.

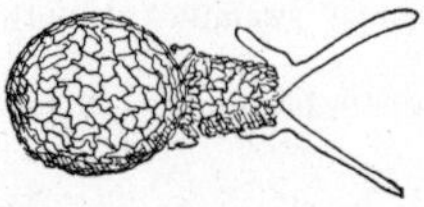

Resembling *Difflugia pyriformis* in appearance, except for the deeply constricted neck. The internal partition has one round opening and one or two other apertures, the latter being closed by transparent opercula. Pseudopodia few, long, and move rapidly. Found with species of *Difflugia*. Average length 150 μ.

FIG. 307. *Pontigulasia spectabilis.* × 100. (After Penard.)

74 (73) Shell with a short neck; aperture partially closed by a transverse diaphragm. . . . . *Cucurbitella* Penard.
Representative species. . . *Cucurbitella mespiliformis* Penard 1902.

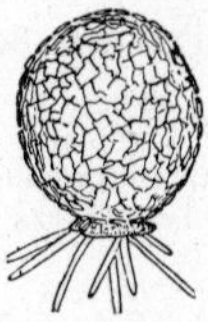

The neck is quadrilobate with an undulating margin. On the inside of the neck is a transverse peristome covered with sand grains, resulting in the rounded aperture being much smaller than the diameter of the neck itself. Pseudopodia numerous, straight. Found at the bottom of ponds and lakes. Length from 125 to 140 μ.

FIG. 308. *Cucurbitella mespiliformis.* × 125. (After Penard.)

75 (58) Shell primarily of formed elements. 76

76 (81) Shell not compressed, of small siliceous particles, aperture lunate with inferior and superior lips. 77

77 (78) Shell hemispherical or elliptical, superior lip with pores. Large size.
Bullinula Penard.
Representative species. . . . . . . *Bullinula indica* Penard 1907.

Shell brownish, of small siliceous plates, closely cemented together. Superior lip slightly overlapping the inferior lip. Nuclei numerous. Diameter 190 to 200 μ. Habitat mosses.

FIG. 309. *Bullinula indica.* × 120. (After Penard.)

78 (77) Shell hemispherical, superior lip without pores. Small size.
Plagiopyxis Penard . . 79

79 (80) Inferior lip rounded, dipping far into the interior of the shell.
Plagiopyxis callida Penard 1910.

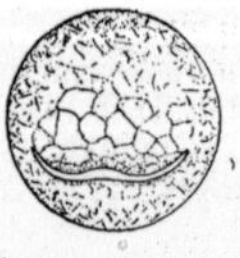

Shell gray, yellow, or brown in color, usually smooth and clear. The lips overlap to such an extent that the aperture is difficult to observe. Pseudopodia large at the base with furcate extremities. Nucleus single. Diameter 92 to 103 μ. Habitat mosses.

Fig. 310. *Plagiopyxis callida.* × 150. (After Wailes and Penard.)

80 (79) Inferior lip triangular, slightly dipping into the interior of the shell.
Plagiopyxis labiata Penard 1911.

Brown in color. Smaller than the preceding species. Nucleus single. Pseudopodia not observed by Dr. Penard, who reports the species from Australia and Vancouver, B. C. Diameter 80 to 88 μ.

Fig. 311. *Plagiopyxis labiata.* × 155. (After Penard.)

81 (76) Shell more or less compressed; aperture not lunate. 82

82 (83) Plates quadrangular. . . . . *Quadrulella* Cockerell.
Representative species. . *Quadrulella symmetrica* F. E. Schultze 1875.

In this species the shell is normally pyriform, one variety being short and another long. The plates are very transparent, usually regularly arranged in transverse and longitudinal series. Pseudopodia few. Common in sphagnous swamps. Length from 80 to 140 μ.

Fig. 312. *Quadrulella symmetrica.* cv, contractile vacuole. × 175. (After Leidy.)

83 (82) Plates not quadrangular. 84

84 (91) Shell pyriform, sometimes ovoid or rounded, compressed with round, oval, or irregular plates. . . . . *Nebela* Leidy . . 85

85 (88) Shell pyriform. 86

86 (87) Neck long, narrow; plates round. . *Nebela lageniformis* Penard 1890.

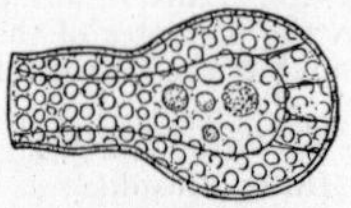

Body of shell oval, prolonged as a tubular neck. There are no lateral pores through the shell as in some species. The plates are round and very clear. Pseudopodia few. Found commonly among mosses; very abundant in some localities. Length 125 μ.

Fig. 313. *Nebela lageniformis.* × 175. (After Penard.)

87 (86) Neck short; plates round or oval. . . . *Nebela collaris* Leidy 1879.

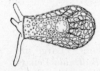

In this species, large, round, and oval plates are usually intermingled. Sometimes foreign elements enter into the composition of the shell. It is a very common species, found abundantly in sphagnous swamps and presents many variations in size and form. Large individuals average about 120 μ.

Fig. 314. *Nebela collaris.* × 150. (After Leidy.)

88 (85) Shell not pyriform. 89

89 (90) Shell rounded, border of aperture smooth.
Nebela flabellum Leidy 1874.

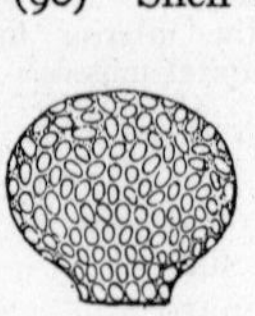

The transverse diameter usually equals or exceeds the length, but apparently transitional forms between this species and the preceding one are sometimes observed. Possibly this is but a variety of *Nebela collaris.* The plates are similar in the two species. Habitat sphagnous swamps. Length 50 to 100 μ.

Fig. 315. *Nebela flabellum.* × 150. (After Leidy.)

90 (89) Shell ovoid; border of aperture crenulate.

Nebela dentistoma Penard 1890.

The shell is very clear with round or oval plates, the arrangement of the plates at the margin of the aperture forming the rounded crenulations. Pseudopodia very active. Found in sphagnous swamps. Length 66 to 130 μ.

FIG. 316. *Nebela dentistoma.* × 160. (After Penard.)

91 (84) Shell ovoid, compressed with round, oval, or irregular plates. . . 92

92 (93) Aperture oval, terminating a short tube formed by the thickened oral membrane. Plates irregular.

Awerinzewia Schouteden.

Representative species. . *Awerinzewia cyclostomata* Schouteden 1902.

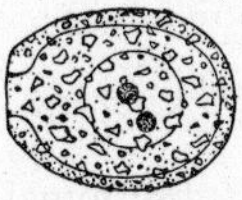

Shell a chitinous envelop covered by siliceous plates, some large, scattering, others small, filling in between the large ones. Sand grains often attached to the posterior border. Color usually violet. Nucleus single. Closely allied to the genus *Heleopera*. Length 135 to 178 μ. Habitat mosses.

FIG. 317. *Awerinzewia cyclostomata.* × 100. (After Penard.)

93 (92) Aperture elliptical or linear, not terminating a tube.

Heleopera Leidy . . 94

94 (95) Chlorophyl always present. . . . . . *Heleopera picta* Leidy 1874.

The shell is very regular in outline, of a yellowish tint, usually with little foreign material attached. The presence of chlorophyl seems to be necessary to the life of the animal. Pseudopodia numerous. Found in sphagnous swamps. Length 100 to 110 μ.

FIG. 318. *Heleopera picta.* × 150. (After Leidy.)

95 (94) Wine-red in color. . . . . *Heleopera rosea* Penard 1890.

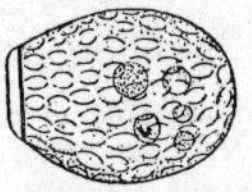

This species may be known by its color, the tint being of variable depths. Sand grains and other foreign elements cover the fundus of the shell. A thin, yellowish lip borders the aperture. Found among mosses in swamps. Length 90 to 100 μ.

FIG. 319. *Heleopera rosea.* × 150. (After Penard.)

96 (23) Pseudopodia sometimes thick, sometimes linear. 97

97 (100) Shell chitinous, densely covered with sand grains, diatom shells, and other foreign elements. . . . *Phryganella* Penard . . 98

98 (99) Large size; foreign elements large, rough.

Phryganella nidulus Penard 1902.

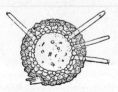

The shell is hemispherical and usually of rough contour. Aperture large. Pseudopodia slender but often accompanied by broad lobes of protoplasm. Found in the ooze of ponds and lakes. Large forms are 200 μ in diameter.

FIG. 320. *Phryganella nidulus.* × 90. (After Penard.)

99 (98) Small size; foreign elements small.

Phryganella hemisphaerica Penard 1890.

Shell hemispherical, composed of small diatom shells and sand grains. Pseudopodia usually slender, sometimes thick. Found in the ooze of ponds and lakes. Diameter 40 to 55 μ.

FIG. 321. *Phryganella hemisphaerica.* × 250. (After Penard.)

100 (97) Shell chitinous, without or sparsely covered with foreign elements. 101

101 (102) Shell occasionally with foreign elements attached. Aperture terminal. . . . . *Cryptodifflugia* Penard. Representative species. . . *Cryptodifflugia oviformis* Penard 1890.

This species has a transparent, yellowish or brownish shell without foreign elements attached. Ovoid in form. The protoplasm does not fill the shell and pseudopodia are seldom extended. Found in marshes. Length 16 to 20 μ.

FIG. 322. *Cryptodifflugia oviformis.* × 450. (After Penard.)

102 (101) Shell without foreign elements. Aperture terminal or subterminal.

Platoum F. E. Schultze.

FIG. 323. *Platoum parvum.* × 725. (After Penard.)

In 1875 Schultze described a form under the name *Platoum parvum.* Ovoid with smooth envelop without structure, slightly elastic, aperture terminal or subterminal. Penard, more recently, observed numerous empty shells and inactive organisms which he provisionally refers to this genus. Some had undulating envelopes with apertures terminal or directed obliquely. Nucleus and contractile vacuole each single. Pseudopodia not observed. Length 16 to 21μ. In preserved material from Alaska, G. H. Wailes found forms which he considers within this genus, probably *P. parvum.* Thus far this is the only record of the genus in North America.

103 (22) Pseudopodia delicate, filiform, usually branched, and pointed.

Family EUGLYPHIDAE . . 104

104 (107) Shell flexible, transparent. . . . . . *Pamphagus* Bailey . . 105

105 (106) Shell spherical. . . . . . *Pamphagus hyalinus* Ehrenberg 1838.

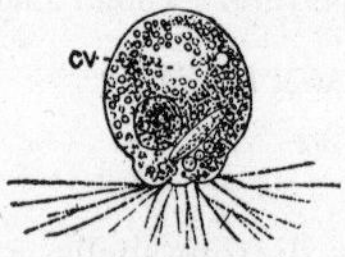

The aperture of the shell is very large and capable of great dilation. Protoplasm is clear, colorless. Nucleus spherical; contractile vacuole single. Pseudopodia numerous, straight, and pointed. Found in clear water. Diameter of shell 30 to 48 μ.

FIG. 324. *Pamphagus hyalinus. cv,* contractile vacuole. × 260. (After Leidy.)

106 (105) Shell ovoid or elongate. . . . *Pamphagus mutabilis* Bailey 1853.

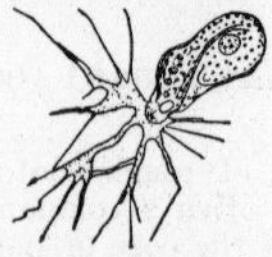

Body very changeable in form. Protoplasm enclosing brilliant granules. Nucleus large, spherical. Contractile vacuoles, one or two. Found in clear water. Length of shell 50 to 70 μ.

FIG. 325. *Pamphagus mutabilis.* × 165. (After Penard.)

107 (104) Shell rigid. 108

108 (113) Shell retort-shaped. 109

109 (110)   Plates small, round, more or less covered by foreign particles.
Campascus Leidy.
Representative species. . . . . . *Campascus cornutus* Leidy 1877.

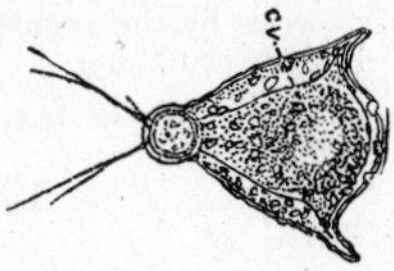

This species has lateral processes developed from the fundus. In common with other species of the genus, a delicate, transparent collar surrounds the aperture, extending perpendicular to it. In common with the genus *Cyphoderia*, the bodies of all species of this genus enclose minute yellow or brown granules very resistant to reagents. Apparently a very rare species. Leidy reports it from but one locality, China Lake, Wyoming, at an altitude of 10,000 feet. Length 112 to 140 μ.

Fig. 326. *Campascus cornutus.* cv, contractile vacuole. × 150.
(After Leidy.)

110 (109)   Plates small, regular, not covered by foreign particles.
Cyphoderia Schlumberger . .   111

111 (112)   Fundus rounded or mamillate.
Cyphoderia ampulla Ehrenberg 1840.

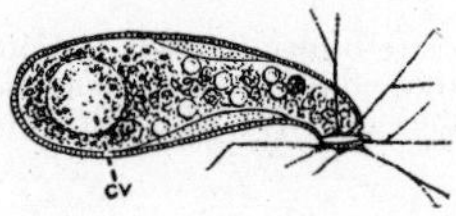

Plates round or oval, cemented together in diagonal rows, presenting a hexagonal appearance. The plates do not overlap. Minute perforations exist between the plates, appearing as fine punctae. Pseudopodia few but very long. Found among mosses, ooze of ponds and lakes. Length 61 to 195 μ. Several varieties of this species are known.

Fig. 327. *Cyphoderia ampulla.* cv, contractile vacuole. × 160.
(After Leidy.)

112 (111)   Fundus tapering. . *Cyphoderia ampulla* var. *papillata* Wailes 1911.

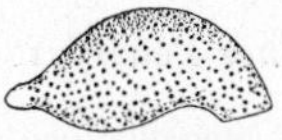

This variety resembles the type species except in the shape of the fundus. The plates are sometimes set very close together in this variety but do not overlap. Found in ooze of lakes. Length 113 to 135 μ.

Fig. 328. *Cyphoderia ampulla* var. *papillata.* ×150. (From a prepared mount.)

113 (108)   Shell straight.   114

114 (115)   Shell without distinct plates, chitinous, covered with sand, dirt, etc. . . . . *Pseudodifflugia* Schlumberger.
Representative species.

Pseudodifflugia gracilis Schlumberger 1845.

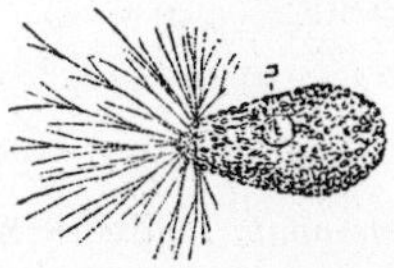

Shell ovoid, elongate, usually yellowish or brownish. Pseudopodia numerous, very long and delicate. Found in the ooze of ponds, lakes, etc. Length 20 to 65 μ.

Fig. 329. *Pseudodifflugia gracilis.* n, nucleus. × 250. (After Leidy.)

115 (114)   Shell with distinct plates.   116

116 (119)   Shell not compressed, with a short flattened neck. Plates round or oval. . . . . *Sphenoderia* Schlumberger . .   117

117 (118)   Margin of neck dentate. . . . *Sphenoderia dentata* Penard 1890.

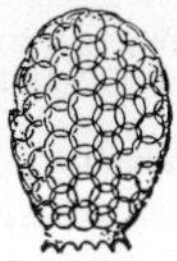

This species may be known by the elongate-oval form of the shell and the presence of the teeth. The plates overlap, giving the appearance of a hexagonal design. Found among sphagnum. Length 35 to 50 μ.

Fig. 330. *Sphenoderia dentata.* × 310. (After Penard.)

118 (117)   Margin of neck not dentate.   *Sphenoderia lenta* Schlumberger 1845.

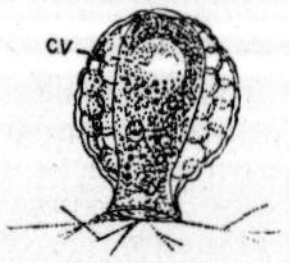

Shell ovoid or rounded with large, round imbricating plates.   The aperture consists of a narrow, elongated opening, extending between two lateral
points opposite each other.   Pseudopodia are numerous and very long.
Habitat sphagnum.   Length from 35 to 50 μ.   Leidy describes a species
under the name *S. macrolepis*, differing from other species by the angular
plates composing the shell.   Habitat sphagnum.   Length 24 to 39 μ.

Fig. 331.   *Sphenoderia lenta.   cv*, contractile vacuole.   × 300.   (After Leidy.)

119 (116)   Shell compressed, without a neck.   120

120 (137)   Aperture terminal.   121

121 (136)   Margin of aperture dentate.   122

122 (125)   Plates elongate-elliptical; margin of aperture finely dentate.
                                                Assulina Ehrenberg . .   123

123 (124)   Large size, rounded.   . . . *Assulina seminulum* Ehrenberg 1848.

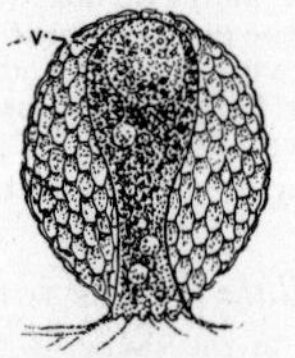

Adult forms of this species are chocolate brown in color.   Contractile vacuole single.   Nucleus very large, elliptical.   Pseudopodia
seldom observed.   Common in sphagnous swamps.   Length 60 to
88 μ.

Fig. 332   *Assulina seminulum.   cv,* contractile vacuole.   × 290.
(After Leidy.)

124 (123)   Small size, oval. . . . . *Assulina minor* Penard 1890.

This species is also brown in color but clearer than the preceding one and
the aperture is more regularly crenulate.   The hexagonal design formed by the
imbricating plates is very symmetrical.   Found among mosses.   Length 35 μ.

Fig. 333.   *Assulina minor.*   × 300.   (After Penard.)

125 (122)   Plates round or oval; margin of aperture with prominent denticles.
              Spines often developed.   . . . *Euglypha* Dujardin . .   126

126 (133)   Aperture circular.   127

127 (130)   Spines at apex only.   128

128 (129)   Spines, one or two. . . . . . . *Euglypha mucronata* Leidy 1878.

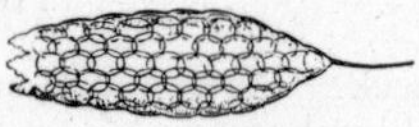

The shell not compressed; plates imbricating, arranged in
longitudinal, alternating rows.   The fundus tapers to a point
which is provided with one or two spines.   Found in sphagnous
swamps.   Reported from North America only.   Length 108 to
140 μ.

Fig. 334.   *Euglypha mucronata.*   × 165.   (After Leidy.)

129 (128)   Spines in a tuft. . . . . *Euglypha cristata* Leidy 1874.

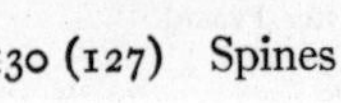

Shell elongated, very little compressed if any, with plates arranged
as in preceding species.   Pseudopodia rarely extended.   Habitat
sphagnous swamps.   Length 33 to 84 μ.

Fig. 335.   *Euglypha cristata.*   × 425.   (After Leidy.)

130 (127)   Spines not at apex only.   131

131 (132) Spines lateral. . . . . *Euglypha brachiata* Leidy 1878.

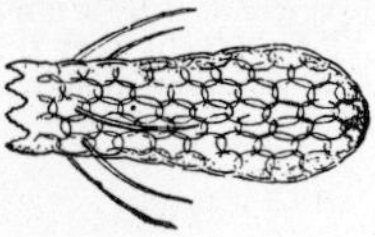

This species may be known by the straight shell, elongate and cylindrical. Plates oval, imbricating in a regular manner. From four to six large, long spines are developed, representing prolongations of some of the lateral plates. Habitat among sphagnum. Length 104 to 128 μ.

FIG. 336. *Euglypha brachiata.* × 180. (After Leidy.)

132 (131) Spines usually absent, scattered when present.
Euglypha alveolata Dujardin 1841.

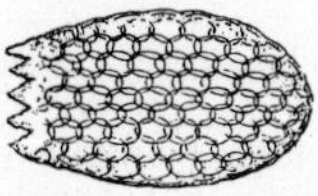

Shell ovoid, elongated, very slightly compressed if any. Plates round or oval, imbricating, presenting a regular hexagonal design. Nucleus large, spherical; contractile vacuoles two in number. Pseudopodia numerous, long and straight. A common species in the ooze of ponds, among algae and mosses. Length 45 to 100 μ.

FIG. 337. *Euglypha alveolata.* × 375. (Original, from a prepared mount.)

133 (126) Aperture oval. 134

134 (135) Plates bordering aperture denticulate.
Euglypha ciliata Ehrenberg 1848.

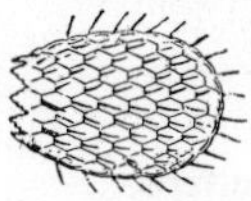

Shell compressed, elongate-oval. Plates oval or round, imbricated. Needle-like spines are produced from the entire surface or in a line around the lateral border of the shell. Habitat sphagnum. Length 40 to 90 μ.

FIG. 338. *Euglypha ciliata.* × 250. (After Penard.)

135 (134) Plates bordering aperture lobed. *Euglypha compressa* Carter 1864.

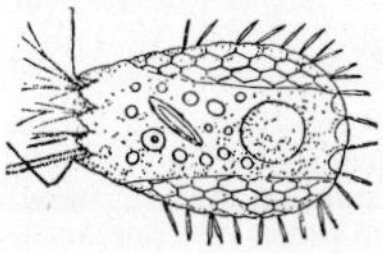

Shell greatly compressed, formed of elliptical plates, imbricating and presenting a hexagonal design. Numerous spines, fusiform in shape, are produced from the lateral border of the shell. Habitat sphagnum. Length 70 to 132 μ.

FIG. 339. *Euglypha compressa.* × 225. (After Leidy.)

136 (121) Margin of aperture not dentate. Shell oval, compressed.
Placocista Leidy.
Representative species. . . . . . *Placocista spinosa* Leidy 1874.

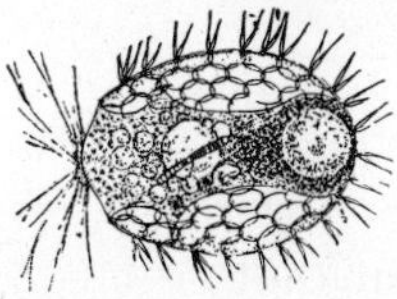

This species may be known by the long, awl-shaped spines which are movably articulated in a line about the lateral border of the shell. Plates oval, imbricating in a regular manner. Habitat sphagnum. Length 100 to 136 μ.

FIG. 340. *Placocista spinosa.* × 170. (After Leidy.)

137 (120) Aperture not terminal. 138

138 (143) Shell elongate-oval, usually compressed; aperture subterminal. Plates rounded. . . . . . *Trinema* Dujardin . . 139

139 (140) Oral extremity broad. . . . *Trinema camplanatum* Penard 1890.

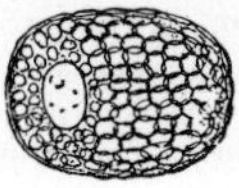

This species is short and broad, the anterior end usually as broad as the posterior extremity. Aperture oval. Habitat mosses. Length 30 to 40 μ.

FIG. 341. *Trinema camplanatum.* × 500. (After Penard.)

140 (139) Oral extremity narrow. 141

141 (142)　Plates distinct, large size. . . . *Trinema enchelys* Ehrenberg 1836.

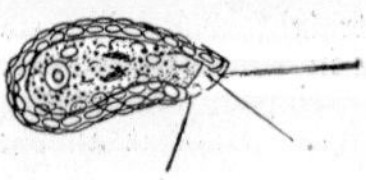

The aperture is circular in this species and surrounded by a number of rows of very minute chitinous plates. Pseudopodia very fine and long, usually few in number. This is the most common species of the genus and is found everywhere among mosses. Length 40 to 100 μ.

FIG. 342. *Trinema enchelys.* × 310. (After Penard.)

142 (141)　Plates indistinct, small size. . . . *Trinema lineare* Penard 1890.

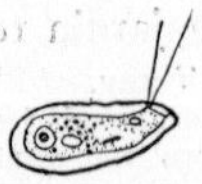

The plates of this small form are indistinct except about the edges, where they may appear as minute undulations. The aperture is round. Habitat as other species. Length 16 to 26 μ.

FIG. 343. *Trinema lineare.* × 500. (After Penard.)

143 (138)　Shell shaped as *Trinema;* aperture subterminal; plates elongate.
　　　　　　　　　　　　　　　　　　　　　　　　Corythion Taranek.
　Representative species. . . . . . *Corythion dubium* Taranek 1882.

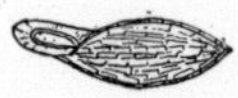

In this species the shape of the aperture is characteristic, its border representing two unequal arcs placed together, the anterior one the longer. The plates are close together but not overlapping. Habitat mosses. Length 35 to 40 μ.

FIG. 344. *Corythion dubium.* × 375. (After Penard.)

144 (2)　Pseudopodia usually anastomosing. 145

145 (158)　Pseudopodia very delicate, usually finely branched.
　　　　　　　　　　　　　　　　　　Subclass **Foraminifera** . . 146

146 (147)　Body without a covering; pseudopodia formed from any part of the surface. . . . . *Biomyxa* Leidy.
　Representative species. . . . . . *Biomyxa vagans* Leidy 1875.

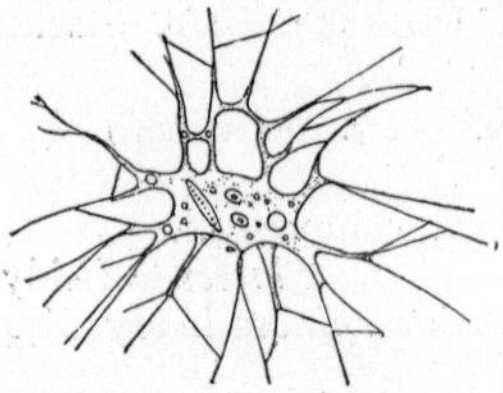

The body moves slowly but continuously, no distinction between ectoplasm and endoplasm being observed. Pseudopodia long, branching and anastomosing, always changing. A granular nucleus and a number of contractile vacuoles are present. Habitat sphagnous swamps. Large individuals may measure 480 μ between the tips of the pseudopodia.

FIG. 345. *Biomyxa vagans.* × 65. (After Penard.)

147 (146)　Body with a distinct covering. 148

148 (153)　Pseudopodia extending from more than one aperture. . . . 149

149 (152)　Envelop elongate, compressed. . . *Amphitrema* Archer . . 150

150 (151)　Envelop transparent, with no foreign particles attached.
　　　　　　　　　　　　　　　　　Amphitrema flavum Archer 1878.

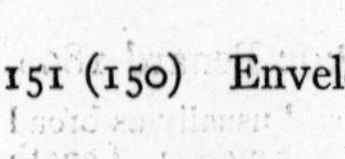

Pseudopodia straight, unbranched, extending from the opposite poles of the envelop. Protoplasm always enclosing chlorophyl. Nucleus single. One or more contractile vacuoles. Habitat mosses. Length 45 to 55 μ.

FIG. 346. *Amphitrema flavum.* × 255. (After Penard.)

151 (150)　Envelop with foreign particles attached.
　　　　　　　　　　　　　　Amphitrema wrightianum Archer 1870.

In this species the apertures at opposite poles are surrounded by short collars. Chlorophyl always present. Pseudopodia often branched. Nucleus single. Contractile vacuoles one or more. Habitat mosses. Length 65 to 70 μ.

FIG. 347. *Amphitrema wrightianum.* × 215. (After Penard.)

152 (149) Envelop spherical. . . . . *Diplophrys* Barker.
Representative species. . . . . *Diplophrys archeri* Barker 1868. 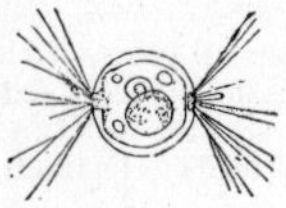
In this species the pseudopodia, which are long and branched, extend from opposite poles of the envelop. The protoplasm always encloses a large spherical globule usually yellow or brown in color. A nucleus and one or more contractile vacuoles are present. Habitat sphagnum. Diameter 8 to 20 μ.

FIG. 348. *Diplophrys archeri.* × 1200. (After Penard.)

153 (148) Pseudopodia extending from a single aperture. 154

154 (155) Envelop very flexible, changeable in shape.
Lieberkühnia Claparède and Lachmann.
Representative species. . . *Lieberkühnia wageneri* C. and L. 1858.

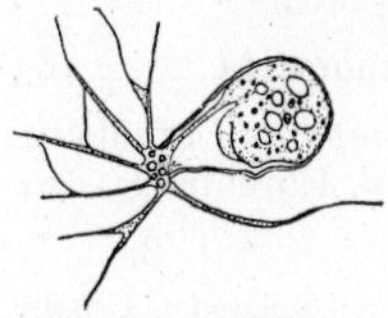

The envelop is normally pyriform but changeable in shape. Pseudopodia long, anastomosing, extending from a protoplasmic peduncle at the aperture. Nuclei as many as 200. Contractile vacuoles numerous. Habitat mosses. Length 96 μ.

FIG. 349. *Lieberkühnia wageneri.* × 130. (After Penard.)

155 (154) Envelop rigid or slightly flexible. 156

156 (157) Body filling the envelop. . . . . *Gromia* Dujardin.
Representative species. . . . . *Gromia fluviatilis* Dujardin 1841. 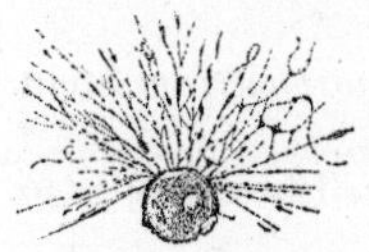
Envelop spherical or ovoid, seldom changing shape. The outer surface of the envelop is covered by a delicate sheath of protoplasm in which minute granules circulate. Pseudopodia numerous, anastomosing. Habitat among aquatic plants. Diameter 90 to 250 μ. This species is identical with *Gromia terricola* Leidy.

FIG. 350. *Gromia fluviatilis.* × 25. (After Leidy.)

157 (156) Body not filling the envelop. . . . . . *Microgromia* R. Hertwig.
Representative species. . . *Microgromia socialis* R. Hertwig 1874. 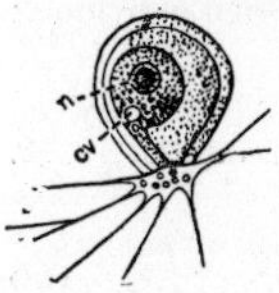
Envelop rigid with a short neck. Pseudopodia long, anastomosing, arising from a peduncle at the aperture. Sometimes colonies are formed. Habitat standing water. Length 20 μ. Conn reports a form from Connecticut which he refers to this species with some doubt as to its identity.

FIG. 351. *Microgromia socialis.* cv, contractile vacuole; n, nucleus. × 545. (After Hertwig.)

158 (145) Pseudopodia ray-like, soft, and anastomosing when touching.
Subclass **Proteomyxa** . . 159

159 (160) Body amoeboid; endoplasm colorless. . . *Nuclearia* Cienkowsky.
Representative species. . . . *Nuclearia simplex* Cienkowsky 1865. 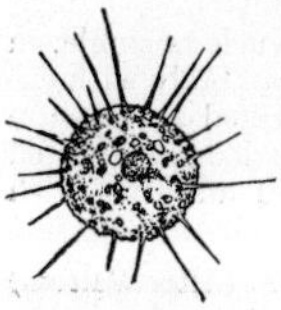
Body normally spherical but capable of changing shape. Pseudopodia arising from all parts of the body. Nucleus central, contractile vacuoles more than one. Diameter 20 to 50 μ. Reported by Conn from Connecticut.

FIG. 352. *Nuclearia simplex.* × 250. (After Conn.)

160 (159)   Body amoeboid; endoplasm red or brown.
Vampyrella Cienkowsky.
Representative species. . . *Vampyrella lateritia* Cienkowsky 1865.

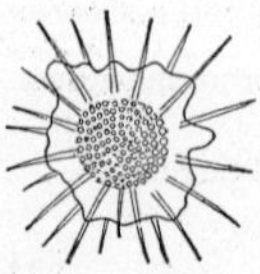

Body spherical or elongated. Pseudopodia arising from all parts of the body or from one point. The nucleus and contractile vacuole usually concealed by the contents of the endoplasm. A gelatinous sheath sometimes surrounds the body. Habitat among algae upon which it feeds. Diameter 25 to 80 μ.

FIG. 353.   *Vampyrella lateritia.*   X 250.   (After Conn.)

161 (1)   Pseudopodia with axial filaments. . . . . . . Class **Actinopoda.**
Fresh-water species included in one subclass.
Subclass **Heliozoa** . .   162

No central capsule between endoplasm and ectoplasm. Pseudopodia ray-like.

162 (165)   With no external envelop . . . . Order **Aphrothoracida** . .   163

163 (164)   Nucleus single. . . . . *Actinophrys* Ehrenberg.
Representative species. . . . . *Actinophrys sol.* Ehrenberg 1830.

Body spherical with protoplasm highly vacuolated. Usually one contractile vacuole which rises and pushes out the surface as a rounded globule before bursting. Pseudopodia extending from all parts of the body. Habitat pond water among aquatic plants; very common. Diameter 40 to 50 μ.

FIG. 354.   *Actinophrys sol. cv,* contractile vacuole.   X 245.   (After Leidy.)

164 (163)   Nuclei many. . . . . *Actinosphaerium* Stein.
Representative species.

Actinosphaerium eichhornii Ehrenberg 1840.

Protoplasm vacuolated with very large vacuoles about the periphery. Nuclei scattered throughout the endoplasm. Pseudopodia extending from all parts of the body. One or more contractile vacuoles. Habitat among aquatic plants. Not common. Average diameter 200 to 300 μ. Some have reported individuals over 1000 μ in diameter.

FIG. 355.   *Actinosphaerium eichhornii. cv,* contractile vacuole.   X 40.
(After Leidy.)

165 (162)   With an external envelop.   166

166 (167)   Envelop gelatinous, without plates or spicules.
Order **Chlamydophora.**

One genus reported in North America.   . . . *Actinolophus* Schultze.
With a pedicel.

Representative species.   . . *Actinolophus minutus* Walton 1905.

Pseudopodia very short, extending from all parts of the body. Nucleus single, in the posterior region. Contractile vacuole not observed. Diameter of body with envelop 12 μ. Length of pedicel 70 μ. Habitat river water. Described by Walton from Ohio. This genus is introduced provisionally. Further knowledge is needed concerning it, as certain species referred to the genus show marked affinities with *Suctoria.*

FIG. 356.   *Actinolophus minutus. cv,* contractile vacuole; *n.* nucleus.   X 350.   (After Walton.)

167 (166)   Envelop with more or less closely united spicules. 168

168 (175)   With a thick protoplasmic envelop in which are imbedded skeletal elements in the form of spicules or plates.
Order **Chalarothoraca** . . 169

169 (172)   Skeletal elements loosely connected. 170

170 (171)   Spicules chitinous, radiating between the pseudopodia.
Heterophrys Archer.
Representative species. . . . *Heterophrys myriopoda* Archer 1869.

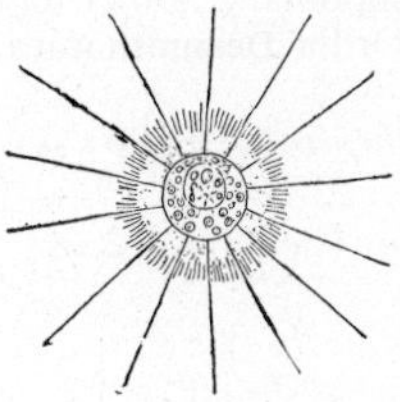

In this species the envelop is mucilaginous, its outer border presenting a villous appearance due to the arrangement of the spicules. Ray-like pseudopodia penetrate the envelop. This organism is known to take possession of spicules from species of related genera, probably from discarded skeletons, and make them a part of its own envelop. Endoplasm usually green with symbiotic algae. Nucleus single. A contractile vacuole is not always observed. Habitat marshes and standing water. Diameter 70 μ.

FIG. 357. *Heterophrys myriopoda.* × 190. (After Penard.)

171 (170)   Spicules siliceous, scattered through the envelop and surrounding the bases of the pseudopodia. . . . *Raphidiophrys* Archer.
Representative species.
Raphidiophrys elegans Hertwig and Lesser 1874.

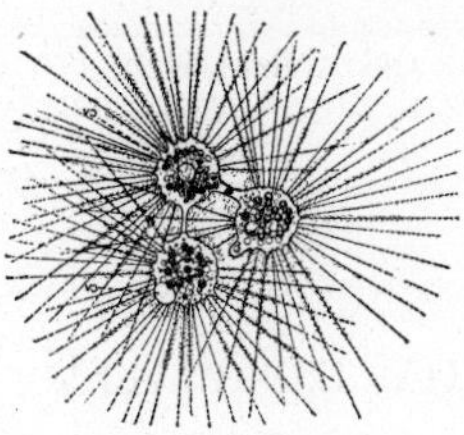

The spicules are semicircular, with their convex surfaces toward the body and pseudopodia. Nucleus single. One contractile vacuole. Chlorophyl sometimes present. Often numbers of these individuals are grouped into colonies, joined by protoplasmic processes. Habitat among aquatic plants. Diameter 30 μ.
R. viridis Archer differs from *R. elegans* in the fusiform spicules and the constant presence of symbiotic algae.

FIG. 358. *Raphidiophrys elegans.* × 150. (After Leidy.)

172 (169)   Skeletal elements closely united, forming a compact envelop. 173

173 (174)   Spicules siliceous, globular, completely surrounding the body.
Pompholyxophrys Archer.
Representative species. . . *Pompholyxophrys punicea* Archer 1869.

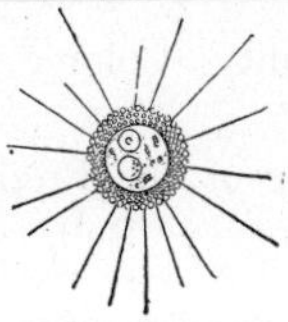

The spicules usually in three rows about the body. Endoplasm reddish. Nucleus spherical, large. No contractile vacuole. Pseudopodia very fine and indistinct. Habitat among aquatic plants in ponds and in swamps. Diameter 25 to 30 μ. Leidy records this species from New Jersey as *Hyalolampe fenestrata* Greeff.

FIG. 359. *Pompholyxophrys punicea.* × 200. (After Penard.)

174 (173) Spicules siliceous, in the form of plates and delicate radiating spines. . . . . *Acanthocystis* Carter.
Representative species. . . *Acanthocystis chaetophora* Leidy 1874.

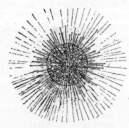

The skeletal plates are oval, arranged tangentially. The spinous rays are of two lengths, the long ones acutely forked, the short ones widely forked at the distal extremities. Nucleus large, usually no contractile vacuole. Endoplasm green in color from enclosed chlorophyl. Habitat among aquatic plants. Diameter of body 50 to 60 μ.

Fig. 360. *Acanthocystis chaetophora.* × 250. (After Leidy.)

175 (168) With a solid envelop, perforated for the pseudopodia. Sometimes stalked. . . . . Order **Desmothoraca.**

One genus reported in North America. . . . *Clathrulina* Cienkowsky.
Envelop with a stalk.
Representative species. . . . . . *Clathrulina elegans* Cienkowsky 1867.

Envelop more or less chitinous, perforated by numerous large, irregular openings. Protoplasm not filling the envelop. Nucleus single. One or more contractile vacuoles. Pseudopodia very delicate, apparently without axial filaments. Habitat sphagnous swamps and among aquatic plants; very common in some localities. Diameter of envelop 60 to 90 μ.

Fig. 361. *Clathrulina elegans.* × 130. (After Leidy.)

IMPORTANT REFERENCES ON PROTOZOA, ESPECIALLY SARCODINA

Bütschli, O. 1883. Protozoa. In Bronn's Klassen and Ordnungen des Thierreichs, vol. 1, pt. 1-3. Leipzig.

Calkins, G. N. 1901. The Protozoa. New York.

1909. Protozoology. New York.

Cash, J., and Hopkins, J. 1905-1909. The British Fresh-water Rhizopoda and Heliozoa. 2 parts. Ray Society, vol. 75.

Cockerell, T. D. A. 1911. The Fauna of Boulder County, Colorado. Univ. Colo. Studies, 8: 227-256.

Conn, H. W. 1905. A Preliminary Report on the Protozoa of the Fresh Waters of Connecticut. State Geol. and Nat. Hist. Survey, Bull. 2; 69 pp., 34 pl.

EDMONDSON, C. H. 1906. The Protozoa of Iowa. Proc. Davenport Acad. Sci., 11: 1–124; 29 pl.

1912. Protozoa of High Mountain Lakes in Colorado. Univ. Colo. Studies, 9: 65–74.

HEMPEL, A. 1898. A list of the Protozoa and Rotifera Found in Illinois River and Adjacent Lakes at Havana, Ill. Bull. Ill. State Lab. Nat. Hist., 5: 301–388; 5 figs.

LANDACRE, F. L. 1908. Protozoa of Sandusky Bay and Vicinity. Ohio Acad. Sci., 4: 421–472.

LEIDY, JOS. 1879. Fresh-water Rhizopods of North America. U. S. Geol. Surv. Territ., vol. 12; 324 pp., 48 pl.

PENARD, E. 1902. Faune rhizopodique du bassin du léman. 714 pp., figs. Genève.

1904. Les Héliozoaires d'eau douce. 341 pp., figs. Genève.

1905. Les Sarcodines des grand lacs. 133 pp., figs. Genève.

1911. Rhizopodes d'eau douce. British Antartic Expedition, 1907–9, 1: 203–262. (Includes a list of Rhizopods from Canada.)

WAILES, G. H. 1912. Fresh-water Rhizopods and Heliozoa from the States of New York, New Jersey, and Georgia, U. S. A.; with Supplemental Note on Seychelles Species. Jour. Linnean Soc., Zoology 32: 121–161; 1 pl.

WAILES, G. H., and PENARD, E. 1911. Rhizopoda. Proc. Roy. Irish Acad., Clare Island Survey, Part 65; 64 pp.; 6 pl.

CHAPTER IX

FLAGELLATE AND CILIATE PROTOZOA

(MASTIGOPHORA ET INFUSORIA)

By H. W. CONN   AND   C. H. EDMONDSON

Professor of Biology, Wesleyan University   *Assistant Professor of Zoology, University of Oregon*

By early observers the term Infusoria was applied to all minute organisms found in water, including not only unicellular animals but many minute plants and not a few multicellular animals, as rotifers, sponges, etc. Later the term was restricted to those one-celled animals which are commonly found in standing water and which move by means of long whip-like processes called flagella or by shorter, hair-like structures called cilia.

At the present time the flagellated forms are included under the subphylum Mastigophora and those possessing cilia, throughout their entire existence or during their embryonic stage only, are grouped under the subphylum Infusoria. Mastigophora and Infusoria are of almost universal distribution, occurring in fresh and salt water, abundant in clear pools and streams as well as in stagnant bodies of water and also in infusions of plant or animal macerations. Some are parasitic, living upon or within the bodies of other animals.

In the Mastigophora flagella are the characteristic structural features. These structures are slender, flexible, whip-like processes drawn out from the body, commonly at one end. The flagellum when single is usually directed forward, and by a lashing movement, a corkscrew twisting, or a mere vibration of its free distal end draws the body forward. Flagella may be numerous and often one or more are directed backward or trail at the side in addition to those extended in advance.

That a close relationship exists between flagella and pseudopodia is easily observed in a number of forms. Some low flagellates possess well-defined pseudopodia, and the flagella of these forms have the appearance of permanent, specialized pseudopodia endowed with the power of vibration. The interchanging of pseudopodia and flagella has been referred to in the case of *Vampyrella* under Sarcodina. The origin of the flagellum has been traced in some forms to the region of the nucleus, which may be considered as evidence in favor of its homology with the axial supports of pseudopodia.

Cilia, which are the conspicuous and for diagnosis the special structural feature of the ciliates, as contrasted with flagella, are short, hair-like processes. They arise from the ectoplasm, not originating from the deeper regions of the body as do flagella. Cilia may be evenly distributed over the surface of the animal or restricted to certain regions or zones. Often fusion of cilia takes place forming vibrating membranelles or large bristle-like cirri or setae. By tufts of cilia certain forms may be temporarily attached to supports. Suctoria, in transition from the embryonic stages to the adult, lose the covering of cilia which is replaced by hollow tentacles, capable of extension and retraction. The tentacles may be pointed or distinctly capitate, the prey being pierced by them and its protoplasm drawn through the hollow tubules into the body of the suctorian.

In Mastigophora and Infusoria the protoplasm is similar in structure to that of lower Protozoa, being alveolar in character. However, in these groups, the protoplasmic contents of the body are not arranged in zones to the extent found in Sarcodina. Great variation exists in the consistency of the body both in flagellates and in ciliates. In some the body is soft and flexible, the ectoplasm permitting rapid changes in shape or even the formation of pseudopodia; others are enclosed by inflexible membranes, sheaths, or well-defined plates. Cup-like loricae are sometimes developed, to the inner surface of which the animal may be fixed, from which it may project, and into which it may retract. In a few of the flagellates a delicate collar is formed about the base of the flagellum. The collar is very transparent, variable in size, and capable of being retracted into the body protoplasm like a pseudopodium.

Many flagellates and ciliates are free swimming, while some may be temporarily fixed by cilia or flagella or by the adherence of a surface to some support. Others are attached by stalks or pedicels which may be rigid, flexible or, in some forms, as *Vorticella*, may contract spirally. Special organs of defense are provided in a few flagellates and many ciliates in the form of trichocysts or stinging, thread-like structures. In at least one genus of flagellates, *Polykrikos*, the stinging threads are highly specialized, resembling nematocysts of Coelenterata. As in Sarcodina, one or more contractile vacuoles are usually present in the flagellates and ciliates, their function being similar in all Protozoa.

Nuclei are present in all Mastigophora and Infusoria but considerable structural variation exists with respect to them in these two groups. In some flagellates the nucleus consists of scattered or grouped particles of chromatin without a nuclear membrane, while in many of the higher Infusoria it consists of a highly differentiated, branched structure. Infusoria differ from other Protozoa, with a few possible exceptions, in the possession of two kinds of nuclei in each cell, a macronucleus and a micronucleus, the former being concerned with the vegetative functions and asexual division, the latter with sexual division. The macronucleus is the larger and often varies greatly from the regular spherical type; the micronucleus is usually very small, spherical, and in close contact with the macronucleus. In but one flagellate, *Polykrikos*, has this differentiation into two nuclei been found. In the key which follows, wherever the term nucleus is mentioned, reference is made to the macronucleus. In many forms of Mastigophora and Infusoria as well as Sarcodina, the nucleus encloses a spherical body which functions as a division center. During the resting stage of the cell the division center resembles a nucleolus in appearance, but during mitosis it elongates, forming a spindle, and indirect division comparable to that in the Metazoa occurs in some of the more complex forms.

The endoplasm of many Mastigophora encloses colored corpuscles or chromatophores, green, yellow, and brown being the prevailing colors. The chromatophores themselves often enclose deeply staining pyrenoid bodies which probably have to do with the construction of starch. Other inclusions as oil droplets, paramylum granules, allied to starch, and pigment spots are common in those forms containing chromatophores. The red "eye-spot" is usually located at the anterior end of the body near the base of the flagellum and probably functions as a sense organ, being stimulated by rays of light. Chromatophores, oil droplets, and pigment spots may sometimes be found in Infusoria but are much less common than among the flagellates.

Generally speaking, the physiological processes in Mastigophora and Infusoria are carried on precisely as in Sarcodina. The presence of chlorophyl in some of the flagellates makes possible the synthesis of food from inorganic elements, but in many of these forms and in nearly all of the ciliates distinct mouths are developed, sometimes permanently open and sometimes open only while food is being ingested. The symbiotic relationship exists with algae in some species of ciliates also. Among Mastigophora food is often whipped down by the flagellum to the soft ectoplasm at its base where ingestion takes place. The delicate collars present in some flagellates assist in food getting. Among ciliates the vibrating cilia, membranelles, and membranes serve to draw food toward the animal by arousing currents of water. In Suctoria the tentacles are organs for securing food, their distal extremities being provided with openings through which the protoplasm of the prey is drawn. Respiration and excretion are similar processes in all Protozoa. The contractile vacuoles assist in the excretion of waste fluids and probably of gases. In some Infusoria there are definite points on the surface where waste solids pass from the body.

Among the Mastigophora, longitudinal fission is the predominating method of reproduction, only a few forms dividing transversely. Usually the chromatophores, "eye-spot" and pyrenoids, if present, divide as well as the nucleus during reproduction. The flagellum sometimes divides longitudinally, and in other forms is cast off, new flagella being developed as the cells separate. In some cases the "eye-spot," pyrenoids, and flagella are duplicated before a division of the cell commences. Many colonial forms of Mastigophora illustrate a highly specialized type of cell division similar to that shown in a metazoan ovum. Among Infusoria simple division is the predominating method of reproduction. Division may be longitudinal, transverse, or diagonal, both nuclei dividing during the process, new structures such as mouth parts and contractile vacuoles usually being formed as division goes on. The production of swarm spores is common among the flagellates, occurring either in the free swimming or encysted condition and developing into the adult either directly or after the fusion of two of them has taken place. Swarm spores are produced in a few species of ciliates during encystment.

Conjugation occurs in both Mastigophora and Infusoria. In some cases the fusion is permanent; in others it is temporary, the cells separating after an interchange of micronuclear material. Conjugation may often be followed by either encystment or the production of swarm spores, or both. Gametes of unequal size are frequently produced, in some cases union between two small gametes taking place, in others a large and a small one uniting. Among Vorticellidae there is a complete fusion of the free-swimming microgamete with the fixed macrogamete. In some of the more complicated flagellates, as *Volvox*, phenomena closely resembling sexual reproduction occur; sex cells are differentiated from somatic cells, ova and sperm are developed, and new colonies are produced as a result of fertilization. Encystment occurs in Mastigophora and Infusoria as in Sarcodina, the condition sometimes being preceded by conjugation or followed by the formation of swarm spores.

In general, methods of collecting, studying and preserving Sarcodina may be employed for Mastigophora and Infusoria. However, these latter are often free-swimming, swift-moving forms, and before any satisfactory study of them can be made their movements must be retarded. An aqueous solution of gelatin will check the movements without killing the animals if a solution of the right consistency is used and this may be obtained by trial. Egg albumen may be substituted for gelatin. A drop of very dilute methyl alcohol added to the water containing Protozoa will usually narcotize them. Evaporation of water from under the cover glass will gradually retard their movements but the larger forms will soon be crushed by the weight of the cover unless the latter is supported by wax feet, bits of paper, or very thin glass. Fine capillary tubes broken into short pieces make useful rollers on which the cover glass may be supported and the protozoan, if under the proper pressure, may then be rotated for study from various aspects.

KEY TO NORTH AMERICAN FRESH–WATER MASTIGOPHORA

1 (131) Flagellated forms with animal characteristics predominating.
Class **Zoomastigophora** . . 2

Confessedly a poor definition, but no better can be given. The beginner will often be in doubt whether forms under consideration are flagellated animals (Mastigophora), or flagellated plants (unicellular algae), or less frequently flagellate stages (spores) of Protozoa and Protophyta. Even authorities are not in agreement regarding the position which should be assigned to specific forms; thus the Volvocina are included in both Protophyta and Protozoa in this book.

2 (118) Without protoplasmic collars. . . Subclass **Lissoflagellata** . . 3

3 (36) Very plastic, often producing pseudopodia. Order **Monadida** . . 4

4 (15) Not forming colonies and without lorica. 5

5 (12) Pseudopodia present; flagella, one or two.
Family RHIZOMASTIGIDAE . . 6
6 (9) Flagellum single. 7

7 (8) Pseudopodia lobe-like or pointed, sometimes branched.
Mastigamoeba Schultze.
Representative species. . . . . *Mastigamoeba longifilum* Stokes 1886.

Body very changeable in shape, often producing distinct pseudopodia; movements usually slow, repent, but sometimes the animal glides forward rapidly without pseudopodia being formed. Flagellum long, very active. Nucleus small, near the anterior extremity; contractile vacuole single, anterior in position. Length 12 to 30 μ. Standing water, among decaying vegetation.

FIG. 362. *Mastigamoeba longifilum.* × 1000. (After Conn.)

8 (7) Pseudopodia ray-like, often capitate. . . . . . *Actinomonas* Kent.
Representative species. . . . . . *Actinomonas vernalis* Stokes 1885.

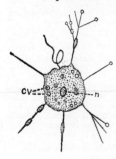

Body subspherical, changeable in shape, free swimming or temporarily attached by a short stalk. Pseudopodia few, radiating from any part of the periphery, simple or branched. Nucleus subcentral; contractile vacuoles several. Diameter about 20 μ. Shallow ponds in early spring.

FIG. 363. *Actinomonas vernalis.* *cv*, contractile vacuole; *n*, nucleus.
× 600. (After Stokes.)

9 (6) More than one flagellum. 10

10 (11)   Pseudopodia ray-like with swellings along their course.   Flagella
          directed forward. . . . . *Acinetactis* Stokes.
          Representative species. . . . . . *Acinetactis mirabilis* Stokes 1886.

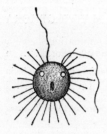

Body subspherical, soft, and plastic.   Short, lobate pseudopodia
often in addition to capitate rays.   Flagella subequal arising at
some distance from each other.   Nucleus central; contractile vacuoles two.   Diameter about 12 μ.   Stagnant pond water.

FIG. 364.   *Acinetactis mirabilis.*   × 700.   (After Stokes.)

11 (10)   Pseudopodia lobe-like.   Flagella two, one trailing.   *Cercobodo* Kraas.
          Representative species. . . . . *Cercobodo* sp.

Species not determined.

FIG. 365.   *Cercobodo* sp.   × 1250.   (After Conn.)

12 (5)   Plastic but not forming pseudopodia.   Flagellum single.
                                        Family CERCOMONADIDAE . . 13

13 (14)   With a posterior tail-like filament. . . . . . *Cercomonas* Dujardin.
          Representative species. . . *Cercomonas longicaudata* Dujardin 1841.

Body elongate-ovate, fusiform, terminating
posteriorly in a long, tail-like filament about
twice the length of the body.   Nucleus spherical, subcentral.   Length 10 μ.   Vegetable
infusions.

FIG. 366.   *Cercomonas longicaudata.*   *cv*, contractile
vacuole; *n*, nucleus.   × 1200.   (After Stein.)

14 (13)   Without a tail-like filament. . . . . *Oikomonas* Kent.
          Representative species. . . . . *Oikomonas steinii* Kent 1880.

Body, in motile condition, exceedingly plastic with a single
flagellum at the anterior end and a lip-like extension which assists in taking food; in sedentary state, pyriform and attached
by posterior extremity.   Nucleus posteriorly located.   Length,
when contracted, about 20 to 30 μ.   Vegetable infusions.   Social.

FIG. 367.   *Oikomonas steinii.*   *cv*, contractile vacuole; *n*, nucleus.
× 440.   (After Blochmann.)

15 (4)   Often forming colonies and often with lorica. . . . .(21) 16
16 (21) Lorica present. . . . . Family BIKOECIDAE . . 17
17 (20) Not forming colonies. 18
18 (19) Body attached in lorica by thread-like peduncle; with peristome
         process. Two flagella. . . . . . *Bicosoeca* James-Clark.
         Representative species. . . . . *Bicosoeca lepteca* Stokes 1885.

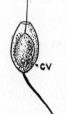

> Lorica subcylindrical with a very short neck in front; drawn out to an acute
> point where attachment is made with the pedicel. Body ovate, obliquely
> truncate in front and projecting slightly beyond the margin of the lorica when fully
> extended. Flagella unequal. Nucleus near the middle of the body; two con-
> tractile vacuoles. A chestnut-brown color of the lorica indicates old age. Length
> of lorica 15 to 18 μ. Pond water among algae.

FIG. 368. *Bicosoeca lepteca.* *cv*, contractile vacuole; *n*, nucleus. × 840. (After Stokes.)

19 (18) Body not attached by thread-like peduncle, no peristome process.
         Flagellum single. . . . . *Codonoeca* James-Clark.
         Representative species. . . . . *Codonoeca inclinata* Kent 1880.

> Lorica ovate, attached obliquely to a pedicel twice its length. Body attached
> to the posterior, inner surface of the lorica without a peduncle. Not projecting
> beyond the margin of the lorica. Flagellum extending considerably beyond
> the aperture. A nucleus and a contractile vacuole in the posterior region of
> the body. Length of lorica 15 μ. Pond water.

FIG. 369. *Codonoeca inclinata.* *cv*, contractile vacuole. × 810. (After Kent.)

20 (17) Forming colonies, with peristome projection.
         Stylobryon de Fromentel.
         Representative species. . . *Stylobryon petiolatum* Dujardin 1838.

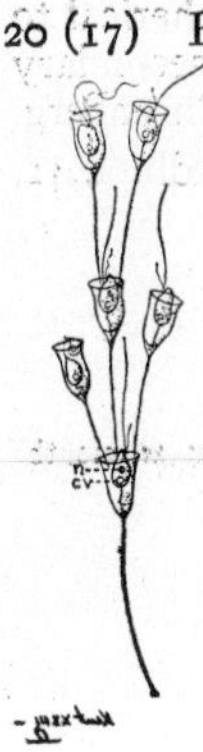

> Each lorica wineglass-shaped, pointed posteriorly, attached to a pedicel
> which arises from within the cavity of the associated lorica. Body plastic.
> Flagella two, unequal in length. Length of lorica 30 to 50 μ. Pond water.
> Often subdividing by spores.

FIG. 370. *Stylobryon petiolatum.* *cv*, contractile vacuole; *n*, nucleus. × 75. (After Kent.)

21 (16)   Without lorica; one or more flagella.
                                        Family HETEROMASTIGIDAE . . 22

22 (29)   Not forming colonies. 23

23 (26)   Flagellum single. 24

24 (25)   Flagellum directed forward. . . . . *Leptomonas* Kent.
          Representative species. . . . . *Leptomonas* sp.

> Body pointed anteriorly and very flexible. Flagellum long and active.
> Often parasitic. Fig. 371 represents a form reported by Conn, taken from a
> watering trough, and assigned to this genus with some doubt.
> Species not determined.

FIG. 371. *Leptomonas* sp. × 875. (After Conn.)

25 (24)   Flagellum trailing. . . . . *Rhynchomonas* Klebs.
          Representative species. . . . . . *Rhynchomonas nasula* Klebs 1886.

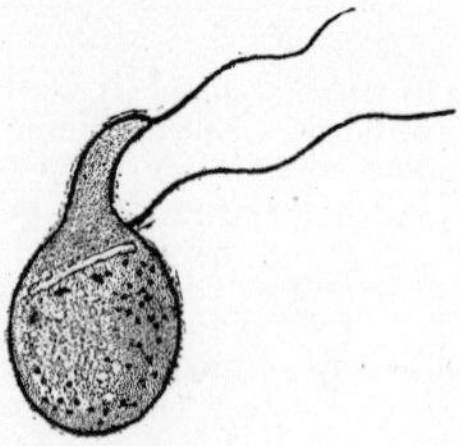

> Body ovate, slightly compressed, anterior end prolonged
> into a movable process. Mouth near the anterior end.
> Nucleus central. Contractile vacuole anterior. Fresh
> water.

FIG. 372. *Rhynchomonas nasula*. × 1500. (After Conn.)

26 (23)   Two or more flagella. 27

27 (28)   Body free or attached by an attenuated posterior end; spherical to
          ovate, with one chief flagellum and one or two secondary
          ones. Moderately flexible. . . . . . *Monas* Ehrenberg.
          Representative species. . . . . *Monas fluida* Dujardin 1841.

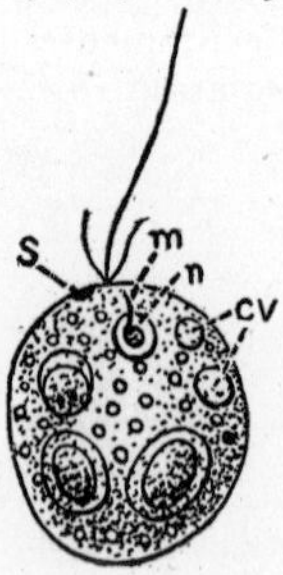

FIG. 373. *Monas fluida*. *cv*, contractile vacuole; *n*, nucleus; *s*, stigma; *m*, mouth.
                                        × 1000.

28 (27)   Free, like *Monas*, but with the anterior end oblique.

Physomonas Kent.

Representative species. . . . . . *Physomonas elongata* Stokes 1886.

Body elongate-ovate, changeable in shape; free-swimming or temporarily attached by a very short pedicel.   Flagella two, unequal.   Contractile vacuole anterior in position.   Length about 12 μ.   Swamp water.

FIG. 374.   *Physomonas elongata.*   *cv,* contractile vacuole; *n,* nucleus.
×1000.   (After Stokes.)

29 (22)   Forming colonies.   Two flagella. 30

30 (33)   One zooid upon the end of each branch. 31

31 (32)   Pedicel rigid. . . . . *Dendromonas* Stein.
Representative species. . . . . *Dendromonas virgaria* Weisse 1845.

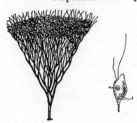

Body of zooid pyriform, compressed, with an anterior, lip-like projection from the base of which arise the two unequal flagella.   Nucleus single; contractile vacuole one or two.   Colony branching dichotomously.   A colony may include over one hundred zooids.   Length of zooid 8 to 10 μ. Pond water.

FIG. 375.   *Dendromonas virgaria.*   Colony × 160; single zooid × 935
(After Blochmann.)

32 (31)   Pedicel flexible. . . . . *Ramosonema* Kent.
Representative species. . . . . . *Ramosonema laxum* Kent 1871.

Zooids pyriform, compressed, obliquely truncate anteriorly.   Pedicel very slender, threadlike.   A colony may include as many as twenty or more zooids.   Length of zooids 8 μ.   Pond water.

FIG. 376.   *Ramosonema laxum.*   *cv,* contractile vacuole; *n,* nucleus.   Colony × 350;
single zooid × 1000.   (After Kent.)

33 (30)   Many zooids upon each branch. 34

34 (35)   Stalk short, branching dichotomously once or twice.

Cephalothamnium Stein.

Representative species. . . *Cephalothamnium caespitosum* Kent 1880.

Zooids irregularly pyriform, in clusters of two or three or as many as six or eight on the summit of a simple or slightly branched pedicel.   Pedicel very short.   Length of zooid about 6 μ.   Fresh water, attached to *Cyclops.*

FIG. 377.   *Cephalothamnium caespitosum.*   × 875.   (After Conn.)

35 (34)   Stalk long, stout, greatly branched. *Anthophysa* Bory de St. Vincent.
Representative species. . . . . . *Anthophysa vegetans* Müller 1786.

Bodies attached in rosette-like clusters, each zooid pyriform in shape, obliquely truncate in front, with two flagella of unequal length. Clusters attached to a branched pedicel or free swimming, moving through the water in a rolling motion. In older stages the pedicel becomes dark brown in color. Length of zooid 5 to 10 μ. In stagnant water.

FIG. 378. *Anthophysa vegetans.* × 500. (After Müller.)

36 (3)   Sometimes plastic but not producing pseudopodia. 37

37 (60)   Chromatophores not present; flagella often numerous. 38

38 (49)   Flagella usually two, one usually trailing; very minute forms.
Order **Heteromastigida** . . 39

39 (40)   Flagella three in number, one directed forward. . . *Elvirea* Parona.
Representative species. . . . . *Elvirea cionae* Parona 1886.

Body ovate to elongate, laterally compressed. The shorter flagellum directed forward. Mouth and nucleus anterior. Fresh water.

FIG. 379. *Elvirea cionae.* × 1200. (After Conn.)

40 (39)   Flagella two in number. 41

41 (42)   Both directed forward. . . . . *Dinomonas* Kent.
Representative species. . . . . *Dinomonas vorax* Kent 1880.

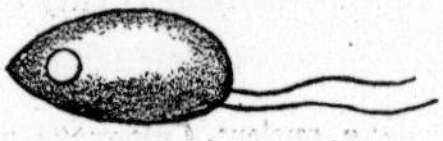

Body persistent in shape, subpyriform, widest posteriorly, slightly curved. Flagella subequal, longer than the body. Length 15 μ. Hay infusions.

FIG. 380. *Dinomonas vorax.* × 1000. (After Conn.)

42 (41)   One flagellum trailing, the other directed forward. 43

43 (46)   Body spiral or oblique. 44

44 (45)   Body not spiral, anterior end oblique; very flexible.
Phyllomitus Stein.
Representative species. . . . . *Phyllomitus amylophagus* Klebs 1886.

FIG. 381. *Phyllomitus amylophagus.* × 1375.
(After Conn.)

45 (44) Body spiral, elongated. . . . . *Spiromonas* Perty.
Representative species. . . . . *Spiromonas angusta* Dujardin 1841.

> Body five or six times as long as broad. Flagella subequal, as long as the body, one directed forward; body sometimes temporarily attached by one. Length 10 μ. Hay infusions.
>
> FIG. 382. *Spiromonas angusta.* × 1000. (After Conn.) There is doubt as to the identity of Conn's form.

46 (43) Body neither spiral nor oblique. 47

47 (48) Kidney-shaped to spherical; flagella arising from a ventral depression, one trailing. Food absorbed by a dorsal vacuole.
Pleuromonas Perty.
Representative species. . . . . . *Pleuromonas jaculans* Perty 1852.

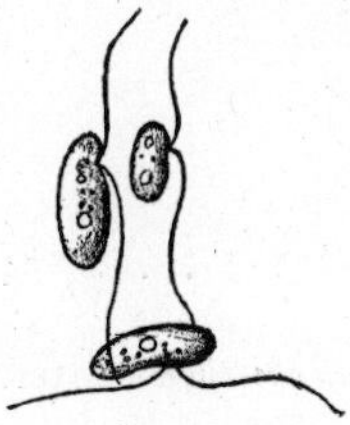

> Body kidney-shaped, very small; sometimes attached by the posterior flagellum. Contractile vacuole anterior; nucleus posterior.
> Length 5 to 9 μ. Stagnant water and infusions. Movements jerking and leaping.
>
> FIG. 383. *Pleuromonas jaculans.* × 1000. (After Conn.)

48 (47) Pear-shaped to spindle-shaped; flagella arising from the anterior end, one trailing. Food not taken in by a dorsal vacuole.
Heteromita Dujardin.
Representative species. . . . . . . *Heteromita ovata* Dujardin 1841.

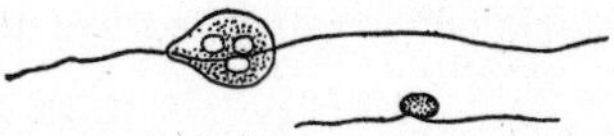

> Body ovate, widest posteriorly. Flagella unequal, the trailing one twice as long as the anterior one. Length 25 to 40 μ. River water with aquatic plants.
>
> FIG. 384. *Heteromita ovata.* × 500. (After Conn.)

49 (38) Flagella usually numerous, frequently arranged in groups.
Order **Phytomastigida** . . 50

50 (53) Flagella two in number. 51

51 (52) Body expanded into two wings; flagella long.
Trepomonas Dujardin.
Representative species. . . . . . *Trepomonas agilis* Dujardin 1841.

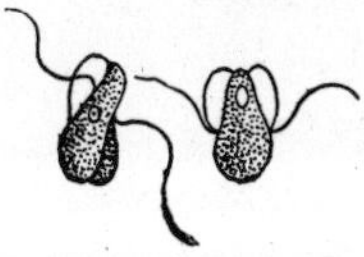

> Very irregular in shape, different appearances being presented from different points of view. The broad, wing-like lateral lobes curve backward nearly to the middle of the body. Length 20 μ. Pond water.
>
> FIG. 385. *Trepomonas agilis.* × 450. (After Conn.)

52 (51) Body not laterally expanded, sometimes attached by a stalk.   Flagella
          arising from the anterior end.   . . *Amphimonas* Dujardin.
    Representative species. . . . . . *Amphimonas globosa* Kent 1880.

Body subspherical, attached by a filamentous pedicel.   Flagella equal, twice the
length of the body.   Diameter 12 μ.   Pond water.

FIG. 386. *Amphimonas globosa.*   × 875.   (After Kent.)

Conn reports a form, found abundantly in the fresh waters of Connecticut, which
he assigns to this genus, with some doubt.   Although never attached by a pedicel,
the two equal flagella would seem to place it here.

53 (50) Flagella four in number. 54

54 (55) With a deep, vertical furrow. . . . . *Collodictyon* Carter.

55 (54) Without a vertical furrow. 56

56 (57) With three flagella directed forward, one trailing.   Body pear-shaped,
          rounded in front, acute behind. . *Trichomastix* Blochmann.
    Representative species. . . . . *Trichomastix* sp.

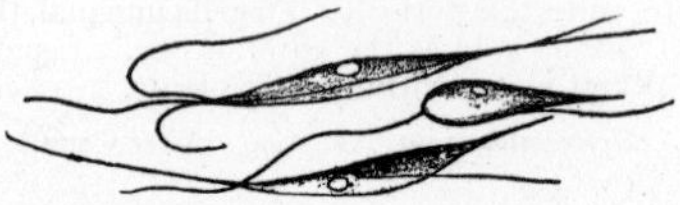

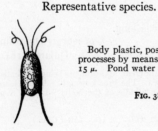

American species observed have not been determined.

FIG. 387. *Trichomastix* sp.   × 750.   (After Conn.)

57 (56) With all four flagella directed forward. 58

58 (59) Body ellipsoidal, with two thread-like processes at the posterior
          end. . . . . *Hexamita* Dujardin.
    Representative species. . . . . . *Hexamita inflata* Dujardin 1838.

Body plastic, posterior end bifid, giving rise to the trailing, flagella-like
processes by means of which it may be temporarily fixed.   Length 10 to
15 μ.   Pond water and infusions.

FIG. 388. *Hexamita inflata.*   × 875.   (After Conn.)

59 (58) Body obovate, obliquely truncate in front; or subpyriform or sub-
         spherical with a rounded front. . . . . *Tetramitus* Perty.
         Representative species. . . . . . *Tetramitus variabilis* Stokes 1886.

Body changeable in form.   Flagella subequal, inserted near the middle of the anterior border.   Endoplasm granular.   Contractile vacuoles two, near the front
border.   Food received at any portion of the surface.   Length 18 to 25 μ.   Standing water with decaying vegetation.

FIG. 389. *Tetramitus variabilis.* × 250. (After Stokes.)

60 (37) Chromatophores usually present. Flagella one or two.
                                              Order **Euglenida** . . 61

61 (87) Elongated forms usually with pointed posterior ends. Chromato-
         phores usually green. Paramylin bodies present.
                                              Family EUGLENIDAE . . 62

62 (69) Naked or with very thin cuticle. 63

63 (68) Flagellum single. 64

64 (65) Attached by a branched stalk, usually surrounded by a jelly-like en-
         velop. . . . . *Colacium* Ehrenberg.
         Representative species. . . . . *Colacium steinii* Kent 1880.

So far as has been determined, no members of this genus have been reported in
North America.   Several species have been reported in Europe.   Usually
attached to *Cyclops* or other fresh-water crustaceans.

FIG. 390. *Colacium steinii.* × 350. (After Kent.)

65 (64) Not attached and not surrounded by a jelly-like envelop. Large
         forms, spindle-shaped, usually green, with an eye-spot.
                                              Euglena Ehrenberg . . 66

66 (67) Body rounded anteriorly, surface smooth.
                                              Euglena viridis Ehrenberg 1830.

Body usually rounded anteriorly with a colorless, tail-like posterior prolongation.   Surface smooth.   Nucleus central; contractile vacuole anterior.
Length 50 to 75 μ.   Common.   The chlorophyl may at times be lost and
the species, no doubt, may then exist on organic substances.

FIG. 391. *Euglena viridis.* cv, contractile vacuole; n, nucleus; pam, paramylum;
st, stigma. × 400. (After Blochmann.)

67 (66) Body cylindrical; surface beaded. *Euglena spirogyra* Ehrenberg 1830.

Body elongate, cylindrical, with a
pointed, tail-like prolongation. Periphery
covered by oblique rows of minute bead-
like elevations.   Color bright green.
Nucleus central, with an elongated starch-
like body anterior and posterior to it.
Eye-spot near the base of the flagellum.
Length 100 to 200 μ. Among algae.

FIG. 392. *Euglena spirogyra.* × 500. (After Conn.)

68 (63)   Flagella two; body spindle-shaped when extended; chromatophores
disk-shaped . . . .   *Eutreptia* Perty.
Representative species. . . . .   *Eutreptia viridis* Perty 1852.

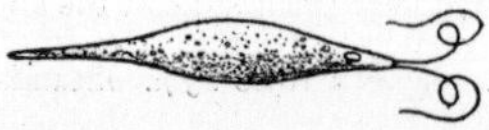

Body very changeable in form.   Flagella equalling the
body in length.   Eye-spot present.   Length, when extended,
100 μ.   Pond water.

FIG. 393.   *Eutreptia viridis.*   × 500.   (After Conn.)

69 (76)   With a thick cuticle or lorica.   70

70 (76)   Lorica present.   71

71 (72)   Lorica beaker-shaped or tube-shaped. . . . . . .   *Ascoglena* Stein.

72 (71)   Lorica spherical or cylindrical, smooth or spiny.
Trachelomonas Ehrenberg . .   73

73 (74, 75)   Lorica smooth, colorless . . *Trachelomonas lagenella* Stein 1878.

Lorica colorless, oval or elliptical, smooth.   An obliquely projecting neck.
Length 20 to 35 μ.   Fresh water.

FIG. 394.   *Trachelomonas lagenella.*   × 600.   (After Stein.)

74 (73, 73)   Lorica spinous, brown. . . . *Trachelomonas hispida* Stein 1878.

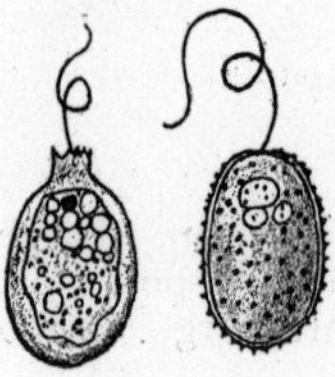

Lorica elongate-oval, with ends broadly rounded.   Surface covered with minute, sharp-pointed spines.   A short, tube-like neck
sometimes present.   Brown in color.   Length 30 to 36 μ.   Pond
water, with other species of the genus.

FIG. 395.   *Trachelomonas hispida.*   × 400.   (After Conn.)

75 (73, 74)   Lorica smooth, brown. . *Trachelomonas volvocina* Ehrenberg 1833.

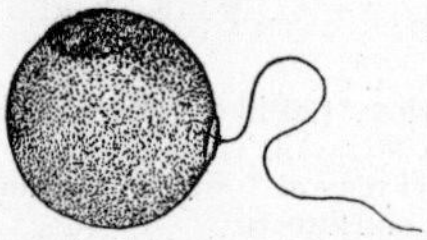

Lorica nearly spherical, surface smooth, usually without a
neck.   Flagellum long.   Color brown.   Diameter 30 μ.   Very
common among algae and other aquatic plants.

FIG. 396.   *Trachelomonas volvocina.*   × 450.   (After Edmondson.)

76 (69)   With a thick cuticle but no lorica.   77

77 (78)   Not flattened, ellipsoidal, with a pointed caudal process.
Chloropeltis Stein.
Representative species. . . . . . .   *Chloropeltis hispidula* Stein 1878.

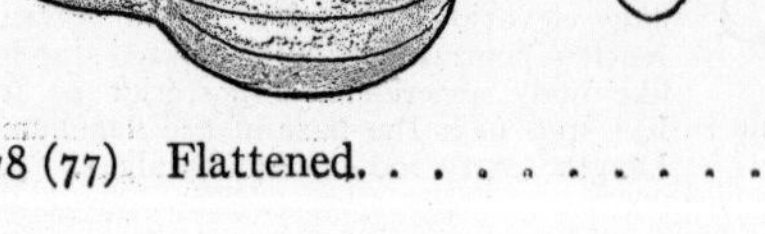

Surface of the body ornamented with minute spines arranged in longitudinal rows.
Endoplasm green, with an eye-spot.   Length
55 μ.   Fresh water, among diatoms.

FIG. 397.   *Chloropeltis hispidula.*   × 600.   (After
Conn.)

78 (77)   Flattened.   79

79 (84)   Posterior border acute or with a caudal appendage. 80

80 (81)   Ellipsoidal, slightly flattened; posterior end acute. Longitudinally or spirally marked. . . . . *Lepocinclis* Perty. Representative species. . . . . *Lepocinclis* sp.

This genus is very closely related to, if not identical with, the preceding one. The form here represented is assigned to this genus by Conn, with some doubt. Species not determined.

FIG. 398. *Lepocinclis* sp. × 1000. (After Conn.)

81 (80)   Round to pear-shaped, asymmetrical, much flattened; caudal process present. . . . . *Phacus* Nitzsch . . 82

82 (83)   Caudal process moderate; not large.
Phacus pleuronectes Nitzsch 1816.

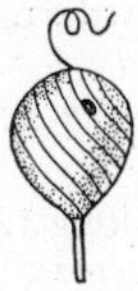

Tail-like projection usually curved. Surface longitudinally striated. Endoplasm green, enclosing one or more large, amylaceous bodies. Flagellum arises from a cleft-like mouth on the anterior border. Length 25 to 75 μ. Among aquatic plants.

FIG. 399. *Phacus pleuronectes*. × 450. (After Conn.)

83 (82)   Caudal process long; size conspicuous.
Phacus longicaudus Ehrenberg 1838.

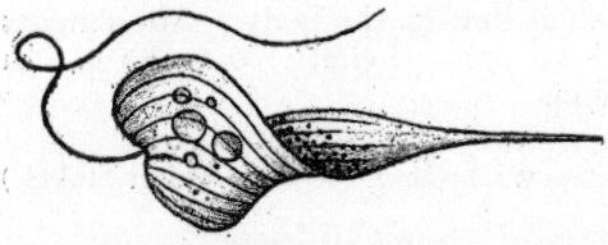

Recognized by its large size and long caudal projection. Body frequently twisted on its longitudinal axis. Length 100 μ.

FIG. 400. *Phacus longicaudus*. × 310. (After Conn.)

84 (79)   Posterior end evenly rounded. 85

85 (86)   Resembling *Phacus* but without caudal appendage.
Cyclanura Stokes.
Representative species. . . . . . *Cyclanura orbiculata* Stokes 1886.

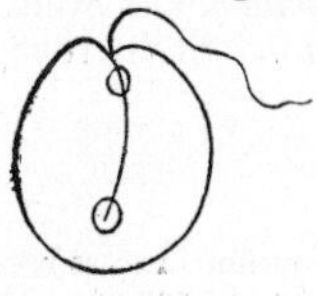

Body ovate or suborbicular, thick, compressed, with a longitudinal keel across the right-hand side. Color green. Contractile vacuole and eye-spot anteriorly placed. Length about 50 μ. Stagnant pond water.

FIG. 401. *Cyclanura orbiculata*. × 325. (After Stokes.)

86 (85)   Oval in outline, rigid, flattened. Chromatophores green, two in number, lateral in position. . . . *Cryptoglena* Ehrenberg. Representative species. . . . . *Cryptoglena pigra* Ehrenberg 1831.

Flagellum single, short. Chromatophores band-like, following the contour of the body. A scarlet eye-spot near the anterior extremity. Length 12 μ. Fresh water.

FIG. 402. *Cryptoglena pigra*. × 1500. (After Conn.)

87 (61)   Colorless forms without eye-spots. Often very plastic. 88

88 (101)   Body elongate, usually with striped membrane. Nutrition saprophytic. Flagella usually two. Family ASTASIIDAE . . 89

89 (94) Body flexible; one or two flagella. 90

90 (93) Flagella two. 91

91 (92) Secondary flagellum very small, directed backward. . *Astasia* Stein.

Representative species. . . . . *Astasia trichophora* Ehrenberg 1830.

FIG. 403. *Astasia trichophora.* × 410.
(After Conn.)

Body elongate, usually wider posteriorly. Primary flagellum very thick at the base and long. Nucleus central; contractile vacuole anteriorly located. Length, when extended, 30 to 60 μ. Common among diatoms and algae.

92 (91) Secondary flagellum about half as long as the primary; both flagella directed forward. . . . . *Distigma* Ehrenberg.
Representative species. . . . . . *Distigma proteus* Ehrenberg 1830.

Body very plastic; when contracted, distended in one or two regions. Endoplasm with dark-colored corpuscles. Nucleus central; contractile vacuole in the anterior region. Length, when extended, 95 μ. Pond water.

FIG. 404. *Distigma proteus.* *cv*, contractile vacuole; *n*, nucleus; *ph*, pharynx. × 330. (After Stein.)

93 (90) Flagellum single; body elongate, tapering posteriorly. A long tubular pharynx. . . . . *Atractonema* Stein.
Representative species. . . . . . *Atractonema tortuosa* Stokes 1885.

Body flexible but persistent in shape, colorless, enclosing oblong dark-bordered corpuscles. Flagellum about half as long as the body. Movements rotary on the long axis. Length 50 to 80 μ. In vegetable infusions.

FIG. 405. *Atractonema tortuosa.* × 625. (After Stokes.)

94 (89) Body not flexible. 95

95 (98) With longitudinal or spiral ridges. 96

96 (97) Elongate or crescentic, with four longitudinal ridges; flagella, two, unequal. . . . . *Sphenomonas* Stein.
Representative species. . . *Sphenomonas quadrangularis* Stein 1878.

Body subfusiform, with the ridges forming a quadrate outline in cross section. Long flagellum stout, four times the length of the shorter one. A large amylaceous corpuscle usually enclosed in the endoplasm. Length 40 μ. Fresh water.

FIG. 406. *Sphenomonas quadrangularis.* × 400. (After Bütschli.)

97 (96) Nearly ellipsoidal, with many spiral ridges. . *Tropidoscyphus* Stein.

98 (95) Without ridges. 99

99 (100) Resembling *Sphenomonas*, but without ridges; flagella two, unequal.
Clostonema Stokes.
Representative species. . . . . . *Clostonema socialis* Stokes 1886.

Body fusiform, with a short, rounded posterior prolongation. Primary flagellum as long as the body; secondary, about one-fourth as long. A long, pharyngeal passage present. Length about 20 μ. In standing water.

FIG. 407. *Clostonema socialis.* × 600. (After Stokes.)

100 (99) Resembling *Clostonema*, but with a single flagellum.
Menoidium Perty. 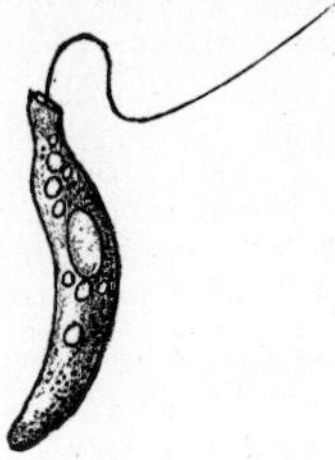
Representative species.
Menoidium pellucidum Perty 1852.
Body lunate, obliquely truncated at the anterior extremity. Posterior end rounded. The short side of the body thin and sharp, the long side rounded. Flagellum equalling the body in length. One or more amylaceous corpuscles usually present. Length 40 to 60 μ. Fresh water.

FIG. 408. *Menoidium pellucidum.* × 500. (After Senn.)

101 (88) Body rigid or plastic, usually symmetrical; one or two dissimilar · flagella deeply sunk in the body. Nutrition holozoic.
Family PERANEMIDAE . . 102

102 (109) Body plastic. 103

103 (108) One flagellum. 104

104 (105) Oval, flattened, very flexible; distinct pharynx and rod-like organ back of the mouth. . . . . *Peranema* Dujardin.
Representative species.
Peranema trichophorum Ehrenberg 1838.

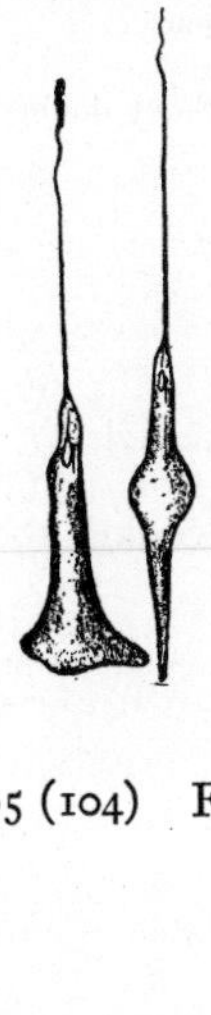

Cuticle finely marked spirally. Flagellum very long, vibratile at the tip only. Nucleus central.

FIG. 409. *Peranema trichophorum.* × 250. (After Conn.)

Conn reports a number of undetermined forms which bear considerable resemblance to the above species and should, without doubt, be assigned to the genus *Peranema*.

105 (104) Flask-shaped; neck-like anterior end with elongated pharynx and rod-like organ. 106

106 (107)   Without sand grains attached. . . . . *Urceolus* Mereschkowsky.
            Representative species. . . . . *Urceolus cyclostomum* Stein 1878.

Anterior extremity obliquely truncate with an expanded rim about the mouth. Pharynx nearly reaching the posterior extremity with its distal end dilated. Surface usually spirally marked. Flagellum about as long as the body. Length 50 μ. Fresh water. Identical with *Phialonema cyclostomum* Mereschkowsky.

FIG. 410.   *Urceolus cyclostomum.*   × 500.   (After Conn.)

107 (106)   With sand grains attached. . . . . *Urceolopsis* Stokes.
            Representative species. . . . . *Urceolopsis sabulosa* Stokes 1886.

Body flexible and elastic, with a short, anterior, neck-like prolongation. Usually densely covered with sand grains. Movements are rapid, the body being held at an angle with the anterior end downward. The long flagellum vibrates strongly at its tip. Food particles are drawn into the oral aperture with considerable force. Length 20 μ. Among algae.

FIG. 411.   *Urceolopsis sabulosa.*   × 625.   (After Stokes.)

108 (103)   Two flagella, one trailing; mouth depression oblique.
                                        Heteronema Dujardin.
            Representative species. . *Heteronema acus* Ehrenberg 1840.

Body very plastic, fusiform when extended. Primary flagellum as long as the body and twice as long as the secondary, trailing one. Nucleus central; contractile vacuole in the anterior extremity. Length, extended, 50 μ. Fresh water.

FIG. 412.   *Heteronema acus.*   × 500.   (After Conn.)

Numerous other forms reported by Conn should, without doubt, be assigned to this genus. The species are undetermined.

109 (102)   Body rigid. 110

110 (111)   One flagellum; body flattened, usually furrowed and keeled.
                                        Petalomonas Stein.
            Representative species. . . *Petalomonas pleurosigma* Stokes 1887.

Body ovate, the posterior end pointed; lateral borders sigmoid. Dorsal and ventral surfaces each traversed by a narrow, longitudinal furrow. Length 15 to 20 μ. Standing pond water.

FIG. 413.   *Petalomonas pleurosigma.*   × 625   (After Stokes.)

111 (110)   Two flagella, unequal. 112

112 (113)   Body with spiral ridges. . . . .   *Tropidoscyphus* Stein.

113 (112)   Body without spiral ridges. 114

114 (115)   Trailing flagellum very prominent, curving around the anterior
            end. . . . .   *Anisonema* Dujardin.
            Representative species.   . . .   *Anisonema acinus* Dujardin 1841.

FIG. 414. *Anisonema acinus.* × 500.
(After Conn.)

Body wider posteriorly, flattened ventrally; anterior vibratile flagellum short.   Mouth near the base of the anterior flagellum. Length 25 μ. Among diatoms. Common.
The genus *Metanema* Klebs resembles *Anisonema* but is
flexible.

115 (114)   Trailing flagellum not prominent. 116

116 (117)   Primary flagellum carried obliquely forward, vibratile only at its
            end.   Body ovate or angular with dorsal side concave.
            No protrusile pharynx. . . . .   *Notosolenus* Stokes.
            Representative species . . *Notosolenus orbicularis* Stokes 1884.

Body with a broad, shallow, dorsal concavity; the ventral surface convex.
Movements somewhat eccentric, the convex surface usually directed downward. Nucleus to the left of the center of the body. Contractile vacuole
near the anterior end. Length 10 to 12 μ. Bottom of shallow ponds.

FIG. 415. *Notosolenus orbicularis.* × 1000. (After Conn.)

117 (116)   Primary flagellum not carried obliquely forward; pharynx pro-
            trusile.   A strong furrow on the ventral surface.
            Entosiphon Stein.
            Representative species. . . *Entosiphon sulcatus* Stein 1878.

Body oval, flattened; anterior border oblique, with a concavity at the
bottom of which is the mouth leading into a long tubular pharynx.
Nucleus posterior.   Contractile vacuole anterior.   Length 22 μ.   Pond
water, among aquatic plants.

FIG. 416. *Entosiphon sulcatus.* × 500. (After Conn.

118 (2)   With protoplasmic collars. . .   Subclass **Choanoflagellata** . . 119

119 (122)   Not forming colonies. 120

120 (121)   No lorica, with or without a stalk. . . . . *Monosiga* Kent.
Representative species.   . . . . . .   *Monosiga ovata* Kent 1880.

Body obovate, the broader end posterior; with a rigid pedicel nearly equal to the body in length. Length of body about 6 μ.   Reported by Conn from the fresh waters of Connecticut.

Fig. 417. *Monosiga ovata.*   × 1000.   (After Conn.)

121 (120)   With lorica, with or without a stalk. . . *Salpingoeca* James-Clark.
Representative species. . . .   *Salpingoeca convallaria* Stein 1878

Lorica campanulate, pointed posteriorly, slightly constricted anteriorly. Pedicel very slender and short.   Zooid nearly filling the lorica.   Length of lorica 15 to 25 μ.   Attached to *Epistylis.*

Fig. 418. *Salpingoeca convallaria.*   × 600.   (After Kent.)

122 (119)   Forming colonies. 123

123 (128)   Without stalks. 124

124 (127)   Colonies enclosed in a gelatinous mass. 125

125 (126)   Forming a flat colony in an irregular jelly. . *Proterospongia* Kent.
Representative species. . . .   *Proterospongia haeckeli* Kent 1880.

Zooids pyriform, plastic; collar long, each zooid bearing a single flagellum.   Colony may contain as many as fifty or sixty zooids, but often not more than six or eight.   The gelatinous support very transparent. Length of zooid 8 μ.   Fresh water.

Fig. 419. *Proterospongia haeckeli.*   × 375.

126 (125)   Colony disk-shaped or arising from a funnel-like, open jelly tube.
Phalansterium Cienkowsky.
Representative species. . . *Phalansterium digitatum* Stein 1878.

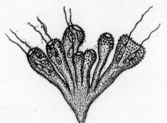

Zooids ovate, plastic.   Flagellum two or three times the length of the body.   Jelly mass coarse, granular, digitiform, and often branching.   Length of zooid 18 μ.   Fresh water.

Fig. 420. *Phalansterium digitatum.*   × 400. (After Bütschli.)

127 (124)   Colony free, not enclosed by jelly. . . . . . . *Hirmidium* Perty.
Representative species.   . . . . . *Hirmidium inane* Perty 1852.

As many as eleven individuals may be included in the colony. Under the name *Desmarella irregularis*, Stokes describes a form with fifty individuals. Length of body, reported by Stokes, 8 to 12 μ. Pond water.

FIG. 421. *Hirmidium inane.* Colony × 155; single zooid × 325. (After Stein.)

128 (123)   With stalks.   129

129 (130)   Stalk simple; many individuals borne at the end of the stalk.
Codosiga James-Clark.
Representative species. . . .   *Codosiga botrytis* Ehrenberg 1838.

Bodies ovate; pedicel slender, rigid. Flagellum long. Collar equalling the body in length. Length of zooid 10 to 15 μ. Attached to aquatic plants.

Kent reports that previous to encystment the collars and flagella of this species may be withdrawn into the protoplasm of the bodies, while the latter become covered with radiating pseudopodia. Occasionally the pseudopodia are produced while the collar is still extended. Spores are formed during encystment.

FIG. 422. *Codosiga botrytis.* × 350. (After Kent.)

130 (129)   Stalk branched, with single individuals or groups on the end of each branch. . . . . *Codonocladium* Stein.
Representative species. . *Codonocladium umbellatum* Tatem 1868.

Kent would refer this species to the genus *Codosiga*, in which genus some forms possess zooids with short pedicels attached to the end of the main stalk.

FIG. 423. *Codonocladium umbellatum.* × 500. (After Conn.)

131 (1)   Plant characteristics evident; chromatophores usually present; often producing colonies. . Class **Phytomastigophora** . .   132

132 (205)   Body without a shell formed of plates; chromatophores yellow, brown, or green. . . . Subclass **Phytoflagellata** . .   133

133 (164)   Chromatophores usually yellow or brown.
Order **Chrysoflagellida** . .   134

134 (137)   Body usually naked but may be enclosed in a jelly mass during resting stages. **135**

135 (136)   Flagellum single; two chromatophores. . *Chromulina* Cienkowsky.

Chrysomonas Stein is very closely related to this genus. Under the name *Chrysomonas pulchra* Stokes describes a species as follows: Body elongate-ovate or obovate, somewhat flexible, three times as long as broad, tapering and slightly constricted posteriorly, curved toward one side anteriorly. Frontal border obliquely excavate. Surface covered with minute hemispherical elevations. Flagellum scarcely equalling the body in length. Nucleus ovate. Contractile vacuoles two, anterior. Length 35 to 40 μ. Color green. Marsh water.

Fig. 424. *Chrysomonas pulchra*. × 400. (After Stokes.)

136 (135)   Flagella, two; two chromatophores. . . . *Ochromonas* Wysotzki.
Representative species. . . . . *Ochromonas* sp.

Species not identified.

Fig. 425. *Ochromonas* sp. × 1000. (After Conn.)

137 (134)   Body enclosed by a membrane or lorica. 138

138 (157)   With a membrane. 139

139 (146)   Not forming colonies. 140

140 (141)   With a close-fitting membrane of plates; flagellum single.
Mallomonas Perty.
Representative species. . . . . *Mallomonas* sp.

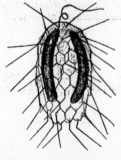

Body elongated, enclosed by a membrane of overlapping plates which bear long, slender spines. Two elongated, yellowish-green chromatophores are within the body. Species not determined.

Fig. 426. *Mallomonas* sp. × 500. (After Conn.)

141 (140)   With a firm cuticle; two flagella. 142

142 (145)   Without chromatophores. 143

143 (144)   Body oval, truncate or concave anteriorly, enclosing refractive bodies. . . . . *Cyathomonas* de Fromentel.
Representative species. . *Cyathomonas truncata* de Fromentel 1874.

De Fromentel identified six or eight species, several of which are but slightly distinguished from each other. Length 12 to 20 μ. Fresh water.

Fig. 427. *Cyathomonas truncata*. × 1200. (After Conn.)

144 (143)   Shaped as *Cyathomonas,* but with pharynx and without refractive
            bodies. . . . . *Chilomonas* Ehrenberg.
            Representative species. . *Chilomonas paramecium* Ehrenberg 1831.

Body elongate-oval, anterior margin with a lip-like projection.   Flagella
subequal in length.   Endoplasm usually enclosing dark-colored corpuscles.
Length 25 to 40 μ.   Stagnant infusions; very common.

Fig. 428.   *Chilomonas paramecium.*   × 350.   (After Conn.)

145 (142)   With two brown or green chromatophores.   Shaped as *Chilo-
            monas.* . . . . *Cryptomonas* Ehrenberg.
            Representative species. . *Cryptomonas ovata* Ehrenberg 1831.

Chlorophyl bands two in number, extending longitudinally through the
body.   Length 50 μ.   Among algae.

Fig. 429.   *Cryptomonas ovata.*   × 350.   (After Conn.)

146 (139)   Forming colonies. **147**

147 (154)   Individuals imbedded in a gelatinous mass. **148**

148 (149)   Spherical colonies; individuals usually with two yellow chroma-
            tophores and eye-spot.   Free-swimming.   Flagella two, un-
            equal. . . . . *Uroglena* Ehrenberg.
            Representative species. . . . . *Uroglena americana* Calkins 1891.

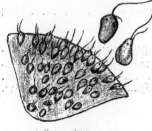

Cells very numerous, arranged around the periphery of a gelatinous mass.   Posterior ends of the
cells rounded, with no means of connection with
each other except by the matrix.
Sometimes found in reservoirs, causing the water
to have a fishy taste.

Fig. 430.   *Uroglena americana.*   Individual cells × 1500.
(After Conn.)

149 (148)   Not colored. **150**

150 (151)   Colonies of dichotomously branching tubes. . *Cladomonas* Stein.

151 (150)   Colonies not of branching tubes. 152

152 (153)   Colony in a gelatinous mass; variable in shape, thread-like, discoidal or round, hollow or sac-like. Individuals with two
equal flagella. . . . . *Spongomonas* Stein.
Representative species. . . . . . *Spongomonas discus* Stein 1878.

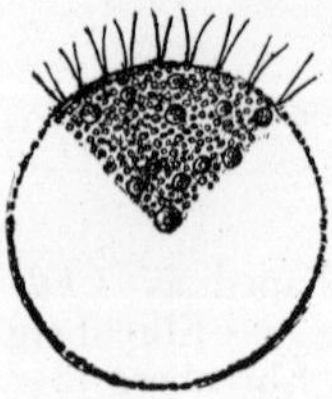

> Colony discoidal, gelatinous mass granular; zooids subspheroidal.
> Flagella two or three times the length of the body. Length of
> zooids 8 μ. Fresh water.

FIG. 431.   *Spongomonas discus.*   × 100.   (After Bütschli.)

153 (152)   Colony formed of jelly-like tubes, closely approximated; individuals
as in *Spongomonas.* . . . . *Rhipidodendron* Stein.
Representative species.
Rhipidodendron splendidum Stein 1878.

> Tubules forming an erect branching colony. Zooids ovate or ellipti-
> cal, usually in the distal extremity of the tubules. Flagella equal, twice
> the length of the body.
> The tubes being hollow are probably secreted or excreted from the
> entire surfaces, rather than the posterior extremities of the zooids.
> The tubes are usually rusty-brown in color and have a granular appear-
> ance. Sometimes as many as two hundred tubes are bound together
> in one mass.
> Length of body 12 μ. Fresh water.

FIG. 432.   *Rhipidodendron splendidum.*   × 250.   (After Stein.)

154 (147)   Individuals not imbedded in a gelatinous mass. 155

155 (156)   Forming spherical colonies. About fifty individuals held loosely
together, each with a delicate membrane, often spiny. Flagella two, unequal. . . . . *Synura* Ehrenberg.
Representative species. . . . . *Synura uvella* Ehrenberg 1833.

> Membranes pyriform, often with posterior stalk-like pro-
> jections; surfaces spiny. Zooids nearly filling membranes.
> Color bands two, extending along the lateral borders. Length
> of body 30 μ. Pond water.

FIG. 433.   *Synura uvella.*   × 600.   (After Conn.)

156 (155)   Forming annular colonies; individuals closely united. Flagella
two, unequal. . . . . *Cyclonexis* Stokes.
Representative species. . . . *Cyclonexis annularis* Stokes 1886.

> From ten to twenty zooids, not in contact in older colonies, leav-
> ing a central, circular space.   Zooids obovate, about twice as long
> as broad.   Length of zooid 10 to 15 μ.   Marsh water.

Fig. 434.   *Cyclonexis annularis.*   × 625.   (After Conn.)

157 (138)   With a lorica.   158

158 (163)   Not forming colonies.   159

159 (162)   Lorica sessile.   160

160 (161)   Lorica beaker-shaped; usually with a peristome process.
Epipyxis Ehrenberg.
Representative species. . . . *Epipyxis utriculus* Ehrenberg 1838.

> Lorica is truncate or slightly everted anteriorly, widest centrally and pointed
> posteriorly.   Body occupies about one-half the cavity of the lorica, and is at-
> tached by a thread-like pedicel to one side of the lorica.   An eye-spot usually
> present.   Nucleus central; contractile vacuole anterior.
> Length of lorica about 40 μ.   Attached to water-plants.

Fig. 435.   *Epipyxis utriculus.*   × 650.   (After Stein.)

161 (160)   Lorica urn-shaped. . . . . *Chrysopyxis* Stein.
Representative species. . . . *Chrysopyxis urceolata* Stokes 1886.

> Zooid occupying the center of the lorica, but in no way attached to it.
> Flagella two, long, diverging.   Yellow chromatophores often present.   Nu-
> cleus centrally located; contractile vacuole posterior.   Length of lorica 12 μ.
> Attached to algae.

Fig. 436.   *Chrysopyxis urceolata.*   × 1200.   (After Stokes.)

162 (159)   Lorica with a pedicel. . . . . *Derepyxis* Stokes.
Representative species.   . . *Derepyxis amorpha* Stokes 1885.

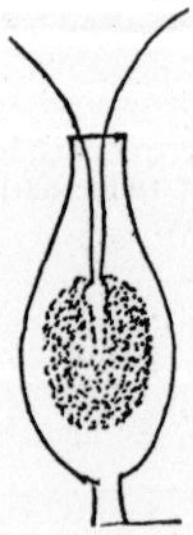

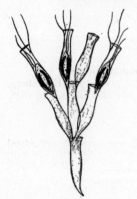

Lorica flask-shaped.   Pedicel about one-tenth as long as the lorica.
Zooid occupying the center of the lorica, subspherical, with the front border
pointed. Endoplasm with two greenish-yellow color bands. Length of lorica
25 to 30 μ. Attached to algae.

FIG. 437. *Derepyxis amorpha.* × 1000. (After Stokes.)

163 (158)   Forming colonies; loricae beaker-shaped.   One primary and one
secondary flagellum. . . . . *Dinobryon* Ehrenberg.
Representative species.   . . *Dinobryon sertularia* Ehrenberg 1838.

Loricae joined to each other without separate pedicels;
the younger individuals being attached by their posterior ends
to the inner, anterior edges of the older loricae. Zooids attached to the bottoms of the loricae by transparent, elastic
ligaments.   Chromatophores and eye-spot present.   Length
of lorica 20 μ. Pond water.

FIG. 438. *Dinobryon sertularia.* × 750. (After Conn.)

164 (133)   Chromatophores green. . . . .   Order **Chloroflagellida** . . 165

165 (168)   Flagella four; not forming colonies. 166

166 (167)   Body enclosed by a lorica. . . . . *Tetraselmis* Stokes.
Representative species. . *Tetraselmis limnetis* Stokes 1887.

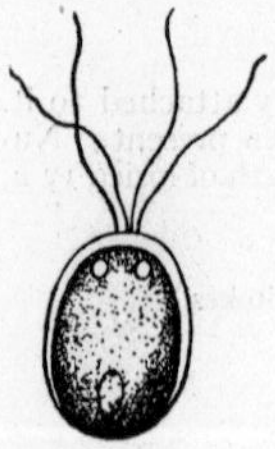

Lorica broadly oval; zooid nearly filling the lorica, green in color.
Flagella exceeding the lorica in length.   An amylaceous corpuscle posteriorly located. Length of lorica 15 μ. Pond water.

FIG. 439. *Tetraselmis limnetis.* × 840. (After Stokes.)

167 (166)   Body not enclosed by a lorica. . . . .   *Carteria* Diesing.

168 (165)   Flagella usually two; often forming colonies.   169

169 (180)   Not forming colonies.   170

170 (177)   Body with closely attached cuticle.   171

171 (172)   Usually without chromatophores; occasionally a colored eye-spot.
            Ellipsoidal, two contractile vacuoles. . *Polytoma* Ehrenberg.
            Representative species. . . . . *Polytoma uvella* Ehrenberg 1838.

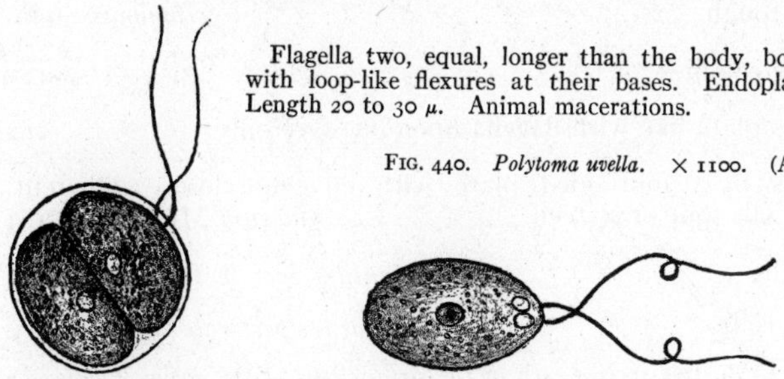

> Flagella two, equal, longer than the body, both extending forward
> with loop-like flexures at their bases. Endoplasm usually granular.
> Length 20 to 30 μ. Animal macerations.
>
> FIG. 440. *Polytoma uvella.* × 1100. (After Conn.)

172 (171)   With chromatophores.   173

173 (174)   Chromatophores numerous; one flagellum trailing.
                                        Trentonia Stokes.
            Representative species. . . . . *Trentonia flagellata* Stokes 1886.

FIG. 441. *Trentonia flagellata.* × 400. (After Stokes.)

Body ovate, the anterior border oblique
and somewhat bilobate, the posterior extremity obtusely pointed. Flagella subequal in length, one extending forward,
often rapidly and spirally vibrating.
Mouth and pharynx conspicuous. Numerous green chromatophores. Length
60 μ. Pond water.

174 (173)   Chromatophores few, sometimes wanting.   175

175 (176)   Spherical or elliptical, with one large chromatophore. An eye-
            spot present. . . . . *Chlamydomonas* Ehrenberg.
            Representative species.
                        Chlamydomonas pulvisculus Ehrenberg 1883.

FIG. 442. *Chlamydomonas pulvisculus.* × 1000. (After Conn.)

176 (175)　Elongate, spindle-shaped; chromatophores two, ribbon-shaped; eye-spot obscure. . . . . *Chlorangium* Stein.
　　　　　　Representative species.
　　　　　　　　　　　　　　Chlorangium stentorinum Ehrenberg 1838.

Flagella terminal, subequal.　Attached during the sedentary stage by a short, thick pedicel, singly or in groups up to ten or twelve zooids.　Length 24 μ.　Pond water, often attached to various Entomostraca.

Fɪɢ. 443.　*Chlorangium stentorinum.*　× 375.　(After Stein.)

177 (170)　Cuticle separated from body mass. 178

178 (179)　Cuticle smooth. . . . . *Haemotococcus* Agardh.

179 (178)　Cuticle rough. . . . . *Coccomonas* Stein.

180 (169)　Forming colonies. 181

181 (186)　Colonies plate-like with flagella upon one face only. 182

182 (185)　Colonies in a four-sided plate with envelop closely adherent. Cells four or sixteen. . . . . . . *Gonium* Müller . . 183

183 (184)　Four cells. . . . . *Gonium sociale* Dujardin 1838.

184 (183)　Sixteen cells. . . . . *Gonium pectorale* Müller 1773.

In this species each of the sixteen cells of the colony produces a daughter colony of sixteen cells.　As the daughter colonies develop, a secondary shifting of the cells takes place resulting in individuals of the adult colonies lying in one plane.

Fɪɢ. 444.　*Gonium pectorale.*　× 350.　(After Stein.)

185 (182)　Colonies in a rounded plate with envelop swollen, oval, or spherical.
　　　　　　　　　　　　　　　　　　Stephanosphaera Cohn.
　　　　　　Representative species. . . *Stephanosphaera pluvialis* Cohn 1853.

Cells four or eight, ovoid or spindle-shaped, with numerous processes.

This form represents a transition from a rosette arrangement of cells to a spherical aggregate, the units being arranged in a rosette but surrounded by a common gelatinous envelop.

Fɪɢ. 445.　*Stephanosphaera pluvialis.*　*A*, copulation of gametes; *B*, spore formation; *C*, cells with protoplasmic processes; *D*, colony of eight cells. *A* × 1325; *B*, *C*, *D* × 425.　(After Hieronymus.)

186 (181)　Colonies spherical, ellipsoidal, or flattened, with flagella not confined to one face. 187

187 (190)　Colonies with cells crowded together. 188

188 (189) Colony ellipsoidal or spherical with cells reaching toward the center.
Pandorina Bory de Saint Vincent.
Representative species.

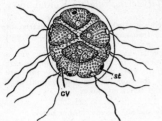

Pandorina morum Bory de Saint Vincent 1824.

Cells sixteen or thirty-two; enclosed within a definite membrane which does not touch the surface of the individuals. Each cell bears two long flagella.

FIG. 446. *Pandorina morum.* *cv*, contractile vacuole; *st*, stigma. × 250. (After Pringsheim.)

189 (188) Colony ellipsoidal with sixteen cells in four rows around a longitudinal axis. Each cell bears four flagella.
Spondylomorum Ehrenberg.
Representative species.

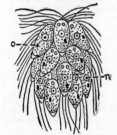

Spondylomorum quaternarium Ehrenberg 1848.

Reproduction occurs by the cells of the colony separating and each individual building up a new colony by cell division.
Colonies often produced in large numbers in pond water. Movements rapid, rotating on the long axis. Green in color. Very favorable conditions are necessary in order that the flagella may be seen and counted.

FIG. 447. *Spondylomorum quaternarium.* *n*, nucleus; *o*, stigma. × 600. (After Stein.)

190 (187) Colonies with cells not crowded together and not reaching toward
the center. 191

191 (194) Colonies spherical, ellipsoidal, or flattened, with cells uniform in
size. 192

192 (193) Colony spherical or ellipsoidal; poles not differentiated by arrangement or size of cells. No tails present.
Eudorina Ehrenberg.
Representative species. . . . *Eudorina elegans* Ehrenberg 1831.

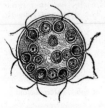

Cells sixteen, thirty-two, or sixty-four; arranged around the periphery of the jelly mass but not in contact with each other. Each cell bears two flagella.

FIG. 448. *Eudorina elegans.* × 250. (From a specimen.)

193 (192)　Colony flattened, horseshoe-shaped, with poles differentiated by
arrangement of cells.　Tails at posterior end.

Platydorina Kofoid.

Representative species.　.　.　.　.　*Platydorina caudata* Kofoid 1899.

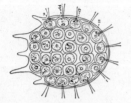

Colony slightly twisted in a left spiral.　Cells sixteen or
thirty-two imbedded in a transparent, gelatinous matrix and
surrounded by a distinct sheath.

Each cell has two flagella, an eye-spot, a nucleus, and a
single chromatophore.　Tails, in sixteen cell colonies, are
three in number; in thirty-two cell colonies five tails are
present.　Movement by rotation on the longitudinal axis.
Length 150 μ.　Plankton of rivers and lakes.

FIG. 449.　*Platydorina caudata.*　× 185.　(After Kofoid.)

194 (191)　Colonies spherical or ellipsoidal; cells differentiated as to size and
function.　195

195 (198)　No protoplasmic processes connecting the cells.　Small vegetative
cells at the anterior pole, large gonidial cells at the posterior
pole.　.　.　.　.　.　.　.　.　.　.　.　*Pleodorina* Shaw .　.　196

196 (197)　Cells sixty-four or one hundred and twenty-eight, about equally
divided between large and small.

Pleodorina californica Shaw 1893.

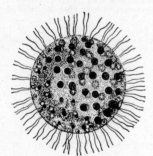

Colony spherical, with gonidial cells two or three
times the size of the vegetative cells.　Cells biflagel-
late, not in contact with each other.

Reproduction asexual, by gonidial cells, in this and
other species of the genus.

Found in ponds, ditches, and streams.

FIG. 450.　*Pleodorina californica.*　× 300.　(After Shaw.)

197 (196)　Cells thirty-two, rarely sixteen or sixty-four.　Vegetative cells,
four in number. .　.　*Pleodorina illinoisensis* Kofoid 1898.

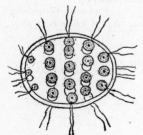

Colony ellipsoidal with cells arranged in five circles;
the polar circles with four cells each, the other three
circles with eight cells each.　The gelatinous sheath
enclosing the colony is of two layers.

Gonidial cells much larger than vegetative cells, the
latter always directed forward during movement.

Each cell with two flagella, an eye-spot, a nucleus,
and a single chromatophore.

Average length 113 μ.　Plankton of rivers.

FIG. 451.　*Pleodorina illinoisensis.*　× 200.　(After Kofoid.)

198 (195)   Protoplasmic processes connecting cells usually distinct. Poles of colony not differentiated by arrangement of vegetative and gonidial cells. . . . . *Volvox* Leeuwenhoek . . 199

199 (204)   Colonies with distinct protoplasmic processes connecting the cells. 200

200 (203)   Protoplasmic processes very stout. . . . . '. 201

201 (202)   Colonies dioecious. . . . . . . *Volvox perglobator* Powers 1908.

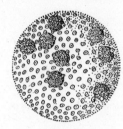

Colonies often exceeding 1 mm. in diameter. Ova or oosperms not infrequently numbering several hundred in a colony. Very common in the United States.

Fig. 452. *Volvox perglobator.* Colony with eight daughter coenobia. Cilia and protoplasmic processes not shown. × 50. (From a prepared mount).

202 (201)   Colonies monoecious. . . . . *Volvox globator* Leeuwenhoek 1788.
The common European species. About one-half the size of the preceding species, and containing fewer reproductive cells. This species probably occurs in the United States but, if so, in much less abundance than *Volvox perglobator.*

203 (200)   Protoplasmic processes slender. . *Volvox aureus* Ehrenberg 1838.
A typical European species but probably occurring in the United States also. Diameter about 850 μ.

204 (199)   Colonies apparently without protoplasmic processes connecting the cells. . . . . . *Volvox spermatosphara* Powers 1908.

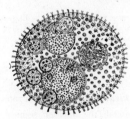

Monoecious forms with ripe sperms arranged in bundles of 32, grouped in sperm spheres in the colonies   Mature colonies often exceed 600 μ in diameter. Widely distributed in the United States.

Fig. 453. *Volvox spermatosphara.* Colony with two daughter coenobia, five egg cells and one sphere of sperm bundles. × 80. (From a specimen.)

205 (132)   Usually with an outer membrane or shell in the form of plates; body usually furrowed; flagella two. Usually colored.
Subclass **Dinoflagellida** . . 206

206 (209)   Without a membrane around the body. 207

207 (208)   Cross furrow extending only around the left side; a longitudinal furrow extending from the central end of the cross furrow to the under part of the body. . . . . *Hemidinium* Stein.

208 (207)   Cross furrow extending entirely around the body; often flattened.
            Gymnodinium Stein.
            Representative species.   . *Gymnodinium fuscum* Ehrenberg 1838.

Body oval, compressed, pointed anteriorly. Color light brown. An
eye-spot reported by Perty. Length 60 to 80 μ. Fresh water.

FIG. 454. *Gymnodinium fuscum.*   × 325.   (After Blochmann.)

209 (206)   With a membrane around the body.   210

210 (211)   Membrane delicate, homogeneous; body without processes, often
            flattened. . . . . *Glenodinium* Ehrenberg.
            Representative species.
            Glenodinium pulvisculus Ehrenberg 1838.

FIG. 455. *Glenodinium pulvisculus.*   × 500.   (After Stein.)

211 (210)   Membrane of distinct plates.   212

212 (213)   Plates without horn-like processes, polygonal, 21 in number.
            Peridinium Ehrenberg.
            Representative species.
            Peridinium tabulatum Ehrenberg 1838.

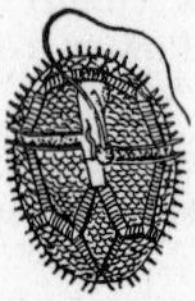

Body ovate, with convex dorsal and concave ventral surface.   Plates
showing a delicate reticulate structure under high magnification.   Color
yellow, green, or brown. Length 45 to 60 μ. Fresh water.

FIG. 456. *Peridinium tabulatum.*   × 320.   (After Stein.)

213 (212)   Plates with long, horn-like processes. . . . . . . *Ceratium* Schrank.
            Representative species. . . . *Ceratium hirundinella* Müller 1786.

Body somewhat quadrilateral, the anterior segment
bearing two nearly straight processes and the posterior
segment a single short one.   Color brown or green.
Length 90 to 170 μ. Fresh water.

FIG. 457. *Ceratium hirundinella.*   × 325.   (After Stein.)

INFUSORIA

1 (208) Cilia present during all stages of existence. . . Class **Ciliata** . . 2

2 (127) Body usually uniformly covered with cilia. 3

3 (104) Cilia similar or slightly lengthened about the mouth; no adoral spiral
zone. . . . . Order **Holotricha** . . 4

4 (59) Without an undulating membrane about the mouth. Mouth closed
except when taking food. Suborder **Gymnostomina** . . 5

5 (6) With a shell of numerous plates arranged in zones around the body.
Cilia projecting between the plates. . . . *Coleps* Nitzsch.
Representative species. . . . . *Coleps hirtus* Ehrenberg 1838.

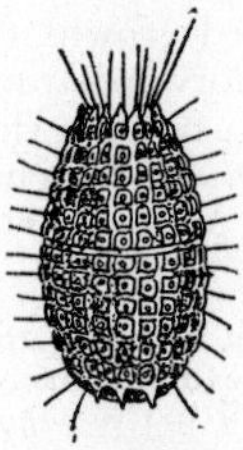

Ovate, persistent in shape. Mouth terminal, bordered by tooth-like
processes, and surrounded by cilia larger than those of the general
surface. Posterior border usually bearing spines. Length 60 μ. Pond
water and old infusions.

FIG. 458. *Coleps hirtus.* × 250. (After Conn.)

6 (5) Without a shell. 7

7 (12) With tentacle-like processes in addition to the cilia. 8

8 (9) Tentacle process single. . . . . *Ileonema* Stokes.
Representative species. . . . . *Ileonema dispar* Stokes 1885.

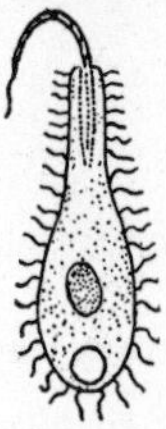

Body flask-shaped, flexible; flattened ventrally, convex dorsally, the
latter surface bearing a row of short, hair-like setae. Tentacle-like process thick at the base, twisted, with a filamentous distal half. Nucleus
subcentral; contractile vacuole posterior. Length 120 μ. Among algae.

FIG. 459. *Ileonema dispar.* × 185. (After Stokes.)

9 (8) Tentacle processes more than one. 10

10 (11) Tentacles very long and numerous, extending between the cilia.
Actinobolus Stein.
Representative species. . . . . . . *Actinobolus radians* Stein 1867.

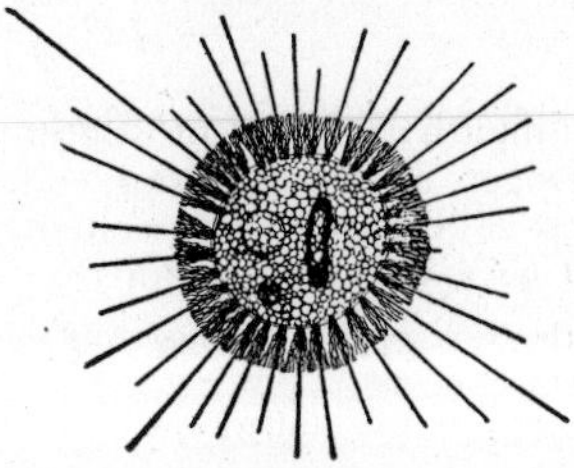

Body ovate or subglobose, the anterior extremity produced as a snout-like projection which carries the mouth
and bears the retractile tentacles and cilia. Nucleus
band-like; contractile vacuole large.

FIG. 460. *Actinobolus radians.* Figure representing individual
with mouth downward. Dimensions undetermined. (After
Calkins.)

11 (10)   Tentacles short, few in number, extending from about the mouth.
                                                      Mesodinium Stein.
Representative species.
          Mesodinium pulex Claparède and Lachmann 1858.

Body turbinate, conical, and tapering anteriorly. A wreath of strong cilia on a constriction halfway between the middle of the body and the base of the snout-like proboscis. According to Claparède and Lachmann three long stylate processes extend in front of the mouth. Length 15 μ. Habitat, reported by Claparède and Lachmann, salt water.

FIG. 461. *Mesodinium pulex.* × 810. (After Kent.)

12 (7)   Without tentacle-like processes. 13

13 (34) Body round, or ovate, or elongate in outline, symmetrical. . . 14

14 (15) Cilia of body confined to two (rarely one) many-rowed crowns or
         circles.   Body thimble-shaped, with broad end forward, from
         the flattened center of which rises an elevation bearing the
         mouth at the apex. . . . . *Didinium* Stein.
Representative species. . . . . *Didinium nasutum* Müller 1786.

Body oval, broadly rounded posteriorly. One wreath of cilia near the base of the proboscis, the other posterior to the middle of the body. Nucleus band-like. Contractile vacuole posterior. Length 100 to 175 μ. Among decaying vegetation.

FIG. 462. *Didinium nasutum. cv,* contractile vacuole. × 95. (After Blochmann.)

15 (14) Cilia not limited to two crowns or circles. 16

16 (27) With pharynx absent or slightly developed. 17

17 (22) Anterior end rounded, not oblique. 18

18 (21) Without a terminal bristle. 19

19 (20) Ellipsoidal to ovate, rounded at both ends.   Mouth anterior, leading
         into a short pharynx.   Uniform ciliation.
                                                      Holophrya Ehrenberg.
Representative species. . . . . *Holophrya* sp.

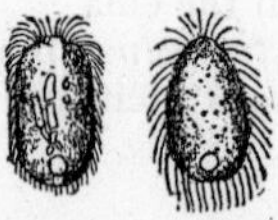

Species not determined.

FIG. 463. *Holophrya* sp. × 300. (After Conn.)

20 (19) Elongated, cylindrical, narrow in front, mouth terminal or subter-
         minal.   No pharynx.   Cilia longer at the anterior end.
         Nucleus divided into small pieces. . . *Chaenia* Quennerstedt.
Representative species. . . . . *Chaenia teres* Dujardin 1841.

Forms observed from the fresh waters of Connecticut are provisionally placed here.

FIG. 464. *Chaenia teres.* × 350. (After Conn.)

21 (18) With a terminal bristle. Similar to *Holophrya* in shape.
Urotricha Claparède and Lachmann.
Representative species.
Urotricha farcta Claparède and Lachmann 1858.

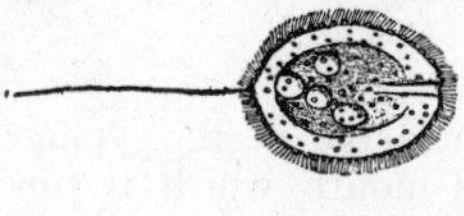

Body obliquely striated; posterior bristle obliquely directed when at rest. Progression by slow forward movement or sudden leaps to one side. Mouth on a small circular prominence at the anterior end. Length 20 μ. Pond water. *Balantozoon* of Stokes agrees with this genus except that only the anterior two-thirds is ciliated.

FIG. 465. *Urotricha farcta.* × 435. (After Conn.)

22 (17) Anterior end oblique. 23

23 (24) With a spiral series of long cilia on either side of a ridge extending from the anterior border to the posterior extremity.
Perispira Stein.
Representative species. . . . . *Perispira strephosoma* Stokes 1886.

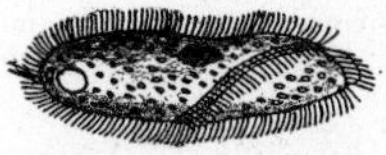

Body elongate-ovate. Cilia of the general surface very fine. Protoplasm filled with dark-colored corpuscles. Length 80 μ. Standing water with sphagnum.

FIG. 466. *Perispira strephosoma.* × 280. (After Stokes.)

24 (23) Without a spiral series of cilia. 25

25 (26) Elongated, with mouth slightly on one side; uniform ciliation. Nucleus single. . . . . *Enchelys* Hill.
Representative species. . . . . . *Enchelys pupa* Ehrenberg 1836.

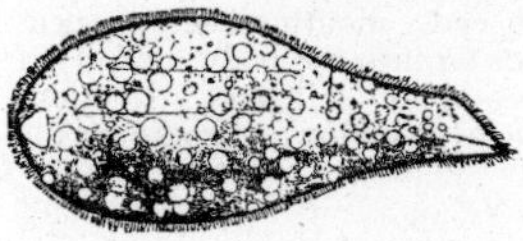

Body inflated, slender anteriorly. Often colored green. Length about 200 μ. Stagnant water.

FIG. 467. *Enchelys pupa.* × 150. (After Conn.)

26 (25) Elongate, sac-like, mouth occupying the oblique surface. Pharynx slightly developed, sometimes with rods. Nucleus bead-like. . . . . *Spathidium* Dujardin.
Representative species. . . . *Spathidium spathula* Dujardin 1841.

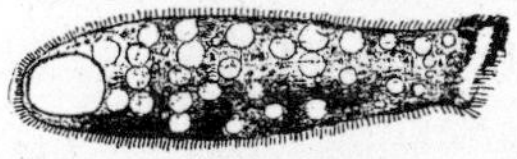

Very difficult to distinguish from forms of the genus *Enchelys.*

FIG. 468. *Spathidium spathula.* × 250. (After Conn.)

27 (16) With pharynx well developed. 28

28 (33) Body greatly elongated. 29

29 (32) Body flattened. 30

30 (31) Flask-shaped with an elongated neck-like anterior end. Proboscis short, retractile. Mouth terminal leading into a long pharynx. . . . *Trachelophyllum* Claparède and Lachmann.
Representative species. . *Trachelophyllum tachyblastum* Stokes 1884.

Body eight or ten times as long as broad; neck slender; pharyngeal passage indistinct, narrow, longitudinally striate. Cilia of surface long, vibrating independently. Nuclei two, subcentral. Contractile vacuole posterior. Length, extended, 120 to 150 μ. Bottom of shallow pools.
FIG. 469. *Trachelophyllum tachyblastum.* *cv*, contractile vacuole; *macn*, macronucleus. × 250. (After Stokes.)

31 (30) Long, ribbon-like; no proboscis. Mouth terminal with an evident
pharynx. Nucleus in the posterior third of the body and a
row of minute vacuoles near one side. . *Flexiphyllum* Conn.
Representative species. . . . . *Flexiphyllum elongatum* Conn 1905.

FIG. 470. *Flexiphyllum elongatum.* × 220. (After
Conn.)

32 (29) Body not flattened; with a long, highly contractile neck; a plug-
like projection carrying the terminal mouth which is surrounded by a crown of long cilia. Body longitudinally or
spirally striated. . . . . *Lacrymaria* Ehrenberg.
Representative species. . . . . . . *Lacrymaria olor* Müller 1786.

A common species found in pond water. Its
swan-like appearance was suggested to the early
observers by its graceful movements, as it swims
about extending its neck here and there in search of
food. Length, neck contracted, 50 to 70 μ.
FIG. 471. *Lacrymaria olor.* *cv,* contractile vacuole; *n,* nucleus. Expanded. × 50. (After Blochmann.) Contracted. × 200. (After Conn.)

33 (28) Body not elongated, spherical to ovate; anterior end not oblique.
Mouth terminal or subterminal, pharynx usually with rods.
Nucleus ovate to ribbon-like. . . . *Prorodon* Ehrenberg.
Representative species. . . . . . . *Prorodon ovum* Ehrenberg 1833.

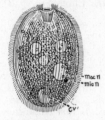

Body oval, evenly rounded at both ends; mouth eccentric, opening into a conical pharynx which leads far into the body. Rods of
pharynx conspicuous. Cilia of posterior border longer. Nucleus
spherical, central. Contractile vacuole posterior. Length 125 μ.
Pond water.

FIG. 472. *Prorodon ovum.* *cv,* contractile vacuole; *macn,* macronucleus; *micn,* micronucleus. × 170. (After Blochmann.)

34 (13) Body asymmetrical with dorsal side arched. 35

35 (48) Mouth subterminal or terminal, body greatly elongated. . . . 36

36 (43) Mouth usually open, pharynx often rod-like. 37

37 (42) Mouth subterminal. 38

38 (39) Anterior end hook-like, bent to the left; elongated, flattened, leaf-
like. Ventral surface flat with ciliated ribs; dorsal surface
curved, without cilia. Mouth on the left anterior edge, leading into a pharynx. . . . . *Loxodes* Ehrenberg.
Representative species. . . . . . *Loxodes rostrum* Müller 1786.

The body of this species is highly vesicular. Nuclei
may be two or more. Wrzesniowski has demonstrated a
racemose system of nuclei. Length 250 to 400 μ. At the
bottom of old infusions.
FIG. 473. *Loxodes rostrum.* × 250. (After Conn.)

39 (38) Anterior end not hook-like. 40

40 (41) Body not elongated; spherical to ovate, slightly flexible; a short
proboscis at the base of which is the mouth. Pharynx
with rods. . . . . *Trachelius* Schrank.
Representative species. . . . . *Trachelius ovum* Ehrenberg 1838.

Neck highly flexible. Mouth circular; pharynx with rods.
Nucleus central; contractile vacuoles numerous. Endoplasm
at the inner end of the pharynx usually spreads out into four
or five broadly diverging ramifications. Length 300 μ. Fresh
water.

FIG. 474. *Trachelius ovum.* X 85. (After Blochmann.)

41 (40) Body greatly elongated, band-like, very flexible; proboscis long with
mouth at the base and a row of long cilia along its ventral
side. . . . . *Dileptus* Dujardin.
Representative species. *Dileptus gigas* Claparède and Lachmann 1858.

Body somewhat compressed, often with a pointed,
tail-like prolongation. A prominent shoulder or
hump often indicates the position of the mouth.
Nucleus moniliform, very long. Contractile vacuoles
numerous in a dorsal row. Trichocysts on the ventral surface of the neck. Length 500 to 800 μ. Pond
water.

FIG. 475. *Dileptus gigas.* X 110. (After Conn.)

42 (37) Mouth terminal; body elongated with a long proboscis. Nucleus
double. . . . . *Lionotopsis* Conn.
Representative species. . . . . . . *Lionotopsis anser* Conn 1905.

FIG. 476. *Lionotopsis anser.* X 230. (After Conn.)

43 (36) Mouth usually closed; pharynx when present, without rods. . . 44

44 (45) With a broad hyaline border; body flattened; proboscis short, mouth
on the left side. Trichocysts well developed on the right
side. . . . . *Loxophyllum* Dujardin.
Representative species. . . . . *Loxophyllum rostratum* Cohn 1866.

Anterior extremity prolonged into a dorsally reflected, uncinate rostrum. Cilia of anterior region
longer. Middle of the dorsal border crenulate, the row
of trichocysts extending from this region forward
nearly to the tip of the rostrum. Nuclei multiple,
central; a number of contractile vesicles posterior.
Length 190 μ. Recorded by Conn from the fresh
waters of Connecticut.

FIG. 477. *Loxophyllum rostratum.* X 200.
(After Conn.)

45 (44) Without a broad hyaline border. 46

46 (47) Body flattened, elongated with an acute proboscis at the base of
which is the mouth. Nucleus single or double.
Amphileptus Ehrenberg.
Representative species. . . . . *Amphileptus gutta* Cohn 1866.

Mouth about one-third the length of the body from the
anterior end. Pharynx a short smooth tube. Cilia even all
over the body. Nucleus-like corpuscles scattered throughout
the cortical region. Contractile vacuole single, posterior.
Length 125 μ. Reported by Conn from Connecticut. Cohn
reports the species from salt water.

FIG. 478. *Amphileptus gutta.* X 335. (After Conn.)

47 (46)   Body flattened ventrally, convex dorsally. With a long neck and usually a tail-like prolongation both of which are hyaline. Mouth a slit at the base of the neck, often invisible. Nuclei usually two; contractile vacuole posterior.

Lionotus Wrzesniowski.

Representative species. . . . . . *Lionotus wrzesniowskii* Kent 1882.

FIG. 479. *Lionotus wrzesniowskii.* cv, contractile vacuole. X 125. (After Kent.)

48 (35)   Mouth usually somewhat posterior, and often with a pharynx; body oval or kidney-shaped. 49

49 (50)   Body completely ciliated, cylindrical to ovate, rounded posteriorly. Mouth about one-third of the way from the anterior end; pharynx with rods. . . . . *Nassula* Ehrenberg.

Representative species. . . . . *Nassula ornata* Ehrenberg 1838.

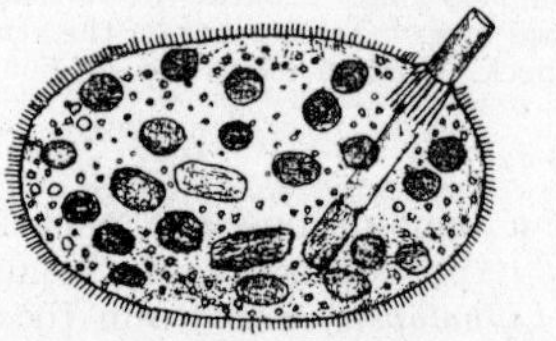

Usually some shade of red or brown in color. Nucleus large, spherical, posteriorly located. Contractile vacuole single. Length 200 μ. Among algae.

FIG. 480. *Nassula ornata.* In act of feeding. X 325. (After Conn.)

50 (49)   Body not completely ciliated; cilia ventral only. 51

51 (56)   Body flattened. 52

52 (55)   Mouth in the anterior half of the body. 53

53 (54)   Body with convex dorsal and flattened or slightly concave ventral surface. Pharynx with rods. . . . . *Chilodon* Ehrenberg.

Representative species. . . . . . *Chilodon cucullulus* Müller 1786.

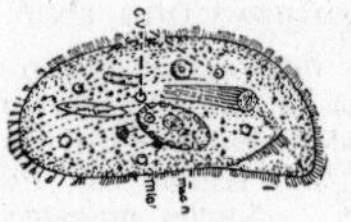

The lip-like extension prominent, a groove leading from it to the mouth. Nucleus oval near the inner end of the pharynx. Contractile vacuoles numerous. Length 125 to 200 μ. Stagnant water and among algae.

FIG. 481. *Chilodon cucullulus.* cv, contractile vacuole; macn, macronucleus; mic, micronucleus. X 110. (After Blochmann.)

54 (53)   Body with ridges on dorsal and ventral surfaces, crenate in cross section, pharynx with rods. . . . . *Chilodonopsis* Conn.

Representative species. . . . . . *Chilodonopsis crenula* Conn 1905.

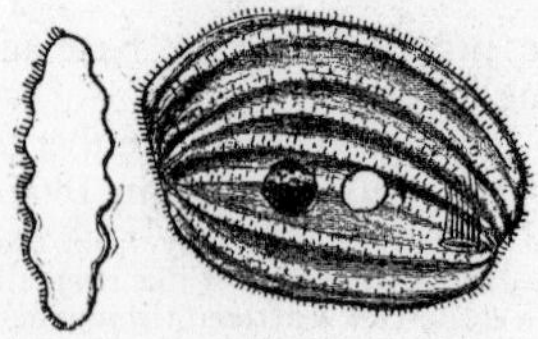

FIG. 482. *Chilodonopsis crenula.* X 335. (After Conn.)

55 (52)   Mouth in the posterior half of the body. . . . . *Opisthodon* Stein.

56 (51)   Body not flattened. 57

57 (58)   Body purse-shaped. . . . . *Phascolodon* Stein.

58 (57)   Body ovate or nearly spherical in outline with a slight lip at the anterior end. Mouth at the base of the lip with no evident pharynx. Cilia ventral in six rows. . . . *Hexotricha* Conn.
Representative species. . . . . . . *Hexotricha globosa* Conn 1905.

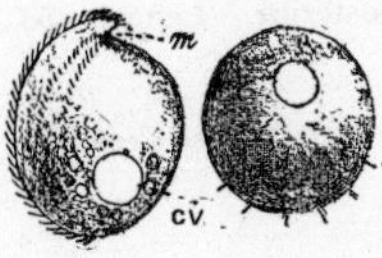

FIG. 483.   *Hexotricha globosa.* Lateral and end views. *cv*, contractile vacuole; *m*, mouth.   X 335.   (After Conn.)

59 (4)   Usually with an undulating membrane or membranes about the mouth. Mouth always open. . . . Suborder **Trichostomina** . . 60

60 (87)   Peristome usually absent; with or without undulating membranes. 61

61 (70)   Without an undulating membrane; pharynx present. 62

62 (65)   One or two broad zones of strong cilia about the body; with a tail-like tuft of cilia. 63

63 (64)   Two broad zones of strong cilia about the body. Body cylindrical, with mouth posterior leading into a short pharynx. Anterior part of the body uniformly ciliated. A band of strong cilia near the middle and posterior end.
Urocentrum Nitzsch.
Representative species. . . . . . *Urocentrum turbo* Müller 1786.

Body broadly rounded anteriorly, rounded or truncate posteriorly. Movement by a rotation on the long axis or swiftly darting from side to side. Contractile vacuole posterior with the band-like nucleus curved about it. Length 100 μ. Pond water.

FIG. 484. *Urocentrum turbo.* *cv*, contractile vacuole; *n*, nucleus. X 200.
(After Kent.)

64 (63)   With an oblique circle of strong cilia near the anterior end. Body somewhat pyriform, rigid, finely ciliated. Two groove-like canals encircling the body. Mouth ventral, posterior to the grooves and leading into a short pharynx.
Calceolus Diesing.
Representative species. . . *Calceolus cypripedium* James-Clark 1866.

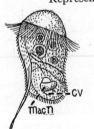

Color light brown. Very similar in movement to *Urocentrum turbo.* Length 80 to 160 μ. Fresh water.

FIG. 485. *Calceolus cypripedium.* *cv*, contractile vacuole; *macn*, macronucleus.
X 200.   (After Kent.)

65 (62) No zones of strong cilia about the body. 66

66 (67) Mouth covering the whole oblique anterior end. Body usually oval or purse-shaped. . . . . *Leucophrys* Ehrenberg.
Representative species. . . . . *Leucophrys patula* Ehrenberg 1838.

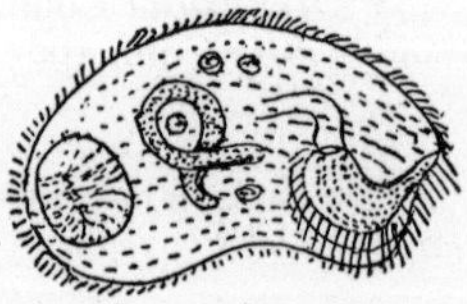

Body oval; pharynx tubular, curved. Nucleus band-like, central. Contractile vacuole posterior. Length 200 μ. Among algae.

FIG. 486. *Leucophrys patula.* × 150. (After Kent.)

67 (66) Mouth at some distance from the anterior end. 68

68 (69) Body ellipsoidal, ciliation regular, mouth a crescent-shaped or spiral slit leading into a pharynx. . . . *Ophryoglena* Ehrenberg.
Representative species. . . . . . *Ophryoglena atra* Ehrenberg 1838.

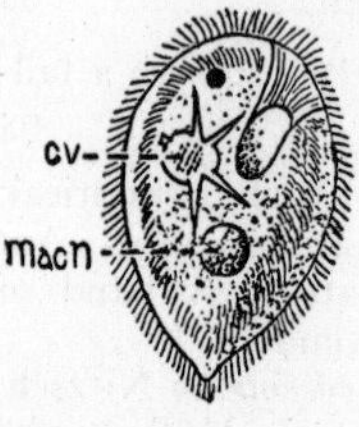

Body with posterior extremity pointed. Endoplasm usually opaque, with a dark blue pigment spot in the anterior region. Nucleus round, posterior; contractile vacuole central. Length 125 to 150 μ. Stagnant water.

cv-

macn-

FIG. 487. *Ophryoglena atra.* *cv*, contractile vacuole; *macn*, macronucleus. × 200. (After Kent.)

69 (68) Body laterally compressed, ovate, with the dorsal surface rounded. Mouth one-third of the distance from the anterior end, with a few, long, fine cilia on its superior wall or roof.
Colpoda Müller.
Representative species. . . . . . *Colpoda campyla* Stokes 1886.

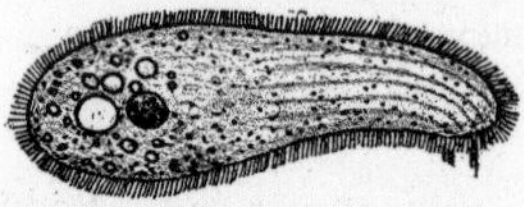

Length of body 55 μ. Standing water with dead leaves.

FIG. 488. *Colpoda campyla.* × 600. (After Conn.)

70 (61) With one or more undulating membranes. 71

71 (76) One membrane present. 72

72 (75) Mouth not terminal. 73

73 (74) Body not flexible; mouth lateral, triangular, following a small peristome and with an undulating membrane in front. Body similar to *Colpoda*, but less compressed. . *Colpidium* Stein.
Representative species. . . . . . *Colpidium striatum* Stokes 1886.

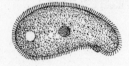

Body twice as long as broad, striated longitudinally, anterior extremity curved ventrally. Nucleus subcentral; contractile vacuole posterior, often leaving several small vacuoles after contraction. Length 50 μ. Infusions.

FIG. 489. *Colpidium striatum.* × 500. (After Edmondson.)

74 (73)   Body very flexible and changeable in shape.   Ovate, covered with
fine cilia, with a long bristle extending from the posterior
border.   Mouth ventral with a vibratile and retractile hood-
like velum. . . . .   *Saprophilus* Stokes.
Representative species. . . . . .   *Saprophilus agitatus* Stokes 1887.

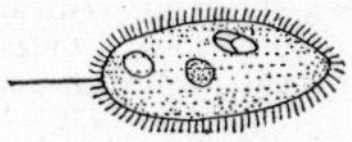

> Body twice as long as broad, compressed, obliquely truncate in front;
> cilia very short and fine.   Body longitudinally striate.   Nucleus sub-
> central.   Contractile vacuole posterior.   Length of body 35 to 45 μ.
> Infusions containing animal matter.
>
> FIG. 490.   *Saprophilus agitatus*.   X 390.   (After Stokes.)

75 (72)   Mouth terminal with a delicate membrane.   Body ovate, elastic;
anterior extremity obliquely truncate. . .   *Trichoda* Müller.
Representative species. . . . . . .   *Trichoda pura* Ehrenberg 1838.

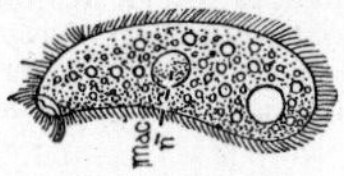

> Length 40 μ.   Often found abundantly in old infusions of pond
> water.   Swift moving, usually rolling on its long axis.
>
> FIG. 491.   *Trichoda pura*.   *macn*, macronucleus.   X 400.   (After Kent.)

76 (71)   Two membranes present.   77

77 (78)   Body elongated, rounded in front, contracting into a tail behind.
One side somewhat flattened, the other convex.   Mouth
triangular, near the anterior end. . . . .   *Dallasia* Stokes.
Representative species. . . . .   *Dallasia frontata* Stokes 1886.

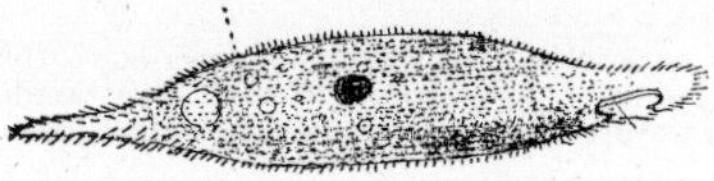

> Body five times as long as broad, ventral
> surface convex, dorsal slightly concave; taper-
> ing posteriorly to a retractile tail-like prolonga-
> tion.   Anterior extremity narrow.   Mouth
> obliquely placed on the ventral surface.   Length
> 150 μ.   Still water, with aquatic plants.
>
> FIG. 492.   *Dallasia frontata*.   X 335.   (After Conn.)

78 (77)   Body not contracting into a tail.   79

79 (84)   With a long, posterior bristle.   80

80 (83)   Without a spiral row of long cilia.   81

81 (82)   Body ovate, slightly compressed, broader behind; ventral surface
straight, dorsal surface curved.   Mouth near or anterior
to the middle, with an extensile membrane.   Cilia densely
arranged in a furrow in front of the mouth.
                                        Uronema Dujardin.
Representative species. . . . .   *Uronema marinum* Dujardin 1841.

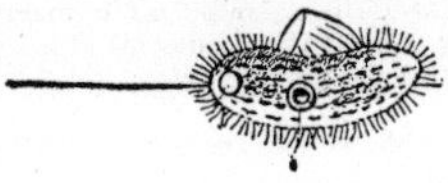

> The cilia are exceedingly vibratile, their movements being ir-
> regular and independent.   Nucleus central.   Contractile vacu-
> ole posterior.   Length 30 μ.   Fresh water, often associated with
> *Cyclidium* but not so numerous.
>
> FIG. 493.   *Uronema marinum*.   X 400.   (After Kent.)

82 (81) Body elongate, nearly cylindrical, the anterior extremity truncate
and slightly curved; a short, curved seta borne on either
side near the anterior end. A long, straight bristle extending from the posterior end. . . . . . . *Loxocephalus* Kent.
Representative species. . . . . *Loxocephalus granulosus* Kent 1882.

Endoplasm granular, mouth on the oblique anterior border although quite indistinct. Nucleus spherical, central.
Contractile vacuole posterior. Length 40 to 70 μ. Often
abundant among decaying vegetable matter. Conjugation
readily occurs in infusions.

FIG. 494. *Loxocephalus granulosus.* × 375. (After Edmondson.)

83 (80) Like *Uronema*, but with an anterior, spiral row of long cilia.
Dexiotricha Stokes.
Representative species. . . . . . . *Dexiotricha plagia* Stokes 1885.

Body about three times as long as broad, bearing minute
hemispherical protuberances. Cilia setae-like; a row of flexible
setae extending from the margin of the mouth obliquely across
the right-hand side of the anterior half of the body. Nucleus
subcentral; contractile vacuole posterior. Length 60 μ. Pond
water.

FIG. 495. *Dexiotricha plagia.* × 315. (After Stokes.)

84 (79) Without a posterior bristle. 85

85 (86) Ellipsoidal to elongate, somewhat acute behind. Mouth lateral,
surrounded by a furrow which extends backward. Pharynx
short with rods. . . . . *Frontonia* Ehrenberg.
Representative species. . . . . *Frontonia leucas* Ehrenberg 1838.

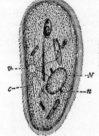

Body elongate-oval, wider anteriorly. Mouth a slit anterior to the
middle of the body. Cilia fine, in longitudinal rows. Contractile
vacuoles, usually two. Trichocysts numerous. Length 250 to 300 μ.
Stagnant water.

FIG. 496. *Frontonia leucas.* c, canal; N, macronucleus; n, micronucleus;
v, vacuole. × 165. (After Calkins.)

86 (85) Ovate, flattened, rounded at each end. Mouth triangular or crescent-
shaped, lateral, in front of the middle of the body.
Glaucoma Ehrenberg.
Representative species. . . . *Glaucoma scintillans* Ehrenberg 1830.

The vibratile membranes extending around the mouth presenting a bilabial appearance. Nucleus large, central. Contractile vacuole posterior. Length 75 μ. Infusions.

FIG. 497. *Glaucoma scintillans.* cv, contractile vacuole; macn. macronucleus; micn, micronucleus. × 350. (After Bütschli.)

87 (60) With a well-developed peristome. 88

88 (101) Mouth not posterior to the middle of the body. 89

89 (98) Not surrounded by a lorica or gelatinous sheath. 90

90 (91) Peristome oblique. Body elongated, slightly flattened, rounded at both ends or slightly truncated in front. Mouth followed by a short pharynx; ciliation regular. . *Paramoecium* Stein. Representative species. . . *Paramoecium caudatum* Ehrenberg 1838.

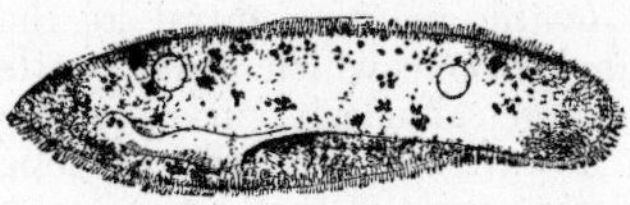

> Perhaps the most familiar ciliated protozoon known. Body with a large central macronucleus and a small micronucleus, and a contractile vacuole in either extremity. Abundantly supplied with trichocysts. Length variable, average 250 μ. Everywhere in infusions.
>
> FIG. 498. *Paramoecium caudatum.* × 170. (After Conn.)

91 (90) Peristome not oblique. 92

92 (97) With one or more membranes well developed in the peristome. . 93

93 (94) Peristome very broad and conspicuous, occupying the entire right side. Body oval, flattened ventrally, convex dorsally; anterior end oblique, posterior end acute. A tuft of long cilia extends from the posterior end. . . . . *Lembadion* Perty. Representative species. . . . . . *Lembadion bullinum* Perty 1849.

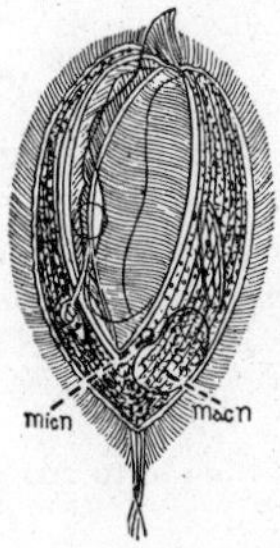

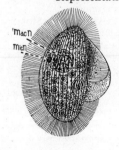

> Nucleus elongated, curved in the posterior region on the left side; contractile vacuole opposite the nucleus. When stimulated the animal swims rapidly backward rotating on its long axis. Length 50 to 100 μ. Among aquatic plants in pond water.
>
> *Hymenostoma* Stokes differs from *Lembadion* in the more posterior, ventral position of the mouth, the greater length of the adoral cilia, the abruptly narrowing membrane and the double contractile vacuole.
>
> FIG. 499. *Lembadion bullinum.* *macn*, macronucleus; *micn*, micronucleus. × 250. (After Blochmann.)

94 (93) Peristome not broad and conspicuous. 95

95 (96) Without a long, posterior bristle. Peristome parallel to the right side with a large projecting membrane. Body oval, flattened dorso-ventrally. Cilia very long. *Pleuronema* Dujardin. Representative species. . . . *Pleuronema chrysalis* Ehrenberg 1838.

> Cilia in length nearly one-half the diameter of the body, stiffened, setae-like. Nucleus central; contractile vacuole anterior. Length 75 to 125 μ. Fresh water. Stokes recognizes two separate genera, *Histriobalantidium*, with long setose bristles among the cilia over the whole body, and *Bothrostoma*, with a long terminal tuft of cilia. Bütschli places them both under *Pleuronema*.
>
> FIG. 500. *Pleuronema chrysalis.* *macn*, macronucleus; *micn*, micronucleus. × 225. (After Blochmann.)

96 (95)　Like *Pleuronema* but with a shorter peristome and one or more long
　　　　　posterior bristles. . . . . *Cyclidium* Ehrenberg.
　　　　Representative species. . . . *Cyclidium glaucoma* Ehrenberg 1838.

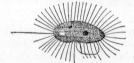

Cilia long and rigid, in longitudinal rows. Nucleus central;
contractile vacuole posterior. Length 20 μ. Very abundant in
stagnant water.

Fig. 501. *Cyclidium glaucoma.* × 625. (After Edmondson.)

97 (92)　Without an oral membrane. Body ovate; mouth ventral at the
　　　　　posterior end of a longitudinal groove which bears on its
　　　　　right-hand border a row of large, arcuately curved setose
　　　　　cilia diminishing in length toward the mouth. A long
　　　　　bristle extending from the posterior end of the body.
　　　　　　　　　　　　　　　　　　　Ctedoctema Stokes.
　　　　Representative species. . . . *Ctedoctema acanthocrypta* Stokes 1884.

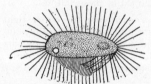

Often very abundant among fresh-water algae.
Trichocysts are numerous and very stout. Length
of body 25 μ.

Fig. 502. *Ctedoctema acanthocrypta.* × 875. (After Stokes.)

98 (89)　With a lorica or gelatinous sheath. 99

99 (100)　Enclosed in a lorica. Animal similar to *Pleuronema*. Lorica oblong-
　　　　　ovate, hyaline, with tapering extremities, the terminal aper-
　　　　　tures about half as wide as the center of the sheath. Animal
　　　　　very active within the lorica. . . . . *Calyptotricha* Phillips.
　　　　Representative species. . . . *Calyptotricha inhaesa* Stokes 1885.

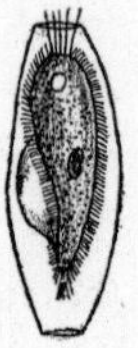

Kellicott reports this species from Ontario. Length of lorica 180 to 200 μ.
Enclosed animal 30 μ. Attached laterally to algae.

Fig. 503. *Calyptotricha inhaesa.* × 100. (After Kellicott.)

100 (99)　Enclosed in a gelatinous sheath to which the animal is not attached.
　　　　　Body ovate; mouth ventral, at the end of a groove on the
　　　　　margin of which is a series of strong cilia. A tuft of long,
　　　　　curved cilia extends from the anterior extremity.
　　　　　　　　　　　　　　　　　　　Cyrtolophosis Stokes.
　　　　Representative species. . . . *Cyrtolophosis mucicola* Stokes 1885.

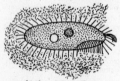

A strange form not uncommon among algae. When the animal
comes to rest, a transparent, sticky substance seems to be exuded
from the body which becomes granular, due to excreta, bacteria
and other foreign bodies which adhere to it. When disturbed
the animal glides out of its covering and another is constructed.
A temporary colony may be built up by the adherence of several
gelatinous sheaths. Length of body 25 μ.

Fig. 504. *Cyrtolophosis mucicola.* × 875. (After Stokes.)

101 (88)　Mouth at the posterior end of the body. 102

102 (103) Body flattened, oval, with spiral furrows. Peristome with a vibrating membrane posterior leading into the mouth. A tuft of long bristles at the posterior end of the body.

Cinetochilum Perty.

Representative species.

Cinetochilum margaritaceum Ehrenberg 1838.

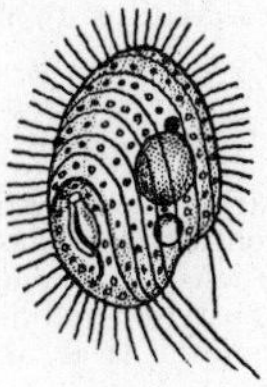

Contractile vacuole posterior, opposite the mouth, with nucleus anterior to it. Length 30 μ. Very common in pond water.

FIG. 505. *Cinetochilum margaritaceum.* × 500. (After Bütschli.)

103 (102) Body nearly oval, ventral surface flat, ciliated; dorsal surface curved, with three longitudinal grooves. Mouth posterior on the left side, with a small, vibrating membrane.

Microthorax Engelmann.

Representative species. . . *Microthorax sulcatus* Engelmann 1862.

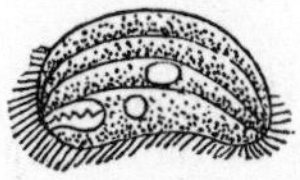

Associated with the preceding species. Length 40 to 60 μ.

FIG. 506. *Microthorax sulcatus.* × 310. (After Kent.)

104 (3) An adoral zone present consisting of cilia fused together into membranellae. . . . . Order **Heterotricha** . . 105

105 (120) With a uniform covering of cilia. 106

106 (115) Peristome not confined to the anterior border of the body. . 107

107 (112) Peristome a long, narrow furrow. 108

108 (111) With an undulating membrane. 109

109 (110) Body flattened, narrow and hook-like in front. Mouth near the middle of the body at the end of the narrow peristome. Membranellae on the left wall of the peristome, on the right an undulating membrane. Colored. . *Blepharisma* Perty.

Representative species. . . *Blepharisma lateritia* Ehrenberg 1838.

Body usually truncate behind; nucleus in the anterior half of the body. Contractile vacuole posterior. Color, peach-bloom. Length 150 μ. Among aquatic plants.

FIG. 507. *Blepharisma lateritia.* × 180. (After Stein.)

110 (109) Body spiral, cylindrical, somewhat pointed at both ends, but contractile; peristome spiral with the mouth near the middle
of the body. Membranellae on the left side of the peristome, a membrane on the right side.
                          Metopus Claparède and Lachmann.
Representative species. . . . . . *Metopus sigmoides* Müller 1786.

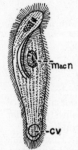

Cilia usually longer at the posterior end. A mass of dark pigment granules in the anterior extremity. Nucleus oval, central; contractile vacuole
posterior. Length 100 to 200 μ. At the bottom of infusions. *Metopides
acuminata* Stokes differs from the above species in the posterior, tail-like
prolongation from which extend a number of long bristles. It is also
smaller in size.

FIG. 508. *Metopus sigmoides.* cv, contractile vacuole; macn, macronucleus. × 220.
(After Stein.)

111 (108) Without an undulating membrane. Body greatly elongated, cylindrical, contractile. Peristome reaching to the middle of
the body. Strong membranellae on the left side of the peristome. Body spirally striated. . . *Spirostomum* Ehrenberg.
Representative species. . *Spirostomum ambiguum* Ehrenberg 1835.

FIG. 509. *Spirostomum ambiguum.* cv, contractile vacuole;
macn, macronucleus. × 30. (After Kent.)

Body ten to fifteen times as long as
broad, but readily contracting into a short
spiral body. Nucleus moniliform. Contractile vacuole posterior, extending forward as a canal. Extended body may
reach 2800 μ in length. Common among
aquatic plants.

112 (107) Peristome a broad triangular area, deeply sunken. 113

113 (114) With an undulating membrane on the right side of the peristome.
Body cylindrical or purse-shaped, sometimes contractile.
Peristome broad in front extending one-third the length of
the body. . . . . *Condylostoma* Dujardin.
Representative species. . . . . *Condylostoma patens* Müller 1786.

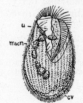

Body broadly ovate, widest posteriorly. Peristome broadly triangular,
extending about half the length of the body. Nucleus moniliform; contractile vacuole irregular. Length 200 μ. Stagnant water.

FIG. 510. *Condylostoma patens.* macn, macronucleus; u, undulating membrane
× 105. (After Kent.)

114 (113) Without an undulating membrane in the peristome. Body purse-shaped, oblique in front; peristome funnel-shaped, opening on the ventral side by a slit reaching as far as the middle of the body. Membranellae on the left side of the peristome. . . . . *Bursaria* Müller. Representative species.

> *Bursaria truncatella* Müller 1786.
>
> Nucleus band-like; contractile vacuoles numerous. Length 500 to 700 μ. Pond water. 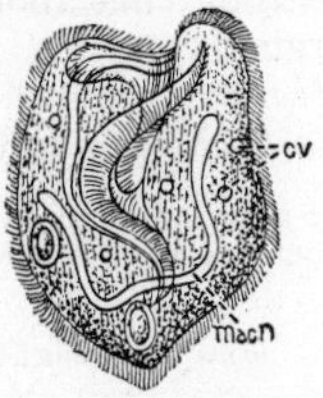
>
> FIG. 511. *Bursaria truncatella.* cv, contractile vacuole; *macn*, macronucleus. × 35. (After Kent.)

115 (106) Peristome confined to the anterior border of the body, with its plane nearly at right angles to the longitudinal axis of the body. 116

116 (119) Posterior end not produced into a tail-like process. 117

117 (118) Body purse-shaped, slightly flattened, anterior end oblique. Peristome enclosing most of the anterior end of the body.
Climacostomum Stein.

118 (117) Body funnel-shaped when extended, fixed or free-swimming, sometimes enclosed in a jelly-like lorica. Peristome, the anterior expanded surface with a spiral row of strong cilia around its border; the left end of the spiral being the lower, leading into the mouth and short pharynx. Surface finely ciliate sometimes bearing, in addition, long slender bristles.
Stentor Oken.
Representative species. . *Stentor polymorphus* Müller 1786.

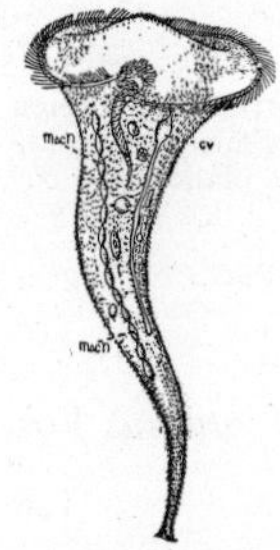

> Body usually containing a cortical layer of chlorophyl granules. Nucleus moniliform. Length, extended, 1200 μ. Among aquatic plants and in infusions. Sometimes found in gelatinous masses on leaves and roots of water plants.
> Another fresh-water form, *Stentor coeruleus* Ehrenberg, blue in color, is also common.
>
> FIG. 512. *Stentor polymorphus.* cv, contractile vacuole; *macn*, macronucleus. × 30. (After Kent.)

119 (116) Posterior end produced into a tail-like process; anterior region helmet-like, rounded anteriorly with a free posterior margin. Mouth ventral in a ciliated groove. Cilia extending from the mouth in a spiral across the anterior border and around the free margin of the anterior portion.
Caenomorpha Perty.
Representative species. *Caenomorpha medusula* Perty 1849.

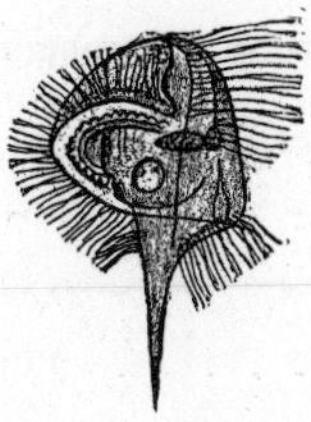

> Movements swift, rotating on the long axis. Length, with tail, 100 to 130 μ. Standing water.
>
> FIG. 513. *Caenomorpha medusula.* × 200. (After Stein.)

120 (105) Cilia restricted to certain limited areas or zones. 121

121 (124) Body not in a lorica. 122

122 (123) Equatorial region of the body bearing a circle of long, fine bristles. Body spheroidal with a spiral wreath of strong cilia about the anterior border. Mouth anterior, marginal.

Halteria Dujardin.

Representative species. . . . . *Halteria grandinella* Müller 1786.

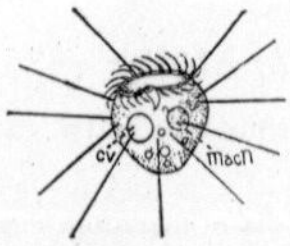

Nucleus round, central, with contractile vacuole near. Moving by a rotary motion accompanied by sudden leaps. Length 25 μ. Common in pond water.

FIG. 514. *Halteria grandinella.* *cv,* contractile vacuole; *macn,* macronucleus. × 400. (After Kent.)

123 (122) Without long, fine bristles, otherwise very similar to *Halteria.*

Strombidium Claparède and Lachmann.

Representative species. . *Strombidium claparèdii* Kent 1882.

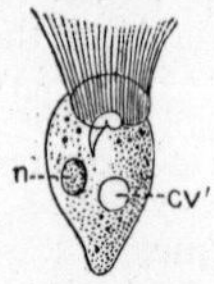

Body somewhat elongate, tapering posteriorly. Length 80 μ. Pond water.

FIG. 515. *Strombidium claparèdii.* *cv,* contractile vacuole; *n,* nucleus. × 100. (After Kent.)

124 (121) Body in a lorica. 125

125 (126) Lorica mucilaginous, attached to some support. Body ovate to pyriform, attached in the lorica by a pedicel. Mouth anterior, surrounded by a wreath of long cilia.

Tintinnidium Kent.

Representative species. . *Tintinnidium fluviatilis* Stein 1867.

The lorica has an uneven surface, frequently with incorporated foreign particles. Body sometimes attached to the bottom, sometimes to the side of the lorica. Length of lorica 125 μ. Attached to aquatic plants.

FIG. 516. *Tintinnidium fluviatilis.* × 200. (After Entz.)

126 (125) Lorica chitinous; otherwise as *Tintinnidium.* . . *Tintinnus* Fol.

127 (2) Body not uniformly covered with cilia. 128

128 (169) Cilia setae-like, usually limited to the ventral surface. Dorsal surface sometimes with bristles. Body flattened.

Order **Hypotricha** . . 129

129 (130) Ventral side uniformly ciliate, except sternum; a group of stronger cilia behind peristome and near posterior end.

Trichogaster Sterki.

130 (129) Ventral surface not uniformly ciliate. 131

131 (166) Many border cilia. 132

132 (157) Ventral cilia numerous, in rows. 133

133 (152) Ventral cilia bristle-like. 134

134 (143) Usually more than two rows of ventral cilia. 135

135 (140) Five or more rows of ventral cilia. 136

136 (137) Peristome with an undulating membrane, body flexible. Three or more frontal styles. Five to twelve anal styles in an oblique row extending to the left. Peristome an elongated triangle.

Urostyla Ehrenberg.

Representative species. . . . . Urostyla trichogaster Stokes 1885.

FIG. 517. Urostyla trichogaster. × 150. (After Conn.)

Ventral surface with closely approximated rows of fine cilia. Anal styles ten or twelve in number. Nucleus single, according to Stokes. Contractile vacuole single, to the left of the peristome. Length 250° to 300 μ. Vegetable infusions. Hemiciplostyla Stokes agrees with Urostyla, but has no anal styles.

Conn found two nuclei in his form and states that it may be a variety of Urostyla grandis Ehrenberg.

137 (136) Peristome without an undulating membrane. 138

138 (139) Elongate, rounded at both extremities, not flexible; five nearly straight rows of ventral cilia. Peristome on the right-hand margin, extending back of the middle, with a row of long cilia or membranellae. Nuclei four to six in number.

Homostyla Conn.

Representative species. . . . . . Homostyla elliptica Conn 1905.

FIG. 518. Homostyla elliptica. × 325. (After Conn.)

139 (138) Kidney-shaped, with six oblique rows of ventral cilia, the posterior row the stronger. No frontal, ventral, or anal styles. Border cilia forming a complete row around the periphery. Peristome reaching to the middle of the body. External parasites on Hydra. . . . . Kerona Ehrenberg.

Representative species. . . . . Kerona pediculus Müller 1786.

FIG. 519. Kerona pediculus. × 250. (After Stein.)

140 (135) Less than five rows of ventral cilia. 141

141 (142) Body elongated anteriorly into a neck; rounded behind, very contractile. Peristome narrow, extending to or beyond the middle. Membranellae long. Two or three oblique rows of ventral setae. No frontal or anal styles.

Stichotricha Perty.

Representative species. . . . . Stichotricha secunda Perty 1849.

Marginal setae long and slender. Nuclei two, with the contractile vacuole between. Often a mucilaginous sheath is secreted by the animal, from which it may project the anterior half of the body or may entirely vacate it and swim freely in water. Length about 200 μ. Among sphagnum.

FIG. 520. Stichotricha secunda. × 235. (After Conn.)

142 (141) Body elliptical to ovate, flexible.   Three unequal rows of ventral
cilia; frontal styles numerous.   No anal styles.   Marginal
setae uninterrupted. . . . . *Eschaneustyla* Stokes.
Representative species. . . *Eschaneustyla brachytona* Stokes 1886.

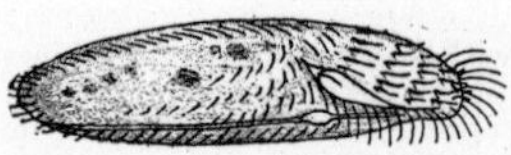

Anterior extremity slightly curved to the left with a constriction beneath the front border.   Frontal styles about
twenty-five in oblique rows.   Nucleus not observed.   Contractile vacuole canal-like along the left-hand border.   Length
about 200 μ.   Standing water with dead leaves.

FIG. 521.   *Eschaneustyla brachytona.*   × 200.   (After Stokes.)

143 (134) One or two rows of ventral cilia. 144

144 (145) One row of about seven large ventral cilia.   Long border and anal
cilia. . . . .' *Balladina* Kowalewsky.

145 (144) Two rows of ventral cilia; body not elongated in front. . . 146

146 (151) Body prolonged posteriorly into a tail-like process. 147

147 (150) Body not flask-shaped. 148

148 (149) No anal styles; body narrow, elongated, sometimes contractile.
The border setae pushed in on the ventral surface.
Uroleptus Stein.
Representative species. . . . . *Uroleptus musculus* Müller 1786.

Body slightly elastic; tail-like process short, conical.   Anterior end curved slightly to the left, the posterior to the
right.   Frontal styles three or four.   Length 200 μ.   Among
aquatic plants.

FIG. 522.   *Uroleptus musculus.*   × 150.   (After Conn.)

149 (148) With a row of seventeen anal styles upon the left side.   In other
respects like *Uroleptus.* . . . . *Amphisia* Sterki.

150 (146) Body flask-shaped, otherwise very similar to *Uroleptus.*
Platytrichotus Stokes.
Representative species. . *Platytrichotus opisthobolus* Stokes 1886.

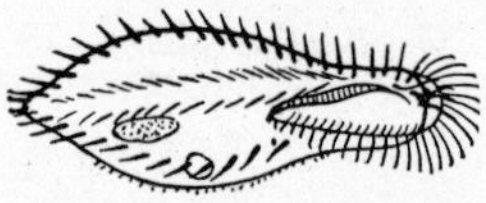

Frontal styles five.   Nucleus single, posterior.   Contractile
vacuole single.   The posterior tip of the body is changeable
in form.   It may be bifid, truncate, or rounded.   Long hispid
bristles are developed from the dorsal surface.   Length 190 μ.
Among sphagnum.

FIG. 523.   *Platytrichotus opisthobolus.*   × 200.   (After Stokes.)

151 (147) Body not prolonged into a tail-like process.   Elongated, rounded at
both ends.   With two uninterrupted rows of cilia on the
ventral surface. . . . . *Holosticha* Wrzesniowski.
Representative species. . . . . *Holosticha vernalis* Stokes 1887.

Frontal styles five or six.   Anal styles from five to eight,
usually branched.   Dorsal bristles numerous.   Nuclei two;
contractile vacuole central.   Length 190 μ.   Shallow pools,
observed with algae.

FIG. 524.   *Holosticha vernalis.*   × 225.   (After Conn.)

152 (133) Ventral cilia setae-like, often in interrupted rows. 153

153 (156) Ventral setae in more than one row. **154**

154 (155) Body elongate-oval, with five to eight frontal styles; ventral setae usually arranged in two or more rows, the inner rows having but few setae. Anal styles five or six, two of which are near the posterior border. . . . . *Pleurotricha* Stein.
Representative species. . . *Pleurotricha lanceolata* Ehrenberg 1838.

Somewhat resembling *Stylonychia* but without caudal setae and with anal styles arranged in two groups. Nuclei two in number, one in front of the apex of the peristome. Length 250 μ. Among algae.

FIG. 525. *Pleurotricha lanceolata.* × 112. (After Edmondson.)

155 (154) Body somewhat rectangular in outline with slightly rounded ends. Three or four oblique rows of ventral setae running from left to right, and three rows parallel to the peristome border. Anal styles five or six. Border cilia uninterrupted.
Onychodromus Stein.
Representative species. . . . . *Onychodromus grandis* Stein 1859.

Body not flexible. Frontal styles from sixteen to twenty-eight, in three rows. Anal styles from five to seven. Nuclei usually four. Length 100 to 300 μ. *Onychodromopsis flexilis* Stokes differs from Stein's form in having a soft, flexible body.

FIG. 526. *Onychodromus grandis.* × 125. (After Conn.)

156 (153) Ventral setae in one oblique row. Body elongate-oval. Five or six frontal styles and as many anal. Peristome triangular, curved, with an undulating membrane.
Gastrostyla Engelmann.
Representative species. . . *Gastrostyla steinii* Engelmann 1862.

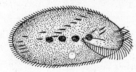

Body evenly rounded at each extremity. Three very large frontal styles near the border. Anal styles five, in an oblique row, not projecting beyond the border. Nuclei four. Contractile vacuole near the middle of the body on the left side. Length 250 μ. Fresh water.

FIG. 527. *Gastrostyla steinii.* × 125. (After Edmondson.)

157 (132) Ventral cilia few, not in rows. 158

158 (165) Not produced posteriorly into a tail-like process. 159

159 (162) Body flexible. 160

160 (161) Border cilia uninterrupted. Narrow, elliptical, rounded at both ends. Five ventral setae and five anal styles. No caudal bristles. Inner right wall of peristome bent toward outer left wall. . . . . *Oxytricha* Ehrenberg.
Representative species. . . . *Oxytricha pellionella* Müller 1786.

Marginal setae set well in on the ventral surface. Anal styles arising near the posterior border and extending nearly their entire length beyond it. Nuclei two. Contractile vacuole on the left side. Length 80 to 100 μ. Common in infusions and fresh water. *Opisthotricha* Kent resembles *Oxytricha* in general characteristics but has three caudal setae.

FIG. 528. *Oxytricha pellionella.* × 335. (After Conn.)

161 (160) Border cilia interrupted at the posterior end. Frontal styles, eight or ten. Five ventral setae and five anal styles. No caudal bristles. Dorsal hispid setae usually present.

Tachysoma Stokes.

Representative species. . . . *Tachysoma parvistyla* Stokes 1887.

Body narrow anteriorly forming a neck-like region. Ten frontal styles. Marginal setae scarcely projecting except posteriorly. Dorsal setae minute. Styles in this form are very small. Length 60 μ. Shallow pools in early spring.

FIG. 529. *Tachysoma parvistyla.* × 450. (After Stokes.)

162 (159) Body not flexible. 163

163 (164) With caudal setae. Elongate-oval in shape with eight frontal, five ventral setae, and five anal styles. Caudal setae usually three, long. Peristome triangular, with an undulating membrane; the inner wall bent away from the outer wall.

Stylonychia Stein.

Representative species. . . . *Stylonychia notophora* Stokes 1885.

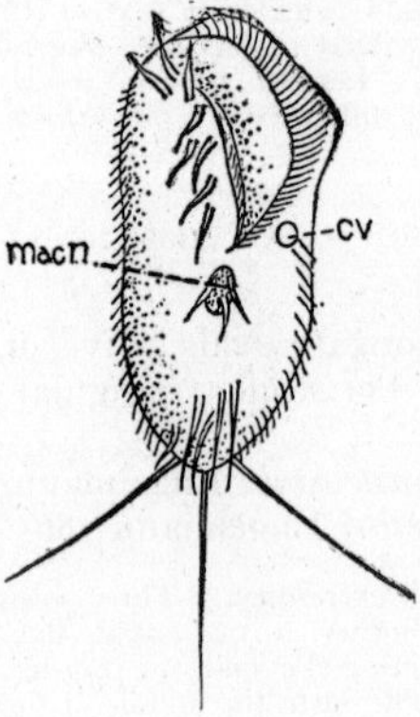

macn

Front border obliquely truncate on the left side. Peristome extending nearly to the middle of the body. Caudal setae widely separated. Nuclei two. Length 120 to 160 μ. Pond water.

FIG. 530. *Stylonychia notophora. cv,* contractile vacuole; *macn,* macronucleus. × 300. (After Conn.)

164 (163) Without caudal setae; with inner wall of peristome bent toward the outer wall. Like *Stylonychia* in other respects.

Histrio Sterki.

Representative species. . . . . *Histrio erethisticus* Stokes 1887.

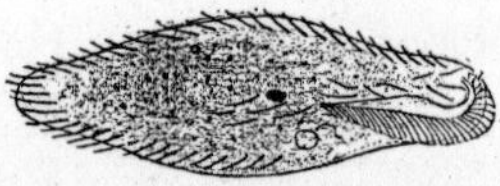

Frontal styles nine; anal styles five, stout, rigid. Marginal setae uninterrupted. Length 150 μ. Shallow pools, with algae.

FIG. 531. *Histrio erethisticus.* × 200. (After Conn.)

165 (158) Produced posteriorly into a tail-like process. Body flexible, with eight ventral setae and five anal styles at the base of the tail.

Urosoma Kowalewsky.

Representative species. . . . . *Urosoma* sp.

Form doubtful as to species.

FIG. 532. *Urosoma* sp. × 335. (After Conn.)

166 (131) Border cilia few or none. 167

167 (168) No caudal setae. Body rounded or oval, dorsal surface usually furrowed. Peristome in the posterior region in the left-lateral border, its right border prolonged into a triangular, lip-like extension. Usually three frontal styles, four or five ventral setae, and five or more anal styles.

Aspidisca Ehrenberg.

Representative species. . . . . *Aspidisca costata* Dujardin 1841.

Dorsal surface with five or six furrows. Nucleus band-like. Length 35 μ. Common in infusions.

FIG. 533. *Aspidisca costata.* × 500. (After Conn.)

168 (167) Caudal setae usually four in number. Body oval, with dorsal convex surface furrowed. Peristome broad, on the left side, extending backward to or beyond the middle of the body. Frontal styles six or eight, a few scattered ventral setae, and five anal styles. . . . . . . *Euplotes* Stein.

Representative species. . . . . . *Euplotes charon* Müller 1786.

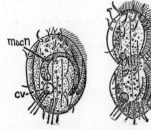

Frontal styles seven; ventral setae three. Nucleus band-like. Length 80 μ. Pond water. Differing from *Euplotes patella* Ehrenberg by its smaller size and greater number of frontal styles.

FIG. 534. *Euplotes charon.* Ventral view and individual in process of division. *cv*, contractile vacuole; *macn*, macronucleus. × 300. (After Kent.)

169 (128) Cilia usually limited to the adoral zone, sometimes with additional rings of cilia. Body cup-like or cylindrical.

Order **Peritricha** . . 170

170 (193) No lorica present. 171

171 (180) Without a stalk. 172

172 (175) With a permanent secondary ring of cilia at the posterior end enclosing an adhesive disk. 173

173 (174) Body short, barrel-shaped, with the posterior end discoidal, the inner border of which is supported by a horny ring, the peripheral zone of which is radially striated and denticulate; the outer border surrounded by a wreath of cilia. Adoral zone extends spirally around the flattened end. Mouth eccentric. Parasitic forms. . . *Trichodina* Stein.

Representative species. . . *Trichodina pediculus* Ehrenberg 1830.

Commonly observed gliding up and down on the tentacles of fresh-water *Hydra*. Height of body 70 μ.

FIG. 535. *Trichodina pediculus.* Individuals adherent to tentacle of *Hydra*. × 50. (After Kent.)

174 (173) Identical with *Trichodina*, except that the chitinous ring is not
denticulate. . . . . *Urceolaria* Stein.

175 (172) Without a permanent secondary ring of cilia. 176

176 (177) With two rings of stiff, spinous processes. . . *Hastatella* Erlanger.
Representative species. . . . . *Hastatella radians* Erlanger 1890.

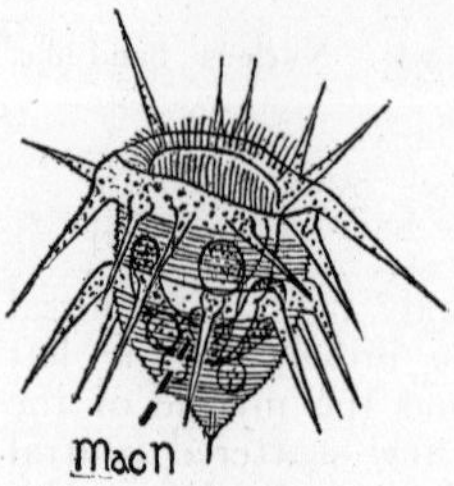

FIG. 536. *Hastatella radians.* *macn,* macronucleus. × 500. (After
Erlanger.)

macn

177 (176) Without rings of stiff, spinous processes. 178

178 (179) Posterior end elongated, usually attached; peristome slightly developed. Ciliated disk small. . . . *Scyphidia* Lachmann.
Representative species. . . . . *Scyphidia fromentellii* Kent 1882.

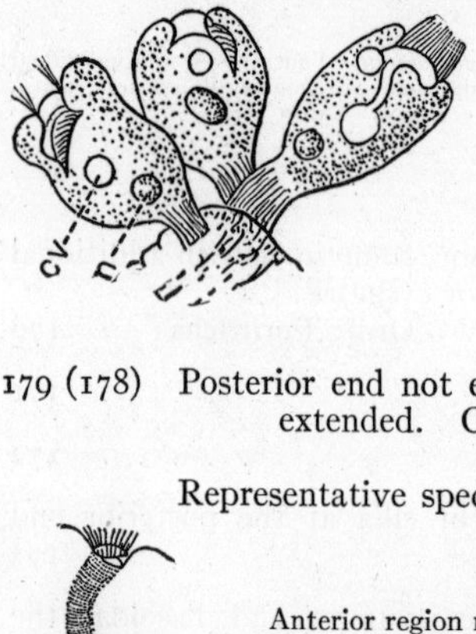

Body truncate anteriorly; stalk-like appendage
longitudinally striated. Length, extended, 80 μ.
On water snails.

FIG. 537. *Scyphidia fromentellii.* *cv,* contractile vacuole; *n,*
nucleus. × 200. (After Kent.)

179 (178) Posterior end not elongated; attached or free. Cylindrical when
extended. Ciliated disk small.
Gerda Claparède and Lachmann.
Representative species. . . . . . *Gerda sigmoides* Kellicott 1885.

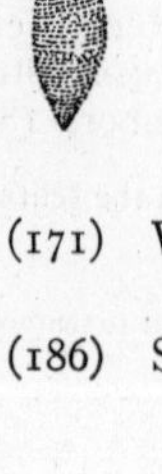

Anterior region narrowed, usually curved. Surface finely striated transversely. Nucleus not observed. Length, extended, 150 μ. Adherent to
fresh-water plants.

FIG. 538. *Gerda sigmoides.* × 160. (After Kellicott.)

180 (171) With a stalk. 181

181 (186) Stalk unbranched. 182

182 (183) Stalk retractile. Body bell-shaped, cuticle often ringed. A series of strong cilia encircle the central, elevated ciliary disk. Mouth eccentric between the peristome and ciliary disk. Nucleus band-like, curved. . . . . . *Vorticella* Ehrenberg. Representative species. . . *Vorticella campanula* Ehrenberg 1838.

Body broadly campanulate, greatly dilated anteriorly, surface smooth. Stalk thick, five or six times the length of the body. Endoplasm often opaque with granules. Length of body 150 μ. Pond water. Social.

FIG. 539. *Vorticella campanula.* × 50. (After Kent.)

183 (182) Stalk not retractile. 184

184 (185) With an operculum. Body ellipsoidal to ovate; the ciliary disk upon a stalk, closing like a lid. Nucleus short or band-like. *Pyxidium* Kent. Representative species. . . . . *Pyxidium ramosum* Stokes 1887.

Body vasiform, widest centrally; surface smooth. Ciliary disk slightly exserted with two circles of long fine cilia. Pedicel very short. Length of body about 100 μ. Pond water on rootlets of *Lemna.*

FIG. 540. *Pyxidium ramosum.* × 335. (After Conn.)

185 (184) Without an operculum. Body elongate-ovate with surface usually transversely striate, stalk short. . . *Rhabdostyla* Kent. Representative species. . . . . *Rhabdostyla vernalis* Stokes 1887.

Body widest centrally, constricted below the peristome border. Ciliary circles two. Nucleus band-like. Length 50 μ. Attached to *Cyclops* and *Cypris* in early spring.

FIG. 541. *Rhabdostyla vernalis.* cv, contractile vacuole. × 660. (After Stokes.)

186 (181) Stalk branched. 187

294   FRESH–WATER BIOLOGY

187 (190)   Stalk retractile. 188

188 (189)   Zooids contracting independently. Bodies bell-shaped. Central
            muscle interrupted at the union of the stalk and the branch.
            Ciliated spiral forming about one and a half circles. Nu-
            cleus horseshoe-shaped. . . . . . . *Carchesium* Ehrenberg.
            Representative species. . . . *Carchesium polypinum* Kent 1882.

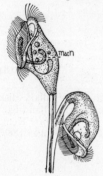

Colonies often reaching a height of one-eighth of an inch. Attached to the under surfaces of stones or floating sticks in fresh-
water pools or running streams. The colony may be the
temporary host of *Amphileptus meleagris*. Length of zooids
50 μ.
Some interesting work has been done on the nucleus of this
species by Miss M. Greenwood. (The Journal of Physiology,
Vol. XX, pp. 427–454.) It was found that the normal activity
causes a drain on the organism which, if not offset by sufficient
repair due to the lack of nutrition, results in the more fluid character of the macrosomes of the nucleus.

FIG. 542. *Carchesium polypinum.* Terminal branch with two zooids;
macn, macronucleus. × 300. (After Kent.)

189 (188)   Zooids contracting together. Bodies very similar to *Carchesium*
            but central muscle continuous, causing all of the zooids to
            contract together. . . . . *Zoothamnium* Stein.
            Representative species. . . . *Zoothamnium adamsi* Stokes 1885.

Bodies about twice as long as broad, tapering to the
pedicel; finely striated transversely. Length of zooids
60 μ. Reported from Niagara River. Attached to
algae.

FIG. 543. *Zoothamnium adamsi.* *cv,* contractile vacuole; *macn*
macronucleus. × 100. (After Stokes.)

190 (187)   Stalk not retractile. 191

191 (192)   Bodies bell-shaped, usually transversely striated; peristomal disk
broad. Stalk containing a canal but no muscle.
Epistylis Ehrenberg.
Representative species. . . . *Epistylis flavicans* Ehrenberg 1830.

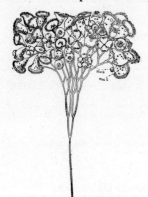

The species may be distinguished by the fact that the
stem is hollow throughout except the joints which are
solid. Another peculiarity is the curvature which each
limb makes as it leaves the point of bifurcation in the
dichotomously branching system.

Five or six circles of strong cilia about the disk. Bodies
usually pale yellow in color. Nucleus band-like, curved.
When old the stalk loses its rigidity and the colony falls
down in a tangled mass. The same decumbent condition of a normal, upright colony may be produced by
removing its customary food supply. Conjugation of
free-swimming microgametes with attached macroga-
metes is common. Length of zooids 200 to 350 μ. Attached to leaves, sticks, stones, etc., in running streams
or fresh-water pools.

Fig. 544. *Epistylis flavicans.* *macg,* macrogamete; *micg,*
microgamete. × 25. (After Kent.)

192 (191)   Bodies elongate-ovate; peristomal disk not broad, elevated a considerable distance. . . . . *Opercularia* Stein.
Representative species. . . . *Opercularia plicatilis* Stokes 1884.

Bodies elongate-ovate, smooth, soft and flexible, about three times
as long as broad. When contracted, zooids are thrown into transverse
folds posteriorly and bear longitudinally plicate, snout-like projections
in front. Protoplasm enclosing green corpuscles. Ciliary circles two.
Stalk rigid, striate longitudinally. Zooids in sessile groups of from ten
to twenty. Length of body 250 μ. Height of colony 2 5 mm. Attached to plants in pond water.

Fig. 545. *Opercularia plicatilis.* × 25. (After Stokes.)

195 (196)   Animals growing in clusters, attached or free-floating, enclosed in a mucilaginous jelly. Zooids attached to a branching stalk, each secreting a jelly-like tube which may remain distinct or fuse with its neighbor forming a jelly mass. Zooids similar in anatomy to *Vorticella*. Usually green.

Ophrydium Ehrenberg.

Representative species. . . *Ophrydium eichhornii* Ehrenberg 1838.

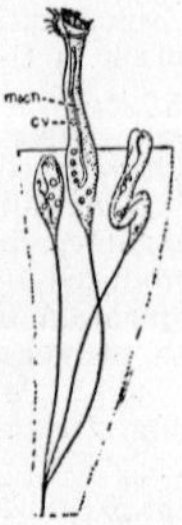

Bodies very plastic, finely striate transversely. Clusters hemispherical, of closely approximated individuals. Some colonies may include as many as one hundred zooids, although this large size is uncommon.

Division of the body has been observed to take place in a transverse direction, which is a rare occurrence in this family.

The anterior portion swims away and settles down to form a new colony, or probably conjugates with some fixed zooid. Length of expanded zooids 250 to 500 μ. Fresh water.

FIG. 546. *Ophrydium eichhornii.* *cv*, contractile vacuole; *macn*, macronucleus. ✕ 50. (After Kent.)

196 (195)   Animals solitary; similar in other respects to *Ophrydium*.

Ophridinopsis Kent.

200 (201)   Lorica with a hinge-like valve that closes the opening when the body retracts. Lorica elongate, subcylindrical. Body elongate with ciliary system as *Vorticella*.

Thuricola Kent.

Representative species. . . . . . *Thuricola valvata* Wright 1858.

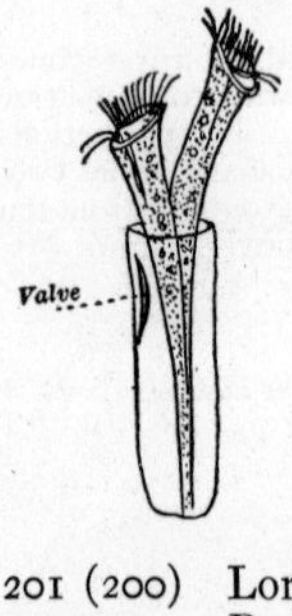

Lorica four or five times as long as broad, with the valve at some distance from the aperture. Length of lorica 120 μ. Fresh water; also reported from salt water. In *Thuricolopsis* Stokes the lorica is provided with a support for the valve. Otherwise as *Thuricola*.

Valve

FIG. 547. *Thuricola valvata.* ✕ 150. (After Kent.)

201 (200)   Lorica without a valve. . *Vaginicola* Claparède and Lachmann.
Representative species. . . *Vaginicola leptosoma* Stokes 1885.

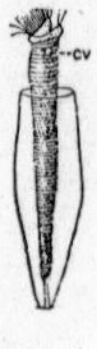

Lorica broadly vasiform, twice as long as broad, inflated posteriorly. Zooid elongate, projecting one-third its length beyond the lorica. Peristome twice as broad as the body. Surface transversely striate. Length of lorica 120 μ. Pond water.

FIG. 548. *Vaginicola leptosoma.* *cv*, contractile vacuole. ✕ 110. (After Stokes.)

203 (204) Without an operculum. Zooid like *Thuricola;* adherent to the bottom of the lorica in a sessile manner or united by a continuation of the supporting pedicel. . *Cothurnia* Ehrenberg. Representative species. . . . . *Cothurnia plectostyla* Stokes 1885.

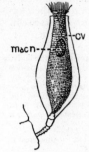

Lorica curved, two and one-half times as long as broad, finely striate longitudinally, also with transverse markings.   Divided posteriorly into two unequal parts by a curved, chitinous partition to which the zooid is attached.   Zooid not protruding much beyond the aperture when extended; transversely striate. Length of lorica 110 μ. Marsh water.

FIG. 549. *Cothurnia plectostyla. cv,* contractile vacuole; *macn,* macronucleus.
× 250. (After Stokes.)

204 (203) With an operculum of chitin developed beneath the peristome and closing the lorica when the animal is retracted.
Pyxicola Kent.
Representative species. . . . . *Pyxicola carteri* Kent 1882.

Lorica subcylindrical, three times as long as broad, anterior margin slightly oblique, walls undulate.   Pedicel very short.   Zooid extending beyond the aperture. Length of lorica 90 μ. Fresh water.

FIG. 550. *Pyxicola carteri.* × 270. (After Kent.)

205 (198) Lorica decumbent. **206**

206 (207) Animal adherent to the posterior extremity of the lorica.
Platycola Kent.
Representative species. . . . . . *Platycola decumbens* Kent 1882.

Lorica oval, depressed.   Zooid extending considerably beyond the aperture, the exserted portion being at right angles to the portion within the lorica. Length of lorica 90 μ. Fresh water.

FIG. 551. *Platycola decumbens.* × 200. (After Kent.)

207 (206) Animal adherent to one side of the lorica which often has a valvular aperture. Zooid adherent to the margin of the aperture.
Lagenophrys Stein.
Representative species. . . . *Lagenophrys vaginocola* Stein 1851.

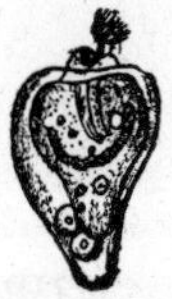

Lorica elongate with two semilunar, lip-like processes partially closing the aperture.   The processes are raised when the zooid is extended and lowered when it is retracted.   Zooid adherent by its narrow peristome to the edge of the aperture. Length of lorica 70 μ. Fresh water. *Stylohedra* Kellicott differs from *Lagenophrys* in having an erect lorica with a pedicel.

FIG. 552. *Lagenophrys vaginocola.* × 210. (After Maupas.)

208 (1)   Cilia present during embryonic stage only.   Tentacles in adult.
Class **Suctoria** . .   209

209 (210)   Tentacles branched.   Animals solitary, sessile, discoidal, or subspherical, with the surface of the integument indurated.
Tentacles flexible, non-contractile, finely perforate at their extremities.   Increasing by gemmation. .   *Dendrocometes* Stein.
Representative species. . . *Dendrocometes paradoxus* Stein 1851.

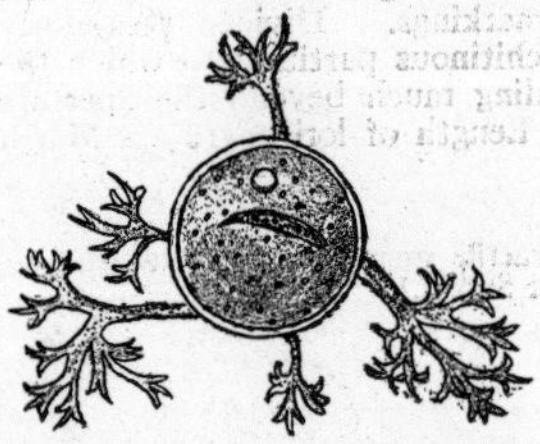

Tentacles equal in length to the diameter of the body,
usually five or less in number.   The distal terminations
of the tentacles are capable of great expansion and, by
means of these, other Protozoa are captured and the protoplasm of their bodies absorbed into the body of the
host.   Nucleus subtriangular.   Diameter of body 80 μ.
Fresh water, sometimes attached to *Gammarus pulex*, a
fresh-water shrimp.

FIG. 553.   *Dendrocometes paradoxus.*   × 170.   (After Stein.)

210 (209)   Tentacles unbranched, contractile.   211

211 (220)   Without a lorica.   212

212 (213)   With a stalk.   Body spherical or pear-shaped.   Tentacles knobbed,
scattered, or in groups.   In some species the animal may
become detached from the stalk and live a free life.
Podophrya Ehrenberg.
Representative species. . . . . . . *Podophrya fixa* Müller 1786.

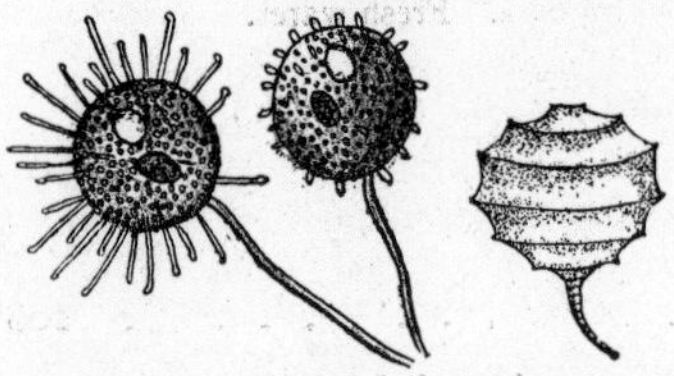

Stalk slender but rigid.   Tentacles slender,
scattered over the surface of the body, usually
not longer than the diameter of the body.   Nucleus oval, central.   Contractile vacuoles often
two.   Diameter of body 55 μ.   Attached to aquatic plants.

FIG. 554.   *Podophrya fixa.*   Active individuals. .   × 210.
(After Conn.)   Cyst.   × 230.   (After Edmondson.)

213 (212)   Without a stalk.   214
214 (215)   Forming colonies.   Animals fused, forming an erect, branching
colony.   Several colonies may be connected by a creeping
stolon.   Suctorial, capitate tentacles borne on the ends of
the branches. . . . .   *Dendrosoma* Ehrenberg.
Representative species. . .   *Dendrosoma radians* Ehrenberg 1838.

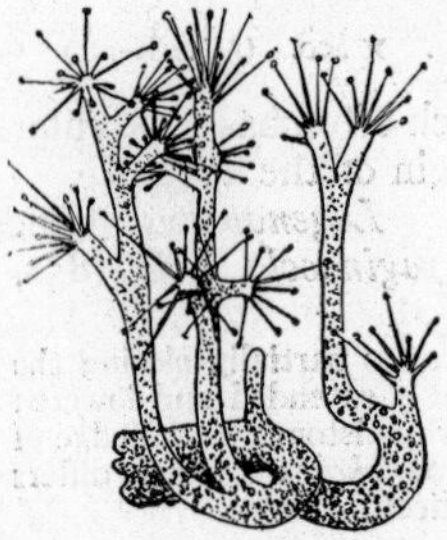

Stolon repent, giving rise to a number of erect branches
tapering distally, themselves often branched.   Nucleus ribbon-
like, ramifying into the branches.   Contractile vacuoles numerous.   Height of colony 1000 to 2500 μ.   Attached to
aquatic plants.

FIG. 555.   *Dendrosoma radians.*   × 30.   (After Blochmann.)

215 (214)   Not forming colonies.   216

216 (217)   Tentacle one, consisting of a single, movable anterior process.
Parasitic on *Cyclops*. . . . . *Rhyncheta* Zenker.

217 (216)   Tentacles numerous. 218

218 (219)   Body spherical, never fixed; knobbed tentacles arising from all
sides. . . . . . . *Sphaerophrya* Claparède and Lachmann.
Representative species. . . . *Sphaerophrya magna* Maupas 1881.

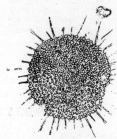

Tentacles not exceeding fifty in number: when fully extended,
equal in length to the diameter of the body. Reproduction has
been observed to take place by transverse division. Diameter
of body 40 μ. Fresh water.

FIG. 556. *Sphaerophrya magna.* × 500. (After Conn.)

219 (218)   Body irregular; knobbed tentacles arising from the lobes of the
margin of the body. Attached by the broad, lower surface.
Trichophrya Claparède and Lachmann.
Representative species. . . . . *Trichophrya sinuosa* Stokes 1886.

Body flattened with lobed margins. Usually not more than five
clusters of tentacles. Nucleus branched. Contractile vacuoles
numerous. Length 55 μ. Attached to aquatic plants.

FIG. 557. *Trichophrya sinuosa.* × 125. (After Stokes.)

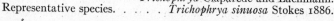

220 (211)   With a lorica. 221

221 (224)   Lorica sessile. 222

222 (223)   Usually cup-shaped or subspherical; tentacles suctorial, sometimes
in groups. . . . . *Solenophrya* Claparède and Lachmann.
Representative species . . . . . . *Solenophrya pera* Stokes 1885.

Lorica irregularly cubical or satchel-shaped, hyaline, widest at the base
of attachment, narrowing anteriorly, with the sides somewhat concave.
Zooid oval, not attached to bottom of lorica. Tentacles arising from the
entire frontal border. Two individuals often in the same lorica. Height
of lorica 40 μ. Width and length nearly the same as height. Attached to
aquatic plants in standing water.

FIG. 558. *Solenophrya pera.* × 225. (After Stokes.)

223 (222)   Posterior end of the body prolonged into a projection. Attached
to *Epistylis*. Two to five long, simple tentacles.
Urnula Claparède and Lachmann.

224 (221)　Lorica with a stalk. Body may or may not fill the lorica. The
end of the lorica may be open or provided with slit-like
openings through which the tentacles extend. Tentacles
suctorial, knobbed, scattered, or in groups.
　　　　　　　　　　　　　　　　　　　　　　Acineta Ehrenberg.
Representative species. . . . . .　*Acineta fluviatilis* Stokes 1885.

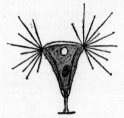

Lorica subtriangular, compressed, very delicate, widest anteriorly, tapering to the attachment with the stalk. Stalk
shorter than the lorica. Two anterolateral openings for the
tentacles. Zooid usually filling the lorica. Length of lorica
40 to 80 μ. Attached to aquatic plants.

FIG. 559.　*Acineta fluviatilis.*　× 315.　(After Stokes.)

IMPORTANT REFERENCES ON MASTIGOPHORA AND INFUSORIA

See list of general works under Sarcodina, p. 236; also the following:

DANGEARD, P. A. 1902. Recherches sur les Eugleniens. Le Botaniste,
8: 97–357; 4 pl., 53 figs.

KENT, S. 1880–1882. A Manual of the Infusoria. 3 vols. London.

KOFOID, C. A. 1898. Plankton Studies, II. Bull. Ill. State Lab. Nat.
Hist., 5: 273–300; 12 pl.

1899. Plankton Studies, III. Bull. Ill. State Lab. Nat. Hist., 5: 419–
440; 1 pl.

PALMER, T. C. 1905. Delaware Valley Forms of Trachelomonas. Proc.
Acad. Nat. Sci., Phila., 57: 665–675; 1 pl.

POWERS, J. H. 1907. New Forms of Volvox. Trans. Amer. Micr. Soc.
27: 123–149; 4 pl.

1908. Further Studies on Volvox, with Descriptions of Three New Species.
Trans. Amer. Micr. Soc., 28: 141–176; 4 pl.

ROUX, J. 1901. Faune Infusorienne des eaux stagnantes des environs de
Genève, 149 pp., 8 pl., 4to., Genève.

STOKES, A. C. 1888. A Preliminary Contribution Toward a History of the
Fresh Water Infusoria of the United States. Jour. Trenton Nat. Hist.
Soc., 1: 71–344; 13 pl.

CHAPTER X

THE SPONGES (PORIFERA)

By EDWARD POTTS,* Media, Pa.

THE zoophytes or plant animals of the old zoologists or, as they are now more correctly designated, the separate groups of sponges and coelenterates, are represented in the fresh waters of North America through a very narrow range both of genera and species. Sponges alone constitute the topic of this chapter. The student of fresh-water sponges must not expect to find them resembling in appearance the familiar forms of commerce, which in fact are exclusively of marine origin. Nor should he look for shapeless masses of jelly; such may be found, but they are not sponges. Yet as animal organisms, sponges, whether fresh-water or marine, are essentially alike. Infinitely variable in form and external appearance and in the character and constituents of their skeletal structure, the vital parts that have clothed them, or do still clothe them if examined in life, are composed alike of protoplasm or sarcode. This forms the delicate tissues, structureless except when viewed through powerful lenses, and builds up the inert framework whether it consists of tough elastic fibers, as in the commercial sponge, or is the fairy-like structure of flint or lime belonging to other sponges found in the ocean, or forms skeletons, as in our fresh-water forms so far as known, always of silex. The active life work of sponges it is impossible to see with the naked eye and very difficult to study even under the microscope. Certain collared cells by means of waving flagella feed the sponge, reject intrusive matter, and create

* The death of Mr. Potts just after the first manuscript of the chapter had been submitted laid upon me the duty of bringing it into conformity with the other chapters of the book without his help. I have endeavored to do this with the least possible change from the original. To make sure that no error was committed in the process I secured the aid of Dr. N. Annandale, Calcutta, India, for whose kind assistance I am deeply indebted. For the present form of the key Mr. Potts is in no wise responsible. I am also indebted to Professor Frank Smith for valuable unpublished data in regard to distribution. — HENRY B. WARD.

the currents that traverse the canals of the body. While the action of these flagella is invisible to the unaided eye, their effect may be seen if some finely divided carmine is added to the water. The particles are sucked into the little pores over the surface and after long wandering, having proved indigestible, are ejected from the larger orifices.

The skeleton of these siliceous sponges, the only part that can be easily preserved for study, is composed of spicules or little needles of hydrated silica (opal), averaging about one one-hundredth of an inch in length, fasciculated or bound together side by side, but breaking joints, to form threads of considerable thickness along the principal lines of the sponge growth but thinner in the connecting links that make the interspaces. The binding material along these threads is not strong and its composition is not certainly known. The terminal spicules projecting around the sponge uphold the filmy dermis a little above the firmer body of the sponge. Where the larger channels unite to form the efferent osteoles the outflowing currents stretch this dermis into little cylindrical tubes or towers, technically called chimneys, with terminal openings through which one may often see rejected particles shot out as from the crater of a volcano.

A few fresh-water sponges in some situations seem to be essentially perennial; others die in hot countries at the onset of the summer season, or among us at the coming of winter, or are broken up by floods, floating ice, etc., so that for a season they disappear from view. The ordinary annual revival of sponge life, the growth after winter or after a period of desiccation, is provided for by the germination of many seed-like bodies, called gemmules; these may generally be found when the sponge matures, fixed as a pavement layer at the base of the sponge or distributed amongst its tissues. The living cells enclosed in these are protected by a firm chitinous coat or shell that is again surrounded by a crust composed of minute air cells, which float the gemmules and promote their distribution to distant places. A variety of minute spicules is normally found embedded in this crust as described under individual species in the key.

Whenever the favorable season arrives, that is in most regions when spring comes or when, in dry regions, the occasional floods reach them, the gemmules in the pavement layers are supposed to germinate where they were deposited; the floating kinds, set adrift, lodge upon any suitable surface and begin their seasonal growth.

Each gemmule is provided with a foramen, or a foraminal aperture, sometimes plain, but often more or less tubular, through which the growing cells usually escape by amoeboid action and appear as a delicate creamy film surrounding the gemmule. Sometimes, however, they escape by the rupture of the whole gemmule. Where this is part of a pavement-layer or one of a group of detached gemmules the escaping currents flow together as a filmy mass, sometimes rounded up like a small pea, otherwise as a spreading film or like the wandering trail of slime left by one of the larger snails. The appearance of the young spicules is nearly coincident with the escape of the cells and they at once begin to arrange themselves according to the habit of the species, forming a network over the supporting surface, upon which is built a superstructure suggesting that of our modern steel-framed buildings. Special interspaces become the chambers lined with the collared flagellate cells already mentioned. The action of these flagella creates currents of water flowing in through myriads of almost invisible pores in the covering, bearing food particles to nourish the growing sponge and then carrying off and discharging useless matter through the larger canals by the efferent osteoles already mentioned.

The study of fresh-water sponges should begin here and follow the cycle of growth from gemmule to gemmule, watching, if it be possible, even the development within their own especial cells of the various classes of spicules, observing in the autumn the gradual gathering together of the germ cells before they are shrouded in chitin or committed to the waters within their floating crusts. Under favorable conditions and constant as well as careful control much of this work may be made independent of the seasons, after germinating the fresh gemmules in shallow glass dishes at home, and in a small way afford excellent opportunity for study; but it will not be found practicable to grow sponges in aquaria excepting as small fragments in very large bodies of water or in vessels in which the water is constantly or frequently renewed.

Those who wish to gather specimens for their cabinets or design to determine genera and species must await the maturity of the various specimens. Observation seems to make it probable that the rarer, filmy sponges complete their growth and mature their gemmules earlier than the more lusty, massive forms. The gemmules of the former have often been seen in August or September resting in slender lines upon standing or floating timbers from which the rest of the sponge has disappeared, though the coarser forms are frequently immature late in November. These dates hold true for the northern United States generally and would of course vary in other parts of the world; but there are undoubtedly individual regions of extreme or atypical climatic conditions within our own area where the sponge calendar when worked out will show a distinctly individual aspect.

A hint as to hopeful localities for collecting may suffice. Do not waste time in hunting along sluggish streams or in shallow, muddy ponds, where, even if the sponges start to grow, they will soon be suffocated by gravitating particles of earthy matter. A reservation should perhaps be made in favor of the lower sides of floating timbers that have long lain in the water, since here gravity protects instead of injures the sponges. Only one other caution seems necessary. As all known fresh-water sponges are siliceous the student will probably fail to find them in waters strongly impregnated with carbonate of lime, though they are recorded from such places.

Perfect drying is to be recommended. The proper classification can be as readily determined from dry as from fresh sponges and it is only when a specimen has some novel character or specific form that it is worth while to preserve it in alcohol. When a wrapper is necessary for transportation or otherwise, be sure to use soft paper, rather than cotton or sawdust.

Other features having proved indeterminate or unreliable, the system is based upon the shapes and positions of the minute spicules found embedded in the gemmule crust. As these can only be satisfactorily seen when the impenetrable crust is made transparent or removed, three microslides from each specimen must be prepared to determine the forms of the skeleton, the dermal or flesh, and the gemmule spicules.

Provide a half dozen or more short test tubes with a stand made by boring holes of suitable diameter in a piece of inch board. First make sure that you have in hand parts of the same sponge only. Place in the first tube a dozen or more clean gemmules, some of them cut in half with a sharp knife, and about an equal bulk from the remainder of the sponge; cover with a few drops of strong nitric acid that has been previously brought to a boil in another tube and set aside, the purpose being to corrode away the crust but not the chitin of the gemmules. In a few minutes, when most of the gemmules incline to settle at the bottom, pour off the acid into the next tube, wash carefully with several lots of pure water, replace it with alcohol and set the tube aside to settle. Put into the acid in the second tube a small quantity of all parts of the sponge, adding more acid if necessary, and boil carefully over a spirit lamp to thorough disintegration. When that is effected fill this tube also with water and set it aside to settle. The smaller spicules settle very slowly. It may be well to shake the tube a little in order to separate the darker particles from the pure white. When the mass has settled, carefully pour off the water with the impurities, wash the residue with fresh water and let it stand, after which a mount may be made from this tube. Spread the spicules evenly and not too thickly on a slide, and let them dry thoroughly before adding balsam and a cover glass. This amount will of course furnish an epitome of the sponge but will not show the exact relations of the minor spicules to the gemmules. This can only be seen after two or more applications of alcohol to the first tube have removed the acid mixture; to keep out the air, cover with benzol until fully ready for the balsam. Distribute a few of the gemmules, with some spicules, upon a second slide and mount in balsam before the air penetrates them. A fragment of the dry filmy dermis mounted in balsam will determine the presence or absence of dermal spicules and fix positively the standing of the sponge according to the key.

If all the smaller spicules distinguished by this process are acerates, that is, more or less cylindrical, whether straight or curved, smooth or spined, pointed or abruptly terminated, the specimen under examination may unhesitatingly be placed in the genus *Spongilla*. All others, unless entirely novel, will show some modification of the birotulate form, *i.e.*, two little wheels or rotules connected by a shaft, and on the numerous variations of these parts depends the position of the species in the key.

KEY TO NORTH AMERICAN FRESH-WATER SPONGES

1 (12)   Gemmules with acerate spicules only. . . *Spongilla* Lamarck . . 2

Spongillidae with long spindle-shaped skeleton spicules, macroscleres, having pointed or rounded ends, and often also with minute simple flesh spicules, or microscleres. Gemmules naked, or with external air-cell layer containing rhabdi, or rod-like spicules.

2 (5)   Sponge branching. 3

Abnormal forms of *S. lacustris* occur in which there are no branches.

3 (4)   Flesh spicules smooth. . . . . *Spongilla aspinosa* Potts 1880.

Sponge evergreen, encrusting, thin, sending out numerous long, slender waving branches from a relatively thick basal membrane. Gemmules few, in scattered branches. Skeleton spicules smooth, straight or slightly curved, rather abruptly pointed. Dermal spicules minute, smooth, straight or curved, slender, gradually pointed. From clear standing water in New Jersey and Virginia.

Fig. 560.   Spicules of *Spongilla aspinosa.* Four types of spicules figured here: ordinary skeleton spicules abruptly pointed at both ends; skeleton spicule, acute or rounded at one end; malformations of skeleton spicules, with processes at or near one end; small smooth dermal spicules; globular or discoidal masses of silica frequently observed in this species. × 100. (After Potts.)

4 (3)   Flesh spicules spined. . . . . . . *Spongilla lacustris* (Linnaeus) 1745.

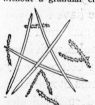

Branches cylindrical or tapering, and rigid. Prefers rapidly running water. Very abundant. Gemmules either apparently wanting or abundant throughout the sponge, with or without a granular crust. Skeleton spicules smooth. Dermal spicules pointed spined acerates. Gemmule spicules whether few or many generally cylindrical, more or less curved, rather sparsely spined. From Boston, Mass., to McDonald Lake, Alaska, in an infinite number of situations and variety of forms. The variety *paupercula* Bowerbank, made an independent species *Spongilla paupercula* by Carter, "is perhaps that one of this group of synonyms about whose identity with *S. lacustris* there may be most hesitation. Its character is somewhat anomalous, as its locality and associations are peculiar. Growing originally in the ponds and reservoirs tributary to the Boston Water supply, Bailey wrote in 1856 that it grew abundantly in the waterpipes by which the city was supplied with water from a small lake." The minute acerates were said to have been smooth which would separate it clearly from *S. lacustris*, but Potts was unable to secure material from the original locality which bore out the contention.

Fig. 561. Skeleton and gemmule spicules of *Spongilla lacustris*, var. *montana.* ×100. (After Potts.)

5 (2)   Sponge without branches. 6

6 (9)   Gemmules in layers or groups. 7

7 (8)   Tubules of gemmules turned upward or outward from the groups.

Spongilla fragilis Leidy 1851.

Sponge encrusting in subcircular patches, thin at edges, occasionally one or more inches thick near the middle. In the most varied situations, apparently preferring standing water, though also in running water. Abundant. Gemmules abundant, primarily in one or more pavement layers. Also in compact groups surrounded by a cellular parenchyma charged with subcylindrical spined acerates. Skeleton spicules smooth, slightly curved, rather abruptly pointed. True dermals wanting. Found in most of the United States.

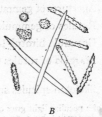

A   B

FIG. 562. *Spongilla fragilis.* A. Section of group of gemmules; a, curved foraminal tubules, always outward; b, envelop with acerate spicules. × 12. B. Three types of spicules figured here: skeleton spicules, smooth, abruptly pointed; variable parenchymal spicules, subcylindrical, subspined; spined, spherical forms frequently seen throughout the species. × 100. (After Potts.)

8 (7)   Tubules of gemmules turned inwards in the groups.

Spongilla igloviformis Potts 1887.

Sponge brown, thin, encrusting. Gemmules in compact hemispherical groups of eight to twelve or more, resting on the flat side, surrounded by a parenchyma of unequal cells, charged with numerous coarsely spined spicules nearly as long as the rather few, less strongly spined skeleton spicules. On the lower side of timbers in cedar swamps, New Jersey. *S. mackayi*, described by Carter from Newfoundland, may belong here.

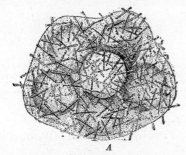

A   B

FIG. 563. *Spongilla igloviformis.* A. Lateral view of dome-shaped group of gemmules. (Foraminal tubules open inward and are invisible.) × 25. B. Two types of spicules figured here: skeleton spicules, weakly spined; "parenchymal spicules" nearly equally long, but more spinous. × 100. (After Potts.)

9 (6)   Gemmules not in layers or groups.   10

10 (11)   Dermal spicules birotulate. . . .   *Spongilla novae-terrae* Potts 1886.

Sponge encrusting, gemmules rather numerous, very large, crust absent or inconspicuous. Skeleton spicules relatively few, slender, gradually pointed, smooth or microspined. Dermal spicules very abundant, minute, birotulate. Gemmule spicules smooth or irregular, furnished with long spines, frequently located near the extremities. Placed by some in genus *Ephydatia*. Found only in shallow water of lakes in Newfoundland (48° N. L.).

FIG. 564. Spicules of *Spongilla novae-terrae*. Representing the slender, smooth or sparsely microspined skeleton spicules; the dermal spicules, birotulates of unequal size; and the spinous gemmule spicules. × 100. (After Potts.)

11 (10)   Dermal spicules acerate. . . . . . .   *Spongilla wagneri* Potts 1889.

Gemmules abundant. Skeleton spicules long, robust, smooth. Dermal spicules very numerous. Gemmule spicules spined, long, curved. Spines most numerous at extremities. Recorded only from brackish water of southwestern Florida.
No figure yet published.

12 (1)   Gemmule spicules of birotulate type, more or less modified.
          Sub-family MEYENINAE Vejdovsky . .   13

13 (47)   Apertures of gemmules not provided with filamentous appendages   14

14 (46)   Rotules of gemmule birotulates nearly equal.   15

15 (37)   Gemmule birotulates of a single class.   16

16 (19)   Margins of rotules entire, *i.e.*, smooth, not serrate.
          Trochospongilla Vejdovsky . .   17

17 (18)   Skeleton spicules smooth. . *Trochospongilla leidyi* (Bowerbank) 1863.

Sponge of a peculiar light gray or drab color, encrusting thin, persistent. Gemmules numerous, each surrounded by a capsule of skeleton spicules. Skeleton spicules short, smooth, robust. Dermal spicules wanting. Gemmule spicules short, birotulate, margins entire and exflected. From Louisiana as well as original field of discovery near Philadelphia. Generally distributed in the Illinois River from the mouth to La Salle according to F. Smith.

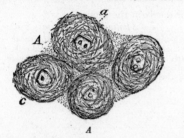

A   B

FIG. 565. *Trochospongilla leidyi.* *A.* Upper surface of portion of a layer of gemmules, each of which is surrounded by a lattice capsule (*c*) of spicules resembling those of the skeleton; at the summit an open space around the foraminal aperture (*a*), more than one being sometimes present. × 50. *B.* Four types of spicules figured here: smooth skeleton spicules, abruptly pointed; same, with rounded terminations; short birotulates with entire margins; same with rotule twisted or exflected; face of rotule; group of rotules as they appear upon the surface of the gemmules. × 100. (After Potts.)

18 (17)   Skeleton spicules strongly spined.
          Trochospongilla horrida (Weltner) 1893.

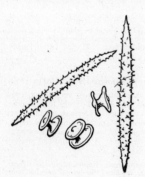

Sponge encrusting, white, gray, yellow, or brown. No gemmule spicules except birotulates which are smooth-margined, low, small. Lives in standing or flowing water. Rare. F. Smith found one specimen each in the Illinois River near Starved Rock and in the Big Muddy River in southern Illinois.

FIG. 566. *Trochospongilla horrida.* Spinous skeleton spicules. × 180. Birotulate gemmule spicules. × 400. (After W. Kükenthal.)

19 (16) Margins of rotules serrated or incised. . *Ephydatia* Lamouroux. . 20

Spongillidae with gemmule spicules of the birotulate type that are uniform or variable in length but not definitely of two classes, long and short, and that have finely or deeply cut margins.

20 (35, 36) Dermal spicules if present neither birotulate nor stellate. . . 21

21 (22) Rays and spines of birotulates subdivided and microspined.
Ephydatia subdivisa (Potts) 1887.

Sponge massive, encrusting, compact. Gemmules few. Skeleton spicules smooth or microspined, abruptly pointed. Birotulates very numerous, robust, shafts frequently spined; rays short but subdivided. From St. Johns River near Palatka, Florida.

Fig. 567. Spicules of *Ephydatia subdivisa*. Three types of spicules figured here: smooth and spined skeleton spicules; long, massive gemmule birotulates, spined and subspined; rotules of same. × 100. (After Potts.)

22 (21) Rays and spines of birotulates entire. 23

23 (24) Margins of rotules very finely serrate. . *Ephydatia millsii* (Potts) 1887.

Sponge encrusting. Gemmules small. Skeleton spicules nearly straight, slender, rather abruptly pointed, entirely microspined. Gemmule birotulates very numerous, very symmetrical, their shafts usually smooth. Rotules sometimes microspined. From Sherwood Lake, near Deland, Florida.

Fig. 568. Spicules of *Ephydatia millsii*. Three types of spicules figured here: microspined skeleton spicule; mature gemmule birotulates with smooth shafts; probably immature forms with less notching on the rotules; face of rotulates lacinulate or delicately notched, and without rays. × 100. (After Potts.)

24 (23) Margins of rotules coarsely dentate. 25

25 (32) Length of birotulates not more than twice the diameter of rotules. . 26

26 (31) Shafts of birotulates generally smooth. 27

27 (30) Skeleton spicules smooth. 28

28 (29) Shafts of birotulates much longer than diameter of rotules.
Ephydatia fluviatilis (auctorum).

Sponge sessile, massive, rarely throwing out short branches an inch or less in length. Prefers standing water. No vesicular cells in parenchyma. Gemmules numerous throughout. Skeleton spicules smooth. Dermal spicules wanting. Rotules of gemmule spicules not deeply indented. Numerous varieties the occurrence of which in North America has not been accurately recorded. The form which Potts describes as present generally throughout the eastern and middle United States is declared by Weltner to be *Ephydatia mülleri*, the second following species. The true *E. fluviatilis* is found in Michigan and Illinois, and is fairly common though not so abundant as *E. mülleri* (*fide* F. Smith).

29 (28) Shafts of birotulates slightly if any longer than diameter of rotules.
                         Ephydatia japonica (Hilgendorf) 1882.

Much like *E. fluviatilis.* Dermal spicules wanting. Birotulates with smooth shaft, short,
never forming more than a single layer on the gemmule. Rotules deeply indented. Gemmule with short, straight, broad, very delicate foraminal tubule. In Potomac River, near
Washington, D. C.

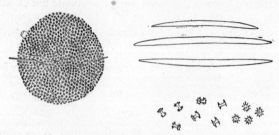

FIG. 569. *Ephydatia japonica.* Gemmule, × 18; birotulates, × 120; skeleton spicules, × 120.
(After Annandale.)

30 (27) Skeleton spicules microspined except at tips.
                         Ephydatia mülleri (Lieberkühn) 1856.

Sponge cushionlike, rarely branched. Vesicular cells abundant
in the parenchyma. Dermal spicules wanting. Shafts of gemmule
birotulates not, or barely, longer than diameter of rotules. Rotules
deeply indented. Eastern and Central United States; Nova Scotia;
Newfoundland; Vancouver Island. Found by F. Smith at Douglas
Lake, Mich., and Tolland, Col.

FIG. 570. Spicules of *Ephydatia mülleri.* Three types of spicules figured
here: skeleton spicules, × 120; birotulate gemmule spicules; same malformed; group of rotulae; single rotules showing an ordinary distribution of
the rays. × 250. (After Potts.)

31 (26) Shafts of birotulates with enormous spines.
                         Ephydatia robusta (Potts) 1887.

Sponge massive, encrusting, thin. Gemmules scarce. Skeleton
spicules pointed, smooth. Birotulates large, generally malformed.
Shafts abounding in spines as long as rays of the rotules. Collected
near Susanville, California. Perhaps only a variety of *E. fluviatilis.*

FIG. 571. Spicules of *Ephydatia robusta.* Three types of spicules figured
here: smooth skeleton spicules; coarsely spined gemmule birotulates; single
rotules; exceedingly misshapen forms. × 100. (After Potts.)

32 (25) Length of birotulates more than twice the diameter of the rotules. .   33

33 (34) Birotulates two or three times longer than the diameter of the rot-
       ules. . . . . *Ephydatia subtilis* Weltner 1895.

Sponge thin, encrusting. Skeleton needles extremely slender, scantily covered with short
spines. Dermal spicules wanting. Gemmules small, spherical; foramen a simple pore, or a
very short tube. Birotulates delicate, slender, of variable length; shaft thin, smooth, long,
Rotules small, split nearly to the center, with 10 to 20 blunt rays. Kissimee Lake, Florida.
No figure yet published.

34 (33) **Birotulates many times longer than diameter of rotules.**
Ephydatia crateriformis (Potts) 1882.

Sponge encrusting, thin. Gemmules small, white, very numerous. Granular crust of gemmules extremely thick, the foraminal tubes in a crater-like depression. Skeleton spicules slender, gradually pointed, sparsely microspined. Birotulates very long and slender, shafts abundantly spined. Rotules of three to six short recurved hooks. In shallow water, rapidly flowing; Schuylkill and Delaware Rivers, Pennsylvania. Found by F. Smith in the Sangamon River, Ill.

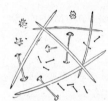

Annandale places this species in *Spongilla* owing to the imperfect development of the rotules (see Fauna of British India; Fresh-water Sponges, 1911, p. 83).

Bowerbank, in 1863, described, under the name of *Spongilla baileyi*, a sponge from a stream at Canterbury Road, West Point, N. Y., which may be the same as this species. The description is too incomplete to allow of an accurate determination. His description is quoted by Potts (1887: 227).

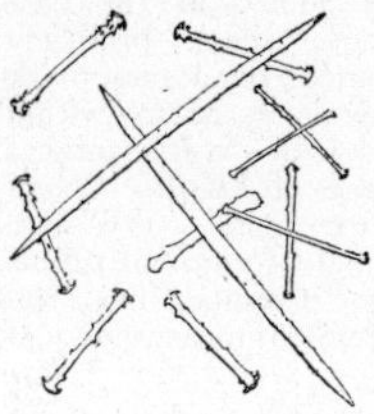

FIG. 572. Spicules of *Ephydatia crateriformis*. Three types of spicules figured here: slender microspined skeleton spicules; mature gemmule birotulates with short hooked rays; supposed immature forms. × 100. (After Potts.)

35 (20, 36) Dermal spicules, minute birotulates.
Ephydatia everetti (Mills) 1884.

Sponge green consisting entirely of slender filaments, little more than a sixteenth of an inch in diameter. Gemmules few, but usually large with a thick crust. Skeleton spicules slender, cylindrical, smooth. Dermal spicules, minute birotulates with slender cylindrical shafts and cap-like rotules notched into five or six hooks. Gemmule birotulates long and club-like; shafts smooth and slender; rotules formed of five or six stout, recurved, acuminate hooks. In cold water, Berkshire County, Mass., and Nova Scotia.

FIG. 573. Spicules of *Ephydatia everetti*. Four types of spicules figured here: smooth, skeleton spicules; gemmule birotulates; end view of rotule formed of hooked rays; minute dermal birotulates. × 100. (After Potts.)

36 (20, 35) Dermal spicules stellate. . . . . *Dosilia* Gray.
Only species yet reported in the United States.
Dosilia palmeri (Potts) 1885.

Sponge massive, subspherical, lobate. Skeleton spicules sparsely microspined, curved, gradually pointed. Dermal spicules star-shaped, consisting of a variable number of arms of various lengths, radiating from a large smooth globular body; arms spined throughout. Gemmule birotulates with long spined shafts, rotules notched. From Colorado River, 60 miles below Fort Yuma, attached to pendent branches flooded by spring freshets.

In the opinion of Annandale, Potts' var. *palmeri* is a different species from Carter's *plumosa* from India. He has seen types of both and is confident both belong to *Dosilia*.

FIG. 574. Spicules of *Dosilia palmeri*. Five types of spicules figured here: robust, microspined skeleton spicule; spined gemmule birotulates; rotules of same, irregularly notched; substellate dermal spicules; imperfect form of same with only two rays; amorphous "Scotch terrier" forms. × 100. (After Potts.)

37 (15) Gemmule birotulates of two distinct classes. 38

38 (41) Dermal spicules stellate. . . . . *Asteromeyenia* Annandale. . 39

Spongillidae with birotulate gemmule spicules of two distinct types and free microscleres in the form of anthasters.

39 (40)　Terminal spines of longer gemmule spicules with a simple curve.
　　　　　　　　　Asteromeyenia plumosa (Weltner) 1895.

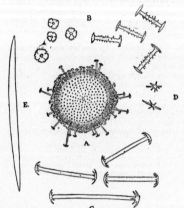

Sponge massive, though brittle and friable. Skeleton spicules slender, smooth, sharply pointed at both ends, nearly straight. Shaft of long birotulates almost smooth, slender, straight; rotules a circle of curved hooks, joined at the base. Short birotulates with stouter shafts, profusely, irregularly, and strongly spined; rotules not markedly convex in profile, irregularly, narrowly, and deeply serrated. Free spicules very minute, abundant, resembling those of *Dosilia*. Gemmules large, spherical, with single, very small aperture having short, straight foraminal tubule. From Pinto Creek, Kinney County, Tex., and Shreveport, La.; one specimen measured 29 × 25 cm.

FIG. 575. *Asteromyenia plumosa. A,* gemmule showing aperture in center, × 35; *B,* short birotulates, × 120; *C,* long birotulates, × 120; *D,* free microscleres, × 120; *E,* skeleton spicule, × 120. (After Annandale.)

40 (39)　Terminal spines of longer gemmule spicules distinctly recurved.
　　　　　　　　　Asteromeyenia radiospiculata (Mills) 1888.

Resembles *A. plumosa.* In profile the rays of the longer gemmule spicule have almost the form of a J. Ohio and Illinois. At Granite City, Ill., specimens were taken from settling tanks of the city water works, measuring 42 × 12 × 8 cm.

FIG. 576.　Spicules of *Asteromeyenia radiospiculata.* × 100. (From mount.)

41 (38)　Dermal spicules acerate if present. . . *Heteromeyenia* Potts . . 42

Spongillidae producing gemmules with birotulate spicules of two distinct classes, long and short. Margins of rotules not smooth but dentate or incised.

42 (43)　Rotules of gemmule spicules of smaller class finely serrated.
　　　　　　　　　Heteromeyenia ryderi Potts 1882.

Sponge massive, often hemispherical. Gemmules numerous, crust thick. foramina short and inconspicuous. Skeleton spicules gradually pointed, entirely spined except at the tips. Dermal spicules wanting. Shafts of long birotulates spined, rotules of three to six short recurved hooks, sometimes umbonate. Rotules of small birotulates nearly as great in diameter as the length of their shafts. Shafts smooth or with few spines. Shallow flowing water, Florida to Nova Scotia, and inland at least as far as Iowa.

FIG. 577. Spicules of *Heteromeyenia ryderi.* Four types of spicules figured here: skeleton spicule; long gemmule birotulates, hooked and spined; short birotulates; surface of rotules, margins lacinulate, surface microspined or granulated; spherical amorphous spicule. × 100. (After Potts.)

43 (42)　Rotules of gemmule spicules of small class coarsely serrate. . .　44

44 (45)   Rotules of gemmule spicules of small class regular mushroom-shaped, shafts usually smooth. . *Heteromeyenia repens* Potts 1880.

Sponge encrusting, thin. Gemmules not abundant. Skeleton spicules rather slender, sparsely microspined, gradually pointed. Dermal spicules nearly straight, entirely spined. Gemmule birotulates of longer class comparatively few; shafts, smooth or with one or a few conspicuous spines often irregularly bent. Rotules dome-shaped, rays incurved like fish hooks. Small birotulates very numerous, about two-thirds the length of the large ones. Quiet, almost stagnant water, New Jersey, Pennsylvania, and Michigan.

Fig. 578. Spicules of *Heteromeyenia repens*. Five types of spicules figured here: microspined skeleton spicules; gemmule birotulates of the longer class, with recurved hooked rays; birotulates of the shorter class with less pronounced rays; rotules of same; small dermal spicules, coarsely spined; amorphous spicule. × 100. (After Potts.)

45 (44)   Rotules of gemmule spicules of small class very irregular, shafts abundantly spined. *Heteromeyenia argyrosperma* Potts 1880.

Sponge minute, encrusting, gray. Gemmules abundant and large. Foraminal tubules somewhat prolonged. Skeleton spicules rather slender, cylindrical, abruptly pointed, sparsely spined. Dermal spicules apparently wanting. Shafts of long birotulates sparsely spined. Rays of rotules few, long, stout, and clawlike. Short birotulates much smaller, abundantly spined. From Pennsylvania, New Jersey, New England States, and Nova Scotia. Found by F. Smith at Douglas Lake, Mich.

Fig. 579. Spicules of *Heteromeyenia argyrosperma*. Three types of spicules figured here: sparsely microspined skeleton spicules; gemmule birotulates of the longer class with one to three hooked rays; spined birotulates of the shorter class. × 100. (After Potts.)

46 (14)   Rotules of gemmule spicules unequal, the proximal being larger.
Tubella Carter.

Only North American species known.
Tubella pennsylvanica Potts 1882.

Sponge minute, encrusting, on stones or timbers in shallow water. Gemmules very numerous, small. Skeleton spicules very variable in length and curvature, entirely spined; spines large, conical. Dermal spicules wanting. Birotulates of gemmules numerous with a large rotule next to the coat and a small distal rotule, varying from the diameter of the shaft to that of the proximal rotule. Margin of large rotule usually entire but margin of small often angular and notched. Shaft smooth. Averse to light and found as a rule under stones and roots. Eastern United States generally. Found by F. Smith at Rhinelander, Wis., and Douglas Lake, Mich.

Fig. 580. Spicules of *Tubella pennsylvanica*. Two types of spicules figured here: spined skeleton spicules; gemmule "inaequibirotulates," or trumpet-shaped spicules; group of rotules seen from above, showing the relative sizes of the rotules; surface of single large rotule. × 100. (After Potts.)

47 (13)   Apertures of gemmules prolonged and divided into filamentous appendages. . . . . *Carterius* Potts . . 48

Gemmules possess a long foraminal tubule, the outer end of which carries an irregularly lobed disc or is provided with long filaments. Not recognized as a separate genus by some recent authors (see Annandale, 1909), but distributed among the preceding genera.

48 (49, 50) Foraminal tubule very long and slender, tendrils short, irregularly waving. . . . . . . *Carterius tubisperma* Mills 1881.

Sponge massive. Gemmules numerous. Length of foraminal tubule one-half to once diameter of gemmule. Skeleton spicules rather slender, gradually pointed, sparsely spined. Dermal spicules long, slender, entirely spined. Gemmule birotulates abundant, irregular in length, suggesting genus *Heteromeyenia*, shaft smooth or with one or more spines, rotules arched, rays numerous, long, incurved. Assigned by Annandale to genus *Heteromeyenia*. In Niagara River, N. Y., Massachusetts, and Michigan.

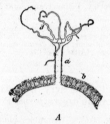

A   B

Fig. 581. *Carterius tubisperma*. *A*. Partial section of gemmule; (*a*), Foraminal aperture prolonged into a long tubule flaring and funnel-shaped at its extremity and divided into several short tendrils (*d*) or cirrous appendages. (*b*), birotulate spicules. × 50. (After Potts.) *B*. Three types of spicules figured here: skeleton spicules; gemmule birotulates; face of rotule; long spined slender dermal acerates. × 100. (After Potts.)

49 (48, 50) Foraminal tubule shorter; tendrils, one or two, enveloping the tubule. . . . . *Carterius latitenta* Potts 1881.

Sponge often encrusting stones in rapidly running water. Gemmules numerous. Cirrous appendages at first flat and ribbon-like, becoming slender and rounded, and occasionally subdividing. Skeleton spicules smooth: or sparsely microspined, gradually pointed. Dermal spicules long, entirely spined. Birotulates stout, shafts with numerous long pointed spines. Rays of rotules deeply cut and sometimes recurved. Annandale believes this and the following species should be assigned to *Ephydatia*. In Pennsylvania, western New York, and Illinois River.

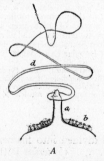

A   B

Fig. 582. *Carterius latitenta*. *A*. Partial section of gemmule; (*a*), foraminal tubule short; (*b*), birotulate spicules; (*d*), one or two long and broad, ribbon-like cirrous appendages. × 30. (After Potts.) *B*. Three types of spicules figured here: skeleton spicules; gemmule birotulates variable in length; face of rotule; spined dermals. ×100. (After Potts.)

50 (48, 49) Foraminal tubule still shorter; tendrils, three to five, very long
and slender. . . . . . . *Carterius tenosperma* Potts 1880.

Sponge forming irregular masses creeping upon and around water plants and roots, less frequently encrusting stones. Gemmules rather numerous. Foraminal tubules about one-fourth
the diameter of the gemmules. Tendrils as much as half an inch long. Skeleton spicules slender, very sparsely microspined, gradually pointed. Dermal spicules slender, nearly straight,
entirely spined. Birotulates with cylindrical shafts, abundantly spined, rotules often irregular.
New Jersey and Eastern Pennsylvania.

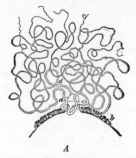
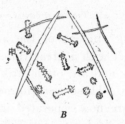

A *B*

Fig. 583. *Carterius tenosperma.* *A.* Section of gemmule, (*a*), short tubule; (*d*), long, slender cirrous
appendages. X 35. *B.* Three types of spicules: skeleton spicules; spined gemmule birotulates with
burr-like rotules; ends of same; long, spinous, acerate dermal spicules. X 100. (After Potts.)

IMPORTANT REFERENCES ON FRESH–WATER SPONGES

ANNANDALE, N. 1909. Report on a Collection of Fresh-water Sponges from
Japan. Annot. Zool. Japon., 7: 105–112, pl. 2.

1909a. Fresh-water Sponges in the Collection of the United States National Museum. Part II. Specimens from North and South America.
Proc. U. S. Nat. Mus., 37: 401–406.

1910. Fresh-water Sponges in the Collection of the United States National
Museum. Part IV. Note on the Fresh-water Sponge *Ephydatia japonica*,
and its Allies. Proc. U. S. Nat. Mus., 38: 649–650.

1911. Fresh-water Sponges in the Collection of the United States National
Museum. Part V. A New Genus proposed, with *Heteromeyenia radiospiculata* Mills as Type. Proc. U. S. Nat. Mus., 40: 593–594.

1911a. Fresh-water Sponges, Hydroids and Polyzoa. Fauna British India.
251 pp., 5 pl.

CARTER, H. J. 1881. History and Classification of the Known Species of
Spongilla. Ann. Mag. Nat. Hist., (5), 7: 77–107, pl. 5–6.

POTTS, EDWARD. 1883. Our Fresh-water Sponges. Amer. Nat., 17: 1293–6.

1887. Fresh-water Sponges; a Monograph. Proc. Acad. Nat. Sci., Phila.,
39: 158–279, pl. 5–12.

1890. Fresh-water Sponges. Microscope, 10: 140–143, 161–163, 193–
196, 257–263, 307–310; pl. 5–6.

WELTNER, W. 1895. Spongillidenstudien III. Katalog und Verbreitung der
bekannten Süsswasserchwämme. Arch. f. Naturges., (pt. I), 61: 114–144.

CHAPTER XI

HYDRA AND OTHER FRESH-WATER HYDROZOA

By FRANK SMITH

Professor of Zoology and Curator of the Museum, University of Illinois

THE student of the animal life of the sea is continually in contact with a great variety of organisms which have radial symmetry and are often striking in appearance, diversity, and abundance. These were formerly included in a great group, Radiata, but are now separated into two very distinct branches (phyla), the Coelenterata and Echinodermata. The latter phylum, which includes the well-known starfishes and sea urchins, is wholly unrepresented in fresh water, while the former, which includes the hydroids, jellyfishes, and corals, with thousands of species in the seas of to-day, has in fresh water scarcely a dozen species and these are relatively insignificant in appearance. The fresh-water Coelenterata are all included in the class Hydrozoa, and hydra is the only one which is abundant, widely distributed, and well known to the ordinary student of zoology. Because of its abundance it is the type form commonly used in zoology classes as an introduction to a knowledge of the phylum.

Among the more obvious structural or morphological characters of hydra is the sac-like body with the capacious chamber which is at the same time body cavity and digestive cavity and of which the mouth is the only opening to the exterior. The animal is attached by one end and at the other shows the mouth surrounded by a circle of tentacles which are evaginations of the body wall and are hollow, their cavities being continuous with the digestive cavity. The body wall as well as that of the tentacles is composed of two cellular layers, the ectoderm and entoderm, separated by a thin, noncellular mesogloea and bounded externally by a delicate cuticula. In some species there is an obvious distinction between an adoral part of greater diameter and more

316

granular opaque entoderm, and a narrowed paler aboral part which is termed the stalk. In other species designated in the key as "not stalked," there is no clearly marked division into such regions. Highly contractile fibers formed by certain cells in both ectoderm and entoderm may bring about either a great elongation of the body and tentacles to thread-like proportions or their contraction to an almost globular form. Certain kinds of ectoderm cells, which are most abundant in the adoral half of the body, especially in the tentacles, give rise to the characteristic nematocysts or "nettling cells" of different shapes and sizes. These contain a fluid secretion which passes out through a thread-like extension of the sac wall, that is forced out when the cell is stimulated. The combined action of a number of these nematocysts on the small organisms encountering them results in the loss of activity or even death of the organisms and so permits their capture and appropriation as food by the hydra.

Spermaries and ovaries develop in the ectoderm layer and at a time of year which seems to be fairly constant for a given species but differs in different species. After fertilization the ovum passes through the early stages of development while still in the ovary and becomes enclosed by a chitinous envelop which has a characteristic shape and surface for each species. This envelop which often is spiny is referred to in the key as the embryonic, chitinous membrane. In some species the embryos are freed from the parent organism and drop to the bottom, while in others they are fastened by the parent to the substratum to which it adheres. The development is direct. In one species (*Hydra oligactis*) the individuals are said to be of separate sexes, or dioecious, but in others hermaphroditism prevails. Asexual reproduction by budding is the prevalent mode of multiplication and very rarely the formation of two individuals by a process of fission has been observed.

Hydra has long been an object of interest and experiment because of its notable powers of regeneration and form regulation and there is now an extensive literature dealing with these phenomena.

Hydra individuals ordinarily maintain an independent existence but in various related groups colonies which often include many individuals arise by asexual reproduction. In some such colonies, besides hydra-like forms or hydranths, another type of individuals is produced which become medusae and separate from the colony as free-swimming forms that develop germ cells which in turn produce a generation of individuals of the hydranth type. In other colonial forms the germ cells are formed by individuals that remain as members of the colony. All the species of Hydrozoa which have a complex colonial organization are with one exception marine.

In the fresh-water colonial hydroid *Cordylophora*, many of the individuals or zooids are nutritive and provide food for the colony and by budding increase its size while other individuals form germ cells; there are no medusae formed. Among the obvious structural features in which this form differs from hydra are the following: the tentacles are not hollow but the entoderm forms a core of large cells which occupies all the space enclosed by the ectoderm and mesogloea; the tentacles are more numerous than in hydra and are irregularly distributed; the cuticula is thick and forms a supporting skeleton for the colony.

Four genera of fresh-water Hydrozoa form free-swimming medusae. Two of these occur in Africa but the two following genera are each known in North America and Europe.

Edward Potts first discovered the *Microhydra* and it has been studied chiefly by him. The hydranth form has no tentacles and it lives independently or forms simple colonies of two or three individuals. The medusae have been seen by him to arise by budding from hydranths but have not been observed when older than a stage attained two or three days after being freed. They have but eight tentacles and no marginal sense organs.

Craspedacusta was first found in the Regent's Park Gardens, London, England, in 1880, and its only occurrence in North America thus far recorded was in Washington, D. C., in 1907 (Hargitt). Only its medusa stage is known with certainty but what is supposed to be the hydranth form is very similar to that of *Microhydra*. The medusa has more than eight tentacles and has marginal sense organs.

The hydra is usually found adhering firmly by the base to submerged objects over which it moves slowly and may be found at various distances from the surface, but not infrequently is suspended from the surface film or even drifts about unattached and thus often becomes a component of the plankton. The hydras multiply so rapidly when conditions are favorable that they often take heavy toll from the plankton organisms, especially the entomostracans and small worms. Since they are probably little used as food by animals useful to man and since they compete with young fish for food, their economic relations to man are unfavorable.

The most favorable conditions for *Cordylophora* are in brackish water and there it attains most luxuriant development but it thrives also in fresh water, although the colonies are there less stalwart and the ascending branches are usually not more than half as large as in colonies from brackish water. It was first known as a brackish water form from Europe and its appearance in fresh water is of comparatively recent date. It has been known for a number of years in the United States, near the Atlantic Coast, where it occurs in both brackish and fresh water. The first recorded appearance in the Mississippi Valley was in the Illinois River in 1909, but it is now known in several states of that region.

This form is a plankton feeder and thus competes with young fish for food. Its most vigorous colonies are found where there is considerable current and in company with Bryozoa it not infrequently invades the pipes of water systems, impedes the flow, and at times vitiates the water itself. *Microhydra* is found associated with bryozoans on the surface of stones in running water near Philadelphia, and is apparently not an abundant form.

In the search after hydra if pond-lily leaves and coarse submerged vegetation be collected from bodies of water in which hydra occurs, and allowed to stand a few hours or days in glass jars, specimens are likely to be found attached to the vegetation or to the sides of the jar or even suspended from the surface film. Hydra may be kept in good condition for long periods of time in well aerated aquaria, if supplied with sufficient food, preferably small entomostracans and worms. At the proper season and temperature they may reproduce sexually as well as by budding.

For ordinary purposes a corrosive sublimate and acetic acid

mixture either hot or cold gives sufficiently good results as a fixative, but for certain cytological studies special methods are recommended; for these one must consult the literature.

Occurring most frequently attached to submerged sticks or twigs *Cordylophora* may also be looked for on the submerged surfaces of walls and piers and also on stems of coarse vegetation. Fixation may be accomplished as with hydra.

It has recently been shown that the Linnaean systematic names in common use for species of *Hydra* must be dropped for the earlier ones of Pallas. Recent literature which deals with the results obtained by several investigators who have worked on *Hydra* shows such conflicting views concerning the status of certain supposed species of this genus, that any classification or key dealing with them must be regarded as tentative. The chief difficulty is with *Hydra oligactis* Pallas (*H. fusca* L.), which by some is believed to have been applied in the past to two specifically distinct forms while others uphold a contrary view.

The treatment of the species of *Hydra* in the following key is based chiefly on the papers of Brauer, Downing, and Koelitz.

KEY TO NORTH-AMERICAN FRESH-WATER HYDROZOA

1 (10) Hydranths with tentacles; no free swimming medusae at any stage of the life history. 2

2 (9) Tentacles in a circle about the oral end; do not form true colonies; have power of slow locomotion. . . *Hydra* Linnaeus . . 3

3 (6) Body not definitely stalked; extended tentacles not very much longer than the body. 4

4 (5) Green; three kinds of nematocysts; embryonic chitinous membrane spherical, with minute elevations; spermaries limited to oral third of body; sexual activity more frequent in summer. *Hydra viridissima* Pallas (*H. viridis* L.) 1766.

5 (4) Pale yellow, gray, or brown; four kinds of nematocysts, diameter of largest 0.0105–0.013 mm.; embryonic chitinous membrane spherical, with coarse branched pointed spines; spermaries only on distal third; sexual activity more frequent in summer. . . . . . *Hydra vulgaris* Pallas (*H. grisea* L.) 1766.

6 (3) Body definitely stalked; extended tentacles much longer than body. . 7

7 (8)   Gray, brown, or reddish; three kinds of nematocysts; diameter of largest less than 0.0105 mm.; embryonic chitinous membrane spherical, with very short spines; spermaries on any part of body except the stalk; sexual activity more frequent in winter. . . . . *Hydra oligactis* Pallas (*H. fusca* L.) 1766.

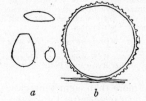

By some it is claimed that *H. oligactis* is strictly dioecious and is in this way distinct from the following species.

FIG. 584. *Hydra oligactis.* (*a*) Nematocysts. (*b*) Embryonic chitinous membrane. × 47. (After Brauer.)

a   *b*

8 (7)   Gray or brown; four kinds of nematocysts, diameter of largest less than 0.01 mm.; embryonic chitinous membrane plano-convex, with only convex side covered with spines; spermaries limited to the oral third of the body; sexual activity more frequent in autumn. . . . . *Hydra polypus* Linnaeus 1758.

Besides the differences between *H. oligactis* and *H. polypus* mentioned above the latter is said to be somewhat smaller and to have somewhat shorter tentacles than the former. By some the validity of any of the differing characters mentioned above is disputed, with the possible exception of the difference in the number of different kinds of nematocysts.

H. pallida Beardsley, a very pale form in Colorado, and *H. corala* Elrod, a very large red form in Montana, may prove to belong to the species listed above, as similar variations of them are known to occur in Europe.

FIG. 585. *Hydra polypus.* (*a*) Nematocysts. (*b*) Embryonic chitinous membrane. × 36. (After Brauer.)

9 (2)   Tentacles irregularly scattered on the body of the hydranth; form true colonies. . . . . *Cordylophora* Allman.

But one species, *C. lacustris* Allman, which occurs in fresh water near Philadelphia, Pa., and near Woods Hole, Mass. It has recently been found in the Illinois River at Havana, and by Mr. W. Donaldson in the Mississippi River at Granite City and East St. Louis, Ill., in the Arkansas River at Little Rock, Ark., and in the Red River at Shreveport, La.

FIG. 586. *Cordylophora lacustris.* (*a*) A branch from a colony. About twice as large as is common in fresh water. (*b*) Female reproductive zooids with embryos in different stages of development. × 20. (After Schulze.)

a   *b*

10 (1)   Hydranths without tentacles; free swimming medusae are formed. . 11

11 (12) Hydranth form most frequently seen; medusae rarely found and
have but eight tentacles. . . . . *Microhydra* Potts.

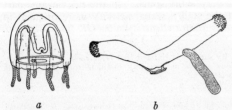

But one species, *M. ryderi* Potts, first described from near Philadelphia, Pa., but since then found in different localities in Europe. The medusae have been seen only when in a very early stage and the adult stages are not known.

a   *b*

Fig. 587. *Microhydra ryderi.* (*a*) Young medusa. × 40. (After Moore from Potts.) (*b*) Hydranths and embryo. × 22. (After Ryder from Potts.)

12 (11) Hydranth form rarely seen; medusae have more than eight tentacles.
Craspedacusta Lankester.

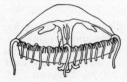

But one species, *C. sowerbyi* Lankester, known in Europe and America. Found only in aquaria according to earlier records, but large numbers were collected by Professor H. Garman in September, 1916, in a creek near Frankfort, Kentucky, the first record of their occurrence in other than artificial surroundings. A second species, *C. kawaii* Oka, has been found in a river of China.

Fig. 588. *Craspedacusta sowerbyi.* × about 4. (After Hargitt.)

Limnocnida Günther is the only other known genus of fresh-water medusae and its distribution so far as recorded is limited to the Eastern Hemisphere. *Limnocnida tanganyicae* (Böhm) 1883 is found in Africa; *Limnocnida indica* Annandale 1912, in India; *Limnocnida rhodesia* Boulenger 1912, in southern Africa.

IMPORTANT REFERENCES ON FRESH-WATER HYDROZOA

Brauer, A. 1909. Die Benennung und Unterscheidung der Hydra-Arten. Zool. Anz., 33: 790–792.

Downing, E. R. 1905. The Spermatogenesis of Hydra. Zool. Jahrb., Anat., 21: 379–426.

Hargitt, C. W. 1908. Occurrence of the Fresh-water Medusa, *Limnocodium*, in the United States. Biol. Bull., 14: 304–318.

Nutting, C. C. 1901. The Hydroids of the Woods Hole Region. U. S. Fish Com. Bull. for 1899: 327.

Potts, E. 1906. On the Medusa of *Microhydra ryderi* and on the Known Forms of Medusae inhabiting Fresh Water. Quar. Jour. Mic. Sci., 50: 623–633; 2 pl.

Smith, F. 1910. Hydroids in the Illinois River. Biol. Bull., 18: 67–68.

CHAPTER XII
THE FREE–LIVING FLATWORMS
(TURBELLARIA)

By CAROLINE E. STRINGER

Head of the Department of Biology, Omaha High School

THE Turbellaria or free-living flatworms are among the most interesting of the simply organized animals because of the remarkable variety shown in their reactions and behavior. They are to be found both in fresh and salt water and sometimes in moist places on land. The fresh-water forms are common in ponds and streams almost everywhere. Many of the smaller forms resemble infusoria in their minute size, shape, and movements. The larger Turbellaria are more readily recognized as worms but are often confused with leeches which they resemble superficially in color and form, although they are easily distinguished by their head-like anterior end, non-segmented body, and lack of posterior adhesive sucker.

Probably the first attempt to describe one of this group dates back to 1744 when Trembley included in his memoir on Hydra what was undoubtedly a planarian. As early as 1776 O. F. Müller separated the Turbellaria and Nemertinea from the parasitic Trematoda, but it was not until 1831 that Ehrenberg gave to these animals the name Turbellaria because of the tiny currents in the water created by the delicate cilia which cover the body. Much confusion existed in their classification until the appearance of Lang's work on structure and relationships in 1881 and in the next year of L. von Graff's monograph on the Rhabdocoelida. Since then considerable attention has been given to the morphological and physiological as well as to the systematic study of the group.

Flatworms may be either cylindrical, thread-like, spindle-shaped, or more or less flattened and leaf-like. They range in length from a fraction of a millimeter to several centimeters. The larger fresh-water forms are usually inconspicuously colored, gray, brown, or blackish or are entirely free from pigment. The smaller forms are often brilliantly colored, yellow, orange, red, or rose; and a few appear green due to the zoochlorellae or symbiotic one-celled plants which live within the mesenchyma. The color is more or less affected by the food contained in the intestine. This is especially true of the non-pigmented or very transparent forms and in many cases examination with a lens will be necessary to show whether pigment is actually present or not.

The anterior end is often modified so as to suggest the form of a head, either by the presence of the various special sense organs, a pair of lobes or cephalic appendages, or by a groove or constriction separating it from the rest of the body. Eyes may or may not be present. If present, the usual number is two, though some forms have four and one genus of planarians, *Polycelis*, is characterized by the possession of a large number of eyes. Accessory eyes or pigment spots are common among certain species. The normal eyes are usually bean-shaped and are black in color although there are many exceptions. Accessory eyes are usually more or less irregular in shape as well as in position.

A pair of sensory pits occurs in the anterior region in many forms. These may be round, oblong, or slit-shaped, and very shallow or deeply sunken. They are connected with special brain ganglia, are usually provided with long cilia, and are regarded as olfactory organs. A few forms possess a statocyst (otocyst) or balancing organ. It consists of a membranous sac filled with a fluid in which a strongly light-refracting statolith (otolith) is suspended. The non-pigmented, light-refracting organs found in *Stenostomum* posterior to the brain and connected with it by nerves are of three types. They may consist (1) of a variable number of spherical bodies arranged in the form of a convex organ, the so-called saucer-shaped or patelliform organ, (2) of a vesicle which contains a strongly light-refracting lens-shaped body on its wall, or (3) of a hollow capsule-like vesicle.

The epidermis consists of a single layer of ciliated cells. The cilia are conspicuous in the rhabdocoels, which are enabled thereby to move freely through the water, and to the unaided eye look much like infusoria. Planarians have a uniform gliding movement but do not swim about unsupported. In addition to the cilia, remarkably long sensory hairs are present in a few forms. The Turbellaria are richly supplied with various kinds of glands. Slime glands occur all over the body and are especially numerous near the anterior and posterior ends. Other glands form the rod-shaped bodies or rhabdites which are either homogeneous and uniformly light-refracting (rhabdoids), or consist of a hyaline outer layer enclosing a fine granular substance (rhammites). The former are extremely variable in shape (spindle-, egg-, rod-, or club-shaped) and originate either in dermal gland cells or in single-celled glands within the mesenchyma, especially in the anterior end where the tracts through which they pass to the surface may appear as conspicuous lines. The rhammites are found only in the mesenchyma. Still other glands produce the pseudo-rhabdites which are irregular in shape, granulated in structure, and have a low light-refracting power. A few forms have nematocysts, or stinging cells, similar to those of the coelenterates, in place of rhabdites. Adhesive cells and adhesive papillae are present in many forms, especially at the posterior end of the body. The external openings, mouth, genital pore, and excretory pores, are extremely variable in position.

In place of the usual body cavity of higher animals, the space between the body and internal organs is filled with a peculiar connective tissue called mesenchyma (parenchyma). In the smaller forms this tissue consists of a few scattered suspensory strands and the space between is filled with fluid. In others there is a network which encloses spaces filled with fluid and richly supplied with cells. The cells may be vacuolated or otherwise modified. The musculature includes bands of circular, longitudinal, and diagonal muscles in the body wall. There are also muscles which extend through the mesenchyma or connect with the internal organs. The digestive apparatus includes the mouth, pharynx, and intestine, all of which play an important part in classification and furnish a ready means of distinguishing the two great groups of fresh-water Turbellaria.

In rhabdocoels (Fig. 589) which include smaller forms, the mouth may be placed at the anterior end or at various points on the ventral surface. The pharynx is represented by three general types, simple, bulbous, and plicate. In the bulbous type a muscular membrane divides the pharynx from the surrounding mesenchyma; the plicate form does not have the dividing membrane, but consists of a cylindrical tube lying within a pharyngeal cavity which opens to the exterior through the mouth. The simple and plicate types of pharynx lie more or less lengthwise and the organ appears as a tube parallel with the surface of the body. The bulbous pharynx is more variable and includes three types, the rosette-shaped, the cask-shaped (dolioliform), and the variable. The intestine has the form of a simple sac; it consists of a blind cylindrical tube, median in position. It is sometimes provided with short lateral diverticula. The walls are thin.

In triclads (Fig. 590) the mouth is on the ventral surface usually just posterior to the middle of the body. The pharyngeal region ordinarily shows externally about the middle of the body, either as a more heavily pigmented or as a lighter colored area. The pharynx is a cylindrical, very muscular tube which lies within the pharyngeal cavity except when protruded while feeding. In a single genus, *Phagocata*, there are many pharyngeal tubes instead of one. The intestine is thin-walled as in the rhabdocoels but has three main branches, a single one extending forward, and two passing back, one on either side of the pharynx to the posterior end of the body. Numerous lateral diverticula are found especially in the anterior region. These may anastomose with each other or remain distinct.

The protonephridial system (water-vascular system or simple kidney) possesses one, two, or four principal canals, with a general antero-posterior direction. The number and position of the openings is variable. The nervous system includes two principal brain ganglia and two main longitudinal nerves with numerous lateral branches. In many forms the longitudinal nerves may be seen as two light lines on the ventral surface.

Reproduction is both sexual and asexual. The Turbellaria are hermaphroditic with the female organs distinct from the maie.

Both sets of organs have a common genital pore or are provided with separate external openings. In many cases the male organs mature earlier than the female and degenerate as the latter develop so that a study of various stages of growth is necessary to give complete knowledge of the organs. The rhabdocoels show great diversity in structure ranging from those with simple ovaries and testes to those with an elaborate system of accessory glands and ducts that much resemble those of the triclads. The male copulatory apparatus or cirrus is often remarkably complex and may, as in *Dallyellia*, present the chief characters for identification of species.

Some rhabdocoels produce two kinds of eggs, the thin-walled transparent summer eggs which may undergo development within the body of the parent, and the thick-walled winter eggs which have a hard, brown shell and develop in the outer world. In other species only the hard-shelled eggs are produced. In the Catenulidae asexual reproduction by the formation of buds or zooids at the posterior end of the body is met with commonly. More than one bud may be produced before separation takes place.

Planarians (Fig. 590) show less variation in the structure of the sexual organs. The testes, usually numerous, lie both above and below the digestive tract and extend from anterior to posterior end. The seminal vesicle opens into the muscular bulb-like cirrus, the apex of which projects into the male genital atrium, which in turn leads into the common atrium. Two ovaries are placed far forward. The numerous yolk glands open into the oviducts as they pass back and either unite to form a common duct which enters the genital atrium or open separately into the posterior part of the uterine duct. Fertilization apparently occurs in the uterus which lies just back of the pharynx.

Some triclads manifest only sexual reproduction; others have regular alternating periods of sexual and asexual reproduction; while a number do not have a definite life cycle since sexual maturity occurs at irregular intervals and often only among a limited number of individuals. In these forms reproduction is ordinarily asexual. *Dendrocoelum lacteum* attains sexual maturity and deposits its cocoons during the winter months. In *Planaria maculata* and *Planaria agilis* sexual organs begin to develop early in the autumn and mature in the spring. After the cocoons are deposited the reproductive organs degenerate and reproduction is again carried on by transverse division into two pieces with subsequent regeneration of the missing parts in each piece. The division plane in most planarians passes just back of the pharynx. In *Planaria velata* there is a division into pieces of various sizes which encyst in a slime layer in response to unfavorable conditions. This slime layer hardens into a shell-like covering. Entire animals may also encyst. Asexual reproduction among planarians may occur at any time of the year and in many species is the usual method of propagation. The factors which control the development of sexual maturity are not fully understood although the food supply unquestionably plays an important part.

Turbellaria undergo no metamorphosis during development but emerge from the egg, resembling the parent except in the lack of sexual organs. In viviparous forms the young develop within the mesenchyma of the parent and make their way to the exterior through the body wall in the posterior region.

Flatworms are extremely responsive to external influences and the larger forms especially give interesting and specific reactions to various kinds of stimuli. If a dish in which they are quietly gliding about is jarred even very slightly, it will cause them to stop and contract until quiet is restored, or if at rest and the dish is moved they respond by becoming active as soon as the disturbance ceases. Violent disturbance induces a highly excited condition with a loss of their more delicate reactions. After being disturbed the animals continue moving about for some time, this period depending on the strength of the stimulus and the physiological condition of the animal. Naturally it depends also upon the species since some are more active than others. They come to rest in some sheltered spot, normally in groups. Light plays an important part in determining their resting place as they show decided negative *photokinesis*. The length of time of the resting period varies greatly. The animals are much more active at night than in day time; this is probably due to their feeding habits.

If the worm is in a normal condition a delicate mechanical stimulus induces a positive reaction, *i.e.*, the animal pauses momentarily, then turns towards the source of the stimulus and glides forward in that direction. A negative reaction is usually given in response to a strong mechanical stimulus. In this case the animal turns away from the source of the stimulus. The positive and negative reactions are given not only in response to weak and strong mechanical stimuli but to changes in temperature and to various chemical stimuli. The food reaction is essentially a positive one. If food is placed in a dish where planarians are gliding about, as they pass near enough to receive the stimulus supplied by the juices of the tissues, they give a positive reaction similar to that following delicate mechanical stimuli. This reaction brings them to the food and as they pass over it the anterior end closes over the food as if testing it. This process completed, the animal moves ahead sufficiently to bring the mouth opening over the food. The pharynx is extruded and the feeding process begins. An interesting reaction is given where a planarian falls dorsal side down, as it rights itself by forming a more or less complete spiral.

There is a constant secretion of slime over the entire body and especially on the ventral surface. Irritation causes an increase in the quantity discharged. The slime layer and rhabdites probably serve the purpose of protection to some extent and aid in holding the prey.

Some Turbellaria occur in shallow quiet pools only; others in larger ponds, lakes, or rivers, while a few species seem to prefer swiftly flowing spring-fed brooks and streams. They are found not only in all kinds of water but under varying temperature conditions as well, since they may be collected during the winter from beneath the ice and also are found in hot springs with a temperature of 47° C. They collect on the under side of stones, sticks, and leaves, conceal themselves among algae and in debris, or cling to the stems of *Chara*, *Ceratophyllum*, and other hydrophytic plants. Certain forms are found near the surface in comparatively open water, and others in the mud or sediment at the bottom of ponds or lakes. Peat bogs and swampy places often furnish a large number of forms.

The regions occupied by different species of planarians are apparently determined by temperature and food supply to a very great extent. Those species which are adapted to low temperatures become sluggish and inactive in higher temperatures, or the reverse, and so will be less likely to find food than forms especially adapted to that temperature. If the food supply is limited this will necessarily lead to a crowding out of those less perfectly adapted to the environment. The development of any one species in a particular region is consequently limited by competition with other species already established in the area. In some cases two or more species may be found in almost equal numbers in the same pond as *Planaria maculata* and *Dendrocoelum lacteum*. In such cases a variety of food usually seems to be abundant, thus reducing the competition which would otherwise lead to the elimination of the weaker. Cannibalism sometimes occurs among individuals of the same species when food is scarce and different species are especially likely to prey upon each other. *Planaria agilis* is a voracious feeder, and will exterminate a culture of *Planaria velata* or *Planaria maculata* in a comparatively short time even if other food is provided. This may account in part for the fact that certain species are always found alone.

Ordinarily a pond or stream shows no evidence of the presence of Planaria even though large numbers of them may be hidden away under stones or leaves. However, one sometimes finds them moving restlessly about in great masses, either all in one general direction or in disorder. Voigt has conducted some interesting experiments with European forms under natural conditions which would indicate that these apparently concerted movements are the result of a response to some stimulus which may promise food, and cannot be regarded as indicating the possession of any inherited tendency toward periodical wanderings. The marine Turbellaria, like the fresh-water forms, hide under stones and among seaweeds. Some find shelter within the shells of molluscs and a few are parasitic.

The land planarians are in general characteristic of tropical and sub-tropical regions where they attain a considerable length and are usually brilliantly colored. In this country one may sometimes find them in greenhouses and gardens, under flower pots or boxes, in moist woods under bark and old logs, or in any moist sheltered place. They are easily overlooked because of the similarity in their appearance to young snails.

Rhabdocoels are especially abundant in pools or ponds which contain much algal or other vegetation. A lens is often necessary to distinguish them from other minute organisms. They may be collected by means of a Birge net or other apparatus used in collecting small animals or simply by gathering carefully plant material, sediment, or debris from the ponds where they live and exposing this material in shallow dishes in the laboratory. The larger triclads are easily collected as they cling to the stone or leaf which conceals them when it is lifted from the water and they may then be removed with the point of a knife, or washed off into a large-mouthed jar. When algae or debris which contains them is disturbed, they contract, remain motionless until the disturbance ceases, and then come to the surface and crawl about excitedly, thus being easily picked up with a large-mouthed pipette.

Most Turbellaria are easily kept in cultures if the water is kept pure. Rhabdocoels should have a supply of unicellular and filamentous algae such as diatoms, *Spirogyra*, etc., and small animals like rotifers, crustacea, and insect larvae, as they use both plant and animal food. Planarians are largely, if not entirely, carnivorous and thrive in aquaria which are supplied with running water so that they may be given a constant supply of food. If this is not possible, they may be kept in ordinary aquarium jars or shallow dishes with or without algae. They will live for weeks without food but become greatly reduced in size. They take food readily, especially at night, and should be fed once or twice a week on earthworms, snails, liver, or almost any soft fleshy animal tissue. The water should be changed after each feeding.

Small forms are easily studied under the microscope if slightly compressed by the cover glass through the absorption of the surplus water with filter paper. A few quince seeds added to the water are of great assistance as they form a jelly which retards movement without injury to the animal. Cells or hollow slides are convenient for work with large forms. Anesthesia may be induced by the use of a solution of one-tenth of one per cent of chloretone, or even less with some species. For preservation hot corrosive sublimate may be used, or a cold solution of the sublimate to which five per cent of glacial acetic acid has been added. Lang's fluid, Chichkoff's mixture, and 30% HNO_3 followed after one minute with 70% alcohol, are all useful killing reagents. Formol is useful for preservation of external characters since the animals retain their shape and color in it better than in most reagents. The larger planarians are especially valuable for study in laboratories where attention is given to animal behavior. Certain forms also afford excellent training in exactness of observation.

The lack of well defined and unvarying external characteristics makes it difficult to identify many Turbellaria. A large part of the material ordinarily collected is sexually immature whereas, as has been noted above, a knowledge of the structure of the sex organs is necessary in certain genera for identification. Preserved material if immature is especially difficult to identify since the body becomes distorted in shape and the color is usually so modified as to be unreliable. The differences in color and form between several of the species of planarians while definite are so slight as to be apparent only after a comparison of living material. In other cases there is a wide variation in color between individuals of the same species.

Until comparatively recently descriptions of many species of Turbellaria were extremely meager. The confusion which has arisen as a result is due to the lack of conspicuous external characteristics which would serve for identification.

KEY TO NORTH AMERICAN FRESH–WATER TURBELLARIA

INCLUDING THE LAND PLANARIANS

1 (78)   Intestine a single blind tube, median in position.

Order **Rhabdocoelida** . . 2

The intestine consists of a simple rod-shaped or sac cavity which rarely has lateral diverticula and never is divided into two distinct post-pharyngeal branches.   Mostly small forms, never more than a few millimeters in length.   The following figures (Figs. 589 and 590) facilitate a comparison of structure in the two great orders, Rhabdocoelida and Tricladida (p. 354).

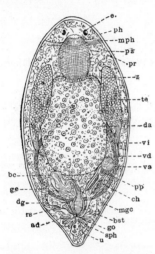

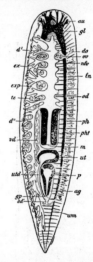

FIG. 589.   Structure of a Rhabdocoel. *Dalyellia rossi.* Compressed.   *ad*, atrial glands; *bc*, bursa copulatrix; *bst*, duct leading from bursa copulatrix; *ch*, chitinous part of the male copulatory organ; *da*, intestine; *dg*, duct of yolk gland; *ge*, ovary; *go*, genital pore; *mgc*, male genital canal; *mph*, retractor muscles of pharynx; *ph*, pharynx; *pp*, cirrus; *pr*, reddish reticular pigment; *pz*, yellow pigment cell; *rs*, receptaculum seminis; *sph*, sphinctor muscle of the uterus; *te*, testes; *vd*, vas deferens; *vs*, seminal vesicle; *vi*, yolk gland; *z*, esophageal cells; *e*, eye; *u*, uterus. $\times$ 50.   (After von Graff.)

FIG. 590.   Structure of a Triclad. Diagram of a Planarian.   *ag*, genital atrium; *au*, eye; *com*, cross commissures of nervous system; *d'*, anterior, and *d''*, posterior branches of intestines; *do*, yolk gland; *ex*, excretory canal; *exp*, excretory pore; *gl*, brain; *gp*, genital pore; *ln*, longitudinal nerve; *m*, mouth; *od*, oviduct; *od'*, common oviduct; *ov*, ovary; *p*, cirrus; *ph*, pharynx; *pht*, pharyngeal pocket; *te*, testes; *ut*, uterus; *utd*, uterine duct; *vd*, vas deferens.   (After Böhmig.)

2 (77)   Pharynx simple, cask-shaped or rosette-shaped.   Connective tissue of body cavity poorly developed.

Suborder **Rhabdocoela** . . 3

The mesenchyma often consists of but a few strands of connective tissue and contains large spaces filled with a perivisceral fluid.

3 (30)   Reproductive organs simple.   Female organs consist of ovary only.

Section **HYSTEROPHORA** . . 4

These forms possess no accessory female organs, *i.e.*, no separate yolk glands, uterus, female copulatory apparatus, etc.   Asexual reproduction among rhabdocoels is found only in this section of the order.

4 (27)   Pharynx simple.   5

5 (20)   Protonephridia with one principal branch, median dorsal in position.
Family CATENULIDAE . .   6

Without eyes but with ciliated pits, non-pigmented light-refracting organs, and in one genus a statocyst. The mouth lies on the ventral side of the anterior end. The pharynx opens into the anterior end of the intestine. Asexual reproduction by budding, thus forming chains of zooids, known for most species. Testes in front of ovary. Both testes and ovary may consist of one or more lobes.

6 (7)   With one statocyst and pre-oval circular groove. . . . . . *Catenula.*
But one species supposed to occur in America.

Catenula lemnae (Anton Dugès) 1832.

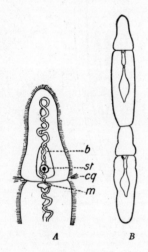

Length of single specimen 1 mm. Rarely 2 to 4 or 8 zooids in a chain. Delicate, white thread-like. Head region set off by a circular groove lined with long cilia. Intestine short and not continuous through chain of zooids.

Graff regards the European species *C. lemnae* as probably identical with the species which was collected in the vicinity of Philadelphia and very incompletely described by Leidy under the name *Anortha gracilis.* Until further collections of the Philadelphia form have been made this must of necessity be a matter open to question, and *C. lemnae* be admitted to the list of American species tentatively.

FIG. 591. *Catenula lemnae.* (*A*) anterior end: *b*, brain; *cg*, ciliated groove; *m*, mouth; *st*, statocyst. × 75. (After von Graff.) (*B*) Chain of two zooids. × 30. (After Mrazek.)

A   *B*

7 (6) Without statocyst or pre-oral circular groove.   With ciliated pits. .   8

8 (19)   Ciliated pits well developed. Without proboscis. *Stenostomum* . .   9

9 (18)   Head region not at all or only slightly set off from rest of body. .   10

10 (17)   Integument colorless.   11

11 (14)   Wall of digestive tract free from pigment.   12

12 (13) Anterior end bluntly pointed, ciliated pits about as far from end of
body as width of body at that point. Posterior end taper-
ing uniformly to a blunt point.

Stenostomum leucops (Anton Dugès) 1828.

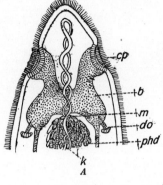

Length of single individuals 0.5 to 1.5 mm. Asexual reproduction by budding 2 to 4 zooids common,
rarely 9 zooids. Intestine continuous through zooids.
Rhabdites small, numerous. Two patelliform organs
which consist of numerous spherical bodies. Male
sexual organs mature in August, female in September.
At this time the animal becomes large, sluggish, and
somewhat reddish-brown in color. The six-lobed
ovary lies under the intestine. The oval-shaped
testes which consist of many closely compacted lobes,
lie above the pharynx and open into the seminal
vesicle which leads through a short canal to the
opening on the dorsal surface. Abundant on plants
in quiet water such as small lakes or ponds. Mass.,
N. Y., Ill., Mich., Neb.

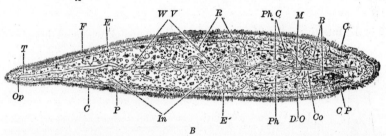

FIG. 592. *Stenostomum leucops.* (*A*) dorsal view of anterior end: *b*, brain; *m*, mouth; *k*, protonephridium; *phd*, pharyngeal glands; *do*, patelliform organ; *cp*, ciliated pit. × 200. (*B*) Entire worm. *cp*,
ciliated pit; *c*, cilia; *b*, brain; *m*, mouth; *ph*, pharynx; *in*, intestine; *wv*, protonephridium; *op*, external
pore of protonephridium. × 100. (After Ott.)

13 (12) Anterior end very bluntly rounded with ciliated pits very near the end.
Posterior end of body narrow and forming a long slender tail,
somewhat spatulate in shape, except where division has
recently taken place, in which case the tail is shorter and
more pointed. . . . *Stenostomum speciosum* Stringer 1913.

Length 2.25 mm. A large rhabdocoel which moves rather slowly and very gracefully. The
ciliated pits are placed close to the blunt anterior end, much farther forward than in *S. leucops*,
also are deeper and narrower than in the latter form. The mouth is about as far from the anterior end as the diameter of the body at that point, and is surrounded by glands. The pharynx
has delicate longitudinal striations. The intestine shows many large highly refractive colorless bodies, probably fat globules. Nothing definite can be said of the light-refracting organs
which were difficult to identify because of the unusual size of the animal. A few specimens
collected from pond with *S. leucops*. Lincoln, Neb.

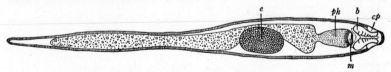

FIG. 593. *Stenostomum speciosum.* *cp*, ciliated pit; *b*, brain; *ph*, pharynx; *m*, mouth with surrounding
glands; *e*, egg. × 45. (Original.)

14 (11) Wall of digestive tract pigmented. 15

15 (16)   Pharynx yellowish-brown.   Intestine except gland cells bright yellow.
Stenostomum tenuicauda von Graff 1911.

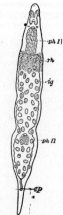

Length in chains of 4 zooids 1.5 mm.   Slender.   Posterior end tapering
to a slender tail ($\frac{1}{4}$ to $\frac{1}{16}$ of entire length).   Point of tail set with adhesive
cells.   Integument colorless and contains masses of small rhabdites measuring
up to 4 |M. in length.   Excretory pore nearer to intestine than end of body.
Two patelliform organs 12 μ across and composed of loosely joined spherical
bodies.   Rochester and Cold Spring Harbor, Long Island, N. Y.

FIG. 594. *Stenostomum tenuicauda.* An undivided chain of four zooids: *rh*, rhabdites;
ig, intestinal glands; *ep*, excretory pore; *ph I, II*, pharynx.   × 40. (After von Graff.)

16 (15)   Intestine yellowish-green between the round glistening oil drops.
Stenostomum agile (Silliman) 1885.

Length of single individual 0.75 mm.   Chains of two zooids measure 1.5 mm.,
those of five, 4 mm.   Light-refracting organs lens-shaped.   Rhabdites small.
Posterior end bears adhesive cells.   Pharynx long and provided with glands
throughout its entire length.   Sexual organs similar to *S. leucops.*   Monroe
Co., N. Y.

FIG. 595. *Stenostomum agile.* (*A*) Anterior end extended; *wgr*, ciliated pit; *lo*, lens-
shaped organ; *esch*, protonephridium; *ph*, pharynx; *da*, intestine; *g*, brain.   × 65. (*B*)
Lens-shaped organ.   × 125. (After von Graff.)

A

B

17 (10)   Integument bright yellow.   . . . *Stenostomum grande* (Child) 1902.

Length of chains of 4 to 6 zooids 2 to 2.2 mm.   Pre-oral region, especially
the rounded beak-like portion, white.   Integument bright yellow, pharynx
somewhat darker yellow, intestine deep orange-yellow.   Rhabdites small,
especially numerous in anterior end.
Two patelliform organs composed of about 25 spherical bodies.   Posterior
portion of nearly cylindrical muscular pharynx sometimes shows folds as a
result of contraction.   Intestine slightly lobed.   Rochester, N. Y.   Brackish
water, Falmouth, Mass.

A

FIG. 596. *Stenostomum grande.* (*A*) Anterior end: *wgr*, ciliated pit; *so*, patelliform
organ; *ph*. pharynx; *da*, intestine. (*B*) posterior end: *eö*, excretory pore.   × 55. (After
von Graff.)

B

18 (9)   Head region distinct from rest of body.
Stenostomum coluber Leydig 1854.

Length 6 mm. Width about one-thirtieth the length. Very slender, white, thread-like with snake-like movements. Head region broader than the rest of the body with blunt point at anterior end. Posterior end abruptly rounded. Asexual reproduction not known. Brackish water, Falmouth, Mass.

Fig. 597. *Stenostomum coluber.* Anterior end: *m*, mouth; *ph*, pharynx; *in*, intestine; *ov*, egg (?); *ns*, protonephridium. × 20. (After Leydig.)

- (8)   Ciliated pits shallow.   A club-shaped proboscis is present.
Rhynchoscolex.
Only one species. . . . . *Rhynchoscolex simplex* Leidy 1851.

Length 4 to 7 mm. Color yellowish-white opaque. Anteriorly abruptly attenuated into a long cylindrical clavate proboscis; anterior end abruptly narrowed, obtusely rounded. Proboscis shows longitudinal and numerous transverse marks. Mouth ventral, at the base of the proboscis. Intestine straight and capacious. A small wriggling worm found among yellowish fragments of vegetable matter and confervae at the bottom of clear brooks in the vicinity of Philadelphia.
Von Graff regards the European species *R. vejdovski* Sekera 1888 as probably identical with this American form.

20 (5)   With two lateral branches of the protonephridium.
Family MICROSTOMIDAE . . 21

Mouth a longitudinal slit on ventral surface, intestine occasionally with side lobes. Protonephridial branches open in anterior end. Testes and ovary either paired or unpaired, with two ventral sexual pores, the male posterior to the female. With or without eyes and ciliated pits.

21 (24)   The intestine extends dorsally and anteriorly beyond the junction
with the pharynx. . . . . . Subfamily MICROSTOMINAE.
Only one genus. . . . . *Microstomum* . . 22

22 (23)   With two reddish-yellow pigmented eye spots.
Microstomum lineare (Müller) 1773.

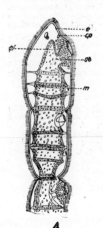

Length of single individuals 1.8 mm. In chains up to 18 zooids with a length of 9 to 11 mm. Slender. Very active. Color yellowish to grayish-brown, rarely rose-colored, with the intestine always darker than the body. Pre-oral portion of intestine short. Two small ciliated pits. Nettle cells or nematocysts in place of rhabdites. Male sexual organs with paired testes; slender chitinous spicule of copulatory organ with curved point. Ovary unpaired and median in position. In fresh and brackish water. Monroe Co. and Ontario Beach, N. Y.; West Twin Lake and Round Lake, Mich.

Fig. 598. *Microstomum lineare.* (*A*) anterior portion of a chain: *e*, eyes; *cp*, ciliated pit; *ai*, pre-oral portion of intestine; *m*, mouth; *oe*, esophagus. × 10. (After von Graff.) (*B*) Chitinous portion of cirrus. Much enlarged. (After Schultze.)

A   *B*

23 (22)   Without eyes. . . . .   *Microstomum caudatum* Leidy.

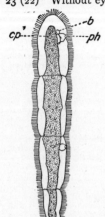

Length 1.5 to 3 mm. Commonly in chains of 2 to 8 zooids. Nematocysts in place of rhabdites. Color of integument white, intestine yellow. Ciliated pits directly dorsal to mouth. Pre-oral portion of intestine short. Anterior end bluntly rounded. Posterior end narrower, bluntly pointed, tail-like, elevated. In standing water and small brooks, Monroe Co., N. Y.; near Philadelphia, and in West Twin Lake, Charlevoix, Mich.

FIG. 599. *Microstomum caudatum.* *b*, brain; *ph*, pharynx; *cp*, ciliated pit. (After Silliman.)

24 (21)   Pharynx opens into anterior end of the intestine, which has short lateral diverticula. . . . . .   Subfamily MACROSTOMINAE. Only one genus. . . . . *Macrostomum* . . 25

25 (26)   Chitinous portion of copulatory organ a broad straight funnel with the slender point bent at a right angle or nearly so and bearing on its convex side the small opening. Vesicula seminalis and vesicula granulorum connected by a narrow tube. . *Macrostomum appendiculatum* (O. Fabricius) 1826.

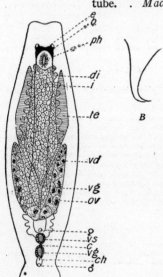

This is the form known as *M. hystrix* Oersted 1843. Length 2 mm. Unpigmented, transparent. Body flattened especially at the ends. The spatulate posterior end set with adhesive papillae. Rhabdoids and long sensory hairs conspicuous. Two eyes, black. Protonephridial tubes open on median dorsal side back of the slit-like mouth. Testes and ovary both paired. Asexual reproduction not known. In running and standing water. Monroe Co., N. Y.; Lincoln, Neb.

FIG. 600. *Macrostomum appendiculatum.* (*A*) Entire worm: *b*, brain; *e*, eye; *ph*, pharynx; *di*, diverticulum of intestine; *i*, intestine; *te*, testes; *vd*, vas deferens; *vg*, ductus seminalis; *vs*, seminal vesicle; *vg*, vesicula granulorum; *ch*, chitinous spicule of cirrus; ♂ and ♀, male and female genital pores; *ov*, ovary. × 35. (After von Graff.) (*B*) Chitinous spicule enlarged. × 350. (After Luther.)

26 (25)   Chitinous spicule of cirrus a straight narrow tube tapering to a
somewhat variably curved point. Vesicula seminalis and
vesicula granulorum separated by a short constriction.
Macrostomum sensitivum (Silliman) 1885.

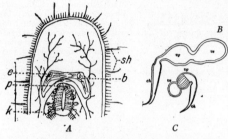

Length 1.5 mm. Color grayish-
white. Intestine yellowish. Broadest through middle. Posterior end
narrowed. Rhabdites present in integument in large numbers, either
singly or in twos and threes. Rhabdite tracts conspicuous in anterior
end. Intestine with lateral diverticula. Protonephridium communicates through a pore with mouth
cavity. Chitinous organ somewhat
variable. Monroe Co., N. Y.; brackish water, Falmouth, Mass.

FIG. 601. *Macrostomum sensitivum.* (*A*) Anterior end: *b*,
brain; *e*, eye with lens; *k*, protonephridium which opens
through the pore (*p*) into the mouth cavity; *sh*, sensory
hairs. × 150. (After Silliman.) (*B*) Male copulatory organ
subjected to pressure. (*C*) Male copulatory organ not under
pressure: *vs*, vesicula seminalis; *vg*, vesicula granulorum; *ch*,
chitinous point. Much enlarged. (*B, C*, after von Graff.)

27 (4)   With a long cylindrical bulbous pharynx. . Family PRORHYNCHIDAE.

The pharynx is remarkably large. The mouth is in the anterior end. Testes with numerous
follicles. Ovary not paired. Two sexual pores, the female pore on the ventral side. The male
sexual organs open near the mouth or unite with it.

Only one genus. . . . . *Prorhynchus* M. Schultze . . 28

28 (29)   Without eyes. . . . . . . *Prorhynchus stagnalis* M. Schultze 1851.

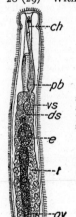

Length to 6 mm., commonly much smaller. White, thread-like. Two ciliated pits. With numerous pear-shaped glands in the integument. Pharynx
about ⅓ of total length of body. Protonephridium with four principal branches,
two dorsal and two ventral. Chitinous portion of cirrus straight and stiletto-
shaped. Monroe Co., N. Y.; brackish water, Falmouth, Mass.

FIG. 602. *Prorhynchus stagnalis.* *ch*, chitinous stiletto; *pb*, bulb-like cirrus; *vs*, seminal vesicle; *ds*, ductus seminalis; *t*, testis follicle; opening of male sexual organs into
pharyngeal pocket; *ov*, ovary; *e*, mature egg. × 15. (After von Graff.)

29 (28)   With two very small eyes, yellowish by transmitted light, whitish by
          reflected light, lying just before the brain in the widest re-
          gion of the pharynx. . *Prorhynchus applanatus* Kennel 1888.

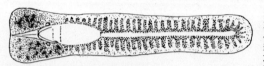

Length 4 mm. White. Body
much flattened at both ends.
Pharynx very muscular. Intestine a slender straight tube
with one diverticulum extending anteriorly under the pharynx and numerous slender very
closely set lateral diverticula.

FIG. 603. *Prorhynchus applanatus.* From life. ✕ 20. (After Kennel.)   Greenhouse, University of Nebraska, Lincoln, Neb.

30 (3)   Female sexual organs divided into ovary and yolk glands.   Male sex
         organs complex. . . . . Section LECITHOPHORA . . 31

Ovary in general small and simple. Yolk glands extremely variable, elongated, lobed, or
forming a network which anastomoses. Chitinous portion of male copulatory organ very
complicated and variable in form.

31 (74)   Proboscis either lacking entirely or if present without a definite
          sheath. . . . . Subsection LIPORHYNCHIA . . 32

This division contains the greater part of the fresh-water Turbellaria.

32 (61)   With a cask-shaped pharynx parallel to the ventral surface or slightly
          inclined and with the end directed forward.   But one genital
          pore. . . . . Family DALYELLIDAE . . 33

With the exception of the genus *Opistomum*, which is not represented in this country, the
pharynx is typically cask-shaped and opens into the anterior end of the intestine. The genital
pore opens on the ventral surface posterior to the mouth. Ovary simple. Yolk glands variable,
female receptaculum seminis and a simple uterus are present. Testes always paired. Chitinous
portion of male copulatory organ often very complex. Pigment eyes usually present, but
without other sense organs. Protonephridium consists of two principal branches which open
on the ventral surface. Rhabdoids and glands of integument prominent.

33 (60)   Without a separate pocket for the chitinous part of the cirrus. .   34

34 (59)   Sexual pore in posterior third of body.   The paired yolk glands un-
          branched and separate. . *Dalyellia* Fleming 1822 . . 35

This is the one commonly known as *Vortex* Ehrenberg 1831.

35 (36)   The chitinous portion of the male copulatory organ is represented
merely by the chitinous tube of the ductus ejaculatorius.
Dalyellia inermis von Graff 1911.

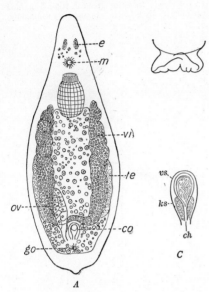

Length 0.6 mm. Flattened. Posterior end
modified into a kind of adhesive disk. Color
white by reflected light. Intestine very
broad and yellow in color. Eyes dull yellow.
Accessory pigment spots irregularly grouped
near the eyes. The locomotor movements
are very quick. Rochester, N. Y.

Fig. 604. *Dalyellia inermis*. (*A*) Ventral view,
slightly compressed: *e*, eye; *m*, mouth; *vi*, yolk
gland; *ov*, ovary; *go*, genital pore; *co*, male
copulatory organ; *te*, testes. ✕ 115. (*B*) Adhesive disk of posterior end. (*C*) Male copulatory organ enlarged: *ch*, chitinous tube; *ks*, vesicula granulorum; *vs* vesicula seminalis. ✕ 300.
(After von Graff.)

36 (35)   Provided with true chitinous organ. 37

37 (38)   Chitinous portion of cirrus consists of a single chitinous spine.
Dalyellia rochesteriana von Graff 1911.

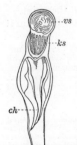

Scarcely 1 mm. long. Closely resembles *D. rheesi*. Colorless, transparent
with very small dermal rhabdites. Brownish mesenchymatous pigment not
so abundant as in *D. rheesi*. Intestine reddish-ocher-yellow. Sexual pore
lies just posterior to the intestine in the beginning of the last third of the
body. Rochester, N. Y.

Fig. 605. *Dalyellia rochesteriana*. Male copulatory organ enlarged: *ch*, chitinous
spine; *vs*, vesicula seminalis; *ks*, vesicula granulorum. (After von Graff.)

38 (37)   Chitinous portion of cirrus consists of more than one piece. . . 39

39 (44)   Chitinous portion of cirrus consists of a number of transverse spines
arranged in a row. 40

40 (41) Spines of unequal size and shape set in a basal piece.

Dalyellia dodgei von Graff 1911.

Length rarely more than 1 mm. Integument colorless. Intestine greenish from contained algae. Mesenchyma mottled with sepia-brown pigment. Eyes black. Found very commonly. Rochester, N. Y.

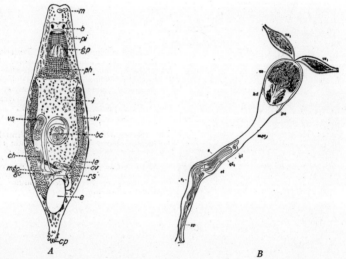

Fig. 606. *Dalyellia dodgei.* (*A*) Ventral view slightly compressed. × 65. (*B*) Male copulatory organ strongly compressed. Explanation of figures: *bc*, bursa copulatrix; *ch*, chitinous organ; *cp*, adhesive papillae; *i*, intestine; *e*, egg; *b*, brain; *ov*, ovary; *go* genital pore; *gp*, grasping papillae of pharynx; *vg*, vesicula granulorum; *m*, mouth; *mgc*, male genital canal; *ph*, pharynx; *pe*, cirrus; *pi*, mesenchyma pigment; *rs*, receptaculum seminalis; *sp*, sperm masses; *te*, testes; *vi*, yolk gland, *vs*, vesicula seminalis. Much enlarged. (After von Graff.)

41 (40) Spines of same size and shape, arranged loosely in a ring without a basal piece. 42

42 (43) With a crown of about 16 spines, tapering from base to the point.

Dalyellia eastmani von Graff 1911.

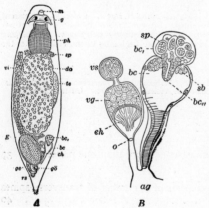

Length 0.3 to 0.5 mm. Color of mesenchymatous fluid pale yellow with spherical bodies which contain cinnamon-brown granules in a clear brown fluid. Rhabdites short and relatively thick and rounded at both ends. Rochester, N. Y.

Fig. 607. *Dalyellia eastmani.* (*A*) Ventral view uncompressed. × 100. (*B*) Male copulatory apparatus. × 600. Explanation of figures: *bc*, bursa copulatrix; *bc,*, blind sack of bursa; *bc,,,*, opening of blind sac; *e*, egg; *g*, brain; *m*, mouth; *ge*, ovary; *go*, genital pore; *rs*, receptaculum seminis; *vs*, vesicula seminalis; *te*, testes; *vi*, yolk gland; *ag*, common atrium; *o*, opening of the male copulatory organs into genital canal; *vg*, vesicula granulorum; *sp*, sperm mass; *ch*, chitinous crown of spines; *da*, intestine; *ph*, pharynx; *sb*, granules of secretion. (After von Graff.)

43 (42)   With a crown of 8 spines, thickened near the middle and tapering
to fine points at both ends.
Dalyellia blodgetti (Silliman) 1885.

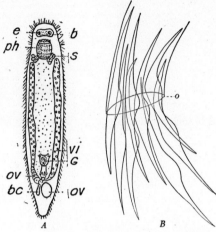

Length 0.6 mm. Color light brown.
A number of sensory hairs on anterior
end. Basal piece of the tube which
encloses the spines is not chitinous but
membranous and placed in the male
genital canal which opens into the
atrium. Erie canal, Rochester, and
Monroe Co., N. Y.

FIG. 608. *Dalyellia blodgetti.* (*A*) Entire: *b*, brain; *vi*, yolk gland; *g*, cirrus; *e*,
eye; *ov*, ovary; *bc*, bursa copulatrix; *ph*,
pharynx; *s*, salivary gland. × 90. (After
Silliman.) (*B*) Crown of spines from chitinous portion of male copulatory organ with
opening (*o*) into the genital canal. From
a strongly compressed preparation. Very
much enlarged. (After von Graff.)

44 (39)   Chitinous portion of cirrus bears two longitudinally placed stalks
on one end of which either one or two longitudinal terminal
branches are set. The terminal branches may be set with
spines. 45

45 (46)   Each chitinous stalk bears two terminal branches, one set with
spines and one with no spines.
Dalyellia fairchildi von Graff 1911.

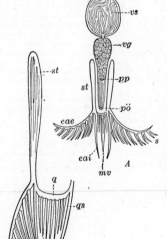

Similar in size and color to *D. rheesi* but more
slender, with a longer tail and the uterus lies posterior to the sexual pore. The egg is round to oval
in shape and measures 108 to 140 μ. Yolk glands
open as in *D. rheesi* through a common yolk duct
but are not lobed, barely notched.

FIG. 609. *Dalyellia fairchildi.* (*A*) Male copulatory
apparatus. × 430. (*B*) Chitinous piece enlarged. ×
850. *ds*, ductus seminalis; *eae*, outer branch with spines
folded; *eai*, inner branch with no spines; *mv*, median
projection; *pö*, opening of cirrus sheath; *pp*, cirrus papillae; *s*, double row of spines; *st*, stalk; *vg*, vesicula granulorum; *vs*, vesicula seminalis; *q*, transverse bar; *qs*,
transverse spines. (After von Graff.)

46 (45) Each chitinous stalk bears a single terminal branch set with
spines. 47

47 (50) The spines on the terminal branch are jointed. 48

48 (49) Each spine consists of three joints.   Stalk long, somewhat variable
in shape. . . . . *Dalyellia rheesi* von Graff 1911.

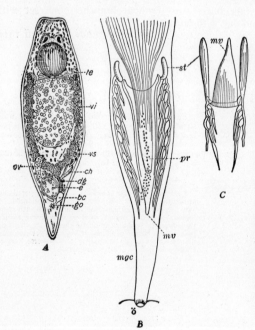

Length 1 mm. When swim-
ming freely the anterior end is
broadly rounded, in crawling,
truncated as shown in figure.
Integument colorless with nu-
m e r o u s delicate rhabdites.
Mesenchyma colored by sepia-
brown to cinnamon-red granules in a clear yellow fluid. In
the living animal the brain
region appears clear white and
the ventral surface lighter in
color than the dorsal, eyes
black. In pools along Erie
canal.

Fig. 610. *Dalyellia rheesi.* (*A*)
slightly compressed: *te*, testes; *vi*,
yolk gland; *vs*, vesicula seminalis;
ch, chitinous portion of cirrus; *dg*,
duct of yolk gland; *bc*, bursa copulatrix; *go*, genital pore; *e*, egg; *ov*,
ovary. × 60. (*B*) Male copulatory apparatus: *pr*, cirrus tube;
mcg, male genital canal; *ŏ*, opening of genital canal into common
atrium; *st*, short stalk of chitinous
piece. × 600. (*C*) Median ventral
grooved piece (*mv*) turned back;
st, variation in stalk. ×600. (After
von Graff.)

49 (48)   Each spine consists of two joints.   Stalk much reduced and variable
in shape. . . . . . .   *Dalyellia articulata* von Graff 1911.

Similar to *D. rheesi* in color and general structure.   Sexual organs differ as shown by a comparison of Figs. 610 and 611.   Same localities as *D. rheesi*.

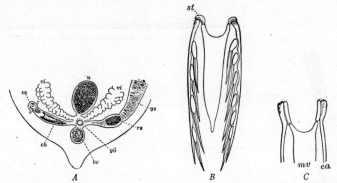

Fig. 611.   *Dalyellia articulata.*   (*A*) Posterior end with sex organs from a strongly compressed specimen: *bc*, bursa copulatrix; *ch*, chitinous part of male organs; *ge*, ovary; *gö*, genital pore; *rs*, receptaculum seminis; *u*, uterus with egg; *vi*, yolk gland; *vs*, vesicula seminalis.   (*B*) Chitinous organ with the reduced stalk (*st*).   (*C*) Chitinous portion of cirrus showing variation from (*B*).   Much enlarged.   (After von Graff.)

50 (47)   The reduced spines on the terminal branch are unjointed and consist
of but one piece.   51

51 (52)   The dorsal transverse bar bears a row of fine spines.
Dalyellia mohicana von Graff 1911.

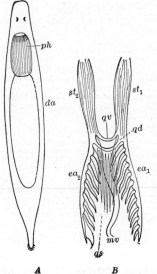

Free swimming, of extremely slender form, similar to *D. rossi*.   Anterior end of the chitinous portion of cirrus not sharply defined.   Differs from *D. rossi* chiefly in structure of the chitinous organ, the stalk of which is not so broad or flat as in that form.   One terminal branch of this organ bears eleven curved teeth, the other seven of the same type and one which is larger and three sided.   The transverse bar bears a row of straight, sharply pointed spines.   Brackish water, Falmouth, Mass.

Fig. 612.   *Dalyellia mohicana.*   (*A*) The animal swimming.   × 60.   (*B*) Chitinous part of cirrus.   Much enlarged.   *ea*, end branch with a row of spines; *st*, stalk; *qd*, dorsal transverse connecting bar, with a row of spines, *qs*; *qv*, ventral transverse bar; *mv*, median projecting piece.   (After von Graff.)

52 (48) The dorsal transverse piece between the longitudinal stalks has a
single median chitinous spine. . . . . · 53

53 (54) The median point is rudimentary; much shorter than the terminal
branches. . . . . *Dalyellia viridis* (G. Shaw) 1791.

Length 5 mm. Unpigmented except during the maturing of the eggs
when there is a brownish pigment, but with a continuous layer of zoochlorellae under the integument giving the characteristic green color.
Rochester, N. Y.

Fig. 613. *Dalyellia viridis.* Chitinous portion of cirrus: *st*, two-parted stalk;
ea, terminal branch. Much enlarged. (After von Graff.)

54 (53) The median point is as long as the terminal branches. 55

55 (56) One terminal branch is not jointed but consists of a single piece
shaped like a plow-share, and does not have spines.
Dalyellia armigera (O. Schmidt) 1861.

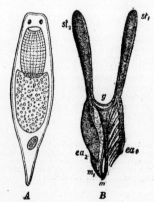

Length 0.6 to 1.5 mm. Color yellowish, reddish, or
brownish-gray. Pharynx very large, almost one-fourth
of entire length of body. Anterior end blunt, tail with
adhesive papillae. Swims actively at the surface of standing and running water. Brooks, Monroe Co., N. Y.;
Lake St. Clair, Mich.

Fig. 614. *Dalyellia armigera.* (*A*) living, uncompressed. × 50.
(*B*) chitinous portion of cirrus: *m*, median point; *ea*, terminal
branch with 3 to 9 (mostly 7 or 8) spines; *ea₂*, terminal branch
shaped like a plow-share; *g*, dorsal and ventral cross pieces;
st, stalk. × 500. (After von Graff.)

56 (55) Both terminal branches bear a row of plates or spines. 57

57 (58)   Terminal spine of only one terminal branch unlike the others in shape. . . . . *Dalyellia rossi* von Graff 1911.

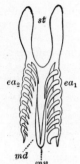

Length a little over 1 mm. Similar in form to *D. rheesi*. Color of mesenchyma bright or dark reddish-yellow to cinnamon-brown. Eyes brown or black. Intestine brownish-yellow. Adhesive cells on short tail. Common at Rochester, N. Y. In brackish water, Falmouth, Mass. See Fig. 589 for view of entire animal.

FIG. 615. *Dalyellia rossi*. Chitinous part of male copulatory organs. *st*, chitinous stalk; *ea₁* and *ea₂*, terminal branches with spines; *mv* and *md*, median ventral and dorsal projections. × 285. (After von Graff.)

58 (57)   Terminal spines on both terminal branches unlike the others in shape. *Dalyellia sillimani* von Graff 1911.

Length 1 mm. Integument colorless with small rhabdites. In heavily pigmented specimens the mesenchyma appears dark brown; those with less pigment show cells filled with yellow fluid and containing brown pigment granules. Intestine ocher-yellow. Eyes black. Rochester, N. Y., in brooks and pools.

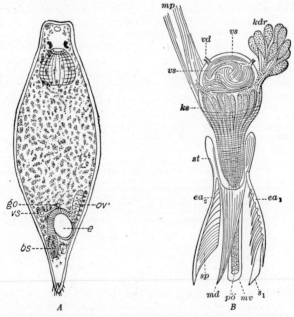

FIG. 616. *Dalyellia sillimani*. (*A*) slightly compressed: *bs*, bursa seminalis; *e*, egg; *ov*, ovary; *go*, sexual pore; *vs*, vesicula seminalis. × 70. (*B*) Male copulatory organ: *ea₁* and *ea₂*, terminal branches of chitinous organ; *kdr*, granular glands of one side; *ks*, granular secretion; *md*, median dorsal chitinous point; *mp*, retractor muscles; *mv*, median ventral grooved chitinous piece; *pö*, cirrus opening; *vd*, vas deferens; *vs*, vesicula seminalis; *s₁*, last chitinous plate of right terminal branch; *sp*, last chitinous plate of left terminal branch; *st*, stalk. × 330. (After von Graff.)

59 (34) Sexual pore anterior to the middle of the body. Yolk glands branched and either separate or united to form a network.

Phaenocora Ehrenberg 1836.

This is the genus formerly known as *Derostomum* Oersted 1843.

Only one species known in this country.

Phaenocora agassizi von Graff 1911.

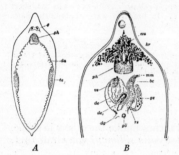

Length 1 to 2 mm. Milk-white. Intestine greenish-yellow. Eyes reddish-yellow. Between the eyes and the pharynx or extending over the anterior end of it there is a zone of so-called crystalloids which appear clear or grayish-brown in transmitted light. This species is an exception for the genus in that it possesses rhabdites. Pharynx cask-shaped, intestine more or less deeply lobed. In pool, Rochester, N. Y.

FIG. 617. *Phaenocora agassizi.* (*A*) slightly compressed: *te*, testes; *da*, intestine; *ph*, pharynx. × 22. (*B*) Anterior part, enlarged: *kr*, crystalloids; *bc*, bursa copulatrix; *mm*, muscles of bursa; *de₁*, proximal, and *de₂*, distal part of ductus ejaculatorius; *dg*, duct of yolk gland; *ge*, ovary; *gö*, genital pore; *rs*, receptaculum seminis; *au*, eye. × 70. (After von Graff.)

A   B

60 (33) With a separate pocket for the chitinous portion of male copulatory organ. Sexual pore lies in last third of body . . *Jensenia*. Only one species known in this country.

Jensenia pinguis (Silliman) 1885.

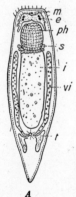

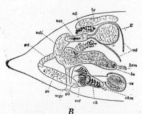

Length about 1.5 mm. Color brown to reddish, darkest in middle of body. Male genital canal divided at its connection with the common atrium, one branch forming the pocket for the chitinous organ while the other leads to the seminal vesicle. Rochester, N. Y.

B

FIG. 618. *Jensenia pinguis.* (*A*) Entire: *m*, mouth; *vi*, yolk glands; *t*, testes; *e*, eye; *ph*, pharynx; *s*, glands; *i*, intestine. × 30. (After Silliman.) (*B*) Sexual organs from animal compressed from side: *bs*, bursa seminalis; *bsm*, retractor muscles of same; *ch*, pocket which contains chitinous organ; *chm*, one of four muscles for same; *e*, egg; *gd*, oviduct; *ge*, ovary; *sd*, shell glands; *te*, testes; *udi*, uterus diverticulum of atrium; *ust*, duct of uterus; *vd*, vasa deferentia; *vs*, vesicula seminalis; *vst*, duct from same; *wgc*, female genital canal. × 60. (After von Graff.)

A

61 (32) Pharynx rosette-shaped, standing perpendicular to the ventral surface. . . . . Family TYPHLOPLANIDAE . . 62

The genital pore lies back of the mouth. Ovary one, testes paired. Other parts of sexual organs variable. Protonephridium with two main branches which may have either one or two openings on the ventral surface or may lead to the surface through the mouth or sexual pore. Eyes, non-pigmented light-refracting organs; ciliated pits may be present. Rhabdoids play an important part in classification. Both summer and winter eggs produced in some species

62 (63)   Genital pore in posterior third of body. . . . Tribe OLISTHANELLINI.

Excretory system opens on [dorsal surface with one asymmetrical or two symmetrically placed openings. Testes dorsal to the yolk glands. Without atrial copulatory organ.

Single genus thus far reported in America. . . . . *Olisthanella*.
Only one species in this country. . *Olisthanella caeca* (Silliman) 1885.

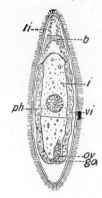

Length 1.3 mm. Without eyes. Without long sensory hairs. Color grayish-white. Sometimes apparently colored, due to food in intestine. Pharynx rosette-shaped and nearly central in position. Intestine large. Rhabdites and tracts prominent. Female organs only are known. Sluggish and found only in mud under stones. Monroe Co., N. Y.

Fig. 619.   *Olisthanella caeca.* *ph*, pharynx; *i*, intestine; *b*, brain; *vi*, yolk gland; *ov*, ovary; *go*, genital pore; *ti*, rhabdite tracts. × 35. (After Silliman.)

63 (62)   Genital pore in anterior two-thirds. 64

64 (71)   Testes ventral to the yolk glands.   Rhabdites only in mesenchyma
tracts. . . . .   Tribe TYPHLOPLANINI . . 65

Protonephridia with two main branches which communicate with the exterior through a transverse branch which leads either to the mouth or to the genital atrium. With or without atrial copulatory organs.

65 (66)   Anterior end of body a retractile proboscis. . . *Rhynchomesostoma*.
Only one species. . . . *Rhynchomesostoma rostratum* (Müller) 1773.

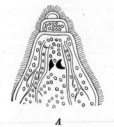

Length 2 mm. European specimens reach a length of 5 mm. when extended. Very transparent. Body fluid rose or yellowish-red in color. Intestine contains yellowish-red oil droplets. Ventral surface flat, dorsal convex. Anterior end of body like a telescopic tube. Pharynx small, lying somewhat before the middle of the body. Rochester, N. Y.

FIG. 620.   *Rhynchomesostoma rostratum.* (*A*) Proboscis partly extended. (*B*) Fully contracted. × 40. (After von Graff.)

66 (65)   Anterior end of body without retractile proboscis. 67

67 (70)   Without atrial copulatory apparatus. 68

68 (69)   With a separate receptaculum seminis, whose short duct is closed by a
muscular ring. Dermal rhabdites present. . . *Strongylostoma.*

Only one species known in this country.

Strongylostoma gonocephalum (Silliman) 1885.

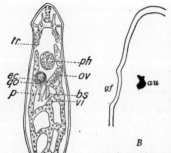

Length 1.2 mm. Mesenchyma yellowish, intestine
with yellowish oil droplets. Eyes carmine red. Small
rhabdites are present. This form differs from the
widely distributed European form, *Strongylostoma
radiatum* Müller chiefly in the possession of two
shallow oval pits which lie close behind the eyes at
the side. The integument is slightly raised around
them and each bears vacuoles and rhabdoids.
Excretory pore opens into mouth. Erie Canal,
Monroe Co., N. Y.

FIG. 621.   *Strongylostoma gonocephalum.*   (*A*) Entire
animal: *tr*, tracts of rhabdites; *ph*, pharynx; *ov*, ovary;
bs, bursa seminalis; *vi*, yolk glands; *p*, cirrus; *go*, genital
pore; *ec*, egg capsule. X 40. (After Silliman.)   (*B*) Out- line of anterior
end with eye (*au*) and shallow pit (*gf*) of one side. Enlarged. (After von
Graff.)

69 (68)   Without a separate receptaculum seminis. . . . . . *Typhloplana.*

Only one species known in this country.

Typhloplana viridata (Abildgaard) 1790.

Length 0.5 to 1 mm. Transparent. Zoochlorellae in the mesenchyma give
it a grass-green color. Tapering at both ends. Without eyes. Anterior
end bluntly pointed, posterior end pointed. Pharynx just anterior to
center. Sexual pore close behind pharynx. Viviparous. The summer
eggs develop within the body of the parent. Winter eggs are as many as
ten in number and yellowish-brown in color.

The pear-shaped bulbous cirrus contains a straight chitinous tube, the
ductus ejaculatorius. The male genital canal is set with small spines; the
small egg-shaped or somewhat elongated testes lie near or back of the pharynx.

Luther and von Graff regard the form collected from Monroe Co., N. Y.,
and described by Silliman under the name of *Mesostoma viviparum*, also
those collected from West Twin Lakes and Old Channel Round Lake,
Charlevoix, Mich., and described by Woodworth under the names *M.
viviparum* and *M. vividatum*, as identical with the European species. There
seems to be no doubt that this is the case. *Typhloplana viridata* was collected by von Graff at Rochester, N. Y.

FIG. 622.   *Typhloplana viridata.*   *pi*, Zoochlorellae; *ph*, pharynx; ♂ , ♀, male and
female genital pore; *pe*, cirrus. X 70. (After von Graff.)

70 (67)   With atrial copulatory apparatus.

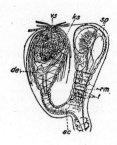

Castrada hofmanni (M. Braun) 1885.

Length 1.5 mm. Unpigmented. Colored green from zoochlorellae in mesenchyma. Cylindrical. Anterior end rounded, posterior end running out to a blunt point. Without eyes. Large rhabdoids in tracts. Pharynx somewhat before the middle of the body with genital pore shortly back of it. Testes are elongated oval to pear-shaped. Yolk glands are deeply lobed. The male copulatory organ and bursa copulatrix are entirely enclosed by the muscular mantle of the atrium copulatorium. Rochester, N. Y.

FIG. 623. *Castrada hofmanni.* Cirrus, bursa copulatrix, and atrium copulatorium. Diagram from preparations subjected to pressure: *vs,* vesicula seminalis; *ks,* granular secretions; *sp,* spermatophore; *rm,* circular muscles; *t,* teeth-like spines; *ac,* atrium copulatorium; *de,* ductus ejaculatorius. Much enlarged. (After Luther.)

71 (64)   Testes dorsal or lateral to the yolk glands. Mesenchyma with rhabdoids outside of tracts. . Tribe MESOSTOMATINI . . 72

Sexual pore lies in anterior two-thirds of body. Protonephridial ducts open through mouth to exterior as in most Typhloplanini and in some cases, mouth, protonephridia, and genital organs have a common external opening. Rhabdites play a very important part in classification. The larger rhabdocoels belong to this group.

72 (73)   With a ventral epidermal pouch and a ductus spermaticus which connects the bursa copulatrix with the female genital canal.
Bothromesostoma.

Only one species known in this country.

Bothromesostoma personatum (O. Schmidt) 1848.

Length 7 mm. Color on anterior and posterior ends and on lateral margins and ventral side a clear brown. In mature specimens the pigment is so massed that together with the dark color of the intestine it gives a dark brown to bluish-black color to the dorsal surface above the intestine. Some specimens show a mixture of brown and black. The oval eyes are about as far distant from the lateral margins as from each other. They are perceptible only in the lighter pigmented specimens. The ventral epidermal pouch occurs somewhat posterior to the eyes. The common opening for mouth, protonephridial ducts, and genital pore is located about the middle of the ventral surface. Both summer and winter eggs are produced. The former produce the viviparous young. Ann Arbor, Mich.

A   B

FIG. 624. *Bothromesostoma personatum.* (*A*) entire animal. × 5. (After Schmidt.) (*B*) Diagram of sexual organs: *bc,* bursa copulatrix; *dsp,* ductus spermaticus; *pm,* opening of cirrus; *rs,* receptaculum seminis; *pg,* genital pore; *dg,* duct of yolk gland; *ph,* pharynx; *no,* opening of protonephridium. Much enlarged. (After Luther.)

73 (72)   Without a ventral epidermal pouch and ductus spermaticus.
                                                      Mesostoma.
Only one species known in America.
                              Mesostoma ehrenbergii (Focke) 1836.

This species attains a length of 12 to 15 mm. in Europe. Greatest length recorded for American specimens is 6 mm. Very transparent. Color pale yellowish to brownish. Intestine yellowish-brown. Thin, flat, and leaf-like in outline. Anterior end tapering, conical. Posterior end tapering sharply and terminating in an acute caudal process. Conspicuous tracts of rhabdites lead to the anterior end. Eyes black. Two shallow pits occur on the dorsal surface of the anterior end, one on either side. Both summer and winter eggs are produced but rarely at the same time. The summer eggs develop and the young embryos may be seen within the body of the parent. From Illinois River; Lake St. Clair, Mich.; Ohio; and Elkhorn River, Neb.

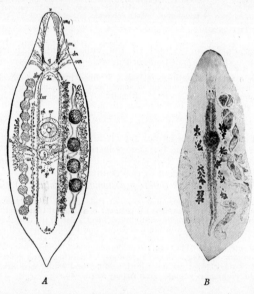

A   B

FIG. 625. *Mesostoma ehrenbergii.* (*A*) Diagram from ventral side showing nervous, digestive, and reproductive systems. Left side shows summer eggs, the right, winter eggs: *bc,* bursa copulatrix; *da,* anterior branch of intestine; *da₁,* posterior branch of intestine; *go,* genital pore; *k,* ovary; *pe,* cirrus; *ph,* pharynx; *rs,* receptaculum seminis; *te,* testes; *u,* uterus; *vd,* vas deferens; *vi,* yolk gland; *vs,* vesicula seminalis; *wgc,* female genital canal; *co,* subesophageal commissure of ventral nerves; *dln,* dorsal longitudinal nerve; *dn,* dorsal nerve of brain; *g,* brain; *lnv,* ventral longitudinal nerve; *nr,* pharyngeal nerve ring; *us,* duct of uterus; *ven,* ventral nerve of brain; *vid,* duct of yolk gland; *vn₁* and *vn₂,* the two pairs of anterior nerves of brain; *x,* chiasma of anterior nerves. × 6. (After von Graff, Vogt, Fuhrmann, and Luther.) (*B*) From life, showing young worms in left uterus. × 9. (After Woodworth.)

74 (31)   With a genuine proboscis which lies within a sheath and communicates with the exterior through an opening at the anterior end.   Pharynx rosette-shaped.
                              Subsection CALYPTORHYNCHIA . . 75

A small group easily recognized by the genuine proboscis. A bursa copulatrix is present. The cirrus is divided into vesicula seminalis and vesicula granulorum. The rosette-shaped pharynx lies on the ventral surface.

75 (76) With a single sexual pore. . . . . . . Family POLYCYSTIDIDAE.
Two ovaries, two yolk glands with finger-like lobes, and two compact testes. Bursa copulatrix small and without a separate external opening.

Single genus thus far found in America. . . . . . . *Polycystis*.
Only one species known in America. . *Polycystis roosevelti* von Graff 1911.

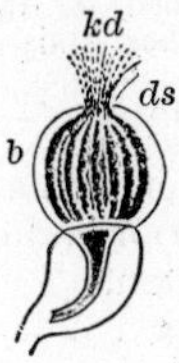

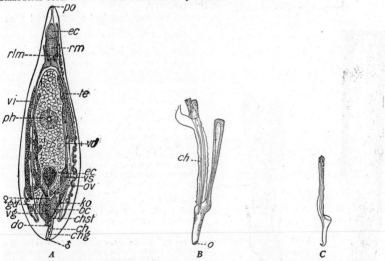

Length 2 mm. Anterior end of body transparent, the rest of the body faintly reddish. A subcutaneous brown pigment between the longitudinal muscle fibers gives a more or less striated appearance. The extremely flexible proboscis lies within its sheath just in front of the brain at the anterior end. The mouth and pharynx lie in the beginning of the second third of the body and the genital pore lies between the second and last third of the body. Posterior end very bluntly rounded, anterior end somewhat narrower. Closely resembles the European species *P. gaetti* Bresslau except in the structure of the chitinous portion of male copulatory organ.

FIG. 626. *Polycystis roosevelti.* Chitinous cirrus tube with bulb (*b*), ductus seminali (*ds*), and the ducts leading from the granular glands (*kd*). × 400. (After von Graff.)

76 (75) With two sexual pores, the male posterior to the female.
Family GYRATRICIDAE.
One or two ovaries, with yolk glands and one compact testes which lies on the left side.

Only one genus known. . . . . *Gyratrix*.
Single species known in America.

Gyratrix hermaphroditus Ehrenberg 1831.
Length 2 mm. White in reflected light. Eyes black. Without rhabdoids or pigment. Capable of contracting into a ball, or extending to almost double its length as long as it remains actively swimming. Stiletto-sheath of male copulatory organ a short wide tube. The very large bursa copulatrix has a separate dorsal opening to the exterior. Egg capsule oval. From peat bog, Rochester, Monroe Co., N. Y.
One subspecies *Gyratrix hermaphroditus hermaphroditus* Ehrenberg. Stiletto-sheath with a hook on the end. The egg capsule is gradually reduced to its stalk and is much elongated. Rhabdoids occur in the terminal cone of the proboscis.

FIG. 627. *Gyratrix hermaphroditus.* (*A*) Ventral view of compressed specimen. *do*, dorsal opening of; *bc*, bursa copulatrix; *ch*, chitinous tube; *chst*, stalk of chitinous tube; *chg*, chitinous stiletto leading from vesicula granulorum; *ec*, egg capsule in uterus; *ov*, ovary; *gd*, granular secretory glands; *ko*, external opening of kidney; *ph*, pharynx; *rlm*, attachment of the long proboscis retractor muscles; *ec*, end cone of proboscis; *rm*, muscular portion of proboscis; *po*, external opening of proboscis sheath; *te*, testes; *vd*, vas deferens; *vg*, vesicula granulorum; *vi*, yolk glands; *vs*, vesicula seminalis; ♂, male and ♀, female genital pores. × 30. (After von Graff.) (*B*) Stiletto-sheath with straight tube. *o*, opening of stiletto sheath; *ch*, chitinous stiletto of cirrus. Much enlarged. (After Hallez.) (*C*) *Gyratrix hermaphroditus hermaphroditus.* Stiletto-sheath with curved point. Much enlarged. (After von Graff.)

77 (2)   Pharynx either variable or cylindrical and lying within a pharyngeal
         pocket.   Connective tissue well developed.
                                                        Suborder **Alloeocoela**.

The intestine is an irregular sac mostly with side lobes and an anterior and posterior branch.
It divides to form a ring in the median ventral region, thus enclosing the slender cylindrical
pharynx which is similar in position and appearance to that of the planarians.
No fresh-water representative of this Suborder has been definitely established for this
country.   It seems clear that some must exist in this region and be found on further study of
the American fauna.

78 (1)   Intestine consists of three main branches, one an anterior branch
         median in position, and two running to the posterior end of
         the body, one on either side of the pharyngeal region.
                                                     Order **Tricladida** . .   79

Mostly larger than in the preceding order.   Pharynx usually median ventral in position, elongated, cylindrical, and lying within a pharyngeal pocket with the free end directed posteriorly.
Compare figures of a typical Triclad (Fig. 590) and Rhabdocoel given on page 333.

79 (104)   Found in fresh-water ponds or streams.   . .   Suborder **Paludicola**.
           Only one family. . . . .   PLANARIIDAE . .   80

Body elongated, flattened, often with conspicuous cephalic appendages.   Inconspicuously
colored.

80 (103)   Pharynx one.   81

81 (82)   With an adhesive disk on anterior end. . . . . . .   *Dendrocoelum*.
          Only one species known in this country.
                                          Dendrocoelum lacteum Oersted 1844.

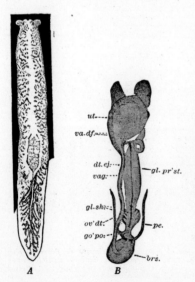

Greatest length 22 mm., breadth 2 to 3 mm.
Color milk-white, creamy, yellowish, or in
larger older specimens sometimes roseate.   No
pigment except in eye spots.   Very translucent.   Intestine colored by contained food.   A
slight constriction just behind the plane of the
eyes sets off the head and produces the rounded,
cephalic appendages.   Posterior end rounded.
Lateral margins nearly parallel when at rest
or contracted.   Median adhesive disk extremely
variable.   Usually about one-third of the broadest diameter of the head.   Inconspicuous in
small specimens.   It is not a true sucker but
consists of a depression into which the glands
open and with the margin somewhat raised.
Two eyes normally but from one to six accessory
eyes are common.   Mass., Mich., Penn., Wis.
What is probably a variety of this species is
described as a non-pigmented eyeless *Dendrocoelum* collected from Mammoth Cave and adjoining caves in Kentucky.

FIG. 628. *Dendrocoelum lacteum.* (*A*) From life. × 4.
(*B*) Sex organs, dorsal view: *brs,* copulatory bursa;
dt ej, ductus ejaculatorius; *gl sh,* shell gland; *gl prst,*
prostate gland; *go po,* genital pore; *ov dt,* oviduct;
pe, cirrus; *ut,* uterus; *va df,* vas deferens; *vag,* vagina.   × 14.   (After Woodworth.)

82 (81)   Without an adhesive disk on anterior end.   83

83 (102)   Normal eyes two or none. . . . .   *Planaria* . . 84

84 (101)   With two normal eyes (sometimes with one or more irregularly placed accessory eyes). 85

85 (94)   Anterior end more or less pointed with angular cephalic appendages. 86

86 (91)   Anterior end bluntly pointed, angle formed by lateral margins of head not less than 60°. Cephalic appendages blunt. Body about as wide just back of appendages as immediately in front of them. 87

87 (88)   Angle formed by lateral margins of head much greater than 60°. Cephalic appendages very inconspicuous, almost entirely wanting in young specimens.
Planaria foremanii (Girard) 1852.

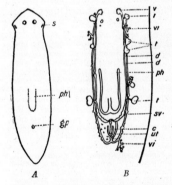

Length of mature specimens 7 to 15 mm., breadth 2 to 4 mm. Color nearly uniform seal-brown or dark gray to slate-black, with an inconspicuous gray area on each cephalic appendage. Eyes gray with a crescent of black pigment on the median side. Body comparatively thick. Ovaries two, ventral, somewhat lobed and situated about halfway from anterior end to pharynx. Testes four or five on each side, unpaired, dorsal and irregularly distributed from region of ovaries to posterior end of pharynx. Does not multiply by fission. Found in small streams in Mass., Penn., Md., Va., and near Washington, D. C.

The species described by Curtis (1900) under the name *Planaria simplicissima* and later by Stevens under the same name clearly must be regarded as synonymous with the species established by Girard in 1852 under the name *P. foremannii*. This species also appears under the name *P. lugubris* in various papers dealing with the physiology of planarians.

FIG. 629. *Planaria foremanii*. (*A*) Outline sketch of large mature specimen: *gp*, genital pore; *ph*, pharynx; *s*, sensory area on cephalic appendages. ×4. (After Stevens.) (*B*) Sexual organs, longitudinal section, dorsal view: *c*, cirrus; *d*, oviduct; *ph*, pharynx; *sv*, seminal vesicles; *t*, testes; *ut*, uterus; *v*, ovary; *vi*, yolk glands; *vl*, vas deferens. ×20. (After Curtis.)

88 (87)   Angle formed by lateral margins of head about 60°. Cephalic appendages distinct. Anterior margin of cephalic appendages of about same length as posterior margin. 89

89 (90)   Color blackish to purplish or brownish by reflected light, blackish
or gray by transmitted light. With many irregular spots
entirely free from pigment. . *Planaria maculata* Leidy 1848.

Length 15 mm. Immature specimens average about 8 to
11 mm. In small specimens the pigment occurs in isolated
patches and spots. In larger specimens the pigment patches
are confluent chiefly in the median region leaving the clear
irregular areas which give a very spotted appearance to the
animal. Smaller spots of deep brown or black scattered
among the larger patches. Frequently with a light median
streak. Posterior half of cephalic appendages with non-
pigmented spots. Ventral surface much lighter than dorsal,
almost entirely free from pigment. Reproduces freely by
transverse fission posterior to pharynx. Sexually mature
specimens not common in most localities. Sluggish. Much
less active than those nearly related species which might
be confused with it. Found commonly among algae and
water plants or under stones where water is comparatively
quiet. Mass., Penn., Ill., Mich., Neb.

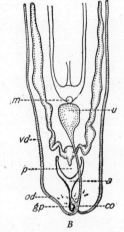

A   B

FIG. 630. *Planaria maculata.* (*A*) From life. × 6. (After Woodworth.) (*B*) Sexual organs, dorsal
view: *u*, uterus; *co*, common oviduct; *od*, oviduct; *a*, atrium; *gp*, genital pore; *p*, cirrus; *vd*, vas deferens; *m*, mouth. × about 35. (After Curtis.)

90 (89)   Color dark reddish-brown to grayish-brown. Uniformly pigmented.
Planaria gonocephala Dugès 1830.

A

Greatest length 25 mm.
Usually not over 15 mm.
Girard describes the color
of this species as often of
a blackish-brown. Pos-
terior margins of auricular appendages free from
pigment. Much lighter on ventral than on dorsal
side. Eyes in a plane joining the apices of the
auricles. Clear areas around eyes sometimes
elongated in an antero-posterior direction. Reproduction asexually common. Mich., Ill.

FIG. 631. *Planaria gonocephala.* (*A*) From life. × 5.
(After Woodworth.) (*B*) Sexual organs, longitudinal
section side view: *ut*, uterus; *od*, oviduct; *de*, ductus
ejaculatorius; *pap*, papilla; *vd*, vas deferens; *ag*, genital
atrium; *vs*, vesicula seminalis; *m*, mouth; *utd*, duct of
uterus; *pdr*, cirrus glands; *pdr*[1], ducts of cirrus glands;
gp, genital pore. Much enlarged. (After Böhmig.)

B

91 (86)   Anterior end rather sharply pointed. Angle formed by lateral margins of head not more than 60°. Cephalic appendages long,
slender, sharply pointed, with anterior margin shorter than
posterior margin. Body distinctly narrower back of cephalic appendages than just in front. 92

92 (93)   Angle of head 50° to 60°. Color a very dark sepia-brown almost
black by reflected light.   . . *Planaria agilis* Stringer 1909.

Length of immature worms usually not over 18 mm.   Mature specimens collected have measured 30 mm.   Well fed specimens in aquaria have attained a length of 55 mm.   Color usually
very uniform.   Ventral surface but little lighter than dorsal.   One variety found only in one
locality and with uniformly colored specimens, shows sharply defined non-pigmented spots.
Under lens a clear light-brown ground with fine dark brown, almost black pigment granules,
either quite uniformly distributed or arranged so as to give the appearance of a very close net
work.   Circum-ocular spaces either oval or slightly pointed at outer anterior region and placed
just in front of or in line with the anterior margins of cephalic appendages.   Some with light
areas on posterior margins of cephalic appendages, others with auricles uniformly pigmented.
A light median streak sometimes present.   Lateral margin of head with a distinct inward curve

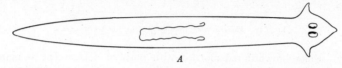

A

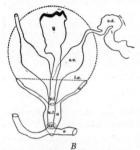

B

just back of tip, also at junction of head with cephalic
appendages.   Wider just in front of appendages than
at any point posterior to them except in large specimens
which are of about same width through pharyngeal region.
Mature specimens much broader proportionally than
immature.   Asexual reproduction the usual method of
propagation in most localities.   Very restless and active.
Collected from small ponds and spring-fed brooks either
among algae or on sandy bottom and often where water
flows swiftly.   Neb., Mo., S. Dak., Wis., and Cal.

Fig. 632.   *Planaria agilis.*   (*A*) Immature specimen from life.
×8.   (*B*) Sexual organs, dorsal view: *u*, uterus; *ut*, uterus tube;
o, oviduct; *gp*, genital pore; *a*, atrium; *sv*, seminal vesicle; *vd*,
vas deferens; *pl*, cirrus lumen; *la*, limit of atrium.   Much enlarged.   (After Stringer.)

93 (92)   Angle of head about 45°.   Color reddish to yellowish-brown.
Planaria dorotocephala Woodworth 1897.

Length of immature specimens 13 mm.   Head about one-sixth of total length of body.   Uniformly colored.   Posterior margins of auricular appendages free from pigment.   Sometimes a
narrow light median streak.   Pigment in spots or patches, not a network or evenly distributed
as in *P. agilis;* ventral side much lighter than dorsal.   Eyes just anterior to plane joining
auricles.   Intestine usually with accessory posterior intestinal trunks which arise either at the
root of the pharynx like the two normal posterior trunks or exist as parallel branches of the
latter.   Those of a side usually unite with each other near their posterior terminations.   Very
active and restless.   Sexual organs have not been described.   Ill., Mich.

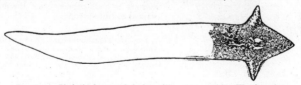

Fig. 633.   *Planaria dorotocephala* from life.   × 7.   (After Woodworth.)

94 (85)   Anterior end clearly not pointed. 95

95 (100)   Anterior end truncated. 96

96 (99)   Margin of anterior end with a median anterior and two lateral
rounded projections giving a sinuous outline. 97

97 (98)   Color gray. . . . . *Planaria velata* Stringer 1909.

Length of mature specimens 15 mm. Color of dorsal side to unaided eye varies from almost white to a very dark gray almost black. Under lens, a colorless groundwork with black pigment granules extremely variable in number. Much lighter in front of eyes and over cephalic appendages. Lighter on ventral surface, over pharynx, and near lateral margins. Preserved material often appears colorless and oval in shape. Encystment of the entire animal or division into a variable number of pieces followed by encystment of the pieces occurs in response to unfavorable conditions. The cysts resemble egg cocoons in appearance and are provided with a shell. Cilia conspicuous. Crete and Omaha, Neb.

FIG. 634. *Planaria velata* from life. × 12. (After Stringer.)

98 (97)   Color brownish-red mottled with purplish dots except at margins.
Planaria unionicola Woodworth 1897.

Length of the one specimen (preserved) from which the description was made 2.8 mm., breadth 1.8 mm. Probably 8 to 10 mm. long when alive and extended. Purple dots occur in masses. Red color absent over an elongated posterior median area extending nearly to the posterior axis of the animal. Appearance of posterior end suggests an injury or transverse division. Color of alcoholic material a deep rusty red. Found creeping on the mantle of *Unio alatus* in Illinois River.

FIG. 635. *Planaria unionicola* from life. About × 3. (After Woodworth.)

99 (96)   Margin of anterior end uniformly curved, not sinuous. Color white.
Planaria truncata Leidy 1851.

Length 10 to 12 mm. Thickness slight. Translucent. Digestive tract variously colored by food. Two crescent-shaped eyes situated far back and near together. Pharynx much elongated and central in position in sexually mature specimens. Intestine with little anastomosis of branches. Ovaries two, sometimes lobed. Testes many. Uterus large with stalk running to left side, dorsal to vasa deferentia and oviducts and entering atrium laterally. Asexual reproduction by fission. Small stream Bryn Mawr campus; rivulet at Newark, Delaware.

A comparison of descriptions of *P. truncata* Leidy and *P. morgani* Stevens and Boring leaves but little doubt that they are identical. The blackish-white color mentioned by Leidy evidently was due to food contained in the digestive tract and not to body pigment since the margin is described as translucent.

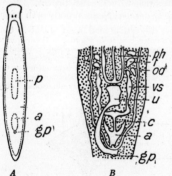

FIG. 636. *Planaria truncata*. (*A*) From life. × 4. (*B*) Dorsal view of sexual organs: *a*, atrium; *c*, cirrus; *gp*, genital pore; *od*, oviduct; *ph*, pharynx; *t*, testes; *u*, uterus; *vs*, vas deferens. × 7. (After Stevens.)

100 (95)   Anterior end rounded in preserved condition (living condition not
known). . . . . *Planaria simplex* Woodworth 1897.

Length 4 mm., greatest diameter 1.8 mm. Color of alcoholic specimen ocher-yellow. Pigment located in spots of nearly uniform size, distributed uniformly over all parts of the body; no clear areas surrounding eyes or at sides of head. General shape ovate. Broadest at one-fifth the total length from the anterior end, tapering from here to rounded posterior extremity. Anterior end rounded, set off from the rest of the body by slight lateral indentions at the level of the eyes. No evidence of cephalic appendages. Mouth one-third of total length from posterior

end. Eye spots elongated, crescentic, facing outward and forward at an angle of 45° to the chief axis of the worm. Intestine of the simple triclad type; no fusion or anastomoses of posterior stems. This description is from a single immature alcoholic specimen. (It is quite possible that the apparent lack of cephalic appendages is due to the effect of the killing fluid.) Collected off N. Y. Point, Lake Mich.

FIG. 637. *Planaria simplex.* From preserved material. × 10. (After Woodworth.)

101 (84) Without eyes. . . . . *Planaria fuliginosus* Leidy 1851.
Length about 5 mm., breadth 4 mm. Body oval, dilated; inferiorly flat, superiorly moderately convex, fuliginous. Eyes none; in their ordinary position a slightly greater accumulation of black pigment upon the upper surface. Mouth a little posterior to the center-Esophagus simple. Rancocas Creek near Pemberton, New Jersey.

102 (83) Normal eyes many, arranged so as to suggest a coronet near the margin of truncated head and extending back near the lateral margins to a somewhat variable distance.
Polycelis.
Only one species known in this country.
Polycelis coronata (Girard) 1891.
Length 8 mm., breadth 2 mm. Color fuliginous or sooty, uniform, somewhat darker on the median dorsal region than on margins. Elongated lanceolate. Anterior margin truncated, weakly bilobed or undulating. The numerous eyes are arranged as a coronet or as an arc of a circle, the arrangement being dependent to some extent on size. Pharynx elongated, central. Collected near Fort Bridger, Wyoming. It is quite possible, as Hallez notes, that this is a synonym of the European *Polycelis nigra.*

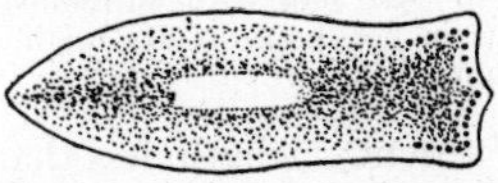

FIG. 638. *Polycelis coronata.* From life. × 5. (After Girard.)

103 (80) Pharynges numerous. . . . . *Phagocata.*
Only one species known in this country.
Phagocata gracilis (Haldeman) 1840.
This species was found and recorded by Haldeman; it was first adequately described by Leidy to whom it is ordinarily attributed.
Largest specimens 35 mm. long, 4.5 mm. wide. Color shiny black by reflected light, greenish-gray by transmitted light. Varies from black to a reddish-brown on one hand or to a light gray on the other. Small specimens at times almost milky-white. Ventral side lighter than dorsal. Lateral margins nearly parallel. Widest through pharyngeal region. Anteriorly sides converge slightly up to about the region of eyes where the diameter increases to form the head with its rounded cephalic appendages. Posteriorly sides converge to a point. Eyes two with elongated circum-ocular areas. The numerous pharyngeal tubes lie in a common chamber and open separately into the intestinal tract. When extruded they reach the exterior through a single orifice. Pools and rivulets, Mass., Penn., Ohio, Wis.

A

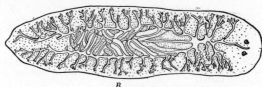

B

FIG. 639. *Phagocata gracilis.* (*A*) Living animal extended. × 4. (*B*) Partial reconstruction to show pharynges and their relation to the intestinal tract. × about 8. (After Woodworth.)

104 (79) Found in moist places on land. . . Suborder **Terricola** . . 105
The so-called land planarians are forms which in a biological sense stand very near the water-living species. They occur only in very moist localities and under circumstances may be taken for fresh-water forms. In general appearance they resemble minute, delicate slugs. When examined under the microscope the structure appears clearly to be that of a flatworm rather than of a mollusk. The few known species are widely and sparsely distributed. They

are likely to be transported in tropical or subtropical vegetation and to make their appearance suddenly and in considerable numbers in greenhouses or in moist shady nooks that have been planted with exotic species. Of one form indeed the proper habitat is not known. Walton has worked out a key and synopsis of the few species reported from North America and adjacent islands. In modified form this is followed here. Almost no records of the occurrence of these forms on this continent have been published, and their numbers as well as their range are sure to be considerably extended when attention is directed to them.

105 (110)   Eyes either absent or numerous; length more than 40 mm. . . .   106

106 (109)   Head anteriorly not broader than remainder of body.
                                        Family GEOPLANIDAE . .   107

107 (108)   Posterior part of head with eyes in two rows; sides margined with orange. . . . . . .   Geoplana nigrofusca (Darwin) 1844.
Length 50 mm.   Found in Mexico; reported also from South America.

108 (107)   Posterior part of head with eyes in one row; sides margined with light brown. . . . . . .   Geoplana stolli (von Graff) 1899.
Length 60 mm.   Thus far known only from a single specimen collected in Guatemala.

109 (106)   Head anteriorly broader than the body. . . . Family BIPALIDAE.
Only one species. . . . .   Placocephalus kewense (Moseley) 1878.

Color dorsally yellow or greenish-yellow with five dark violet longitudinal lines. Length 80 to 250 mm. An introduced species found in hot houses. Its original home is unknown.

FIG. 640.   *Placocephalus Kewense.*   Anterior end. × 1.   (After von Graff.)

110 (105)   Eyes two in number; ventral suckers absent; length less than 30 mm.   111
Rarely the eyes are apparently absent but even here they may be demonstrated in sections. Ventral suckers do occur in the related family Cotyplanidae. Known from Africa and New Zealand.

111 (114)   Eyes small, marginal sense organs present.
                                        Family RHYNCHODEMIDAE . .   112

112 (113)   Color dorsally light brown with two darker longitudinal stripes and transverse area at posterior two-thirds of body.
                                        Rhynchodemus sylvaticus (Leidy) 1851.

Length not over 10 mm. Common in places described by Leidy (1851) in Pennsylvania and rediscovered in Ohio by Walton (1904). Frequents under side of slightly decayed boards, sticks, etc., in company with snails, the young forms of which it closely resembles. Range, Eastern United States.

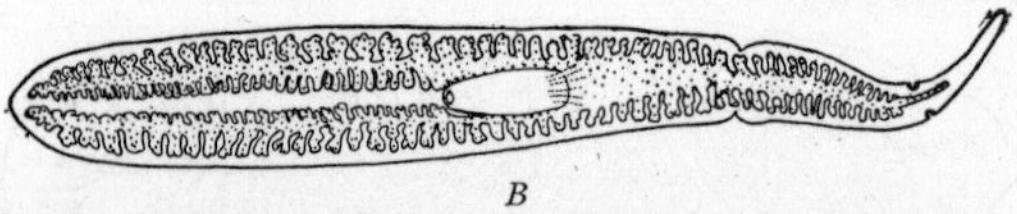

FIG. 641.   *Rhynchodemus sylvaticus.*   (A) Dorsal view of individual from Philadelphia, Pa.   × 5.   (B) Individual from Newport, R. I., showing arrangement of esophagus and structure of intestine.   × about 5.   (After Girard.)

113 (112)   Color dorsally uniformly dark blue.
                                        Rhynchodemus atrocyaneus Walton 1912.
Length 20 mm.   Only two specimens of this form have been reported.   Found at Gambier, Ohio, under decayed boards.

114 (111)   Eyes well developed; marginal sense organs absent.
                                        Amblyplana cockerelli von Graff 1899.
Color dorsally bluish-black with light yellow median stripe longitudinally and yellow "neck band." Length 17 mm. Represented only by two known specimens found in Jamaica.

The following is a list of those forms which are not sufficiently well known to be given their proper place in the key.

Order **Rhabdocoelida**

Section I HYSTEROPHORA

Family CATENULIDAE

Microstomum philadelphicum Leidy 1851

Microstomum variabile Leidy 1851

Section II LECITHOPHORA

Subsection LIPORHYNCHIA

Family TYPHLOPLANIDAE

Typhloplanid from Canandaigua Lake, N. Y., von Graff 1911

Typhloplanid from Irondequoit, N. Y., von Graff 1911

Mesostoma pattersoni Silliman 1885

Family DALYELLIDAE

Dalyellia bilineata (Woodworth) 1896

Dalyellia marginatum (Leidy) 1847

Derostoma elongatum Schmarda 1859

Subsection CALYPTORHYNCHIA

Rhynchoprobolus papillosus Schmarda 1859

The following Rhabdocoels are of very doubtful position and relationships

Vortex (?) *cavicolens* Packard 1883

Plagiostoma (?) *planum* Silliman 1885

Acmostomum crenulatum Schmarda 1859

Order **Tricladida**

Dendrocoelum sp. Pearl 1903

A brief description of these doubtful species will serve to promote their rediscovery and further study. Each description is taken from the original account of the species which is also the only record of it yet published.

Microstomum philadelphicum Leidy 1851.

Body linear, slightly attenuated posteriorly; head conoidal with the apex surmounted by a small oval papilla; tail obtusely rounded. Respiratory fovea subhemispherical, placed at the base of the cone of the head. Mouth oval, projectile; esophagus keg-shaped, intestine narrowed, cylindroid, dilated at the commencement. Colorless, translucent, ciliated, increasing by transverse segmentation, always observed in the process of forming two segments. Length 0.9 mm. Found in water of marshes and ditches near Philadelphia.

Microstomum variable Leidy 1851.

Body broad, linear; anteriorly and posteriorly obtusely rounded. Respiratory fovea longitudinally oval, lateral. Intestine very broad. Colorless, increasing by twos. Length from 0.3 to 1 mm. No nematocysts or rhabdites. Found with *Microstomum philadelphicum.* Also a chain of 4 individuals was collected in algae culture from shore, Charlevoix, Mich., by Dr. H. B. Ward.

Typhloplanid from Lake Canandaigua, N. Y., von Graff 1911.

Length 1 mm. Anterior end set off from the rest of the body by depressions at the sides, probably sensory pits. Broadest through middle of body which measures about one-fourth the length. Spindle-shaped rhabdites in glands and tracts of anterior end. Pigment is present in the form of large reddish-brown granules which mostly lie lengthwise of the body, sometimes branched, and enlarged at posterior end. The pigment forms a reticulation between and passes over the irregularly shaped eyes. Eyes twice as far apart as they are distant from the margin of the body. Pigment of eyes the same as that of the body, only much closer compacted so that they are deeper in color.

The mouth lies in the anterior third of the body. In the uncompressed animal the pharynx

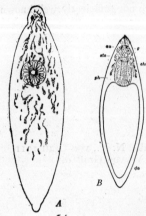

shows as a typical rosette-shaped pharynx. This form is unusual in that the rosette-shaped pharynx does not lead into the intestine from its ventral side, but opens into its anterior end so that when compressed its axis becomes directed forward. Intestine yellowish and extending almost to the posterior end, and having the general shape of the body.

FIG. 642. Typhloplanid from Lake Canandaigua, N. Y. (*A*) Swimming freely, showing the dorsal pigmentation. × 55. (*B*) Slightly compressed with pharynx directed forward. × 40. *au*, eyes; *da*, intestine; *ehv*, anterior branches of protonephridium; *g*, brain; *ph*, pharynx; *stz*, rhabdite glands. (After von Graff.)

Typhloplanid from Irondequoit, N. Y., von Graff 1911.

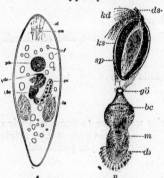

Length o.5 mm. Without pigment and color-less apart from the brownish-red eyes and the oil drops of the intestine. Eyes irregular in shape and almost twice as far from the side of the body as from each other. The mouth lies on the boundary between the first and second thirds of the body. The anterior end shows many tracts of rhabdites. Collected from a reedy swamp.

FIG. 643. Typhloplanid from Irondequoit, N. Y. (*A*) The animal slightly compressed. × 80. (*B*) Male copulatory organ. × 320. *au*, eye; *bc*, bursa copula-trix; *dr*, gland cells; *ds*, ductus seminalis; *f*, fat drops; *ge*, ovary; *gö*, genital pore; *kd*, granular glands; *ks*, granular secretion; *m*, muscles; *ph*, pharynx; *st*, tracts of rhabdites; *te*, testes. (After von Graff.)

Mesostoma pattersoni Schmarda 1885.

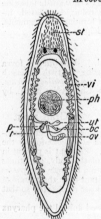

Length 3 to 3.5 mm., o.6 mm. broad through middle. Color in reflected light brownish except anterior to the eyes which appears grayish from the rhabdites. Intestine yellowish. Body fluid with many cells which contain granules. Eyes directly above the brain. Pharynx rosette-shaped, not far from middle of body.

FIG. 644. *Mesostoma pattersoni*. *st*, tracts of rhabdites; *ph*, pharynx; *vi*, yolk gland; *ut*, uterus; *bc*, bursa copulatrix; *ov*, ovary; *p*, cirrus; *t*, testes. × 20. (After Silliman.)

Dalyellia bilineata (Woodworth) 1896.

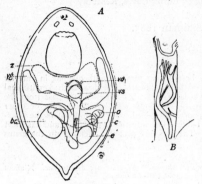

Length 0.96 mm., breadth 0.24–0.32 mm. Anterior end truncated, posterior end pointed. Pharynx dolioliform, in anterior third of body, traversed by two prominent, lateral, nearly longitudinal bands of light chocolate-brown, and numerous other pale indistinct longitudinal lines. Zoochlorellae in central part of the body, posterior fifth free from them, transparent-brown. Egg dark chocolate, 120 μ × 80 μ.

The figures given here are those which were in possession of Woodworth with the material when the description was written and the species named.

FIG. 645. *Dalyellia bilineata.* *A*, compressed. × about 50. *vd*, vas deferens; *vs*, vesicula seminalis; *o*, ovary; *c*, chitinous portion of cirrus; *e*, egg; *bc*, bursa copulatrix; *yg*, yolk gland. *B*, chitinous piece. × about 200. (Unpublished sketch by Ward.)

Dalyellia marginatum (Leidy) 1847.

Blackish, narrow lanceolate, anteriorly truncate; marginate margin delicately striate; mouth large; pharynx large and oblong; eyes two, anterior, distant, each consisting of two round masses of black pigment in contact with each other and of which one is larger than the other; generative orifice one-fourth the length of the body from the posterior extremity. Length 2 mm. A single specimen found in ditches near Philadelphia, Pa. Digestive cavity consists of a large capacious sac extending as far back as the posterior third of the body and

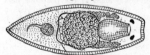

having a cecum upon each side of the proboscis. The cirrus has a yellow color and consists of a round granular mass with a moderately long and bent spiculum projecting from its posterior part. This is the form described by Leidy under the name *Prostoma marginatum.*

FIG. 646. *Dalyellia marginatum.* × about 20. (After Girard.)

Derostoma elongatum Schmarda 1859.

FIG. 647. *Derostoma elongatum.* × about 25. (After Schmarda.)

The body is long, ribbon-shaped, flattened. Posteriorly uniformly tapering. Color reddish-gray. Length 2 mm. Without eyes. Mouth opening elliptical. Pharynx long, cask-shaped. From brackish water in swamp, New Orleans, La.

Rhynchoprobolus papillosus Schmarda 1859.

FIG. 648. *Rhynchoprobolus papillosus.* × about 9. (After Schmarda.)

Body somewhat compressed, anteriorly rounded, posteriorly gradually tapering. Color clear yellow. Length 5 mm. Without eyes. Proboscis short, round, externally set with small papillae. Mouth opening central. Pharynx rosette-shaped. From brackish water, Hoboken, N. J.

Vortex (?) *cavicolens* Packard 1883.

Found in X cave, one of the Carter caves, Kentucky. Body flat, elongated, narrow lanceolate-oval, contracting in width much more than is usual in *Vortex* (Dalyellia). Pharynx is situated much farther back from anterior end of body than is usual in *Vortex*, being placed a little in front of the middle of the body; it is moderately long, being oval in outline. The body behind suddenly contracts just before the somewhat pointed end. The genital outlet is about one-half as wide as the pharynx and orbicular in outline. Apparently eyeless. White. Length 4 mm., breadth 1.5 mm. Brooks, Carter Caves, Kentucky.

Plagiostoma (?) *planum* Silliman 1885.

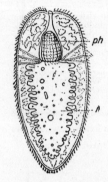

Length 1.5 mm., breadth 0.7 mm. Mouth opening in anterior end. Pharynx lies within a sheath and has both longitudinal and transverse muscle layers. Radial muscle fibers pass from the base of the pharynx to the body wall. Without eyes or other sense organs. The poorly developed brain lies in front of the pharynx as a transverse band. The intestine is capacious and has short lateral diverticula. This species probably belongs to the genus *Prorhynchus*.

FIG. 649. *Plagiostoma* (?) *planum*. *ph*, pharynx; *d*, intestine. X about 30. (After Silliman.)

Acmostomum crenulatum Schmarda 1859.

The body is cylindrical, yellowish, 1 mm. long. Pharynx cylindrical, protractile with six deep lobes on its margin. Otolith large and spherical contained within a transparent capsule which is located at the end of the first third of the body. The ovaries form a large spherical mass in the posterior part of the body. The cirrus is short knife-shaped and has a slight double curve. Found in brackish water, Hoboken, N. J.

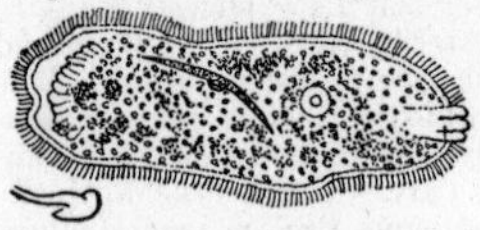

FIG. 650. *Acmostomum crenulatum*. From life. X about 30. (After Schmarda.)

Dendrocoelum sp. Pearl 1903.

Agrees with description of *Dendrocoelum lacteum*, except in respect to the color. Color ranges from a light grey to nearly black, and is uniform. Found about Ann Arbor, Mich.

IMPORTANT REFERENCES ON NORTH AMERICAN FRESH-WATER TURBELLARIA

GRAFF, L. VON. 1882. Monographie der Turbellarien. I Rhabdocoelida. Leipzig.

1904–1912. Bronn's Klassen und Ordnungen des Tierreichs. IV. Bd., Würmer: Vermes, Turbellaria, Acoela, and Rhabdocoela. Leipzig.

1911. Acoela, Rhabdocoela und Alloeocoela des Ostens der Vereinigten Staaten von Amerika. Zeitschr. f. wiss. Zool., 99 : 321–428. Taf. I–VI.

SILLIMAN, W. A. 1885. Beobachtungen über die Süsswasser-Turbelarien Nordamerikas. Zeitschr. f. wiss. Zool., 41 : 48–78; Taf. III, IV.

WOODWORTH, W. McM. 1897. Contributions to the Morphology of the Turbellaria II. On some Turbellaria from Illinois. Bulletin Mus. Comp. Zool. Harvard Coll., 31 : 1–16; 1 plate.

CHAPTER XIII

PARASITIC FLATWORMS

By HENRY B. WARD

Professor of Zoology in the University of Illinois

THE parasitic worms do not all belong to a single systematic division. Coming in many cases from widely separated groups, they often show much closer relationship to certain free-living forms than to each other. But because of a likeness in manner of life these forms were grouped together by early students of animal life as the Helminthes and in fact were long regarded as related by reason of similarities in appearance and habit. There are five such groups, usually ranked as classes; they are Trematoda or flukes, Cestoda or tapeworms, Nematoda or roundworms, Acanthocephala or proboscis-worms, and Gordiacea or hair-worms.

In any given host only a few parasitic species may be found or again the number of individuals and species of parasitic worms in a single host may be very large. I have taken 5000 flukes from a single fish (*Amia*), and even larger figures are recorded. At a given time the variety of species may be limited; yet as the kinds of parasites change with the food, the season, and the region, the total number found in a certain host may be very large; thus over one hundred species of parasitic worms are reported from man and thirty or forty from some well-known and widely-studied fish or aquatic birds. Some parasites are found in more than a single host species, a few infest a wide range of animals, and others occur in one host only; all in all, parasites are far more numerous than free-living animals both in number of individuals and of species.

The abundance of parasites varies greatly under different conditions of existence. Desert animals are not without them, but they are much more numerous and more varied in water-living animals than in hosts from any other habitat.

Representatives of some or all groups of parasites occur in the various aquatic vertebrates and invertebrates, and while in a certain sense they are not inhabitants of fresh water, they infest aquatic animals and their life histories form a part of aquatic biology. To be sure some species of parasites never come into contact with the external world but are transferred from host to host with the material in which they are living and others are entirely dependent upon terrestrial animals as hosts. Such parasites have no direct relation to fresh-water life and will be entirely omitted in the present discussion. However, in the large majority of parasitic forms the parasitic stage alternates with a longer or shorter non-parasitic period. During this period of free existence the species is a dweller in fresh waters alongside of their normal inhabitants, possessed of similar organs of locomotion and other adaptations to a free existence, often unrecognized in their true nature, and properly regarded as members of the shore or bottom fauna or plankton. This fact alone compels their consideration in any discussion of aquatic life.

Contrasted with this stage is the parasitic period which is more extended, usually embracing almost all of the life history. In it the worm remains with its host, dependent upon the latter for protection, locomotion, and subsistence, showing structural modifications which aid in maintaining this dependence and indicating by the absence of organs calculated to provide for successful independent activity the changes which the parasitic habit has induced in its original structure.

As already indicated most parasites show distinct adaptations to the conditions under which they live. To be sure some, such as certain small parasitic nematodes, are indistinguishable from their free-living relatives, but such instances are rare. The large majority have lost organs usually found in free forms and have gained structures of significance only for a parasitic existence. Furthermore, both loss and gain are relative and graded, rather than absolute and unrelated. Thus in some flukes the alimentary system is about as well developed as in the free-living Turbellaria, and of much the same type (*cf.* Figs. 678 and 639*B*); in other flukes the system is greatly reduced (*cf. Microphallus*, Fig. 697); and finally in the cestodes it is entirely lacking. The same conditions prevail in the threadworms. Most of the true Nematoda have a well-developed and functional digestive system; in Mermis the system is active during early life and becomes inert and degenerate in the adult stage. Finally in the Acanthocephala there is no trace of an alimentary system at any stage in the life-history. The gains are no less marked. Hold-fast organs, like suckers and hooks, enable the parasite to maintain its position against the constant and vigorous movements of the host. Such organs of similar structure appear in widely separated groups, *e.g.*, suckers in flukes and threadworms.

While these structural likenesses between parasitic worms of different groups are striking and important, they are in a real sense superficial and do not serve to conceal more than temporarily the fundamental differences in structure between the various groups.

The flatworms (Plathelminthes) are soft-bodied, usually elongate and somewhat flattened forms. In the phylum are included the free-living Turbellaria (Ch. XII) and Nemertina (Ch. XIV), as well as two classes of parasitic worms: the Trematoda or flukes, and the Cestoda or tapeworms. The other three classes of parasitic worms named previously are grouped together under the phylum Nemathelminthes or roundworms, which forms the topic of a separate chapter. The structure of each group will be discussed separately, but certain biological features are general enough to deserve brief mention first.

Aquatic animals possess some external parasites; among them the species of ectoparasitic flatworms, rare in fresh water, belong to a single subdivision of the flukes or Trematoda; all other flukes and the Cestoda which are all parasitic live as endoparasites in some part of the host organism where they find better protection than on the surface. The most common place of residence is the alimentary canal or its adnexa, air-bladder, lungs, liver, etc. Parasites occur regularly in the body cavity and other serous spaces, in the kidney and bladder, in the sex organs, in the heart and blood vessels, encysted in the skin, connective tissue and muscle, and finally in the nervous system, even entering the eye or brain and its cavities.

Parasites may be collected by opening an animal in a dissecting dish of suitable size and examining the contents of various organs. The parasites usually betray their presence by sluggish movements of the body which make even minute objects conspicuous in a mass of debris. A watchmaker's lens held in place at the eye by a spring is of service in recognizing and sorting out the smaller forms, and long bristles or a camel's hair pencil are useful in picking out the forms for study and preservation. Doubtful objects should be examined under a higher magnification whereupon the firm, definite outline of a parasite enables the student to distinguish it even when motionless from partly digested fragments of food, blood clots, or other foreign bodies of similar size and texture.

Parasitic flatworms may be kept some hours in weak normal salt solution for examination or even in tap water, but deteriorate so that for careful study material should be preserved as soon as possible. For preservation an aqueous solution of corrosive sublimate is most satisfactory, and the precise method of handling suggested by Looss gives results well worth the extra time and trouble because of the greater ease with which future work may be carried on. Because of the great similarity in external form between different types, a determination can be safely reached only after a worm has been stained and mounted in toto, or sectioned in case of large and opaque specimens.

The parasitic flatworms have received relatively little attention in North America; it is consequently a difficult matter to prepare a synopsis that is of value to the student, for from our knowledge of the group in other parts of the world it is safe to assert that the known forms do not constitute more than a small fraction of those that actually exist on this continent. Another difficulty which presents itself is the impossibility of defining clearly the limits of the topic. I have endeavored to include in the key all North American parasitic flatworms thus far recorded from fresh-water animals whenever the record permits of any reasonable interpretation. I have omitted a few records so brief or indefinite that a diagnosis was impossible. There is included also a considerable number of parasites from distinctly land animals, the life history of which is certainly bound up with stages parasitic in the fresh-water fauna. On the other hand I have omitted all clearly marine species and all from hosts commonly frequenting the sea and most likely to become infected there.

The parasitic flatworms fall readily into two great classes, the Trematoda or flukes and the Cestoda or tapeworms. Some authors would make a third intermediate group out of the few forms which are known as Cestodaria and resemble the flukes in having a simple body and the tapeworms in details of internal anatomy. In this work they are treated with the tapeworms. As apart from these few cases flukes and tapeworms can be fairly readily distinguished, it is advantageous for the student to have each group treated separately in a distinct section of the chapter; and to this treatment the following brief synopsis may serve as an introduction.

> Body soft, flattened, shaped more or less like a simple scale, leaf, band, or ribbon. . . . . Phylum Plathelminthes.

The external surface may have hooks, spines, or scales, or be provided with warts or rugosities, but it does not possess a tough, shiny, smooth, resistant cuticula. In a few cases the body is cylindrical, conical, or spindle-shaped and does not display the characteristic flattening mentioned in the key.

> Intestine present . . . . . . Class Trematoda . . page 369.
> Intestine absent . . . . Class Cestoda . . . . page 424.

Sometimes the intestine is so rudimentary or so thoroughly concealed by other organs that its presence is difficult to determine. It is, however, the only absolute diagnostic characteristic which in the last analysis separates a fluke from a tapeworm.

TREMATODA

The trematode or fluke is usually flattened, oval, seed-shaped, or rarely rodlike, attenuate, or globular in shape. With few exceptions one finds on the surface one or more cup-shaped suckers. The number and arrangement of these constitute a means of subdividing the group. Careful examination under magnification discloses pores or openings and also in some cases hooks or spines on the surface. Many of the flukes are transparent and permit the observer to identify the main internal organs.

The alimentary system which usually starts at the forward tip of the body or close to it and in the anterior or oral sucker is commonly shaped like a tuning fork (triclad). More rarely it is rodlike (rhabdocoel), or branching (dendritic). A sphincter, the pharynx, is ordinarily found on the esophagus and the true digestive region consists of the two branches, the ceca or crura, which vary greatly in length.

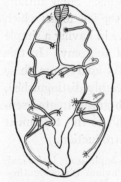

FIG. 651. *Microphallus opacus.* Excretory system, dorsal view. Reconstructed from series of transverse sections. × 30. (After Wright.)

The excretory system (Fig. 651) usually opens at the opposite end of the body, and is I-, Y-, or U-shaped. The main branches are distinct, containing in life a clear fluid with a slightly yellowish or bluish tinge. The finer branches can be traced only with difficulty. They terminate in the essential excretory elements known as "flame cells" which may be distinguished readily only in the living animals under high magnification. In the larger tubes one finds commonly highly refractive granules of excretory material.

Of the nervous system one can usually see irregular masses (ganglia) right and left of the alimentary canal, near its anterior end. They are joined to form a sort of collar around the esophagus, and from them nerves pass anteriad and posteriad throughout the body. Further details of structure can be followed only by special methods and in well-preserved specimens.

Special sense organs are not common. A few of the ectoparasitic trematodes, which are rare in fresh water, have pigmented eye-spots near the brain, and the free-swimming stages of endoparasites show similar structures which with rare exceptions are wanting in the adult internal parasites.

The reproductive system is the most conspicuous part of the worm but is exceedingly complicated and often difficult to follow. Yet it is the most important feature in the classification of the group. Most flukes are hermaphroditic, and contain complete organs of both sexes. The arrangement of these organs in a simple, typical case is given in the accompanying diagram (Fig. 652). In many species an enormous accumulation of eggs in the uterus

obscures all other structures in the body. The eggs are covered
with a firm chitinous shell which is often opaque but in other cases
is transparent enough to permit one
to follow the gradual development
of the enclosed embryo.

The development of most ectoparasitic trematodes is simple and
not different from that of free-living
flatworms. There emerges from the
egg-shell in due time a ciliated larva
which swims about in the water until
it finds a new host to which it
attaches itself. In endoparasitic
trematodes the life cycle is more
complicated in all cases and extremely involved in some. Only a
general outline of conditions can be
given here.

The eggs of the fluke reach the
external world in the feces or dis-
charges from the host. Within the
egg-shell is developed a minute
larva, the miracidium, evidently
adapted by its ciliated covering to
a free existence. Sooner or later the
egg arrives in water where the shell
opens and the larva escaping swims

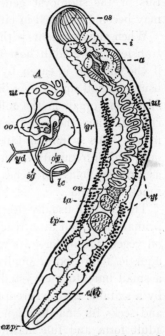

FIG. 652. *Azygia sebago.* Dorsal view. × 16.
A, female reproductive system in dorsal aspect.
Semi-diagrammatic to show relation of organs
to ovarian complex, ovary drawn in outline only.
Highly magnified. *a,* acetabulum; *exb,* excretory bladder; *exp,* excretory pore; *i,* intestine; *lc,* Laurer's canal; *oo,* ootype; *ov,* ovary;
sg, shell gland; *ta,* anterior testis; *tp,* posterior
testis; *ut,* uterus; *vt,* vitellaria; *yd,* yolk duct;
yr, yolk reservoir. (Original.)

about in search of a new host. The latter is not the species which
shelters the adult but an intermediate host which for almost all flukes
is a mollusk, in the tissues of which the miracidium changes to an
irregular sac (sporocyst); this produces within itself a new generation (redia) which also in this host produces a third generation
(cercaria). The miracidium possesses an eye-spot (not always
pigmented) and often a boring apparatus at the anterior end.
These structures are lost in the metamorphosis into a sporocyst,
a stage so simply constructed that the young rediae escape by the
rupture of the wall. A redia is characterized by the presence of a

rhabdocoel intestine with pharynx, an oral sucker, and usually a birth pore.   The redia generation may be repeated and either this or the sporocyst generation be eliminated, so that the cycle may become modified in either direction.

When development within the mollusk is completed and the transfer to the adult host takes place, the transfer may be direct if the mollusk is eaten by a suitable host.   Yet this is not the usual method since the ordinary cercaria possesses a well-developed swimming organ in the tail which characterizes this stage and is cast off when the larva reaches a new host or a place of encystment.   This swimming tail is reduced in a few types and wanting only very infrequently.   In other cases various modifications, such as bristles, folds, branches, lateral membranes, etc., increase its functional value.

The cercaria usually deserts the snail and actively seeks out its primary host, but after reaching the outer world it may also encyst on vegetation or force its way into a second intermediate host, an aquatic arthropod or small fish, and encyst there.   Here it rests, a small immature encysted distome, until the tissue is consumed by a suitable host, whereupon it is set free in the alimentary canal and seeks its final location to attain after a period of growth the adult form and full maturity.   Life histories are known among trematodes only in the most fragmentary way and the field offers inviting prospects to the student.

As appears from the account just given two free-living stages recur in the development of most flukes.   The miracidium normally depends on active migration through the water to reach and infect the secondary host.   In spite of the constant and abundant production of such larvae their occurrence in plankton or other fresh-water collections is not recorded.   This may be due to the extreme delicacy of the larvae which go to pieces almost as soon as collected.

When infected snails are kept in an aquarium, the cercariae swarm out at certain times in great numbers and can be seen swimming actively about in the water.   They conduct themselves under such circumstances like true plankton organisms: protozoa, rotifers, and entomostraca in the same aquarium.   Yet although such larvae are produced in great abundance and infected mollusks are also abundant and widely distributed, there are few records of cercariae in reports on aquatic life.

Leidy found cercariae free in the Delaware River and in a Wyoming pool. Wright discovered the remarkable anchor-tailed cercaria among weeds, and I have taken several forms including the striking *Cercaria gorgonocephala* in the tow with a plankton net. None the less among the fresh-water organisms that are least known one may well list the free-swimming stages of parasitic worms.

From this survey of the life history it is evident that the degree of trematode infection depends: first, on the presence of water at the time when the cercariae or miracidia swarm out; and second, on the occurrence of mollusks in the region to act as intermediate hosts. Hence flukes are rare in arid areas and also in regions lacking in lime where mollusks are all but wanting.

In general, infection is seasonal and may be traced to the climatic conditions because periods of excessive moisture permit the swarming of the larvae, whereas during dry months the egg-shells remain unbroken. The study of the adult parasites has shown that in most cases observed the flukes produce eggs continually and seem to display equal reproductive activity in all parts of the year. The number of flukes found in a given host does not appear to vary seasonally although it does vary widely in individual hosts.

The fishes, amphibians, reptiles, birds, and mammals that occur in and around various fresh-water bodies shelter a multitude of species of trematodes. The group has never been studied carefully on this continent and data available include mostly casual or fragmentary observations on a few of its members. Pratt made the first general list of these species. Since then a number of students of individual genera or groups of flukes have added to the count. Even this has only made a start at recording the North American species in the region which has been studied and one can hardly venture to predict the number of species in parts of the country where no collections at all have been made. The total trematode fauna of North America is greatly beyond any present records and cannot be estimated from the data at hand.

Even concerning the forms listed it must be confessed that our knowledge is very imperfect.

In preparing the key I have followed the plan so admirably formulated by Looss and worked out in various groups by Braun, Lühe, and Odhner. The data on larval forms (Cercariae) are adapted from Cort and Faust.

KEY TO NORTH AMERICAN FRESH–WATER TREMATODA

1 (169)   Adult forms; sex organs developed and functioning. 2

2 (28)   Posterior organs of attachment powerfully developed; those at anterior end absent or if present poorly developed and paired. Chitinous hooks and anchors almost always present.
Subclass **Monogenea** . . 3

Excretory pores anterior, double, dorsal; uterus short usually containing only a single egg. Development simple, direct. Most forms are ectoparasitic on body surface or gills. In fresh-water hosts found in urinary bladder (Amphibia) or respiratory passages (turtles).

3 (8)   Posterior organ single. Vagina unpaired. No genito-intestinal canal.
Order **Monopisthocotylea** Odhner . . 4

4 (5)   Two suckers at anterior end, entirely independent of the oral cavity. A single large posterior sucker.
Family TRISTOMIDAE van Beneden 1858.

Monogenetic, ectoparasitic trematodes with a single large round terminal sucker, often armed with hooks, and with two smaller yet conspicuous lateral suckers at the anterior end. Mouth ventral just behind anterior suckers. Many forms parasitic on gills of marine fishes; a few reach fresh water through the movements of migratory fish.

Only species reported from North America.
Nitzschia sturionis (Abildgaard) 1794.

Reported by Linton from gills of sturgeon (*Acipenser sturio*) at Woods Hole. May be carried at times into fresh water.

5 (4)   Anterior end expanded, bearing special structures of some sort and yet never true suckers alone.
Family GYRODACTYLIDAE van Beneden and Hesse 1863 . . 6

Small, slender, elongate trematodes with anterior end variably provided with specialized structures, only rarely true suckers and then associated with other special organs. Posterior disc without suckers, usually with two or four huge hooks in the center and a considerable number of small marginal hooklets.
On the skin and gills of fishes.
The genera reported from fresh water all fall in the section of the family in which the anterior end is provided with two or four retractile cephalic tips in which open ducts of numerous dermal glands.

6 (7)   Posterior disc with two large central hooks. No eyes.
Gyrodactylus von Nordmann 1832.

Anterior end provided with two lateral contractile lappets. Large central hooks of posterior disc turned ventrad, shaped like fish hooks and bound together at the roots by a special clamp piece. Marginal hooks sixteen, simple. Viviparous.
On skin and gills of many fresh-water fish, especially Cyprinidae. At times numerous enough to destroy the external dermal layer and leave the fin rays naked. May cause death of host.
Reported only twice in North America; from young lake trout in Maine and small-mouthed black bass, Ontario, Canada. Species uncertain. Cause of serious epidemic among young fish at hatchery (Craig Pond); also on wild fish in same stream.

7 (6)   Posterior disc with four large central hooks.   Two pairs of eyes.
Ancyrocephalus Creplin 1839.

Anterior end bluntly triangular with two inconspicuous lobes on each side, but no distinct cephalic lappets.   Posterior disc bears four large, heavy hooks and clamp, and fourteen or sixteen small marginal hooks of which two lie before and two behind the large hooks.   Oviparous.
On the gills of many fresh-water fish.
Two species, determination doubtful, reported by Cooper from Ontario, Canada.   On the gills of young black bass.   Also from rock bass and sunfish.

8 (3)   Posterior organs multiple (two to many parted).   Vagina double.
Genito-intestinal canal present.
Order **Polyopisthocotylea** Odhner . . 9

Suckers at anterior end, if present, open into oral cavity.   Posterior end with variable but well-developed organs of attachment consisting of hooks and suckers grouped on a terminal field or disc.

9 (12)   With two oral suckers and with genital hooks. 10

10 (11)   Posterior disc with eight, less often four (five) small peculiar sucking organs.
Family OCTOCOTYLIDAE van Beneden and Hesse 1863.

Elongate, flattened ectoparasitic trematodes.   The posterior organ of attachment has — usually in two parallel symmetrical rows — eight, more rarely four or six, small suckers braced with a characteristic chitinous framework or armed with hooks.   Extra hooks occur often on the disc.   Genital pore always armed with hooks.   Eggs supplied with one or two long filaments.   On gills of marine and fresh-water fishes.
These parasites are rare in fresh water yet no doubt other genera than the two cited here do occur.   The American representatives are not well known and only the first is more than an accidental member of the fresh-water fauna.   For this reason no effort has been made to incorporate them in the key.

Mazocraes Hermann 1782.

One species, formerly known as *Octobothrium sagittatum*, is reported by Wright from the sucker (*Catostomus teres*).

Plectanocotyle Diesing 1850.

Reported from the gills of *Roccus americanus* which enters fresh water to spawn so that this parasite may be taken at times in that habitat.

11 (10)   Posterior disc with a large number of small suckers.
Family MICROCOTYLIDAE Taschenberg 1879.

Elongate ectoparasitic trematodes with two small anterior suckers connected with the oral cavity and with the posterior end expanded into a foot-like region bearing a multitude of minute suckers.   Eggs with large filaments at both poles.
Body and posterior organ of attachment symmetrical.

Microcotyle van Beneden and Hesse 1863.

A genus parasitic on the gills of marine fishes.   G. A. and W. G. MacCallum report three species from the rock bass (*Roccus lineatus*) which ascends rivers along the Eastern Coast for spawning.   Hence these parasites might be taken in fresh water, though no record of such an occurrence has been found.

12 (9)   Anterior end pointed, without suckers or other special organs.
Family POLYSTOMIDAE van Beneden 1858 . .   13

Elongate, flattened monogenetic trematodes with simple anterior end, and with prominent adhesive disc at posterior end.   Posterior disc with hooks and either two or six large powerful suckers.   Mouth subterminal, intestine triclad, often dendritic, with anastomoses.   Male genital pore and uterine orifice median, ventral, postpharyngeal.
On body surface, gills, and in urinary bladder of amphibians; in pharynx and cloaca of reptiles.

13 (27)   Posterior disc with six suckers. **14**

14 (26)   Posterior disc terminal; suckers large.
                                            Polystoma Zeder 1800 . .   15

Six suckers in a circle or in two rows somewhat separated in the median line.   In the center of each sucker a small hook, and others on anterior and posterior margins of shield; between posterior acetabula two large hooks.   Vagina double, one pore on each side near the anterior end.   Eggs without polar filament.   Genital atrium with circle of hooks.

Several species in reptiles and amphibians.   Not common but widely distributed.   *P. integerrimum* Zeder, type of the genus, is not reported from North America.   American species worked out by Stunkard.

All North American forms fall in the section of the genus characterized by the presence of a short uterus containing a single egg; to these forms a new subgeneric name should be given.

Polystoma (*Polystomoides*) Ward.

15 (23)   Great hooks present on caudal disc and well developed.   16

16 (22)   Genital hooks of equal length. **17**

17 (18, 21)   Not more than 16 genital hooks.
                                P. (*Polystomoides*) *hassalli* Goto 1899.

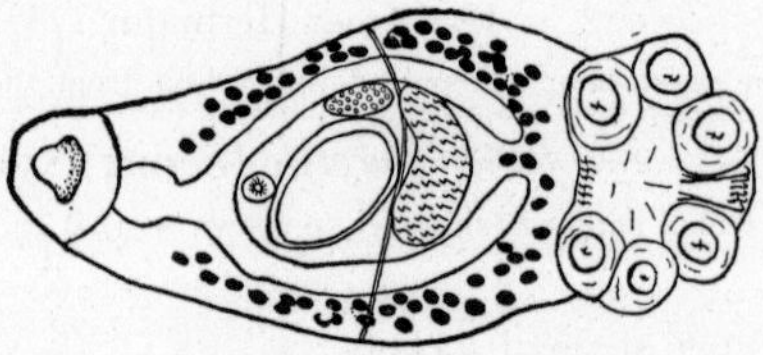

Length 1.3 to 2 mm.; width 0.4 to 0.65 mm. Caudal suckers 0.12 to 0.16 mm. in diameter. Caudal disc with 18 hooks, the largest 0.125 mm. and the smallest 0.033 mm. long.   Cirrus hooks 0.028 mm. long with a winglike process at the middle.   Uterus contains only a single large egg measuring 0.11 by 0.25 mm. to 0.18 by 34 mm.

Urinary bladder of *Cinosternum pennsylvanicum, Aromochelys carinatus, A. odoratus, Chelydra serpentina*; Maryland, North Carolina, Texas, Iowa.

Fig. 653.   *Polystoma hassalli.* Ventral view.   ✕ 18.
          (After Stunkard.)

18 (17, 21)   Genital hooks 32.   19

19 (20)   Acetabula large, adjacent, not contiguous; pharynx smaller than
          oral sucker. . .   *P.* (*Polystomoides*) *coronatum* Leidy 1888.

Body 3.15 by 0.83 mm.   Caudal suckers 0.37 mm. in diameter.   Caudal disc with one pair of great hooks, 0.132 mm. long, one pair of intermediate hooks, 0.051 mm. long, and small hooks, 0.02 mm. long.

From the common food terrapin (Leidy).

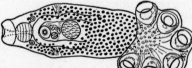

Fig. 654.   *Polystoma coronatum.* Ventral view.
          ✕ 9. (After Stunkard.)

20 (19) Acetabula small, widely separated; pharynx equal in size to oral
         sucker. . . . *P. (Polystomoides) microcotyle* Stunkard 1916.

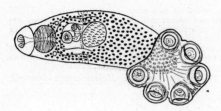

Body 3 by 0.78 mm. Caudal suckers
0.28 mm. in diameter. On caudal disc one
pair of great hooks, 0.116 mm. long, one
pair of intermediate hooks, 0.061 mm.
long, and small hooks, 0.017 mm. long.
Genital coronet of 32 equal and similar
hooks.

In mouth of *Chrysemys marginata*;
Creston, Iowa.

FIG. 655. *Polystoma microcotyle.* Ventral view.
X 9. (After Stunkard.)

21 (17, 18) Genital hooks more than 32 in number.
             P. (Polystomoides) megacotyle Stunkard 1916.

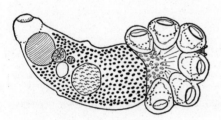

Body 2.5 to 2.7 by 0.71 to 0.78 mm.
Genital coronet 36 to 42 equal hooks.
Caudal suckers large, crowded. On caudal
disc one pair of great hooks, 0.116 mm.
long, one pair of intermediate hooks,
0.058 mm. long, and small hooks 0.017
mm. long.

From mouth cavity of *Chrysemys marginata*; Creston, Iowa.

FIG. 656. *Polystoma megacotyle.* Ventral view.
X 12. (After Stunkard.)

22 (16) Genital hooks unequal in length.
         P. (Polystomoides) oblongum Wright 1879.

Up to 2.5 mm. long and 1.5 mm. wide. Caudal suckers 0.2 mm. in diameter. Large hooks
on caudal disc 0.15 mm. and small hooks 0.015 mm. long. Genital coronet of 32 hooks, alternately large and small, with free end sharply curved.
From urinary bladder of *Aromochelys odoratus*; Canada.

23 (15) Great hooks of caudal disc reduced in size or absent. 24

24 (25) Genital hooks 16 in number.
         P. (Polystomoides) orbiculare Stunkard 1916.

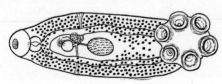

Length 2.7 to 3.7 mm.; width 0.9 to
1.2 mm. Caudal suckers 0.3 mm. in
diameter. On caudal disc only a single
minute hooklet 0.016 mm. long, in the
base of each sucker; no large hooks.
Genital coronet of 16 equal and similar
hooks. Egg spherical, 0.21 to 0.24 mm.
in diameter.

In urinary bladder of *Chrysemys marginata* and *Pseudemys scripta*; North
Carolina, Illinois, Iowa.

FIG. 657. *Polystoma orbiculare.* Extended. Ventral
view. X 10. (After Stunkard.)

25 (24)   Genital hooks 32 in number.

P. (*Polystomoides*) *opacum* Stunkard 1916.

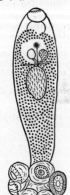

Length 3 to 4 mm., width 0.8 to 1 mm.   Caudal suckers 0.4 mm. in diameter.   On caudal disc many small hooklets 7 to 9 μ long, and one larger pair, 75 μ long; no great hooks present.   Genital coronet of 32 (33?) equal hooks.   Egg oval, 0.25 by 0.2 mm.

Vitellaria of large compact follicles under dorsal surface from pharynx to caudal disc except over ovarian complex; so extensively developed as to obscure internal organs and render body opaque.

In esophagus of *Trionyx ferox* and of *Malacoclemmys lesueurii*; Texas.

FIG. 658.   *Polystoma opacum.*   Extended.   Ventral view.   X 7.   (After
Stunkard.)

26 (14)   Posterior disc overhung by a flap bearing four hooks.

Diplobothrium F. S. Leuckart 1842.

Elongate, ectoparasitic trematodes with slender posterior end.   Six short stalked suckers arranged in two longitudinal rows and armed with chitinous hooks, stand just anterior to slender caudal tip which carries two hooks on each side.

One species (*D. armatum*) reported on the gills of the lake sturgeon (*Acipenser rubicundus*) from St. Lawrence River.

27 (13)   Posterior disc with two suckers. . . . . *Sphyranura* Wright 1879.

Caudal lamina considerably wider than slender body, with two immersed suckers, two large hooks behind them, and sixteen small hooks arranged seven along each side of the lamina and one in each sucker. Two contractile bladders anteriorly, each with a dorsal pore.   No lateral vaginae.   Oviparous.

Only species known.

Sphyranura osleri R. R. Wright 1879.

On the skin of *Necturus lateralis* in the Great Lakes region.   Corresponds to larval stage of *Polystoma* in having only two terminal suckers.

FIG. 659.   *Sphyranura osleri.*   Ventral surface.   X 20.   (After Wright and
MacCallum.)

28 (2) Organs of attachment one or two suckers of which the anterior is always single and median; without chitinous hooks or anchors; accessory suckers rare. Subclass **Digenea** . . 29

Excretory organs empty by a single pore at or near posterior end. Uterus usually long, containing masses of eggs, rarely only a few. Development complex, with alternation of hosts and most often also of generations.

With rare exceptions adults endoparasitic in visceral organs, usually alimentary system of vertebrates. Isolated adults occur in mollusks and insects which are the normal hosts for young stages.

For key to free living larval stages see section on Cercaria, 171 (170) in this key.

29 (30) Anterior sucker not perforate; mouth on mid-ventral surface; no oral or ventral suckers. . . Order **Gasterostomata** Odhner.

Pharynx and esophagus present. Intestine sacculate, simple. Vitellaria lateral in anterior region of body. Germ glands behind intestine, in posterior region. Testes two; cirrus elongate; pore ventral near posterior end. Ovary simple, opposite or in front of anterior testis.

Single family. . . . . BUCEPHALIDAE Poche 1907.
Only genus known. . . . . *Bucephalus* von Baer 1826.

Anterior end bears large sucker with ventral orifice and small muscular papillae at lateral angles.

The adult, better known as *Gasterostomum*, has been reported only from Canada though to judge from the abundance of the characteristic two-tailed cercaria it must occur frequently in other regions.

Stomach, intestine, and ceca of black bass and *Boleosoma nigrum*. Early stages encysted in young black bass, rock bass, perch, and minnow.

Cercariae parasitic in Unionidae, especially in sex organs. Pennsylvania, Illinois, Iowa, Canada. Not common; occurring in fifteen species of Unionidae out of forty-four examined; in susceptible hosts only 4 per cent of individuals affected (Kelly).

Representative North American species.
Bucephalus pusillus (Stafford 1904).

FIG. 660. *Bucephalus pusillus*. Ventral view. X 75. (After Cooper.)

30 (29) Mouth at or near anterior tip of body ordinarily surrounded by oral sucker; another sucker if present median, behind mouth on ventral surface or at posterior end.
Order **Prosostomata** Odhner . . 31

31 (36) Intestine simple, rhabdocoel; oral sucker very poorly developed; ventral sucking organ a powerful, conspicuous, adhesive disc or a series of smaller suckers.
Suborder **Aspidocotylea** Monticelli.

Terminal or subterminal mouth surrounded by funnel-shaped expansion of skin, but not by true sucker. Holdfast organs ventral, usually in form of large sucking disc distinctly set off from body and subdivided into numerous sucking alveoli, but never carrying chitinous hooks or anchors; or in place of disc single series of small disconnected suckers. Alimentary canal simple, rhabdocoel. Sexual organs simple. Development with or without alternation of hosts and generations. Endoparasitic, or rarely ectoparasitic, in mollusks and cold-blooded vertebrates.

Forms not numerous, little known, grouped together at present into a single family. . . ASPIDOGASTRIDAE Poche 1907 . . 32

32 (33)   Adhesive organ oval, composed of four rows of alveoli.

Aspidogaster von Baer 1826.

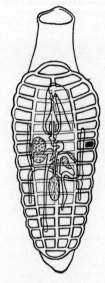

Ventral sucking disc large, equal in breadth and nearly so in length to entire body; oval in outline with four convergent longitudinal rows of quadrangular sucking grooves.   Margin notched, with sense organs.   Mouth terminal; intestine extending into posterior end. Sexual pore median; in depression between ventral shield and fore-body.   Ovary small; testis single, same size as ovary.   Uterus moderately long; ova large.   In fishes and mollusks.

Representative American species.

Aspidogaster conchicola von Baer 1826.

The common North American species in fresh water, *Aspidogaster conchicola* v. Baer, is also the most common parasite of the Union-idae.   From pericardial and renal cavities of various species of the group; St. Lawrence River; Havana, Illinois; North Judson, In- diana; Iowa; Pennsylvania.   Kelly reported thirty-seven cut of forty-four species of Unionidae and 41 per cent of the 1577 individuals examined were parasitized by this species.   Occasionally found in the intestine of various fishes into which it has been introduced when its proper host, the mussel, was taken as food.

FIG. 661. *Aspidogaster conchicola.*   Anterior end of ventral sucker as seen from below combined with genital system, partly diagrammatic.   Uterus and yolk follicles left out.   Est.   X 35.   (After Stafford.)

33 (32)   Adhesive disc oval, composed of three rows of alveoli. 34

34 (35)   Mouth subterminal, not surrounded by buccal disc.

Cotylaspis Leidy 1857.

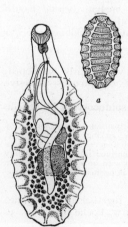

Ventral shield much as in *Aspidogaster*, save that the alveoli are in three longitudinal rows, the central alveoli being elongated transversely.   Marginal sense organs present, also two eyes. Ovary dextral, smaller than single testis in posterior end.   Ova not numerous, large.

Of several species known, *Cotylaspis insignis* Leidy 1857, is most frequent.   It is adherent to surface of host in angle between inner gill and visceral mass (Kelly); or branchial cavity (Leidy) of many species of Unionidae: Havana, Ill.; Grand Rapids, Mich.; Lake Chatauqua, N. Y.; Cedar River, Ia.; Schuylkill River, Penn.   Kelly examined over 1600 individuals of 44 species which belong in 24 separate host species and found 18 per cent infected.   The number in a single host is small.

Representative American species.

Cotylaspis cokeri Barker and Parsons 1914.

C. cokeri Barker and Parsons occurs in the intestine of *Malacoclemmys lesueurii.*

FIG. 662. *Cotylaspis cokeri* X 30. *a.* Ventral view of sucking disk X 15.

35 (34)   Mouth terminal, surrounded by expanded buccal disc.
Cotylogaster Monticelli 1892.

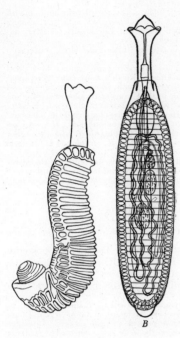

Ventral disc composed of single median row of grooves greatly elongated transversely and surrounded by marginal row of small, circular alveoli. Mouth in center of discoidal expansion of anterior tip of forebody. Long prepharynx and esophagus. Ovary and two testes just behind it form linear series posterior to center of body. Laurer's canal present. Embryo with large posterior sucker; development unknown.
Parasitic in intestine of fishes.

Single North American species.
Cotylogaster occidentalis Nickerson 1900.

In intestine of sheepshead (Aplodinotus grunniens), Minnesota. Rare.

Fig. 663. *Cotylogaster occidentalis.* *A.* Lateral view of an entire alcoholic specimen in which the anterior portion is retracted. × 8. *B.* Diagram showing relation of organs as seen from the dorsal side, the animal being represented as straightened horizontally with the dorsal cone projected backward. Magnified. (After Nickerson.)

B

36 (31)   Intestine forked; oral sucker distinctly developed; ventral sucker if present simple.   37

In one genus (*Cryptogonimus*) the ventral sucker consists of two small acetabula close together; in a few genera it is more or less intimately connected with a genital sucker surrounding the sexual pore, but in no case does it consist of a series of small sucking organs or have a complex, many-parted structure.

The forms embraced under this heading in the four suborders which follow, stand in sharp contrast with those of the suborder Aspidocotylea just preceding. In fact the latter are so distinct in general appearance, in structure, and in development, that they have regularly been grouped heretofore apart from the orders which follow. They were generally included under the Monogenea (p. 374) until Monticelli revived the original view that they should be regarded as an independent subdivision of equal rank intermediate between the Monogenea and the Digenea (p. 379). Their very recent inclusion in the latter group has been well justified; yet even with that the striking differences noted above must be kept clearly in mind.

The forms which follow fall naturally into four groups ranked here as suborders; they are easily distinguished by a single external feature, the adhesive apparatus, consisting of suckers which in number and arrangement are characteristic of each group. Thus the holostomes have in addition to the oral and ventral suckers a special adhesive organ behind the latter. This special organ is variable in form and character. In the amphistomes one finds an oral and a terminal sucker, but no other adhesive organs. The distomes possess an oral and a ventral sucker but none further back, while finally the monostomes have only one sucker and that is circumoral in location.

These long recognized groups are already beginning to break up under the influence of more careful study, and as noted in the next section steps have been taken to eliminate the monostomes as an independent subdivision, distributing its members among other groups.

37 (48) No ventral sucker present; oral sucker only adhesive organ present.
Suborder **Monostomata** Zeder . . 38

Endoparasitic trematodes with flattened body and single sucker which surrounds mouth at anterior end. Intestinal crura often unite in posterior end of body. Genital pore usually ventral or marginal in anterior region, or rarely median posterior. Life history relatively unknown. For developmental stages see 174 (183) in this key.

Forms not well known, though frequent especially in reptiles (turtles) and birds; rarely also mammals. North American records scanty.

Most of the forms described from this continent as "Monostomum" cannot be located except generally in this section since the data are lacking on which a more exact determination depends. It is indeed likely that some of them were wrongly placed in this group and more complete knowledge of their structure will result in their transfer to some other section. Until the specimens are restudied they must all be regarded as uncertain. Such doubtful forms are those listed as *Monostoma* sp. in Stiles and Hassall's Catalog (1904) and the following:

Monostoma affine Leidy from muskrat, *M. amiuri* Stafford from bullhead, *M. aspersum* Vaill of Pratt from salamander, *M. incommodum* Leidy from alligator (which later the author conjectured to be in fact a distome), *M. ornatum* Leidy from frog, *M. spatulatum* Leidy from "fish."

Odhner contends that the monostomes are isolated members of other groups that have lost all suckers save the oral and that they should be classed in the various families from which they have sprung. For practical reasons it will be necessary to retain the group at least until its forms are much better known.

38 (45) With two compact testes, and follicular vitellaria. 39

39 (44) Body elongated. Not parasitic in dermal cysts. ; 40

40 (41) Intestinal crura connected at posterior end. Testes near posterior
         end, within crura, asymmetrical. Ovary between testes,
         and intercecal but opposite to them.
         Family CYCLOCOELIDAE Kossack 1911.

Large monostomes with thick, muscular body, somewhat flattened. Esophagus short, no pharynx. (Kossack designates the structure which lies near the mouth as the pharynx; I have called it the oral sucker. He says these forms do not possess an oral sucker.) Intestinal

branches simple or with small ceca on the inner side connected at posterior end by continuous arch. Genital pore median, ventral to and near oral sucker. Receptaculum seminis and Laurer's canal wanting. Vitellaria well developed, lateral and sometimes dorsal to intestine; transverse duct just in front of posterior testis. Uterine coils numerous, regular, transverse, occupying space between posterior testis and fork of intestine. Eggs numerous, without polar filaments.

Air passages of water birds; frequently reported as in body cavity.

Only American genus. . . . *Cyclocoelum* Brandes 1892.

Intestinal crura simple, genital pore near sucker, or at anterior margin. Cirrus sac small, rarely extending beyond fork of intestine. Vitellaria extracecal from fork of intestine to posterior end, not continuous with opposite side. Reproductive glands in posterior region in arch of intestine at corners of triangle. Ovary smaller than testes, on side opposite them. Uterine coils do not extend laterad beyond the intestinal branches. Eggs thick-shelled, large.

The species designated by Leidy as "probably *Monostoma mutabile* Zeder" belongs here if his determination be accepted. It was collected from the gray snipe (*Gallinago wilsoni*).

FIG. 664. *Cyclocoelum mutabile.* × 3. (After Kossack.)

41 (40) Intestinal crura end blindly at posterior end. Testes symmetrical, in
         posterior region, outside of crura. Ovary intercecal, between
         testes. . . . Family NOTOCOTYLIDAE Lühe 1909 . . 42

Small monostomes with elongated flattened body tapering and rounded at both ends. On ventral surface several (3 to 5) rows of small excrescences or papillae with unicellular dermal glands. Esophagus short, no pharynx; intestinal ceca simple, long, not united in posterior region. Genital pore median, not far from oral sucker. Cirrus sac elongate enclosing only part of the convoluted seminal vesicle. Testes symmetrical, near posterior end, outside intestinal crura. Ovary between testes. Vitellaria lateral, anterior to testes. Uterine coils behind cirrus sac, transverse, regular, not extending outside intestinal crura. Eggs with long filaments at both poles.

42 (43) With conspicuous longitudinal rows of papillae on ventral surface.
Metraterm barely half as long as cirrus sac.
Notocotylus Diesing 1839.

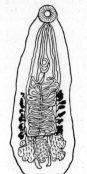

Body attenuated in front, broadly rounded behind. Ventral surface with three rows (in *N. quinqueserialis* with five rows) of glandular masses which open into protrusible grooves.
European species reported from cecum of water birds.

Representative American species.
Notocotylus quinqueserialis Barker and Laughlin 1911.

In North America one species; in the cecum of the muskrat. Nebraska, Michigan.

FIG. 665. *Notocotylus quinqueserialis.* Ventral view. Magnified. (After Barker and Laughlin.)

43 (42) Ventral rows of papillae poorly developed. Metraterm about equal in length to cirrus sac. . . . . . *Catatropis* Odhner 1905.
Body tapering only slightly, about equally rounded at both ends. Ventral surface with three rows of poorly developed gland masses; the middle row opens on a low keel or ridge; the lateral rows contain each eight to twelve small wart-like, non-retractile prominences. Metraterm well developed, as long as cirrus sac.
European species in cecum and rectum of water birds.

Representative American species.
Catatropis filamentis Barker 1915.
Only North American species; in the duodenum of the muskrat.

FIG. 666. *Catatropis filamentis.* Ventral view. Magnified. (After Barker.)

Nudocotyle novicia, very recently described by Barker from the muskrat, is placed in this family despite some striking morphological differences. The form is small (0.7 to 0.9 mm. long by 0.5 to 0.65 mm. wide), thick-bodied, and without ventral glands. The genital pore is lateral and well behind the middle of the body, being thus far removed from the intestinal bifurcation. The heavy pyriform cirrus pouch encloses part of the convoluted seminal vesicle. Vitellaria in compact masses lie extracecal and just behind the middle of the body. Transverse uterine coils extend over the intestinal crura nearly to the lateral margins of the body; they fill the anterior half and are limited posteriorly by the cirrus pouch and vitellaria. The eggs measure 20 to 24μ by 10 to 13μ and have long heavy polar filaments.
Parasitic in intestine of muskrat; Minnesota.

44 (39) Body compressed, broader than long. Parasitic in pairs in dermal cysts. . . . . Family COLLYRICLIDAE Ward.
Small to moderate sized monostomes with thick but not muscular body, smooth skin; oral sucker and pharynx present; ceca long, capacious, not united. Genital pore ventral near center of body; vitellaria follicular, scanty, antero-lateral. Ovary much lobed, asymmetrical. Testes oval, symmetrical behind ovary. Uterus in irregular coils showing a tendency to antero-posterior direction. Terminal region of uterus enlarged.
Parasitic in dermal cysts on abdominal surface. Usually two in each cyst. In birds.

Only American genus. . . . . *Collyriclum* Kossack 1911.
Submoderate sized trematodes with dorsally arched and ventrally flattened body. Oral sucker weak, pharynx small, intestinal crura simple, very broad. Genital pore median, just

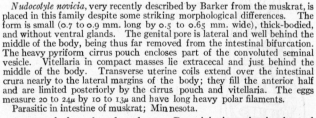

anterior to center. Vitellaria in seven symmetrical groups, marginal in anterior region. Testes symmetrical. Ovary in front, strongly lobed. Coils of uterus irregular, mostly lateral in posterior half of body. Eggs very small.

Representative American species. . . . . *Collyriclum colei* Ward.

The single European species, formerly known as *Monostoma faba*, was reported for North America as the cause of an epidemic among sparrows at Madison, Wisconsin. The life history is unknown; the supposition that avian insect parasites act as the intermediate host is extremely improbable. It attacks only young sparrows and infected birds are found only during or just after a wet period (Cole).

The parasite has been found again in Boston, Mass. These specimens differ clearly from the European form in numerous minor details, such as ovary, yolk glands, dermal spines, etc., and demand recognition as a distinct species under the name given here.

FIG. 667. *Collyriclum colei*. × 9. Detail of surface. × 105. (Original.)

45 (38)   With elongate tubular testes and vitellaria.
Family HERONIMIDAE Ward . . 46

Moderate sized monostomes with thick, elongate, soft body somewhat flattened, tapering both towards pointed anterior and bluntly rounded posterior end. Skin smooth. Oral sucker weak, pharynx large, esophagus short, ceca simple, extending to but not united at posterior end. Vitellaria compact, tubular, shaped like inverted V. Uterus in four longitudinal regions. Genital pore ventral to oral sucker near anterior tip. Testes tubular, lobed or with short branches, united into V-shaped organ with apex anteriad. Copulatory apparatus poorly developed.

Lungs of reptiles. Northern North America.

Two genera imperfectly known which may prove to belong in a single genus.

46 (47)   Vitellaria extend only half way from ovary, to posterior end. Seminal receptacle present. . . *Heronimus* MacCallum 1902.

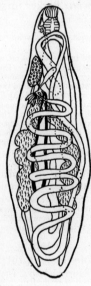

Oral sucker small, pharynx large, no esophagus, simple intestinal crura which reach the posterior end but do not unite. Ovary oval or bean-shaped, lateral in anterior third of body; receptaculum present but no Laurer's canal. Uterine loops intracecal; terminal section of uterus sacculate. Vitellaria small, elongate, not follicular, tubular (?). Genital pore ventral to oral sucker. Testes Y-shaped with coarse lobes, in median third of body, with median stem directed anteriad.

Only species known.
Heronimus chelydrae MacCallum 1902.

In lungs and air passages of river snapping turtle (*Chelydra serpentina*), Ontario, Canada.

FIG. 668. *Heronimus chelydrae*. From above, combined with dorsal view showing male genital apparatus. (Excretory vesicle not shown.) Magnified. (After MacCallum.)

47 (46) Vitellaria extend from ovary to posterior end of body. Seminal
receptacle absent. . . . *Aorchis* Barker and Parsons 1914.

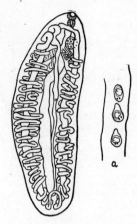

Oral sucker small, weak, pharynx large, esophagus short,
intestinal ceca long, not united at posterior end. Ovary entire,
just behind fork of intestine. Vitellaria compact, tubular,
coarsely lobed or with short irregular branches extending almost
entire length of body. Two divisions of uterus looped or coiled
around intestinal ceca. Other two divisions straight longitudinal tubes. Terminal division conspicuous, heavy, dark band
through length of the body in the median plane. Testes
elongate, tubular, irregularly lobed. Genital pore ventral,
near anterior tip of body. Eggs with short polar stalk at one
end.

Type species.
Aorchis extensus Barker and Parsons 1914.

Lungs of *Chrysemys marginata*, Mississippi River (Minnesota)
and also, in various turtles from Michigan, Indiana, Illinois,
Nebraska.

FIG. 669. *Aorchis extensus*. Only anterior portion of testes shown
in drawing. X 8. *a*, Embryos in uterus; note conspicuous eye spots.
X 22. (Original.)

48 (37) Ventral sucker present, usually single though varied in form and
position; never represented by numerous small organs in
series. 49

The acetabulum or ventral sucker proper is a closed organ, not possessing any inner opening
or connecting with any special organ or system. It may be so insignificant in size as to be
difficult to distinguish, in which case the form is erroneously diagnosed as a monostome as has
often occurred. On the other hand it may be as wide as the body or wider and so powerful
as to distort the form of the animal. It may be sessile or be borne on a stalk or peduncle.

In some species a special secondary sucking organ is developed around the genital orifice
and this may even become so highly differentiated as to exceed in size or include the true ventral sucker. Those forms which possess this highly developed adhesive organ ordinarily have
the body divided into two distinct regions.

In location the acetabulum is near the posterior end in the group of amphistomes and at or
anterior to the center of the body in the distomes and holostomes. The latter are readily
recognized by the peculiar adhesive organ and the separate regions of the body even though
the details of form are very variable in different genera.

49 (62) Acetabulum terminal or subterminal and posterior to the reproductive glands. . . . . Suborder **Amphistomata** Nitzsch.

Endoparasitic trematodes with oral opening anterior and terminal. Oral sucker powerful,
oval or more elongate, often with two dorso-lateral muscular pockets. Acetabulum conspicuous, much larger than oral sucker, at or very near posterior end. Body muscular, thick, little
flattened and often conical, tapering anteriad. Skin without spines but regularly provided
with sensory or glandular papillae. Excretory bladder sacculate, with median ventral pore
near posterior end. Genital pore ventral, median, in anterior region. Testes large anterior
to small ovary. Vitellaria follicular, lateral, paired. Uterus simple, with few coils. Eggs
numerous, small, plain. Development complex with alternation of generations and hosts.

Only family recognized.
PARAMPHISTOMIDAE Fischoeder 1901 . . 50

50 (61) Oral sucker terminal; acetabulum simple, not divided. 51

51 (52) No postero-lateral pockets on pharynx.
Subfamily PARAMPHISTOMINAE Fischoeder 1901.

None of these forms is parasitic as adults in aquatic animals. One species occurs in domestic ruminants in North America. The redia and cercaria develop in some fresh water snails as
is known of the related European forms. Compare 185 in this key.

52 (51) Postero-lateral pockets present on pharynx. 53

53 (56) Testes two, more or less deeply lobed.
                Subfamily CLADORCHIINAE Fischoeder 1901 . . 54

Amphistomes with more or less strongly flattened body, and with acetabulum usually conspicuously ventral, rarely only terminal. Testes branching or lobed. Cirrus sac incomplete or nearly wanting.

In this subfamily belongs possibly the "*Amphistoma grande* Diesing" of Leidy from the terrapin which does not seem to conform to the species designated. The description is inadequate for a final diagnosis.

54 (55) Pharyngeal pockets small, not affecting external boundary of oral
        sucker. . . . . *Stichorchis* Fischoeder 1901.

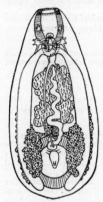

Body noticeably attenuated anteriorly, broadly rounded posteriorly. Margins rounded, dorsal surface high, arched, ventral flattened. Acetabulum ventral. Pharynx lacking; crura not much separated from lateral margins. Cirrus sac small, genital sucker not conspicuous. Vitellaria well developed, mostly behind testes and median to crura, as well as partly dorsal and ventral to same.

North American species.
      Stichorchis subtriquetrus (Rudolphi) 1814.

One species, *St. subtriquetrus*, the true *Amphistoma subtriquetrum* Rud. In intestine of the beaver; Quebec, Ontario.

FIG. 670. *Stichorchis subtriquetrus.* Dorsal view to show arrangement of parts. Magnified. (After Duff.)

55 (54) Pharyngeal pockets large, conspicuous, modifying greatly outline of
        oral sucker. . . . . . . *Wardius* Barker and East 1915.

Moderate sized amphistomes with prominent pharyngeal pockets, and large subterminal sucker. Esophagus well developed, without differentiated regions; crura long and wavy. Testes slightly lobed, tandem, in center of body. Ovary median, behind testes near posterior sucker. Genital pore posterior to bifurcation of intestine. Vitellaria extend outside crura from oral to posterior sucker.

Only one species.
      Wardius zibethicus Barker and East 1915.

In cecum of muskrat. Regarded by these authors as the "*Amphistomum subtriquetrum* Diesing" of Leidy (1888).

FIG. 671. *Wardius zibethicus.* Ventral view, specimen compressed. Magnified. (After Barker.)

56 (53) One or two testes, spherical. 57

PARASITIC FLATWORMS

387

57 (58) Vitellaria consist of few large follicles or form paired compact organ. No cirrus sac. . . Subfamily DIPLODISCINAE Cohn 1904.

Moderate sized amphistomes with conical body, round in transsection, attenuated anteriorly. Terminal sucker very large. Intestinal crura extend to terminal sucker, relatively broad. Vitellaria a few large follicles on each side which may be condensed into a more or less compact but lobed organ. In alimentary canal of Amphibia and Reptilia.

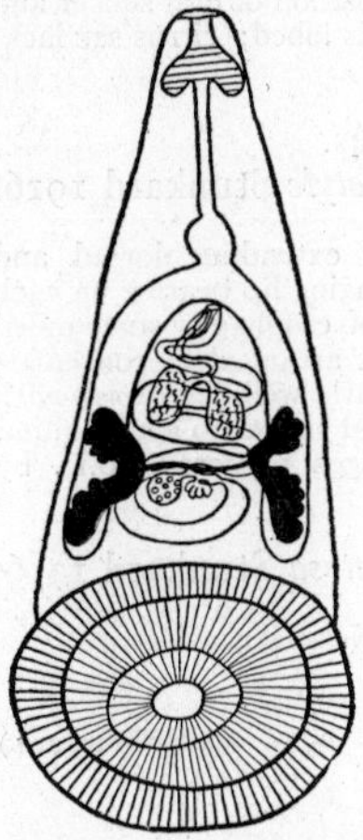

Only North American genus.

Diplodiscus Diesing 1836.

Two testes confluent in older specimens. Genital pore near oral opening. Esophagus long, pharynx-like enlargement at bifurcation of intestine, not sharply marked off. Excretory vessels looped into coils, some above and some below intestine.

Only North American species.

Diplodiscus temperatus Stafford 1905.

Rectum of various frogs. Canada, Pennsylvania, Indiana, Nebraska, Minnesota.

FIG. 672. *Diplodiscus temperatus*. Adult worm somewhat contracted, drawn from the ventral side as a transparent object. Magnified. (After Cary.)

58 (57) Vitellaria consist of small scattered lateral follicles. Cirrus sac present. . . . Subfamily SCHIZAMPHISTOMINAE Looss 1912. Representative North American genus.

Allassostoma Stunkard 1916 . . 59

Large oral invaginations open independently into oral sucker; no preoral sphincter; esophageal bulb composed of concentric muscle lamellae. Hermaphroditic duct present. Germ glands median, near center of body. Both testes anterior to ovary. Vitellaria consist of small scattered lateral follicles, in posterior region with median follicles also. Laurer's canal opens in mid-dorsal line anterior to excretory pore.

59 (60) Large worm (over 10 mm. long) with small suckers.

Allassostoma magnum Stunkard 1916.

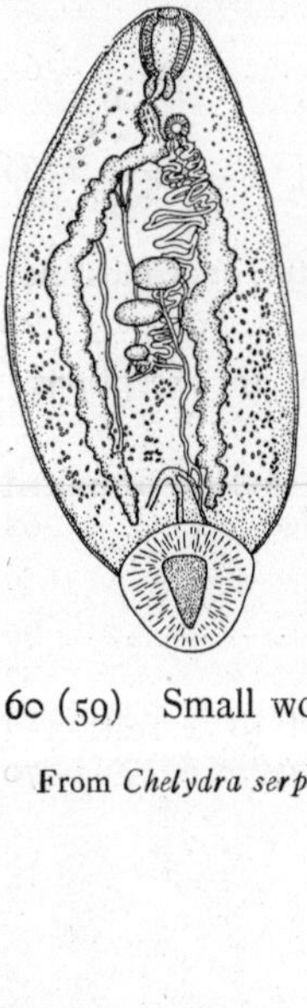

Length 10 to 12 mm., breadth 3 to 5 mm., thickness 1.5 to 2 mm. Living worm clear, slow-moving, capable of great extension. Acetabulum sub-terminal, ovoid, wider anteriad, 2 to 2.5 mm. long by 2 mm. wide. Oral sucker terminal, 0.9 to 1.35 mm. long by 0.6 to 0.9 mm. wide; oral pockets arise at posterior end of oral sucker by separate lateral openings and extend dorsad and caudad.

Testes oval, 0.27 to 0.35 by 0.45 to 0.9 mm., long axis transverse, located near center of body and slightly oblique. Ovary median, spherical or oval, 0.28 to 0.35 by 0.33 to 0.57 mm. in diameter. Vitelline follicles small, sparse, anteriorly extracecal, but posteriorly also intracecal. No receptaculum seminis and no vitelline reservoir. Eggs 0.1 by 0.13 mm.

In intestine of *Pseudemys;* Illinois, Missouri.

FIG. 673. *Allassostoma magnum*. Ventral view. X 2. (After Stunkard.)

60 (59) Small worm (length about 3 mm. or less) with large suckers.

Allassostoma parvum Stunkard 1916.

From *Chelydra serpentina;* Urbana, Ill.

61 (50)   Oral sucker, subterminal; acetabulum divided by transverse ridge
into two pockets. . . .   Subfamily ZYGOCOTYLINAE Ward.

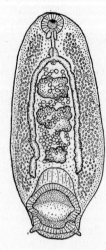

Differs from all other subfamilies in position of oral sucker and
peculiar character of acetabulum.   Testis lobed; [cirrus sac lacking.

Representative American genus.
Zygocotyle Stunkard 1916.

Acetabulum consists of anterior part extending dorsad and
anteriad into body, and posterior overhanging lip bearing on each
side conical projection.   Posterior end of esophagus surrounded
by muscular bulb in which fibers are not arranged in concentric
lamellae as in other amphistomes.   Vitellaria well developed, with
large follicles, in extracecal region from oral sucker to acetabulum.
Uterus and germ glands intracecal.   Eggs numerous, 0.14 by
0.083 mm.

Type species. . . Zygocotyle ceratosa Stunkard 1916.

From intestine of Anas platyrhynchos; Nebraska.

FIG. 674. Zygocotyle ceratosa. Ventral view. × 5. (After Stunkard.)

62 (49)   Acetabulum conspicuously ventral and usually anterior to center of
body.   Reproductive organs completely or largely posterior
to acetabulum. 63

63 (160) No holdfast organs present except oral and ventral suckers.   No
sharp separation between anterior region with holdfast
organs and posterior region with genital organs.
Suborder **Distomata** . . 64

64 (159) Hermaphroditic distomes. 65

65 (148) Ovary anterior to testes. 66

66 (107) Coils of uterus do not extend posteriad beyond testes, or at most not
beyond the posterior testis. 67

Bunodera (103 in this key) and Cryptogonimus (106) are exceptions.

67 (106) Acetabulum a single typical sucker which may be stalked or united
with special genital sucker but is not divided. 68

68 (105) Not more than two testes present. 69

69 (74)   Both ovary and testes dendritic; uterus limited to a restricted
area. 70

70 (73) Large flattened distomes; ovary and testes both highly branched; uterus median, a short series of transverse coils.

Family FASCIOLIDAE Railliet 1895.

Large distomes with muscular, more or less broad and flattened leaf-shaped body. Ventral sucker powerful, close to anterior end. Intestinal crura extend to posteror end. Excretory bladder tubular, extends anteriad beyond testes. Genital pore median, at anterior margin of acetabulum. Cirrus and cirrus sac well developed. Ovary lateral, in front of acetabulum, testes symmetrical, postacetabular. Vitellaria extensive, reaching posterior end. Uterus short, in condensed coil, entirely preovarian. Eggs very large, thin shelled, in moderate numbers. Development with alternation of hosts and generations.
Parasites in intestine and gall ducts of Mammalia.

Reported in North America.

Subfamily FASCIOLINAE Stiles and Hassall 1898 . . 71

71 (72) Anterior tip distinctly set off from main body; vitellaria both dorsal and ventral to intestinal branches. *Fasciola* Linnaeus 1758.

Very large distomes with leaf-shaped body having so-called "cephalic cone" set off at anterior end, and pointed posterior end. Skin spinous. Acetabulum large, at junction of cephalic cone and main body. Esophagus short, with pharynx and prepharynx. Intestinal crura near median line, extend to posterior end, provided on mesial aspect with short branches and on outer side with long branches which again may be branched. Uterus in front of acetabulum, forming a rosette. Vitellaria richly developed in lateral area, and in posterior region also on both surfaces of body. In the gall passages of herbivores, very rarely in man.

Type species. . . . *Fasciola hepatica* Linnaeus 1758.

An introduced species (*F. hepatica*) common in sheep and cattle in limited regions; Long Island, N. Y., introduced from Texas, Gulf States, California. The North American intermediate host is not known. Stiles suspects *Limnaea humilis* Say.

FIG. 675. *Fasciola hepatica.* × 3. (Original.)

72 (71) No distinct anterior conical portion. Vitellaria ventral to intestinal branches. . . . . *Fascioloides* Ward.

Body very large, broad, thick, without separate anterior portion or cephalic cone, posterior end bluntly rounded. Vitellaria confined to region ventral to intestinal branches.

Type species. . . . . *Fascioloides magna* (Bassi) 1875.

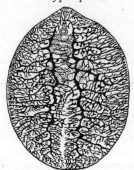

In liver and lungs of North American herbivores both domestic and wild; usually included in former genus. On the advice of Odhner a new genus is made for the North American form. First discovered in a European zoological garden parasitic in the wapiti, it is known to occur in many hosts and to be widely distributed from Maine to California. It is especially abundant in parts of the South. Egg and embryo are said by Stiles to agree with those of the last species.

FIG. 676. *Fascioloides magna.* Intestinal crura and branches drawn as solid black lines. Natural size. (Original.)

Another genus, *Fasciolopsis*, common as a parasite of man in some parts of the East, has been reported in North America a few times as a human parasite. Apparently all these cases have been imported and the parasite has not so far as known gained a foothold on this continent.

73 (70) Distomes moderate in size, thick bodied; ovary and testes lobed
         or coarsely branched; uterine coil chiefly lateral to acetab-
         ulum. . . . . Family TROGLOTREMATIDAE Odhner 1914.

Distomes of small to moderate size with compressed body. Skin with spines in groups.
Ventral surface flat, dorsal arched. Musculature and suckers poorly developed. Intestinal
crura do not reach posterior end. Excretory bladder Y-shaped, or tubular. Genital pore
close to acetabulum. Cirrus sac lacking. Testes symmetrical, postacetabular. Ovary
dextral, immediately in front of testes, lobed or branched. Laurer's canal present. Vitellaria very extensive, covering dorsal surface save for narrow median strip. Uterus long, in
open loops, or shorter in tight coil; eggs in first case small, in second moderately large.
    Parasites of birds and carnivores, living usually by pairs in cyst-like cavities.
    The monostome, *Collyriclum colei*,(p. 384), is regarded by Odhner as properly a member of
this family.

        Only American genus. . . . . . . *Paragonimus* M. Braun 1899.

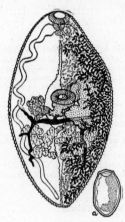

Body opaque, thick, nearly rounded in cross section. Skin
with spines. Pharynx almost spherical, crura wavy with irregular
walls. Testes lobed, symmetrical, in hindbody. Ovary lobed,
lateral, pretesticular, and postacetabular. Vitellaria extend entire length of body, lateral and dorsal. Laurer's canal and
rudimentary receptaculum present. Uterus in coil, postacetabular, opposite ovary. Eggs large, thin-shelled, laid before cleavage begins.
    Encysted, in pairs usually, in lungs of mammals.

    Single American species.
              Paragonimus kellicotti Ward 1908.

    Parasitic in dog, cat, and pig. Ohio, Illinois, Wisconsin,
Minnesota, Kentucky. Confused in records with the human
lung fluke (*P. westermanii* Kerbert) which has been positively
determined in North America only in a few human cases, all of
which are probably imported from Asia.

    FIG. 677. *Paragonimus kellicotti.* Total preparation, ventral surface.
The vitellaria are represented on the left side and omitted on the other
side in order to show ovary, testis, vitelline ducts and intestine normally
obscured by them. × 3.8. *a*, egg from same specimen. × 150.
(After Ward and Hirsch.)

74 (69) Ovary and testes entire or lobed but not dendritic. 75

75 (82) Oral sucker surrounded by a reniform collar open ventrally and
         bearing a series of strong spines.
                    Family ECHINOSTOMIDAE Looss 1902 . . 76

    Elongate distomes, very variable in size. Acetabulum powerful, close to anterior end.
Oral sucker small, weak or degenerate; anterior end surrounded laterally and dorsally by
skin fold or "collar" which carries large spines ("spikes") definite in number and arrangement. "Corner spines" on ventro-median lobe usually differ from others, *i.e.*, "marginal
spines." Skin in anterior region at least richly provided with fine dermal spines. Pharynx
and esophagus present; intestinal crura extend almost to posterior tip. Excretory bladder
Y-shaped with numerous lateral branches. Genital pore median, near acetabulum or between
it and fork of intestine. Cirrus and cirrus sac well developed. Germ glands postacetabular,
usually median; ovary pretesticular, sometimes lateral. Vitellaria lateral, well developed,
reaching posterior end. Uterus between ovary and acetabulum, with scanty lateral loops,
or none. Laurer's canal present, receptaculum seminis absent. Eggs large, thin shelled, not
numerous. Development with alternation of hosts and generations. For characteristic
cercariae see 224 (220) in this key.
    Parasites of intestine, rarely of gall ducts, in mammals and birds.

76 (81) With well-developed oral sucker. Parasitic in intestine. . . . 77

77 (80) Anterior region not enlarged. Spines in a double row. 78

78 (79) · Uterus long and much coiled. . . . . *Echinostoma* Rudolphi 1809.

Echinostomes of moderate size with elongate body. Collar with double unbroken row of spines. Oral and ventral suckers close together. Cirrus sac reaches ordinarily center of acetabulum. Cirrus long, not spinous, when contracted it lies in coil. Vesicula seminalis twisted, not bipartite. Pars prostatica present. Vitellaria lateral, posttesticular, extending in places towards median line. Uterus long, much coiled. Eggs large.

A mixed group of unplaced and unrelated species, many of which are not well enough known to determine their true place in the family. Several uncertain North American species are reported under this generic name from chickens (Hassall), and muskrat (Leidy). Some forms from the muskrat are more perfectly described by Barker *et alii.*

79 (78) Uterus short, coils few, open. . . . *Echinopharyphium* Dietz 1909.

Small echinostomes, slender. Much like last genus except in absence of pars prostatica. Cirrus sac long, often extending dorsad, or posteriad to center of acetabulum. Uterus short; eggs not numerous, large.

The placing of *Distomum flexum* Linton from the black scoter (Yellowstone Lake) in this genus is probably correct. Another species has been reported by Barker and Bastion from the muskrat.

80 (77) Spines in a single row. Subfamily ECHINOCHASMINAE Odhner 1910.

Spines in a single row interrupted at the mid-dorsal line, with 20 to 26 spines only. Cirrus sac when present pyriform, not projecting behind the center of the acetabulum. Vesicula seminalis not coiled, distinctly bipartite.

Several genera common in Europe.

Only genus yet recorded from North America.
Stephanoprora Odhner 1902.

Small, elongate echinostomes. Cirrus sac well developed, cirrus short but muscular, often apparently entirely preacetabular. Testes median, close together, in posterior half of body. Vitellaria lateral, never preacetabular, often nearly confluent along median line. Uterus not long; eggs of moderate size.

Representative American species.
Stephanoprora gilberti Ward.

The species reported by Gilbert from the loon (*Gavia immer*) and from Bonaparte's gull (*Larus philadelphia*) near Ann Arbor, Michigan, probably belongs to this genus. It cannot be *Echinostoma spinulosum* Rud., as designated.

FIG. 678. *Stephanoprora gilberti.* × 7α (Original.)

81 (76) Oral sucker degenerate. Parasitic in gall ducts.
Pegosomum Rátz 1903.

Echinostomes of moderate size with lance-shaped muscular body. Collar poorly developed, with single row of blunt spines. Skin spinous. Oral sucker entirely degenerate. Pharynx present. Fork of intestine not near acetabulum which is powerful and near center of body. Cirrus sac large, mostly preacetabular. Testes median, in posterior half of body. Ovary dextral, postacetabular and pretesticular. Vitellaria from pharynx to posterior end, confluent in median line, only in front of genital pore. Uterus short. Eggs large, not numerous.

In gall ducts of Ardeidae. Only one species reported from North America as *Distomum asperum* Wright from *Ardea minor.*

82 (75) Oral sucker without collar and spines. 83

A condition not represented in the key is found in the ACANTHOCHASMIDAE where the large funnel-shaped oral sucker opens at the anterior tip and is surrounded by a crown of prominent spines. *Acanthochasmus coronarium* (Cobbold) was taken from the alimentary canal of an *Alligator mississipiensis* that died in England. According to Odhner *Cryptogonimus* and *Caecincola* are members of this family which have lost the crown of spines. *Deropristis* may also be related to it.

83 (94) Genital glands median in linear series in posterior region of body. 84

84 (91)   Uterus between ovary and acetabulum, possessing an ascending ramus only. Testes ordinarily behind ovary and close to it, or rarely (*Leuceruthrus*) near acetabulum and separated from ovary by coils of uterus. 85

In *Deropristis hispida*, a peculiar distome found in *Acipenser* in Europe and reported once by Stafford in the lake sturgeon from Canada the arrangement of the germ glands differs from either plan noted in the key line above. Two oval testes are median in posterior end; median ovary lies near large receptaculum, separated from acetabulum and testes by about equal distances which are filled by uterine coils. Uterus has short descending ramus which extends posteriad from ovarian complex to anterior testis, and long ascending ramus from this point to genital pore on median anterior margin of acetabulum. Vitellaria are extracecal, in uterine region. Cirrus sac and seminal vesicle, nearly median and postacetabular, are both well developed, but rather distinctly separated. The relationship of the genus is not clear and the American record needs confirmation, hence this form is not included in the key.

85 (88)   Body muscular; cirrus sac present.

                                    Family AZYGIIDAE Odhner 1911 . . 86

Infra-medium to large distomes. More or less elongate, flattened, with thick, muscular body. Suckers powerfully developed. Skin smooth, on contraction drawn into irregular transverse folds. No prepharynx. Pharynx powerful, esophagus very short, intestinal crura reach posterior end. Excretory bladder Y-shaped with very long branches reaching even to anterior end. Genital pore median, in front of and above acetabulum; genital sinus spacious. Uterus with ascending limb alone, extending direct from ovary to genital pore in closely laid transverse loops. Laurer's canal present; receptaculum seminis wanting. Vitellaria follicular, lateral, extracecal, not reaching to posterior end. Eggs 45 to 85 μ long, with cap; when deposited they contain each a ripe embryo, regularly nonciliated.

Stomach parasites of fishes.

86 (87)   Germ glands form series in posterior region; ovary anterior, not far separated from testes. . . . .   *Azygia* Looss 1899.

Distomes of moderate size or larger, with slightly flattened, much elongate, nearly cylindrical muscular body, rounded at both ends (Fig. 652). Genital pore close to acetabulum. Cirrus sac present. Seminal vesicle long and coiled. Uterus intercecal, in center third of body. Vitellaria extend at least between acetabulum and posterior testes. Ovary and testes behind middle of body. Main stem of excretory bladder splits behind testes; lateral branches do not unite in anterior region. Eggs 45 by 21 μ with thin shell and albumen covering.

Azygia is a powerfully muscular type and is usually much distorted in the process of preservation so that a lot of specimens taken from the same host at the same time present marked external differences in the preserved condition. Such extreme specimens have been the basis for various new genera, *e.g.*, *Megadistomum* of Leidy and Stafford, *Mimodistomum* of Leidy und *Hassallius* of Goldberger. The same factor has led to the separation of too many as species.

Despite many records of its occurrence the common European *A. lucii* (= *A. tereticolle*) has not been found in North America. Several species peculiar to this continent occur in *Amia calva*, *Micropterus salmoides* and *dolomieu*, *Esox lucius* and *reticulatus*, *Ambloplites rupestris*, *Salvelinus namaycush*, *Lucioperca*, *Lota lota*, *Salmo sebago*. Maine, St. Lawrence, Great Lakes, Wisconsin.

87 (86)   Testes just behind acetabulum, separated from ovary by coils of uterus. . . . .   *Leuceruthrus* Marshall and Gilbert 1905.

Anterior end rounded, posterior end pointed. Oral sucker ventral, prominent, acetabulum one-half as large. Intestinal crura slender, straight, extending nearly to posterior end. Excretory vesicle forking at ovary. Testes small, postacetabular, oblique to each other. Uterus at first confined to area between intestinal crura, ovary and testes, later filling posterior three-fourths of body. Vitellaria lateral, in posterior half of body. Laurer's canal present.

One species known (*L. micropteri*) from mouth and stomach of black bass and bowfin in Wisconsin and Indiana.

Odhner advocates the association of this genus with *Azygia* from which it differs primarily only in the fact that the testes have moved from their original place behind the ovary and have been drawn anteriad by the shortening of the sperm ducts to a location a little posterior to the acetabulum. This is the relation they hold in *Hemiurus*, marine distomes descended from the Azygiidae.

FIG. 679. *Leuceruthrus micropteri*. Ventral view showing internal topography. After a press preparation. Very slightly diagrammatic. Magnified. (After Goldberger.)

88 (85) Body flat, thin, transparent; no cirrus sac present.
                    Family OPISTHORCHIIDAE Lühe 1901 . . 89

Elongate flattened transparent distomes with weak musculature. Suckers close together and very weak. Intestinal crura reach fully or nearly to posterior end. Excretory bladder Y-shaped with short branches and long stem. Genital pore close in front of acetabulum. No cirrus or cirrus sac. Coiled seminal vesicle. Germ glands in series in posterior region, ovary in front of testes. Vitellaria outside intestinal crura, moderately developed, not reaching posterior end. Uterus long, preovarian, in transverse loops, mostly postacetabular. Eggs very numerous, small, light yellowish brown in color.

Parasites of gall passages of Amniota.

An important parasite of man, *Clonorchis sinensis*, which belongs to this family has been introduced several times into this continent but apparently has not gained a footing.

89 (90) Neither uterine coils nor vitellaria extend anteriad beyond
                    acetabulum. . . . . . . *Opisthorchis* R. Blanchard 1895.

Anterior end conical, posterior end broader. Main stem of excretory bladder S-shaped, passing between testes, anterior forks of Y short. Vitellaria in groups.

In gall ducts of mammals, birds, and (?) fishes. Young distomes encysted in skin and connective tissues, especially subdermal tissue of fishes.

Several species in North America; best known *O. pseudofelineus* Ward 1901 in the cat.

FIG. 680. *Opisthorchis pseudofelineus*. From liver of cat. X 5. (Original.)

90 (89) Uterine coils and vitellaria both in part anterior to acetabulum.
                    Metorchis Looss 1899.

Small to moderate sized distomes with short, compressed body tapering anteriad. Skin spinous. Testes slightly lobed, nearly symmetrical. Coils of uterus compact, extending clearly over crura to margins. Vitellaria compact, extending anterior to acetabulum.

A single American species *M. complexus* (Stiles and Hassall) from the liver of cat. New York, Maryland, District of Columbia. Peculiar in extent and arrangement of vitellaria and in position of testes. May need to be transferred to a new genus when its structure has been worked out.

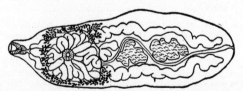

FIG. 681. *Metorchis complexus*. Magnified. (After Stiles and Hassall.)

91 (84) Ovary anterior, near acetabulum, separated from one or both testes
                    by coils of ascending and descending rami of uterus.
                    Subfamily TELORCHIINAE Looss 1899. . 92

Small to middle sized distomes with slender, elongate, spinous, somewhat flattened body. Anterior region very mobile; posterior region stable. Acetabulum small, in anterior region. Pharynx present, esophagus variable, crura long. Testes tandem, both in posterior end or one there and the other not far behind ovary. Laurer's canal and receptaculum seminis present. Vitellaria lateral, elongate, outside intestinal crura. Uterus in coils or loops between ovary and testes or when one testis is near ovary, between ovary and posterior testis. Eggs numerous, small.

In the intestine of reptiles.

92 (93)   Genital pore anterior to and near acetabulum; cirrus sac very long extending far behind acetabulum to round ovary.

                                                    Telorchis Lühe 1899.

Small to middle sized distomes. Musculature light; hence worms translucent. Testes close together, near posterior end, separated from ovary which lies at the end of the cirrus sac and near the center of the body, by a mass of uterine coils. Excretory vesicle long, median, extends anteriad about to ovary where it forms two lateral branches.

Species distinguished by length of esophagus and direction and extension of uterine coils. *Cercorchis* Lühe with esophagus and having uterine coils entirely intercecal, grades into *Telorchis* s. str. Lühe (without esophagus and with uterus coiled beyond ceca), and cannot be accepted as a valid subgenus.

Apparently confined to reptiles; six or more species in North America. Revision of genus by Stunkard.

FIG. 682.   *Telorchis medius.*   Ventral view.   × 28.   (After Stunkard.)

93 (92)   Genital pore dorso-lateral, separated by marked interval from acetabulum.   Cirrus sac entirely preacetabular.

                                              Protenes Barker and Covey 1911.

Two species, *P. leptus* Barker and Covey and *P. angustus* (Stafford) in North America. From *Chrysemys marginata* and *C. picta.*

94 (83)   Ovary lateral; testes either median or slightly lateral.   95

95 (96)   Ovary separated from acetabulum by coils of uterus.

                                              Plagioporus Stafford 1904.

Small, fusiform distomes with acetabulum larger than oral sucker and anterior to middle of length. Skin smooth. Pharynx and esophagus present; crura extend to posterior end. Testes median, close together in center of postacetabular region. Ovary small, lateral, just in front of anterior testis. Uterus from ovary to acetabulum. Genital pore lateral, on level of intestinal bifurcation. Cirrus sac large, preacetabular, obliquely transverse. Vitellaria lateral, from esophagus to posterior end.

Only species known. . . . . . .   *Plagioporus serotinus* Stafford 1904.

Intestine of large-scaled sucker (*Moxostoma macrolepidotum*) in Canada.

96 (95)   Ovary close to acetabulum, at least not separated from it by coils of uterus.   97

97 (104)   Testes large, in posterior region of body, separated from ovary by small uterus with few eggs; or when eggs are numerous, they extend beyond testes into posterior end (*Bunodera* only). . .   Family ALLOCREADIIDAE Odhner 1910 . .   98

Distomes of small to moderate size; body attenuated and mobile anteriorly. Suckers well developed. Pharynx and esophagus present; crura long, but not reaching posterior end. Genital pore near acetabulum or not more than halfway to oral sucker, median or slightly lateral. Ovary lateral, behind but not far from acetabulum. Testes large, proximate, in posterior region halfway or more from acetabulum to posterior end. Vitellaria lateral. Eggs large.

Parasites of fishes; rarely of higher vertebrates.

98 (103)   Uterus short with few coils, between anterior testis and acetabulum.

                        Subfamily ALLOCREADIINAE Odhner 1905 . .   99

Acetabulum at end of first third or fourth of total length. Excretory bladder single, undivided, sac-shaped, rarely pyriform. Genital pore preacetabular, median or slightly lateral. Cirrus and sac large, well developed. Testes large, proximate, median or oblique in posterior region. Ovary spherical or lobed, close between acetabulum and testes, not median. Vitellaria lateral, well developed, partly covering crura, often confluent behind testis. Eggs not numerous, usually large.

99 (100)   Oral sucker smooth; not provided with muscular papillae around anterior end. . . . . *Allocreadium* Looss 1900.

Esophagus long, not dividing until just before the acetabulum. Excretory bladder very short, ending at posterior margin of posterior testes. Ovary spherical, lateral; vitellaria exclusively ventral. Cirrus and sac rather short; prostate well developed. Genital pore median. Eggs without filament, large (60 to 90 μ) with light yellow shell.

Intestine of fresh-water fishes.

Several species from stomach and intestine of sheepshead, pumpkinseed, sturgeon, sucker, dace, minnow, and gall-bladder of red-finned minnow. Collected in Great Lakes region, Lake Erie, Ontario; Lake Sebago, Maine. Synopsis of genus by Wallin.

Young forms of *A. commune* Olsson encysted in Mayfly nymph (*Blasturus cupidus* Say) with eggs and living miracidia in body cavity of nymph (Cooper).

Representative American species.

Allocreadium lobatum Wallin 1909.

Length 4 to 7 mm., breadth 1 to 1.5 mm. Suckers equal, 0.46 to 0.5 mm. in diameter. No prepharynx; pharynx 0.24 to 0.3 mm. long by 0.22 mm. broad.

Testes lobed; cirrus sac extends to center of acetabulum. Ovary spherical; vitellaria postovarial, profuse, confluent behind posterior testis. Receptaculum large, pyriform, between ovary and anterior testis. Uterus compact, between anterior testis and acetabulum. Eggs very numerous, 67 to 85 μ long by 46 to 57 μ broad.

FIG. 683. *Allocreadium lobatum.* Uterus indicated by dotted area, added from slide. × 19.   (After Wallin.)

100 (99)   Six oral papillae surround anterior end. 101

101 (102)   Genital pore anterior to fork of intestine.

Crepidostomum Braun 1900.

Bifurcation of intestine just anterior to acetabulum. Excretory bladder elongate. Cirrus sac muscular; pore anterior to fork of intestine; testes large, round, median, halfway from acetabulum to posterior end. Vitellaria confluent behind testes. Uterus short, with few eggs, between acetabulum, ovary, and anterior testis. In intestine of fresh-water fishes. Several species not adequately described.

Representative American species.

Crepidostomum cornutum (Osborn) 1903.

Probably the best known species in the North American fauna is *C. cornutum* (Osborn) from the stomach and pyloric ceca of black bass, rock bass, channel cat, perch, sunfish, darter, etc. Immature forms encysted in viscera of various crayfish, Ontario, Canada. The worm manifests precocious sexual maturity as the larger cysts contain many eggs already extruded. Very young forms have been taken from Mayfly nymphs (*Hexagenia*) by Cooper.

FIG. 684. *Crepidostomum cornutum.* Ventral view; compressed. × 20. (After Osborn.)

102 (101) Genital pore posterior to fork of intestine.   .   *Acrolichanus* Ward.
(Syn. *Acrodactyla* Stafford 1904 preocc.)

Body uniform in width or slightly constricted behind oral sucker which is noticeably larger (0.325 mm.) than the acetabulum (0.275 mm.) located about at center of body. Ovary posterior and close to acetabulum, slightly lateral. Vitellaria from pharynx to posterior end. Uterus tubular, short, with few eggs. Genital pore midway from acetabulum to oral sucker. Cirrus large, with broad lumen at anterior end. Cirrus sac reaching to posterior border of acetabulum or even a little beyond. Testes spherical, close together, median, or slightly oblique, halfway from acetabulum to posterior end..

Representative American species.
Acrolichanus petalosa (Lander) 1902.

One species, *A. petalosa* (Lander), is common in intestine of Lake sturgeon (*Acipenser rubicundus*) in the Great Lakes and St. Lawrence River.

"This is the *D. auriculatum* Wedl of Linton and it is upon the authority of Looss that I use the above specific demonstration" (Stafford). The comment of Odhner that *Acr. petalosa* is a synonym of *Acr. lintoni* appears to be incorrect.

Fig. 685. *Acrolichanus petalosa;* type specimen. × 39. (Unpublished drawing
by C. H. Lander.)

103 (98)   Uterus dorsal to both testes, extending nearly to extreme posterior
end. . . . . . .   Subfamily BUNODERINAE Looss 1902.

Small distomes, with elongate body, and smooth skin. Anterior region small, muscles moderately developed. Oral sucker with circle of six muscular mammiform processes, often a collar-like expansion. Acetabulum equal to or larger than oral sucker. Pharynx and esophagus present, crura long. Genital pore between ventral and oral suckers. Ovary close behind acetabulum and lateral. Testes oblique, in posterior half of body. Uterus with descending and ascending rami in sacculate form, dorsal to testes in posterior region. Laurer's canal and receptaculum seminis present. Vitellaria lateral, well developed, extending from pharynx to caudal end. Eggs large.

Type genus. . . . . . *Bunodera* Railliet 1896.

Esophagus long, forebody narrow. Fork of intestine somewhat anterior to acetabulum. Cirrus sac without muscular tissue in wall. Testes oblique, far back in body. Vitellaria not confluent, not reaching posterior end. Uterus with descending and ascending rami, greatly enlarged, not coiled, extending to posterior end and covering testes on ventral side of body.

Recorded in North America.
Bunodera luciopercae (O. F. Müller) 1776.

One species *B. luciopercae* (O. F. Müller) (= *Dist. nodulosum* Zeder) reported by Stafford from perch.

Fig. 686. *Bunodera luciopercae.* Ventral view. × 47. (After Looss.)

104 (97) Testes small, in center of body, separated from ovary by dense uterine coils with masses of eggs; no eggs posterior to testes. . . . . *Auridistomum* Stafford 1905.

Elongate, slightly constricted at center, with lateral auricle on each side of oral sucker. Skin covered with fine scales. Acetabulum smaller than oral sucker, located in center of anterior half of body. Pharynx present; crura extend to posterior end. Excretory vesicle very long, extending nearly to acetabulum, dividing into short lateral branches directed anterial. Testes oblique, near center of body; cirrus sac large, extending from posterior margin of acetabulum to genital pore located between suckers and posterior to fork of intestine. Ovary postacetabular, dextral. Laurer's canal in fork of excretory duct; wall thick. Vitellaria continuous from right to left both above and below crura and excretory duct, extending anteriad to posterior margin of acetabulum. Eggs 31 by 17 μ.

Only species known. . *Auridistomum chelydrae* Stafford 1900.

Intestine of *Chelydra serpentina*.

FIG. 687. *Auridistomum chelydrae.* Vitellaria changed to correspond with later account of author. Ventral view. Magnified. (After Stafford.)

105 (68) Testes numerous, in two longitudinal series.
Pleorchis Railliet 1896.

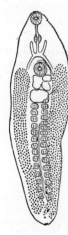

Inframedium sized distomes with oval, somewhat flattened body. Skin spinous. Suckers small, equal, separated by only one-fourth body length. Oral sucker subterminal. Prepharynx prominent, pharynx small, esophagus extended, crura with single branch directed anteriad. Excretory system unknown.

Genital pore preacetabular. Cirrus sac absent (?). Testes numerous in two rows near median plane in posterior half of body. Vitellaria in two broad lateral bands from acetabulum to posterior end. Other organs confined to small area between anterior testes and fork of intestine mostly, behind acetabulum. Uterus short; ova scanty, 48 μ long.

Reported by Leidy from lungs of musk turtle (*Aromochelys odorata* Latr.) as *Monostoma molle.* Shown by Stiles and Hassall to be distome, somewhat like *Distoma polyorchis* Stossich. Position and relationship dependent finally on more perfect knowledge of structure which awaits discovery of new material.

FIG. 688. *Pleorchis mollis.* Magnified. (After Stiles.)

106 (67) Acetabulum represented by two small suckers set close together in depression on mid-ventral surface near center of body; genital cloaca opens between the two suckers.
Subfamily CRYPTOGONIMINAE Osborn 1903.

Very small, spinous distomes of uniform width throughout, with bluntly rounded ends. Oral sucker very large and prominent. Ventral sucker double, minute, withdrawn into pocket; genital pore between the two. Prepharynx, pharynx, and short esophagus present; crura extend to anterior margin of testes. Excretory vesicle Y-shaped, fork at oviduct, anterior

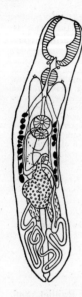

branches reach to posterior margin of pharynx. Testes elongate, parallel, dorsal, in posterior third of body; seminal vesicle convoluted, large; no cirrus or sac. Ovary ventral, proximate to testes, slightly lobed; Laurer's canal (?); vitellaria lateral, in central region. Uterus with descending ramus on right, slightly coiled, extending to posterior end, ascending ramus returning on left, crossing anterior to ovary and passing on right to genital atrium. Eggs small, dark, about 20 by 10 μ.

Type genus. . . . *Cryptogonimus* H. L. Osborn 1903.

The genus has been placed in the Acanthochasmidae; see note under 82 (75). Even if that action be justified it occupies a position sufficiently isolated to demand rank in a separate subfamily as indicated here.

Only species known in North America.
Cryptogonimus chyli Osborn 1903.

In stomach and intestine of *Micropterus dolomieu* and *Ambloplites rupestris;* Lake Chautauqua, New York; St. Mary's River, Michigan; Canada. Young distomes encysted in small black bass, rock bass, and minnows (Cooper).

FIG. 689. *Cryptogonimus chyli.* Ventral view with spines omitted and coils of uterus simplified. × 9. (After Osborn.)

107 (66)　Coils of uterus extend well beyond testes into posterior portion of body. 108

108 (109)　Mouth surrounded by a crown of six muscular papillae which are outgrowths of oral sucker. . . . . *Bunodera.*

See note under 66 in this key and description with figure under 103.

109 (108)　Mouth without crown of papillae. 110

110 (115)　Vitellaria represented by small solid more or less lobed organ on each side of body just anterior to ovary.
Family GORGODERIDAE LOOSS 1901.

Muscular distomes with slender mobile anterior region and flattened posterior region. Suckers muscular; acetabulum especially projects noticeably beyond surface of body. Skin without spines but often with fine papillae. Esophagus long without, or short with pharynx. Crura simple, extend to posterior end. Excretory bladder simple tubular, extending from dorsal pore near posterior end to region of ovarian complex. Genital pore median, between acetabulum and fork of intestine; without male copulatory organs. Ovary lateral, post-acetabular; Laurer's canal or receptaculum seminis present. Testes lateral, oblique or symmetrical. Uterus in numerous open loops chiefly postovarian. Eggs relatively large with thin, faintly colored shell.

Only one subfamily reported in North America.
GORGODERINAE LOOSS 1899 . . 111

Small to submedium in size, sometimes slender, sometimes broad in posterior region. Esophagus relatively long, without muscular pharynx. Testes more or less oblique and within intestinal crura. Laurer's canal present but no receptaculum seminis. Vitellaria not far apart.
In urinary bladder and ducts of fishes and amphibians.

111 (114) Body elongate, lanceolate without conspicuous well marked anterior
and posterior regions. 112

112 (113) Testes subdivided, forming on one side a series of four and on the
other five parts; in all nine separate lobes.

Gorgodera Looss 1899.

Testis on ovarian side has five parts; the opposite testis lies further anteriad and is divided into four parts only. In well-developed adults these
organs are completely concealed by the coils of the uterus filled with dark
brown, almost black eggs.

Found in the bladder of various Amphibia: *Rana* and *Salamandra* (?).
At least two species in North America.

Representative American species.

Gorgodera minima Cort 1912.

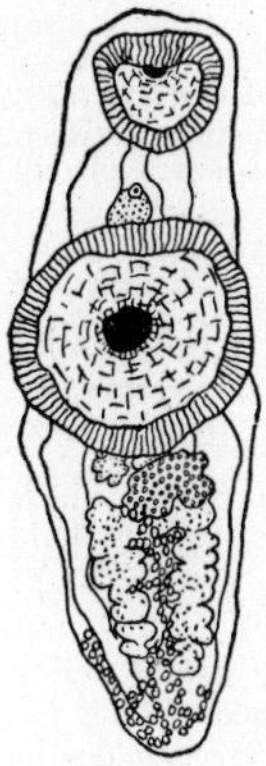

FIG. 690. *Gorgodera minima.* Ventral view. Young specimen with but few
eggs. × 72. (After Cort.)

113 (112) Two simple testes, elongate-oval, not divided.

Gorgoderina Looss 1902.

Testes are elongate and have irregular notched margins but do not divide into sections.
Vitellaria have only few lobes. Much like the former genus. Adults are difficult to distinguish
after the uterine coils cover the testes.

Found in the bladder of Amphibia: *Bufo, Rana* and *Salamandra* (?). Three species known
from North America.

Representative American species.

Gorgoderina attenuata Stafford 1902.

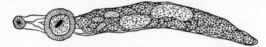

FIG. 691. *Gogoderina attenuata.* Ventral view. × 24. (After Cort.)

114 (111) Body elongate; slender anterior region distinct from broad posterior region. . . . . *Phyllodistomum* M. Braun 1899.

No sharp line of division marks the transition between the two regions
of the body. The vitellaria are solid masses only slightly indented
marginally. The testes are oblique, well separated from each other,
and only weakly lobed if at all.

In urinary bladder of fishes and amphibians.

Representative American species.

Phyllodistomum americanum Osborn 1903.

One species (*P. americanum* Osborn) reported from North America
in *Amblystoma;* two others doubtful from pike (*Esox lucius*), bull-head
(*Ameiurus nebulosus*), and perch (*Perca flavescens*) in Canada.

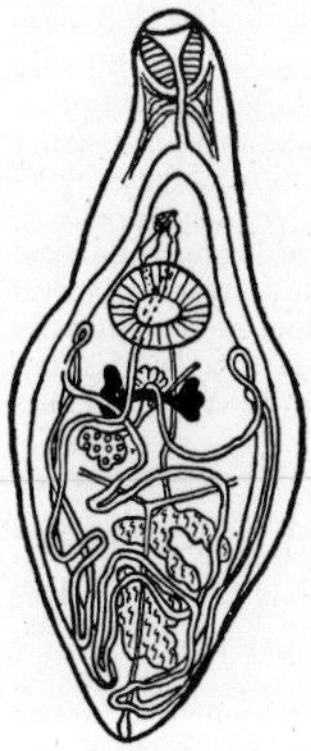

FIG. 692. *Phyllodistomum americanum.* Ventral view. × 16. (After
Osborn.)

115 (110) Vitellaria composed of distinctly separated follicles. 116

116 (119) Vitellaria confined to extreme anterior region of body, not extending posteriad further than acetabulum. 117

117 (118) Vitellaria extend across entire body in anterior region, reaching
nearly to acetabulum.
Genital pore on ventral surface.

Subfamily BRACHYCOELIINAE LOOSS 1899.

Intestinal crura short, not extending posteriad to acetabulum. Genital pore median, between
suckers. Testes lateral, near acetabulum. Ovary lateral, pretesticular. Uterine coils fill
entire posterior region. Eggs numerous, small.
A single species *Brachycoelium hospitale* Stafford 1903 is recorded from North America.
Genital pore marginal.

Subfamily PLEUROGENETINAE LOOSS 1899.

Intestinal crura of variable length. Genital pore sinistral, often marginal. Cirrus sac
large, pyriform, with coiled vesicula seminalis and muscular cirrus. Eggs 23 to 40 μ long.
Intestines of Anura; a single species in *Chamelion.*
The family description as written by Odhner will not take in the American genus which
Looss and he think should certainly be included here. Until more data are available it is
unwise to make a new place for this single genus.
Only North American genus yet described.

Loxogenes Stafford 1905.

Small distomes, with broad, thick, heart-shaped body indented at posterior end. Skin spinous. Suckers small, poorly
developed, nearly equal; acetabulum near center of body.
Pharynx present; esophagus very short; crura short, somewhat inflated, not reaching even to center of body. Excretory
vesicle divides near pore, lateral branches inflated, terminating behind testes. Ovary pyramidal, lobed, preacetabular,
between testes, slightly dextral. Vitellaria ventral, extend
across entire body from pharynx nearly to acetabulum.
Laurer's canal and small receptaculum present. Uterus
chiefly postacetabular, with longitudinal folds in two groups
one on each side of body. Testes oval, small, lateral at ends
of crura, in line with acetabulum or slightly posterior. Cirrus sac long and narrow, preacetabular, sinistral, with coiled
cirrus. Sexual pore dorsal, sinistral, midway between center
and margin at level of fork in intestine. Ova small, 24 by
14 μ, numerous.

FIG. 693. *Loxogenes arcanum*
Dorsal view. X 10. (After Osborn.)

In thick-walled closed cysts on pylorus, liver, and bladder
of various frogs. The single species *L. arcanum* (Nickerson) is encysted in pairs. Massachusetts, Minnesota, Ontario.

118 (117) Vitellaria consist of small groups of follicles lateral to pharynx in
extreme anterior region.

Caecincola Marshall and Gilbert 1905.

Very small distomes; anterior end truncate, posterior end bluntly
rounded. Entire body spinous. Oral sucker very large, acetabulum
much smaller. Mouth terminal, prepharynx and esophagus equal, rather
long, pharynx prominent, ceca short but wide. Excretory vesicle Y-
shaped, extending anteriad beyond pharynx. Testes very large, ovoid,
in posterior half; no copulatory organs; seminal vesicle large, bipartite.
Ovary lobed, anterior to right testis; vitellaria scanty, far anterior, lateral
to pharynx. Uterus poorly developed, a few open loops, above and behind testes, extending nearly to posterior end of body. Receptaculum
seminis dorsal to ovary. Assigned by some to the family Acanthochasmidae; see note under 82 (75) in this key.

Type species.
Caecincola parvulus Marshall and Gilbert 1905.

One species known (*C. parvulus*) in ceca and stomach of large-mouthed
black bass in Wisconsin.

FIG. 694. *Caecincola parvulus.* Ventral view; ovary drawn somewhat to one
side to show underlying parts. X 95. (After Marshall and Gilbert.)

119 (116) Vitellaria not confined to extreme anterior region. 120

120 (123) Intestinal crura short, diverging, not passing acetabulum. . 121
121 (122) Testes symmetrical, lateral, postacetabular.

Subfamily MICROPHALLINAE Ward 1901.

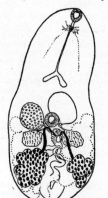

Small distomes having pear-shaped body with mobile anterior region containing alimentary system. Suckers small, prepharynx, pharynx and long esophagus present; crura short, not surpassing acetabulum. Excretory system V-shaped. Genital pore sinistral, rarely postacetabular. No cirrus-sac. Seminal vesicle immediately preacetabular. Testes symmetrical, behind acetabulum. Ovary dextral, alongside of acetabulum. Vitellaria symmetrical, behind testes, in form of a lobed mass of follicles. Uterus coiled in posterior region, extending anteriad about as far as posterior margin of acetabulum. Eggs small, very numerous.

In intestine of water birds and fishes.

Representative American genus.

Microphallus Ward 1901.

One species (*M. opacus*) in *Amia calva, Micropterus dolomieu, Anguilla chrysypa, Ictalurus punctatus, Perca flavescens;* the young distome encysted in crayfish.

FIG. 695. *Microphallus opacus.* Ventral view; dotted line represents limits of coils of uterus, filled with eggs. × 37. (After Ward.)

122 (121) Testes oblique, in center of body, posterior to acetabulum.

Protenteron Stafford 1904.

Small distomes. Broadest at center, narrowed behind. Skin spinous. Oral sucker terminal, 0.186 mm., acetabulum 0.62 mm. in diameter. Prepharynx longer than pharynx or esophagus. Crura short, diverging, not passing acetabulum. Black eye spots lateral to pharynx. Testes oblique in center of body behind acetabulum. Ovary in front of left testis. Uterus reaching posterior end. Vitellaria lateral, short, from fork of intestine to near ovary. Cirrus (and sac ?) extending posteriad to ovary. Eggs 22 by 11 μ.

Type species. . . . . . *Protenteron diaphanum* Stafford 1904.
Intestine of *Ambloplites rupestris;* Montreal, Canada.

123 (120) Intestinal crura extend beyond acetabulum. 124
124 (125) Uterus forms rosette in center of body.

Centrovarium Stafford 1904.

Small distomes, tapering somewhat towards both rounded ends. Ventral sucker larger than oral, at end of anterior third of body. Crura terminate opposite center of ovary. Testes behind ends of crura, not conspicuous. Uterus rosette-shaped, in center of body. Vitellaria lateral, from esophagus to anterior margin of testes.

Only species known.
Centrovarium lobotes (MacCallum) 1895.

Delicate worms, 1 to 3 mm. long. Suckers relatively small and weak. Ovary deeply lobed. Acini of vitellaria more or less confluent imparting a tubular appearance to the organ. Eggs very numerous, small, pyriform, 32.5 by 15 μ, with thick brown shell. Intestine of *Esox lucius, Stizostedion vitreum, Ambloplites rupestris, Anguilla chrysypa;* Ontario, Canada.

FIG. 696. *Centrovarium lobotes.* Dorsal view. Magnified. (After MacCallum.)

125 (124) Uterus more or less elongated or in coils but not in form of a central rosette. 126

126 (129) Genital pore near oral sucker on left margin of body.
Subfamily PROSTHOGONIMINAE Lühe 1909. . . 127

Small to medium sized distomes with body somewhat flattened and elongate. Skin spinous. Pharynx present, esophagus variable, crura half or three-quarters length of body. Excretory bladder Y-shaped, sometimes with caudal vesicle. Genital pore marginal, dorsal or anterior to oral sucker. Cirrus sac long, slender, cylindrical, extending to or beyond intestinal bifurcation. Testes behind acetabulum and ovary. Ovary close to acetabulum, vitellaria extracecal in central portion of body. Receptaculum seminis and Laurer's canal present. Uterus in coils in posterior region, chiefly behind testes.

127 (128) Testes symmetrical; ovary lobed; uterine coils pass between testes.
Prosthogonimus Lühe 1899.

From the bursa Fabricii of various water birds in Europe. Reported from North America in a hen's egg and also from two birds.

128 (127) Testes oblique or tandem; ovary entire; uterine coils do not pass between testes. . . . . Cephalogonimus Poirier 1886.

Genital pore dorsal or anterior to oral sucker. Uterus passes from ovarian complex directly posteriad between crura and testes, on right side of body, forms mass of coils behind testes and passes anteriad on left to genital pore. Vitellaria not always entirely extracecal. Testes round or irregular. Eggs numerous, moderate in size, development unknown.
Two species in intestine of frogs, Toronto and Montreal; and of soft-shelled turtles (Aspidonectes and Amyda), Minnesota.

FIG. 697. *Cephalogonimus americanus.* Living animal, from ventral surface. Magnified. (After Stafford.)

FIG. 698. *Cephalogonimus vesicaudus.* Entire worm from dorsal surface, somewhat flattened. Magnified. (After Nickerson.)

FIG. 697.

FIG. 698.

129 (126) Genital pore anterior to acetabulum, from nearly median to marginal in position.
Family PLAGIORCHIIDAE Lühe *char. emend.* . . 130
(Syn. *Lepodermatidae* Odhner 1910.)

More or less elongate distomes with moderately flattened to cylindrical body; rarely (*Ochetosoma*) strongly flattened. Skin usually spinous over entire body. Prepharynx, pharynx, and esophagus present; crura very variable in length. Excretory bladder typically Y-shaped with median stem dividing into two short branches behind complex of Mehlis' gland. Genital pore usually just in front of acetabulum, slightly left of median line. Cirrus sac crescentic, powerful, with prominent longitudinal fibers, containing cirrus, vesicle, and prostate; rarely (*Astiotrema*) reduced. Ovary on posterior margin of acetabulum, dextral, rarely sinistral. Testes usually oblique, rarely symmetrical or median, close behind ovary. Laurer's canal present, except in *Pneumonoeces;* receptaculum seminis variable. Vitellaria lateral, variable in extent. Uterus extends posteriad to end of body and then anteriad to pore, simple or complicated by coils filling posterior region. Eggs very numerous, small, thin-shelled, measure 20 to 50 μ.

130 (139) Receptaculum seminis present (except *Plagiorchis*); crura reach
posterior end (except *Styphlodora*). 131

131 (138) Vesicula seminalis fills greater part of cirrus sac; pars prostatica
follows after it and is very short.
Subfamily PLAGIORCHIINAE Lühe 1909. . . 132

132 (135) Genital pore near oral sucker. 133

133 (134) Testes median or nearly so. . . . . *Pneumonoeces* Looss 1902.
Medium sized distomes, with body elongate, thick, and only slightly flattened, tapering anteriorly. Acetabulum small. Oral sucker large, pharynx well developed, esophagus short, intestinal crura long, extending to posterior end. Genital pore just behind oral sucker, median,
ventral. Cirrus sac greatly elongate, reaching acetabulum. Ovary near acetabulum. Testes
postovarian, slightly oblique. Large seminal receptacle between testes and ovary. No Laurer's
canal. Vitellaria lateral in middle region of body. Uterus much coiled, extending to extreme
posterior end. Eggs numerous, small, dark shelled.
In lungs of Anura; widely distributed and abundant. Develop perhaps from Xiphidiocercariae. North American species well worked out and described with key by Cort.

Representative American species.
Pneumonoeces coloradensis Cort 1915.

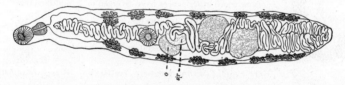

FIG. 699. *Pneumonoeces coloradensis.* Fully developed specimen, ventral view. *o*, ovary; *sr*, seminal
receptacle. × 27. (After Cort.)

134 (133) Testes lateral and symmetrical or nearly so. *Pneumobites* Ward.
Much like *Pneumonoeces* but body larger, thicker, with testes lobed, elongate, lateral and
symmetrical or only slightly oblique. Extracecal longitudinal folds of uterus pronouncedly
longer than in *Pneumonoeces*. Ovary lobed. Vitellaria with many very small acini in each
group. Eggs small.
In lungs of Anura. Two species in North America: *P. longiplexus, P. breviplexus.* Cort,
who grouped these in *Pneumonoeces*, called attention to their close relationship. The points
of resemblance constitute also characteristic differences from other species in *Pneumonoeces*
sufficient to justify their being made an independent genus.

Type species. . . . . . *Pneumobites longiplexus* (Stafford) 1902.

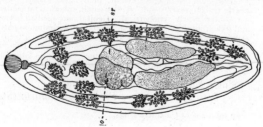

FIG. 700. *Pneumobites longiplexus.* Dorsal view. *o*, ovary; *sr*, seminal receptacle. × 13.
(After Cort.)

135 (132) Genital pore near acetabulum. **136**

136 (137) No conspicuous pharyngeal glands. . . . *Plagiorchis* Lühe 1899.

Body elongate oval, somewhat attenuated at both ends, covered with minute spines. Pharynx and esophagus of approximately equal length, crura reach posterior end, or near it. Genital pore just anterior to acetabulum, median or slightly sinistral. Cirrus sac curved around and reaching posterior margin of acetabulum, with large vesicula seminalis. Testes round to oval, oblique, separated by uterine branches. No receptaculum seminis. Ovary spherical, at inner end of cirrus sac. Vitellaria with many closely crowded follicles usually reaching posterior end. Uterine coils partly pretesticular, chiefly posttesticular. Eggs numerous.

In intestine of insectivorous vertebrates, chiefly birds, but also amphibians, reptiles and mammals, infection probably through insects.

Little specialized forms that constitute the type of the family and from which other genera have diverged in several directions.

North American species.

Plagiorchis proximus Barker 1915.

Reported from the muskrat in North America.

FIG. 701. *Plagiorchis proximus.* Ventral view. × 25. (After Barker.)

137 (136) Conspicuous pharyngeal glands present.

Glypthelmins Stafford 1905.

Small, oval distomes with rounded ends and cylindrical body. Skin spinous. Acetabulum smaller than oral sucker, anterior to middle of body. Pharynx and esophagus present, pharyngeal glands conspicuous; crura nearly reach posterior end. Testes small, spherical, at center of body, postacetabular, nearly symmetrical. Genital pore median between acetabulum and fork of intestine. Cirrus sac overlaps acetabulum in part. Ovary small at left of acetabulum, receptaculum seminis present. Uterus with numerous short transverse coils within crura between testes and posterior end, spreading somewhat beyond ends of intestine. Vitellaria lateral from fork of intestine nearly to end of crura. Eggs small, numerous.

Single North American species known.

Glypthelmins quieta (Stafford) 1900.

In intestine of Canadian frogs.

FIG. 702. *Glypthelmins quieta.* Magnified. (After Stafford.)

138 (131) Vesicula seminalis at inner end of cirrus sac, continued to outer end by long, tubular pars prostatica.

Styphlodora Looss 1899.

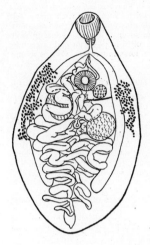

Body somewhat attenuated anteriad, but broadened posteriorly, with rounded ends. Skin covered with fine spines. Pharynx and esophagus present; crura do not reach posterior end. Genital pore median, preacetabular. Cirrus sac encloses coiled vesicula seminalis. Cirrus powerful. Testes oblique, close together in center of body. Vitellaria poorly developed. Receptaculum seminis present, but small. Uterus intercecal, but spreading to margin beyond ends of crura. Eggs numerous.

In intestine of reptiles.

One North American form described by Goldberger as *Styphlodora bascaniensis* from the liver (?) of *Bascanion constrictor*, Virginia, is a doubtful member of this genus.

Fig. 703. *Styphlodora bascaniensis.* Ventral view. Magnified. (After Goldberger.)

139 (130) No receptaculum seminis, intestinal crura half to three-fourths body length, at least never reaching posterior end.

Subfamily RENIFERINAE Pratt 1902 . . 140

Crura of medium length, reaching beyond center of body but not into posterior tip. In every case an open space or uterine coils intervene between the crura and posterior end of body.

No receptaculum seminis.

Testes at ends of crura, more or less symmetrical.

In mouth, air passages, lungs, esophagus and stomach of snakes.

A group clearly worked out and defined by Odhner, richly represented in North America where occur five out of the seven genera already described.

140 (141) Genital pore marginal or nearly so. . . . . *Renifer* Pratt 1902.

Small distomes with elliptical, ventrally flattened body covered with fine spines. Suckers moderately developed; acetabulum larger, anterior to middle. Mouth subterminal; pharynx present; esophagus short; intestinal ceca reach beyond acetabulum, about to center of body. Excretory vessel Y-shaped. Genital pore marginal, about level of fork of intestine. Testes both symmetrical just behind center of body near ovary which is lateral at right posterior margin of acetabulum. Cirrus sac large, reaching to or beyond acetabulum with convoluted seminal vesicle. Vitellaria submoderate in size, lateral, in central third of body. Uterus with descending and ascending limb, passing between testes nearly to posterior tip; capacity provided by increase in breadth of tube and not by extension in length and formation of coils.

Representative American species.

Renifer ellipticus Pratt 1903.

Mouth and air passages of *Heterodon platyrhinus.* Only one certain North American species, *R. ellipticus* Pratt 1903, type of the genus.

Fig. 704. *Renifer ellipticus.* Ventral view. X 15. (After Pratt.)

141 (140) Genital pore median or nearly so. 142

142 (143) Testes oblique, separated by greatly enlarged branch of uterus.
Dasymetra Nicoll 1911.

Body moderately flattened, spinous. Pharynx large, crura wide, not reaching posterior end. Excretory vesicle Y-shaped, with many side branches. Genital pore median, slightly preacetabular. Cirrus sac short, plump; cirrus long. No receptaculum seminis; Laurer's canal present. Vitellaria branching, lateral. Uterus coiled in posterior end, ascending ramus wide, nearly straight, metraterm long, muscular. Ova 35 μ long.

Type and only species.
Dasymetra conferta Nicoll 1911.

Length 3.5 to 4.6 mm., maximum width 1 to 1.4 mm., near center. Spines long, straight. Oral sucker 0.56 mm. in diameter. Acetabulum same size or little less, about 1.7 mm. from anterior end. Pharynx 0.28 mm. in diameter; esophagus short; crura wide, enlarged at ends. Excretory tubules pigmented. Testes oblique, separated by uterus. Ovary at right posterior margin of acetabulum. Vitellaria lateral, extend from genital pore to posterior border of right testis; follicles large. Uterus spacious; descending ramus dorsal, small; posterior coil behind ends of intestinal crura; ascending ramus irregular, broad, extending to acetabulum. Metraterm with thick muscular walls. Ova dark brown, 33 to 37 by 16 to 19 μ.

In mouth (?) of diamond water-snake (*Tropidonotus rhombifer*); North America, locality unknown.

{ FIG. 705. *Dasymetra conferta.* Ventral view. X 15. (After Nicoll.)

143 (142) Testes lateral, symmetrical. 144

144 (145) Topography inverted, *i.e.*, genital pore right and ovary left of median line. . . . . *Pneumatophilus* Odhner 1910.

Broad, flat distomes of submedian size with moderately developed suckers. Greatest width behind center, tapering to anterior end, rounded posteriorly. Skin spinous. Suckers in anterior third of body, acetabulum slightly larger. Genital pore dextral, near fork of intestine, half way between suckers. Oral sucker slightly subterminal, pharynx present, esophagus very short. Crura extend to or just beyond testes, with numerous short lateral projections on outer margin. Excretory vesicle Y-shaped, slender. Stem reaches to anterior margin of testes. Testes opposite, just behind center of body, lobed. Cirrus sac and cirrus moderate in size. Ovary at left posterior margin of acetabulum. Laurer's canal, but no receptaculum seminis. Vitellaria extracecal, extend from level of genital pore to anterior part of testes. Uterus with descending and ascending limb passing between testes; thrown into transverse loops that fill posttesticular region.

In the lung and trachea of *Heterodon platyrhinus* and *Tropidonotus sipedon.*

One species in North America, originally described by Leidy as *Distoma variabile* var. b., and listed later by Pratt as *Renifer variabilis* taken by Odhner as type of the new genus.

FIG. 706. *Pneumatophilus variabilis.* Dorsal view. X 12. (After Pratt.)

145 (144) Topography direct, *i.e.*, genital pore left and ovary right of median line. 146

146 (147)   Cirrus sac does not extend posteriad beyond acetabulum.
Lechriorchis Stafford 1905.

Distomes of submoderate size oval, narrower behind, ventral sucker much larger than oral (?), one-third body length from anterior end. Skin spinous. Pharynx and esophagus present; crura extend to [posterior margin of ?] testes, two-thirds length of body. Testes large, nearly symmetrical, almost in contact. Cirrus sac large, dorsal and anterior to acetabulum on right side. Genital pore at fork of intestine. Ovary small, spherical, at the end of cirrus sac, on right posterior margin of acetabulum. Uterus extends directly posteriad to end of body and then anteriad, ascending limb greatly expanded. Vitellaria [lateral ?], nearly entire length of ceca. Eggs dark brown.

Two species from North America; type *L. primus* in lung of garter snake. The only well-described species is one which Stafford says belongs here; it is *L. elongatus* (= *Renifer elongatus* Pratt) in mouth of *Heterodon platyrhinus*. *Renifer megasorchis* Crow 1913 from the uterus of *Natrix rhombifera* may belong here.

FIG. 707. *Lechriorchis elongatus*. Dorsal view. × 15. (After Pratt.)

147 (146)   Cirrus sac extends posteriad beyond posterior margin of acetabulum. . . . . *Zeugorchis* Stafford 1905.
Small, elongate elliptical distomes with subterminal oral sucker and spinous skin. Acetabulum near center of body. Pharynx and esophagus present, crura extend to testes only. Testes oval, lateral, separated. Cirrus sac large, dorsal, extending posterior to acetabulum. Genital pore in fork of intestine. Ovary small, spherical, at end of cirrus sac. Uterus with descending and ascending limbs, reaches to posterior end; eggs very numerous. Vitellaria lateral along crura, but also covering same and approaching median line dorsally. Excretory bladder median, large, with evident lateral branches.

Single North American form, type species.
Zeugorchis aequatus Stafford 1905.
In esophagus and stomach of garter snake; Canada. This form is very inadequately described and its position is somewhat a matter of conjecture. Odhner believes it should be placed in this subfamily.

148 (65)   Ovary posterior to one or both testes. 149

149 (152)   Ovary posterior to both testes. 150

150 (151)   Uterine coils anterior to ovary, between it and acetabulum; testes small, oblique, nearly symmetrical, widely separated from each other, lateral near acetabulum. . . . *Leuceruthrus*.
For description and figure consult 87 (86) in this key.

151 (150)   Uterine coils posterior to ovary, between it and posterior end; testes large, oblique or nearly median, forming with acetabulum and ovary almost a continuous median series.
Family DICROCOELIIDAE Braun 1915.
Elongate, flattened, transparent distomes of moderate size with weak suckers and poorly developed musculature. Acetabulum near anterior end. Intestinal crura do not reach posterior end. Excretory bladder tubular, reaching anteriad to center of body. Genital pore median, between suckers, near fork of intestine. Cirrus sac small, cirrus conspicuous. Germ glands postacetabular with testes symmetrical, oblique, in median series in front of ovary. Vitellaria occupy central region of body mostly outside of intestinal crura. Uterus long with descending and ascending branches in transverse coils, mostly filling area behind ovary. Eggs moderate in size, very abundant, thick shelled, dark brown.
Parasitic chiefly in gall ducts of Amniota.

Type genus. . . . . *Dicrocoelium* Dujardin 1845.
Body tapering towards both ends, more anteriad. Testes oblique, close together. Vitellaria lateral, symmetrical, small. Genital pore with cirrus sac between ventral sucker and fork of intestine. Uterus prominent, filling entire body behind germ glands which lie between acetabulum and center of body.

The common European species (*D. dendriticum*, the old *Distoma lanceolatum*) is said by Leidy to be frequent in sheep in several western states, but Stiles and Hassall report it as apparently not in North America. I have never seen a specimen collected here. Confusion with *Opisthorchis* and similar forms is common in earlier records.

North American genus. . . . . *Halipegus* Looss 1899.

Moderate sized distomes with muscular body, round in cross-section, and powerful suckers. Pharynx large, esophagus short, crura extending to posterior end. Genital pore close to pharynx. No cirrus. Testes lateral, near posterior end, symmetrical. Ovary close behind right testis; vitellaria just behind ovary and composed of group of 4 to 5 large follicles on each side. Uterus in crowded transverse coils, filling almost entire body. Eggs extremely numerous, small, with long polar filament. In mouth and pharynx of amphibia.

North American species. . . . *Halipegus occidualis* Stafford 1905.

In mouth and eustachean tube of *Rana catesbiana*; Canada, Massachusetts.

152 (149) Ovary between testes. 153

153 (156) Ovary median or nearly so, hence directly behind anterior testis. 154

154 (155) Genital pore between acetabulum and pharynx.
Sphaerostoma Stiles and Hassall 1898.

Small distomes with actively mobile, powerful anterior region and broad posterior region. Suckers powerful. Pharynx present, esophagus long, crura reach into caudal end. Cirrus sac large, cirrus muscular. Testes separate, anterior one near acetabulum on right, posterior one near caudal tip, median. Ovary intermediate but slightly to left of median line. Vitellaria extensive, lateral, from pharynx to posterior end. Uterus in few coils between posterior testis and acetabulum. With few, large eggs.

This genus has not yet been reported from fresh-water fishes in North America. Linton has found it in marine fishes in the Woods Hole region and it is common in Europe in Cyprinidae and many other fresh-water fishes so that it is very likely to be found on this continent in similar fresh-water hosts.

155 (154) Genital pore some distance behind acetabulum, just anterior to anterior testis. . . . . *Clinostomum* Leidy 1856.

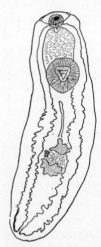

Middle sized distomes with flattened body. Oral sucker small and retracted at times so that the body wall rises around it like a collar. Acetabulum near oral sucker, larger, very muscular, with triangular orifice. No pharynx, short esophagus and long crura provided with lateral pockets. Cirrus sac present. Vitellaria lateral, strongly developed, confluent behind testes. Uterus inverted U-shaped, reaching forward nearly to acetabulum, with expansion on distal branch of U.

Several species in North America. Not clearly distinguished in records. Adults are parasitic in the pharynx and esophagus of fish-eating birds such as herring gull, various herons, bittern, eagle, stork. Young forms encysted in frogs and fish (minnows, perch, bluegill, bullhead, rock bass, pike, black bass, trout, etc.). Cort has shown that the young encysted in amphibia are a different species from those in fish. Widely distributed in eastern North America at least. The larval stages are so abundant in some regions that food fish are rendered unfit for use by the middle of June. The cysts are deserted by late fall and the fish are free from infection in winter.

Distoma oricola Leidy from the mouth of *Alligator mississippiensis* is undoubtedly a related form as Pratt surmised. It falls in this family but too little is known of its structure to justify assigning it to a definite genus.

FIG. 708. *Clinostomum marginatum.* Larval stage from perch. × 19. (After Cort.)

FIG. 709. *Clinostomum marginatum.* Young adult from heron. × 19. (After Cort.)

156 (153) Ovary lateral and slightly posterior to anterior testis, but not directly behind it. 157

157 (158) Genital pore at posterior end. . . *Leucochloridium* Carus 1835.

Small distomes with compressed muscular body. Both suckers and pharynx large and powerful. Esophagus short, crura very slender, reaching nearly to posterior end. Excretory pore dorsal near caudal tip. Cirrus sac present. Laurer's canal present; receptaculum wanting. Vitellaria lateral, conspicuous, extracecal. Uterus in loops ascends on one side of acetabulum, crosses body, and descends on the other side. Eggs small, thick shelled.

In the cloaca of birds, not reported in North America. The larval stage in *Succinea* is a sporocyst which sends into the tentacles of the snail branches that are banded in color and are bitten off by birds. Reported in a personal letter by Mr. Bryant Walker who found it in *Succinea ovalis* in Michigan.

158 (157) Genital pore ventral, median, just anterior to posterior testis.
Hasstilesia Hall 1916.

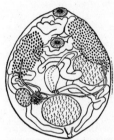

Very small oval distomes, nearly round in cross section. Skin with minute spines in anterior region. Suckers small, nearly equal. Pharynx and esophagus present, equal in length; crura irregular, reach to posterior end of body. Excretory bladder minute with two delicate lateral branches. Genital pore ventral, slightly dextral, midway from acetabulum to posterior end. Cirrus sac flask-shaped, large; cirrus long. Testes large, one in extreme posterior region, nearly median, the other near center of body on left. Ovary small, round, ventral to right intestinal cecum, near anterior margin of posterior testis. Vitellaria lateral in anterior half. Uterus in anterior region of body, moderately developed, mostly pretesticular but with a single loop between the testes.

Eggs 13 by 20 μ.

Single American species.

Hasstilesia tricolor (Stiles and Hassall) 1894.

Fig. 710. *Hasstilesia tricolor.*
Magnified. (After Stiles.)

In small intestine of *Lepus;* abundant, Maryland, District of Columbia, Virginia.

159 (64) Distomes of separate sexes.
Family SCHISTOSOMATIDAE Looss 1899.

Adults parasitic in blood vessels of man, cattle, and birds; not yet found in North America. Cercariae very similar to those of this family occur in North American snails. Compare furcocercous cercariae 241 (246) in this key.

160 (63) Special adhesive organ behind acetabulum. Anterior region with holdfast organs usually distinctly separated from posterior region with genitalia. . . . . Suborder **Holostomata** Lühe.

The genus *Cyathocotyle* without differentiated regions has not been recorded in North America.

Only family represented.
Family HEMISTOMIDAE Brandes 1888 . . 161

Distomes with body more or less distinctly divided into two regions. Anterior region spoon or cup-shaped, serving as adhesive organ. Suckers poorly developed, but with peculiar postacetabular sucking organ. Posterior region cylindrical or ovoid. Intestinal crura extend to posterior end. Excretory bladder in form of subcutaneous network. Genital pore at posterior end. Neither cirrus sac nor cirrus. Ovary and testes in series in posterior region. Vitellaria conspicuously developed. Uterus short with few, very large, thin-shelled eggs. No alternation of generations. Develop with intermediate host but without alternation of generations.

Parasitic in intestine of Amniota.

161 (166)   Adult forms with developed sex organs.   162

162 (165)   Dorsal surface without special suckers.   163

163 (164)   Anterior region flat, with foliate margins sharply set off from
            posterior region. . . . . .   *Hemistomum* Diesing 1850.

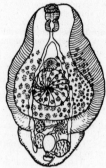

Anterior region more or less in the form of a cone opening anteriorly and ventrally. Acetabulum often covered by special ventral holdfast organ, not larger than oral sucker, in one case entirely
lacking. Sexual pore dorsal.

North American species.
Hemistomum craterum Barker and Noll 1915.

Length 0.75 to 1.89 mm. Cephalic region 0.62 to 0.79 mm. long
by 0.41 to 0.49 mm. wide. Caudal region 0.28 to 0.47 by 0.20 to
0.36 mm. Adhesive disk large, flattened cone with crateriform
top, without papillae.
An unnamed species is recorded from *Didelphis virginiana* by C.
Curtice.

FIG. 711. *Hemistomum craterum.* Ventral view. Magnified. (After
Barker.)

164 (163)   Anterior region cup shaped, with anterior circular entrance.
            Strigea Abildgaard 1790.

Frequently called *Holostomum*, a name of later date.
Anterior region sharply set off from posterior by circular groove. Flattened lateral region
united ventrally to a cup, with mouth at anterior end. Concealed in this cup small acetabulum and posterior adhesive organ in form of a papilla extending to mouth of cup. In genital
pore a well developed genital cone; opening terminal.

North American species. . . . . . *Strigea cornu* (Rudolphi) 1819.

Recorded from *Ardea herodias* in Maryland by Stiles and Hassall.
Another species described by Leidy as *Holostomum nitidum* from the small intestine of *Rana
pipiens* is according to Stafford a distome, and if so could not be placed here.

165 (162)   With row of suckers on dorsal surface.
            Polycotyle Willemoes-Suhm 1871.

Type species. . . . .   *Polycotyle ornata* Willemoes-Suhm 1871.

Length 4.5 mm. Posterior region growing larger posteriorly, longer than anterior. In
mid-dorsal line 14 or 15 suckers.
In intestine of *Alligator lucius;* Charleston, S. C.

FIG. 712. *Polycotyle ornata.* × 25. (After Willemoes-Suhm.)

166 (161)   Larval forms; sex organs wanting or only partly developed. .   167

Sometimes difficult to separate from adults and hence noted here as well as later.
Compare under Holostome Cercariae, 250 (184) in this key.

167 (168)   Larval forms with an oval sucker-like depression on each side of the oral sucker. . . . . *Tetracotyle* Filippi 1854.

Body pyriform or oval. On each side of oral sucker an oval groove, not muscular, with pores of special (cystogenous ?) glands.
Encysted in mollusks and vertebrates. European forms belong to various species of *Strigea*. Ruttger found these larvae in *Limnaea stagnalis* and fed them to ducks; ten days later he obtained mature holostomids (species not given). Leidy recorded *T. typica* from *Limnaea catascopium* and *Physa heterostropha* (cf. 251 in this key). Other undescribed species encysted in North American frogs.

168 (167)   Larval forms without sucker-like depressions at the side of the oral sucker. . . . . . . *Diplostomulum* Brandes 1892.

Body flattened with lateral margins turned ventrad in anterior region; short tip represents posterior region. On anterior margin near oral sucker group of gland pores on each side. Several species encysted in body of fishes, or free in optic bulb of similar hosts. Belong to various *Hemistomum* species (cf. 252 in this key).
A form is frequent which has been identified as *D. cuticola* (v. Nordmann), the larva of *Hemistomum denticulatum* (Rud.) common in Europe. It has been reported from sunfish, perch, bluegill, pumpkin-seed, minnows, horned dace, rock bass, small-mouthed black bass, pike, and other fish from Canada to Iowa. Not a few of the larger cysts contain two worms, one usually much smaller than the other.
Cooper found a form in the optic lens in young *Micropterus dolomieu* which he identified as *Diplostomulum volvens* (von Nordmann).

169 (1)   Larval forms; sexual organs entirely wanting or at most only partly developed. 170

A few encysted forms are described that contain eggs and are apparently sexually mature.

170 (171)   Young flukes, encysted or free, always without caudal appendage. *Agamodistomum* Stossich 1892.

Many immature forms whose relationship to adult types has not yet been determined. The group is artificial, temporary, and collective, including all agamic flukes with two suckers. Agamic forms in other groups have been given special names as noted in connection with the description of the adults.
Forms of this sort are mentioned frequently without specific names. Named forms are also on record, *e.g. A. apodis* (Packard 1882) from the ovisac of *Apus* from Kansas, a unique record of a distome in a phyllopod crustacean, but without data adequate to fix the species.
All forms described as encysted cercariae belong in this subdivision rather than in the next since the two marks of distinction between the two are the tail, which is cast off when the larva encysts, and the cystogenous glands, pure larval organs, that are emptied in this process and disappear.
Various species which belong here have been recorded without description under other names as "*Heterostomum echinatum* Diesing" of Leidy from the oviduct of *Paludina* "quite common," and *Distomum centrappendiculatum* of the same author from *Helix arborea*.

171 (170)   Caudal appendage present, usually simple, sometimes modified, even greatly reduced, rarely absent. . *Cercaria* . . 172

No hard and fast line can be drawn between this group and the last since a few tailless cercariae are known. Furthermore the transition in any case will be instantaneous when the cercaria under stimulation casts off its tail, which happens normally as well as in cultures.
Small, barely visible, microscopic, free-living forms of simple trematode structure, having a triclad alimentary canal. A tail, single, double, branched, setose, or otherwise modified is nearly always present, and is the efficient organ of locomotion. Rarely the tail is rudimentary or entirely lacking and the form can be classified here only by its strong resemblance in other features to the tailed larvae. The reproductive organs are always rudimentary, and sometimes entirely wanting. At most one can distinguish masses or cords of cells that indicate the location of future organs. Faust has found that these agree fully with adult conditions. Prominent larval organs are the stylet, a boring spine in the anterior tip above the oral sucker, simple eyes appearing as pigment spots on the anterior dorsal region usually near the brain, conspicuous dermal glands that in one group are designated stylet glands and in another are assigned a cystogenous function and are perhaps always digestive in character; they present varied features in different species. All of these constitute useful specific characters.
Very few North American species have been described and the brief records that exist are in most cases adequate only for the definition of groups rather than species in the true sense. Most of the following subdivisions of the key are to be regarded in that light.
Some names in use like *Cercaria bilineata* Hald. can have even no general significance since the original reference contains no data that will fix the species.

172 (173)   Mouth opening some distance from anterior end, near center of ventral surface.   Intestine rhabdocoel.
                                        Gasterostomous or rhabdocoelous cercariae.
Alimentary canal short, simple, rod-shaped.   Swimming organ in the form of two long narrow appendages directed obliquely right and left from posterior end of body in the only known type.   Larval stages of Bucephalidae, such as the well-known *Bucephalus polymorphus* von Baer of Europe.
Not yet reported on this continent though the adult (see 29 in this key) is known here.

173 (172)   Mouth opening at or very near anterior end of body.   Intestine triclad. . . . .   Prostomatous cercariae . .   174

174 (183)   Only one sucker, and that around mouth opening.
                                        Monostome cercariae . .   175
All yet studied have a pair of lateral pigment spots on the dorsal surface, the simple eyes. Some have also a medium pigment area between the lateral eyes or slightly anterior to them.

175 (178)   Cercariae without median eye in cephalic region.   176
Under the designation "median eye" is included always an optic cup with pigment lining and an optic cell; part of these are found in certain developmental stages but in species included under this heading disappear so that the structure never becomes complete.

176 (177)   Six pairs of large gland cells in tail.
                                        Cercaria urbanensis Cort 1914

Length 0.27 to 0.54 mm., width 0.11 to 0.2 mm., tail 0.2 to 1.2 mm. long and 0.05 mm. at base.   Develops in rediae.   An active swimmer.   Encysts on solid objects.   Cysts shaped like thick discs.   Moves over surface by aid of two projections one at each postero-lateral angle of body and with cuticular knob in tip.   Heavily pigmented, especially near anterior end.   A pair of lateral eyes; intermediate pigment nucleus present in later stages, but no optic cup or cell at any time.   Cystogenous glands abundant.   From *Physa gyrina* at Urbana, Illinois.

Fig. 713.   *Cercaria urbanensis*, mature, ventral view.   Cystogenous glands not shown. × 70.   *a*, posterior locomotor projection.   × 216.   (After Cort.)

177 (176)   Six groups of paired gland cells in tail, each pair dove-tailing into the one next anterior. . . . .   *Cercaria konadensis* Faust.
Cercaria 0.4 to 0.46 mm. in length, 0.1 to 0.16 mm. in width.   Tail 0.4 to 0.45 mm. long by 0.03 to 0.04 mm. diameter at base.   This species possesses no median pigment area in cephalic region.   Glands of posterior locomotor organ large and prominent.   Cercariae and rediae aspinose.   Germ balls arise from central germinal rachis in subdistal region of redia.
From liver of *Lymnaea proxima* Lea, Bitter Root River, Corvallis, Montana.

178 (175)   Cercariae with median eye or median pigment area in cephalic region.   Larger species than preceding.   179

179 (180)   Distinct mobile, evertible spinose pharynx.
                                        Cercaria pellucida Faust.
Length 0.4 to 0.7 mm., width 0.18 to 0.2 mm.   Tail 0.5 mm. in length, 0.07 mm. in diameter at base.   No large gland cells in tail.   Rediae provided with multispinose evertible piercing organ in prepharynx region.   Germ balls arise from central germ cells in distal region of redia.   From liver interstices of *Physa gyrina* Say, Bitter Root River, Fort Missoula and Corvallis, Montana.

180 (179)   No evertible spinose pharynx mentioned (imperfectly known species).   181

181 (182) Body dark brown, or blackish.

Cercaria hyalocauda Haldeman 1842.

Very imperfectly known. The form described under this name by Evarts (1880) has a body 0.47 mm. long and 0.24 mm. wide with a tail 0.55 mm. long and 0.1 mm. wide in maximum. Cyst 0.32 mm. in diameter. Body dark brown or blackish. Two eye spots and smaller, less distinct pigment mass between. Tail semitransparent, corrugated when contracted, active long after detachment from body.

Evarts' description of the living organism shows it is much like *C. urbanensis* though easily distinguishable by greater size of larva and cyst. Haldeman's account is entirely inadequate to differentiate the form and suffices only to place it in this group. Taken in numbers from *Physa heterostropha* Say by Evarts.

182 (181) Body white. Doubtful form.

Cercaria (Glenocercaria) lucania Leidy 1877.

Length 0.5 mm. White, ovoid, with conical tail equal to or longer than body and frequently moniliform. Two eyes with intermediate black pigment spot and smaller scattered pigment spots near them. Produced in bright orange-colored sporocysts which are cylindrical and bluntly rounded at the ends. Leidy calls this a *Monostoma*, and all data given agree with that conclusion except that his description lists an acetabulum which would make it a distome cercaria. Abundant in *Planorbis parvus* found near Philadelphia, Pa.

183 (174) More than one sucker. 184

184 (250) Oral sucker well developed; genital atrium not modified. . 185

185 (190) Second sucker ventral and at posterior end of body.

Amphistome cercariae. . . 186

According to studies on European species the cercaria of *Paramphistoma cervis* lacks pockets in the oral sucker and has a connection between the longitudinal excretory vessels. It belongs to one subfamily. All other known cercariae in this group belong to another subfamily. They have the pockets in the oral sucker and a muscular enlargement of the esophagus at the bifurcation of the intestinal crura.

186 (189) Cercariae separate, not attached in bunches. 187

Very likely one of the species described below is the larval form of *Diplodiscus temperatus* Stafford, see 57 (58) in this key.

187 (188) Anterior half of body pigmented. . . *Cercaria inhabilis* Cort 1914.

Large, pigmented form, sluggish in movement. Swims slowly in open water, does not progress on substratum. Two large eye spots with lenses. Cystogenous glands thickly developed both dorsally and ventrally. Tail lightly attached above acetabulum and easily lost. Location of genital organs distinctly indicated by four dense masses of nuclei connected by fine lines.

From *Planorbis trivolvis*, Lawrence, Kan., and Urbana, Ill.

Fig. 714. *Cercaria inhabilis*, mature, ventral view. Cystogenous glands not shown.
× 44. (After Cort.)

188 (187)   Pigment in limited area near eyes.

Cercaria diastropha Cort 1914.

Smaller than last, eye spots larger in proportion.   Pigment confined to limited area near eyes.   Tail always shorter than body.   Genital organs distinctly marked out.

FIG. 715.   *Cercaria diastropha*, mature, dorsal view.   Cystogenous glands not shown.
× 60.   (After Cort.)

189 (186)   Cercariae grouped in bunches with individuals united by tips of tails, which are very long and slender.

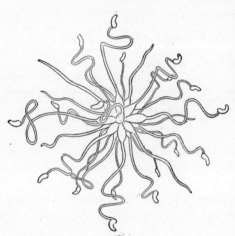

Such forms, designated *Rattenkönig-cercarien* by their discoverer, Leuckart, are as rare as they are striking.   *C. clausii* from the marine fauna, the only form of this type known previously, was determined by Odhner to belong to *Phyllodistomum folium*.   The striking peculiarity in that the cercariae are joined in groups is evidently not of fundamental importance as the marine form (*C. clausii*) and the species noted here belong to different orders of trematodes.

North American species.
Cercaria gorgonocephala
Ward 1916.

Fifty or more cercariae in a single bunch.   Tail, *i.e.*, stalk, enlarged at base with thick wall.   Yellow pigment in body.   Stalk marked by two longitudinal lines of dark pigment, attached to postero-dorsal aspect of worm.

FIG. 716.   *Cercaria gorgonocephala*.   Free-hand sketch from life.   × 40.   (Original.)

190 (185)   Second sucker ventral, not at or near posterior end of body.
Distome cercariae . .   191

Some distome cercariae are readily recognizable by characteristic features of adult structure like the collar and spines of the Echinostomidae which are as prominent in the cercaria as in the adult, and apparently identical in form and arrangement.   In the majority of cases, however, the various groups of distome cercariae at present recognized are purely arbitrary as they are based on superficial characters.   But the system cannot be rewritten until much more is known of the origin of all of these larval organs and until a large number of species has been studied.

191 (247)   Tail present in larva.   192

The name Cercaria is applied strictly only to such larvae as possess a tail, though the tail may be thrown off at an early period.

192 (234)   Tail not conspicuously modified in form or divided into regions.   193

193 (233)   Tail slender, never as broad as body of cercaria.

Cercariae leptocercae . . 194

The long, slender, unbranched tail, which even in maximum contraction does not reach the width of the body, and in extension is twice the body length or more, is found in the majority of distome cercariae. The anterior end of the body furnishes data for the subdivision of these forms.

194 (199)   Anterior end rounded, entirely devoid of spines.

Gymnocephalous cercariae . . 195

So far as known these forms develop in rediae. Many exist on this continent which have not been reported, for many adults are listed in the earlier sections of this key which must possess such larvae as one may infer from European studies on related species. These cercariae are conveniently subdivided on the structure of the tail which in all is a prominent organ but which in some does not function as a swimming organ.

195 (196)   Tail simple, not provided with fin-folds or terminal sucking organ.

Three different forms may be noted without attempting to analyze them in the key.

Cercaria (Gymnocephala) ascoidea (Leidy) 1877.

Length 0.25 to 0.4 mm. Body, white clavate; tail long, narrow, cylindrical, pointed. Cephalic end triangular and slightly constricted from rest of body. Acetabulum at or behind center of body often protruded into a cone or expanded into a cup. No eyes. In movement excessively elongated. Rediae white; head distinct from cylindrical body, with birth pore and caudal prolongation.

Abundant in *Planorbis parvus* and found free in water containing that species. Leidy is in error in identifying this form as *Cercaria minuta* Nitzsch of Europe.

Cercaria agilis Leidy 1858.

Body pyriform, oral sucker large, acetabulum slightly larger, near middle of body. Tail as long as body, clavate, transversely plicate. White. Very active.

Found in Delaware River; ordinarily with snails. Common.

Cercaria fasciolae hepaticae.

Larva of the well-known sheep liver fluke, not yet reported but undoubtedly frequent in certain regions and years as the adult is known to be abundant at certain points in North America.

196 (195)   Tail modified, having fin-folds or terminal organ. 197

197 (198)   Tail provided with dorsal and ventral fin-folds.

Cercaria reflexa Cort 1914.

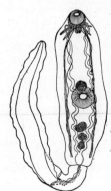

Develops in rediae. Encysts in same snail as redia inhabits or other snail of the same species. Tail as long as body or longer, provided with dorsal and ventral fins. Cystogenous glands abundant. Esophagus long, fine; also crura; bifurcation at anterior level of acetabulum. Genital organs marked out by four masses of nuclei. Cort believes this form is undoubtedly related to the Echinostomes, but the spines are not yet developed. All other characters accord with this view. From *Lymnaea reflexa*, Chicago, Illinois.

Compare 232 (231) in this key.

Fig. 717. *Cercaria reflexa*, ventral view. Cystogenous glands not shown.
× 60. (After Cort.)

198 (197)   Tail long with terminal organ for attachment.
Megalurous cercariae.

Single American species known.

Cercaria megalura Cort 1914.

Develops in rediae. Cystogenous glands abundant. Does not swim in open water or use tail as swimming organ, but as a stalk, becoming attached by the adhesive organ, a group of unicellular glands at the tip. The tail has the power of elongating very greatly. In this position the worm waves or wriggles about in a serpentine fashion. When taken up in a pipette it encysts quickly and this seems to be normal on contact with fresh water.

From *Pleurocera elevatum*, Sangamon River, Ill., and *Goniobasis virginica*, Princeton, N. J. Adult unknown. Reproductive organs indicated by two masses of nuclei joined by line.

199 (195)   One or more spines present at anterior end. 200

200 (224)   Anterior end provided with single median boring spine.
Stylet cercariae . . 201

These forms called Acanthocephala by Diesing and Xiphidiocercariae by Lühe are numerous and perhaps not closely related; even if the stylet cercariae do belong to different adults, their assemblage in a single group is convenient.

Small, slender-tailed cercariae with rounded anterior margin, bearing a dagger-shaped boring spine or stylet, usually in the upper lip of the oral sucker. The form of this organ is very definite in each species and varies between different species distinctly enough to form i1 many cases a valuable mark for diagnosis. Eye spots are usually wanting. Development in sporocysts is most frequent and encystment in a second intermediate host usual in species of which the development is known.

201 (217)   Tail slender, not provided with special organs (bristles, fin-fold) or regions. 202

202 (203)   Stylet glands few in number, not more than four on each side. Tail attached to median posterior extremity, not arising from distinct caudal pocket.   . .   Cercariae microcotylae.

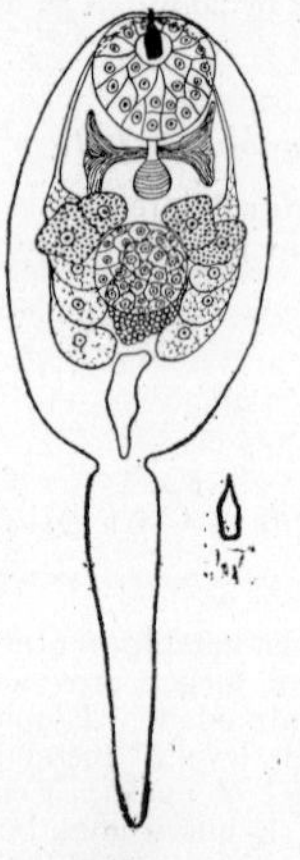

Very small. Body less than 0.2 mm. long. Stylet glands 3 to 4 only, near acetabulum. Excretory bladder small, forking more or less acutely at anterior end. These forms are all minute and further study may disclose the presence of a caudal pocket with minute spines in some or all species. Two species; not analyzed in key.

Median stem of excretory bladder elongate, club-shaped.
Cercaria leptacantha Cort 1914.

Body oval; circular in cross section, 0.12 mm. long by 0.063 mm. wide. Tail slender, shorter than body. Stylet small. Not fully developed. Surface in living specimen with highly refractive prominent globules of different size.

Produced in oval thin-walled sporocysts from *Campeloma decioum* Hartford, Conn.

FIG. 718.   *Cercaria leptacantha*, immature, ventral view.   *a*, stylet, ventral view.
X 320.   (After Cort.)

Median stem of excretory bladder short.
Cercaria caryi Cort 1914.

Very small; stylet glands present, few in number. Acetabulum small; develops in sporocysts. From *Goniobasis virginica*, Princeton, N. J.

FIG. 719.   *Cercaria caryi*, ventral view.   From Cary's material.   X 140.   (After Cort.)

203 (202)   Stylet glands more numerous, six or more on each side. Tail arising from posterior caudal pocket, ventral to excretory bladder. . . . .   Polyadenous cercariae . . 204

204 (210)   Caudal pocket present, distinct, devoid of hooks or spines. . 205

205 (206, 207)   Ceca short, lateral trunks of excretory bladder circumscribe
acetabulum. . . . .   *C. brevicaeca* Cort 1914.

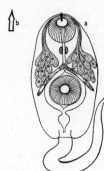

Body elongate oval, 0.3 mm. long, 0.14 mm. wide.   Tail caducous,
slender in length about equal to body.   Oral sucker 0.082 mm., acetabulum 0.087 mm. in diameter.   Stylet glands 10 to 12 on each side.
Intestinal ceca short.   Anterior half of body spinous.   A poor swimmer.
Found in sausage-shaped sporocysts in liver of *Physa analina*
from Manhattan, Kansas.

FIG. 720.   *Cercaria brevicaeca; a,* free hand drawing, ventral view.   Cystogenous glands not shown.   ✕ about 100.   *b,* stylet, ventral view.   ✕ 290.
(After Cort.)

206 (205, 207)   Ceca arise directly from pharynx region, excretory bladder
muscular, crenate, capable of great distension.
Cercaria crenata Faust.

Body length 0.25 mm., width 0.13 mm.   Tail weak, 0.15 to 0.16 mm. in length, 0.02 to 0.03
mm. wide at base.   Body oblong-ovate, with deep pocket at posterior extremity for reception
of tail.   Stylet glands 13, 8 in outer series and 5 in inner series, minute, extending to mid-
acetabular region.   Esophagus lacking.   Sporocysts small oblong-ovate.   In liver tissue of
Lymnaea proxima Lea from springs at Fort Missoula, Montana.

207 (205, 206)   Ceca undeveloped, excretory bladder bicornuate. . . .   208

Cort regards these forms as a natural group characterized by development in elongate sac-
s'iaped sporocysts in Gastropoda, with a slender tail, not usually shorter than the body, with
a small post-central acetabulum, a stylet 30 μ long, with six or more stylet glands on each
side in front of acetabulum, and a bicornuate excretory bladder.   He considers that they probably belong to the Plagiorchiinae.   Nothing is known regarding the development of the
American species.

208 (209)   Six stylet glands on each side.   *Cercaria isocotylea* Cort 1914.

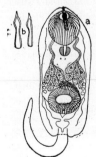

 ̄ Develops in sporocysts.   Tail small, very extensile.   Suckers relatively large.   Stylet glands just in front of ventral sucker.   Excretory
pore dorsal, at base of tail.   Genital glands indicated by nuclear mass
dorsal and anterior to acetabulum, and a larger mass dorsal and posterior, but connected with the former by a band on left margin of acetabulum.
From *Planorbis trivolvis* at Urbana, Illinois.

FIG. 721.   *Cercaria isocotylea; a,* ventral view.   ✕ 207.   *b,* stylet, ventral and
side view.   ✕ 290.   (After Cort.)

209 (208)   Twelve stylet glands on each side.   *Cercaria polyadena* Cort 1914.

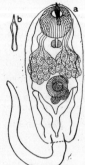

Encysts readily. Tail active, easily detached, somewhat larger than in last species. Oral sucker smaller, stylet glands more numerous. Body also larger than former species. Genital system marked out by S-shaped nuclear mass, elongate and dorsal to acetabulum.

FIG. 722. *Cercaria polyadena;* a, ventral view. Cystogenous glands not shown. X 207. b, stylet, ventral view. X 290. (After Cort.)

210 (204)   Caudal pocket distinct, provided with hooks or spines that are mostly situated in postero-lateral sacs. 211

211 (212)   Digestive tract naked, ceca rudimentary.
Cercaria dendritica Faust.

Body length 0.38 to 0.40 mm., width 0.16 to 0.17 mm. Tail small, 0.16 mm. in length, 0.04 mm. wide at base. Body obovate, muscular; cuticula thick. Caudal pocket lined with spines. Excretory bladder large, muscular, bicornuate; tubules dendritic. In long oval sporocysts in liver of *Lymnaea proxima* Lea, sloughs of Bitter Root River, Fort Missoula, Montana.

212 (211)   Digestive tract provided with special glands, in addition to stylet glands.   Ceca developed. 213

213 (214)   Glands along entire course of digestive tract. Three median spines on lip of caudal pocket. . *Cercaria glandulosa* Faust.

Body length 0.45 mm., width 0.2 mm. Tail length 0.35 mm. by 0.05 to 0.06 mm. at base. Body oblong-ovate, acetabulum slightly behind center of body, smaller than oral sucker. Esophagus long, ceca short, unicellular glands along entire digestive system. Cuticula delicate. Eight cephalic glands. Body filled with cystogenous glands. In sporocysts, in liver of *Physa gyrina* Say, Bitter Root River, Corvallis, Montana.

214 (213)   Glands in pharynx region only, spines confined to pockets of caudal pocket. 215

215 (216)   Ceca attenuate, excretory bladder with long median shank.
Cercaria diaphana Faust.

Body oblong-ovate to ovate. Acetabulum median, about half size of oral sucker. Pharynx small, surrounded by great mass of unicellular glands. Cephalic glands 8, anterior to cecal bifurcation. Stylet set with an internal spine at anterior end. Body length 0.2 to 0.26 mm., width 0.10 to 0.12 mm. Tail 0.15 mm. in length by 0.04 mm. wide at base. In oblong sporocysts in liver tissue of *Lymnaea proxima* Lea, Bitter Root River, Corvallis, Montana.

216 (215)   Ceca inflated, excretory bladder bicornuate, inflated.
Cercaria micropharynx Faust.

Body minute, ovate, covered with fine spines. Acetabulum mid-ventral, smaller than oral sucker. Pharynx extremely small, esophagus short, ceca inflated. Digestive glands in prepharynx region only. Body length 0.18 mm., width 0.09 mm. Tail 0.14 mm. in length by 0.03 mm. at base. In oval sporocysts with well-developed excretory tracts. Liver of *Lymnaea proxima* Lea, Rattle Snake Creek, Missoula, Montana.

217 (201)   Tail modified, not of simple form. 218

218 (223) Tail provided with fin-like fold, but of normal length.

Cercariae ornatae . . 219

219 (220) Eye spots present. . . . . *Cercaria racemosa* Faust.

Body length 0.29 mm., width 0.11 mm. Tail 0.22 mm. in length by 0.04 mm. wide at base. Body ovate, oral sucker small, acetabulum somewhat smaller. Esophagus long, ceca short, extending around acetabulum. Excretory tubules multi-dendritic. Tail with lateral ruffled fin-folds. Stylet delicate, attenuate. In polygonal sporocysts in liver of *Lymnaea proxima* Lea, sloughs of Bitter Root River, Fort Missoula, Montana.

220 (219) Eye spots lacking. 221

221 (222) Stylet small, without thickened region.

Cercaria hemilophura Cort 1914.

Body oval, 0.38 mm. long, 0.14 mm. wide, densely covered with small spines. Tail about length of body, extensile to double body length, with fin half as wide along ventral surface of distal half. Oral sucker 0.065 mm., acetabulum 0.049 mm. in diameter. Stylet small, without thickened region.

Produced in orange-colored, elongate and non-branching sporocysts, much twisted together. In *Physa gyrina* from Rockford, Illinois.

Fig. 723. *Cercaria hemilophura; a,* ventral view. Cystogenous glands not shown. X 80. *b,* stylet, side view. X 290. (After Cort.)

222 (221) Stylet heavy. . . . . *Cercaria platyura* Leidy 1890.

Length 0.8 mm., body 0.4 by 0.12 mm., tail 0.36 by 0.06 mm. at base, width with membranous alae 0.14 mm. Body ovoid, head rounded, oral sucker large (0.08 mm.) with heavy stylet. Acetabulum 0.06 mm. Tail nearly as long as body, stout, tapering, corrugated, with broad, costate, lateral membrane.

Taken free in a pool with *Lymnaea*, at Fort Bridger, Wyo.

223 (218) Tail short and peculiarly modified. . . . Microcercous cercariae.

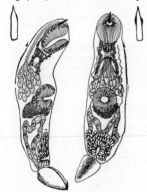

Tail short, stumpy, with powerfully developed muscles. Not a swimming organ, but used as a prop or lever. In the Cotylocercous cercariae of Dollfus the organ is still further modified into a type of sucker. This latter group develops in sporocysts and is mostly marine.

Only species thus far recorded in North America.

Cercaria trigonura Cort 1914.

Body 0.24 mm. long, 0.06 mm. wide. Tail 0.05 mm. long by 0.024 mm. wide. Oral sucker 0.049 mm. long by 0.039 mm. wide. Acetabulum just back of center of body, 0.04 mm. in diameter. Cuticula covered with fine spines. Tail short, blunt, easily detached, triangular, folded into groove. Just anterior prominent gland opening into the head of this groove. Stylet dorsal to oral sucker. Stylet glands small but numerous. Excretory system bicornuate, thick walled. Free in tissues of snails; rediae in same host. No tendency to encyst noted.

Found in *Campeloma decisum* from Hartford, Conn.

Fig. 724. *Cercaria trigonura,* lateral and ventral views. X 170. Each with stylet. X 400. (After Cort.)

224 (200)   Anterior end with fleshy collar and crown of spines.
Echinostome cercariae . . 225

These cercariae develop in rediae which have collar, birth pore, and posterior locomotor appendages. They are characterized by the conspicuous collar and spines, also found in the adult distome. The esophagus is long and the ceca reach to the posterior end of the body. The tail is long and powerful.

225 (228)   Collar spines in a single, if sometimes slightly irregular row. . 226

226 (227)   Collar spines 42, rounded at both ends; excretory trunks doubly reflexed in cephalic region. . . . . *Cercaria biflexa* Faust.

Acetabulum in posterior third of body. Great number of cephalic glands in 2 series, 50 to 60 in each series, lateral to digestive ceca. Excretory tubes reflexed twice in cephalic region preliminary to entering lateral trunks. Bladder long, with median swelling; scaleriform anastomosis of excretory tubules in tail. Body length 0.45 to 0.5 mm., width 0.13 to 0.15 mm. Tail about same length as body, powerful. Encysts within redia. Redia with "feet" in posterior third of body. In liver tissue of *Physa gyrina* Say, near Buckhouse Bridge, Bitter Root River, Montana.

227 (226)   Collar spines 36, acute at distal end; excretory trunks arising from triangular anastomosis in cephalic region.
Cercaria trisolenata Faust.

Deltoid anastomosis of tubules from 3 flame cells in cephalic region, preliminary to entering lateral trunks. Excretory bladder obtruncate. Acetabulum spinose in posterior third of body. Readily encysts in free state, easily drops tail. Body length 0.45 mm., width 0.1 mm. Tail short, about 0.2 mm. Rediae with lateral "feet" about one-third distance from anterior end. In liver of *Physa gyrina* Say and *Planorbis trivolvis* Say. Entire length of Bitter Root River, Montana.

228 (225)   Collar spines in mature cercariae in two alternating rows; excretory trunks reflexed once. 229

229 (230)   Excretory bladder long, attenuate; 43 equal spines.
Cercaria rubra Cort 1914.

Cysts large, spherical, thick-walled, transparent. Collar has forty-three equal spines in two alternating rows; four spines on each side of mid-ventral line point in. Encysted above gills in *Campeloma decisum*, Hartford, Conn. No redia found. Known only in encysted stage which is really an *Agamodistomum* and not a *Cercaria*.

Fig. 725. *Cercaria rubra* in *Agamodistomum* stage freed from cyst, ventral view. X 130. (After Cort.)

230 (229)   Excretory bladder ovoid to depressed spheroid, excretory trunk reflexed almost entire length. 231

231 (232) Tail simple, unmodified. . . . . . *Cercaria trivolvis* Cort 1914.

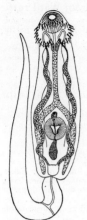

Both rediae and cercariae in *Planorbis trivolvis*, Urbana, Illinois. Moves actively in free water and on solid bodies; found encysted in same host with rediae and cercariae. Nuclei of sex organs in two masses, connected by slender thread. Collar carries thirty-seven equal spines in two alternating rows; two or three spines near mid-ventral line point inward.

FIG. 726. *Cercaria trivolvis*, mature, ventral view. Cystogenous glands not shown. × 65. (After Cort.)

232 (231) Tail with lateral fin-folds. . . . . *Cercaria reflexa* Cort.

Though without oral spines in the stage originally discovered and described this species probably belongs here among Echinostomid cercariae. For description see 197 (198) in this key.

233 (194) Tail simple but heavy, when contracted exceeding in breadth the body. . . . . Rhopalocercous cercariae.

Listed from North America.
Cercaria (*Rhopalocerca*) *tardigrada* Leidy 1858.

Reported by Leidy from *Anodonta* species. The true *R. tardigrada* is *Dist. duplicatum* v. Baer renamed and is the larva of *Phyllodistomum folium* according to Lühe. Perhaps Leidy's form is the larva of some American species in that genus.
No North American cercariae have yet been well described which fall into this subdivision though both of the species listed by Lühe for Central Europe belong to genera, *Allocreadium* and *Phyllodistomum*, which are reported here. These are not closely related genera and the group of cercariae does not appear to be a natural one as at present constituted.
Note that Odhner believes that the larva of *Phyllodistomum folium* occurs in bunches, as stated in 189 (186) of this key.

234 (192) Tail well developed and highly modified. 235

235 (240) Base of tail envelops body of young distome.
Cystocercous cercariae . . 236

The anterior end of the tail is expanded in the form of a bladder into which is folded the body of the young distome that lies thus in a sac or chamber.

236 (237) Chamber globular, small. Tail simple, slender. European type.
Cercaria macrocerca Filippi 1854.

These forms of which several have been described in Europe are the young forms of *Gorgoderinae* (110 in this key). The adults have been reported from this country, but this larval form is yet to be identified here.

237 (236) Chamber large; round. Tail flat, forked, anchor-shaped with broad terminal flukes; powerful swimming organ. . . 238

These move by rapid alternate lateral jerks of the anchor flukes. As the distome is thus pulled along by the tail, the usual orientation of a cercaria is reversed. The adults are unknown.

238 (239) Distome fills three-fifths of stem of anchor.

Cercaria wrightii Ward 1916.

Length 0.75 mm., width 0.133 mm. Flukes measure 0.53 by 0.1 mm. Young distome 0.45 by 0.1 mm. Genital rudiment forms rod-like mass partly preacetabular and partly postacetabular.

Originally described as a free-swimming sporocyst by R. R. Wright, it was shown by observations of Braun on the European *C. miriabilis* to be a highly modified cercaria. Found in an aquarium at Toronto.

239 (238) Distome fills less than half of stem of anchor.

Cercaria anchoroides Ward 1916.

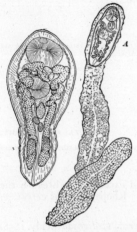

Length 2 mm., width 0.24 to 0.34 mm.; flukes curved, tips 0.84 mm. apart. Young distome 0.64 by 0.288 mm. Germ glands already laid down in middle third of body. Ovary postacetabular, pretesticular; testes oblique. Genital pore preacetabular. Adult unknown.

FIG. 727. *Cercaria anchoroides.* Young distome just set free. × 73. *a,* Cercaria complete. × 27. (Original.)

240 (235) Tail of cercaria does not envelop young distome, but is modified in form. 241

241 (246) Modification consists in forked end.

Furcocercous cercariae . . 242

The long slender tail is split in its distal region and terminates in two slender branches, one-third to one-half the length of the entire structure. An unnatural group as this modification has apparently arisen more than once in different types.

242 (243) Cephalic glands with short ducts, never reaching acetabulum.

Cercaria douthitti Cort 1914.

Develops in sporocysts. Tail bifid; nearly twice as long as body. Oral sucker very large. Two pigment eye-spots with lenses. Eight large cephalic glands in posterior region with ducts opening into or through oral suckers; no stylet found. Single genital nuclear mass at posterior extremity of body. Found in *Lymnaea reflexa* from Chicago, Ill.

FIG. 728. *Cercaria douthitti,* ventral view. × 98. (After Cort.)

243 (242) Cephalic glands open into ducts posterior to acetabulum. . . 244

244 (245) Cephalic region crowned with spines; two eye-spots present.
Cercaria gracillima Faust.

Body length 0.13 to 0.16 mm., width 0.02 to 0.03 mm. Cephalic glands in posterior third of body. A pair of flame cells (in pockets) in posterior third of excretory trunks. Eye-spots lying directly lateral to cephalic ganglia, unpigmented. Genital rudiment extends anterior to acetabulum. Tail about twice body length, furcae of same length as undivided portion. In long attenuated sporocysts in liver of *Physa gyrina* Say, near Buckhouse Bridge, Bitter Root River, Montana.

245 (244) Cephalic region crowned with two small tubercules; eye-spots
lacking. . . . . *Cercaria tuberistoma* Faust.

Body length 0.2 mm., width 0.05 to 0.06 mm. Tail about 0.32 mm., furcae equal in length to undivided portion. Cephalic glands small; excretory system simple, most anterior tubules of tail reflexed, bladder muscular. In sporocysts, either dumbbell shaped or attached at one end. No birth pore. Cercariae escape by splitting wall of sporocysts. In liver tissue of *Physa gyrina* Say, Bitter Root River, Corvallis, Montana.

246 (241) Modification consists of lateral spines in rows.
Setiferous cercariae.

None yet recorded from North America. A small group, mostly marine.

247 (191) Tail apparently entirely wanting. 248

The tail may be small and easily lost or actually not developed.

248 (249) Develop in rediae or unbranched sporocysts. . . . *Cercariaeum.*

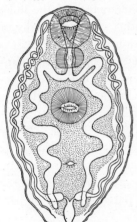

The young distomes possess no cyst or protective membrane. Found not infrequently in our fresh-water mussels. Species not described. Adults unknown. One of the European species is thought to be the larva of *Asymphylodora*.

Cercariaeum helicis (Leidy) 1847.

Total length 0.85 mm.; breadth 0.6 mm., active and very extensive. Body white, oval, with oval tail. Oral sucker marked by radial lines; acetabulum central, equal in size to oral sucker, 0.15 mm. in diameter. Pharynx oval. Intestine large, sinuous, extending to end of body. Excretory bladder small; lateral vessels double. Genital pore postacetabular.
In pericardial cavity of *Helix alternata* and *H. albolabris.* The "first" and "third" stages of Leidy's later account are clearly not the same species as the "second stage" to which the name *Distoma helicis* was originally given.
Called later *D. vagans* also by Leidy. Diesing makes it *Cercariaeum vagans*. Possibly a cercaria which has thrown off its tail but has not encysted.

FIG. 729. *Cercariaeum helicis.* Second stage; highly magnified.
(After Leidy.)

249 (248) Develop in branching sporocysts. . . . . . . *Leucochloridium*

The remarkable species is known in Europe in the adult form as a parasite of singing birds and in the sporocyst stage in certain snails, *Succinea.* See 157 in this key. It has no free-living period.

250 (184) Oral sucker rudimentary, much smaller than acetabulum. Genital atrium modified into sucking organ.
Holostome cercariae . . 251

Genital opening posterior, ventral to excretory pore.

251 (252)   Anterior part of body hemispherical to cup-shaped; two lateral
           sucking discs also present. . . *Cercaria flabelliformis* Faust.

Typical tetracotyle form.   Body length 0.48 to 0.56 mm., width 0.44 mm.   Animal slipper-shaped, with two posterior and two lateral lappets around sucking discs.   Anterior part of excretory system fan-shaped.   In rediae or encysted in tissues in liver of *Physa gyrina* Say, Bitter Root River, Corvallis, Montana.
Compare 167 (168) in this key.

252 (251)   Anterior part of body lamellate or only slightly patelliform.
                                       Cercaria ptychocheilus Faust.

Hemistomum larva.   Body length 0.48 to 0.63 mm., width 0.17 to 0.37 mm.   Posterior portion abbreviated.   Atrial chamber posteriad, well-developed.   Varying number of mucous glands, situated in posterior part lateral to genital atrium, empty into the latter.   Encysted within semitransparent ovoid membrane, with discoid attachment to mesentery of *Ptychocheilus oregonensis* Richardson, Bitter Root River, Stevensville and Carlton, Montana.
The encysted form described by Faust is really a Diplostomulum, *i. e.*, the stage succeeding the true Cercaria.   Compare 168 (167) in this key.

CESTODA

The cestode or tapeworm is as the name suggests more or less like a band or ribbon, and in the majority of cases the band is subdivided by cross-markings into a series of links or proglottids. In a few primitive tapeworms the body consists of but a single link and the general appearance is so similar to that of the fluke as to make distinction difficult. In some other cases, especially of fish tapeworms, the ribbon-like body is not subdivided by external cross-markings, but the internal structure shows the potential presence of proglottids, for the organs are multiplied successively in the undivided body as they are in the segmented body of the ordinary tapeworm. Most tapeworms are distinctly flattened so that one may speak of surfaces and margins. A few species are, however, so nearly circular in cross section that it is difficult to use such terms. Abnormal individuals of the flattened species have been described which are three-cornered or prismatic in cross section; these represent partially fused or partially split chains.

One can usually recognize two or three fairly distinct regions in the ordinary tapeworm: the head or scolex, the neck, and the chain or strobila. The head is more or less enlarged, globular or oval, and not infrequently provided with an apical extension designated a rostellum, which in some forms is held withdrawn in a pocket under most circumstances. The head is commonly supplied with suckers and sometimes hooks also by which it attaches itself to the

tissue of the host. In some tapeworms the head carries long sucking grooves or bothria, and in others round cup-shaped suckers or
acetabula. More complicated hold-fast organs are developed on
the scolex in certain groups of cestodes parasitic in marine hosts.
A slight constriction behind the head has been given the name of
"neck"; many cestodes have no neck. The body usually increases in caliber from the head toward the opposite end. The
partition lines of proglottids are at first very indistinct, and become more marked as one goes backward along the chain. The
form of the proglottids also changes from the scolex toward the
other end of the worm. Much has been made of these and other
minor details of external
appearance in the descriptions of cestodes. They
are not adequate for the
determination of many
species and moreover are
not of fundamental significance. Unfortunately very
few cestodes are transparent and it is not easy to
study the internal structure, since the specimen
must first be subjected to
a time-consuming technic.
Methods for the prepara-
tion of cestode material
were outlined briefly in the
general section of this chapter (page 368). Specimens
must be kept flat and ex-
tended or they are difficult
to study and interpret correctly.

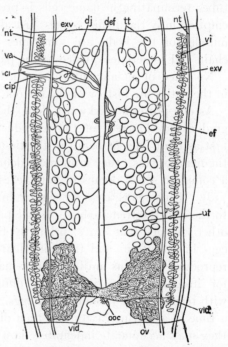

FIG. 730. *Ophiotaenia filaroides.* Mature proglottid, un-
flattened, showing relationships of organs. Abbreviations
used in this and following figures: *ci*, cirrus; *cip*, cirrus-pouch;
def, vas deferens; *dj*, ductus ejaculatorius; *ef*, vasa efferentia;
exv, excretory vessel, ventral; *nt*, lateral nerve; *ooc*, oocapt;
ov, ovary; *ut*, uterus; *va*, vagina; *vi*, vitellaria. × 52. (After La Rue.)

Each proglottid may be
considered as a unit of structure as it contains a complete set of
reproductive organs (Fig. 730). With rare exceptions tapeworms

exhibit the same condition of hermaphroditism that was described for the flukes, since all organs of both sexes are represented in a single proglottid. The reproductive organs of one proglottid have usually no connection with those preceding or following; other organs are continuous throughout the chain. One may readily observe at the side of the proglottid the main longitudinal nerve trunks which connect with a complicated series of enlargements or ganglia in the scolex. These main nerve trunks are joined by cross-connectives in each proglottid. Near them and parallel to them are the main canals of the excretory system, and these also are joined by transverse vessels. A network of finer tubes terminating in flame cells is present in each proglottid and empties into the main vessels just described. The longitudinal muscles of the body are sometimes continuous throughout the chain and sometimes divided at the partitions.

No trace of an alimentary system has been found at any time in the entire life history of the cestode.

As one proceeds backward along the chain one can observe the gradual development of the reproductive organs. These appear first as faint lines or bands in the tissue, outlining the positions of the main organs; they grow more definite until at sexual maturity a complete set of organs of both sexes can be demonstrated (Fig. 730). The organs are very similar in character and interrelation to those of the trematodes. As one passes further along the chain other changes take place, primarily the gradual accumulation of eggs in the uterus and the coincident gradual shrinkage of other reproductive organs until the latter may ultimately disappear save for insignificant vestiges. Two different plans are observable with regard to the production of eggs. The latter may be held for a time in a uterine cavity and then discharged through a pore, or they may accumulate indefinitely in a blind uterine sac until they come to occupy nearly the entire volume of the proglottid. Where the latter condition prevails, the last proglottids of the chain have been reduced to mere egg cases that are cut off periodically, either singly or in groups, and carry to the outer world masses of ova for the dissemination of the species.

Some cestodes have a free-living stage which hatches from the egg in the form of a spherical ciliated larva (**Fig.** 731) that for a short time carries on an existence in the outer world. This larva occurs among the fish tapeworms. The external layer of large ciliated cells may be regarded as an embryonic membrane within which is a narrow fluid filled chamber containing a smaller spherica mass that in fact is the true cestode larva, known as an onchosphere. This larva derives its name from the presence of three pairs of long slender hooks arranged at equal intervals around one pole of the sphere and provided with special muscles that serve to push the hooks out and then away from the center so as to open up tissue and force the larva through it.

FIG. 731. *Diphyllobothrium latum.* Free swimming embryo. Magnified. (After Schauinsland.)

In most cestodes the onchosphere, surrounded by two or more membranes characteristic in form in particular groups, is retained within the egg-shell until the mass is brought passively into the alimentary canal of a suitable host. Here the onchosphere is set free by digestion and bores its way out of the alimentary canal into the body cavity or vascular spaces. It may remain there free and undergo further development, or by active or passive migration reach a point where it encysts and remains fixed during the period of growth. During this period it develops to one of the larval forms of the group. These forms differ in different subdivisions of the class Cestoda. Among the lower forms they are small, oval or elongated, spindle-shaped, solid-bodied larvae known as plerocercoids, and in the highest groups of cestodes they become large fluid-filled vesicles known as cysticerci or bladder-worms. Other types occur among other kinds of cestodes.

These larval forms almost without exception develop in an intermediate host. In some cases the larva wanders out later and achieves actively the infection of the adult or final host, but in most instances it is held in the body of the intermediate host until the latter is eaten. Thereupon it is set free by digestion, migrates to the organ which is its normal seat, and enters upon a period of growth that brings it to the fully matured adult form.

Certain important changes have occurred during this larval growth period. These are most marked in the bladder-worm cestodes. The fully developed cysticercus shows a completely formed scolex that corresponds in detail with the scolex of the adult cestode save that it is reversed and lies turned into the internal cavity of the bladder. When the bladder-worm reaches its final location the head is everted and appears with the armament of suckers and hooks that characterizes the adult. This scolex attaches itself in the region appropriate for the adult and the bladder remnant is lost by digestion while the neck continues to grow in length until it has produced a full-sized adult worm. The formation of proglottids and the growth within them of the reproductive organs proceeds slowly as the worm lengthens, the oldest proglottids being found regularly at the end furthest from the scolex.

The life histories of North American cestodes are entirely unknown and can only be inferred to be similar to related species that have been studied in the Old World. The evidence furnished by the latter indicates clearly that tapeworms are not bound up with an aquatic existence in some stage as are the flukes. Certain cestodes have aquatic larvae and others bladder-worm stages in aquatic invertebrates, or vertebrates, but many of the species parasitic in birds and mammals pass the larval period in terrestrial hosts (insects, land snails, birds, mammals) and have no relation to the aquatic fauna at any time. Such forms do not belong rightly in such a synopsis as this; but the data available are insufficient to mark out clearly which forms belong to the freshwater fauna during some phase of their existence and which are entirely unconnected with it.

Cestodes are found as parasites in all types of fresh-water vertebrates. The adults occur most frequently in the alimentary canal or pyloric ceca. Certain kinds, chiefly larval forms, are found in the body cavity and the encysted stages, the bladder-worms, may be encountered in almost any tissue, even in the brain; yet they are most frequent in connective tissue and seem to find the liver a preferential location. Usually only a few cestodes are found in an individual host, but they may occur in such numbers that the cavity of the alimentary canal is stuffed full and the wall of the body is markedly distended. The distribution of various species is probably nearly concurrent with that of the particular hosts.

North American cestodes are very imperfectly known and the large part of the data available concerns species parasitic in birds and mammals. Because of the lack of definite knowledge it has been necessary to decide upon somewhat artificial limits, and the synopsis has been made to include all cestodes reported in North America from fresh-water hosts and all likely to have developmental stages in fresh-water hosts even though such stages have not yet been identified on this continent. Among the various hosts from which tapeworms are reported the water birds are most difficult to group correctly. Many of them visit both fresh and salt-water bodies, and most of them feed at times and places on terrestrial plants and insects either intentionally or incidentally. Consequently, the source of a given infection is difficult to determine and some errors have no doubt been made in these cases; yet, thanks to Ransom's careful and extensive work, avian cestodes are better known than those from any other host group in North America.

The data on North American cestodes are not only scanty but also so indefinite as to be of little value in the attempt to prepare a systematic outline of the group. Early references are to "cestodes" or "Taenia," and even in later years the same habit has prevailed. Most existing records of the occurrence of tapeworms in aquatic hosts cannot be referred to known genera. For these reasons the appended synopsis must be presented with an apology. Among the Proteocephalidae I have been able to depend on the work of La Rue and for bird cestodes I have made free use of Ransom's monograph. Outside of these groups there is little definite knowledge of the North American forms.

KEY TO NORTH AMERICAN FRESH–WATER CESTODA

1 (122) Adult worms; sex organs developed. **2**

2 (7) Body simple, not divided into joints or proglottids. A single set of genital organs. . . . . Subclass **Cestodaria** . . 3

   The few forms included here are often designated the monozootic cestodes, and sometimes are regarded as a separate class intermediate in position between Trematodes and Cestodes. In external appearance they resemble the flukes but are readily distinguished from them by the entire absence of an alimentary canal. The internal structure is much like that of tapeworms but the sexual organs are never duplicated.

3 (4) Anterior end not peculiarly modified. No suckers, hooks, or specialized scolex region. . . . . *Amphilina* Wagner 1858.
Large, oval, flattened forms, parasitic in body cavity of fishes. Anterior end usually notched, but occasionally extended in the form of a small papilla bearing the pores of a group of unicellular glands. Male genital pore at posterior end. No cirrus sac present. Female pore slightly anterior to male pore, separate from it. Uterus long, uterine pore at anterior end. Embryo with circle of *ten* hooks at one pole.
Not yet reported from North America but present.

4 (3) Anterior end with unarmed, poorly developed adhesive organ, imperfectly set off as scolex from rest of body.
                              Family CARYOPHYLLAEIDAE Claus 1885 . . 5
Body elongate, flattened, with nearly parallel sides and primitive scolex. Neck may be present or wanting, as also a caudal appendix. All genital pores ventral, median, near posterior end; cirrus anterior; uterus and vagina open together into a genital atrium.

5 (6) Caudal appendix present in adult. Two distinct sucking grooves on rudimentary scolex. . . . . . *Archigetes* Leuckart 1878.
Sexually mature in oligochaetes. A form which undoubtedly belongs here has been described to me as found in native earthworms. It has not been recorded in the literature. The species known are 2 to 6 mm. long and parasitic in the body cavity of Tubificidae.

6 (5) No sucking grooves present. Caudal appendix lacking in adult though present in larval form. . *Caryophyllaeus* O. F. Müller 1787.
Expanded anterior end very mobile, irregularly folded but without definite sucking grooves. Intestinal parasites of Cyprinid fishes. Larvae parasitic in body cavity of Tubificidae.

7 (2) Body multiplex, usually divided externally into joints or proglottids; always containing successive sets of reproductive organs generally corresponding to such subdivisions even in cases where external proglottid markings are lacking.
                                      Subclass **Cestoda** s. str. . . 8
Elongate, ribbon-like forms in which the reproductive organs are serially duplicated, each set constituting a reproductive unit, usually though not always set off from adjacent units by internal septa and external boundaries. These forms are often spoken of as the true tapeworms, or polyzootic cestodes.

8 (29, 30) Scolex with a single terminal or with two opposite sucking organs, never with four suckers or accessory proboscides.
                                      Order **Pseudophyllidea** . . 9
Scolex rarely armed with hooks, never provided with rostellum, or extrusile proboscides. The two sucking grooves sometimes combined by complicated growth of their margins into a funnel-shaped or tubular organ which may be united with that of the opposite side to a terminal sucker of peculiar form. External jointing is rarely lacking, but often indistinct in certain regions at least. Uterine pore present, on the surface of the proglottid. Uterus in the form of rosette-shaped coils or of a large sacculate uterine cavity.
Characteritic fish parasites in one or more stages of the life history.
Lühe places the Caryophyllaeidae (see above), as the first family under this order, grouping them as monozootic Pseudophyllidea in contrast with all other families as polyzootic. For practical reasons they are treated here under the Cestodaria.

9 (28) Adult forms with developed reproductive organs. 10
The larval forms are sometimes hard to distinguish from adults. Consult also 28(9).

10 (13) Eggs thin-shelled, without lid. Uterine pore ventral; cirrus and vagina open dorsal and posterior to uterine pore, or marginal. . . Family PTYCHOBOTHRIIDAE Lühe 1902 . . 11
Scolex with two separate bothria, rarely replaced by a pseudoscolex. No neck; external segmentation always present but incomplete or obscured by secondary folds in many cases. Reproductive organs single in each proglottid. Cirrus and vaginal pores posterior to uterine pore, marginal or median and then on opposite surface from uterine pore. Ovary and shell gland median; testes in two lateral fields. Uterus in form of a single spacious cavity, never

of a rosette. Eggs thin-shelled, without lid. Embryonal development in uterus; all eggs of an entire worm may be in many cases at the same stage of development, at a given season. Lühe makes two subfamilies, Ptychobothriinae and Amphicotylinae.

11 (12) Genital pore on surface of proglottid.

Bothriocephalus Rudolphi 1808.

Scolex distinctly elongated, bothria not well developed. External segmentation incomplete between successive proglottids; serrate marginal incisions distinct but markings on surface of proglottids often imperfect or wanting. Vitellaria in cortical layer, continuous from proglottid to proglottid, as are also testes. No seminal receptacle. Beginning of uterus a convoluted canal (uterine duct) which opens into spherical uterine cavity. Uterine pore median, ventral; orifice of cirrus and vagina median, dorsal.

Many entries under this name really belong in other genera of the family. A revision of the group is necessary before one can say which are true species of this genus.

12 (11) Genital pore at margin of proglottid.

Abothrium van Beneden 1871.

Scolex not elongate, with two bothria powerful but not deep. Segmentation uncertain among older proglottids because of surface wrinkles; even oldest proglottids much broader than long. Nerve trunks near margin, dorsal to cirrus and vagina. Testes exclusively between nerve cords in two lateral fields. Vitellaria irregular, also in two broad lateral fields, mostly between longitudinal muscle bundles, separated at proglottid limits. Ovary reniform, ventral, median. Shell gland dorsal to ovary. Uterine sac in ripe proglottids filling almost entire medullary region. Uterine pores ventral, in median longitudinal furrow on strobila.

Representative North American species.

Abothrium crassum (Bloch) 1779.

Reported from salmon in Lake Sebago, Maine; not uncommon in the Great Lakes trout.

13 (10) Orifice of cirrus and vagina on same surface as uterine pore and anterior to latter or marginal. Eggs thick-shelled, with lid.

Family DIPHYLLOBOTHRIIDAE Lühe 1910 . . 14

Scolex and sucking organs variable in form, or replaced by pseudoscolex. Segmentation usually distinct. Receptaculum seminis sharply set off from vagina near inner end. Uterus long, convoluted tube, in form of central rosette; without uterine sac except in *Haplobothrium*. Eggs thick-shelled with lid.

14 (27) Genital pore on surface of proglottid. 15

15 (24) All genital pores exclusively on one and the same surface of the strobila. 16

16 (19) Scolex very short, not set off from the rest of the worm.

Subfamily LIGULINAE Monticelli and Crety 1891 . . 17

Scolex roughly triangular, more or less drawn out to a point with contraction of worm. Bothria median, small, weak. Genital organs in adult fully developed just behind scolex. Testes form dorsal layer in lateral fields of medullary parenchyme. Yolk follicles in lateral part of cortical area. Ovary median, ventral; shell gland median, dorsal.

Adult in intestine of water birds; larva in body cavity of teleosts, attaining full size and forming advanced rudiments of sexual organs, found occasionally in water, having been set free by rupture of abdominal wall of intermediate host.

17 (18) External evidences of proglottid formation limited to anterior end or entirely lacking. . . . . *Ligula* Bloch 1782.

When fully grown jointed only at anterior end, but the divisions do not agree with the internal segmentation of reproductive organs. Bothria poorly developed. Larvae without segmentation and without bothria, live chiefly in Cyprinids. Adults in water birds; stay in definitive host only brief.

Several species have been reported and described by various authors, all too briefly to permit of positive identification. The parasites come from chub, sucker, and trout; New York, Pennsylvania, Maryland, Yellowstone Park, Arizona.

18 (17) Proglottid formation evident externally throughout entire worm, even in larval condition. . . *Schistocephalus* Creplin 1829.

Apex of scolex pitted, retractile. Bothria poorly developed. Segmentation complete. Suckers and proglottids visible in larva. Adults in water birds; larvae in abdomen of *Gasterosteus*.

At least one adult and one larva are found in North America. No records have been published.

19 (16) Scolex more or less elongate, distinctly set off from rest of worm. 20

20 (21) Scolex similar in form to first proglottids, separated by sharp boundaries; no unjointed region (neck).

Subfamily HAPLOBOTHRIINAE Cooper.

Proglottid formation evident externally only in anterior part of strobila. Large median dorsal and two smaller ventro-lateral excretory vessels. Both vitellaria and testes medullary. Cirrus covered with minute spines. Uterus sharply divided into uterine duct and large uterine sac.

Type and only genus. . . . . *Haplobothrium* Cooper 1914.

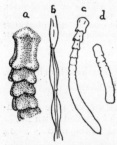

FIG. 732. *Haplobothrium globuliforme. a,* scolex and first three proglottids; X 20; *b,* twenty-third, twenty-fourth, and twenty-fifth proglottids, lateral view, showing disappearance of auricular appendages; X 6; *c,* young scolex showing beginning of proglottid formation; X 11; *d,* smallest plerocercoid observed; X 11. (After Cooper.)

Scolex small, simple; rectangular, excavated dorso-ventrally to form simple bothria, and also slightly laterally. Apex slightly extended to form low pyramidal disc; posterior end of scolex modified as auricular appendages which with edges of apical disc bear minute spines. No neck. Proglottids elongate and auriculae decrease posteriad until segmentation near end is indicated only by successive sets of reproductive organs. Large median dorsal and two small ventro-lateral excretory trunks. Testes small, numerous (80) in 2 lateral fields. No genital sinus. Cirrus and vagina open close together well anterior on ventral surface. Uterine pore ventral also, anterior to posterior end of uterine sac. Ovary horse-shoe shaped, ventral, posterior. Large yolk-reservoir.

Uterus in 2 regions formed very early, viz.: coiled thin-walled uterine canal and capacious uterine sac which when filled occupies almost entire central field of proglottid. Eggs with opercula, carrying ciliated larva.

Type species.

Haplobothrium globuliforme Cooper 1914.

Intestine of *Amia calva.* The uterine sac and the armed cirrus exclude this genus from the family in which it was placed formerly. It certainly shows some points of resemblance to the Triaenophorinae and has been included in a new subfamily which at present stands isolated in a position intermediate between that and the following family.

21 (20) Scolex separated from first proglottids by unjointed region (neck).

Subfamily DIPHYLLOBOTHRIINAE Lühe 1910 . . 22

Proglottid formation always evident externally. Genital organs single or double in each proglottid. Vitellaria cortical; testes medullary in position. Vas deferens with muscular bulb before entrance to cirrus sac. No spines on cirrus.

Adults in intestine of Amniota; larvae so far as known in fishes, reproductive organs wanting at time of transfer to definitive host.

22 (23) One set of reproductive organs in each proglottid.

Diphyllobothrium Cobbold 1858.

The most famous member of this genus is the broad fish tapeworm of man, *D. latum,* commonly referred to as *Bothriocephalus latus,* though it is very distinct from that genus as reference to the section will show. This species has become established on the North American continent, having been introduced no doubt by immigrants from infected territory in Europe.

Possibly related species. . . . . [*Dibothrium*] *cordiceps* Leidy 1871.

Length of adult 2 m.; scolex cordiform 2 by 0.6 to 0.8 mm., neck short. Widest about 15 to 25 cm. from head, where proglottids are 7.5 mm. long, 4.5 mm. broad, 0.5 mm. thick.

Genital pores median, ventral, approximated but distinct; cirrus pore most anterior. Cirrus large, oval. Testes in lateral fields, dorsal. Vagina with vesicle near distal end. Ovary posterior, ventral, transverse to main axis. Shell-gland dorsal, near ovary and posterior to it. Uterus in lateral coils, approaching form of rosette. Ova 70 by 35 μ.

Adult in white pelican; larvae in muscles and body cavity of trout; Yellowstone Lake, Wyoming.

The name of this form cannot be accepted as *Dibothrium* is only a synonym of *Bothriophalus* and the location of the genital pores rules this species out of that genus as at present defined. Furthermore its exact position and true relationship must remain uncertain until its structure is better known.

23 (22)   Two sets of reproductive organs in each proglottid.
Diplogonoporus Lönnberg 1892.

Very large cestodes parasitic in whales, seals, and occasionally in man.

The human parasite, *D. grandis*, is reported by Ashford and King from Porto Rico so it may easily reach the southeastern coast of North America (see also *Sparganum mansoni*).

24 (15)   Genital pores of different proglottids found on both surfaces of strobila, alternating irregularly from proglottid to proglottid. . Subfamily CYATHOCEPHALINAE Lühe 1899 . .   25

Scolex unarmed, variable in form, not longer than wide, with two median or one apical sucking organ in form of acetabula. External proglottid limits not marked, or absent. Genital organs single in each proglottid; all pores median. Vagina and uterus open in common female genital atrium provided with sphincter and located posterior to male pore. Adults in fishes.

25 (26)   Apical sucking organ single, undivided by transverse fold.
Cyathocephalus Kessler 1868.

Scolex with single apical sucking organ in form of a cup, and without evidence in shape or structure of its origin from fusion of two bothria located on surface. Proglottid limits distinct externally. Sphincter of female genital atrium poorly developed. Adults in fishes.

Type species. . . . . . . *Cyathocephalus truncatus* (Pallas) 1781.

Reported by Linton from pyloric ceca of common whitefish, Lake Superior.

26 (25)   Apical sucking-organ single but divided by transverse fold indicating its double origin. . . . . . *Bothriomonus* Duvernoy 1842.

Scolex large, approximately spherical, with single apical sucking organ like acetabulum, yet divided transversely by a fold which indicates its origin from two bothria typical of family. No external proglottid boundaries. Sphincter of female genital atrium well developed. In *Acipenser oxyrhynchus;* Wabash River, Indiana.

Type species. . . . . . . *Bothriomonus sturionis* Duvernoy 1842.

27 (14)   Genital pore at margin of proglottid.
Subfamily TRIAENOPHORINAE Lühe 1899.

Scolex always with typical bothria, not very deep; flattened apex of scolex projects above bothria as a more or less distinct annular cap. Marginal genital pores alternating irregularly; uterine pore, median on ventral surface, anterior to marginal genital pore. Reproductive organs single in each proglottid. No muscular bulb at inner end of cirrus sac. Receptaculum seminis small. Uterus in coils, but never in rosette form, somewhat enlarged near its terminus.

Adults in intestine of fishes and marine turtles; larvae in fishes, mostly unknown.

Type genus . . . . *Triaenophorus* Rudolphi 1793.

Scolex with 4 three-pointed hooks. No external proglottid markings. Testes occupy all medullary layer not taken by other organs. Vitellaria continuous in cortical layer, interrupted only at genital pores. Ovary and shell gland adjacent to margin bearing genital pore. Uterine pore usually not median but on surface at right of median line when marginal pore is sinistral and *vice versa*.

Adults in intestine of fishes; larva encysted in fishes. Present in North America; no species definitely recorded as yet.

28 (9) Immature forms; sexual organs wanting or at least as yet only partly developed. . . . . *Sparganum* Diesing 1855.

Larval stages, without sex organs; not yet at a period in which specific determination is possible. Many undescribed forms in various hosts; three known forms are listed below. The first named is not yet reported for this continent; the second and third are definitely recorded for United States of America.

Sparganum mansoni (Cobbold) 1882.

Large forms, 8 to 36 cm. long; o.1 to 12 mm. broad. Two longitudinal grooves on dorsal surface; one median longitudinal groove on ventral surface. In connective tissue and body cavity of man. Japan. The probable adult, *Diplogonoporus grandis* has been reported from Porto Rico.

Sparganum proliferum (Ijima) 1905.

Small form, 1 to 12 mm. long, 2.5 mm. broad. Body usually irregular in form. Multiplication in cysts by formation of supernumerary heads and transverse division. Encysted in subdermal connective tissue and elsewhere; in man, Florida, U. S. A., and Japan.

Sparganum sebago Ward 1910.

Length 25 to 36 mm., breadth 1.8 to 0.36 mm. Head with keyhole-shaped bothria. Body elliptical in cross-section with slightly thickened margins. No segmentation developed and no sex organs. In spleen and body cavity of *Salmo sebago;* Maine.

29 (8, 30) Scolex with two or four sucking grooves, and also at apex four protrusile proboscides armed with many hooks.

Order **Trypanorhyncha.**

The four long slender cylindrical proboscides are conspicuous enough to render the determination of adult or larva easy. The adults are found in the spiral valve of sharks and rays; the larval forms occur encysted in migratory fish. They are among the rarest of finds in fresh-water collecting and are present in North America though no species are recorded as yet.

30 (8, 29) Scolex with four sucking organs (exceptionally replaced by a pseudoscolex) but without extensile proboscides. No uterine pore. 31

31 (54) Vitellaria with very numerous follicles, distributed on each side in longitudinal marginal zone, rarely in the entire surface zone of the proglottid. . . . . Order **Tetraphyllidea.**

Sucking organs 4, cup-shaped, small, or very mobile stalked or unstalked modified bothridia. Small apical sucking organ frequent. Pseudo-scolex exceptionally present. External segmentation evident, but less conspicuous at end of chain. Genital organs single in each proglottid. No uterine pore, but uterus opens in median ventral line by rupture of wall. Testes numerous. Ovary posterior, median, usually with two wings. Eggs thin-shelled, without lid; embryonal development in uterus.

Adults in intestine of cold-blooded vertebrates.

Only family in North America in fresh-water hosts.

Family PROTEOCEPHALIDAE La Rue 1911 . . 32

Heads small. Suckers sessile and without accessory areola. Fifth sucker functional, vestigial, or lacking. No rostellum. Genital organs in general as in other Tetraphyllidea. Genital pores marginal, irregularly alternating. Vitellaria lateral, follicular, follicles closely grouped about a central conducting tubule. Ovary bilobed, posterior. Oocapt, ootype, shell gland, and uterine passage present. Uterus with lateral outpocketings and one or more preformed ventral uterine openings. Vitellaria, testes, ovary and uterus within the inner longitudinal muscle-sheath.

Habitat: In fresh-water fish, amphibians, and aquatic reptiles.

32 (53) Head without lappets or folds of tissue around suckers. 33

33 (46) Testes in one broad mass between vitellaria; parasitic in fresh-water fish. . . . . *Proteocephalus* Weinland 1858 . . 34

Head globose or conical, flattened dorsoventrally. No rostellum. No spines or hooks. Suckers circular or oval. Fifth sucker functional or vestigial, rarely lacking. Musculature well developed. Eggs with three membranes.

34 (41)   Functional fifth or apical sucker, absent or vestigial. 35

35 (38)   Testes number 100 or more. 36

36 (37)   Genital pore on lateral margin near center of proglottid.
          Proteocephalus macrocephalus (Creplin) 1825.

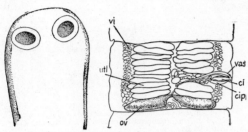

As much as 40 cm. long by 1 to 1.8 mm. broad, or perhaps more. Proglottids very numerous; first much broader than long; mature, broader than long or nearly quadrate; ripe, longer than broad. Suckers 0.095 to 0.106 mm. in diameter. Fifth sucker vestigial. Testes 100 to 120, irregularly scattered between vitellaria, lying in one or two layers, usually one. Cirrus-pouch short, about 0.16 mm. long; ratio to proglottid breadth 1 : 6 to 1 : 8. Uterine pouches 7 to 14 on either side. Habitat: In intestine of *Anguilla vulgaris* and *A. chrysypa* Raf.

FIG. 733. *Proteocephalus macrocephalus.* *a*, Head. × 70; *b*, ripe proglottid showing female reproductive organs. × 40. (After La Rue.)

37 (36)   Genital pore on lateral margin anterior to center of proglottid.
          Proteocephalus perplexus La Rue 1911.

Length as much as 155 mm.; maximum breadth 1.7 mm. First proglottids much broader than long; mature proglottids 1.70 mm. broad by 0.595 mm. long; ripe proglottids quadrate or longer than broad. Suckers, 0.340 to 0.459 mm. long by 0.255 to 0.272 mm. broad. No vestige of fifth sucker.

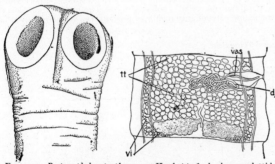

Genital pore at end of first fourth or half of proglottid. Cirrus-pouch 0.30 to 0.344 mm. long, extending to one-third or one-fifth width of proglottid. Testes 135 to 155 in number, in one layer anterior to ovary. Vagina anterior to cirrus-pouch, never crossing same. Vitellaria extend to posterior margin of proglottid and parallel to it. Uterus with 20 to 25 lateral pouches on each side.

Habitat: In intestine of *Amia calva* and *Lepisosteus platostomus.* Illinois, North Carolina.

FIG. 734. *Proteocephalus perplexus.* *a*, Head, × 36; *b*, ripe proglottid, reconstruction showing male reproductive organs (*tt*, testes), and ovary. Note also position of sphincter vaginae (*vas*). × 36. (After La Rue.)

38 (35)   Testes number less than 100. 39

39 (40)   Suckers with pointed apex and shallow cavity.
          Proteocephalus singularis La Rue 1911.

Strobila long, slender, up to 170 or even 250 mm.; maximum breadth 0.90 to 1.0 mm. Head small, suckers large. No vestige of fifth sucker. First proglottids broader than long; mature proglottids 0.85 mm. broad by 0.34 to 0.37 mm. long; ripe proglottids longer than broad or quadrate. Old spent proglottids up to 2.0 mm. long by 0.4 mm. broad.

Genital pore at end of first one-fourth to one-half of proglottid. Testes 75 to 80 or 90, in a .

single layer. Vas deferens large mass of coils in mid-field. Cirrus-pouch slender, nearly straight, muscular, length two-fifths to one-third proglottid width.

Vagina always anterior to cirrus-pouch, never crossing latter. Beginning region of vagina narrow. Uterus with 20 to 25 lateral outpocketings.

In intestine of *Lepisosteus platostomus*, Illinois.

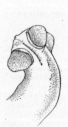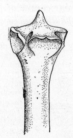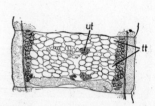

FIG. 735. *Proteocephalus singularis. a*, Head; apical prominence contracted; *b*, apical prominence extended, × 50; *c*, ripe proglottid, frontal section showing arrangements of testes, vitellaria and ovary; vagina and cirrus-pouch not shown, × 36. (After La Rue.)

40 (39)   Suckers round or oval with smooth contour.
             Proteocephalus ambloplitis (Leidy) 1887.

Large, 280 to 410 mm. long, 2 to 2.5 mm. in maximum breadth. Surface of body rough, with transverse and longitudinal furrows. Scolex prominent. Fifth sucker vestigial. Young proglottids 12 to 15 times broader than long. Mature and ripe proglottids broader than long, about quadrate, or rarely longer than broad. Vitellaria not posterior to lobes of ovary. Genital sinus at end of first fourth of proglottid. Uterus with 15 to 20 lateral outpocketings on each side. Cirrus-pouch pyriform, muscular, two-sevenths to two-fifths of proglottid breadth. Coils of vas deferens many, extending to middle of proglottid. Testes 70 to 100 in number.

Intestine of *Ambloplites rupestris, Micropterus salmoides, M. dolomieu, Amia calva·* New York, Michigan, Minnesota, and Wisconsin.

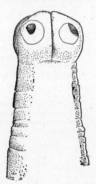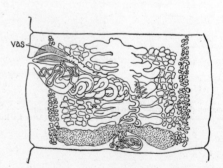

FIG. 736. *Proteocephalus ambloplitis. a*, Head, × 25. (After La Rue); *b*, ripe proglottid, frontal section showing main parts of male and female reproductive systems, magnified. (After Benedict.)

·41 (34)   Well-developed (functional) fifth sucker present.   42

42 (43)   Cirrus-pouch extends half way across proglottid.
Proteocephalus exiguus La Rue 1911.

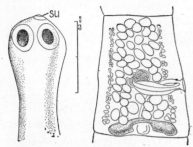

Strobila short, slender, length 9 to 38 mm., maximum breadth 0.425 to 0.8 mm. First proglottids longer than broad or nearly quadrate; mature and ripe proglottids longer than broad, ripe proglottids considerably larger, 0.680 to 1.190 mm. long by 0.460 to 0.595 mm. broad. Suckers 0.058 mm. broad, 0.069 to 0.085 mm. long. Genital pore near middle of lateral margin of proglottid. Testes 34 to 54 in number, in one layer. Vas deferens forming mass of coils in mid-field. Vagina anterior to cirrus-pouch, crossing it near middle. Uterus with 9 to 14 lateral pouches on either side.

In intestine of *Coregonus nigripinnis*, *C. prognathus*, and *C. artedi*, Lake Michigan.

FIG. 737. *Proteocephalus exiguus. a*, Head, *su*, fifth sucker, × 93; *b*, mature proglottid, × 60. (After La Rue.)

43 (42)   Cirrus-pouch less than one-third breadth of proglottid. 44

44 (45)   Testes in one layer. . . . .   *Proteocephalus pinguis* La Rue 1911.

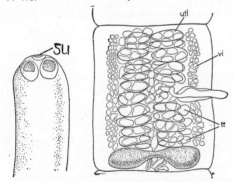

Strobila short, slender, length up to 90 mm., maximum breadth 1.24 mm. First proglottids very short. Mature and ripe proglottids nearly quadrate or in a few ripe proglottids length exceeding the breadth.

Genital pore at or near middle of lateral margin of proglottid. Testes 54 to 70, in a single layer. Cirrus-pouch short, stout, 0.13 to 0.14 mm. long by 0.05 to 0.06 mm. broad, 1 : 3 or 1 : 4 in breadth of proglottid. Vagina anterior, but vaginal opening always dorsal to cirrus-pouch. Vagina crossing inner end of cirrus-sheath. Uterus with 10 to 14 lateral pouches on either side.

In intestine of *Esox reticulatus* Le Sueur, and *E. lucius* Linn., Maine, Michigan, and Wisconsin.

FIG. 738. *Proteocephalus pinguis. a*, Head in dorsal or ventral view, × 45; *b*, ripe proglottid, *utl*, lateral uterine pouches, ventral view, × 63. (After La Rue.)

45 (44)   Testes in two layers. . . . . .   *Proteocephalus pusillus* Ward 1910.

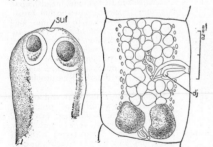

Very small, weak; length 30 to 50 mm., maximum breadth 0.350 mm. Proglottids few. First proglottids broader than long, mature proglottids longer than broad, ripe proglottids much longer (0.84 to 1.4 mm.) than broad (0.18 to 0.35 mm.)

Genital sinus at end of first one-third to two-fifths of proglottid. Testes 44 to 70 in number, in two layers. Coils of vas deferens few, anterior to cirrus-pouch. Vagina never crossing cirrus-pouch. Uterus with 10 to 16 lateral pouches on each side.

Habitat: Intestine of *Salmo sebago* Girard and *Cristivomer namaycush* Walbaum; Sebago Lake, Maine, Lake Temagami, Ontario.

FIG. 739. *Proteocephalus pusillus. a*, Head, showing fifth sucker, × 70; *b*, mature proglottid, toto, × 63. (After La Rue.)

46 (33) Testes lie in two lateral fields between vitellaria; parasitic in amphibians, aquatic snakes, and lizards.
Ophiotaenia La Rue 1911 . . 47

Head globose or somewhat tetragonal. No rostellum. No hooks or spines. Suckers circular or oval, with margins entire. Fifth sucker vestigial. Neck usually long. Testes in
two long lateral fields anterior to ovary. Musculature weak.
In aquatic snakes and Amphibia.

47 (48) Vagina always anterior to cirrus-pouch, not crossing latter.
Ophiotaenia filaroides La Rue 1909.

Worms attenuate, small, thin, flat. Length 80 to 110 mm., maximum breadth about 0.80
to 0.90 mm. Suckers deep, muscular, oval, maximum diameter 0.165 to 0.184 mm. First
proglottids 0.30 to 0.36 mm. broad by 0.10 to 0.17 mm. long; mature proglottids quadrate or
longer than broad; ripe proglottids from 1.6 mm. to 4.0 mm. long by 0.8 mm. to 0.75 mm.
broad.

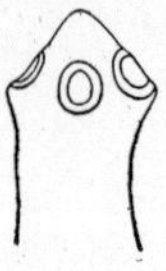

Genital pore at end of first fifth of proglottid. Testes 70 to 114 in number.
Few coils in cirrus-pouch. Cirrus-pouch about 0.22 mm. long by 0.11 mm.
broad. Vitellaria with large follicles. Uterus with 25 to 35 lateral pouches on
each side. (For structure of mature proglottid consult figure 730, page 425.)
Intestine of *Amblystoma tigrinum* (Green); Nebraska and Kansas.

FIG. 740. *Ophiotaenia filarioides.* Head of adult, magnified. (After La Rue.)

48 (47) Vagina either anterior or posterior to cirrus-pouch. 49

49 (52) Genital pore anterior to middle of margin of proglottid. 50

50 (51) Testes number 90 to 160. *Ophiotaenia lönnbergii* (Fuhrmann) 1895.

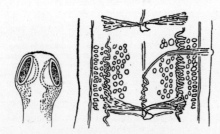

Length 170 to 190 mm., breadth up to
1.35 mm. Scolex 0.50 to 0.60 mm. broad.
Suckers measure 0.24 to 0.26 mm. long
by 0.14 to 0.22 mm. broad. First proglottids about 0.5 mm. long by 0.50 mm.
broad; mature proglottids 0.85 to 1.0
mm. square, or longer than broad,
measuring as much as 2.5 mm. long by
0.45 to 0.5 mm. broad. Ripe proglottids
not observed.

Genital pore situated at end of first
one-third or two-fifths of proglottid.
Testes 90 to 160 in number, extending
lateral of excretory vessels and a few

FIG. 741. *Ophiotaenia lönnbergii.* *a,* Head, *b,* mature
proglottid, magnified. (After Fuhrmann.)

into midzone. Cirrus-pouch 0.185 to
0.280 mm. long by 0.05 to 0.085 or 0.10
mm. broad, with large mass of coils.
Uterus with 25 to 40 lateral pouches.

posterior to it. Vagina never crosses cirrus-pouch.
In intestine of *Necturus maculosus* Raf.; Ohio, Indiana.

51 (50)   Testes number 150 to 215.   .   *Ophiotaenia perspicua* La Rue 1911.

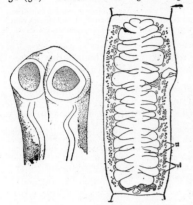

Length up to 360 mm., maximum breadth about 2.0 mm. First proglottids short, mature proglottids quadrate (2.0 mm.) or somewhat longer than broad, ripe proglottids as much as 3.8 mm. long by 1.2 mm. broad.

Genital pore situated near middle or at end of first third of proglottid. Testes 150 to 215. Vas deferens in ripe proglottids heavy mass of coils reaching from end of cirrus-pouch to mid-field. Ratio of length of cirrus-pouch to proglottid breadth 1 : 4 to 1 : 3. Vagina anterior or posterior to but not crossing cirrus-pouch. Uterus with 20 to 30 lateral pouches on each side.

Habitat: *Natrix* (*Nerodia*) *rhombifer* Hallowell; Illinois, Oklahoma.

Fig. 742. *Ophiotaenia perspicua.* a, Head, × 23; b, ripe proglottid, showing uterine pouches, and testes. (After La Rue.)

52 (49)   Genital pore at or near center of margin of proglottid.
Ophiotaenia grandis La Rue 1911.

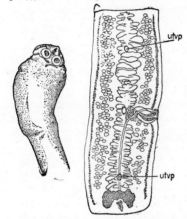

Very long (fragments 200 mm.), 2.75 to 4.25 mm. broad in ripe proglottids. First proglottids much broader than long; proglottids with developing sexual organs quadrate or nearly so; ripe proglottids quadrate or much longer than broad. Head large, 1.0 to 1.2 mm. broad at base of suckers. Suckers about 0.34 by 0.36 mm. Testes large, numerous, 200 to 250. Cirrus-pouch 0.24 to 0.26 mm. broad, 0.64 to 0.75 mm. long, enclosing few or no coils of ductus ejaculatorius. Uterus with 40 to 60 lateral outpocketings on each side.

In intestine of *Ancistrodon piscivorus* Holbr., locality not known.

Fig. 743. *Ophiotaenia grandis.* a, Head, showing swollen region back of head, × 8; b, mature proglottid, ventral view showing reproductive organs and ventral uterine pores (*utvp*). × 10. (After La Rue.)

53 (32)   Many lappets or folds of tissue about suckers.
Corallobothrium Fritsch 1886.

Scolex with four suckers situated on the flat anterior face of the head. Many irregular folds and lappets of tissue about margin of anterior surface; may enclose suckers as in a corolla. No rostellum. No hooks nor spines. Neck broad, short. Habitat: In Siluridae.

Marshall and Gilbert report the occurrence of two species in the common bullhead. I have an undescribed species taken from a channel-cat at Milford, Neb.

54 (31)   Vitellaria condensed, in a single mass, in medullary layer, usually immediately posterior to ovary, rarely anterior to it.
Order **Cyclophyllidea** . . 55

' Scolex with 4 cup or saucer-shaped suckers and in the center an apical organ or rostellum of varied form. Hooks common on rostellum, very rare on suckers. Segmentation well developed, only rarely absent (Fimbriariidae); proglottids set free after full maturity. No uterine pore; rarely a secondary connection to the exterior permits the escape of ova. Testes in medullary layer, ordinarily numerous. Ovary bilobed; vitellarium compact, single, near ovary

with shell gland between. Eggs thin-shelled, no lid; onchosphere with one or more membranes. Bladder-worm in vertebrates and invertebrates.
The great majority of forms commonly designated *Taenia* are included here. Number
and form of hooks on which older systems are based form unreliable means for the distinction
of species. In immature forms the organs utilized in this key are undeveloped and a determination can only be approximate.

55 (117)   Body flattened.   Distinct and regular external boundaries corre-
           sponding to internal grouping of organs in the strobila.   56

56 (57)   Suckers carry on anterior and lateral surface auricular appendages.
          Vitellarium anterior to ovary.
                              Family TETRABOTHRIIDAE Fuhrmann 1907.

Scolex unarmed, without rostellum.   Neck short.   Proglottids
except oldest always much broader than long.   Reproductive organs
single in each proglottid.   Genital pores unilateral; genital cloaca
deep.   Cirrus-pouch small and nearly spherical, united with genital
cloaca, by muscular cloacal canal.   Eggs with three transparent envelopes.   Adults in birds and mammals.

          Type genus.   .   *Tetrabothrius* Rudolphi 1819.

With characters of the family.
Scolex unarmed, quadrate.   Suckers large.   Sexual pore always
dextral.

FIG. 744.   *Tetrabothrius*   The hosts are aquatic birds, largely marine.   Nearly twenty species
macrocephalus. Scolex; mag-   are described, a number of which occur in North American birds:
nified. (After Lühe.)   (gull, grebe, heron, loon), that frequent fresh-water bodies.

57 (56)   Suckers simple without appendages of any sort.   Vitellaria not
          anterior to ovary but posterior to it, or in the same trans-
          verse plane with it. 58

58 (59)   Genital pores median, on flat surface of proglottids.
                              Family MESOCESTOIDIDAE Fuhrmann 1907.

Scolex without rostellum or hooks.   Suckers unarmed.   Reproductive organs single in
each proglottid.   Genital pores median on ventral surface.   Vagina opens in front of or beside
cirrus-pouch.   Eggs in terminal proglottids inclosed in single thick-walled egg-capsule. Adults
in mammals and birds.

          Type genus. . . . .   *Mesocestoides* Vaillant 1863.

With characters of the family.
Few species; almost never in aquatic forms.   No North American records although the
genus occurs here.

59 (58)   Male genital pores at margin or very close to it.   Female pores
          when present similarly located. 60

60 (104)   Female genital pore present and located near male pore. . . . 61

61 (103)   Uterus transverse or irregular, not elongated in median line of
           proglottid. 62

62 (102)   Reproductive organs simple in each proglottid or if genital pores
           are double, the organs are also double. 63

63 (64)   Scolex provided with three to many rows of hooks.
                              Family DIPYLIDIIDAE Lühe 1910.

No forms in fresh-water hosts.

64 (63)   Scolex provided with one or two rows of hooks or without any
          hooks. 65

65 (70) Rostellum hassock-shaped with a multitude of very small hooks arranged in a double row.
Family DAVAINEIDAE Fuhrmann 1907 . . 66

Scolex with rostellum usually broader than high and armed with very many minute hammer-shaped hooks. Margins of suckers usually with small hooks. Genital organs usually single, rarely double in each proglottid. Testes numerous. Onchosphere with two thin membranes.

66 (67) Uterus divides into numerous separate parenchyme-capsules.
Davainea R. Blanchard 1891.

Rostellum armed with double row of hooks; dorsal excretory vessels present. Reproductive organs single in each proglottid. Genital pores unilateral or occasionally irregularly alternate. Uterus breaks down into egg capsules each containing one or several eggs. Adults in mammals and birds. Numerous species; mostly in scratching birds. D. anatina is reported from the domestic duck in Europe. No North American records.

67 (66) Uterus not breaking up into separate parenchyme-capsules. . . 68

68 (69) No parauterine organ; uterus sac-shaped. Rostellum broader than scolex with several thousand hooklets.
Ophryocotyle Friis 1870.

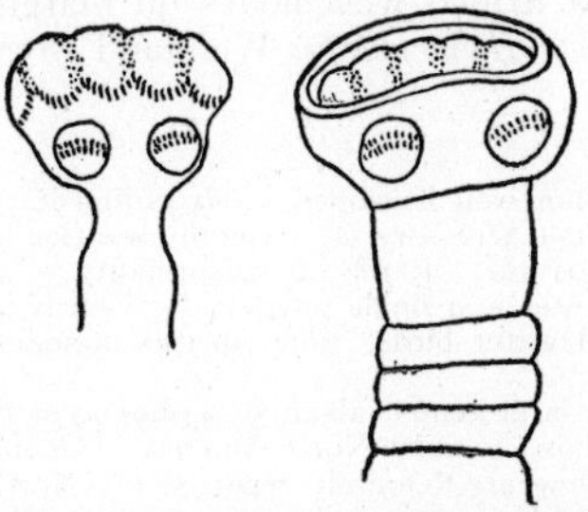

Rostellum broader than rest of scolex; suckers armed only near anterior border. Reproductive organs single in each proglottid. Uterus sac-like, persistent.
Three species in European shore and water birds some of which occur in North America.

FIG. 745. Ophryocotyle proteus. Head and neck with retracted and extended infundibulum; magnified. (After Stiles.)

69 (68) Uterus coiled in posterior end of proglottid; thick-walled parauterine organ in anterior region. Rostellum small; with not to exceed a few hundred hooklets.
Idiogenes Krabbe 1868.

Small cestodes. Genital pores unilateral. Cirrus-pouch very large, with retractor. Parauterine organ develops in front of uterus; eggs finally pass directly into it from uterus and it is transformed into single thick-walled egg capsule. Adults in birds.
A few species in water birds; none recorded as yet in North America.

70 (65) Rostellum sac-like, or lacking. 71

71 (82) Not more than four testes in each proglottid.
Family HYMENOLEPIDIDAE Fuhrmann 1907. . . 72

Scolex armed with 8 to 40, usually 10 hooks, with points directed posteriad when at rest, on a more or less elongated rostellum which rarely is rudimentary and unarmed. Genital pores strictly unilateral in entire strobila. Genital ducts dorsal to excretory ducts and longitudinal nerve. Female glands median. Onchosphere with three membranes. Adults in birds and mammals.

72 (73) In each proglottid normally 4 testes. . . Oligorchis Fuhrmann 1906.
A single species in North America; not reported in aquatic birds.

73 (72) In each proglottid normally less than four testes. 74

74 (79) In each proglottid normally three testes. 75

75 (76)　Strobila broad, lancet-shaped.　Ovary and vitellarium ante-poral,
alongside of testes. . . . . 　*Drepanidotaenia* Railliet 1892.

Scolex very small, with 8 hooks.　Neck wanting.　No accessory sac in genital atrium.

Type species. . . . . . . 　*Drepanidotaenia lanceolata* (Bloch) 1782.

Adult in intestine of ducks and geese; cosmopolitan.　Bladder-worm in various Cyclopidae
and *Diaptomus*.

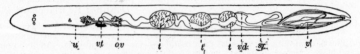

Fɪɢ. 746.　*Drepanidotaenia lanceolata.*　Transverse section of proglottid; *u*, uterus; *vt*, vitellaria;
ov, ovary; *t*, testes; *vd*, vas deferens; *sr*, seminal receptacle; *v*, vagina; magnified.　(After Wolffhügel.)

76 (75)　Strobila slender or even filiform.　Ovary and vitellarium ventral to
testes or between them. 77

77 (78)　Suckers entirely unarmed, or at most armed with hooks on margin
only. . . . . 　*Hymenolepis* Weinland 1858.

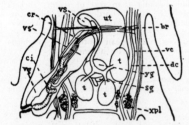

Fɪɢ. 747.　*Hymenolepis megalops.*　Dorsal view
of mature segment (no. 172).　Reconstruction from
sections; *br*, retractor of cirrus-pouch; *ci*, cirrus;
cr, retractor of cirrus; *dc*, dorsal excretory canal; *gc*,
genital cloaca; *nt*, main lateral nerve; *sg*, shell
gland; *t*, testis; *tm*, transverse muscles; *ut*, uterus;
vc, ventral excretory canal; *vg*, vagina; *vs*, seminal
vesicle; *vs'*, seminal vesicle of cirrus-pouch; *xpl*,
plexus of excretory vessels; *yp*, yolk glands.　× 90.
(After Ransom.)

Rostellum well developed, rarely rudimentary
or absent.　Accessory sac generally wanting in
genital atrium.　Rarely as abnormality 2, 4,
5, or 6 testes in a single proglottid.　Chiefly in
land and water birds; some species in mammals.

A very large genus; about 50 species occur in
aquatic hosts found in North America.　Among
them a few are definitely reported for North
America.　*H. compressa* (Linton) 1892 from the
scoter and canvas-back.　*H. fusus* in which
Fuhrmann places Linton's *Taenia filum* from
gulls at Yellowstone Lake.

H. megalops described by Ransom (with other
species from land birds) from the pintail duck;
Missouri River, Mo.

78 (77)　Suckers armed on borders and also in cavity with small hooklets;
sacculus accessorius always present.
Echinocotyle Blanchard 1891.

Rostellum armed with single crown of ten slender hooks with dorsal
root and blade about equal in length and ventral root rudimentary.
Suckers large, flat, oval, poor in musculature, armed on borders and in
middle with several rows of small hooklets.　Muscular, spinous sacculus
accessorius always present.　Adults in birds.

Type species. . 　*Echinocotyle rosseteri* Blanchard 1891.

Five species in shore and water birds of Europe.　Hosts mostly found
in North America also.

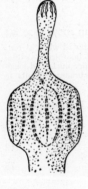

Fɪɢ. 748.　*Echinocotyle rosseteri.*　Head with extended rostellum; × 250.
(After Blanchard.)

79 (74) In each proglottid normally less than three testes. 80

80 (81) Two testes in each proglottid. . . . . *Diorchis* Clerc 1903.

Rostellum with single crown of ten hooks having long dorsal and short ventral roots, or exceptionally very short dorsal root and ventral root nearly as long as the blade. Entire surface of suckers may be armed with minute spines. Inner longitudinal muscle layer consisting of 8 bundles, 4 dorsal and 4 ventral. Two testes in each proglottid. Ovary and vitellarium always median. Adults in birds.

Four or more species in European water birds. Most of the host species occur in North America. *D. acuminata* and *D. americana* were both collected by Ransom from the coot in Nebraska.

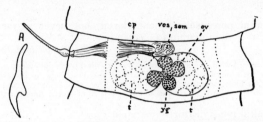

FIG. 749. *Diorchis acuminata.* *a*, Hook from rostellum; sexually mature segment; *cp*, cirruspouch; *ov*, ovary; *t*, testis; *ves sem*, seminal vesicle; *yg*, yolk gland; magnified. (After Ransom.)

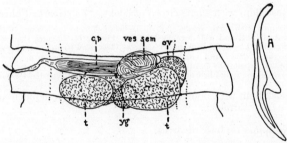

FIG. 750. *Diorchis americana.* *a*, Hook from rostellum; magnified; sexually mature segment at high focus to show male organs, dorsal view; magnified; *cp*, cirrus-pouch; *ov*, ovary; *t*, testes; *ves sem*, seminal vesicle; *yp*, yolk gland; magnified. (After Ransom.)

81 (80) One testis in each proglottid. . . . . . *Aploparaksis* Clerc 1903.

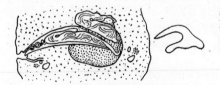

Strobila small and slender. Rostellum armed with a single crown of 10 hooks, with ventral root as long or nearly as long as blade. Suckers unarmed. One testis dorsal. Seminal vesicle large. Ovary and vitellarium always median. Adults in birds.

Type species.
Aploparaksis filum (Goeze) 1782.

FIG. 751. *Aploparaksis filum.* Transverse section of proglottid, female reproductive organs not shown; × 36. (After Clerc.) Hook from rostellum, × 750. (After Krabbe.)

A dozen species described from avian hosts both terrestrial and aquatic; nearly all of the species are found in North American host species.

82 (71) At least six testes normally in each proglottid. 83

83 (83a)   Rostellum entirely lacking.   Scolex unarmed, very muscular.
                             Family ANOPLOCEPHALIDAE Kholodkovsky 1902.
Not found in fresh-water hosts.

83a (83)   Rostellum present and armed with one or two rows of hooks.
                         Family DILEPIDIDAE Fuhrmann 1907 . .   84

With rostellum armed with single or double crown of hooks rarely in broken zig-zag row, exceptionally rudimentary.   Points of hooks directed posteriad.   Suckers unarmed.   Genital pores marginal (see 84 just below).   Sex organs in each proglottid simple or double.   Uterus sacculate or lobed, simple.

Onchosphere with three membranes.   Many genera chiefly found in birds, rarely in reptiles or mammals.

84 (85)   Genital pores submarginal, dorsal, but never as far as half way from margin to median line.
                             Trichocephaloides Ssinitsin 1896.

Rostellum powerful with single crown of hooks.   Genital pores unilateral, subdorsal.   Cirrus short and thick with long bristles; no seminal vesicle.   Testes few, in posterior region of segment.   Uterus sac-like; eggs few.   Adults in birds.

Few species in shore birds; parasites not reported from North America.

85 (84)   Genital pores distinctly marginal.   86

86 (93)   Genital pores uniformly unilateral.   87

87 (88)   Rostellum with single crown of hooks.   *Lateriporus* Fuhrmann 1907.

Rostellum armed with single crown of 12 to 16 hooks (120 to 170 μ long), with long dorsal and short ventral root, and well-developed blade.   Proglottids broader than long.   Genital canals pass dorsal of longitudinal excretory vessels.   Testes 12 to 30 in number, situated posterior and lateral to ovary and vitellarium.   Uterus sac-like, filling entire medullary parenchyma in terminal proglottids.   Adults in birds.

Five or more species, found in Europe in Anseriformes; not yet reported for North America.

88 (87)   Rostellum with double crown of hooks; rarely rudimentary and unarmed.   89

89 (92)   No spines on base of cirrus.   90

90 (91)   Testes not in front of but behind ovary and vitellarium.
                                  Dilepis Weinland 1858.

Rostellum armed with double crown of hooks having long dorsal and short ventral root and long blade.   Inner longitudinal muscle layer consisting of numerous bundles.   Proglottids broader than long.   Genital canals pass dorsal of the longitudinal excretory vessels and nerve.   Vas deferens coiled, seminal vesicle not developed.   Testes in medullary portion typically numerous (40 to 50), but may be reduced in number (7).   Uterus sac-like with few or numerous outpocketings.   Adults in birds and mammals.

Many species from various birds including fresh-water types found in North America. *D. transfuga* from the spoonbill determined for North America by Ransom.   *D. unilateralis* for the green heron by Stiles and Hassall, and by A. J. Smith; also for the little blue heron by Leidy.

91 (90)   Testes very numerous, entirely surrounding the female glands.
                                Cyclorchida Fuhrmann 1907.

Rostellum armed with double crown of hooks, which have a very large dorsal root and small hook portion.   Genital canals pass between longitudinal excretory vessels.   Cirrus-pouch communicates with genital cloaca by narrow canal opening upon large papilla.   Uterus ventral, growing laterally between the excretory vessels into the cortical parenchyma and filling entire proglottid.   Adults in birds.

In heron, crane, etc., in Europe.   Not recorded for North America.

92 (89) Root of cirrus with one or two pairs of powerful hooks lying in special pockets; genital canals pass between longitudinal excretory vessels.
Gryporhynchus Nordmann *1832*.
(Syn. — *Acanthocirrus* Fuhrmann 1907.)

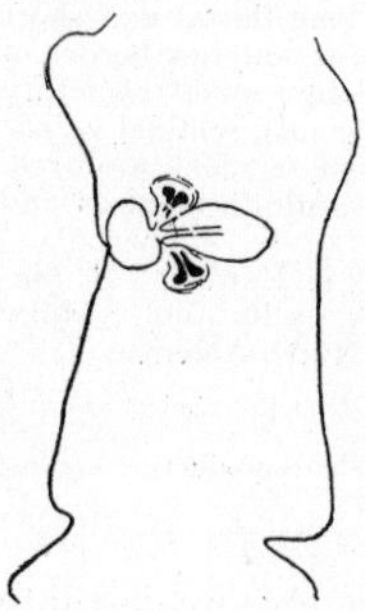

Genital canals pass between the longitudinal excretory vessels. In genital atrium lateral to root of cirrus two special pockets with one or two pairs of powerful hooks in each. Uterus sac-like. Adults in birds.

Three species or more in herons; not reported from North America.

FIG. 752. *Gryporhynchus cheilancristrotus.* Proglottid with contracted cirrus-pouch; short heavy hooks in pockets at opening of cirrus-pouch into genital cloaca. Magnified. (After Clerc.)

93 (86) Genital pores not unilateral but alternating. 94

94 (97) Genital pores regularly alternating. 95

95 (96) Rostellum with single crown of hooks. Less than 30 proglottids; scolex large; no neck. . . . . *Amoebotaenia* Cohn 1899.

Proglottids much broader than long. Testes rather numerous (12 or more), in posterior portion of segment. Uterus sac-like, fills entire medullary portion of terminal proglottids. Adults in birds.

Four or five species, some in shore birds that occur in North America.

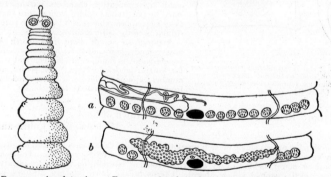

FIG. 753. *Amoebotaenia.* Anterior end, magnified. (After von Linstow.)

FIG. 754. *Amoebotaenia cuneata.* *a*, dorsal view; *b*, ventral view; magnified. (After Cohn.)

96 (95) Two rows of hooks on rostellum. . . *Cyclustera* Fuhrmann 1901.

Rostellum with double crown of hooks. Longitudinal musculature in three layers. Genital canals pass between the longitudinal excretory vessels and open into a very muscular cloacal canal. Testes numerous, scattered throughout entire dorsal medullary portion of proglottid. Ovary and yolk gland surrounded by ring-like uterus with secondary branches. Eggs with two shells. Adults in birds. *C. capito*, the type species, is reported by Ransom as found in the roseate spoonbill in North America.

97 (94) Genital pores alternate irregularly. 98

98 (99)   Uterus sac-like. . . . .   *Anomotaenia* Cohn 1900.

Rostellum with double crown of hooks, with long dorsal and short ventral root, and long blade. Genital pores near anterior border of segment. Genital canals pass between the longitudinal excretory vessels and dorsal of the nerve. Vas deferens coiled, seminal vesicle absent. Testes numerous, in posterior portion of segment (or rarely laterally on both sides of the female glands). Adults in birds and mammals.

Many species from both land and water birds in Europe. *A. constricta* from the fish crow, determined for U. S. A. by Ransom. Many European hosts of other species are found in North America.

Fig. 755.   *Anomotaenia constricta.*   Male and female reproductive organs, magnified.   (After Volz.)

99 (98)   Uterus branching and in ripe proglottids incompletely divided into numerous small communicating compartments. 100

100 (101)   One crown of hooks on the rostellum.   *Choanotaenia* Railliet 1896.

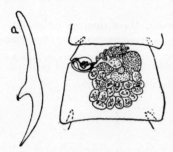

Scolex small. Rostellum armed with single crown of hooks usually with long dorsal and short ventral root. Proglottids numerous, rarely less than 30; oldest often longer than wide. Genital pores irregularly alternate near anterior border of proglottid. Genital canals pass between longitudinal excretory vessels and dorsal of nerve. Vas deferens coiled, seminal vesicle absent. Testes numerous, in posterior region of, or more rarely laterally on each side of, the female glands. Uterus subdivided into numerous small communicating chambers incompletely separated by partitions infolded from wall so that in some cases eggs appear almost as if isolated in parenchyma. Adults in birds and mammals.

A dozen species or more from North American hosts; land, shore and water birds represented. *Ch. infundibulum* is common in chickens and is recorded for North America generally. *Ch. porosa* occurs in a number of aquatic birds; it is reported by Linton from gulls at Yellowstone Lake.

Fig. 756.   *Choanotaenia . infundibulum* a, Hook from rostellum; magnified; segment showing reproductive organs; magnified. (After Ransom.)

101 (100)   Rostellum armed with double crown of hooks.
Monopylidium Fuhrmann 1899.

Reproductive organs single in each proglottid. Genital canals pass between longitudinal excretory vessels and dorsal to longitudinal nerve or to both excretory vessels. Testes numerous (20 to 40 or more), behind ovary and vitellarium or laterally on both sides of latter. Vas deferens coiled; seminal vesicle absent. Uterus breaks down into egg capsules, each containing usually one egg. Adults in birds.

A dozen species in European hosts which include some shore birds found in North America.

102 (62)   Reproductive glands simple, central in each proglottid; ducts and pores double, one set on each side.
Diploposthe Jacobi 1896.

Rostellum armed with single crown of ten hooks. Suckers unarmed. Inner longitudinal muscle layer, except for two or three small bundles lateral beyond excretory vessels, developed in median portion consisting of about ten dorsal and ten ventral bundles of unequal size. Outer longitudinal muscle layer of numerous equally developed bundles, interrupted where genital canals pass through. Outside thin layer of diagonal fibers, at posterior end well-developed muscle ring. Genital pores marginal, one on each side. Testes few (3 to 7) in posterior portion of proglottid. Two vasa deferentia. Seminal vesicles present on each side

armed with strong hooks. Female glands single, median; two vaginae. Eggs with three membranes.

The type species, *D. laevis*, from various ducks and geese found in North America. No record of any species on this continent.

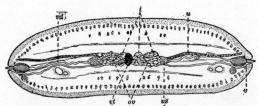

Fig. 757. *Diploposthe laevis*. Optical section of ripe proglottid; *vd*, vas deferens; *t*, testes; *u*, uterus *vt*, vitellaria; *ov*, ovary; *vs*, seminal vesicle; *v*, vagina; × 22. (After Jacobi.)

103 (61) Uterus with median stem and lateral branches; female genital glands in posterior end of proglottid.

Family TAENIIDAE Ludwig 1886.

Scolex usually with well-developed rostellum armed with double crown of hooks, rarely with rudimentary unarmed rostellum. Suckers unarmed. Terminal segments longer than broad. Reproductive organs single in each proglottid. Genital pores irregularly alternate. Vas deferens coiled, seminal vesicle absent. Testes numerous, scattered. Double ovary posterior, median, posterior to which is the yolk gland. Egg with thin outer membrane, and thick brown radially striated inner shell. Adults in mammals and birds.

Taenia Linnaeus 1758.

Forms rightly included here are as adults characteristic parasites of higher carnivorous land animals and the larval forms (cysticerci) also occur in land-living herbivorous or omnivorous mammals.

Eggs are distributed widely by surface waters. Larval stages occur rarely in aquatic mammals, *e.g.*, *Cysticercus fasciolaris* the bladder-worm of *Taenia crassicollis* of the cat which Stiles and Hassall, and later Linton also, have reported from the muskrat.

104 (60) Female genital pore not adjacent to cirrus and male pore. . . 105

105 (112) Proglottids without lateral appendages. Female genital pore is entirely lacking.

Family ACOLEIDAE Fuhrmann 1907 . . 106

Thick-bodied cestodes with rostellum usually armed. Proglottids short. Musculature very powerful. Cirrus sac very large; cirrus armed with strong spines. Eggs with 3 membranes. In birds.

106 (111) Hermaphroditic forms. 107

107 (110) Male and female genital organs simple. 108

108 (109) Testes numerous; seminal receptacle very· large; uterus a transverse tube anterior to ovary. Male genital pores regularly alternate. . . . . *Acoleus* Fuhrmann 1899.

Scolex small with armed rostellum. Reproductive organs single. Cirrus-pouch passes ventral of longitudinal excretory vessels and nerve. Vagina closed, functions as very large seminal receptacle. Adults in water birds.

Type species. . . . . *Acoleus armatus* Fuhrmann 1899.

From the black-necked stilt; parasite not reported from North America.

109 (108) Testes few; seminal receptacle very small; uterus encircling ovary; male pores irregularly alternate.

Gyrocoelia Fuhrmann 1899.

Rostellum armed with single crown of hooks arranged in zig-zag row having eight angles. Reproductive organs single in each proglottid. Cirrus-pouch passes between longitudinal excretory vessels and dorsal of nerve. Uterus ring-like, with numerous outpocketings, and with opening in terminal proglottids both dorsally and ventrally in median line of posterior margin. Adults in birds.

In water birds; not reported in North America.

110 (107)   Male reproductive organs double and female single in each proglottid with two vaginae functioning as large seminal receptacles. . . . . *Diplophallus* Fuhrmann 1900.

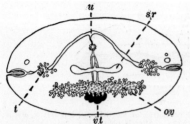

Large forms with small scolex and armed rostellum. Testes numerous, in two lateral fields
fully separated by median female glands.   Cirrus sac powerful, cirrus slender, very long.
Vagina a blind transverse canal. Uterus at
first transverse tube; later irregular, and finally
taking in entire medullary region.

Type species.
Diplophallus polymorphus
(Rudolphi) 1819.

FIG. 758. *Diplophallus.* Schematic transverse
section of ripe proglottid; *t*, testes; *u*, uterus; *sr*,
seminal receptacle; *ov*, ovary; *vt*, vitellaria. (After
Wolffhügel.)

From the black-necked stilt; parasite not recorded from North America.

111 (106)   Dioecious, entire strobila male or female; male with a double
set, female with a single set of reproductive organs in each
proglottid. . . . . *Dioicocestus* Fuhrmann 1900.

Female thicker and broader than male. Vagina irregularly alternating, reaching almost to
the edge of the segment. Testes numerous, divided more or less plainly into two symmetrical
groups. Eggs with three envelopes. Male ducts paired in every proglottid. Adults in
birds.

Type species. . . . . . *Dioicocestus paronai* Fuhrmann 1900.

Several species from grebe and ibis; parasite not recorded from North America.

112 (105)   Proglottids carry lateral foliate or digitate processes. Female
genital pore, when present, separate from marginal male
pore. . .   Family AMABILIIDAE Fuhrmann 1907 . .   113

Rostellum with simple crown of hooks. Proglottids short with lateral margins prolonged
into processes. Musculature weakly developed. Cirrus sac large; cirrus spinous. Duct
united with receptaculum seminis, designated as accessory vagina, opens in cases on surface or
on margin opposite male pore.
In water birds.

113 (114)   Male sexual organs double in each proglottid. Accessory vagina
with surface opening. Uterus a network.
Amabilia Diamare 1893.

Scolex very small with armed rostellum. Male reproductive organs double with one pore
on each side of proglottid. .Cirrus armed with strong spines. Testes numerous, in median
field. Female organs median, single set in each proglottid. Uterus forming network consisting of dorsoventral ring with dorsoventral anastomoses. Accessory vagina opening ventrally, communicating (?) with canal from excretory system opening on ventral surface of
proglottid in median line. Adults in birds.

Type and only species. . . . . *Amabilia lamelligera* (Owen) 1832.

114 (113)   Male organs single in each proglottid. Uterus sac-like.. . .   115

115 (116)   Rostellum thick, powerful. Male pores alternate irregularly.
Female pore, when present, on surface of proglottid.
Schistotaenia Cohn 1900.

Rostellum very large, armed with heavy hooks. Between rostellum and suckers an annular
thickening covered closely with small three-cornered hooks. Testes numerous, dorsal, posterior, across entire width of proglottid, reaching maturity later than female glands. Ovary
and vitellarium large. Male duct runs between excretory canals, accompanying vagina which
ends blindly near cuticula.
Type species *S. macrorhyncha* in the horned grebe. Parasite not recorded from North
America.

116 (115)   Rostellum long, slender.   Male pores alternate regularly.   Female
pore, when present, always marginal.

Tatria Kowalewski 1904.

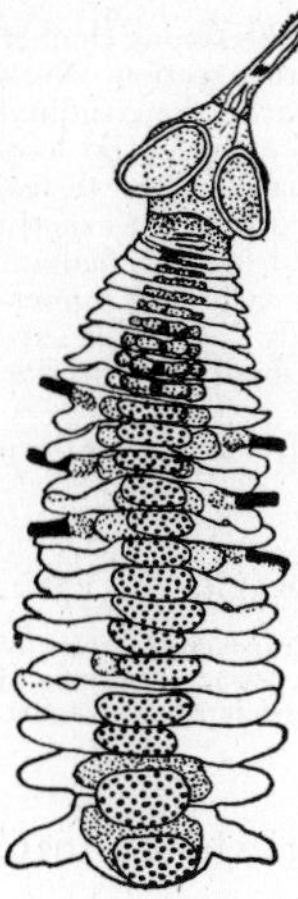

Rostellum with single crown of 10 to 14 large hooks and behind them
numerous rows of small conical hooks.   Suckers and posterior portion
of head covered with minute spines.   Segments not numerous.   Cirrus-
pouch large.   Testes not numerous.   Male and female canals pass between longitudinal excretory vessels.   Distal end of vagina instead of
opening to exterior turns posteriad into next following proglottid and
opens into seminal receptacle there.   Seminal receptacles median; accessory vagina present opposite cirrus-pouch. sometimes with opening.
Adults in birds (Urinatores).

The type species (*Tatria biremis* Kowalewski 1904) occurs in the
horned grebe and has not been reported for North America.   In 1887
Leidy reported *Taenia scolopendra* Diesing from this host and that species
is placed here by some authors.

FIG. 759.   *Tatria biremis*.   Forma major; proglottids with lateral appendages,
X 30.   (After Kowalewski.)

117 (55)   External division of strobila into proglottids lacking.   118

118 (119)   Anterior portion of strobila folded and coiled to form large pseudoscolex;   strobila   grooved   transversely,   without   true   proglottid limits. . .   Family FIMBRIARIIDAE Wolffhügel 1898.

Scolex small, unstable, frequently lost, with rostellum armed with single row of hooks.
Pseudoscolex conspicuous.   Strobila with transverse grooves which produce appearance of
segmentation.   Three pairs of longitudinal excretory vessels.   Reproductive
organs not segmentally arranged.   Genital pores marginal, irregular, generally
unilateral.   Testes numerous, arranged in transverse rows.   Uterus not persistent, breaking down into a large number of egg sacs.   Egg spindle-shaped with
thin transparent shell.   Adults in birds (Anseriformes).

Type genus. . . . .   *Fimbriaria* Frölich 1802.
(Syn. — *Epision* Linton 1892.)

Two well-known species both occur in North American water birds; a third,
F. plicata (Linton) 1892 is recorded from the American scoter.

FIG. 760.   *Fimbriaria plicata*.   Lateral view of head and anterior part of body of
smallest specimen.   X 8.   (After Linton.)

119 (118)   Scolex small, simple.   Strobila round or nearly so.   Without proglottid boundary except at extreme posterior end.

Family NEMATOTAENIIDAE Lühe 1910 . .   120

Scolex unarmed, without rostellum.   At extreme posterior filiform end of strobila a few
separate proglottids visible externally; these are much longer than thick, separate readily, and
move about independently a long time.   Genital pores alternate irregularly.   Cirrus and
vagina pass dorsal to excretory canals and nerve trunks, open into genital atrium marginal
in location.   Male organ dorsal, female ventral.
In intestine of Amphibia.

120 (121)   Two testes in each proglottid. . . . .   *Nematotaenia* Lühe 1899.

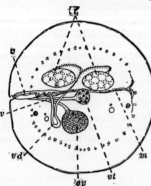

Strobila thicker near anterior end becoming thinner and eventually filiform, circular in cross-section. Neck short, cirrus-pouch long, passing within longitudinal muscle layer. Vas deferens long, with ventral loop between ovary and excretory canals. Two testes, dorsal and symmetrical. Vitellarium almost exactly in center of body. Ovary ventral, nearly median; uterus horseshoe-shaped, breaks up early into numerous capsules with 2 to 4 eggs, usually 3, in each capsule becoming ultimately 13 to 30 small dark uterine capsules.

Records of its occurrence in North America are open to question.

Type species.
Nematotaenia dispar (Goeze) 1782.

Fig. 761. *Nematotaenia dispar.* Transverse section of ripe proglottid; *c*, cirrus; *t*, testes; *m*, retractor muscle of cirrus; *vt*, vitellaria; *ov*, ovary; *vd*, vas deferens; *v*, vagina. Magnified. (After Fuhrmann.)

121 (120)   One testis in each proglottid.   . . .   *Cylindrotaenia* Jewell 1916.

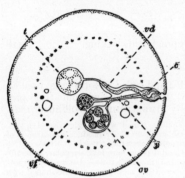

Strobila thickest near center, becoming thinner towards both ends. Neck long. Single testis round, on aporal side of proglottid just dorsal to transverse diameter. Cirrus-pouch short, ending at longitudinal muscle layer. Vas deferens short, nearly straight. Uterus breaks up into capsules each containing 4 to 6 eggs, becoming enclosed later in two conical organs, one dorsal and one ventral, which are large transparent uterine capsules.

Type species.
Cylindrotaenia americana Jewell 1916.
Perhaps *Taenia pulchella* Leidy 1851 belongs here.

Fig. 762. *Cylindrotaenia americana.* Transverse section of ripe proglottid; *t*, testes; *vd*, vas deferens; *c*, cirrus; *v*, vagina; *ov*, ovary; *vt*, vitellaria. Magnified. (After Jewell.)

122 (1)   Larval forms; reproductive organs undeveloped.   123

Usually small and unsegmented though some bladder-worms reach considerable size and even show the beginning of proglottid formation. On the whole these larvae show little or no organ differentiation and are distinguishable from adults by the absence of characteristic structures. Most larvae are encysted but there are numerous free forms.

123 (124)   Four long proboscides covered with hooks.

Trypanorhyncha (p. 434).

Very rare but easily recognized.

124 (123)   No proboscides with hooks present.   125

125 (126)   Scolex and sucking organs hardly differentiated at all and the latter when present never more than two.

Larvae of Pseudophyllidea.

(See also *Sparganum*, p. 434.)
The anterior end of these and other larvae is often rolled in so that its exact character is difficult to determine.

126 (125) Four suckers on the scolex of the larva. . *Cysticercus* . . 127

The head of the larva is inverted so that these suckers are in the center of the mass and may easily be overlooked. In the narrower sense the term cysticercus is applied to the large thin-walled bladder-worm having a cavity of considerable size filled with watery fluid in which the scolex grows from a polar papilla that subsequently hollows out giving in reverse the scolex of the adult. This larva belongs to the terrestrial fauna and occurs only accidentally in aquatic forms like the muskrat which have become a part of the aquatic fauna secondarily.

127 (128) Entire larva solid parenchyma tissue. Scolex invaginated with apex at bottom of infolding. . . . . *Plerocercoid.*

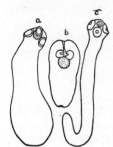

Caudal region not differentiated at all or only very poorly indicated. In general structure the Bothriocephalid larvae with two sucking grooves are like the true plerocercoids with 4 acetabula.

Larvae prominently of Proteocephalidae, also of Cyclophyllidea from reptiles. One special form known as *Gryporhynchus* has been identified as the larva of *Dilepis* or some allied genus.

FIG. 763. *Proteocephalus* plerocercoid; *a*, from the body cavity; *b*, from cyst, suckers drawn within body. Note large end organ, shaded; *c*, from intestine; optical sections, × 10. (After La Rue.)

128 (127) Spaces in larva between folds of tissue. Scolex in natural position, surrounded by cyst. . . . . *Cysticercoid.*

Usually with caudal appendage in a posterior hollow of the cyst, and on the tail the embryonic hooklets of the onchosphere. In form and texture the cyst varies greatly. Calcareous bodies abundant, mostly on the invaginated layer between the cyst and the scolex which corresponds to the neck when the larval head is evaginated.

Very frequent among Cyclophyllidea. Relationship between the cysticercoid and the adult may be inferred from careful examination of the scolex and its armature.

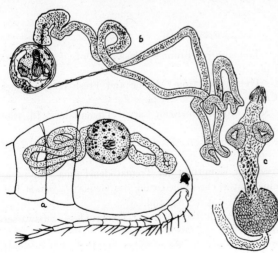

No records exist of the presence in North America of these forms. For convenience in recognizing them a figure is included of an abundant European form likely to occur here also in similar aquatic hosts. While these cysticercoids are most frequently recorded from Copepoda, Ostracoda, and other small aquatic crustacea, they occur also in *Lumbriculus* and other small annelids, and more rarely in small snails and slugs.

FIG. 764. *Drepanidotaenia fasciata. a*, body of *Cyclops agilis*, containing larval tapeworm (cysticercoid); *b*, same larva with enormously long tail, isolated from the crustacean; *c*, cysticercoid with extended head, magnified. (After Mràzek.)

REFERENCES ON NORTH AMERICAN PARASITIC WORMS

IMPORTANT GENERAL WORKS

COBBOLD, T. S. 1864. Entozoa. 480 pp. 82 figs. London.
1879. Parasites. 508 pp. London.

DIESING, C. M. 1850, 1851. Systema helminthum. Vienna. 2 vols.; 679 and 588 pp.

DUJARDIN, F. 1845. Histoire naturelle des helminthes, ou vers intestinaux. Paris. 654 pp. Atlas, 12 pl.

LEIDY, J. 1904. Researches in Helminthology and Parasitology. Smith. Inst., Misc. Coll., vol. 46, Art. III, 281 pp. (Reprint of Leidy's contributions from 1845 to 1891. With a bibliography.)

LINSTOW, O. VON 1878. Compendium der Helminthologie. 382 pp. 1889. Nachtrag. 157 pp. Hannover.

LOOSS, A. 1901. Zur Sammel- und Conservirungstechnik von Helminthen. Zool. Anz., 24: 302–304, 309–318.

SMITH, A. J. 1908. Synopsis of Studies in Metazoan Parasitology. Univ. Penn. Med. Bull., Feb., 68 pp. 10 pl.

STILES, C. W., and HASSALL, A. 1894. A Preliminary Catalog of the Parasites Contained in the Collections of the U. S. Bureau of Animal Industry, U. S. Army Medical Museum, etc. Vet. Mag., 1: 245–253, 331–354.
1902–1912. Index-Catalog of Medical and Veterinary Zoology. (Authors.) Bur. An. Ind., Bull. No. 39; 36 parts, 2766 pp.

WRIGHT, R. R. 1879. Contributions to American Helminthology, Proc., Can. Inst., n.s. 1: 54–75, 2 pl.

TREMATODA

BRAUN, M. 1879–93. Trematodes. Bronn's Klass. u. Ord. d. Tierreichs, Vol. 4, 925 pp., 34 pl. Leipzig.

COOPER, A. R. 1915. Trematodes from Marine and Fresh-Water Fishes. Trans. Roy. Soc. Can., (3) 9: 181–205, 3 pl.

CORT, W. W. 1915. Some North American Larval Trematodes. Ill. Biol. Monogr., 1: 447–532; 8 pl.

LOOSS, A. 1894. Die Distomen unserer Fische und Frösche. Biblth. Zool., Heft. 16, 296 pp., 9 pl.
1899. Weitere Beiträge zur Kenntniss der Trematoden-Fauna Aegyptens, zugleich Versuch einer natürlichen Gliederung des Genus Distomum Retzius. Zool. Jahrb., Syst., 12: 521–784, 9 pl.

LÜHE, M. 1909. Parasitische Plattwürmer. I: Trematodes. Süsswasserfauna Deutschlands, Heft 17, 217 pp., 188 figs.

ODHNER, T. 1910. Nordostafrikanische Trematoden. I. Fascioliden. Swedish Zool. Exp., 23 A; 170 pp., 6 pl.

1911–1913. Zum natürlichen System der digenen Trematoden I–VI. Zool. Anz., vols. 37–42.

PRATT, H. S. 1900. Synopses of North American Invertebrates, XII. The Trematodes. Part 1. Heterocotylea. Am. Nat., 34: 645–662; 50 figs. 1902. Part 2. Aspidocotylea and Malacocotylea. Am. Nat., 36: 887–910, 953–979; 8 pl.

STILES, C. W. and HASSALL, A. 1908. Index-Catalog of Medical and Veterinary Zoology. Subjects: Trematoda and Trematode Diseases. Hyg. Lab., Bull. No. 37, 401 pp.

CESTODA

BRAUN, M. 1894–1900. Cestodes. Bronn's Klass. u. Ord. d. Tierreichs, Vol. 4, p. 927–1732, 25 pl. Leipzig.

LA RUE, GEO. R. 1914. A Revision of the Cestode Family Proteocephalidae. Ill. Biol. Monogr., 1: 1–350, 16 pl.

LÜHE, M. Parasitische Plattwürmer. II. Cestodes. Süsswasserfauna Deutschlands, Heft 18, 153 pp., 147 figs.

RANSOM, B. H. 1909. The Taenioid Cestodes of North American Birds. U. S. Nat. Mus., Bull. 69, 141 pp.

STILES, C. W. and HASSALL, A. 1912. Index-Catalog of Medical and Veterinary Zoology. Subjects: Cestoda and Cestodaria. Hyg. Lab., Bull. No. 85, 467 pp.

CHAPTER XIV

THE NEMERTEANS

By WESLEY R. COE

Sheffield Scientific School of Yale University

Among the fresh-water animals of the northern half of the United States occurs a slender little worm of a beautiful reddish color belonging to the group of Nemerteans. These worms can be easily distinguished from the other flatworms (Platyhelminthes) by the slenderness of the body, and from the other groups of worms by their perfectly smooth, ciliated bodies and their leisurely creeping movements. The presence of the proboscis armed with a formidable calcareous stylet which can be thrust out of the opening at the anterior end of the body is proof that the worm is a nemertean.

These nemerteans live along the shores of lakes and streams, as well as in pools and artificial basins of water and aquaria. Quiet, shallow areas of water with a dense growth of water plants are particularly favorable. The worms may be found creeping over the stems and leaves of the water plants, among the dead leaves and debris at the bottom, on stones and objects in the water, and oftentimes beneath the stones along the shore. The under sides of floating leaves, as lily pads, particularly those partially decayed, often harbor numbers of these tiny worms. They are, however, local in distribution and are seldom found in abundance over a very wide area. When common in a shallow inlet a few yards wide, a further search for a mile along the shore of a lake or stream may fail to reveal a single specimen.

The worms are usually from 10 to 18 mm. in length when fully extended, but may contract to a small fraction of their former length. They rarely exceed 1 mm. in diameter. The color varies considerably, shades of red, orange, or vermilion being most common, while the smaller specimens are often pale yellowish or flesh colored. The anterior half of the body is more brightly colored

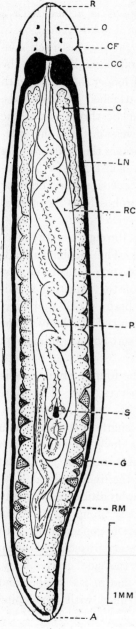

than the posterior portion, where the intestinal lobes and reproductive glands modify the brilliancy of the coloring. Some individuals have a cast of reddish brown.

On the anterior end of the body are usually six black pigment spots, or ocelli, arranged symmetrically in three pairs (*o*, Fig. 765). Smaller specimens may have but four ocelli, and occasional irregularities occur in which the number may be five, seven, or eight.

It is to the internal organization of the body, however, that one must look for those characters which are mainly used in the classification of the nemerteans. These structures must be studied in most species by means of serial sections, but, fortunately, the fresh-water forms are so nearly transparent that the principal organ systems of the body may be studied in the living animal. It is only necessary to place the worm on a slide with a small drop of water and flatten the body beneath a cover glass. When such a specimen is examined under the low powers of a microscope the principal anatomical features are easily made out.

Particularly characteristic is the proboscis, a strong muscular organ (*p*, Fig. 765) contained in the rhynchocoel and enclosed by the proboscis sheath. This organ extends from the anterior extremity nearly to the posterior end of the body.

FIG. 765. *Stichostemma rubrum* (Leidy). Diagram of living individual flattened beneath a cover glass, showing internal anatomy: *A*, anus; *C*, pyloric cecum; *CF*, cephalic furrow; *CG*, cerebral ganglia; *G*, gonad; *I*, intestine; *LN*, lateral nerve; *O*, ocellus; *P*, proboscis; *R*, rhynchodaeum; *RC*, rhynchocoel; *RM*, retractor muscle of proboscis; *S*, central stylet and basis.

Back toward its posterior third, the proboscis is armed with a needle-like calcareous stylet (*s*) resting upon a solid conical basis. Beside the central stylet there are two lateral pouches each containing 2, 3, or 4 accessory stylets of size and shape similar to the central stylet. The proboscis is considerably longer than the sheath in which it lies coiled and to which it is attached at both ends. By means of its powerful musculature it can be thrust out of the anterior end of the body. This process of eversion turns the anterior part of the proboscis inside out and brings the central stylet to the end of the everted organ, where it constitutes a formidable weapon of defense or offense. After eversion the retractor muscle at its posterior end withdraws the proboscis to its original position.

The mouth and proboscis open together through the rhynchodaeum (*r*) at the anterior end of the body. The esophagus leads into a broad stomach, and this into the intestine with its numerous lateral lobes. At the anterior end of the intestine a pair of pyloric ceca (*c*) extend forward to the brain. The short rectum leads to the opening at the posterior end of the body. The nemerteans feed upon other worms and soft-bodied animals of various kinds.

The central nervous system consists of the four cerebral ganglia and a pair of large longitudinal lateral nerves (*ln*). These are easily seen in the living worm.

The excretory system extends the entire length of the body as a series of delicate tubes with several efferent ducts leading to each side of the body. The three longitudinal trunks of the blood vascular system are often distinctly seen in the living animal.

The fresh-water nemerteans are hermaphroditic, and usually protandric. The gonads are arranged serially along each side of the body between the intestinal lobes. Each gonad bears both male and female genital products, which are discharged when mature through a small pore opening on the side of the body. The male sexual elements are formed first, and in the smaller and evidently younger worms the gonads are filled with developing spermatozoa. Later, and after the discharge of a portion of the spermatozoa, the eggs begin their development.

As a rule a single egg is formed in each gonad, although sometimes there are two. Even when the eggs are fully formed there remains in each gonad a portion of the spermatozoa previously formed. This fact has led certain investigators to conclude that self-fertilization may sometimes occur. The eggs are fertilized after deposition, however, and the gregarious habits of the worms presumably insure the presence of spermatozoa from other individuals which may effect cross fertilization in whole or part.

The eggs are deposited in a double string embedded in a jelly which attaches them to the water plants or other objects on which the worms are found. They are beautiful objects by which to illustrate the processes of fertilization, maturation, cleavage and the development of the embryo.

The worms may be kept alive for a long time in aquaria containing water plants, and under suitable conditions will continue to live and breed year after year. They thrive under the conditions found in botanical gardens, where large basins of water are used in the cultivation of exotic water plants.

Although the nemerteans are represented by numerous genera and species in the oceans in all parts of the world, only a few forms occur in fresh water and a few others in moist places on the land.

In North America only a single genus is known from fresh water, and of this genus the described species are so closely similar as to lead to some doubt as to whether more than a single species is actually represented.

In 1850 Leidy published a brief and imperfect description of a nemertean found in the vicinity of Philadelphia, which species he described as *Emea rubra*. Silliman later found the same or a very similar species in New York State, to which he gave the name *Tetrastemma aquarium dulcium*, and included Leidy's species therein. Montgomery, in 1896, described under the name *Stichostemma asensoriatum*, a similar species from Pennsylvania, while apparently similar forms have been recorded from Connecticut, Illinois, Nebraska, and Washington. The worms are thus known to occur from the Atlantic to the Pacific coasts and have probably been observed at numerous unrecorded localities in the intervening territory.

But whether the nemerteans from these widely separated localities represent a single or several distinct species is not yet definitely known. Since fresh-water nemerteans similar to ours are found in England, Germany, and other parts of Europe, and in Asia and Africa, a careful study of specimens from many American localities is necessary to settle the question of nomenclature. For it is not improbable that some of the localities mentioned have been stocked with forms transported from other parts of the country, or from other quarters of the world. The importation of cultivated water plants furnishes ideal conditions for the introduction of the nemerteans associated with them.

A recent study indicates that the species found in Connecticut is identical with that recorded by Montgomery from Pennsylvania. This species differs in certain anatomical details from any of the described exotic forms, but is evidently synonymous with Leidy's *Emea rubra*. Since there is nothing in the published descriptions of specimens from other North American localities to indicate a specific distinction it is at present possible to recognize but a single species, to which the name *Stichostemma rubrum* (Leidy) should be applied.

IMPORTANT REFERENCES ON FRESH-WATER NEMERTEANS

Böhmig, L. 1898. Beiträge zur Anatomie und Histologie der Nemertinen. [*Stichostemma graecense* (Böhmig), *Geonemertes chalicophora* (Graff).] Zeit. f. wiss. Zool., 64: 479–564.
  Detailed account of the structure of a fresh-water form.
Bürger, O. 1895. Die Nemertinen des Golfes von Neapel und der angrenzenden Meeres-abschnitte. Fauna u. Flora v. Neapel, Monogr. 22.
  Important monograph on the European nemerteans.
Child, C. M. 1901. The Habits and Natural History of Stichostemma. Am. Nat., 35: 975–1006.
Hartmeyer, R. 1909. Nemertini. Die Süsswasserfauna Deutschlands, Heft. 19: 47–48.
Montgomery, T. H., Jr. 1895. *Stichostemma eilhardi* nov. gen. nov. spec. Ein Beitrag zur Kenntnis der Nemertinen. Zeit. f. wiss. Zool., 59: 83–146.
  Anatomical study of a fresh-water nemertean.
  1896. *Stichostemma asensoriatum* n. sp., a Fresh-water Nemertean from Pennsylvania. Zool. Anz., 19: 436–438.
  Description of a fresh-water nemertean from Pennsylvania.

CHAPTER XV

FREE-LIVING NEMATODES

By N. A. COBB

U. S. Department of Agriculture

PRACTICALLY any collection of sand, mud, debris or aquatic vegetation, from standing or running water, in any part of the country, will yield, on examination with a hand lens, minute slender organisms which whip themselves about by means of more or less rapid contortions of the whole body. This type of movement identifies them as nematodes; it differs from that of other small organisms in that, though often vigorous and conspicuous, it is in one plane only, the dorso-ventral plane of the body, and in that the length and proportions of the body meanwhile remain unchanged. In pure water, moreover, this thrashing about seems to produce no locomotion; the animal remains in the same spot unless among vegetation, debris or particles of soil. When quieted by stupefying or killing, these freshwater nematodes ("threadworms" or "roundworms") are seen to be more or less cylindroid unsegmented, without locomotor appendages, varying in length up to a centimeter or more. They belong to a group in the animal kingdom comparable in number and importance with the insects; nematodes of other sorts live free in the soil, and in the sea, and infest as parasites an immense variety of plants and other animals. They are inconceivably abundant. A tablespoonful of ooze from the bottom of the ocean may contain thousands of specimens. The number of nematodes in the top six inches of an acre of ordinary arable soil is shown by statistical calculations to reach thousands of millions. The number of eggs vastly exceeds even that of adults; for they are usually very prolific, a single female sometimes producing hundreds of thousands of eggs.

Even the free-living soil and water nematodes have become adapted to an astounding variety of habitats; they occur in arid deserts, at the bottom of lakes and rivers, in the waters of hot

459

springs and in polar seas. They were thawed out alive from Antarctic ice by members of the Shackleton expedition. An examination of beet seeds imported into the United States disclosed the presence on them of several species of nematodes. The tap water of even well-conducted cities often contains nematodes. Their microscopic eggs and larvae, even more readily than the adults, are transported from place to place by an exceedingly great variety of agencies. They are carried by the wind, by flying birds and running animals, they float in all the waters of the earth, and are shipped from point to point throughout the civilized world in vehicles of traffic. Sometimes the eggs and larvae are so resistant to dryness that if converted into dust they revive again when given moisture, even after as long a period as a quarter of a century. There are beneficial nematodes, though knowledge of this phase of the subject is in its infancy. Some nematodes feed exclusively on their injurious brethren. Others devour baneful micro-organisms. Their adaptations in these respects appear to be similar to those of insects.

The small fraction of the fresh-water nematodes of North America at present known, comprises only about thirty genera, but these present such a variety of form that a thorough knowledge of them insures a fair understanding of all the free-living nematodes.*

The number of nematode species is enormously greater than commonly supposed. Since most species of vertebrates are infested by one or more nematodes, and with comparatively few exceptions a given parasitic nematode infests but one host, it may be estimated that more than 80,000 nematode species infest the forty odd thousand species of vertebrates. Insects, also much infested, will add many thousands of species. The molluscs, crustaceans, and various groups of worms are also infested, and investigation continues from this source also to augment the number of known species of parasitic nematodes.

Numerous as the parasitic species are, it is certain that the species of nematodes living free in soil and in water far

---

* In an attempt to distinguish the parasitic nematodes from the aquatic and soil-inhabiting nematodes, the latter are usually assigned to the group of free-living nematodes, — an arbitrary classification not based on natural relationships.

outnumber them; and the number of free-living individuals is so great that they probably constitute one of the important mechanical as well as biological factors in soil, and in the bot-

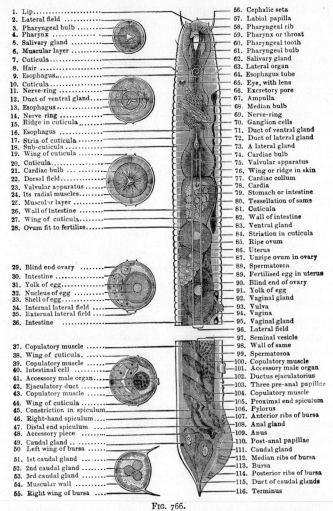

1. Lip	56. Cephalic seta
2. Lateral field	57. Labial papilla
3. Pharyngeal bulb	58. Pharyngeal rib
4. Pharynx	59. Pharynx or throat
5. Salivary gland	60. Pharyngeal tooth
6. Muscular layer	61. Pharyngeal bulb
7. Cuticula	62. Salivary gland
8. Hair	63. Lateral organ
9. Esophagus	64. Esophagus tube
10. Cuticula	65. Eye, with lens
11. Nerve-ring	66. Excretory pore
12. Duct of ventral gland	67. Ampulla
13. Esophagus	68. Median bulb
14. Nerve ring	69. Nerve-ring
15. Ridge in cuticula	70. Ganglion cells
16. Esophagus	71. Duct of ventral gland
17. Stria of cuticula	72. Duct of lateral gland
18. Sub-cuticula	73. A lateral gland
19. Wing of cuticula	74. Cardiac bulb
20. Cuticula	75. Valvular apparatus
21. Cardiac bulb	76. Wing or ridge in skin
22. Dorsal field	77. Cardiac collum
23. Valvular apparatus	78. Cardia
24. Its radial muscles	79. Stomach or intestine
25. Muscular layer	80. Tessellation of same
26. Wall of intestine	81. Cuticula
27. Wing of cuticula	82. Wall of intestine
28. Ovum fit to fertilize	83. Ventral gland
	84. Striation in cuticula
	85. Ripe ovum
	86. Uterus
	87. Unripe ovum in ovary
	88. Spermatozoa
29. Blind end ovary	89. Fertilised egg in uterus
30. Intestine	90. Blind end of ovary
31. Yolk of egg	91. Yolk of egg
32. Nucleus of egg	92. Vaginal gland
33. Shell of egg	93. Vulva
34. Internal lateral field	94. Vagina
35. External lateral field	95. Vaginal gland
36. Intestine	96. Lateral field
	97. Seminal vesicle
	98. Wall of same
37. Copulatory muscle	99. Spermatozoa
38. Wing of cuticula	100. Copulatory muscle
39. Copulatory muscle	101. Accessory male organ
40. Intestinal cell	102. Ductus ejaculatorius
41. Accessory male organ	103. Three pre-anal papillae
42. Ejaculatory duct	104. Copulatory muscle
43. Copulatory muscle	105. Proximal end spiculum
44. Wing of cuticula	106. Pylorus
45. Constriction in spiculum	107. Anterior ribs of bursa
46. Right-hand spiculum	108. Anal gland
47. Distal end spiculum	109. Anus
48. Accessory piece	110. Post-anal papillae
49. Caudal gland	111. Caudal gland
50. Left wing of bursa	112. Median ribs of bursa
51. 1st caudal gland	113. Bursa
52. 2nd caudal gland	114. Posterior ribs of bursa
53. 3rd caudal gland	115. Duct of caudal glands
54. Muscular wall	116. Terminus
55. Right wing of bursa	

FIG. 766.

Diagram of Nematode structure. Above, anterior end of female. Below posterior end of male. (After Cobb.)

toms of lakes and oceans. The aquatic nematode species exist in enormous numbers, in both fresh and salt water, while the number of individuals is past computation. The unavoidable conclusion is that there must be hundreds of thousands of species of nematodes.

Nearly all the tissues of the fresh-water nematodes are comparatively colorless and transparent, and whatever decided color the body possesses is usually confined to the intestinal region. The cells of the intestine itself are sometimes colored by the presence in them of granules of a faint yellowish or brownish tint, and the middle portions of the body are thus rendered yellowish or brownish. The color of the ingested food, showing through the tissues of the body, is also sometimes a color factor. The food varies in color from nearly black to colorless, and the body is correspondingly tinted. Species feeding on the juices of plants are usually nearly colorless, e.g., species of *Tylenchus* and *Aphelenchus*. A few species possess colored eye-spots near the head. In some species the esophagus contains yellowish or brownish pigment.

Most genera, and even some species, of fresh-water nematodes have a world-wide distribution. The small size and the vitality of the individuals favor their transportation in a great variety of ways, one of the most efficient vehicles being the feet of flying water-fowl. Possibly some of the aquatic species are as resistant to dryness as are rotifers, and, as "dust," are blown about in the same manner. Certain species of plant-infesting nematodes will revive after many years of desiccation.

Another cause of this wide distribution is the fact that fresh-water nematodes adapt themselves to a great variety of depths and temperatures. They are found as near the poles as are any other organisms. They occur in practically every body of water where extreme conditions do not preclude life of any kind. Few organisms are so easy to find.

The outer covering of a nematode is composed of a non-cellular layer usually divided into two parts, the cuticula and the subcuticula. These groups are not easily defined, but the natural division line is probably between the outer layers that are to be shed at the next moult, and all the other layers. Thus the subcuticula in turn becomes the cuticula. The cuticula is composed of about three layers and the subcuticula of about an equal number. Though some of the markings usually to be seen in the cuticula are due to sense organs or to pores, most of them are inherent structural markings. These markings are used as specific, and in some cases as generic, characters.

The cuticula of almost any species, if examined with sufficient care, will show transverse striations, ranging in the various species from a few score to upwards of a thousand. Many species described by earlier writers as destitute of these striations really possess them. When very fine the transverse striae are best seen at the extremities of the organism. In some genera the striae are apparently due to the constant bending of the body in the dorso-ventral plane. This peculiar motion, which is universal among nematodes, and continuous from birth to death, unceasingly stretches and then compresses the dorsal and ventral surfaces. At the time when the one is stretched the other is compressed. This

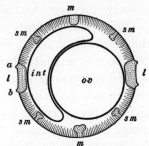

FIG. 767. Diagrammatic cross-section through the middle of a nematode. *ov*, ovary; *int*, intestine; *m*, median fields; *l*, lateral fields; *sm*, submedian fields; *a*, *b*, cuticular "wings" on the lateral fields. The median, lateral, and submedian lines are imaginary lines opposite the letters *m*, *l*, and *sm*, respectively, these lines being, of course, in no sense organs, but only convenient descriptive terms. The line shading between the fields represents muscle cells. (After Cobb.)

results in characteristic appearances, such as the more pronounced striation of the dorsal and ventral surfaces, the interruption and variation of the striations near the lateral lines, and the presence on the lateral fields of various longitudinal striations. In some genera the striations are compound, that is, each transverse striation is resolvable into a row of dot-like markings, either round or elongated. These secondary markings may be again resolvable, the result being a very complex series of exceedingly minute markings. The transverse striations are usually more or less plainly interrupted near the lateral lines. Oblique striae, such as are to be found in the large parasitic nematodes, sometimes occur in the fresh-water species, in some Mermithidae, for instance.

The longitudinal striations are of two kinds: (1) True striations of the cuticula due to certain stiffening structures or "wings," and (2) internal markings due to the attachment of the cells of the muscular layer and of the lateral fields. The longitudinal striations, when they are really cuticular structures, are likely to appear in some multiple of four. Since they occur on each side of the two lateral lines, and, naturally, in a symmetrical way, the smallest number possible is four. Two on each side of each lateral line would make eight in all, a state of things exemplified in *Iota*. In *Diplogaster* the number is about sixteen to thirty-two, and apparently these numbers also prevail in some *Dorylaimi*.

The various elements of the cuticula originate in certain cells in the longitudinal fields, which early in the development of the embryo become separated from the ectoblastomere group of cells. One of the first two somablastomeres, the primary ectoblastomere, divides and spreads systematically over the endoblastomeres. By further divisions the primary ectoderm thus formed gives rise among other things to the cuticula. The nuclei of the ectoblast cells destined to form the cuticula of the embryo arrange themselves in longitudinal lines. Increasing, and functioning from these lines they become specially active at each moult in producing a new layer of cuticula. At moulting time the activity of the cuticula-forming cells in the lateral fields is indicated by an increase in the size of the nuclei and the growth from them of excessively fine elements forming the cuticula. The lateral fields appear to be the leading members of this group of cuticula builders. This is in harmony with the greater abundance and variety of the lateral cuticular structures.

In the course of its development a nematode sheds its skin about four times, — and often appears to be about as active during the moulting period as at other times. In some species the changes that take place at the time of moulting are of a striking character, reminiscent of the metamorphoses in other groups, though no true metamorphosis takes place. Thus we have in the last moult of the males in some species of *Iota* a marked alteration, *viz.*, the loss of the oral spear. This so alters the appearance of the male that one unfamiliar with the facts would not class the adult males in the same genus as the females.

During the moulting period the cuticula is thicker and looser, — sometimes very loose. The lining of the mouth and esophagus, as well as that of the rectum, is shed at the same time as the outer cuticula. At this time, therefore, the mouth parts take on unusual appearances. If the pharynx is armed with teeth these are often seen in duplicate. In a moulting *Dorylaimus*, for instance, one may see the old spear or tooth and behind it a second smaller one, and in some cases even a third. The nature, or the presence, of striations may become more evident, or less evident, at the moulting period than at other times. Remnants of old skin attached to newly moulted individuals have sometimes given rise to erroneous deductions and to errors in taxonomy.

The nervous system centers in the so-called nerve-ring, which in free-living species encircles the esophagus near the middle of the neck. This ring is composed of interwoven nerve-fibers which, taken together with the groups of nerve cells immediately in front of and behind them, form what is undoubtedly a rudimentary brain. (See *Rhabdolaimus*.)

Eyes, or rather eye-spots, are known in one or more species of the following fresh-water genera: *Dorylaimus*, *Diplogaster*, *Spilophora*, *Cyatholaimus*, *Chromadora*, and *Monhystera*. The visual organs in their most complete form consist of well-defined subspherical cuticular lenses placed in front of collections of reddish, violet, or blackish pigment-granules. Usually two such organs are placed symmetrically, one on either side of the esophagus, between it and the body wall, and in a dorsally sublateral position. Nerves pass backward from the eyes to the nerve-ring. It is doubtful whether the lenses form images that are perceived, though no doubt the more perfect of the lenses found in nematodes are capable of forming excellent images. Probably the lenses serve merely to collect and condense light. Usually the eye-spots are mere collections of pigment without lenses. Eye-spots, or what appear to be such, may occur embedded in the esophagus. It is probable that the great majority of species, even when without specialized visual organs, perceive light by its direct action on the nervous system. A few experiments will convince anyone that many eyeless species distinguish the direction from which the light comes. There is no satisfactory evidence that nematodes hear.

At various points on the surface of the cuticula there are found innervated papillae and setae, which appear in most cases to be tactile organs. Sometimes, however, they are associated with glands, as, for instance, in the case of the supplementary organs of the males. These papillae, hairs, and setae all belong to the same general class of structures, but various terms are applied to them in accordance with their size and location. The special hairs found on and near the lips are known as cephalic setae, in contradistinction to the large hairs or setae sometimes found at the posterior extremity, the caudal and terminal setae. The setae are no doubt mainly tactile in function, though it seems certain that some of the cephalic setae and papillae serve also as organs of taste and smell.

FIG. 768. Head of a nematode (diagrammatic). 1, side view; 2, front view, showing triangular mouth opening in the middle. The ventral side to the right in 1 shows the ampulla and excretory duct. As the right side of the head is towards the spectator the lateral organ appears as a left-handed spiral. The arrangement of the cephalic setae is characteristic, the lateral ones being single, while the submedian are in pairs whose members are of unequal size. (After Cobb.)

The similar organs found on the general surface of the body are called hairs or somatic setae. These probably follow a definite law in their distribution, but are so small that the exact distribution is difficult to make out and has been studied in but few cases. While it is not established that their distribution accords with a segmentation theory, this matter is worthy of careful study. Sometimes the hairs occur in harmonic repetition on successive groups of annules. The papillae of the cuticula are setae that do not project beyond the surface, or not far enough to entitle them to be called setae. They should not be confounded with pores, or with mere projections of the surface of the cuticula. Neither of these latter are innervated. Tactile structures supplementary to the sexual organs are found on the tail end of the male both in front of and behind the anus, generally toward the ventral side. They are much more rare in the female, being located, when present, near the vulva.

What are known as the amphids or lateral organs are of such widespread occurrence among free-living nematodes as to make it seem certain that their function is of fundamental importance, but what the function is remains a mystery. The amphids are two lateral, symmetrically-placed external cephalic organs. The exterior part has the form of a circle, spiral, helix, or elongated figure, the helix or spiral being the fundamental form of the main cuticular outer lateral markings that serve so good a purpose in characterizing species. These external markings are undoubtedly in some species connected with internal series of lateral organs arranged in two rows, one along each lateral field, extending throughout the length of the body. One more or less plausible theory concerning the amphids is that which proposes to regard them as breathing organs. It is only very exceptionally that they are known to have special direct connection with the central nervous system. Such connection would be expected, if, as some suggest, they are organs of sensation. Their apparent homologues found in some parasitic nematodes seem rudimentary. Possibly they are organs of equilibration.

In describing the digestive system it is necessary to consider the mouth parts, the salivary or mouth glands, the esophagus, the intestine, and the rectum. Roughly speaking, the mouth parts may be divided into two main groups: those adapted to biting and those adapted to sucking. The various forms of the pharyngeal cavity in the biting group are shown in the adjacent illustrations, together

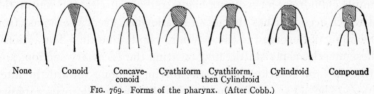

None   Conoid   Concave-   Cyathiform   Cyathiform,   Cylindroid   Compound
                 conoid   then Cylindroid

FIG. 769. Forms of the pharynx. (After Cobb.)

with their corresponding nomenclature (Fig. 769). The formation of the pharynx in the sucking groups is more uniform. The soft-lipped species are intermediate in form and are adapted to seizing and swallowing various microscopic organisms, both plant and animal.

The mouth cavity or pharynx is usually more or less strongly lined with cuticula, and often furnished with cuticular parts serving various purposes according to the food habits of the species. Where the lips are muscular and mobile, not infrequently they are supplied with rather complicated gripping organs arranged like the jaws of a lathe chuck. This arrangement of the mouth parts is well illustrated in *Enoplus;* the reverse motion for ripping tissues open is shown in *Ironus* (Fig. 781). *Mononchus* (Fig. 782) shows the development of six muscular lips with opposing pharyngeal teeth used in seizing prey. There are a number of genera in which the pharynx is armed with from one to three prominent teeth of problematical function. In some of these cases the teeth are the outlets of an equal number of glands located in the wall of the esophagus. The secretions of these glands are probably salivary in nature, or possibly in some cases venomous, or even, as has been suggested, excretory. These suppositions rest on structural and food-habit considerations, rather than on an examination of the nature of the secretions. The saliva theory is strongly supported by the nature of these glands, whether their form, number, position, or structure is considered, but they sometimes empty through fang-like projections in carnivorous species that one would think could profit by the use of venom in much the same way that serpents do.

The nematode esophagus is an organ of which every cross-section is usually substantially circular, though the diameter may vary much in the various parts. The central canal is usually trique-trous in cross-section (Fig. 766). The lining is uniformly cuticular and varies considerably in thickness in the various species. In the simple cylindrical form of esophagus, radial muscles, the contraction of which accomplishes the act of swallowing, everywhere pass from the lining of the organ to the exterior cylindroid wall. The action of these muscles is peristaltic, first creating the necessary suction, and, after the food is sucked in, rapidly forcing it along toward the intestine. The act of swallowing is often lightning-like in its rapidity.

In addition to this general radial musculature the esophagus sometimes presents spherical or ellipsoidal muscular swellings, or bulbs, often supplied with a central cuticular valve, for exerting more powerful suction than could be produced by the narrower tubular part. The presence of bulbs denotes certain methods of feeding, — either the lips need to be fastened securely to the source of food in order to facilitate the stabbing action of the oral spear, or it is necessary to exert unusual suction in order to ingest the food. There may be one, two, or three of these bulbs, or none. The corresponding forms of the esophagus are shown in the accompanying illustration (Fig. 770), to which the appropriate names are appended. In rare cases the esophagus is not clearly marked off from the intestine, but there nearly always exists between these two parts of the alimentary canal a distinct constriction, known as the cardiac constriction. In the immediate vicinity of this constriction small organs are sometimes found, apparently of a glandular nature, though their functions are still veiled in obscurity. Here also occur definite nerve cells which are probably to be regarded as the center of an involuntary nervous system.

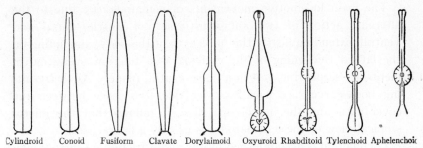

Cylindroid   Conoid   Fusiform   Clavate   Dorylaimoid   Oxyuroid   Rhabditoid   Tylenchoid   Aphelenchoid

FIG. 770.   Forms of the esophagus.   (After Cobb.)

The intestine is a tubular canal extending from the esophagus to near the anus. Usually rather uniform in diameter, it is occasionally somewhat expanded just behind the esophagus to form a rudimentary stomach, if one may judge from the histology of this part of the organ. The cells at this part of the intestine are often markedly different in structure and chemical reaction from those farther back. In almost any species a sufficiently careful examination will show that some of the anterior cells of the intestinal tube differ from those farther back, and hence it appears certain that the anterior part of the intestine serves a digestive function, while the remaining part serves as an intestine proper. There are also well differentiated cells in the wall of the posterior part of the intestine, indicating here also a subdivision of functions.

The intestine ends in a short tubular conoid region leading to the anus, and known as the rectum. This part is more or less muscular and serves to extrude the feces. In *Dorylaimus* and its congeners, just preceding the rectum there is a short very distinct part of the alimentary canal known as the pre-rectum. In spite of the definiteness of its structure its function is unknown. Emptying near the anus there are usually to be found a number of small unicellular glands, called anal glands, perhaps serving as accessories in defecation. The anal muscles are muscular strands passing from the transverse slit-like anus to the body walls near the lateral fields.

There is no vascular circulatory system. These organisms are so small that the colorless "blood" is aerated without the need of special vessels. The movements of the body serve to propel the body-fluid irregularly about through the body cavity and among the organs.

The main locomotive movements of nematodes are due to the alternate action of two antagonistic sets of muscle, dorsal and ventral, extending nearly the full length of the body, and acting on the lateral thickening of the cuticula as a fulcrum. The movements are serpentine, but in a dorso-ventral plane. As the resulting body-curves are usually wider than the space between the cover glass and the microscope slide, it follows that the microscopical view of these nematodes is usually a lateral view.

Locomotion is accomplished by the aid of friction on surrounding solid objects, such as the stems or roots of plants, grains of sand or other particles. Comparatively few of the aquatic species can swim, and even these seem uneasy and frightened when they find themselves floating free in the water. Most of the aquatic species are supplied with three unicellular caudal glands and a terminal spinneret, whose main, and probably sole, function is to cement the tail temporarily to various objects. From this attachment as a base the nematode moves its head in various directions in search of food, or of its mates. Some species, for instance some species of *Chromadora*, attach themselves alternately first by the head by suction, and then by the spinneret, executing movements like those of the common caterpillars known as "inch-worms."

The excretory organ of the free-living nematodes consists of a unicellular* gland, the renette, lying in the body cavity, not far from the junction of the intestine and esophagus. It empties through a duct leading forward to a ventral excretory pore, usually located somewhere between the lip region and the intestine. There are a number of genera in which the renette has not yet been seen. Its homologue in the large parasitic species is renal in nature,— at least in one case.

Through the study of the free-living species the supposed excretory function of the lateral fields, long believed in, has been dis-

* Rarely two to many-celled and double.

proved. The apparent connection in the parasitic species between the excretory organ and the lateral fields is incidental, the action of the body muscles tending to locate such long slender tubular organs in the region of least motion, namely the lateral region. In these parasitic species the organ is often bifurcated a little behind the excretory pore (apparently on account of the increased size of the whole organism), and thence backward the tubular elements are attached to or lie in or near the lateral fields. This suggests that the mystery surrounding the excretory organ in some of the free-living species may perhaps be solved by search directed toward the discovery of a bilaterally symmetrical renette. *Dorylaimus*, a genus containing some of the largest free-living nematodes, is a case in point. The renette cell often has smaller companion cells in its immediate rear.

The caudal glands, so common in the tail end of the free-living nematodes, serve to cement the tail end to any convenient object. In thus attaching themselves nematodes sometimes show great skill and pertinacity. The terminus of the tail bears a minute spinneret through which the secretion of the glands is forced out, and by means of which its flow may be regulated, much as in the case of spiders. The secretion is a cementing substance insoluble in water. The caudal glands are normally three in number and are usually located single file in the anterior part of the tail, or somewhat farther forward in front of the anus. Two of the ducts often unite to form one duct; sometimes all three unite. Just in front of the pore in the spinneret the ducts may enlarge to form one or more ampullae. Caudal glands are absent in most of those species in which the males are supplied with lateral caudal flaps constituting the bursa. It is possible that the secretion of the bursal ribs, or tubes, is of the same general character as that of the three caudal glands, and that these two sets of glands are homologous. The ribs of the bursa, when the full complement is present, consist of three groups. This is at least suggestive. The females of such species sometimes have lateral pores on or near the tail.

The sexual organs originate from a few cells set off for the purpose early in the development, which for a time remain rather quiescent near the center of the body. As the nematode approaches maturity these sexual cells resume their activity and begin to divide and to produce a symmetrically two-parted elongated group of cells, one part extending forward and the other backward. Primarily the sexual organs of both sexes are double, and the normal development at first always forecasts a double organ. This forecast is often fulfilled, but in many species one of the halves has deteriorated or become vestigial. Where this is the case the symmetry of the early development is soon lost and the group of developing sexual cells then becomes one-sided.

At the last moult, or the penultimate, the sexual opening in the cuticula makes its appearance. This is always on the ventral side, and in the male invariably corresponds with the anus; in the female it is independent and nearer the middle of the body, usually very near the middle when the internal organs are double and symmetrical, and farther back, or more rarely farther forward, when there is only one ovary.

The female sexual system is very commonly double, each half of it being tubular and consisting of (1) an ovary, (2) a seminal receptacle, (3) a uterus, (4) a vagina; this latter of course in common with the other half of the apparatus. These parts may lie in linear succession in the body cavity, or, as is more often the case, the series may be folded near its middle, that is, between the ovary and the uterus, so that the ovary is reflexed and extends back toward the vulva.

The more usual forms of female apparatus are as follows:

1. Of two parts, each reflexed.
2. Of two parts, each outstretched.
3. Single and reflexed.
4. Single and outstretched.

When the organ is single it may extend either forward or backward from the vulva, though it usually extends forward. Letting **F** represent the vulva, - an outstretched organ, and ' a reflexed organ, the various forms may be abbreviated as follows:

$$\text{'F'} \qquad \text{-F-} \qquad \text{'F} \qquad \text{F'} \qquad \text{-F} \qquad \text{F-}$$

and this is the form in which the facts are presented in the measurement formulae for the females, except that **F** is replaced by the percentage measurement figure representing the position of the vulva.

As the male organ may be either double or single, outstretched or reflexed, the corresponding abbreviations for the usual forms of male apparatus are as follows:

$$-M \qquad =M \qquad \text{'}M \qquad \text{'}M \qquad -M-$$

and this is the form in which the facts are presented in the formulae for males. As the testes always lie in front of the sexual opening, the datum point of the reference signs in this case is the point where the testes join the vas deferens, not the sexual opening, as in the females. The percentage figure representing the extent of the male sexual organs dates from the anus. Species with reflexed testes are comparatively rare among fresh-water nematodes, the commonest forms being -M- and -M.

The blind, free, or distal end of the female sexual tube is usually found to contain only cells of extremely small size, observable with difficulty. In consequence little is known about the primordial sexual products in these free-living species. The interior of the main part of this segment of the tube, the ovary, is filled with developing oocytes, which generally soon arrange themselves in single file. The oocytes increase rapidly in size, so that they are ripe by the time they reach the entrance to the uterus. At this point they undergo synapsis, meet the spermatozoa, and are fertilized, and then receive their shells, cuticular coverings acquired in the uterus. The spermatozoa usually collect together at the end of the uterus, which, in some instances, has a special form adapted to their reception, and in all cases must be at least physiologically adapted to attract and retain them. Some species have special receptacles for the spermatozoa in the shape of large tubular branches of the uterus, — genuine spermathecae.

The entrance to the uterus from the ovary is narrow, and this slender part of the sexual tube is armed with delicate annular muscles adapted to moving the ova on into the uterus. The uterus varies much in size. Frequently in the small species a single egg completely fills it; in the larger fresh-water species each uterus may become large enough to carry a score or more of eggs. In the larger parasitic species this capacity is enormously greater, so that the number of eggs in the uterus may reach tens of thousands, or even hundreds of thousands.

The vagina is usually short and more or less muscular, especially near the vulva, where its wall is usually thicker. At the thickest part it suddenly diminishes in massiveness, and in the case of the double-ovaried species forks to form two short tubular branches which join the uteri. The walls of these two short tubes, as well as those of the part nearer the vulva, are supplied with encircling muscle fibers which by their peristaltic action force the egg onward and outward in the process of deposition. The vulva is a transverse slit-like opening whose length varies up to about one-half the width of the body. Muscular fibers radiate from its cuticular margin to the ventral submedian parts of the body wall, and serve by their contraction to open the orifice.

The subspherical to elongate eggs are covered with cuticular shells of varying thickness, usually smooth, but sometimes bearing projections. In the greater number of fresh-water species the eggs are deposited before segmentation begins, but in some genera fully developed embryos are formed in the eggs before deposition. A few species are viviparous. The period of gestation varies widely. In some cases the formation of the embryo occurs within the space of a few hours to a day or two, in other cases weeks are necessary.

The structure of the testes resembles that of the ovaries, but the resulting sexual cells, the spermatozoa, are smaller. The primordial germ cells at the blind end of the testis multiply to form the grandmother-cells of the spermatozoa, which grow to a considerable size, so that it is usually easy to locate the part of the testis where they are maturing, — generally the middle or proximal part. These grandmother-cells, or spermatocytes, have the number of chromosomes characteristic of the males of the species, and they proceed to the formation of the spermatozoa by a process of sudden double division of the chromosomes such that each spermatocyte gives rise in most of the known cases to four spermatozoa, two with half the number of chromosomes characteristic of the females and two with one less chromosome than this. All these spermatozoa are supposed to be potent, but there is a dearth of experimental evidence.

The oocytes follow a similar course but only one of the last four female cells is potential, the other three being the so-called polar bodies which are left at the periphery of the egg to disintegrate and disappear. The polar bodies are to be looked for in eggs that have just entered the uterus, and can be observed to advantage only in stained specimens, though they may sometimes be seen in the living material. The fundamental facts connected with fertilization and inheritance in animals were first worked out largely through the instrumentality of the eggs of various species of nematodes. In this respect they are classical objects.

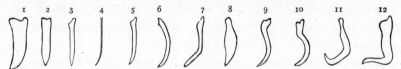

FIG. 771. Forms of spicula. 1. Broad, tapering, blunt. 2. Elongate. 3. Slender. 4. Setaceous. 5. Elongated, tapering. 6. Elongated, arcuate. 7. Elongated, bent. 8. Fusiform, slightly arcuate. 9. Arcuate, strongly cephalated. 10. Sickle-form. 11. Hamate. 12. L-shaped. (After Cobb.)

The male intromittent organs, the spicula, are usually two in number, and in nearly all free-living species the two are identical in form and size. Each spiculum is usually a straight, curved, or bent, elongated framework of cuticula, commonly one to two times as long as the anal body diameter. Exceptionally it may be very long and slender. The main portion of its shaft is usually of uniform size, while the free or distal end commonly terminates in a somewhat blunt point, which, however, may be variously modified. The anterior or proximal end is often swollen or cephalated, for the attachment of muscles.

The muscle for protruding the spiculum more or less insheaths it, and is attached to the proximal end of the spiculum and to the body wall, or to an accessory piece, near the anus, so that its contraction moves the spiculum toward the anus and thus protrudes it. The retractor muscle is attached to the proximal end of the spiculum and thence usually passes forward and toward the dorsal side of the body, where it is attached to the body wall; its contraction thus tends to pull the spiculum back into the body. It is usually rather easy to observe these retractor muscles of the spicula, but difficult to observe the protruding muscles.

In order that these muscles may act to better advantage the spicula often slide in grooved pieces of cuticula named the accessory pieces. These accessory pieces are usually from one-fourth to two-thirds as long as the spicula themselves, and not uncommonly possess an inward or backward extending apophysis whose function is to anchor them firmly in position, or serve for the attachment of special muscles. Long-necked unicellular glands are often seen to empty into the cloaca near the distal ends of the spicula. These probably serve a special purpose at mating time. The form of the spicula and of their accessory pieces is useful in distinguishing the various species, and as these organs are usually viewed in profile the various terms used to describe them are understood to apply to this aspect. The various forms and terms are shown in the accompanying illustrations, Fig. 771.

Among the male accessory organs the bursa is, in a number of genera, the most important, though there is no trace of it in the greater number of the fresh-water genera. The bursa is a thin, transparent flap-like expansion of the lateral cuticula of the tail end of the male, and serves as a copulatory clasping organ. It may consist of two distinct halves, one on each side of the tail, and each ending short of the extremity, or the two parts may extend to the extremity and coalesce to form a continuous flap encompassing the tail. The bursa springs from the submedian or lateral regions, though it is usually on the ventral side of the lateral lines and, furthermore, is bent toward the ventral side. Typically the flaps spring from the body somewhat in front of the anus, grow wider as they pass backward, and reach their maximum development about opposite the anus; thence onward they usually diminish, — though in some cases not very much. In its maximum development the bursa may possess flaps as wide as the body itself; from this maximum it varies to rudiments that may easily be overlooked (pp. 484, 493).

The bursa functions as a male clasping organ through the presence of muscular fibers adapted to close it ventrally, and through the presence of so-called ribs which appear to be in the main, if not altogether, tubular outlets for a cement-like secretion used to fasten the male more or less permanently to the female at mating time. No chemical examinations have been made of the cement substances of the bursa and the caudal glands, but both are insoluble in water and seem otherwise similar. Some genera in which no bursa is developed, nevertheless have papillae, as they have been called, located according to the same general law as the ribs of the bursa. (*Diplogaster, Cephalobus.*)

One striking fact will be forced on the attention of the collector of nematodes early in his work, and that is the comparative rarity of the males. In many of the species the males have never been seen, and in most species the females are from five to twenty times as common as their mates. There is reason to think that in some species the males are very short-lived, and that this is the reason they are so rarely seen. The males are often so much smaller than the females that they are easily overlooked, or mistaken for young, so that in such cases the rarity of the males may easily be over-estimated. In a few species the males appear to be more common than the females, at least at times. Hermaphroditism and par-thenogenesis are frequent. (See p. 495.)

As the ova approach the narrow duct leading to the uterus they rapidly acquire yolk of a distinctly granular character. In the case of the numerous species having reflexed ovaries, the oviduct is located near the flexure, and is so small and short that it is usually impossible to see it except when the organs are immature. Passing through the oviduct, the ovum enters the uterus, where for a short distance the cells of the uterine wall are unusually well developed, apparently to furnish the material for the shells of the eggs. Here too the eggs are fertilized. The proximal limit of the shell-gland is often very definite. The rest of the uterus is thin-walled and connects with the vagina through a narrow muscular duct, mainly responsible for forcing the eggs into the outer world. The eggs at the time of deposition are usually soft and pliant, so that they easily pass through the vulva, even when relatively large.

The fresh-water nematodes are typical of the entire group of free-living nematodes in that while most of them are oviparous, some are ovi-viviparous and others viviparous. The eggs in most of the known fresh-water species are smooth shelled. In the segmentation the first division is a slightly unequal one, one blastomere giving rise to the somatic tissues, the other to the sexual organs.

There are various organs that have been observed in the free-living nematodes whose functions are problematical, such as (1) the double organ in the females only of some species of *Oncholaimus*, located in the posterior part of the body and connecting with the exterior through openings in the subdorsal region; (2) the gland-like pair of organs seen in the females of *Diplogaster*, and apparently also of *Rhabditis* and other related genera; and (3) the long-necked paired glands sometimes emptying into the male cloaca. It is conceivable that some of these serve a sexual function, such as the secretion of a substance whose odor or taste is of service in enabling the nematodes to locate their mates.

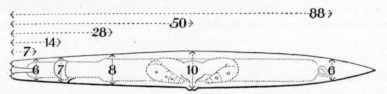

FIG. 772. Diagram in explanation of the descriptive formula used for nematodes; 6, 7, 8, 10, 6 are the transverse measurements, while 7, 14, 28, 50, 88 are the corresponding longitudinal measurements. The formula in this case is:

$$\frac{7. \quad 14. \quad 28. \quad 50. \quad 88.}{6. \quad 7. \quad 8. \quad 10. \quad 6.}$$

The measurements are simply percentages of the length, and the formula, as printed in the key, may be regarded as somewhat in the nature of a conventionalized sketch of the nematode with dimensions attached.

The measurements are taken with the animal viewed in profile; the first is taken at the base of the pharynx, the second at the nerve-ring, the third at the cardiac constriction (base of the "neck"), the fourth at the vulva in females and at the middle (*M*) in males, the fifth at the anus. (After Cobb.)

It seems reasonably clear that fresh-water nematodes have marked seasonal development, at least in some species. Adults of many species can be found at all times of the year. Freezing does not necessarily kill them. Although the fresh-water nematodes are so widespread, and so abundant at all seasons, it is not always easy to isolate them for examination without the use of special methods. Few of these nematodes exceed two to three millimeters in length, and they are so slender and transparent as to make it practically impossible to examine them without the aid of a lens.

However, when special methods are employed they may easily be collected. A few centigrams of mud or sand from a place where nematodes are believed to exist is disseminated in a watch glass of water, and the sediment examined carefully for the characteristic wavy non-progressive motion exhibited by these little organisms. When discovered, the specimens are captured with a fine-pointed pipette or medicine dropper and ejected with a minimum of other material into a second watch glass, from which they are removed on a very fine-pointed needle and placed in a drop of clear water on a microscope slide. These operations are best performed on the stage of a dissecting microscope, under a lens magnifying five to ten diameters.

To collect specimens in large numbers it is best to make use of more elaborate methods. A coarse sieve with meshes two to three millimeters across is used to remove objects larger than nematodes. To gather the nematodes, the material that comes through

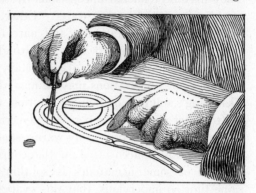

FIG. 773. Measuring the length of the camera lucida drawing of a nematode. The head end of the drawing lies near the left-hand cuff. The pharynx is shown, and near it, next the knuckle of the little finger, is the oblique nerve-ring. The cardiac constriction lies this side of the end of the forefinger, and the vulva on the farther side. Mention should be made of the presence of the error resulting from the attempt to measure a curved line with a straight measure. The aim should be to reduce this error so much that it can safely be neglected. One means of reducing this error may here be mentioned, namely, reducing the "step" of the divider legs in proportion to the sharpness of the curve to be measured. Another method may also be mentioned, but it is to be used with caution, and only as the result of experience. By a number of careful trials it will be found that a measurement nearer the truth can be obtained by following a path somewhat on the outside of the curves of the median line on the drawing or image being measured, but care must be exercised in adopting this method not to overshoot the mark. Where the curve is sharp it is of course safer to go *always* a *little* on the outside of the curve. I consider it to be sufficiently accurate after a little practice to dispense with actually drawing in a median line on which to measure. It is easy to keep sufficiently near the middle by eye. Of course, with a reliable map-measure all these difficulties disappear. The map measurer, an instrument to be had from most dealers in drawing instruments, has a small milled wheel that may be so rolled along a crooked line as to measure its exact length.

To obtain the percentage figures used as terms of the formula simply divide each of the various transverse and longitudinal measurements by the total length. Using a slide rule these divisions occupy only two to three minutes. (After Cobb.)

this coarse sieve is passed through sieves of finer and finer mesh until the limit of fineness is reached. About the finest mesh obtainable is that of the finest miller's bolting silk (0.25 to 0.5 mm.), which, when stretched over appropriate rings made of bottomless dishes will allow fine mud to pass through while it will retain all but the smallest nematodes. By successive siftings practically all the nematodes can be secured.

The sifting can be supplemented by gravity methods. Aquatic nematodes are lighter than sand and heavier than water. If the water containing the nematodes be violently agitated and then be allowed to rest for a few seconds the sand will have subsided to the bottom, and the nematodes may be decanted off if the pouring be managed expeditiously. Then, if the nematode-containing water be allowed to rest for from two to four minutes in a vessel two to three inches deep the nematodes will have largely settled to the bottom and the supernatant muddy water may be carefully decanted away. The residue will contain an abundance of nematodes that may be captured as described above.

Fresh-water nematodes are so active that it is practically impossible to examine them without first anesthetizing or killing them. They may be rendered unconscious by the use of a small amount of chloroform dissolved in water. Ether, chloral hydrate, tobacco smoke and other anesthetics and narcotics are also used in this way. Specimens treated thus are wonderfully transparent, and display to a maximum advantage certain features of the anatomy.

Permanent preparations may be made by killing and fixing with Flemming's solution or Bouin's solution, washing, and then changing to water containing 5 per cent glycerine and very slowly evaporating in a closed, preferably warm, space such that the solution becomes fully concentrated in the course of a few days. The cuticula of some nematodes is so thin and flexible, and at the same time so impervious, that this evaporation process sometimes has to be prolonged to several weeks to prevent crumpling, but many kinds can be successfully treated in two to three days. If the specimens have been blackened by the Flemming's solution, they may be satisfactorily bleached in a few hours or days by adding a few drops of dioxide of hydrogen solution to the glycerine in which they lie after evaporation. They are removed to pure glycerine one by one as they become bleached, and then are mounted in glycerine jelly. Specimens treated in this way make excellent material for examination, but may deteriorate in the course of years. Again, the specimens may be killed by suddenly heating in water on a glass slide until they become motionless, and can then be examined at once, or evaporated as above described in 5 per cent glycerine.

The residue from the subsidence and sifting methods, already described, may be added suddenly to an equal volume of boiling-hot concentrated solution of corrosive sublimate and allowed to cool. When the specimens have remained in this solution for twenty-four hours or more they may be picked out one by one on the point of bamboo splinters and differentiated into alcohol, and thence successively into acid carmine in 70 per cent alcohol, 70 per cent alcohol with 1 to 2 per cent hydrochloric acid, absolute alcohol, oil of cloves and Canada balsam. The specimens thus treated are more permanent than those resulting from the glycerine treatment described above and are the only satisfactory ones for many cytological studies. These various treatments may affect the relative proportions of the organism differently, especially those of the neck. It is therefore best when noting measurements of specimens

FIG. 774. Skeleton camera lucida drawing used to compute the nematode formula. (After Cobb.) The head end lies to the left. This gives the following formula.

$$\frac{1.9 \quad 8.6 \quad 14.8 \quad 46 \quad 95}{2.8 \quad 5.2 \quad 7.4 \quad 10.4 \quad 4.3}.81 \text{ mm}.$$

for descriptive purposes to indicate how the specimens were treated.

The student cannot expect to examine the finer details of the anatomy or indeed to make satisfactory progress without the patient use of a good oil immersion objective under favorable conditions.

The formula is made to convey much additional information, by interspersing suggestive signs. Thus the successive signs in the adjacent formulae indicate lips,[1] papillae on the lips,[2] a pharynx of uniform diameter without armature of any kind,[3] no amphids,[4] a renette whose excretory pore is located a little behind the nerve-ring,[5] about 600 transverse striae resolvable into rows of dots,[6] no wings to the cuticula,[7] a median esophageal bulb two-thirds as wide as the middle of the neck,[8] a cardiac bulb three-fourths as wide as the base of the neck,[9] two symmetrically reflexed ovaries, occupying 71 per cent of the length of the body,[10] no caudal glands or spinneret,[11] a single outstretched testis occupying 63 per cent of the length of the body,[12] a bursa beginning in front of the anus and including the entire tail,[13] 4 bursal ribs or supplementary organs on either side in front of the anus, and 5 ribs on either side behind the anus.[14]

$$\left\{= \frac{1.2}{1.2} - \frac{11}{3.3}/ \div \frac{17}{4.3} - - \frac{'55'71}{4.9} - - \frac{93.8}{1.6} \quad 1.8 \text{ mm}\right.$$

$$\left\{= \frac{2.3}{1.9} - \frac{16}{3.4}/ \div \frac{26.}{3.3} - - \frac{-M63}{37} - \frac{96.3}{4\ 2.6\ 3}\right. \quad 1. \text{ mm}$$

TABLE

Terminology Relating to Striation of Cuticula.

Number of Striae to the Millimeter	Corresponding Text Term	Corresponding Formula Line
100 down	Very coarse	
250 ±	Coarse	
500 ±	Rather coarse	
750 ±	Rather fine	
1000 ±	Fine	
1500 up	Very fine	
	None	

---

[1] Conventionalized contour of the front of the head. [2] Conventionalized contour of the lips. [3] Conventionalized outline of the pharynx. [4] Absence of **mark indicat-**

KEY TO NORTH AMERICAN FRESH–WATER NEMATODA

1 (64) Intestine normal and functional throughout; anus present in both
sexes. 2

The forms which are included here are typical nematodes. They possess an alimentary
canal which is complete and functional during the entire life of the individual. They are
free living in the adult as well as in the larval stage of existence. With the free-living forms
are sometimes found parasitic forms so similar in structure that a knowledge of their source is
needed to determine whether the species is parasitic or not. No note is taken of the parasitic
forms and the following statements apply only to the true free-living nematodes.

They are all relatively small in size and so transparent that the internal structure can be made
out clearly in the living animal. In these respects as well as in detail of internal structure they
stand in distinct contrast to the other group included under the alternative heading in the
key. Families which include only parasitic species are not mentioned in this key.

2 (13) Oral end armed with protrusible spear or sting. 3

3 (8) Spear with bulbous base. 4

4 (5) Cuticula with 70 to 100 coarse, retrorse annules. . . . . *Iota* Cobb.

Genus consisting of a considerable number of species, found in swamps and in acid
soils. These nematodes are covered with retrorse scales, or bristles, so that it is practically impossible for them to move in any other direction than forward. Near the head the remarkably
large and powerful spear can be seen through the skin. When, in order to make punctures, this
spear is thrust out, the nematode is not pushed backward, because of the friction which its
scales offer to surrounding soil particles. But often the males of *Iota* lose the spear at the last
moult and become relatively longer and more slender and smoother, and then they look very
unlike the females.

Representative species. . . . . *Iota octangulare* Cobb 1914.

$$\left\{ \rightarrow \frac{14.}{11.} \; \frac{21.}{12.} \; \frac{25.}{12./} \; \frac{-85^{57}}{9.} \; \frac{92}{6.} \;\text{———} .4 \; mm. \right.$$

Male unknown. Habitat: Dismal Swamp, Va.

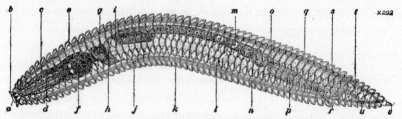

FIG. 775. *Iota octangulare.*
a, mouth opening; *b*, lip region; *c*, spear muscles; *d*, shaft of spear; *e*, base of spear; *f*, cuticular tube
of esophagus; *g*, nerve-ring; *h*, posterior portion of esophagus; *i*, flexure in ovary; *j*, body muscles;
k, cuticula; *l*, one of the eight longitudinal rows of modified cuticula; *m*, ovum; *n*, muscles of body wall;
o, sublateral modification of the cuticula; *p*, uterus; *q*, subdorsal modification of the cuticula; *r*, vulva;
s, muscles of the body wall; *t*, rectum; *u*, anus; *v*, terminus. (After Cobb.)

5 (4) Cuticula with 200 or more finer or almost invisible annules. 6

ing amphids. [5] Oblique line, conventionalized drawing of the outlet of the excretory
duct, placed just behind the measurements relating to the nerve-ring. [6] Character
of the line running through the formula (see adjacent table), and dots placed on either
side of the line. [7] Absence of short horizontal lines above and below main line, such
marks being used when wings are present. [8] Horizontal stroke under two-thirds of
the nerve-ring width measurement. [9] A corresponding stroke under three-fourths of
the width measurement for the base of the neck. [10] Single quotation marks around the
measurement indicating the position of the vulva, and 71 used as an exponent. [11] Absence of spinneret mark, — an angular sign used to indicate spinneret. [12] Dash in
front of the M and 63 used as an exponent. [13] Curved marking under the transverse
anal measurement, extending to the end of the formula line of the male. [14] 4 and 5
used as sub-figures before and after the anal diametral measurement with ditto marks
to indicate that the ribs occur on both sides.

6 (7) Esophagus with a distinct median bulb, and a more or less distinct posterior swelling. Males with bursa. . *Tylenchus* Bastian.

Genus consisting of numerous species, many of them parasitic in plants and sometimes highly injurious. Aquatic species are rather uncommon. A single species found parasitic in a marine alga. Principally owing to its economic importance the genus has a very extensive literature.

Representative species. . *Tylenchus dipsaci* Kühn 1857.

$$\overleftarrow{\left(-\; \tfrac{.9}{.8}\; \cdot\; \tfrac{8.}{1.8}\; \rightleftharpoons \tfrac{13.}{2.}\; \cdot\; \cdot\; \tfrac{81}{2.2}\; \cdot\; \tfrac{93.}{1.2}\right.}\; 1.5\,mm.$$ This species is found parasitic in onion and hya-

$$\overleftarrow{\left(-\; \tfrac{.9}{.8}\; \cdot\; \tfrac{8.}{1.7}\; \rightleftharpoons \tfrac{12.}{1.9}\; \cdot\; \cdot\; \tfrac{M}{2.}\; \cdot\; \tfrac{93.}{1.4}\right.}\; 1.4\,mm.$$ cinth bulbs, and in a number of other plants, and is very harmful. The spear, *b, i,* Fig. II, is shot forth by the muscles, *f,* and is used to puncture the cells of the host plant. The spear is tubular, and the juices of the host are sucked through the spear into the intestine by means of the bulb, *c.* Often referred to in literature as *Tylenchus devastatrix.*

Habitat: Europe, America, Australia, and probably throughout the temperate regions.

FIG. 776. *Tylenchus dipsaci.* Kühn.

I, a female; II. head of the same more highly magnified; III, tail of a male; IV, view from below, of the female sexual opening; V, cross-section of the neck passing through the median sucking-bulb; VI, front view of the penes and their accessory parts; VII, cross-section through the middle of a female, showing how the body-cavity is filled completely by the ovary (*w*) and the intestine (*z*).

a, lip region; *b.* tip of spear; *c,* median sucking-bulb; *d,* nerve-ring; *e,* excretory pore; *f.* muscles for moving the spear forward; *g,* posterior esophageal swelling; *h,* excretory gland; *i,* hind end of spear, three-bulbed: *j.* loop in ovary; *k,* right spiculum; *l,* muscles for opening the vulva; *m,* the vulva; *n,* glandular (?) bodies; *o,* bursa; *p,* hind end of ovary; *q,* uterus containing spermatozoa and one segmenting egg; *r,* segmenting egg; *s.* vagina; *t,* the vulva or female sexual opening; *u,* blind end of posterior rudimentary ovary; *v.* intestine, showing its cellular structure; *w,* cross-section of an egg; *x,* anus; *y,* wings of the cuticula; *z,* cross-section of the intestine. (After Cobb.)

7 (6) Esophagus with only one swelling, corresponding to the median bulb of *Tylenchus.* Males without bursa. . . *Aphelenchus* Bastian.

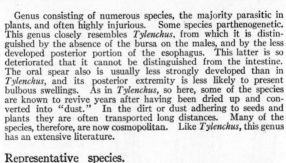

Genus consisting of numerous species, the majority parasitic in plants, and often highly injurious. Some species parthenogenetic. This genus closely resembles *Tylenchus,* from which it is distinguished by the absence of the bursa on the males, and by the less developed posterior portion of the esophagus. This latter is so deteriorated that it cannot be distinguished from the intestine. The oral spear also is usually less strongly developed than in *Tylenchus,* and its posterior extremity is less likely to present bulbous swellings. As in *Tylenchus,* so here, some of the species are known to revive years after having been dried up and converted into "dust." In the dirt or dust adhering to seeds and plants they are often transported long distances. Many of the species, therefore, are now cosmopolitan. Like *Tylenchus,* this genus has an extensive literature.

Representative species.

Aphelenchus microlaimus Cobb 1891.

$$\overleftarrow{\left(-\; \tfrac{.5}{.7}\; \cdot\; \tfrac{5.}{1.3}\; \cdot\; \tfrac{10.}{1.2}\; \cdot\; \tfrac{69-49}{2.2}\; \cdot\; \tfrac{95.3}{1.}\right.}\; .7\,mm.$$ Habitat: Douglas Lake, Michigan.

$$\overleftarrow{\left(-\; \tfrac{.9}{.8}\; \cdot\; \tfrac{?}{1.3}\; \cdot\; \tfrac{11.}{1.7}\; \cdot\; \tfrac{M}{2.4}\; \cdot\; \tfrac{95.1}{1.}\right.}\; .66\,mm.$$

FIG. 777. *Aphelenchus microlaimus.*

a, the lips; *b,* the spear; *c,* the nerve-ring; *d,* sucking-bulb; *e,* excretory pore; *f,* ventral gland; *g,* blind end of testicle; *h,* intestine; *i,* cuticula or skin; *j,* spermatozoon; *k,* right spiculum or penis; *l,* piece accessory to the spicula; *m,* anus; *n,* papilla; *o,* terminus. (After Cobb.)

8 (3) Spear without a bulbous base. 9
9 (10) Esophagus with a median bulb; males with bursa.

Dolichodorus Cobb.

This genus is distinguished from *Tylenchus* by the peculiar lobed bursa without ribs, by the relatively long and slender oral spear and peculiar lip region, and by the presence of a double sexual organ in the female. There are few Tylenchi the females of which possess two ovaries.

Representative species. . . . *Dolichodorus heterocephalus* Cobb 1914.

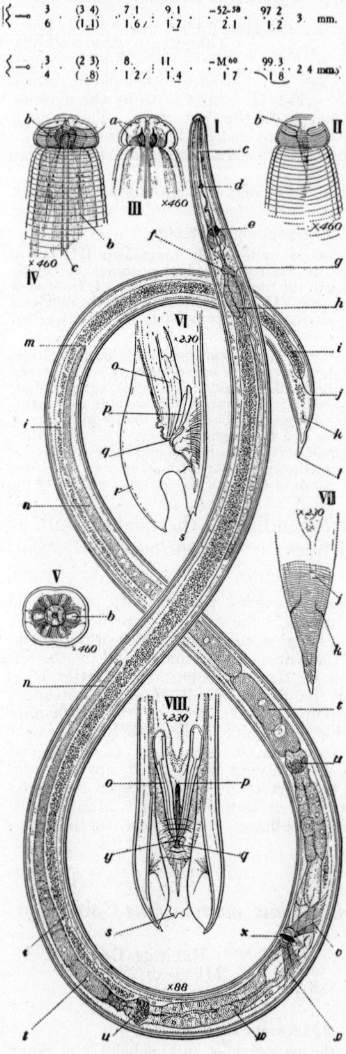

$\lvert{\leftharpoondown}\ \frac{3}{6}\cdot\frac{(3.4)}{(1.1)}\cdot\frac{7.1}{1.6\prime}\cdot\frac{9.1}{1.7}\cdot\frac{-52\text{-}30}{2.1}\cdot\frac{97.2}{1.2}\ 3\ \text{mm}.$

$\{{\leftharpoondown}\ \frac{3}{4}\cdot\frac{(2.3)}{(.8)}\cdot\frac{8}{1.2\prime}\cdot\frac{11}{1.4}\cdot\frac{-M.60}{1.7}\cdot\frac{99.3}{1.8}\ 2.4\ \text{mm}.$

The transverse striae are resolvable with high powers under favorable conditions into rows of exceedingly minute, somewhat irregular elements. The flaps of the bursa are striated in much the same manner as the cuticula, and the margins of the flaps are distinctly thickened. The spermatozoa are small and numerous and it appears that the reduction divisions take place in a short segment of the testis not far from the blind end. The organs obscurely figured in connection with the head appear to be the outlets of glands located in the neck.

The "cardiac swelling" *h* appears to have the same structure as in some species of *Tylenchus*, in which it is known to be caused by the presence of glands exterior to the esophagus, and therefore not properly to be regarded as a cardiac swelling of the ordinary kind. In the Tylenchi mentioned, these glands empty through a minute duct which enters the esophagus, passes through the median bulb on the dorsal side of its valvular apparatus, and, continuing, empties into the pharynx at the base of the spear. These so-called salivary glands are designated at *g* in I, under *Tylenchus dipsaci* (Fig. 776). Similar structures may occur in the present species.

Inequality of the ovaries is characteristic of a vast number of species of nematodes and may have a deep morphological significance. It is nearly always the posterior ovary which is the smaller. Every degree of inequality exists even to the extinction of one ovary. The smaller branch may produce smaller and what appear to be inferior eggs, and may even cease to function as a reproductive organ and function merely as a minor part of the other branch, serving, for instance, either as an extension of the uterus, or as a seminal receptacle.

Habitat: Douglas Lake, Michigan; Silver Spring, Florida.

FIG. 778. *Dolichodorus heterocephalus.*
I, nearly side view of a female; II, lateral view of surface of head, more highly enlarged; III, sagittal section of head; IV, dorso-ventral view of head; V, front view of head; VI, side view, posterior extremity of male; VII, ventral view of posterior extremity of female; VIII, ventral view of posterior extremity of male.
a, papilla; *b*, cephalic organ of unknown significance; *c*, spear; *d*, base of spear; *e*, median bulb; *f*, nerve-ring; *g*, excretory pore; *h*, cardiac swelling; *i*, intestine; *j*, anus; *k*, lateral caudal pores; *l*, terminus; *m*, blind end of posterior ovary; *n*, ovary; *o*, left spiculum; *p*, accessory piece; *q*, distal end of accessory piece; *r*, left flap of bursa; *s*, terminus of male; *t*, ovum; *u*, spermatozoa; *v*, vaginal muscles; *w*, uterus; *x*, vulva; *y*, anus. (After Cobb.)

10 (9) Esophagus with only an elongated posterior swelling; no bursa. . 11

11 (12) Pharynx simple, male supplementary organs not in fascicles.

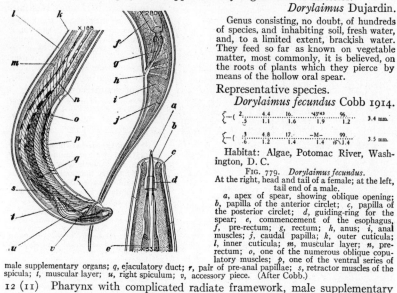

Dorylaimus Dujardin.

Genus consisting, no doubt, of hundreds of species, and inhabiting soil, fresh water, and, to a limited extent, brackish water. They feed so far as known on vegetable matter, most commonly, it is believed, on the roots of plants which they pierce by means of the hollow oral spear.

Representative species.

Dorylaimus fecundus Cobb 1914.

$$\left\{-\left(\frac{2.}{.5}\quad\frac{4.4}{1.1}\quad\frac{16.}{1.6}\quad\frac{\cdot 43'43}{1.9}\quad\frac{96.}{1.2}\right.\right.\quad 3.4\ mm.$$

$$\left\{-\left(\frac{3.}{.6}\quad\frac{4.8}{1.2}\quad\frac{17.}{1.4}\quad\frac{-M-}{1.4}\quad\frac{99.}{\text{19}\backslash 1.4}\right.\right.\quad 3.5\ mm.$$

Habitat: Algae, Potomac River, Washington, D. C.

Fig. 779. *Dorylaimus fecundus.*

At the right, head and tail of a female; at the left, tail end of a male.

a, apex of spear, showing oblique opening; *b*, papilla of the anterior circlet; *c*, papilla of the posterior circlet; *d*, guiding-ring for the spear; *e*, commencement of the esophagus; *f*, pre-rectum; *g*, rectum; *h*, anus; *i*, anal muscles; *j*, caudal papilla; *k*, outer cuticula; *l*, inner cuticula; *m*, muscular layer; *n*, pre-rectum; *o*, one of the numerous oblique copulatory muscles; *p*, one of the ventral series of the male supplementary organs; *q*, ejaculatory duct; *r*, pair of pre-anal papillae; *s*, retractor muscles of the spicula; *t*, muscular layer; *u*, right spiculum; *v*, accessory piece. (After Cobb.)

12 (11) Pharynx with complicated radiate framework, male supplementary organs in fascicles. . . . . *Actinolaimus* Cobb.

Genus represented in all parts of th world, and proposed for species similar to *Dorylaimus labyrinthostomus*, in which the pharynx is more or less immobile, radially striated and elaborately constructed.

Representative species.

Actinolaimus radiatus Cobb 1913.

$$\left\{c\ \frac{.3}{.9}\quad\frac{6.4}{1.5}\quad\frac{19.}{1.7}\quad\frac{\cdot 29'}{2.}\quad\frac{93.}{1.4}\right.\quad 3.9\ mm.$$

$$\left\{c\ \frac{.9}{1.8}\quad\frac{13.}{3.}\quad\frac{41.}{3.6}\quad\frac{-M-}{2.}\quad\frac{99.7}{\mathcal{N}1.4}\right.\quad 4.1\ mm.$$

The esophagus begins as a tube about one-third as wide as the corresponding portion of the neck. It continues to have this width for some distance. Considerably in front of the middle of the neck it expands rather suddenly. The cells of the brownish intestine contain granules of variable size, arranged so as to give rise to a rather obscure tessellation. The tail of the female is concave-conoid to the hairfine terminus. The tail of the male is hemispherical-conoid. Immediately in front of the anus are two ventral papillae placed side by side. In addition to these there are ventral papillae arranged in three raised and conspicuous groups or fascicles. These three groups form a series whose length is about equal to the distance from the posterior group to the end of the tail. The two equal, slightly arcuate, rather acute spicula are about twice as long as the anal body diameter. The surface of the tail carries a number of innervated papillae, at least as many as six, and probably quite a number of others.

Habitat: Roots of plants and among algae, Potomac River and its banks, Arlington Farm near Washington, D.C.; Douglas Lake, Mich.

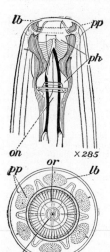

Fig. 780. *Actinolaimus radiatus.*

lb, lip region; *pp*, innervated papillae; *ph*, pharynx; *on*, onchus or spear; *or*, mouth opening. (After Cobb.)

13 (2) Oral end without protrusile spear or sting. 14

14 (37) Pharynx armed with one or more refractive, cuticular teeth. . . 15

15 (16)   Number of teeth three, equal, small, mobile, well forward near the mouth. . *Ironus* Bastian.

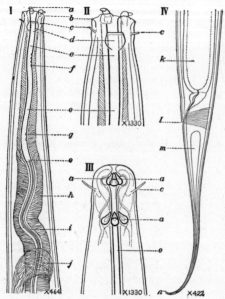

Genus with about six known species, confined to fresh water, though there is a very similar genus, *Thallasironus* de Man, for the reception of similar marine forms. Some species hermaphroditic. Salivary glands in esophagus.

Representative species.
Ironus americanus
Cobb 1914.

$$\zeta = c \quad \frac{3.7}{1.6} \quad \frac{9.}{2.3} \quad \frac{21.}{2.7} \quad \frac{\cdot52\cdot30}{2.9} \quad \frac{92.5}{1.3} \quad 2.3\ mm$$

From the size of the apparently matured ova it is assumed that the eggs are considerably elongated. It is unlikely that more than one is contained in the uterus at a time.

Habitat: Deer Bottom, Pikes Peak region, Colorado.

FIG. 781. *Ironus americanus.*
I, head and anterior portion of neck; II, head, lateral view, "teeth" extruded; III, head, "teeth" withdrawn with second set formed in preparation for the next moult; IV, tail end of female.

a, one of the three pharyngeal teeth, shown extruded; *b*, papilla; *c*, cephalic seta; *d*, amphid; *e*, pharynx; *f*, toothlet; *g*, toothlet; *h*, esophagus; *i*, lining of esophagus; *j*, nerve-ring; *k*, intestine; *l*, anus; *m*, caudal gland; *n*, terminus. (After Cobb.)

16 (15)   Number of teeth one; or more than one, and unequal. 17
17 (22)   Teeth, at least one of them, usually massive; thick, more or less papillate lips closing over the capacious pharynx. . . . 18
18 (19)   Main tooth dorsal (sometimes all nearly obsolete); lips thick, armed with papillae; no setae. . . . . *Mononchus* Bastian.

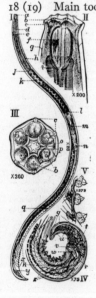

Genus of a score or more species, some in fresh water, others in soil, where they hunt and devour nematodes and other small organisms. The movements, especially those of the head, are often very active. The males are very rare. The name Mononchus indicates the presence of a single pharyngeal tooth, but sometimes there are one or two additional teeth; sometimes all are absent. The relatively powerful lips can be everted, and are utilized to grasp the prey and force it against the pharyngeal teeth. In some species the wall of the pharynx bears series of minute rasp-like denticulations. Some species are hermaphroditic.

Representative species. *Mononchus major* Cobb 1893.

$$\zeta = o \quad \frac{1.6}{1.6} \quad \frac{6.}{2.2} \quad \frac{19.}{2.6} \quad \frac{\cdot55\cdot25}{2.9} \quad \frac{95}{1.5} \longrightarrow 3.4\ mm.$$

$$\zeta = o \quad \frac{1.5}{1.5} \quad \frac{6:6}{2.3} \quad \frac{19.}{2.9} \quad \frac{-M-}{2\ 8} \quad \frac{95}{\cap 2.3} \longrightarrow 3.4\ mm.$$

This elegant species is a soil-inhabiting form sometimes found in wet places. No American species are figured as yet. The adjacent illustrations are derived from Australian specimens.

FIG. 782. *Mononchus major.*
I, side view of male; II, side view of head of same; III, front view of head; IV, side view of tail; V, details of male papillae.

a, mouth; *b*, lip-papilla; *c*, lip; *d*, esophagus; *e*, nerve-ring; *f*, pharyngeal tooth; *g*, innervated papilla of skin; *h*, esophagus; *i*, base of pharynx; *j*, cardiac collum; *k*, intestine; *l*, flexure in testicle; *m*, blind end of testicle; *n*, vas deferens; *o*, lip; *p*, mouth opening; *q*, ejaculatory duct; *r*, spicula; *s*, ejaculatory duct; *t*, accessory piece; *u*, post-anal papillae. *v*, spicula; *w*, ejaculatory duct; *x*, ventral row male papillae; *y*, anus; *z*, three anal glands. (After Cobb.)

19 (18) Main tooth submedian. Lips thin; setae present. 20
20 (21) Males without bursa. . . . . *Oncholaimus* Dujardin.

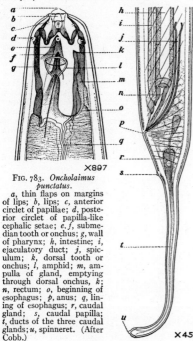

X897

FIG. 783. *Oncholaimus punctatus*.

a, thin flaps on margins of lips; *b*, lips; *c*, anterior circlet of papillae; *d*, posterior circlet of papilla-like cephalic setae; *e*, *f*, submedian tooth or onchus; *g*, wall of pharynx; *h*, intestine; *i*, ejaculatory duct; *j*, spiculum; *k*, dorsal tooth or onchus; *l*, amphid; *m*, ampulla of gland, emptying through dorsal onchus, *k*; *n*, rectum; *o*, beginning of esophagus; *p*, anus; *q*, lining of esophagus; *r*, caudal gland; *s*, caudal papilla; *t*, ducts of the three caudal glands; *u*, spinneret. (After Cobb.)

X457

Genus of numerous species, nearly all marine. A few species only in brackish and fresh water. Cosmopolitan, extending well into the polar seas. Some attain a length of 25 to 30 mm. The individuals sometimes occur in enormous numbers.

The pharyngeal teeth vary in number, form, and size, and afford good specific characters. The segments of the esophagus frequently contain much-branched "salivary" glands emptying through the pharyngeal teeth.

The female sometimes possesses a peculiar pair of relatively large organs of unknown significance emptying through pores toward the tail end.

Representative species.
Oncholaimus punctatus Cobb 1914.

$$\zeta = \zeta \, \frac{1.9}{1.2} \quad \frac{10.}{2.2} \quad \frac{21.}{2.8} \quad \frac{-M-40}{2.5} \quad \frac{92.}{1.8} \; 2.1 \text{ mm.}$$

It is rather difficult to observe the finer details of the cuticula on account of the presence in it of *numerous dot-like elements*, which are arranged *in longitudinal groups*, of which the widest are the lateral groups. The longitudinal arrangement of the granules is continuous throughout the body, but it is most marked on the lateral fields. There are six lips.

Habitat: Fresh-water ponds, Cape Breton Island, Dominion of Canada.

21 (20) Males with bursa.
Oncholaimellus de Man.

Much like *Oncholaimus*, but males have narrow bursa. Spicula unequal, or equal. Two species known; the type *O. calvadosicus* de Man is marine.

Representative species.
Oncholaimellus heterurus Cobb 1914.

$$\zeta = \zeta \, \frac{9}{.8} \quad \frac{8.5}{1.5} \quad \frac{18.}{1.8} \quad \frac{-M-53}{1.8} \quad \frac{91.}{1.4} \; 1.2 \text{ mm.}$$

There are six lips, each bearing on its anterior surface, near the margin of the head, a somewhat outward pointing, minute, innervated papilla. The cells composing the intestine contain scattered granules, which give rise to a very obscure tessellation, and also certain doubly refractive granules. The posterior testis is the smaller. This is a doubtful *Oncholaimellus*, since there are no pharyngeal teeth, and the amphid varies from that of the type species, as do the spicula, which in the type species are unequal.

Habitat: Fresh-water pond near Ocala, Fla.

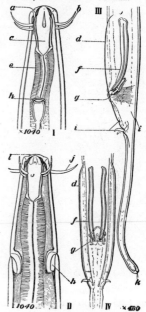

FIG. 784. *Oncholaimellus heterurus*.

I, side view of head; II, ventral view of head; III, side view of tail end of male; IV, ventral view of anal region of male. *a*, excretory pore; *b*, submedian cephalic seta; *c*, pharynx; *d*, left flap of bursa; *e*, esophagus; *f*, left spiculum; *g*, accessory piece; *h*, amphid; *i*, male post-anal seta and papilla; *j*, lateral seta; *k*, spinneret; *l*, thin lips. (After Cobb.)

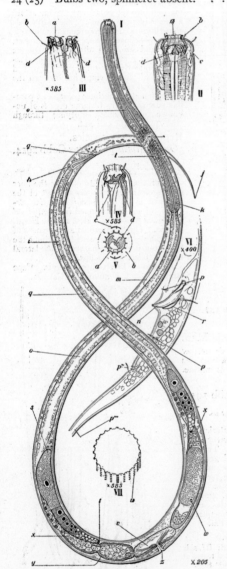

Genus with more than a score of known species, mostly found in fresh water but also in many moist situations in soil and between the sheaths of grasses, etc. Some species hermaphroditic. A number of the species appear to be at least facultative parasites. They are often found in dead insects and caterpillars, whose death they apparently have caused. Other species are found in decaying mushrooms, animal excreta and foul pools. Many of the species are easily reared in decayed meat and various other culture media. Many thrive best in the presence of bacteria.

Representative species.

Diplogaster fictor Bastian 1865.

$$\text{\textsf{ʒ}} \Big(\tfrac{1.3}{1.3} \cdots \tfrac{11.}{1.4} \cdots \tfrac{14.}{1.4} \cdots \tfrac{\cdot 51^{\cdot 35}}{1.7} \cdots \tfrac{88.}{1.4} \cdots \Big) \; 1.5 \text{ mm.}$$

$$\text{\textsf{ʒ}} \Big(\tfrac{9}{1.4} / \tfrac{12.}{1.4} \cdots \tfrac{15.}{1.4} \cdots \tfrac{-M^{.35}}{1.5} \cdots \tfrac{86.6}{1.6 7} \overset{\curvearrowright}{\curvearrowleft} \Big) \; 1.6 \text{ mm.}$$

Striae resolvable near the head into rows of refractive dots arranged in longitudinal as well as transverse lines. A short distance behind the head the longitudinal rows arrange themselves in pairs. These pairs indicate the locus of about twenty-four longitudinal cuticular ribs or wings, which extend from the middle of the neck to near the anus. On the tail these ribs again resolve themselves into double rows of dots. The thin-shelled eggs appear to be deposited before segmentation begins, something rather unusual in this genus.

Habitat: Spring, Washington Country Club, Chevy Chase, Md.

FIG. 785. *Diplogaster fictor.*

I, side view of female; II, head of the same, seen in dorso-ventral view, lips nearly closed; III, head of the same, lateral view, lips nearly wide open; IV, head of the same, lateral view, lips partially closed; V, front view of mouth, partially closed; VI, lateral view, posterior portion of a male specimen; VII, somewhat diagrammatic perspective view showing markings of the cuticula.

a, one of the lips; *b*, one of the six cephalic setae; *c*, amphid; *d*, one of the two more or less evertible pharyngeal hook-shaped teeth; *e*, median esophageal bulb; *f*, nerve-ring; *g*, anus; *h*, rectum; *i*, intestine; *j*, terminus; *k*, posterior esophageal bulb; *l*, nerve cells; *m*, renette cell (?); *n*, left spiculum; *o*, lumen of the intestine; *p'*, pre-anal male seta; *p''*, *p'''*, *p''''*, post-anal male setae and papillae; *q*, one of the cells of the intestine; *r*, accessory piece; *s*, flexure in anterior ovary; *t*, blind end of anterior ovary; *v*, vagina; *w*, synapsis in egg in the anterior uterus; *x*, one of the spermatozoa in the vagina; *y*, uterus; *z*, vulva. (After Cobb.)

26 (27) Lateral dots much accentuated. . . . . . . *Spilophora* Bastian.

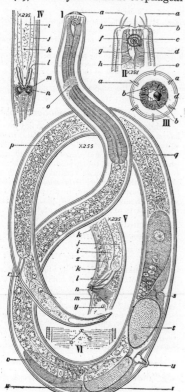

The striae are resolvable into rows of dots which are much accentuated on the lateral fields.

Genus of a score or more known species, aquatic, mostly marine.

Representative species.

Spilophora canadensis Cobb 1914.

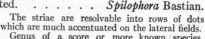

Lateral wings (*j*) are very prominent, and posteriorly are somewhat scalariform. The females have symmetrically reflexed ovaries.

Habitat: Fresh-water ponds, Cape Breton Island, Dominion of Canada.

FIG. 786. *Spilophora canadensis.*

a, mouth opening; *b*, dorsal tooth; *c*, pharynx; *d*, base of the pharynx; *e*, esophagus; *f*, nerve cells; *g*, nerve-ring; *h*, excretory pore; *i*, valvular apparatus of the bulb; *j*, longitudinal row of cuticular markings characteristic of the genus; *k*, intestine; *l*, renette cell; *m*, nucleus of renette cell; *n*, cell accessory to the renette cell; *o*, blind end of testicle; *p*, reversal of the striations of the cuticula; *q*, vas deferens; *r*, spiculum; *s*, anus; *t*, caudal gland; *u*, spinneret. (After Cobb.)

27 (26) Striae composed of dots; the lateral ones little if any accentuated. 28
28 (29) Pharynx without esophageal bulb. . . . . *Cyatholaimus* Bastian.

Pharynx is cup shaped then conoid, and longitudinally ribbed.

Genus of a score or more of aquatic species, nearly all marine but found also in brackish and fresh waters. Cyatholaimi are found in all tropical and temperate seas, and the individuals are numerous. In most habitats both sexes will be found. Diatoms are sometimes found in the intestine. Though not shown in the species here figured, the renette seems always present, and is often well developed.

Representative species.

Cyatholaimus truncatus Cobb 1914.

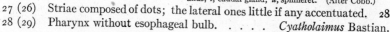

Habitat: Silver Springs, Fla.

FIG. 787. *Cyatholaimus truncatus.*

I, side view of a female; II, side view of head; III, front view of the same head; IV, ventral view of anal region of male; V, lateral view of the same; VI, lateral view in the middle of the body showing cuticular markings and pores.

a, submedian cephalic seta; *b*, labial papilla; *c*, amphid; *d*, dorsal tooth; *e*, lateral cephalic seta; *f*, one of the twelve ribs of the vestibule; *g*, small submedian pharyngeal tooth; *h*, base of the pharynx; *i*, ejaculatory duct; *j*, intestine; *k*, one of the four male pre-anal supplementary organs; *l*, one of the spicula; *m*, anal muscles; *n*, one of the accessory pieces; *o*, nerve-ring; *p*, one of the cells of the intestine; *q*, lumen of the intestine; *r*, anus; *s*, blind end of reflexed ovary; *t*, egg; *u*, vulva; *v*, flexure in anterior ovary; *w*, junction of the ovary and uterus; *x*, pores in the cuticula; *y*, one of the three caudal glands; *z*, male gland (?). (After Cobb.)

29 (28)　Pharynx less conspicuously ribbed; cardiac bulb distinct. . . . **30**

30 (35)　Dorsal tooth well developed. **31**

31 (34)　Pharynx cyathiform then conoid, joining esophagus indefinitely.　**32**

32 (33)　Amphids spiral, inconspicuous slits or none. . . *Chromadora* Bastian.

Genus, aquatic, mostly marine but abundant in fresh waters. Twenty to thirty species known. Found in American fresh waters, no species yet described. Species highly developed, usually of small size. Many possess eye-spots near the head. The males usually have a number of pairs of special unicellular glands emptying through slender ducts into the cloaca. These glands are usually arranged in series of pairs toward the dorsal side of the body some distance in front of the spicula. Amphids, fairly well developed, usually difficult to see because of their peculiar form and position; far toward front of head, usually seen more or less in profile. Cardiac bulb relatively shorter than in *Spilophora*, and not so distinctly subdivided. Males usually have well-developed series of ventral supplementary organs; such organs are less common and less well developed on males of *Spilophora*. Lateral elements of the transverse striae sometimes modified, but rarely reaching degree of differentiation shown in *Spilophora*.

Representative species. . *Chromadora minor* Cobb 1893.

$$\begin{array}{l} \stackrel{.6}{1.7} \cdots \stackrel{.9}{3.2} / \cdots \stackrel{.15}{3.7} \cdots \stackrel{.48'}{4.8} \cdots \stackrel{.86}{2.8} \cdots \rangle \text{ 1. } \textbf{mm.} \end{array}$$　Habitat: Pacific Ocean,

$$\begin{array}{l} \stackrel{.6}{1.3} \cdots \stackrel{8.3}{2.7} / \cdots \stackrel{.14}{3.1} \cdots \stackrel{-M.}{3.8} \cdots \stackrel{.89}{16} \langle 2.7 \cdots \rangle \text{ 1.13 mm,} \end{array}$$　California, and Australia.

Fig. 788.　*Chromadora minor.*

I, male of *Chromadora minor;* II, one of the ventral accessory organs of the same nematode; III and IV, head and anal region of the same nematode.

a, pharynx; *b,* eye-spots; *c,* esophagus; *d, h,* ventral supplementary organ; *e,* nerve-ring; *f,* excretory pore; *g,* gland of supplementary organ; *i,* renette cell; *j,* organ of unknown nature, accessory to the renette cell; *k,* blind end of testicle; *l,* cephalic seta; *m,* ribs of pharyngeal opening; *n,* papilla; *o,* dorsal tooth; *p,* pharynx; *q,* one of the striae of the cuticula; *r,* subcephalic seta; *s,* dorsal eye-spot; *t,* intestine; *u,* one of the ventral male supplementary organs; *v,* ejaculatory duct; *w,* one of the supplementary organs; *x,* anus; *y,* left spiculum; *z,* accessory piece.

33 (32)　Amphids spiral, well developed. . . . . *Achromadora* Cobb.

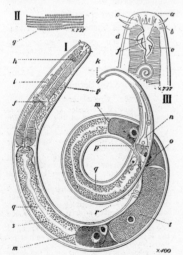

Genus proposed for the reception of *Chromadora minima* Cobb and similar soil and fresh-water species. Distinguished from *Chromadora* by the presence of well-developed spiral amphids. The dorsal tooth is farther back and is opposed by a small ventral "pocket" as shown in the figure of *Achromadora minima*. Species found, probably, in all parts of the world. Known from Australia, Fiji, and various parts of United States and Europe.

Representative species.

Achromadora minima (Cobb) 1914.

$$\begin{array}{l} \stackrel{}{\gtrless} \cdots \stackrel{2.8}{2.5} \cdots \stackrel{10.}{3.6} \cdots \stackrel{17.}{3.9} \cdots \stackrel{.45'}{4.4} \cdots \stackrel{87}{2.8} \cdots \rangle \text{ .51 mm.} \end{array}$$

Male unknown. Habitat: Soil, El Paso, Texas. Potomac River, Washington, D. C.

Fig. 789.　*Achromadora minima.*

I, lateral view of a female; II, lateral view, cuticular markings; III, lateral view of head.

a, cephalic papilla; *b,* cephalic seta; *c,* one of the ribs of the pharynx; *d,* dorsal pharyngeal tooth; *e,* subventral (?) pharyngeal tooth; *f,* pharynx; *g,* cuticular markings; *h,* amphid; *i,* nerve cell; *j,* nerve-ring; *k,* spinneret; *l,* excretory pore; *m,* flexure of ovary; *n,* one of the caudal glands; *o,* blind end of posterior ovary; *p,* anus; *q,* intestine; *r,* vulva; *s,* one of the granules of the intestine; *t,* egg. (After Cobb.)

34 (31) Pharynx cyathiform then prismoid, ending behind very definitely; amphids distinct. . *Ethmolaimus* de Man.

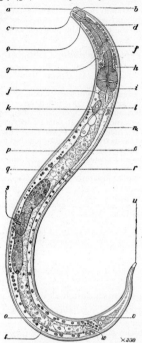

Genus of two known species, one European, one American. Closely related to *Chromadora*, from which it is readily distinguished by the narrow uniform posterior portion of the pharynx, which is usually surrounded by a comparatively distinct pharyngeal bulb.

Representative species.
Ethmolaimus americanus Cobb 1914.

$$\xi = \alpha \frac{2.5}{2.4} \quad \frac{10.}{3.4'} \quad \frac{18.}{3.9} \quad \frac{{}^\cdot54''27}{5.6} \quad \frac{90.3}{2.1} > \quad .6 \text{ mm.}$$

Labial papillae, apparently 12. Onchus thumb-shaped, forward pointing, attached to a distinctly thickened rib of cuticula which extends from the lip region back to the base of the pharynx, and is thicker anteriorly than posteriorly. Fully developed ova are nearly twice as long as the body is wide, and one-third as wide as long. Form, size, and number of eggs unknown.

Habitat: Spring, Washington Country Club, Chevy Chase, Md.

FIG. 790. *Ethmolaimus americanus.* Lateral view of a female. *a*, lips; *b*, minute dorsal and ventral pharyngeal teeth; *c*, one of the four cephalic setae; *d*, amphid; *e*, pharynx; *f*, nerve-ring; *g*, excretory pore; *h*, nerve cells; *i*, cardiac bulb; *j*, beginning of the intestine; *k*, renette cell (?); *l*, beginning of main portion of the intestine; *m*, one of two pairs of unicellular organs of unknown significance; *n*, cuticula; *o*, one of the cells of the intestine; *p*, subcuticula; *q* and *r*, body cavity; *s*, vulva; *t*, nucleus of one of the muscle cells; *u*, spinneret; *v*, one of the caudal glands; *w*, anus.

35 (30) Dorsal tooth minute, amphids circular. . . . *Microlaimus* de Man.

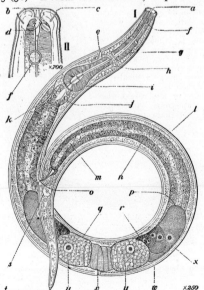

Amphids well developed.

Genus of few species from Europe and North America.

Representative species.
Microlaimus fluviatilis Cobb 1914.

$$\xi = \infty \frac{1.6}{1.9} \quad \frac{8.5}{3.5'} \quad \frac{15.5}{4.3} \quad \frac{{}^\cdot44''27}{4.7} \quad \frac{85.}{2.6} > \quad .83 \text{ mm.}$$

The eggs appear to be deposited before segmentation begins. Specimens with one, and those with two, ovaries, appear to be about equally numerous; as no other difference has been detected, they are included for the present under the same name and description.

Habitat: Maple River, Michigan.

FIG. 791. *Microlaimus fluviatilis.*

I, lateral view of female; II, head of the same.

a, mouth opening; *b*, one of the six cephalic papillae; *c*, one of the four cephalic setae; *d*, one of the small pharyngeal teeth; *e*, excretory pore; *f*, spiral amphid; *g*, esophagus; *h*, nerve-ring; *i*, cardiac bulb; *j*, preliminary portion of the intestine; *k*, renette cell; *l*, body cavity; *m*, lumen of intestine; *n*, one of the cells of the intestine; *o*, anus; *p*, flexure in posterior ovary; *q*, uterus; *r*, blind end of posterior ovary; *s*, one of the three caudal glands; *t*, spinneret; *u*, eggs; *v*, vulva; *w*, cuticula. (After Cobb.)

36 (23) Esophagus plain. . . . . *Cryptonchus* Cobb.

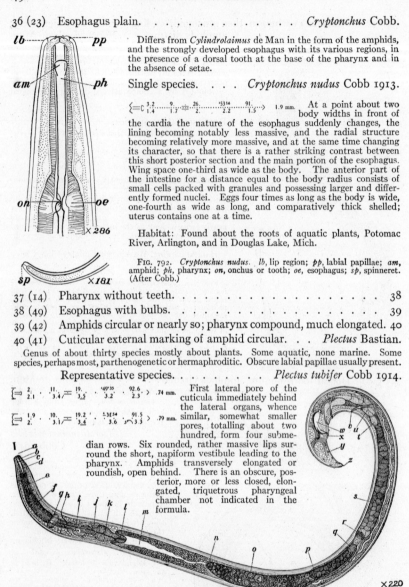

Differs from *Cylindrolaimus* de Man in the form of the amphids, and the strongly developed esophagus with its various regions, in the presence of a dorsal tooth at the base of the pharynx and in the absence of setae.

Single species. . . . *Cryptonchus nudus* Cobb 1913.

$\left\{ = c\,\dfrac{3.2}{1.4}\cdots\dfrac{9.}{1.7}\,\overline{}\,\dfrac{26.}{2.}\cdots\dfrac{^{\cdot53\,14}}{2.2}\cdots\dfrac{91.}{1.5}\cdots\right\rangle$ 1.9 mm.   At a point about two body widths in front of the cardia the nature of the esophagus suddenly changes, the lining becoming notably less massive, and the radial structure becoming relatively more massive, and at the same time changing its character, so that there is a rather striking contrast between this short posterior section and the main portion of the esophagus. Wing space one-third as wide as the body. The anterior part of the intestine for a distance equal to the body radius consists of small cells packed with granules and possessing larger and differently formed nuclei. Eggs four times as long as the body is wide, one-fourth as wide as long, and comparatively thick shelled; uterus contains one at a time.

Habitat: Found about the roots of aquatic plants, Potomac River, Arlington, and in Douglas Lake, Mich.

FIG. 792. *Cryptonchus nudus.* *lb,* lip region; *pp,* labial papillae; *am,* amphid; *ph,* pharynx; *on,* onchus or tooth; *oe,* esophagus; *sp,* spinneret. (After Cobb.)

37 (14) Pharynx without teeth. 38
38 (49) Esophagus with bulbs. 39
39 (42) Amphids circular or nearly so; pharynx compound, much elongated. 40
40 (41) Cuticular external marking of amphid circular. . . *Plectus* Bastian.

Genus of about thirty species mostly about plants. Some aquatic, none marine. Some species, perhaps most, parthenogenetic or hermaphroditic. Obscure labial papillae usually present.

Representative species. . . . . *Plectus tubifer* Cobb 1914.

$\left\{ \Rightarrow \dfrac{2.}{2.1}\cdot\dfrac{11.}{3.4}\,\overline{}\,\dfrac{19.}{3.5}\cdot\dfrac{^{\cdot49\,35}}{3.2}\cdot\dfrac{92.6}{2.3}\,\right\rangle$ .74 mm.   First lateral pore of the cuticula immediately behind the lateral organs, whence

$\left\{ \Rightarrow \dfrac{1.9}{2.}\cdot\dfrac{10.}{3.1}\,\overline{}\,\dfrac{19.2}{3.4}\cdot\dfrac{^{\cdot M\,34}}{3.6}\cdot\dfrac{91.5}{3.3}\,\right\rangle$ .79 mm.   similar, somewhat smaller pores, totalling about two hundred, form four submedian rows. Six rounded, rather massive lips surround the short, napiform vestibule leading to the pharynx. Amphids transversely elongated or roundish, open behind. There is an obscure, posterior, more or less closed, elongated, triquetrous pharyngeal chamber not indicated in the formula.

FIG. 793. *Plectus tubifer.* Male.

a, mouth; *b,* papilla-like cephalic setae; *c,* lateral organ; *d,* pharynx; *e,* posterior chamber of pharynx; *f,* esophagus; *g,* nerve-ring; *h,* excretory pore; *i,* renette cell; *j,* glandular (?) cell; *k,* cardiac bulb; *l,* cardia; *m,* intestine; *n,* blind end of anterior testicle; *o,* spermatocyte; *p,* flexure in posterior testicle; *q,* blind end of posterior testicle; *r,* junction of testicles; *s,* vas deferens; *t,* glandular (?) organ; *u,* muscle to one of the three supplementary organs; *v,* anterior supplementary organ; *w,* spiculum; *x,* anus; *y,* one of the caudal papillae; *z,* spinneret. (After Cobb.)

41 (40) Chitinous marking of amphid not circular. . . . *Chronogaster* Cobb.

Genus closely related to *Plectus*, differing in much elongated cardia, connecting posterior esophageal bulb and intestine. Ovary single in *Chronogaster*, double in *Plectus*.

Single species known. . *Chronogaster gracilis* Cobb 1913.

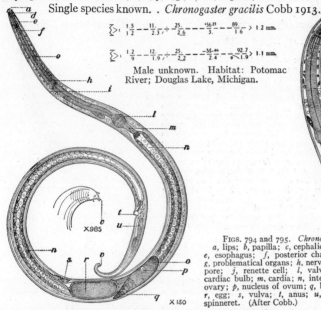

$$\gtrless \cdot \; \frac{1.5}{1.2} - - \frac{11.}{2.3} \cdot \div \frac{25.}{2.6} - - - \frac{{}^{\prime}56.{}^{21}}{3.} - - \frac{89.}{1.6} > 1.2 \text{ mm.}$$

$$\gtrless \cdot \; \frac{1.2}{9} - - \frac{12.}{1.9} \cdot \div \frac{25.}{2.2} - - - \frac{-M-46}{2.4} - \frac{92.7}{9 \sim 1.9} > 1.1 \text{ mm.}$$

Male unknown. Habitat: Potomac River; Douglas Lake, Michigan.

FIGS. 794 and 795. *Chronogaster gracilis.*
a, lips; *b*, papilla; *c*, cephalic seta; *d*, pharynx; *e*, esophagus; *f*, posterior chamber of pharynx; *g*, problematical organs; *h*, nerve-ring; *i*, excretory pore; *j*, renette cell; *l*, valvular apparatus in cardiac bulb; *m*, cardia; *n*, intestine; *o*, flexure in ovary; *p*, nucleus of ovum; *q*, blind end of ovary; *r*, egg; *s*, vulva; *t*, anus; *u*, caudal gland; *v*, spinneret. (After Cobb.)

42 (39) Amphids apparently absent; pharynx simple 43

43 (44) Esophagus with two bulbs; males with bursa. *Rhabditis* Dujardin.

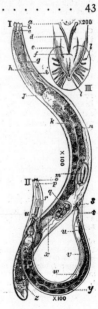

Genus of numerous species, some parasitic, especially in insects. Several marine species and a number in fresh water. Common in decaying matter. Reproduction wonderfully varied, ranging from parthenogenesis, through hermaphroditism of varying degree to complete bi-sexuality. Many species microbivorous. In some species there is a marked alternation of generations.

Bursa better developed in species of *Rhabditis* than in any other fresh-water nematodes. Other genera presenting this feature are *Tylenchus*, *Dolichodorus*, and *Oncholaimellus*. Bursa (Fig. III) consists of two thin lateral extensions of cuticula containing rays or ribs, often tubular, constituting outlets of cement glands, always well supplied with nerve endings. Form of bursa and arrangement of its rays form good generic and specific characters.

Representative species. *Rhabditis cylindrica* Cobb 1898.

$$\gtrless = \; \frac{1.2}{1.2} - - \frac{11.}{3.3} \cdot \div \frac{17.}{4.3} - - - \frac{{}^{\prime}55{}^{71}}{4.9} - - \frac{93.8}{1.6} \quad 1.8 \text{ mm.}$$

Habitat: Wet soils.

$$\gtrless = \; \frac{2.3}{1.9} - - \frac{16.}{3.4} \cdot \div \frac{26.}{3.5} - - - \frac{-M^{63}}{3.7} - - \frac{96.3}{4 \, 2.6} \, 3 \quad 1. \text{ mm.}$$

FIG. 796. *Rhabditis cylindrica* Cobb.
I, side view of female; II, side view of attached male; III, ventral view of male tail.
a, proximal end of spiculum; *b*, lip; *c*, base of pharynx; *d*, right spiculum; *e*, bursa; *f*, anus; *g*, median bulb; *h*, nerve-ring; *i*, excretory pore; *j*, cardiac collum; *k*, intestine; *l*, one of the ribs of the bursa; *m*, egg containing embryo; *n*, flexure in ovary; *o*, lips; *p*, pharynx; *q*, segmenting egg; *r*, median bulb; *s*, vulva; *t*, intromitted spicula; *u*, ejaculatory duct; *v*, testicle; *w*, blind end of testicle; *x*, blind end of reflexed ovary; *y*, intestine; *z*, anus. (After Cobb.)

44 (43) Esophagus with only one well-developed bulb; males without
     bursa. 45

45 (46) Pharynx long and narrow. . . . . *Rhabdolaimus* de Man.
Genus of four known species, three European, one American.

    Representative species. . . . . . *Rhabdolaimus minor* Cobb 1914.

$$\Subset (\tfrac{4.6}{2'.4} \cdots\cdots \tfrac{15}{3.7} \cdots\cdots \tfrac{25}{3.8} \cdots\cdots \tfrac{'51''28}{4'.} \cdots\cdots \tfrac{77.5}{2.} \cdots > 28 \text{ mm.}$$

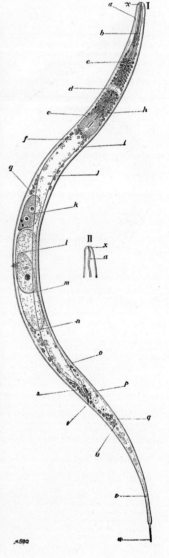

The cuticula appears to be destitute of any but very
fine transverse striations, most clearly visible near the
head. Careful focussing appears to indicate the
presence on the outer margin of the head of almost
invisible papilla-like organs which may perhaps be
the representatives of cephalic setae. There are no
lips. The thin-shelled, smooth eggs are relatively
large and elongated and have been seen in the uterus
one at a time. They are about four to five times as
long as the body is wide and about one-fifth as wide as
long. They appear to be deposited before segmentation begins. The eggs are so large in proportion to the
size of the ovaries that they push the ovaries first to
one side and then the other as they develop, so that
both ovaries may occasionally appear to be either in
front of or behind the vulva. The specimen figured
was so twisted that the head presents the dorso-
ventral view, and the tiny amphids (*a*) therefore
appear in profile. The figure shows well the typical
distribution of nerve cells, large numbers in front of
and behind the nerve-ring, a smaller collection in the
cardiac region, and other collections in the anal region.
The long, slender spinneret is characteristic of the
genus.

The figure illustrates the general features of the central nervous system, which in nematodes consists of a
ring of nerve fibers encircling the esophagus, and having connected with it a number of more or less spherical
nerve cells, shown dark in the figure. Under favorable
circumstances each one of these cells can be seen to be
connected with others, and directly, or indirectly, with
the ring of fibers. The whole, therefore, constitutes a
rather complicated, coordinated system of nerve cells.
In many species the cells, such as those shown at *c* and
h, are arranged in longitudinal groups, and even where
the groups are not apparent, as here, the connections
among the cells are undoubtedly systematic and correspond with the longitudinal grouping that is evident
in other genera. From the central nervous system
extend forward and backward nerves, — ventral, dorsal, lateral, and to a lesser extent submedian, connected
by commissures. Special collections of nerve cells
occur on the ventral side near the cardia, vulva, and
anus. The exterior indications of the nerves are found
in papillae and setae, usually corresponding in position
with the main branches of the nervous system.

Habitat: Mud, Beach pool, Pine Point, Douglas
Lake, Michigan.

FIG. 797. *Rhabdolaimus minor.*

I, lateral view of female; II, head of the same, showing
amphid. The head in I is twisted, so that the amphid
appears as if ventral, or nearly so.

a, amphid; *b*, long, narrow pharynx; *c*, anterior group
of nerve cells; *d*, nerve-ring; *e*, cardiac bulb; *f*, wall of
the intestine; *g*, flexure in anterior ovary; *h*, posterior
group of nerve cells; *i*, body cavity; *j*, lumen of intestine;
k, ovum; *l*, blind end of posterior ovary; *m*, egg; *n*, flexure
in posterior ovary; *o*, cuticula; *p*, caudal glands; *q*, subcuticula;
r, vulva; *s*, rectum; *t*, anus; *u*, nerve cells (?); *v*, duct of
caudal glands; *w*, spinneret; *x*, lip region. (After Cobb.)

46 (45) Pharynx not long and narrow. 47
47 (48) Striae not resolvable into rows of dots. . . . . *Cephalobus* Bastian.

Genus of numerous species, frequent about the higher plants, doubtless often at least "semi-parasitic." Occasionally species in fresh water. Common in decaying vegetable matter. Some species are parthenogenetic, others hermaphroditic. Found on the surface of insects.

Cephalobus resembles *Rhabditis*, but may readily be distinguished by the form of the pharynx and the nature of the male caudal armature. The pharynx of *Cephalobus* is almost never cylindroid or prismoid as in *Rhabditis*. On the contrary it tends to taper more or less regularly from the base of the lips backward. Though simple in form the pharynx is usually compounded of two or three series of short cuticula elements separated from each other by transverse breaks. In a considerable number of species the lips are modified so as to bear more or less complicated forward pointing cuticula appendages.

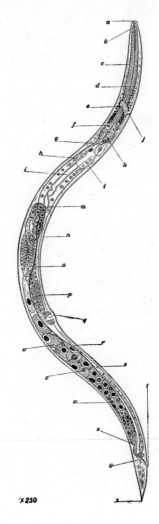

Such forms are intermediate between the typical Cephalobi and other genera, such as *Acrobeles* and *Wilsonema*. The males of the Cephalobi do not possess a bursa, at most showing faint indications of such a structure. Nevertheless the papillae or ribs found accompanying the bursa in *Rhabditis* are present in *Cephalobus*, though they sometimes are less numerous than on typical Rhabdites.

Not infrequently the ovary functions in the first instance as a testis. Spermatocytes appear in the young ovary even before an external sexual opening exists. The developing spermatozoa descend the oviduct and enter the uterus. Later the oocytes develop and are fertilized by the spermatozoa previously produced in the same organ, — at least this happens in some instances, and hence is assumed to happen in all. So far no differences have been discovered between spermatozoa produced in this way by these syngonadic females and those produced by the rarely occurring males. It is therefore fair to assume that the sperm cells so commonly produced in this way are potent. As in *Rhabditis* the renette often takes the form of two long slender lateral ducts ending blindly near the anus. Some species may be revived after remaining months or even years in a dry condition.

Representative species.

Cephalobus sub-elongatus Cobb 1914.

$$\left\{ > \quad \frac{1.8}{1.6} \cdots \frac{15.}{3.7} \cdots \frac{23.}{3.6} \cdots \frac{^{6}51}{4.3} \cdots \frac{94.}{2.1}^{\circ} \quad \text{6 mm.} \right.$$

The thin, transparent, colorless layers of the naked cuticula are traversed by about seven hundred plain, transverse striae, resolvable with high powers without very much difficulty. There are three rather distinct, bluntly conoid lips, which are rounded in front; each of them apparently has two inconspicuous innervated papillae. The intestine is composed of cells of such a size that probably only about two are required to build a circumference. The nerve-ring surrounds the esophagus obliquely, and is accompanied by nerve cells, of which the greater number are behind the nerve-ring and in front of the cardiac bulb.

Habitat: Moss Bog, W. End of Douglas Lake, Mich.

FIG. 798. *Cephalobus sub-elongatus.*
Lateral view of a female.
a, lips; *b*, pharynx; *c*, anterior portion of esophagus; *d*, posterior extremity of anterior portion of esophagus; *e*, nerve-ring; *f*, cardiac bulb; *g*, beginning of intestine; *h*, one of the cells of the intestine; *i*, lumen of the intestine; *j*, excretory pore; *k*, cardiac valve; *l*, renette cell; *m*, flexure in single ovary; *n*, cuticula; *o*, ovary; *p*, spermatozoon in uterus; *q*, vulva; *r*, nucleus in ovum; *s*, body cavity; *t*, anus; *u*, ripe ovum; *v*, unripe ovum; *w*, oocyte; *x*, blind end of ovary; *y*, rectum; *z*, terminus. (After Cobb.)

'x 250

48 (47)   Striae resolvable into rows of dots, altered on lateral fields.
Teratocephalus de Man.

Interesting genus of few species, with movable cuticular lips. Species have thus far been found only in fresh water and wet soils, but the genus appears to have a world-wide distribution, at least in temperate regions. *Teratocephalus* seems related to *Cephalobus* from which, however, it differs strikingly in the formation of the lips and pharynx. It is difficult to determine the functions of the movable cuticular labial elements (*a*). The most reasonable assumption appears to be that they are biting organs.

,Representative species. . . . . *Teratocephalus cornutus* Cobb 1914.

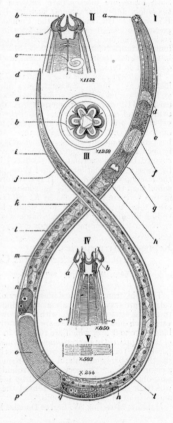

The cuticula is traversed by about 1500 transverse striae, resolvable into rows of minute dots, which are modified on the lateral fields. The movements of which the lips are capable are plainly indicated in Figs. II and IV. The relatively large eggs are extremely mobile, so that they pass out through the relatively small vulva without difficulty. Contact with water, however, appears to harden the shell so that after deposition the eggs have a more definite and rigid form. These phenomena are characteristic of the eggs of many genera, especially those in which the eggs are of relatively large size. In the present species the eggs are deposited before segmentation begins. The general form of the tail, and its terminus, would seem to suggest the presence of caudal glands, but none have been seen.

The cardiac bulb so strongly developed in this species is similar to that found in *Rhabditis, Plectus, Cephalobus*, etc. It consists of three movable valves rolling against each other, that can be pulled backward by appropriate muscles. The arch over them meanwhile remains rigid; thereby a vacuum (suction) is produced. The minute striation on these valves has suggested that they are triturating organs, but the food habits would not seem to necessitate such an assumption. It seems more likely that the striations are due to such a disposal of the cuticula as will give to the organs the necessary strength and efficiency. These valves act rapidly, often several times per second.

Habitat: Maple River, Michigan.

FIG. 799. *Teratocephalus cornutus.*

I, lateral view of a female; II, lateral view of head, more highly magnified; III, front view of head; IV, dorso-ventral view showing lips wide open; V, cuticula showing lateral field.

a, one of the six movable, cuticular lips; *b*, one of the four submedian cephalic setae; *c*, amphid; *d*, nerve-ring; *e*, excretory pore; *f*, organ of unknown significance; *g*, cardiac bulb; *h*, intestine; *i*, anus; *j*, rectum; *k*, cuticula; *l*, one of the cells of the intestine; *m*, lumen of the intestine; *nn*, flexures in ovary; *o*, egg; *p*, vulva; *q*, blind end of posterior ovary; *u*, terminus. (After Cobb.)

49 (38)   Esophagus without bulbs.   50

50 (57)   Pharynx none.   51

51 (56)   Caudal glands and cephalic setae present.   52

52 (55)   Amphids spiral. 53

53 (54)   Male supplementary organs papillate. . . . . .   *Bastiana* de Man.

Named in honor of the English nematologist Henry Charlton Bastian, 1837–1914.

Genus of slender nematodes with rather simple mouth parts. Males with a ventral row of small supplementary organs extending over the greater part of the length of the body. Half a dozen species known. Occurs in Europe, America, Japan, and Australia.

Representative species. . . . .   *Bastiana exilis* Cobb 1914.

$$\substack{\text{\large$\{$}\\ \text{\large$\{$}} \circ \; \frac{2}{5} - - \frac{8.}{.8} \rightleftharpoons \frac{18.}{1.} - - - \frac{58.}{1.5} - - - \frac{89.}{1.1} \quad 1.4 \text{ mm.}$$

$$\substack{\text{\large$\{$}\\ \text{\large$\{$}} \circ \; \frac{4}{5} - - \frac{6.}{1.2} \rightleftharpoons \frac{19.}{1.\%} - - - \frac{-M.60}{2.} - \frac{92.}{90^{\cdot}1.2} \quad 1.4 \text{ mm.}$$

The moderately thick layers of the transparent, colorless, naked cuticula are traversed by about eight hundred transverse striae, which do not appear to be further resolvable. These striae exist in the outer as well as the inner cuticula, so that the entire contour of the body is crenate. Rather conspicuous lateral wings are present, the optical expression of which is two distinctly refractive longitudinal lines opposite the lateral fields, separated from each other by a distance somewhat greater than the width of one of the annules of the cuticula. There is a circlet of at least six cephalic setae, of which the four submedian are the longer, and are somewhat longer than the head is wide. Possibly each of these latter is accompanied by a shorter seta, thus making ten in all. Apparently labial papillae are present, but they have not been sufficiently clearly seen to permit of enumeration. From the rather raised anus the conspicuous rectum, which is twice as long as the anal body diameter, extends inward and forward. The tail is conoid, but tapers more rapidly near the acute terminus. Nothing is known concerning the renette.

Habitat: Fresh water, Tynne Station, Fla.

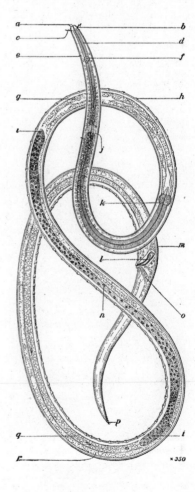

FIG. 800.   *Bastiana exilis.*

Lateral view of a male specimen.
a, one of the six cephalic papillae; *b*, one of the posterior set of four submedian cephalic setae; *c*, one of the anterior set of six cephalic setae; *d*, esophagus; *e*, cervical seta; *f*, amphid; *g*, one of the cells of the intestine; *h*, one of the numerous male supplementary organs; *i*, blind end of the two testes; the two testes join each other at *n*, the complete development of the spermatozoa taking place between the locations indicated by *i* and *n*; the junction of the testes with the vas deferens is on the far side of the body and is not shown; *j*, nerve-ring; *k*, posterior extremity of esophagus (pseudo-bulb); *l*, left spiculum; *m*, cuticula; *n*, spermatozoon; *o*, anal muscle; *p*, terminus; *q*, vas deferens; *r*, intestine. (After Cobb.)

×350

54 (53) Male supplementary organs protusile tubes. *Aphanolaimus* de Man.

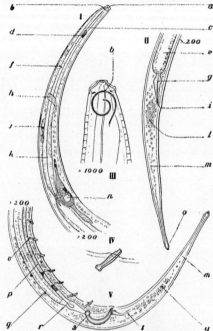

Genus of fresh-water nematodes, of which nearly a dozen species are known. Hermaphroditism occurs.

Representative species.
Aphanolaimus spiriferus Cobb 1914.

$$\left(\varrho \; \frac{.5}{.7} \cdot \frac{9.}{1.5} \cdot \frac{20.}{2.1} \cdot \frac{\cdot ^{50}.43}{3.1} \cdot \frac{88.}{1.9} \cdot \right) \; 1.5 \; mm.$$

$$\left(\varrho \; \frac{.2}{.7} \cdot \frac{10.}{1.1} \cdot \frac{14. (?)}{2.} \cdot \frac{M^{64}}{2.4} \cdot \frac{82.}{, 1.9} \cdot \right) \; 1.5 \; mm.$$

Viviparous. Two embryos and developing egg have been seen in each uterus at the same time. Eggs, about as long as body is wide, and less than half as wide as long.
Habitat: Potomac River, Washington, D. C.

FIG. 801. *Aphanolaimus spiriferus.*

I, lateral view, anterior end of female; II, lateral view, posterior end of female; III, lateral view of head, more highly magnified; IV, male supplementary organ; V, lateral view of posterior extremity of male.

a, mouth opening; *b*, amphid; *c*, lumen of esophagus; *d*, pigmented eye-spots (?); *e*, intestine; *f*, nerve cell; *g*, rectum; *h*, nerve-ring; *i*, anus; *k*, esophagus; *l*, caudal gland; *m*, duct of caudal gland; *n*, glandular body at base of neck; *o*, spinneret; *p*, ejaculatory duct; *q*, intestine; *r*, anterior end of cloaca; *s*, right spiculum; *t*, backward pointing accessory piece; *u*, nerve cells (?); *v*, male supplementary organs. (After Cobb.)

55 (52) Amphids circular or ellipsoidal. . . . . *Tripyla* Bastian.

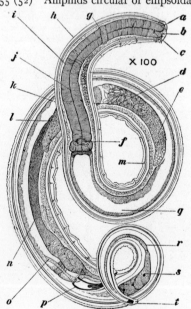

Genus of toward twenty fresh-water species, some at least carnivorous.

Representative species.
Tripyla lata Cobb 1914.

$$\underset{\natural}{\overset{\circ}{\natural}} 0 \frac{1.1}{2.3} \quad \frac{7.}{3.1} \quad \frac{20}{3.5} \quad \frac{\cdot ^{54}49}{4.,} \quad \frac{8..5}{3.2} \; 2.4 \; mm.$$

$$\underset{\natural}{\overset{\circ}{\natural}} 0 \frac{.7}{2.1} \quad \frac{7.}{3.2} \quad \frac{20.}{3.9} \quad \frac{-M^{-50}}{4.8} \quad \frac{82.8}{20 \cdot 4.1} \; 2.4 \; mm.$$

In lumen of pharynx at a point removed from anterior extremity a distance a little greater than radius of head, minute inward-pointing dorsal tooth, having a length about equal to width of one of the annules of cuticula, proving that pharynx extends backward a distance equal to width of head. In some specimens not far behind this point distinct transverse fold in lining of esophagus.

Habitat: Alpine Lakes, Bald Mountain, Colorado.

FIG. 802. *Tripyla lata.*

a, labial papilla; *b*, lip; *c*, amphid; *d*, spermatozoon; *e*, spermatocyte of anterior testis; *f*, base of esophagus, pseudo-bulb; *g*, nerve-ring; *h*, cuticula; *i*, esophagus; *j*, lining of esophagus; *k*, intestine; *l*, posterior testis; *m*, male supplementary organ; *n*, vas deferens; *o*, retractor muscle of spiculum; *p*, right spiculum; *q*, intestine; *r*, duct of caudal gland; *s*, caudal gland; *t*, spinneret. (After Cobb.)

56 (51) Caudal glands and cephalic setae absent. . . . *Alaimus* de Man.

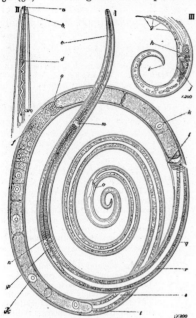

The species of this small genus have a rather simple structure. All are slender. Some appear to be parthenogenetic.

Representative species.
Alaimus simplex Cobb 1914.

$$\Big[\; \cdot \frac{.2}{.3} \cdots \underset{.8}{\overset{!!}{\cdots}} \cdots \underset{.9}{\overset{19}{\text{cm}}} \cdots \underset{1.1}{\overset{35^{\cdot}41}{\cdots}} \cdots \underset{.6}{\overset{92}{\cdots}} \cdots \; \; 2. \; \text{mm}. $$

$$\Big[\; \cdot \frac{.2}{.3} \cdots \underset{.6}{\overset{7}{\cdots}} \cdots \underset{.7}{\overset{15}{\text{cm}}} \cdots \underset{.9}{\overset{68}{\underset{M}{\cdots}}} \cdots \underset{\cdot.7}{\overset{94}{\cdots}} \cdots \; \; 2 \; 3 \; \text{mm}. $$

Very minute striations in subcuticula at extremities, under favorable conditions. Obscure traces of lateral wings. Eggs apparently deposited before segmentation begins. Whether two testes or only one not determined. Broad, rounded, blunt end of testis, located as far behind base of neck as latter is behind anterior extremity.
Habitat: Big Lake, Fla.

FIG. 803. *Alaimus simplex.*

I, lateral view of a female; II, anterior extremity, lateral view; III, posterior extremity of a male, lateral view.
a, lip region; *b*, pharynx; *c*, amphid; *d*, amphid, enlarged; *e*, group of spermatozoa at posterior portion of ovary; *f*, blind end of ovary; *g*, male supplementary papillae; *h*, left spiculum; *i*, terminus; *j*, submedian elevation or flap indicating rudimentary bursa; *k*, egg; *l*, vulva; *m*, nerve-ring; *n*, posterior extremity of esophagus; *p*, modified cells of anterior intestine; *q*, cuticula; *r*, wall; *s*, lumen of intestine; *t*, flexure in single ovary. (After Cobb.)

57 (50) Pharynx present. 58

58 (59) Pharyngeal cavity relatively large, amphids very small if any.
Prismatolaimus de Man.

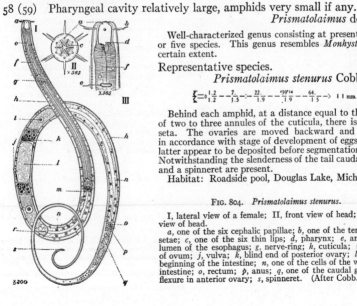

Well-characterized genus consisting at present of four or five species. This genus resembles *Monhystera* to a certain extent.

Representative species.
Prismatolaimus stenurus Cobb 1914.

$$\textstyle\sum = 0\frac{1.2}{1.2} -- \frac{7.}{1.5} -; -\frac{22.}{1.9} -- \frac{{}^{\cdot 39^{\cdot}14}}{1.9} -- \frac{64.}{1.5} -\rightarrow \; 1\,1\;\text{mm}. $$

Behind each amphid, at a distance equal to the width of two to three annules of the cuticula, there is a short seta. The ovaries are moved backward and forward in accordance with stage of development of eggs. These latter appear to be deposited before segmentation begins. Notwithstanding the slenderness of the tail caudal glands and a spinneret are present.
Habitat: Roadside pool, Douglas Lake, Michigan.

FIG. 804. *Prismatolaimus stenurus.*

I, lateral view of a female; II, front view of head; III, side view of head.
a, one of the six cephalic papillae; *b*, one of the ten cephalic setae; *c*, one of the six thin lips; *d*, pharynx; *e*, amphid; *f*, lumen of the esophagus; *g*, nerve-ring; *h*, cuticula; *i*, nucleus of ovum; *j*, vulva; *k*, blind end of posterior ovary; *l*, egg; *m*, beginning of the intestine; *n*, one of the cells of the wall of the intestine; *o*, rectum; *p*, anus; *q*, one of the caudal glands; *r*, flexure in anterior ovary; *s*, spinneret. (After Cobb.)

59 (58) Cavity small, amphids usually well developed. 60

60 (61) Form of cavity conoid, open in front; circular amphids considerably
behind it. . . . . *Monhystera* Bastian.
A large, aquatic genus of which about one hundred species are known. Many marine.
Some found in soil. Many species feed upon diatoms. Probably no other nematode genus
is so widespread as *Monhystera*. In any collection from land or from fresh or salt water the
first specimen to come to view often proves to be a *Monhystera*. The species are very numerous and the individuals surprisingly so. Brightly colored eye-spots are more common than in
any other fresh-water genus.

Representative species. . . . . *Monhystera sentiens* Cobb 1914.

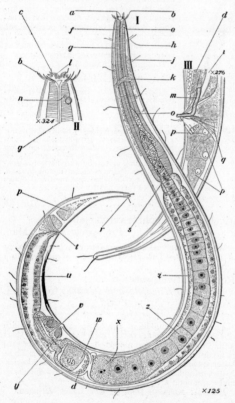

$$\tfrac{^{\nu}}{\circ}\,\circ\ \tfrac{.6}{_16} - - \tfrac{7}{31} - \div \tfrac{22}{43} - - - \tfrac{-72.62}{48} - - - \tfrac{88.}{3.1}\,\text{\female}\ \text{1.6 mm.}$$

$$\tfrac{^{\nu}}{\circ}\,\circ\ \tfrac{7}{_16} - - \tfrac{9.}{29} - \div \tfrac{22}{33} - - - \tfrac{-M.71}{42} - - \tfrac{87.}{3.3}\,\text{\male}\ \text{1.5 mm.}$$

The striae are more readily visible
toward the extremities, especially the
posterior extremity. The lips appear
to be three in number, and are longitudinally striated or fluted. The
anterior portion of the intestine is
somewhat bulbous in form, and is
separated from the esophagus on
the one side and the true intestine on
the other, by a pair of constrictions.
This portion may perhaps be looked
upon as a strongly developed cardia.
The lateral fields vary in width in
different parts of the body. A little
in front of the anus they are about
two-fifths as wide as the corresponding portion of the body, and contain
rather numerous scattered nuclei of
such a size that about eight would be
required to reach across the field.
A little farther forward the field is
narrower. Anteriorly it is wider
again. The blind end of the anterior
testis is located a short distance behind
the nerve-ring, while the blind end of
the posterior testis is located about as
far in front of the anus as the terminus is behind it. The testes are
broad and in some parts appear to
fill up the main portion of the body
cavity.
Habitat: Sand bar off Plummer's
Island, Potomac River.

Fig. 805. *Monhystera sentiens.*

I, side view of a female; II, side view of head of the same; III, side view of posterior extremity of a
male.

a, pharynx; *b*, submedian cephalic seta; *c*, lateral cephalic seta; *d*, spermatozoon; *e*, amphid; *f*, lining
of esophagus; *g*, esophagus; *h*, subcephalic setae; *i*, lumen of intestine; *j*, nerve cells; *k*, nerve-ring;
l, striated lip region; *m*, left spiculum; *n*, cell-nucleus associated with amphid; *o*, blind end of
single ovary; *pp*, the three caudal glands; *q*, anal muscles; *r*, spinneret; *s*, beginning of intestine; *t*, anus;
u, one of the cells composing the intestine; *v*, vulva; *w*, egg, the spermatozoa "*d*" being outside of the egg
"*w*"; *x*, egg in synapsis; *y*, vaginal glands; *z*, ovum. (After Cobb.)

61 (60)   Form of cavity various, closed in front, amphids opposite it.   62

62 (63)   Lateral organs or amphids inconspicuous. . . . . *Trilobus* Bastian.
Fresh-water genus of which about half a dozen species are known. Known to feed upon diatoms in one case and upon rotifers in another. Hermaphroditism occurs.

Representative species. . . . . . . *Trilobus longus* (Leidy) 1851.

$$\text{♀}^{\,a}\ \dfrac{1.3}{2.}\ \cdots\ \dfrac{7.}{2.8/}\ \cdots\ \dfrac{19.}{3.8}\ \cdots\ \dfrac{\cdot46'\,40}{4.6}\ \dfrac{89.}{2.3}\ \cdots\!\!\!>\ 1.2\ mm.$$

$$\text{♀}^{\,a}\ \dfrac{1.3}{2.}\ \cdots\ \dfrac{8.}{2.6/}\ \cdots\ \dfrac{14.}{3.2}\ \cdots\ \dfrac{-M-}{3.8}\ \dfrac{92.}{6^{-}2.7}\ \cdots\!\!\!>\ 1.2\ mm.$$

The lips bear papillae but their number is not known.   The intestine frequently contains diatoms in large numbers, indicating that these are a common source of nourishment of this species.   The longitudinal fields are distinctly developed, and about one-fourth as wide as the body.   From the slightly elevated vulva the vagina leads inward at right angles to the ventral surface fully half way across the body.   The reflexed ovaries pass about two-thirds of the way back to the vulva.   Two or three eggs may occur in each uterus at one time.   These are somewhat ellipsoidal and thin shelled, being about two-thirds as long as the body is wide and about two-thirds as wide as long.   The eggs appear to pass through at least the early stages of segmentation before being deposited.   The walls of the vagina present the peculiarity of being very thick, and composed of six to seven concentric layers so that the organ is considerably broader than it is deep.   Its internal wall presents the peculiarity of staining strongly with carmine.

Trilobus longus, the only American fresh-water nematode outside the *Mermithidae* that had been adequately characterized previous to the inception of this chapter, was described by the famous Philadelphia naturalist, Dr. Joseph Leidy, in 1851.   At that time extremely little was known about the free-living fresh-water nematodes, and no one dreamed of their vast number and variety.   The peculiar male supplementary organs of *Trilobus* did not fail to attract attention, and it is owing to this fact that Leidy's name is associated with the striking species selected as a representative of the genus.

Habitat: Mud about the bases of aquatic plants, in pools, ditches, rivers, and lakes throughout the country.

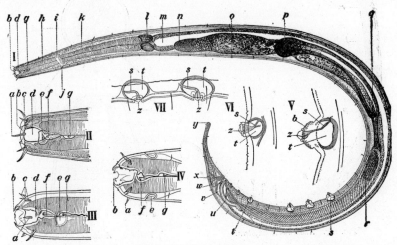

FIG. 806.   *Trilobus longus.*

I, male; II, head, lateral view; III, head, lateral view; IV, head, ventral view; V, anterior supplementary organ; VI, posterior supplementary organ; VII, two supplementary organs from an exceptional female.

a, lateral seta; b, papilla; c, submedian seta; d, pharynx; e, lateral organ; f, tooth; g, tooth; h, esophagus; i, nerve-ring; j, excretory pore; k, body muscles; l, glandular (?) organs; m, intestine; n, blind end anterior testicle; o, testicle; p, junction of testicles; q, blind-end posterior testicle; r, vas deferens; s, nerve of supplementary organ; t, cavity of supplementary organ; u, left spiculum; v, accessory piece; w, the three caudal glands; x, anus; y, terminus; z, apex of supplementary organ.   (After Cobb.)

63 (62)   Lateral organs or amphids more or less conspicuous spirals or circles.
Anonchus Cobb.

Genus of which a single species is known.   There are indications of folds surrounding the mouth opening, so that in all probability the lips may be opened outward as in *Mononchus*.

Single species known.   . . . . . *Anonchus monhystera* Cobb 1913.

$$\dot{\underleftarrow{=}}\circ\; \frac{1.4}{2.1} - - \frac{8.2}{3.\,} - \frac{17.}{3.4} - - \frac{'50\,23}{4.3} - - \frac{85.}{2.4} - \rangle \quad \text{1. mm.}$$ Lateral fields occupied by about forty internal ellipsoidal bodies, rather equally spaced in two series.

$$\dot{\underleftarrow{=}}\circ\; \frac{1.}{2.1} - - \frac{8.6}{3.\,} - \frac{16.}{3.3} - - \frac{M}{2.9} - \frac{86.}{18\diagdown2.9} - \rangle \quad \text{1. mm.}$$ Cardia slender, as long as the neck is wide.   The twenty tubular male supplementary organs are continued to the head by a series of about seventy minute ventral depressions.
Habitat: Mud about the roots of aquatic plants, Potomac River.

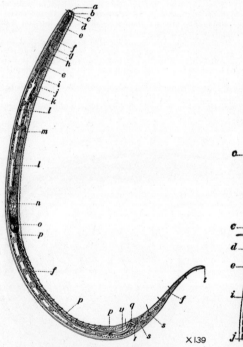

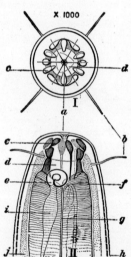

FIG. 807.   *Anonchus monhystera*.

FIG. 808.   *Anonchus monhystera*.

a, mouth opening; *b*, pharynx; *c*, cephalic seta; *d*, lateral organ; *e*, esophagus; *f*, cellular body in lateral field;   *g*, nerve-ring; *h*, excretory pore; *i*, cardia; *j*, anterior end of intestine; *k*, renette cell; *l*, lumen of intestine; *m*, blind end of testicle; *n*, testicle; *o*, spermatozoa; *p*, one of the numerous supplementary organs; *q*, anus; *r*, accessory piece; *s*, one of the caudal glands; *t*, terminus; *u*, right spiculum. (After Cobb.)

a, mouth opening; *b*, cephalic seta; *c*, chitinous element, anterior portion of pharynx; *d*, pharynx; *e*, spiral amphid; *f*, radial musculature of esophagus; *g*, lumen of esophagus; *h*, cuticula; *i*, ampulla of gland (?); *j*, body wall. (After Cobb.)

64 (1)   Posterior region of intestine atrophied; anus vestigial or absent.
Family MERMITHIDAE . . 65

The forms included in this group are of some size, being notably larger than those in the first section of the nematodes. These often reach 10 to 20 cm. in length. They are more or less opaque so that the internal structure cannot usually be determined by superficial examination of the living animal. The intestinal region of the alimentary canal is reduced to a mere cord of cells without any cavity, or may be entirely wanting for a portion of the length. The anus if discernible at all in the female has the form of a mere shallow dent in the external surface of the cuticula to which the vestigial remnant of the intestine is attached. In the male the terminal portion of the intestinal canal persists as the genital duct cloaca and the anus functions as its orifice, but the intestinal tube is atrophied in front of the point at which the sexual canal joins it. These forms are parasitic in larval life and do not feed during the adult stage of their existence. The latter may be passed either in water or in the soil, though the species are more frequently reported from the latter. By virtue of likeness in habit and to some extent also in external form Mermithidae are often regarded as related to the "hair snakes" (Gordiacea) to which, however, they bear no real structural resemblance. They are the so-called "cabbage worms" which from time to time enjoy transient newspaper notoriety on account of their supposed poisonous character whereas really they are harmless.

The American Mermithidae are very little known. The following key to the established genera will be of service to the student in allotting any of his discoveries to the proper genus.

65 (66)   Hypoderm with only two longitudinal fields; cuticula with crisscross fibers; spicula two. . . . . *Neomermis* von Linstow.

66 (65)   Hypoderm with more than two longitudinal fields. 67

67 (78)   Longitudinal fields six. 68

68 (73)   Cuticula without criss-cross fibers. 69

69 (70)   Spicula two. . . . . *Mesomermis* Daday.
Representative species. . . . . *Mesomermis virginiana* Cobb 1914.

There are minute longitudinal striations throughout the body. These are interrupted on the lateral lines where there is a distinct wing. There is no distinct pharynx. The mouth pore is very minute and is located a little toward the ventral side of the middle of the front of the head. The cuticula is penetrated on the head by a number of innervations which end in minute depressions on the surface of the head. Near the mouth opening there is one of these depressions on the dorsal side, and apparently a similar one on the ventral side, while nearer the outer margin of the head there are two ventral submedian and two dorsal submedian similar depressions. Pores occur also here and there on the body, as well as on the neck. The lateral organs present the following appearance when seen from the side: They appear to project from the surface of the body very slightly, beginning as a tube having a length about one-third as great as the corresponding diameter of the head. This tube has very thin walls, and, a short distance in, apparently near the surface of the body, a second element appears in the form of a circle inside that representing the contour of the outer tube. This appears to constitute a sort of core in the midst of which are a number of refractive elements, resembling nerve fibers, which pass inward and backward toward the lumen of the esophagus. Some of these elements are longer than others. The focus passing inward picks up one, then two, then several more, so that by the time a view is obtained that is wholly inside the body there are seen a half dozen or more of these elements. It is impossible in this view to pick up the internal connections of these refractive elements. The lateral fields are about one-third as wide as the body. The tail of the male bears several series of innervated papillae. These papillae are arranged on the ventral submedian lines as well as on the ventral line. The ventral papilla just in front of and just behind the anus are double. In the submedian rows there are four on the tail — one opposite the anus, one a little farther back, a third near the middle of the tail, and a fourth considerably farther back. In front of the anus on each side there are eight submedian papillae occupying a distance more than twice as great as the length of the tail; the distance between the successive papillae increases with the distance from the anus, so that the space between the seventh and eighth is about two-thirds as great as the diameter of the body. Of the median papillae on the tail there are three, two near the anus and one just in front of the middle of the tail, with possibly a fourth farther back. Of the median papillae in front of the anus there are two near the anus, and ten additional ones about coextensive with the submedian papillae, and distributed in the same manner. There are two outstretched testes, the posterior a little shorter than the anterior.

{ o   8⁄13   6.⁄2.   11.⁄1.8   –M–⁵⁵⁄2 3   96.⁄6\2.2₄   1.8 mm.   Habitat: Cranberry bog, Arlington Farm, Virginia.

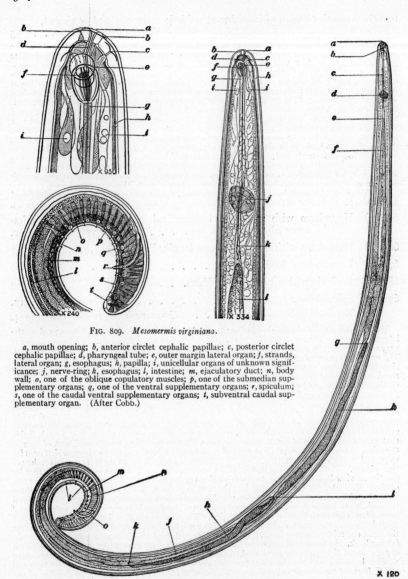

FIG. 809. *Mesomermis virginiana.*

a, mouth opening; *b*, anterior circlet cephalic papillae; *c*, posterior circlet
cephalic papillae; *d*, pharyngeal tube; *e*, outer margin lateral organ; *f*, strands,
lateral organ; *g*, esophagus; *h*, papilla; *i*, unicellular organs of unknown significance; *j*, nerve-ring; *k*, esophagus; *l*, intestine; *m*, ejaculatory duct; *n*, body
wall; *o*, one of the oblique copulatory muscles; *p*, one of the submedian supplementary organs; *q*, one of the ventral supplementary organs; *r*, spiculum;
s, one of the caudal ventral supplementary organs; *t*, subventral caudal supplementary organ. (After Cobb.)

FIG. 810. *Mesomermis virginiana.*

a, mouth opening; *b*, lateral organ; *c*, esophagus; *d*, nerve-ring; *e*, posterior end esophagus; *f*, intestine;
g, blind end anterior testicle; *h*, testicle; *i*, junction of testicles; *j*, intestine; *k*, blind end posterior
testicle; *l*, ventral supplementary organs; *m*, submedian supplementary organs; *n*, oblique copulatory
muscles; *o*, spiculum. (After Cobb.)

IMPORTANT REFERENCES ON FREE–LIVING NEMATODES

BASTIAN, C. 1865. Monograph of the Anguillulidae. Trans. Linn. Soc., Lond., 25: 73–84; 5 pl.

BÜTSCHLI, O. 1873. Beiträge zur Kenntnis der freilebenden Nematoden. Nova acta caes. leop., 36: 144; 11 pl.

COBB, N. A. 1913. New Nematode Genera Found Inhabiting Fresh-Water and Non-Brackish Soils. Jour. Wash. Acad. Sci., 3: 432–444.

1914. The North American Free-living Fresh-Water Nematodes. Trans. Amer. Micr. Soc., 33; 69–134; 8 pl.

DE MAN, J. G. 1884. Die frei in der reinen Erde und im süssen Wasser lebenden Nematoden d. Niederländischen Fauna. 206 pp.; 34 pl.

JÄGERSKIÖLD, L. A. 1909. Freilebende Süsswassernematoden. Süsswasser-fauna Deutschlands, Heft 15; 46 pp.; 65 figs.

MAUPAS, E. 1899. La mue et l'enkystement chez les Nématodes. Arch. zool. expér. (3), 7: 562–628; 3 pl.

1900. Modes et formes de reproduction des Nématodes. Arch. zool. expér. (3), 8: 462–624; 11 pl.

MICOLETZKY, H. 1913. Freilebende Süsswassernematoden der Ostalpen. Sitzber. Kais. Akad. Wiss. Wien, Math.-naturw. Kl., Abt. I, 122 : 111–122, 543–548.

STEINER, G. 1913–1914. Freilebende Nematoden aus der Schweiz. Archiv. Hydrobiol. und Planktonk., 9: 259–276, 420–438.

CHAPTER XVI

PARASITIC ROUNDWORMS

By HENRY B. WARD

Professor of Zoology in the University of Illinois

THE roundworms or Nemathelminthes constitute a group of
convenience into which are put three classes that have little in
common except general external appearance. But even in this
feature differences of a real character appear on closer examination
and the study of internal anatomy fails to show any intimate
agreement in the fundamentals of structure. The three classes
embraced in this phylum are the Nematoda or true roundworms,
the Gordiacea or hairworms, and the Acanthocephala or proboscis roundworms. All agree in the elongated generally cylindrical
form, and in the uniform or monotonous external appearance.
The Nematoda show nearly always some taper toward one or both
ends, being thus spindle-shaped rather than truly cylindrical, and
possess a smooth, glistening, colorless external surface. The Gordiacea are larger, more uniformly cylindrical with blunt rounded
ends and an exterior at least faintly colored in whole or in part.
The Acanthocephala show a roughened surface sometimes with
imperfect rings around the body, and the form usually like a
carrot is always somewhat irregular. These differences are general
and subject to exception but with practice one can usually separate
members of the three groups at sight, and the structure is so different that it is wise to consider each group separately in an independent section of the chapter.

Biologically the three classes show certain contrasts. The Nematoda include many free-living forms and many others purely
parasitic, but most of the latter have brief free-living stages during
which they achieve the transfer to a new host. The Gordiacea are
parasitic during early life and spend the adult existence free in
water bodies. The Acanthocephala are among the most highly
specialized of parasites as they have no free-living stages at all

and as there is no trace of an alimentary canal at any stage of development.

In collecting parasites one may find adult Nematoda and Acanthocephala side by side in the same intestine but the latter rarely occur outside the alimentary canal and nematodes often do. The Gordiacea are parasitic in larval stages normally in the body cavity of Insecta and are found only infrequently in other hosts. They are most commonly found as adults in general aquatic collecting and are well known even to the casual observer of life in ponds and ditches under the popular designation of "Hair Snakes."

The technic of handling the roundworms is not simple. Parasitic nematodes are collected in the manner already described for parasites in general (p. 368), but owing to the very resistant cuticula and delicate structure of these worms great care is necessary to avoid injuring specimens seriously. Those which are loose can be picked up with a fine camel's hair brush. This instrument is most convenient in the handling of small species. Many species are so firmly attached to the intestinal wall that it is difficult to remove them without injury. Gentle manipulation if prolonged will usually loosen the hold, but the body is easily lacerated by grasping it with forceps other than very lightly or the mouth parts are often torn by pulling the worm too hard. Encysted forms should be freed from the cyst under a dissecting lens with fine, sharp needles. A very good needle is made of a glass rod drawn out to a point. Most nematodes are very sensitive to changes in osmotic pressure and are badly disfigured by rapid changes. Living specimens should not be put into distilled water or normal salt solution. Tap water is fairly good and for nematodes from fresh-water fish a 0.3 per cent salt solution is best, but material should not be left in such a fluid longer than absolutely necessary.

The resistant cuticula prevents the entrance of cold killing solutions so thoroughly that these worms live even hours in fluids that kill other parasites promptly. Hot fluids coagulate the body proteins and preserve specimens well extended. No successful methods of narcotization have yet been worked out. The killing fluid recommended by Looss is all in all most useful; it is made by adding to alcohol (70 to 85 per cent) from 5 to 10 per cent glycerine. This fluid is heated over a flame in a beaker or thin watch glass until it begins to volatilize, or more precisely to a temperature of 56° to 60° C. The worms in a minimum amount of fluid are dropped into the beaker, whereupon most forms straighten at once. Specimens are preserved permanently in this mixture and by allowing it to evaporate slowly one can bring them gradually into strong glycerine in which they can be studied. This method is especially good for mounting in toto. For histological details nematodes should be killed in a mixture containing equal parts of acetic acid, alcohol, and water, which has been saturated with corrosive sublimate and to which has been added 0.25 per cent osmic acid.

Formol can be used to advantage only in the lactophenol quick method. Nematodes are killed in 2 to 5 per cent formol and after lying there 2 hours are gradually transferred to a solution composed of 1 part glycerine, 1 part lactic acid, 1 part phenol, and 2 parts water. The transfer should be timed to bring them at the end of 6 hours into the pure solution.

Lactophenol specimens are mounted in the same fluid in a prepared cell. Glycerine-alcohol material is mounted in strong glycerine into which it has been carried gradually by evaporation. When material must be stained and embedded for sectioning, or mounted in balsam, treatment is very difficult and results are uncertain. In general all changes must be gradual and as deliberate as possible. The simplest method is to employ a string siphon made by placing three stender-dishes in a stair-step series, with the worms in the middle dish and the fluid into which they are to be transferred in the top dish while the waste flows into the bottom dish. String siphons lead into and out of the center dish and the amount of the flow is regulated by the size of the string.

The differentiator (Fig. 811) is a very valuable aid in nematode technique. Worms are placed in the small tube a and the tube b is filled with the fluid into which they are to be transferred. The very fine tip regulates the flow of the fluid. When in absolute alcohol they can be taken out and brought into a clearing fluid by the siphon method, or the differentiator may safely be used by extending the fine tip e, and leaving out the mixing chamber. The best clearing fluids are synthetic oil of wintergreen (methyl salicylate) and xylol. As stains, Delafield's hematoxylin, Ehrlich's acid hematoxylin, and Mayers' para-carmine give good results. For sections the first two are advised, also a stain made by saturating a one per cent phenol solution with thionin. Special methods were worked out on the nervous system by Goldschmidt. Nematodes may also be studied by staining *intra vitam* by thionin without phenol and by methylene blue.

When specimens are to be transferred to balsam or damar, it is wise to pierce the body wall with a fine needle. Some skill is necessary to avoid injury to internal organs. When transferring the worms to thin balsam place them in paper cups and allow the medium to dialyze into them. Sections are difficult to make but possible by the use of very hard paraffin and great care in making the transfers. Vacuum embedding is helpful in securing good infiltration.

For Gordiacea the alcohol-glycerine method is useless; on the whole the corrosive sublimate-acetic mixture works best, but should be used warmed to 56° or 60° C. In other respects the instructions for nematode technic apply here also.

The Acanthocephala are best killed and fixed in the corrosive sublimate-acetic mixture and do not come out well in glycerine-alcohol. In general methods used for flatworms work well with these forms also, but for more precise results on any of the roundworms each worker must develop a special technic. (Compare further Looss, Ransom, Magath.)

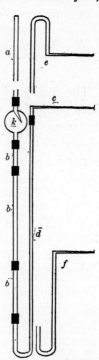

FIG. 811. Differentiator for dehydrating. *a*, reservoir; *b*, object holders; *c*, filter and regulation device; *d*, safety tube; *k*, mixing chamber. The reservoir should be two meters long, and is shown sectioned in the figure. In filling avoid bubbles. *e*, end piece of differentiator for clearing fluids; *f*, end piece of differentiator for alcohols. (After Magath.)

The following distinctly artificial key may be used to separate the three classes of Nemathelminthes; it must be supplemented by reference to the longer discussion in the opening paragraph of this chapter.

A (B)   With anterior, protrusible proboscis covered with rows of recurved
        hooks. . . . .   Class **Acanthocephala** (page 542)
B (A)   Without proboscis at anterior end. C
C (D)   Adult free-living, aquatic, long, cylindrical, with posterior end bifid
        or bluntly rounded. . . . . .   Class **Gordiacea*** (page 535)

The family of the Mermithidae (page 534) agrees in some of these particulars with the Gordiacea, although the structure shows that these species are true Nematoda and not Gordiacea; they are readily distinguished by the acutely pointed posterior end and terrestrial habit.

D (C)   Adult usually spindle-shaped, tapering rather than cylindrical. Pos-
        terior end never bifid or bluntly rounded, usually acutely
        pointed, occasionally peculiarly modified in form.
                                            Class **Nematoda** . . E
E (F)   Free-living during entire life cycle. Adults small, transparent.
                                    Free-living Nematoda (page 459)
F (E)   Parasitic during most or all of the life cycle. Larvae small, transpar-
        ent; adults variable in size, often more or less opaque.
                                            Parasitic Nematoda

Parasitic Nematoda

The nematodes are easily recognized by their appearance, which has given them the common name of round- or threadworms. Most of them are small, measuring only a few millimeters in length and a fraction of a millimeter in diameter, and resemble a fragment of a violin string. A few of the larger sorts reach a length of several centimeters or even a meter. The external surface is usually smooth and glistening and the body is not divided into joints or segments. In some cases a fine surface striation is present which appears under a lens as delicate circular grooves; the exterior may also bear irregular beaded tubercles or fine scales, spines, or hairs. When present these are usually confined to certain regions and the remainder of the surface has the typical nematode appearance.

The body tapers slightly towards one or both ends and only very rarely can one find marked differences in diameter or dis-

* Some authors designate the class Nematomorpha and rank the Gordiacea as an order under it.

tinguish adjacent regions by other prominent features. As a rule the anterior end is slightly blunter whereas the posterior end is more pointed. The uniformity of external appearance is very characteristic of nematodes. This creates an impression of monotony in structure and renders their classification difficult. The smaller forms are somewhat transparent in life but the larger species are opaque.

One may also recognize a nematode easily by its peculiar type of movement, which in a liquid medium consists of a more or less rapid and violent coiling and twisting alternately right and left without appreciable progress, but is modified by the presence of solid particles in the fluid into a powerful serpentine movement winding in and out among the debris. This grows in effectiveness as the material becomes more nearly solid and the particles are less readily pushed aside by the twisting of the worm.

In external features the parasitic species appear somewhat different from the free-living forms. On the whole they are much larger, thicker and more opaque. Few species are as minute as free forms and only these minute types approach the free species in transparency. The external form is also more monotonous since the delicate hairs and scales that distinguish free species are almost entirely wanting. Eyes, amphids, and setose tactile organs such as already described for free-living types are not present in parasitic species.

Parasitic nematodes occur in nearly all water-living vertebrates; they are also often found in insects. In crustaceans and worms they are much less frequent and in any other forms their presence is unusual. While adult forms are found in all hosts, yet the immature stages are more frequent in hosts from the lower groups mentioned and less common in the higher vertebrates. The encysted worms are usually larval forms. The adults frequent commonly the alimentary canal, though some species occur regularly in connective tissue and rarer types in other parts of the body. Encysted larvae may be found almost anywhere.

In structure the parasitic threadworms manifest great similarity to the free-living species and in view of the detailed treatment given the latter in the last chapter it will be necessary in the present general discussion to refer prominently only to points of contrast or to features peculiar to parasitic forms. For further structural details the student should consult that discussion which should be read in connection with the following description. Some parasitic nematodes are apparently indistinguishable from free-living species, others are classed in the same genera or families, but there are also large groups that contain no free-living species and are highly modified for a parasitic existence. In general the smaller transparent species show the greatest similarity to the free-

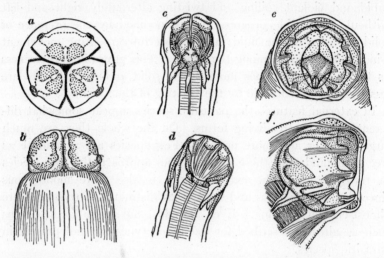

FIG. 812. *Ascaris lumbricoides*. *a*, top view of head; dorsal lip with two sensory papillae and ventral lips with one each; the shaded areas indicate the muscle attachment. *b*, lateral view, showing ventral lips. Magnified. (After Leuckart.) *Camallanus ancylodirus*. *c*, ventral view of head, × 135; *d*, lateral view of head, × 135. (Original.) *Necator americanus*. *e*, head of young male, dorsal view, × 160; *f*, head of young female, from the right, × 160. (After Looss.)

living species whereas the large opaque forms depart most widely from that type. In general organology, microscopic structure of cells and their arrangement in layers, as well as in fundamental features of reproduction and development, the parasitic nematodes agree substantially with the free-living forms and manifest their recent differentiation from them.

The anterior end or "head" of a nematode is usually slightly truncated or bluntly rounded and shows under a lens the presence of lips, papillae, spines, teeth and other special structures.

In reality the numerous modifications of the anterior end may be reduced to a few fundamental types (Fig. 812). In the first, the tip of the body is unarmed or at most provided with a few minute papillae arranged around the mouth opening which is a minute circular orifice. In a second, three lips are present, a large dorsal and two smaller ventro-lateral, which border a triangular mouth. In a third, the oral aperture is a dorso-ventral slit guarded by two lateral jaws often called lips but very distinct in form and function from the triple labia of the second type. In the fourth class one finds a hollow cup-shaped capsule with an entire margin which in lateral aspect resembles the jaws of the third type but is very unlike them in general plan. The capsule is a powerful sucking organ, the jaws act as a grasping organ like a vise or pincers, the lips are weaker and more varied in movement. These main types of oral apparatus are modified in so many directions that it is often difficult to comprehend the general type involved in a complicated case.

The mouth cavity may be tubular, funnel-shaped, or even expanded into a globular or oval capsule or pharynx. Following this region comes the esophagus which is either muscular or capillary. The muscular type is prominent, thick walled, and triangular in cross section (Fig. 813, *a*), with the muscle fibers perpendicular to the lumen. By the contraction of these fibers the cavity is enlarged and the organ acts as a pump to draw in food. The esophagus may be differentiated into two regions, one clearly muscular and the other granular, or the single muscular region may have large (salivary?) gland cells in its wall.

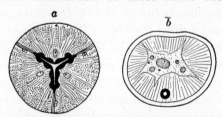

FIG. 813. *a, Ancylostoma duodenale.* Trans-section of the esophagus, magnified. (After Looss.) *b. Trichosoma contortum.* Transverse section of esophagus, magnified. (After von Linstow.)

It is frequently terminated by a spherical bulb which contains a valvular apparatus. In some cases this bulb is double. The cavity is lined by an inturned layer of the external cuticula which terminates at the bulb. This is the type of esophagus found in free-living forms (see Chapter XV, p. 461, Fig. 766). The capillary esophagus (Fig. 813, *b*), consists of a minute chitinous tube surrounded by a row of granular cells but without muscle elements. It does not terminate in a bulb though the end of the cell row may be slightly enlarged.

The esophagus opens directly into the following region which is commonly termed the intestine. It is the digestive portion of the canal and is without any cuticular lining. The cavity is of considerable size and lined by large cells rich in protoplasm. This region changes gradually into the narrow terminal section of the canal, known in the female as the rectum, or in the male as the cloaca, since the duct of the sex gland joins it to form a common passage way.

The tail is ordinarily sharply pointed though sometimes the point is short and in other cases long drawn out. The anal opening is ventral, a little anterior to the tip of the body. In a few instances the anus is terminal and the tail is rounded or of peculiar form. In several families its true character is obscured in the male because lateral wings or folds of cuticula cover it. These folds may be low, narrow, keel-like ridges along the sides or may have developed into wide semi-circular wings forming together a clasping organ known as the bursa. Protoplasmic strands in the wings appear like ribs of an umbrella; they vary in form and number and are much used in the diagnosis of species. Numerous papillae occur on the ventral surface of the male both in front of and behind the anus. They vary greatly in size and arrangement in different species and constitute another useful feature in the determination of genera and species. A prominent cup-shaped sucker is found on the ventral surface in front of the anus in some species and one can often see in the body behind the anal orifice a few large unicellular structures which are interpreted as glands.

Between the head and the tail there are very few external features to be noted. A minute excretory pore lies in the mid-ventral line not far from the middle of the esophagus. In the female the sexual pore also is found on the ventral surface; in some families it is near the head, in others near the tail, and again in the center of the body. Its location is an important characteristic in defining the various groups.

A circumesophageal nerve ring with lateral ganglia is a conspicuous feature in most nematodes. It lies not far from the excretory pore, a short distance behind the anterior end of the esophagus.

A cross section of the body shows on the exterior the thick non-cellular cuticula; within it the hypoderm or sub-cuticula which is cellular but without cell walls. This layer is thin except at the median and lateral fields which are visible externally as faint streaks and hence often called "lines"; here it projects inward between the muscle cells. The major part of the body wall consists of the muscular layer, a single layer of large cells with longitudinal but no circular or cross fibers; these cells have a conspicuous protoplasmic body on the inner side next the body cavity. The muscle layer is divided into four areas separated by the median and lateral fields of the hypodermis; rarely the presence of submedian fields makes eight such muscle areas. Each of the four muscle areas may contain many muscle cells (the Polymyaria) or be limited to a longitudinal series of two muscle cells (the Meromyaria).

The cuticula of nematodes is usually said to be " chitinous " but as this layer is soluble in alkalis, digested by the action of enzymes, and contains a very high percentage of nitrogen, it is not chitin; consequently Reichard correctly classes it as a protein. Glycogen occurs in large amount in nematode tissues and is supposed to furnish them oxygen and energy.

The body cavity is large but not lined by a peritoneal epithelium. It is in fact formed by the breaking down of connective tissue cells, the remnants of which may still be observed in well preserved specimens, especially at the anterior end. Both reproductive and digestive organs are free in this cavity since mesenteries are lacking. In full-grown worms the space of the body cavity is almost entirely filled by the greatly enlarged and much convoluted reproductive organs which press upon each other, the alimentary canal, and the body wall so as to leave only small irregular cavities here and there.

The reproductive system is exceedingly simple. In both sexes it has the form of a long tube in which the various regions are continuous and only slightly distinguished from each other in form. The fine inner end of the tube produces the reproductive cells, eggs or sperm. In the female the fully developed eggs are pushed into a slightly larger region in which fertilization takes place. Sometimes the fertilized eggs are provided with a heavy shell and are soon ejected to carry out their development in the outer world. In other cases they are retained in a sac-like uterus until development is more or less advanced. In certain families the entire development is carried out within the uterus and the female brings forth living young. The organs in these cases differ in length and capacity rather than in fundamental structure.

In the male the reproductive system consists of but a single tube, emptying as already stated into the cloaca, whereas the windings of the tube lie in the body in front of this region. In the female the tube may be single but is most frequently double or Y-shaped. The short stem of the Y connects with the female pore, the branches extend in coils into the body. One branch may pass anteriad and the other posteriad or both may lie nearly parallel in the same part of the body. One branch may be greatly reduced and by its final disappearance give to the system the form of a single tube such as is found in the male. Various intermediate stages occur.

In connection with the terminal portion of the male duct are usually found pieces of cuticula shaped like hooks or needles, and known as the spicules. There may be only one spicule or if two are present they may be equal or unequal. Finally an accessory piece furnishes in some species a link or groove in which the spicules proper are held and through which they are extruded. These spicules are easily seen both on account of their high refractive index and because in many preserved specimens they project conspicuously from the anal opening. In transparent forms the student may detect under the microscope the spicule sac, dorsal to the intestine, in which the spicules are housed and also special sets of muscles by which they are operated. The number, length, and exact shape of these organs serve as features for specific diagnoses.

The development of parasitic nematodes introduces all variations from extreme simplicity to some of the most complex life histories known among animals. The early development is simple.

Within the egg-shell is formed in direct fashion a minute worm which on hatching displays the main features of nematode structure. This embryo may require weeks or months for its growth and may wait within the shell for years before it is passively introduced into a new host; or it may break out from the shell and spend a period in moist earth or water awaiting the time when in one way or another it is brought into a suitable host. In most cases the embryo of a parasitic nematode spends a brief period at least as a free-living larva, and always in an aquatic environment, but this may be semi-fluid mud as well as open water. Frequently it undergoes in this stage or earlier the first of the four characteristic molts and within the cast cuticula of the embryonic form enters upon a resting stage well protected against drying out. In this condition it may be transported by wind or water, or attached to other objects, even such living agents as the feet of reptiles, birds, or mammals, and thus be carried far in attaining the location where by some chance it is introduced into the body of a new host. When this new host is reached it may be the same as the original host in which case further molts bring the worm in a short time to the adult condition. In other instances the larva reaches an intermediate host in which it becomes encysted in muscles or viscera and after a period of growth is ready for transfer to the final host. This change involves the consumption of the flesh with the encysted larva by a suitable final host, whereupon digestion sets the worm free, the active development is resumed, and the adult form reached after a period of growth.

Most often the larval parasite is taken into a new host with water or food. In some cases the free-living larva does not depend on chance to carry it but gains entrance by its own activity. Thus the hookworm larva, living in moist earth, when brought suitably in contact with the skin of an available host burrows into it and completes its life history during its devious wanderings in that host.

As an illustration of the life history of a typical aquatic species may be taken the development of *Camallanus lacustris*, formerly often designated *Cucullanus elegans*. This development was worked out and described by Leuckart somewhat as follows:

The female is viviparous and produces myriads of young. The larva at birth (Fig. 814, *a*) has an awl-shaped tail equal to one-third the total length; no trace of the adult lips are seen; the esophagus is simple, as also the intestine, and a single cell is the only trace of genital organs present. A boring spine lies dorsal to the mouth.

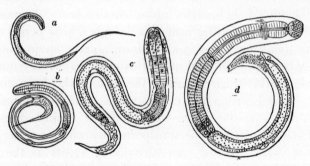

FIG. 814.　Development of *Camallanus lacustris; a,* youngest stage of larva; *b,* second stage from body cavity of Cyclops; *c,* at end of second stage showing jaws forming; *d,* third stage with larval jaws complete. Magnified.　(After Leuckart.)

The larva soon gains entrance to a small aquatic animal (*e.g.,* Cyclops) through the mouth and bores its way into the body cavity where the first molt occurs. After this the worm (*b*) has grown in size, lost its long tail in part and acquired a bipartite esophagus. A period of growth follows towards the close of which the lips of the adult are laid down (*c*) and the second molt discloses an oral armature (*d*) which though smaller and differently marked than that of the mature worm, yet displays its likeness even to the beginning of the dorsal and ventral labial tridents so conspicuous in the adult *Camallanus.* The genital area is still insignificant and the tail carries three small spines near the tip which survive in the adult female only. The double esophagus is fully differentiated even to the valve cells at the lower end and the nerve ring is well developed.

In summer these changes require only 3 days but in winter they may last 3 weeks. No further change ensues until the parasites are brought into the alimentary canal of a suitable fish host. Here set free from the larval host by digestion, the worm grows rapidly to 1 mm. in length, molts and assumes the sexually differentiated form of the adult. Ten to fourteen days after introduction into a fish the young worms have become fully matured and pair.

In most cases the larval *Camallanus* is introduced directly into the final host from the first intermediate host, but in others encystment in a second intermediate host becomes an enforced preliminary to the attainment of the final host. This takes place when the intermediate host is eaten by some species other than the final host; the larva is set free by digestion but immediately encysts again, usually in the intestinal wall. Such erratic encysted larvae occur in a wide variety of unusual hosts (Seurat).

Too many complications enter into individual cases to be discussed in detail here. It is necessary to mention briefly, however, one type of life history of a different character. Among the Filariidae, the adult is parasitic in the connective tissues or body cavity of the host and is viviparous. The embryos are produced in enormous numbers and invade the blood stream from which they are drawn out by biting insects such as the mosquito. After a period of development in the mosquito they escape into the final host when the insect is biting again, and now are ready to develop into the adult parasite. In this case no part of the life-history is spent in the outer world and the only link which connects the life-history to aquatic biology is the intermediate host which may be, like the mosquito, a typical aquatic organism in early life.

The nematode life histories which have been partly worked out are mostly those of the parasites of man and the domestic animals. Almost nothing is known of the development of parasites from characteristic aquatic hosts and the field offers enticing opportunities to the student.

Concerning other phases in the biology of parasitic nematodes little or nothing has been ascertained. Observations are too scanty to furnish data on their length of life, on seasonal variation, or on factors that influence their frequency. Their distribution evidently cannot transcend that of the hosts and in many cases falls far short of conforming to that, but the conditions which affect such variations are beyond safe conjecture.

No satisfactory outline for the classification of parasitic nematodes has yet been worked out and the very imperfect knowledge of North American forms makes it impossible to do more than group the few records available into an arbitrary key. A natural classification lies far in the future and collecting in any region will surely result in extending greatly the list of species included in the subjoined key. Parasites from terrestrial hosts have not been included in the synopsis; doubtless many of them depend upon water for their transfer during a free-living stage from one host to another and some of them may even utilize aquatic species as intermediate hosts, just as the guinea worm larva occurs in a fresh-water copepod and reaches the human host in drinking water. The nematode parasites of fishes, amphibians, and aquatic species among reptiles, birds, and mammals may safely be assigned to the fresh-water fauna. They are included here so far as described from North America.

Undoubtedly the larvae of the hookworms (*Ancylostoma duodenale* and *Necator americanus* of man; *Uncinaria stenocephala* of the dog), of the parasite of Cochin China diarrhoea (*Strongyloides stercoralis*), and of many other parasites which occur in North America are aquatic organisms and live for considerable periods in pools of water or in moist earth, awaiting an opportunity to gain entrance into a suitable host. Yet as immature forms they can be differentiated with great difficulty if at all, and do not show the structural features that characterize the adults to which they belong. Hence they are only noted collectively in the subjoined key. The adults which parasitize land animals are not included in the list.

KEY TO NORTH AMERICAN PARASITIC NEMATODA

1 (4) Immature. Sexual organs only partly developed, if at all.

Agamonema Diesing 1851 . . 2

A collective name for the group of imperfect, larval nematodes not yet developed so that the worms can be definitely classified. Many such forms occur encysted in fish, and the group was originally proposed to hold fish parasites. Now it is used to include all agamic nematodes that cannot be referred to a more definite group. The rudiment of the sexual organs can usually be seen as a large cell or a discrete mass of a few cells, lying near the center of the worm. In older individuals this sexual rudiment has begun to grow out into a long cord of cells which marks the place of the future reproductive system. In these forms the lips, papillae, and other features of special adult structure are wanting or only generally and indefinitely laid down. Sometimes distinct characters, such as the three lips of the Ascaridae which are, however, easily confused with similar conditions in other groups, may enable one to assign these immature forms to a definite family, subfamily, or genus, and other collective names are then applied to such forms, e.g., *Agamomermis*. These larval forms are very similar and are apt to be confused because of their general resemblances.

2 (3) Free-living in moist earth or water. Many embryonic and larval stages of parasitic nematodes.

Not distinguishable from free-living nematodes except by exact data concerning specific forms which are available only in a few cases. Such are the larvae of the human hookworms (*Ancylostoma duodenale* or *Necator americanus*), of *Strongyloides stercoralis*, known to be present generally in infected areas. They depend for their development upon the opportunity of entering a new human host.

3 (2) Encysted in the viscera or flesh of various fishes.

Agamonema capsularia (Rudolphi) 1802.

The name covers what is probably a wide variety of different species from different sources. Thus worms under this name are listed from migratory fishes, and these are very likely to represent encysted larvae of marine adults; and also from fresh-water fishes in which case they are doubtless of fresh-water origin. The descriptions of these forms are brief, general, and inadequate to differentiate larval forms of different genera.

Among the other species recorded from North America are:

Agamonema papilligerum, a single specimen of which was found by Leidy in Philadelphia, in the body cavity of a pike. Later regarded by him as young *Filaria solitaria*.

Agamonema piscium from the white fish, listed by Stiles and Hassall in the collection of the Army Medical Museum.

Such forms may be found in other hosts than fishes like the embryos recorded by Leidy as: *Nematoideum integumenti lumbriculi limosi*, encysted in the skin of a mud-inhabiting annelid.

4 (1) Mature. Sexual organs developed; worms active, not encysted. . . 5

Most adults are easily recognized as the eggs can be seen in the female and the sperm mass in the male. The open sexual pore in the female and the spicules in the male when exserted aid in reaching a diagnosis.

5 (6) Small transparent nematodes; in general appearance identical with free-living forms. Few eggs in uterus.

Not a very satisfactory means of separating this group from certain species in the subsequent divisions which approach rather closely to the brief description of the key line above. In case of doubt regarding a specimen the student should try also the latter alternative, 6 (5) of the key.

These forms are all minute (less than 5 to 6 mm. long). Furthermore they are simple in structure and not easy to differentiate from free-living species. They possess a double esophageal bulb and ventral glands often in lieu of lateral excretory canals. The male has two similar spicules and in some cases a bursa. The female sexual pore is found in the posterior half of the body and the uterus contains only a few thin-shelled eggs.

One family, the Anguillulidae, includes the vinegar eel, the paste eel, various plant parasites of some economic importance, and many free-living forms. These do not show any alternation of generations in the life history.

Only group containing animal parasites.

Family ANGIOSTOMIDAE Braun 1895.

Characterized by heterogony. Otherwise very much like the Anguillulidae, and united to them by many authors. Parasitic generation contains no males.

Only genus recorded for North America. . *Angiostoma* Dujardin 1845.

Representative species in North America.

Angiostoma nigrovenosum (Goeze) 1800.

In *Bufo lentiginosus;* lung. District of Columbia. Listed by Stiles and Hassall under the name *Rhabdonema nigrovenosum* as in the Bureau of Animal Industry Collection.

6 (5) Nematodes larger than free-living species; almost always distinctly less transparent and often even opaque. Uterus contains many eggs. 7

The unsatisfactory character of the key at this point has already been noted. The nematodes which follow are usually well differentiated parasites, recognizable by one or another typical structure not present in the previous group. They are, however, distinguishable from the latter only in general aspect and the key is open to doubt in a few cases.

7 (75) Esophagus prominent, muscular, with triradiate lumen.
                               Suborder **Myosyringata** . . 8

8 (15) Bursa present in male and conspicuously developed. 9

9 (14) Male with broad bursa traversed by system of rays. Buccal capsule usually well developed in both sexes.
                  Superfamily STRONGYLOIDEA Weinland 1858 . . 10

With the spherical buccal capsule may easily be confused the bivalve oral armature of some of the Spiruroidea. The former presents in cross-section an unbroken circle, or oval. The latter is distinctly composed of two pieces interrupted along lines of division. In the former the mouth opening is a ring that may be dentate or serrate but is still complete; in the latter the mouth opening is a slit having at opposite points two deep acute angles. A buccal capsule is wanting in the three forms described here.

The bursa in the strongyles is a conspicuous broad flaring organ, supported generally by six paired rays and one unpaired median ray, all extending outwards from a common center much like the ribs of an umbrella.

Only a very few strongyles have been reported in North America from aquatic hosts and these few are not representative of the majority of the group to which belong the hookworms and other well-known and abundant parasites of land animals. The three species cited here are in truth so unlike typical strongyles that it is difficult to bring them into the key.

Since the group is very large and complex and only three species are to be considered here no effort has been made to outline the families or the numerous other subdivisions. The key is merely a convenient way of separating these few species. It is not unlikely that other genera are represented in the same and other aquatic hosts.

10 (11) In reptiles and amphibians. . . . *Strongylus auricularis* Zeder 1800.

No buccal capsule; 30 longitudinal ridges on the body. Spicules bifid or trifid at the distal end.

Reported by Leidy in 1856 from the intestine of *Bufo americana* and *Cistudo carolina* in Philadelphia. No other data accompany the record so that it cannot be verified at present. At least two species are included in European records under this name.

The genus *Strongylus* is grouped by Railliet and Henry under the family Strongylidae, subfamily Strongylinae, tribe Stronglyeae.

Ransom is uncertain as to the genus in which Zeder's or Schneider's species should be placed but thinks they evidently belong in the family Trichostrongylidae. Probably Leidy's form will fall in the same group.

11 (10) In mammals. 12

12 (13) From frontal sinus of aquatic carnivore.
                            Filaroides van Beneden 1858.

Railliet and Henry include this genus in the subfamily Metastrongylinae.

Only species known . . *Filaroides mustelarum* van Beneden 1858.

No description of the North American form has been given as yet. Identified as European species from host and effect.

In frontal sinuses of various Mustelidae: skunk, weasel, mink, and otter, from northeastern North America. Produces large asymmetrical postorbital swellings.

13 (12) From intestine of aquatic rodent.
                      Trichostrongylus fiberius Barker and Noyes 1915.

Capsule absent in both sexes. Male 2.8 mm. long, 0.013 to 0.09 mm. broad. Bursa with broad lateral lobes and narrow dorsal lobe. Spicules short and heavy.

Female 4.7 mm. long, 0.03 to 0.135 mm. broad. Vulva near posterior end. Eggs oval, 0.059 by 0.036 mm., shell thick.

Intestine of muskrat. Nebraska.

The genus *Trichostrongylus* is type of the subfamily Trichostrongylinae.

FIG. 815. *Trichostrongylus fiberius.* Posterior end of male. X 150.
(After Barker.)

14 (9) Male with bell-shaped bursa encircling posterior end; no supporting ribs in bursa. No buccal capsule.

Family DIOCTOPHYMIDAE Railliet 1915.

Mouth surrounded by one or two circles of papillae, 6, 12, or 18 in number. Esophagus very long, without bulb. One ovary; vagina very long. Vulva near anterior end; anus terminal in female. One long spicule. Eggs with very thick pitted shells. Large worms, in some genera armed with spines near anterior end.

Only genus parasitic in North American aquatic hosts.

Dioctophyme Collet-Meygret 1802.

Anterior end unarmed; mouth surrounded by six papillae.

Only species known. . . . . . . *Dioctophyme renale* (Goeze) 1782.

FIG. 816. *Dioctophyme renale.* Anterior end of female. × 3. (After Riley and Chandler.)

Color blood red; six circumoral papillae and 150 along lateral lines. Male up to 40 cm. long, 4 to 6 mm. broad. Anus terminal, surrounded by circular bursa without ribs. Spicule 5 to 6 mm. long. Female up to 1 m. long, and 12 mm. broad. Anus crescentic, terminal. Sex pore only 50 to 70 mm. from anterior tip. Uterus single. Eggs oval; shell brown, very thick, deeply pitted except at poles.

In pelvis of kidney of seal, otter, dog, wolf, etc. Rare in man. Reported from mink and dog in Pennsylvania by Leidy. Found in dogs at Chicago, Illinois. Intermediate host probably a fish.

The giant among nematodes; a dangerous and little-known parasite. Another form which may belong here was collected in Florida by Wyman from the water-turkey or snake-bird and described as "nearly if not identical with *Eustrongylus papillosus* Diesing in *Plotus anhinga* from Brazil." The species last mentioned was included in the genus *Hystrichis* by Molin, but as the identification of Wyman was not final it is impossible to enter *Hystrichis papillosus* definitely among North American species.

15 (8) Bursa absent or weakly developed in male. True buccal capsule wanting. 16

Compare the discussion under 9 (14) in this key. The caudal alae, often but incorrectly called a bursa, when present consist of long, narrow wings not projecting conspicuously from the body but parallel to it and not supported by radiating ribs, but having at most a series of canals at right angles to the body.

16 (51) Very long, slender forms, with or without lips. 17

17 (26) Esophagus slender, simple, no bulb.

Superfamily FILARIOIDEA Weinland 1858 . . 18

The anterior end is usually plain and no lips are present though in some cases a few minute oral papillae can be recognized. The esophagus has only a single region. The posterior end of the male is rolled into a close spiral of two or more coils. The vulva lies far anteriad and the forms are usually ovoviviparous. The group as now conceived is much more sharply limited than formerly.

18 (19) Anus wanting in adult; vulva lacking in adult female.

Family DRACUNCULIDAE Leiper 1912.

The famous guinea-worm of man known since ancient times belongs in this group. After impregnation the sexual pore disappears and no trace of it has been found in the adult. The females grow to a relatively enormous size coincident with the development of great numbers of minute embryos which fill the uterus. The larvae develop in aquatic organisms, probably Copepoda, Ostracoda, etc.

Only North American genus. . . . . *Ichthyonema* Diesing 1861.

Mouth surrounded by four low papillae. No buccal cavity. Esophagus funnel-shaped at origin. One esophageal gland with large nucleus. Polymyarian. Uterus broad, traversing entire body, with short ovary at each end. Embryos develop in uterus. No anus, vulva, or vagina present in adult. Male much smaller than female; with two spicules and accessory piece. Females parasitic in body cavity of Teleostei.

Single North American species recorded.

Ichthyonema cylindraceum Ward and Magath.

Male unknown, probably minute. Mature female 100 mm. long, of nearly equal diameter (0.48 mm.) everywhere. Delicate, semi-transparent, and very fragile owing to thin body wall. Lateral lines broad, light colored, conspicuous. No lips or papillae. Esophagus 1.09 mm. long, 0.066 mm. in diameter. Vulva and vagina atrophied, no vestiges discernable. Female unimpregnated; uterus crowded with undeveloped ova almost spherical, 44 μ in diameter.

In abdominal cavity of *Perca flavescens;* Lake St. Clair.

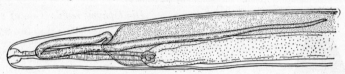

FIG. 817. *Ichthyonema cylindraceum.* Anterior end of female. × 35. (After Ward and Magath.)

19 (18)   Anus present in adult; vulva persistent in female.

Family FILARIIDAE Claus 1885.

A large group not well known and imperfectly subdivided into a number of subfamilies, leaving many other forms still unplaced. Most of the species are connective tissue parasites and the majority inhabit terrestrial hosts.

Forms that have not been described from this family exist in North American aquatic hosts. Those recorded are few in number and imperfectly known. The following classification is purely temporary. The genus *Filaria* has been used as a convenient receptacle for all slender roundworms that did not show conspicuous features of external anatomy adequate to place them definitely elsewhere. Unless the proper location of a species could be determined clearly it has been left under this general heading even though its original location in this genus appears to have been an error.

Type genus. . . . . *Filaria* O. F. Müller 1787 . . 20

Among the forms recorded as *"Filaria"* are some that have no usable description or in a few cases none at all and must be recognized, if at all, by their host, habit, or geographic location. Such are *"Filaria ardearum"* Stiles and Hassall 1894, cited from *Ardea herodias,* in Leidy Collection.

Filaria amphiumae Leidy 1856 encysted in the stomach wall of *Amphiuma means;* alcoholic specimens in Philadelphia.

Filaria cistudinis Leidy 1856 from the heart of *Cistudo carolina,* Pennsylvania.

Filaria spec. Leidy 1882, a red worm from the musculature and peritoneum of the black bass. *Filaria nitida* Leidy 1856 from *Rana pipiens;* later from fish and reptiles. "Probably young of *F. solitaria."* (Two species ?)

20 (25)   Anterior end without lips. 21

21 (22)   Anterior tip lacks both lips and papillae.

Filaria wymani Leidy 1882.

No lips or papillae. Female 65 by 0.5 mm., sexual pore near center (?); viviparous. Eggs 0.02 mm. long; embryos 0.15 mm. Male half as large, with coiled caudal end; one spicule. Coiled on back of cerebrum of *Plotus anhinga* in Florida. Males rarer than females. Probably not *Pelecitus (Filaria) helicinus* (Molin 1860) with which Leidy later identified it.

22 (21)   Anterior tip with minute papillae. 23

23 (24)   Oral papillae in two series of 4 to 6 each.

Filaria solitaria Leidy 1856.

Body cylindrical, rose-red with more deeply tinged extremities. Length up to 150 mm., breadth 1 mm. Slightly narrower towards both ends. Tail obtuse; anus terminal, transverse, with prominent lip. Esophagus tortuous, one-sixth length of body.

Beneath dorsal skin of *Rana pipiens;* also in muscles of *Anguilla chrysypa* in Delaware River. In peritoneum of *Chelonura serpentina, Emys serrata,* and *Esox reticulatus.* Most frequent during winter and spring. Railliet thinks two species are involved.

24 (23) Only two small conical papillae near mouth.
Filaria physalura Bremser 1811.

Living worm pink with brown intestine and white uteri prominent. Female 30 to 45 cm. long, 1 to 1.5 mm. broad. Head obtuse. Mouth with two small conical papillae. Male 35 mm. long, 0.615 mm. broad; tail curved with short quinquecostate alae which are 0.35 mm. long. Spicule recurved.

In abdomen of kingfisher; Pennsylvania. "Determination not positive" (Leidy).

25 (20) Anterior end provided with two lips. Each lip carries two blunt hooks. . . . . *Filaria cingula* von Linstow 1902.

Length 15 to 25 cm., diameter 0.53 mm. Anterior end bluntly rounded; dorsal and ventral, triangular lips with two blunt hooks in each. Cuticula embossed with low, rounded transverse ridges on dorsal and ventral surfaces. Pharynx narrow, 0.375 mm. long, with bulbous enlargement at end. Esophagus triangular, 15 by 0.13 mm. Lateral fields broad. Two ovaries. Vulva? Embryos 0.33 by 0.014 mm. Viviparous.

In skin of *Cryptobranchus alleghaniensis;* Ohio river. Identification with von Linstow's meager description uncertain.

Fig. 818. *Filaria cingula.* Optical section of the two anterior millimeters; *l,* lips; *p,* pharyngeal bulb; *o,* ovary; *e,* esophagus; *u,* uterus; *h,* hooks; *r,* ridges. Magnified about 50. (After Krecker.)

26 (17) Esophagus with two separate regions, more or less differentiated.
Superfamily SPIRUROIDEA Railliet and Henry 1915 . . 27

The mouth has two lips, or is without any. Esophagus with partition dividing it into two regions which may be differentiated as anterior muscular and posterior granular region, and may be much alike in appearance.

Male with lateral alae near posterior end of body. Alae in general long, not much if any wider than body, without ribs or radiate, branching supports.

Most of these forms were previously included with the Filarioidea from which they are most easily distinguished by the double esophagus.

27 (42) Anterior end simple, without prominent lateral valve-like lips. . 28

28 (41) Tail in female simple, not modified in the form of a sucker-like structure. 29

29 (40) Male with preanal papillae and without ventral ridges. 30

30 (37) Preanal papillae in male single not stalked and paired, also few in number. . . . . Family SPIRURIDAE Oerley 1885 . . 31

There are several subfamilies which contain numerous parasites of terrestrial hosts.

31 (34) Anterior end plain, unornamented by external ridges or frills.
Subfamily SPIRURINAE Railliet 1915 . . 32

The mouth has two small lips, or none. The pharynx is simple or wanting. The vulva is at the center of the body, or anterior.

32 (33)   Mouth without lips.   Male without caudal alae.
Haplonema Ward and Magath.

Anterior end flexed or coiled, provided with lateral alae.
Esophagus muscular, without bulb, divided into two regions by
partition near center.   Posterior end of male without bursa, with
two pairs of preanal papillae and three pairs of postanals.
Spicules two, equal.   Vulva near center of body; ovary double,
laid in transverse loops near anterior and posterior ends.   Oviparous.

Only North American species.
Haplonema immutatum Ward and Magath.

Body moderately robust.   Males 10 mm. long, 0.2 mm. broad;
females 15 mm. long, 0.31 mm. broad.   No lips present;   three
minute oral papillae.   Esophagus divided about equally; anterior
and posterior regions not distinctly differentiated.   Spicules 0.75
mm. long, 0.02 mm. broad, flat, ribbon-shaped.   Eggs 65 by 45 μ,
with moderately thick, smooth shell.   Vulva five-eighths of
length from anterior tip.

FIG. 818A. *Haplonema im-*
mutatum. Anterior end showing lateral alae. X 22. (After
Ward and Magath.)

From intestine of *Amia calva;* Lake St. Clair, Michigan, and
Fairport, Iowa.

33 (32)   Mouth with well-developed lips.   Male with caudal alae joined
anteriorly across ventral surface of body.
Physaloptera Rudolphi 1819.

Mouth elongated dorsoventrally; bounded by 2 lateral, thick lips each carrying a toothed
process and 2 broad submedian papillae.   Caudal end of male with lateral alae and 10 pairs
of papillae, of waich 4 are stalked and in each ala, whereas 6 are sessile and on body.   Spicules
2, unlike.   Vulva in anterior region.   Eggs very thick-shelled.

Species reported in North America but not adequately known.

Physaloptera constricta Leidy 1856.   In stomach of *Tropidonotus sipedon*;   Pennsylvania.
Also *Physaloptera contorta* Leidy 1856.   In stomach of numerous turtles;   Pennsylvania.

34 (31)   Anterior end with sinuous cuticular thickening or cervical frill.
Subfamily ACUARIINAE Railliet, Henry, and Sisoff 1912.

Anterior end provided with bands, epaulets, or similar ornaments.   Mouth with two simple
lateral lips, pharynx and esophagus differentiated into two distinct regions.   Caudal end of
male with lateral alae; four pairs of preanal papillae; postanals variable.   Eggs with thick
shell, containing embryos when deposited.
In digestive tract of birds.   A numerous and varied group.

Only genus yet recorded in North American aquatic hosts.
Acuaria Bremser 1811 . . 35

The cervical frill consists of two or four simple or complex loops draped from the tip of the
head back over the anterior region of the body.   Vulva in posterior region.   Two unequal
spicules.   In esophagus, crop, or gizzard of birds.   Often called *Dispharagus* in records.

35 (36)   With trifid cervical papilla. . .   *Acuaria triaenucha* (Wright) 1879.

Male unknown.   Female 10 mm. long, 0.43 mm. broad.   With cervical frill;
lateral loops 0.18 mm. from anterior end at top and extend 0.405 mm. posteriad.
Cervical papilla a trident spine, at base 0.06 mm. from end of frill, and 0.06
mm. long.   Eggs 27 by 18 μ.
Single female taken from gizzard of *Botaurus minor* in Canada by R. Wright
and described as *Filaria triaenucha.*

FIG. 819.   *Acuaria triaenucha.*   Cervical papilla.   X 233.   (After Wright.)

36 (35) No trifid cervical papilla present.

Acuaria ardeae (A. J. Smith) 1908.

Male unknown. Female 17 by 0.7 mm. Two lateral lips, each with double papillae. From base of each lip two prominent submedian ridges on surface extend posteriad nearly to center of body, then dorsad and ventrad respectively to join similar lines on opposite side. Esophagus 2 mm. long, in two sections: anterior narrow region 0.8 by 0.05 to 0.09 mm., posterior wider region 1.2 by 0.2 mm. Anus 0.35 from tip of tail which is bent strongly dorsad. Vulva near center of body; no eggs developed.

In *Ardea herodias.* Described originally as *Dispharagus ardeae* by A. J. Smith.

37 (30) Preanal papillae in male numerous, grouped in pairs and stalked.

Family THELAZIIDAE Railliet 1916.

Head naked or provided with cuticular thickenings or helmet-like covering. Mouth with 2 to 6 very small lips or without any, followed by a long vestibule or a short buccal capsule. Esophagus composed of two distinct regions. Males with or without lateral alae in caudal region, with a linear row of numerous preanal papillae, often paired; postanal papillae less numerous; 2 spicules, almost always unequal. Female with double uterus; vulva variable in location. Oviparous or viviparous.

Only genus in North American aquatic hosts.

Cystidicola Fischer 1797 . . 38

No valid record exists for the European *C. farionis* in North America.

38 (39) In air-bladder of salmonid fishes.

Cystidicola stigmatura (Leidy) 1886.

Length: male, 12 to 25 mm.; female, 20 to 40 mm. Width: male, 0.25 mm.; female, 0.45 mm. Mouth circular with 2 minute lateral teeth. Buccal capsule tubular, 0.12 to 0.24 mm. long. Anterior region of pharynx 0.5 to 0.6 mm. by 0.054 mm., posterior region 2.1 to 2.4 mm. by 0.1 mm. Male with narrow lateral membranes on caudal end ; 5 pairs of single postanal papillae, 9 pairs of double preanal papillae. Two unlike spicules; one slender 0.8 to 0.9 mm. long, 0.01 mm. wide; other trowel-shaped, 0.16 mm. long, 0.18 mm. wide. Female sexual pore near center of body;

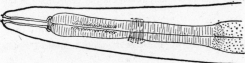

FIG. 820. *Cystidicola stigmatura.* Anterior end of female. X 85. (After Ward and Magath.)

uterus with anterior and posterior branches both well developed and symmetrical. Ova thin shelled, containing developed embryo when laid, 44 by 27 μ.

In air-bladder of Great Lakes trout, white fish, and lake herring. Lake Erie, Lake St. Clair, Lake Michigan, Lake Ontario (Leidy).

In half or more of fish examined. Reported by Wright as *Ancyracanthus cystidicola* and by Leidy as *Filaria stigmatura.*

39 (38) In heart of white fish. . . . . . Cystidicola serrata (Wright) 1879.

Length 11 mm. With several small teeth around anterior end instead of two as in former species. Only a single specimen found by Ramsay Wright at Toronto. Perhaps an immature specimen, either migrating in blood stream, or accidentally introduced into this peculiar location.

40 (29) Male with conspicuous ventral ridges near posterior end; preanal papillae absent or inconspicuous. Body spinous.

Spinitectus Fourment 1883.

Mouth without lips or papillae. Except at extreme tip the body is encircled in the anterior half or more by rows of spines pointing backward. The ventral surface in the male carries several parallel series of rugosities just anterior to the anus.

Representative North American species.

Spinitectus gracilis Ward and Magath.

Mature female 17 to 19 mm. long, 0.14 broad; male 12 mm. long, 0.075 mm. broad. About 130 rows of spines with 40 to 50 in each row. Anterior tip free from spines for 0.12 mm. in

female, o.1 in male. Vulva one-fourth total length from caudal tip. Spicules two, large, heavy, unequal. Ova 41 by 24 μ, thick-walled.
In intestine of black crappie, sheepshead, and white bass at Fairport, Iowa. Abundant.

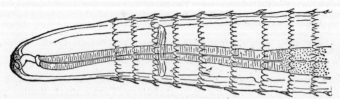

FIG. 821. *Spinitectus gracilis.* Anterior end of female. × 220. (After Ward and Magath.)

41 (28)　Posterior end in female modified to form a sort of sucker by which the parasite is attached to the stomach wall.
Hedruris Nitzsch 1821.

Head with 4 lips: 2 lateral, slender, each with 2 papillae; 2 median, thinner, overlapping laterals almost completely. Vulva near anus. Tail of female modified to form with included spine, the caudal tip, an adhesive organ or sucker. Eggs elliptical, with lid-like areas at both pointed poles, contain developed embryos. Male spirally wound around female. Tail strongly compressed laterally: 6 pairs postanal papillae, 1 pair just preanal. Spicules 2, similar, very short, apparently grown together.

Type species. . . . . *Hedruris androphora* Nitzsch 1821.

Reported from *Amblystoma mexicana* and *Nanemys guttata* by Stiles and Hassall. The form described by Leidy in 1851 as *Synplecta pendula* certainly belongs in this genus if not in this species.

Also recorded . . . . *Hedruris siredonis* Baird 1858.

In British Museum collection. From "stomach of *Siredon mexicanus* from Mexico." Male not found.

42 (27)　Anterior end provided with heavy, lateral, valve-shaped lips. . . 43

43 (48)　Lips red or brown, very conspicuous. Esophagus with two well differentiated, distinctly separated regions. No preanal sucker in male.
Family CAMALLANIDAE Railliet and Henry 1915 . . 44

Body nearly cylindrical, with heavy oral armature having the appearance of a bivalve shell, which is really 2 thick, lateral, valve-like lips probably functioning as jaws and not a buccal capsule. Each valve marked by longitudinal ridges terminating at the inner margin of the mouth in minute teeth. Mouth an elongated oval; inner opening of oral cavity to esophagus round, encircled by heavy basal ring of chitin. Several (2 to 4) heavy chitinous rods diverge from common center at each side of capsule along sides of body beneath cuticula, forming a fork or "trident."
Esophagus bipartite, anterior region muscular, club-shaped; posterior dark, granular (glandular?); valve to intestine.
Tail of male surrounded by narrow, poorly developed caudal alae with stalked papillae. A single spicule with accessory piece or two nearly equal spicules. Female sexual pore towards center of body. Viviparous; embryos develop in crustacea and insect larvae.
Parasitic in alimentary canal of fishes and reptiles.

Single genus known. . . . . *Camallanus* Railliet and Henry 1915.

These forms are often cited as *Cucullanus* and *Dacnitis.* Railliet and Henry have recently cleared up the confusion previously existing in the group.

44 (45) With anterior end bent ventrad.
              Camallanus ancylodirus Ward and Magath.

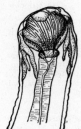

Mature female 25 mm. long, 0.56 mm. broad; male 15 mm. long, 0.38
mm. broad. Oral armature in female 0.142 to 0.168 mm. long by 0.18 to
0.187 mm. broad; in male 0.126 mm. long by 0.12 mm. broad. Trident
with 3 or 4 roots, in female 0.21 and in male 0.18 mm. long. Spicules nearly
equal. Vulva three-fifths of length from anterior end.
In intestine of German carp. Fairport, Iowa.

Fig. 822. *Camallanus ancylodirus.* Head of male. × 70. (After Ward and
               Magath.)

45 (44) With anterior end attenuated, not bent. 46

46 (47) Vulva one-third total length from anterior tip. No spines on caudal
              tip. . . . . . *Camallanus oxycephalus* Ward and Magath.

Female slenderer than preceding species, 25 mm. long, 0.27 mm. broad, straight through
entire length. Oral armature smaller. First esophagus 0.47 by 0.085 mm.; second 0.57 mm.
wide. Male unknown. In intestine of white bass and black crappie.

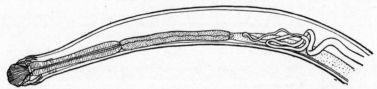

Fig. 823. *Camallanus oxycephalus.* Anterior part of female. × 70. (After Ward and Magath.)

47 (46) Vulva behind center of body. Three small spines on caudal tip of
              female. . . . . . . *Camallanus trispinosus* (Leidy) 1851.

Mouth large, valves with 8 radiating lines on each side of unstriated median band, making
16 rays on each valve. Male 6 mm. long, 0.12 to 0.16 mm. broad. Anus 0.08 mm. from caudal
tip. Two spicules, 0.12 and 0.43 mm. long. Female 12 mm. long, 0.24 to 0.27 mm. broad.
First esophagus 0.38 by 0.12 mm; second 0.46 mm. long. Anus 0.022 mm. from caudal tip
which bears three minute points. Vulva with prominent lips.
In small intestine of *Emys guttata*, *E. reticulata*, *E. serpata*, *Chelydra serpentina*. Philadelphia (Leidy).

48 (43) Lips not conspicuous; esophageal regions similar in structure, not
              sharply separated. Male with preanal sucker.
                          Family CUCULLANIDAE Stossich 1898 . . 49

Mouth elliptical, with long axis dorso-ventral, bounded by two lateral valves recalling those
of *Camallanus*. Esophagus pestle-shaped but without bulb, two regions appear alike in
structure, short, separated only by transverse partition. Male without caudal alae; two
equal spicules; preanal sucker without horny ring. Female with vulva not far from center
of body.
In intestine of fishes.
There are in North America numerous species of this genus. Only a few have been described
adequately. In the past these forms have often been recorded as *Dacnitis* Dujardin 1845
and assigned to the Heterakidae.

49 (50) With anterior end bent dorsad. No intestinal cecum present.

Cucullanus O. F. Müller 1777.

Anterior end flexed dorsad 60 to 90 degrees. Spicules with accessory piece. Ovary double.

Representative species in North America.

Cucullanus clitellarius Ward and Magath.

Body uniform in diameter except for clitellar-like swelling 1 mm. long, and 1.5 mm. from anterior tip. On each oral margin three small papillae. Male 10 mm. long by 0.38 mm. broad. Esophagus 1.45 by 0.12 to 0.22 mm. Spicules gouge-shaped, 1.62 by 0.035 mm.; accessory piece dagger-shaped, 0.06 by 0.015 mm. Two small preanal papillae; 4 pairs of postanals. Females 12 to 17 by 0.5 mm. Esophagus 1.6 by 0.13 to 0.32 mm. Vulva two-thirds of length from anterior end. Uterus and ovary double. Ova 63 by 46 μ.
In intestine of lake sturgeon; Lake St. Clair.

50 (49) Anterior end straight; well-developed intestinal cecum present.

Dacnitoides Ward and Magath.

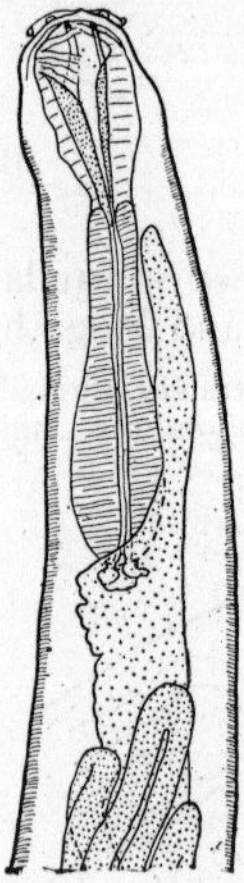

Much like *Cucullanus* except that anterior tip is not flexed, an accessory piece is lacking and only a single ovary is developed. The intestine possesses a prominent cecum extending anteriad to the nerve ring.

Representative species in North America.

Dacnitoides cotylophora Ward and Magath.

Male 4 to 6 mm. long, 0.2 mm. broad. Each lateral valve with anterior marginal cuticular thickening bearing 3 papillae. Esophagus 0.5 to 0.6 by 0.06 to 0.12 mm. Boundary between esophageal regions at nerve ring. Spicules 0.89 by 0.005 mm. Caudal papillae: one pair on anterior margin of sucker, four pairs between sucker and anus, a single medial papilla just in front of anus and four pairs postanal.

Female 4 to 5.5 mm. long, 0.28 mm. broad. Anus 0.14 from posterior tip with 4 slender spines midway between. Vulva one-eighth of total length behind center of body. Posterior uterine branch has no ovary. Ova 65 by 40 μ.
In intestine of yellow perch and wall-eyed pike; Lake St. Clair.

FIG. 823a. *Dacnitoides cotylophora*. Head of female, showing oral armature, esophageal regions, intestine, cecum, and anterior coils of ovary. × 57. (After Ward and Magath.)

51 (16) Stout bodied forms with conspicuous lips. 52

52 (55) Two heavy lips. Body covered on anterior region at least with dentate or spinous plates.

Family GNATHOSTOMIDAE Railliet 1893.

Body covered in whole or part by circles of dentate cuticular plates. Anterior tip enlarged, provided with simple spines, separated by nuchal constriction. Two large fleshy lips. Esophagus large, muscular. Vulva behind middle of body. Two equal spicules. No bursa. In male two pairs of preanal papillae and two postanals.

Type genus. . . . . *Gnathostoma* Owen 1836 . . 53

Entire body or anterior end covered with abundant spines, often many pointed. Head separated by circular constriction, with circles of simple spines. Two large, fleshy lips. Spicules 2, unequal; vulva behind center of body. Male with two pairs of postanals.
Two species reported from North American.

53 (54) Anterior plates palmate with eight spines each.

Gnathostoma horridum (Leidy) 1856.

Female 66 mm. long, 3 mm. broad. Male unknown.
Taken from stomach of *Alligator mississippiensis* in Georgia and originally described by Leidy as *Cheiracanthus horridus*.

54 (53) Anterior plates tridentate. . . . *Gnathostoma sociale* (Leidy) 1858.

Female 30 mm. long, 1.5 mm. broad. Male 24 mm. long, 1 mm. broad.
Taken from stomach of mink (*Putorius vision*) in Philadelphia and originally described by Leidy as *Cheiracanthus socialis*.

55 (52) Relatively thick, heavy-bodied forms. Mouth with three lips, more or less conspicuous. Always oviparous.

Superfamily ASCAROIDEA Railliet and Henry 1915 . . 56

One large dorsal and two smaller ventral lips, right and left of medial line; secondary lips (interlabia) may be intercalated. Buccal capsule never present. Dorsal lip bears regularly two papillae and ventral lips one each. Lips rarely greatly reduced (or absent?).

56 (68) Polymyaria. Usually 'arge opaque species. 57

For discussion of term Polymyaria see page 515.

57 (67) Lips prominent. No ventral sucker in male.

Family ASCARIDAE Cobbold 1864 . . 58

Male usually has two spicules. Female with abruptly conical posterior end.

Type genus. . . . . *Ascaris* Linnaeus 1758.

No fringes or tentacles on the lips. A large and complex group. Differentiated usually on the basis of the form of the lips which present many modifications in minor details.

A number of forms have been recorded under the name *Ascaris* which are so inadequately described that their exact systematic position must depend on their rediscovery and further study. Such are:

Ascaris longa Leidy 1856 of which a single female specimen was taken from the intestine of the wood ibis in Georgia.

Ascaris penita Leidy 1886 from the intestine of the terrapin.

Ascaris cylindrica Leidy 1849 from the intestine of *Helix allernata* in Pennsylvania.

Ascaris entomelas Leidy 1851 from the lungs of *Rana halecina*, which the description says is "not *Ascaris nigrovenosa* Zeder" (= *Angiostoma nigrovenosum* q.v.).

Ascaris tenuicollis Rudolphi 1819, from the stomach and intestine of *Alligator mississippiensis* or encysted on viscera. Reported frequently.

Probably most of these do not belong in the genus *Ascaris* in the strict sense and very likely not in the family of the Ascaridae as at present defined. These species are not well known and often determinations have evidently been based on general factors that are not truly diagnostic.

58 (59) Lips relatively small, without intermediate lobes; dental plates with serrate edges on inner margins.

Ascaris lanceolata Molin 1860.

Male 20 to 25 by 0.5 mm.; female 25 to 40 by 0.8 mm. Lips much like those of *Heterakis*. Tail of male with oval groove on ventral surface, and parallel longitudinal furrows on dorsum; lateral to these merely cuticular folds (weakly developed alae?). Papillae: about 19 preanal and 12 postanal with one row of long papillae in an arc. In stomach of *Alligator mississippiensis*. Georgia.

FIG. 824. *Ascaris lanceolata*. Dorsal lip, inner aspect. X 80. Ventral view of tail of male. X 6. (After von Drasche.)

59 (58) Lips well developed; with intermediate lobes or interlabia. . . 60

60 (64) With serrate dental plates on inner border of lips. 61

61 (62, 63) Tail of male with 6 pairs of postanal papillae.

Ascaris sulcata Rudolphi 1819.

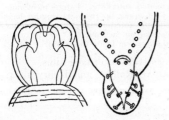

Male 35 mm. long; female 97 to 100 mm. long. Body attenuate anteriorly, distinctly ringed. Lips very large, hexagonal; lobes indistinct; interlabia very small. Tail of male with 6 postanal papillae and many (±64) preanals. Bursa broad. Eggs irregularly elliptical, large.

Reported in 1887 by Leidy from the stomach of terrapin, Pennsylvania.

FIG. 825. *Ascaris sulcata*. Dorsal view of lips, and posterior end of male. Magnified. (After Stossich.)

62 (61, 63)   Tail of male with 4 pairs of postanal papillae.

Ascaris ardeae Smith 1908.

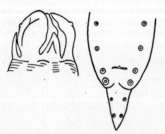

Female up to 80 mm. long and 1.8 mm. broad. Head rounded with 3 prominent lips and well-marked interlabia. Superior lip with finely denticulate anterior and lateral borders. Tail acutely conical, vulva 30 mm. from head. Ova 0.105 to 0.11 mm. by 0.096 to 0.1 mm.; shell colorless marked by thick-set pits.

Male 72 mm. by 1.5 mm. Spicules double, equal, brownish, 1.3 mm. long. Tail incurved, bluntly rounded with small acutely conical tip. Papillae: 2 pairs on conical tip also 2 pairs postanal and 5 pairs or more preanal.

In *Ardea herodias*.

FIG. 826. *Ascaris ardeae*. Lateral view of anterior end, showing two of the lips (partly in profile) and two of the interlabia. Ventral surface of male tail. (Note the second pair of papillae from tip of tail as uncertain.) Magnified. (After A. J. Smith.)

Much like *A. serpentulus* Rudolphi reported by Leidy from same host. Probably Leidy's record concerns this species. The true *A. serpentulus* was collected by A. J. Smith from a European crane in the Philadelphia Zoological Gardens.

63 (61, 62)   Tail of male with 3 pairs of postanal papillae.

Ascaris microcephala Rudolphi 1819.

Male 15 to 45 mm., female 45 to 70 mm. long. Body greatly attenuated anteriorly. Lips quadrangular, with anterior margin concave and angles projecting. Interlabia as long as lips. Cervical papillae in dorsal and ventral lines. Tail of male obliquely truncated; papillae small, 3 postanal and 31 preanal. Ova 72 by 59 μ.

In crop, esophagus, stomach and intestine of various herons, and bittern. Florida to Canada.

FIG. 827. *Ascaris microcephala*. Dorsal view of head. Magnified. (After von Linstow.)

64 (60)   Without serrate labial plates. 65

65 (66)   With interlabia. . . . . *Ascaris helicina* Molin 1860.

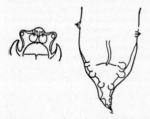

Male 6 to 8 by 0.1 to 0.2 mm.; female 13 to 28 by 0.3 to 1 mm. Three interlabia. Lips almost quadrangular with auricles on anterior corners. Tail of male with 5 postanal and 4 large lateral preanal papillae. Vulva anterior, or almost in center of body.

In stomach of *Alligator mississippienis*.

FIG. 828. *Ascaris helicina*. Dorsal lip, inner aspect. × 55. Tail of male. × 85. (After von Drasche.)

66 (65)   Neither interlabia nor dental plates in oral armature.

Ascaris mucronata Schrank 1790.

Length 52 mm., breadth 0.75 mm. Body much attenuated anteriorly. Lateral membrane broad on head, disappears on neck. Greatest breadth of upper lip twice its length; base broader than anterior margin; lateral margins divided into anterior straight and posterior arcuate portion. Tail of male with 2 rows of preanal papillae on each side.

From *Alligator mississippiensis*. Listed by Stiles and Hassall in Leidy Collection.

67 (57)   Lips distinct, not large.   Male with ventral sucker near anus.

Family HETERAKIDAE Railliet and Henry 1914.

None known from aquatic hosts. Likely to be confused with *Cucullanus* (*cf.* page 530) which has a preanal sucker without horny ring. There are in North America numerous species of this genus.

68 (56)   Meromyaria.   Small transparent forms. 69

For discussion of term Meromyaria see page 515.

Lips simple, inconspicuous. Vulva anterior. Caudal end of female distinctly elongate. Separated from Ascarids by some authors.

69 (70)   Without esophageal or intestinal cecum.

Family OXYURIDAE Cobbold 1864.

The few North American records cannot be safely assigned on the basis of the present distinction between this family and the next. Consequently they are left where they were placed originally.

Among forms recorded from North America which cannot be placed at present owing to imperfect knowledge of their structure are:

Oxyuris dubia Leidy 1856 reported from *Bufo americanus* and *Salamandra rubra*. Male unknown.

North American genus. . . . . · . . . . *Spironoura* Leidy 1856.

Mouth surrounded by circular, papillated lip. Tail of male spiral, acute, tuberculate. Spicules two, curved, ensiform, costate. Tail of female conical, acute. Vulva at posterior third.

Type species. . . . . *Spironoura gracile* Leidy 1856.

Female 16 by 0.25 mm.; male 8 by 0.25 mm. with two rows of three papillae on tail. Found in stomach of *Emys serrata* and *Siredon mexicanus*.

Also recorded. . . . . *Spironoura affine* Leidy 1858.

Female 9 by 0.4 mm.; male 6 by 0.3 mm., with two papillae on each side of tail near end. Found in cecum of *Cistudo carolina*.

70 (69) With cecum on esophagus or intestine, or on both.

Family HETEROCHEILIDAE Railliet and Henry 1915 . .   71

71 (74) With papillae on tail of male and with ceca on both esophagus and intestine. . . . .   *Contracoecum* Railliet and Henry 1912.

72 (73) Without circle of spines on tail.

Contracoecum spiculigerum (Rudolphi) 1809.

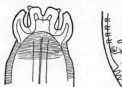

Male 18 to 90 mm., female 30 to 154 mm. long. Lips small; interlabia well developed with a small notch at outer margin. Intestine with diverticulum at anterior end. Tail of male with 7 postanal papillae many (± 40) preanals in 2 lateral series. Spicules very long, usually well extended, and recurved. Vulva anterior. Ova irregularly reticulate 0.11 to 0.12 mm. long.

Reported by Leidy in 1856, 1882, and 1868 from the stomach of cormorant, white and brown pelicans, and water turkey. Florida to Dakota.

FIG. 829. *Contracoecum spiculigerum.* Anterior end and tail of male. Magnified. (After Stossich.)

73 (72) With circle of spines on tail.

Contracoecum adunca (Rudolphi) 1809.

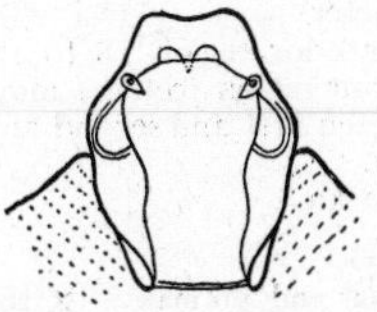

Male 30 to 31 mm., female 30 to 65 mm. long. Weak lateral cuticular membranes. Linstow says interlabia are present. Esophagus with cecum extending posteriad 0.6 mm., and intestine with similar extension 0.41 mm. anteriad. Tail of male short, conical, coiled; 27 preanal papillae in simple series, and 3 postanals. Tip of tail ringed with fine spines. Spicules long (1.92 mm.), equal, somewhat enlarged at proximal end.

In intestine and pyloric appendages of shad. Pennsylvania, Maine. Probably of marine origin though taken from fish in fresh water.

FIG. 830. *Contracoecum adunca.* Dorsal view of upper lip. Magnified. (After von Linstow.)

74 (71) Without papillae on tail of male and with single intestinal cecum.
Hysterothylacium Ward and Magath.

Anterior end with narrow lateral wings. Lips three, not prominent. Esophagus long, slender, with terminal bulb. Intestine with short simple cecum at anterior end, extending posteriad. Males with two equal spicules. Females unknown.

Type species. . . *Hysterothylacium brachyurum* Ward and Magath.

Male 32 mm. long; maximum width 0.66 mm. Lateral ala one-quarter width of body. Esophagus 3.1 mm. long, 0.1 to 0.13 mm. broad; bulb with three teeth; cecum 0.94 by 0.08 mm. Spicules 0.72 mm. long, 0.045 mm. wide. Pyriform sperm vesicle prominent. In stomach of black bass; Lake St. Clair.

75 (7) Esophagus slender, non-muscular; lumen a capillary chitinous tube traversing a row of granular cells.
Suborder **Trichosyringata** . . 76

76 (77) Anus lacking; alimentary canal non-functional in adult. Adults free living. . . . . . Family MERMITHIDAE Braun 1883.

These forms are only distantly related to aquatic biology as the adults occur free in soil, or less often on plants as the famous "cabbage-snake." The early life is spent as a parasite in the body cavity of some insect or crustacean from which they occasionally escape into an apple or other peculiar environment.

They are very slender, greatly elongated, threadworms in which the alimentary canal is transformed in the adult into a fat body. The eggs are spherical, with two peculiar stalked, tasselated appendages at the poles. The adults are fully considered in the chapter on Free-living Nematodes (consult page 503).

The Mermithidae are often confused with Gordiacea to which they bear a certain superficial resemblance. The differences are discussed later (page 535).

77 (76) Alimentary canal complete and functional. Adults always parasitic. . . Family TRICHINELLIDAE Stiles and Crane 1910.

Esophagus formed by capillary tube traversing chain of cells. Anterior region of body slender, posterior region swollen. Anus terminal. Male with single spicule (or none?). Female with one ovary. Vulva near junction of anterior and posterior body regions.

The well known human parasite, *Trichinella spiralis*, commonly called trichina, is included in this group though in another subfamily from the following.

Subfamily TRICHURINAE Ransom 1911 . . 78

78 (79) Anterior region of body very slender and much longer than posterior region . . . . . . *Trichuris* Roederer and Wagler 1761.

In North American aquatic host.

Trichuris opaca Barker and Noyes 1915.

1 m m.

Male 22 to 28 mm. long; anterior region 13 to 19 mm. long, 0.06 to 0.08 mm. thick; posterior region 7 to 9 mm. long, 0.14 to 0.16 mm. thick. Spicule 2 mm. long; sheath 0.18 mm. long, 0.07 mm. in diameter.

Female 22 to 30 mm. long; anterior region 18 to 19 mm. by 0.06 to 0.07 mm.; posterior region 10 to 11 mm. by 0.23 to 0.25 mm. Vulva between first and second anterior eleventh of posterior region.

Duodenum of muskrat. Nebraska.

FIG. 831. *Trichuris opaca.* Posterior end of male. X 20.
(After Barker.)

79 (78) Anterior region not much slenderer than posterior region and equal
              to it in length or shorter. . . . . .   *Capillaria* Zeder 1800.

In North American aquatic host.

Capillaria ransomia Barker and Noyes 1915.

Length 19 to 20 mm.; breadth of male 0.01 to 0.03 mm., of female 0.022 to 0.065 mm.
Bursa of male small, with 2 lateral lobes.   Spicule 1.36 mm. long, 0.007 mm. broad.   Vulva
in anterior fourth of body.   Eggs 0.05 by 0.02 mm. with prominent plugs.
Duodenum of muskrat.   Nebraska.

GORDIACEA

The Gordiacea are familiar to all as the hairworms or "hair
snakes" frequently found in the country in drinking troughs,
springs, brooks, ponds, or indeed any body of water, large or small.
In general appearance these worms are very much like the nematodes but the more fully their internal organization has become
known by study the less they seem to resemble that group in detail, and the present tendency is to separate them as an independent class.   Some even make the group an independent phylum.

The body resembles a bit of fine wire or a tough root fiber in
appearance.   It is nearly cylindrical, usually with blunt or rounded
anterior end and a caudal extremity of modified form, often swollen,
lobed, or curled in a loose spiral.

Certain nematodes, especially *Mermis* which occurs free in soil
in the adult stage, resemble the hairworms so much externally that
they are often confused with them.   The two differ greatly in
internal structure and somewhat in less important external features; but by their pointed anterior end, tapering body, and
smooth, finely striated and somewhat transparent cuticula the
true nematodes are usually easily distinguished from the Gordiacea with blunt head, cylindrical body, and roughened, ordinarily
also papillate, irregular cuticula.   *Mermis* in particular is most
readily distinguished by the pointed posterior end and when alive
by the active anterior region.

In the Gordiacea a single orifice serves as the common outlet of
the reproductive and alimentary systems, alike in both sexes; it is
located near the posterior end.   There are no lateral lines and the
male never possesses spicules.

These animals are so opaque that little or no internal structure
is visible on examination either with the naked eye or with the

aid of a microscope. The most of the features on which classification is based are external and must be regarded as arbitrary
and trivial. The internal structure can be studied only with
difficulty by complicated technic and may be passed here without
description.

In one respect the Gordiacea differ from the parasitic worms
heretofore considered: the adults are free-living and it is only the
young stages which carry on a parasitic existence. Probably the
free aquatic stage is merely a reproductive period, even though it
is prolonged for several weeks or months. The worm when loaded
with eggs is round and plump, but the spent female is often wrinkled
and flattened.

Gordius deposits its eggs in a long white or grayish cord which
may be several feet long and apparently many times the bulk of
the female worm. In some species the cord breaks up into shorter
pieces. The worms are often observed in knotted masses, consisting of two or more worms coiled together. In some cases at
least they are coiled about the egg strings and remain for many
days in this position, thus in a sense exercising protection over the
developing embryos. It is commonly said that the Gordiacea deposit their eggs in brooks or other running water, but I have found
some species in abundance on water plants and in knotted masses

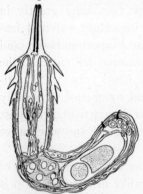

along the shore of Lake St. Clair, Lake
Erie, and Lake Michigan. Rarely I
have seen a conspicuous windrow of
adult worms and egg masses extending
for some distance along the water's
margin of an inland lake and probably
washed up there by wave action. The
minute embryo (Fig. 832) which hatches
from these eggs after a brief period
possesses a conspicuous proboscis and
set of hooks at the anterior end. By
this powerful boring apparatus the embryo forces its way into some aquatic

FIG. 832. Embroyo of *Paragordius
varius* with extended proboscis. × 1000.
(After Montgomery.)

insect, often the mayfly larva. Further changes are not known
except that in the body cavity of various adult insects, such as

beetles, grasshoppers, and crickets, are found well-grown and nearly mature larvae of the hairworms. On escaping into the water from these insects, the worms become sexually mature and the cycle is completed. Villot denied the necessity of an intermediate host, but others have held that the hairworm undergoes two and perhaps more changes of host during the complete life cycle. When the worm escapes from an insect it swims about actively in the water but even where the capillary esophagus is not closed so that the taking of food is absolutely precluded, the worms probably take no nourishment in the aquatic stage.

Hairworms in an early or late larval condition have been recorded as parasites not only in the insects cited above but also less frequently in spiders, oligochaetes (*Lumbriculus*), snails, and rarely in distomes, fish, and amphibians (?). In the last three types their presence is no doubt purely accidental. Adults in the free-living stage have been reported a number of times as human parasites. Here their presence is also fortuitous and is doubtless due to the accidental swallowing of specimens in water or in food eaten uncooked.

The number of species of Gordiacea in North America is not large and thanks to the splendid work of Montgomery the group is well known. The following synopsis is based on his papers. The range of species has been somewhat increased by my own collections from regions not represented in his records. I have also been given valuable unpublished data by H. G. May. Even yet there are no records from the southeastern or northwestern United States and only a single record each from Canada and Alaska. The absence of records from any region indicates lack of study in that region rather than scarcity of material.

Only three well-marked genera are known: Gordius, Chordodes, and Paragordius, all of which are represented in this continent.

KEY TO NORTH AMERICAN GORDIACEA

1 (8) Anterior region distinctly attenuated, coming nearly to a point; usually lighter than the rest of the body and without a dark ring. . . . . *Chordodes* Creplin 1847 . . 2

Caudal end simple, not lobed; in female somewhat enlarged. External surface complicated; several types of areoles present.

Because the males and females are distinctly unlike in external appearance they come out as separate groups in the key. The cross references carry the student back to the other sex in each case. It will be noted that the key line which ultimately determines the species is usually alike in both sexes.

2 (5)　Caudal end slenderer than preceding region of body, with tendency to
　　　　roll into spiral form. . . . . (Males of *Chordodes*) . . 3

The cloacal orifice is ventro-median and the ventral surface possesses a shallow furrow or
groove from this orifice to the posterior extremity.

3 (4)　Cuticular areoles longer than high; small circular pits upon and be-
　　　　tween them. . . *Chordodes occidentalis* Montgomery 1898.

For female of this species consult 6 in this key.
Male up to 255 mm. long, 1.5 mm. broad.　Color light brown to
black; tip of head yellowish white.　A western species; Montana,
Wyoming, California, Arizona, Texas, Mexico.
An Acridiid is known to serve as host for this species.

FIG. 833.　Head and surface areoles of *Chordodes occidentalis* ♀.　Highly
magnified.　(After Montgomery.)

4 (3)　Cuticular areoles higher than long.
　　　　　　　　　　　　　　Chordodes morgani Montgomery 1898.

For female of this species consult 7 in this key.
Male 64 to 220 mm. long.　Color dull chocolate brown, except anterior end which is always
white.　Papillae of several types; the most regular conical with short spine, and the highest
papillae with a few spines on the summit of each being typical.
The species manifests a high degree of individual and sexual variation.　Recorded from
Pennsylvania, Maryland, Michigan, Ohio, Florida, Iowa, and Nebraska.　*C. puerilis*, origi-
nally described from two males, belongs here.
A Blattid is known to serve as host for this species.

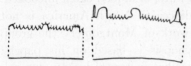 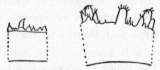

FIG. 834.　Cuticula of *Chordodes morgani* ♀
in transverse section.　Highly magnified.　(After
Montgomery.)

FIG. 835.　Cuticula of *Chordodes morgani*
♂ in transverse section.　Highly magnified.
(After Montgomery.)

5 (2)　Caudal end swollen, somewhat knob-shaped; also marked off by a
　　　　slight constriction.　No tendency to roll into a spiral.
　　　　　　　　　　　　　　　　　　　(Females of *Chordodes*) . . 6

The females of *Gordius*, which may easily be confused with these, never have more than a
slight swelling at the caudal end and this is not marked off by a constriction.

6 (7)　Cuticular areoles longer than high; small circular pits upon and be-
　　　　tween them . . *Chordodes occidentalis* Montgomery 1898.

For male and range of this species consult 3 in this key.
Anterior region much attenuated; head pointed.　Areoles low.　Color yellowish brown with
darker neck ring and black mouth spot.

7 (6)　Cuticular areoles higher than long.
　　　　　　　　　　　　　　Chordodes morgani Montgomery 1898.

For male and range of this species consult 4 in this key.　The variable papillae are also
noted there.
Female up to 222 mm. long.　In the largest females the cuticula in surface view is like that
of the males, except that the large papillae are less numerous.　Color averages lighter than in
the male.

8 (1) Anterior region very slightly or not at all attenuated. Tip white, usually followed by a distinct dark ring. 9

Caudal end lobed; in female if not lobed then of uniform caliber with body or slightly enlarged, but not set off by a distinct constriction.

9 (10) Anterior region slightly attenuated, tip obliquely truncate; dark ring very broad. . . . . . . *Paragordius* Camerano 1897.

Caudal end trilobed in female and only bilobed in male. All males of *Gordius* also have the caudal end bilobed.

Montgomery rightly emphasized the absence of cloacal musculature in the male and the exceedingly long cloaca in the female as most significant generic features to which the caudal lobes were subordinate in value. For mere diagnostic purposes the latter are convenient.

Only species in North America. . . *Paragordius varius* (Leidy) 1851.

Males more slender and considerably longer than females; up to 350 mm. long, 0.9 mm. wide; female up to 290 mm. long, 2 mm. wide.

The long trilobed tail of the female, the long cylindrical caudal lobes in the male, the obliquely truncated head, and the usually very dark-colored ring around the head make its identification easy.

Montgomery found the larva only in *Achaeta abbreviata* (*Gryllus assimilis*). Found by Minnie E. Watson in the same host at Urbana, Illinois, and by H. G. May in the same host and also in *Nemobius fasciatus* at Douglas Lake, Michigan.

From New England to New York, Virginia (and southward?; it is reported from Guatemala); also Kansas and California. I have specimens from Lake Erie, Lake St. Clair, Lake Michigan, and Nebraska.

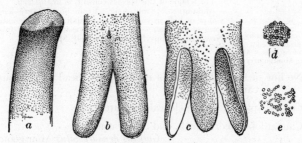

FIG. 836. *Paragordius varius*. *a*, lateral aspect of head. × 25. (Original.) *b*, ventral view of tail. × 25. (Original.) *c*, dorsal view of tail (female). × 25. (After Stiles.) *d*, surface view of cuticula in male and *e*, in female. Highly magnified. (After Montgomery.)

10 (9) Anterior region not attenuated, tip usually rounded.

Gordius Linnaeus 1758 . . 11

Caudal end bilobed in male; simple, not enlarged in female.

11 (22) Caudal end bilobed, spirally inrolled. . (Males of *Gordius*) . . 12

12 (13) Arcuate cuticular ridge anterior and lateral to cloacal pore.

Gordius alascensis Montgomery 1907.

Female not known; male 120 mm. long, slender, cylindrical. Head rounded. Caudal lobes without hairs or spicules. Areoles irregular, interconnected. Color dark brown with darker neck ring.

FIG. 837. *Gordius alascensis*. Cuticular areoles, lateral and ventral views of tail. Magnified. (After Montgomery.)

13 (12)   No cuticular ridge anterior and lateral to cloacal pore. **14**

14 (15)   Behind cloacal pore sharp V-shaped ridge.

Gordius villoti Rosa 1882.

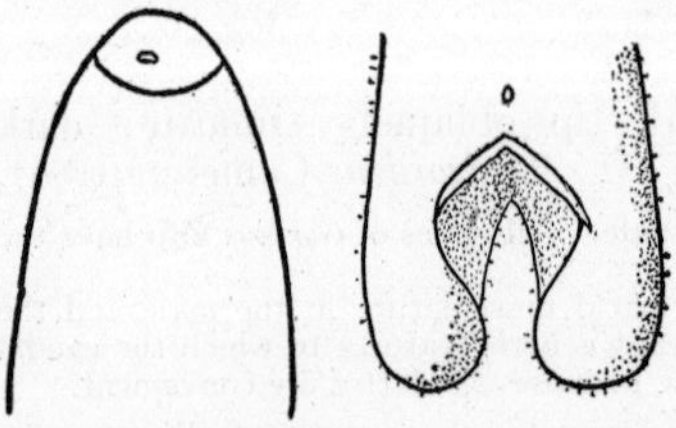

For female of this species consult 23 in this key. This species was described by Montgomery as *G. aquaticus*. Several subspecies have been distinguished. In the typical form the cuticula is marked with large light spots.

Male up to 655 mm. long, 1.3 mm. broad, equal in diameter throughout; both ends obtuse; no true areoles present.

From Canada, New England, New York to South Carolina; westward to South Dakota, Montana, and California; south to Oklahoma, Texas and Mexico. Various Acridiidae serve as hosts for this species. Also found in Locustidae by H. G. May.

FIG. 838.   *Gordius villoti* ♂ ; ventral view of anterior and posterior ends of body. Magnified. (After Montgomery.)

15 (14)   Cuticula behind cloacal pore without sharp, V-shaped ridge. . . **16**

Paragordius varius which might be confused here is readily distinguishable by the truncated anterior end.

16 (17)   On each side of cloacal pore a longitudinal line of hairs.

Gordius lineatus Leidy 1851.

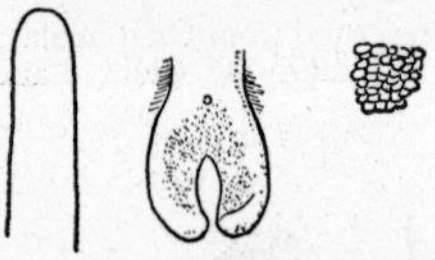

FIG. 839. *Gordius lineatus* ♂ ; anterior and posterior ends, and surface view of cuticula. Magnified. (After Montgomery.)

For female of this species consult 28 in this key.

Male up to 278 mm. long, 0.6 mm. broad; very slender. Pale yellow or buff in color; areoles small.   Perhaps only a young form of *G. villoti*. Most of the specimens taken from springs. New York, Pennsylvania, Maryland, Michigan.

17 (16)   No line of hairs along side of cloacal pore; head not obliquely truncated. 18

18 (21)   Conical spicules behind cloacal aperture. 19

19 (20)   Caudal lobes short, thick, and nearly conical.

Gordius densareolatus Montgomery 1898.

For female of this species consult 29 in this key.

Male up to 290 mm. long, 1.1 mm. broad. Body robust. Conical spines on ventral surface of caudal lobes. Color deep chocolate, with black ring about cloacal aperture. Wyoming, Montana, California.

FIG. 840.   *Gordius densareolatus* ♂ .   Ventral view of posterior end.   Magnified. (After Montgomery.)

20 (19)   Caudal lobes nearly cylindrical.

Gordius longareolatus Montgomery 1898.

Female of this species unknown.

Male 115 mm. long, 0.5 mm. broad. Longitudinally arranged elongate areoles characteristic and of rounded-conical form without median groove. No hairs between areoles. Color deep olive brown; tip of head white. California.

FIG. 841. *Gordius longareolatus* ♂ ; head, tail in ventral aspect, and cuticular areoles. Magnified. (After Montgomery.)

21 (18)   No conical spicules behind cloacal aperture; caudal lobes cylindrical. . . . . . *Gordius platycephalus* Montgomery 1898.

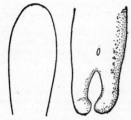

For female of this species consult 30 in this key.
Male up to 216 mm. long, 1 mm. broad. The flattened
anterior end is characteristic, but Montgomery found one
specimen apparently of *G. densareolatus* with this feature and
could explain it only as a hybrid form. Canada, Pennsylvania, and Guatemala.

FIG. 842.   *Gordius platycephalus* ♂; head and tail in ventral
aspect. Magnified. (After Montgomery.)

22 (11)   Caudal end straight, not enlarged nor lobed.
(Females of *Gordius*) . . 23
Compare 5 in key.

23 (24)   No elevated cuticular areoles on surface of body.
Gordius villoti Rosa 1882.
For male and range of this species consult 14 in this key.
Largest female 705 mm. long, 1.9 mm. broad. One variety (*G. villoti difficilis* Montgomery) has cuticular areoles at the ends of the body only. The other varieties are like the
males marked with light spots or plain. Montgomery found some points of difference from
the European type, and the American form may prove on further study to be a separate
species.

24 (23)   Elevated cuticular areoles cover the entire surface of the body.   25

25 (26)   Paired dark stripes occur in median lines.
Gordius leidyi Montgomery 1898.

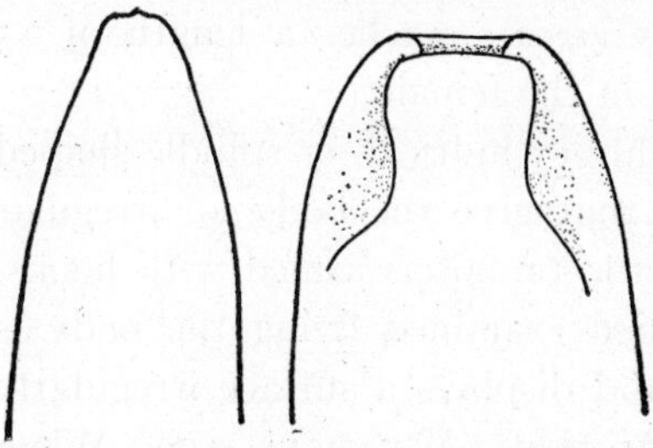

Male of this species is unknown. Female
295 mm. long, 1.5 mm. broad. Sharply distinguished from all other species in the genus
by the peculiar truncated form of the posterior
end and the two narrow parallel stripes of
intense reddish brown in the median line of
the dorsal groove.
In the Leidy collection; source unknown.

FIG. 843.   *Gordius leidyi* ♀; head and tail in dorsal aspect. Magnified. (After Montgomery.)

26 (25)   Dark stripes in median lines are lacking. 27
The unknown female of *Gordius longareolatus* probably falls here.

27 (30)   Areoles not elongated in long axis of body; head not flattened. .   28

28 (29)   Areoles close-set, tending to produce longitudinal ridges.
Gordius lineatus Leidy 1851.
For male and range of this species consult 16 in this key.
Female up to 283 mm. long, 0.8 mm. broad; like male very slender. Deeper buff color as
against the pale, transparent yellowish white of the male. In the female the cloacal orifice is
surrounded by a narrow reddish-brown ring.

29 (28)   Areoles more or less confluent, tending to produce transverse rows;
head usually cylindrical.
Gordius densareolatus Montgomery 1898.
For male and range of this species consult 19 in this key.
Female up to 395 mm. long, 1.7 mm. broad. Body robust. Head white, followed by light
buff ring and broad reddish brown ring; cloacal pore surrounded by thin black ring and broader
circular reddish brown area; body generally chocolate or yellowish brown. Cloacal aperture
in a ventral depression.

30 (27)   Areoles not elongated, usually separated; head usually flattened;
interareolar groups of fine hairs.
Gordius platycephalus
Montgomery 1898.

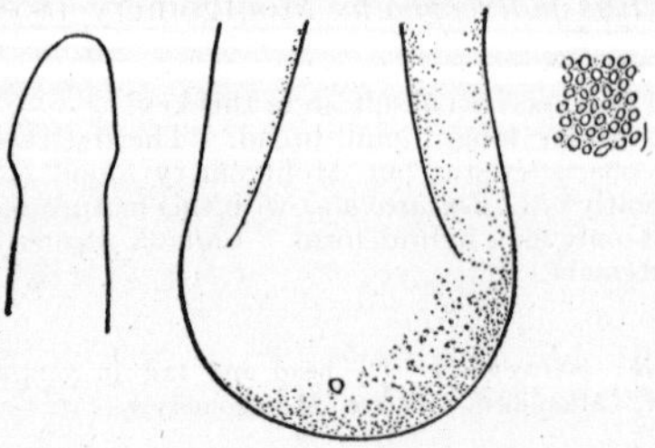

For male and range of this species consult 21
in this key.   Female up to 335 mm. long, 1.4
mm. broad.   Posterior end slightly enlarged.
Color brown;   tip of head lighter;   dark ring
around neck.

FIG. 844. *Gordius platycephalus* ♀ ; head in dorsal
aspect, tail in ventral aspect, and surface view of
cuticula.   Magnified.   (After Montgomery.)

ACANTHOCEPHALA

The Acanthocephala or proboscis roundworms constitute a most
remarkable group both in the extreme adaptation to the parasitic
habit which they manifest and in the unique structure which presents little or no parallel to any other type of animal.   Most of
them are small, measuring only a few millimeters in length although
the common parasite of the pig, *Gigantorhynchus hirudinaceus*
(commonly called *Echinorhynchus gigas*), reaches a length of 15
cm. in the male and 30 to 50 cm. in the female.

In form they are elongate, roughly cylindrical, or spindle-shaped
but with several distinct regions that give the body an irregular
form.   These regions are a retractile proboscis armed with hooks,
a neck, and a body proper.   When examined living the body is
often flattened or slightly bent, and displays a surface irregularly
roughened or marked by transverse ridges of varying size.   When
removed to normal salt solution or preserved in other fluids, they
tend to assume a smooth rounded form, sometimes with slight
regular annulations that suggest segmentation but in fact do not
extend beyond the dermal layer.

At the anterior end the proboscis, which is retractile and in preserved specimens often partly or wholly withdrawn into the body,
presents a variable form being in various species cylindrical, globose, filiform, spindle-shaped, and even more complex; it may be
long or short, straight, oblique, or at right angles to the long axis.
The particular form is characteristic of the genus or species and useful
in diagnosis.   The proboscis bears always a considerable number of

recurved hooks which are arranged in rows. One can distinguish both longitudinal and circular rows and as the hooks alternate they form a quincunx pattern. The number, form, and arrangement of the hooks are again diagnostic features. Usually the hooks are strongly recurved but they may be almost straight and often the form varies from tip to base of the proboscis. The form of the root is also subject to variation in different species. In a few cases the hooks differ on the dorsal and ventral sides of the proboscis.

In most species a neck intervenes between the proboscis and the body proper. It is nearly always unarmed and usually short. At times it is externally very sharply marked off from the body or again difficult to distinguish. Internally a cuticular fold or septum divides the hypoderm of the proboscis and neck completely from that layer in the body. The circular insertion of a retractor muscle at this point also separates these regions from each other.

The body proper forms the major part of the animal. It is usually unarmed but may bear small spines of definite form and arrangement on some portion of the external surface.

The body wall has on the exterior a thin cuticula which is not conspicuous as in nematodes. The subjacent hypoderm possesses in one group a few very large and prominent nuclei which were seen by early investigators though their true nature was not divined. These nuclei usually show as swellings or prominences on the surface. In most Acanthocephala, however, the hypoderm has many small nuclei which cannot be seen on casual observation. Two elongate organs, the lemnisci, are projections of the hypoderm posteriad into the body cavity. They originate at the line between neck and body proper and vary in size and form in different species. Their function is unknown. The body wall contains a system of lacunae which is conspicuous both in living and preserved specimens as two longitudinal vessels with smaller anastomoses usually numerous and irregular.

The proboscis sheath, usually a closed muscular sac, is attached at the base of the proboscis, or rarely inside that organ. The proboscis can be inverted into the sheath. The brain lies within the sheath concealed between the retractor muscles. Its precise location may be determined by the retinacula, a pair of nerve cords passing from it directly through the sheath and obliquely to the body wall.

No trace of an alimentary system has been found in the adult or in any stage of development. Nutrition is thus provided for entirely by absorption.

The sexes are separate in all cases. The genital pore in both is at or very near the posterior tip. The male is smaller and more slender than the female and often distinguished externally by a bell-shaped bursa that surrounds the genital pore. This is a muscular fold which is held within the body except at coition and may be forced out by the contraction accompanying the preservation of the specimen. Two oval testes lie usually in the center of the body one behind the other. Farther back is a group usually of a few large cells, the cement glands.

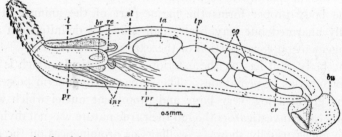

Fig. 844. *Acanthocephalus ranae.* Entire male. *br*, brain; *bu*, copulatory bursa; *cg* cement glands; *cr*, cement receptacle; *inr*, invertor of neck region; *l*, lemniscus; *pr*, proboscis receptacle; *pt*, posterior testis; *re*, retinacula; *rpr*, retractors of proboscis receptacle; *sl*, suspensory ligament; *ta*, anterior testis. X 30. (After Van Cleave.)

In the female a ligament extends through the center of the body cavity from end to end. The ovary, which is present only in the larval stage, produces great numbers of ova that later, surrounded by a heavy covering of three distinct membranes, float free in the body cavity. A complicated apparatus known as the uterine bell, located in the body cavity near the posterior end, performs rhythmic contractions that discharge from the body all well-developed embryos and return to the body cavity all that are not sufficiently matured.

The life history of Acanthocephala is almost unknown. Those parasitic in terrestrial hosts develop probably without any relation to the aquatic fauna as *Gigantorhynchus hirudinaceus* of the pig finds its intermediate host in terrestrial beetle larvae. Of forms from aquatic hosts it is inferred that the ripe embryos discharged into the water with the feces of the host attain by chance a suitable intermediate host which is probably a crustacean or insect and in that develop to the end of the larval stage. When this intermediate host is eaten by the final host the parasite reaches the place in which it can complete its development.

Almost no records have been published of Acanthocephala from North American fresh-water hosts. My own collections and recent papers by Van Cleave, to whom I am indebted also for valuable unpublished data, give at best an imperfect survey of the field. The system used, which follows in the main Lühe's work, is also confessedly artificial and incomplete.

KEY TO NORTH AMERICAN ACANTHOCEPHALA

1 (10) In hypoderm and lemnisci only a few giant nuclei.
Family NEOECHINORHYNCHIDAE Ward . . 2

Primitive Acanthocephala with hypoderm consisting of a syncytium in which are six giant nuclei, ordinarily arranged so that five lie in the mid-dorsal line and one in the mid-ventral. One lemniscus contains two giant nuclei and the other only one. These nuclei are usually conspicuous on external examination.
Proboscis sheath contains only a single layer of muscles. Cement gland a compact mass. Neck lacking. Muscles weakly developed. Lacunar system with simple circular connections.

2 (9) Proboscis globose, or nearly so; with three circles of hooks.
Neoechinorhynchus Stiles and Hassall 1905 . . 3

Proboscis short, globose, with few hooks. Hooks of anterior row much larger than those in center and basal rows. Cement gland with eight nuclei.

3 (4) Twelve hooks in each circle.
Neoechinorhynchus gracilisentis (Van Cleave) 1913.

Body small, tapering slightly toward both ends, bent into a crescent. Mature females 1.7 to 4 mm. long; maximum width 0.38 mm. just anterior to center of body. Males 1.5 to 3 mm. long, maximum breadth 0.3 mm. Proboscis slightly longer than wide with constriction between second and third row of hooks. Hooks delicate, in anterior row curved, 15 to 17 μ long, in middle row 12 to 15 μ long, in basal row nearly straight, 15 to 20 μ long. Embryos spindle-shaped, 36 to 40 μ long by 10 μ broad.

In intestine and ceca of hickory shad; Illinois River; October to May.

FIG. 845. Neoechinorhynchus gracilisentis. Proboscis, × 95; hooks and embryos, × 310. (After Van Cleave.)

4 (3) Six hooks in each circle. 5

5 (8)   Terminal hooks over 90 µ long.   Embryos under 50 µ long. 6

6 (7)   Body 8 to 32 mm. long.   Embryos very small.
                    Neoechinorhynchus emydis (Leidy) 1852.

Body much elongated, cylindrical. Female 10 to 32 mm. long, 0.7 mm. in maximum width. Male 8 to 11 mm. long by 0.7 mm. broad. Proboscis globose, 0.175 mm. long. Hooks large, in anterior row strongly recurved, 95 to 103 µ long, in middle row 49 to 59 µ long, in basal row 35 to 54 µ long, nearly straight. Embryos very small, oval, 16 by 11 µ.

Originally described by Leidy from the intestine of various species of *Emys* from Pennsylvania and Maryland. Frequent in *Malacoclemmys geographicus* (Lesueur) and *Pseudemys elegans* Max from the Illinois River.

Fig. 846.   *Neoechinorhynchus emydis*. Proboscis, × 75; hooks and embryos, × 230.   (After Van Cleave.)

7 (6)   Body 2 to 13 mm. long.   Embryos about 40 µ long.
                    Neoechinorhynchus tenellus (Van Cleave) 1913.

Body small, both ends curved strongly ventrad. Posterior two-thirds of body markedly attenuated. Female 3.5 to 13 mm. long, 0.6 mm. in maximum breadth; males 2 to 8 mm. long, 0.5 mm. broad. Proboscis nearly cylindrical, 0.150 mm. long by 0.135 mm. wide. Anterior hooks 90 to 110 µ long, heavy; middle hooks 38 µ long; basal hooks 27 µ long. Embryos 37 to 45 by 12 to 16 µ.

Intestine of *Esox lucius* L. from Lake Marquette near Bemidji, Minnesota.

Fig. 847.   *Neoechinorhynchus tenellus*. Proboscis, × 75; hooks and embryo, × 230.   (After Van Cleave.)

8 (5)   Terminal hooks usually less than 90 µ long.   Embryos over 50 µ long.
                    Neoechinorhynchus cylindratus (Van Cleave) 1913.

Large, straight-bodied. Female 10 to 15 mm. long, 0.7 mm. in maximum width, just behind proboscis. Male 4.5 to 8.5 mm. long, 0.5 to 0.7 mm. in maximum breadth near anterior end. Proboscis slightly broader (0.172 mm.) than long (0.15 mm.). Anterior hooks 79 to 97 µ long, heavy, strongly recurved, center hooks 37 µ long, basal hooks 21 to 25 µ long. Embryos 49 to 51 µ long by 15 to 21 µ broad.

In intestine of *Micropterus salamoides* (Lacép.). Pelican Lake, Minnesota, and of *Anguilla chrysypa*, Woods Hole, Massachusetts.

Fig. 848.   *Neoechinorhynchus cylindratus*. Proboscis, × 75; hooks and embryos, × 230.   (After Van Cleave.)

9 (2)   Proboscis long.   Numerous irregular circles of about six hooks each.
Tanaorhamphus Ward.

The extreme length of the proboscis and the large number of hooks serve to contrast this with the previous closely related genus. Hooks in the anterior row are not conspicuously larger than those following. The cement gland has 16 nuclei.

Only species known.
Tanaorhamphus longirostris (Van Cleave) 1913.

Body robust, posterior end flexed slightly ventrad. Females average 6.2 mm. long, and 0.63 mm. in maximum breadth. Males average 4 mm. long, and 0.47 mm. in maximum breadth. Proboscis cylindrical with slight constriction one-third distance from base to outer end, bent ventrad 60 degrees. Hooks in about 20 circular rows of six to ten hooks each. Anterior hooks 54 μ long, successive hooks gradually smaller until within a few rows of the base where they become abruptly smaller; basal hooks 16 μ long. Embryos oval 27 μ long by 8 to 10 μ broad.
In intestine of hickory shad from Illinois River; not abundant but probably most frequent in summer and wanting in January to April.

Fig. 849.   *Tanaorhamphus longirostris.*   Proboscis, × 75; embryos, × 230.
(After Van Cleave.)

10 (1)   In hypoderm many small nuclei, not conspicuous externally. . .   11
The proboscis sac has a double muscular wall.

11 (36)   Proboscis and neck simple, without bulbous enlargement even in fully developed specimens.   12

12 (27)   Hooks in each circular row all alike; no contrast between different sides of proboscis.   13

13 (24)   Proboscis sheath attached at posterior end of proboscis.   14

14 (19)   Body of parasite entirely free from spines at all points.   15

15 (16)   Retinacula emerge from proboscis sheath at blind posterior end which contains ganglion.   *Acanthocephalus* Koelreuter 1771.
In marine and fresh-water fishes and Amphibia, larvae in Isopoda.

Representative North American species.
Acanthocephalus ranae (Schrank) 1788.

Body elongate, club-shaped, largest near neck. Proboscis short, cylindrical. Twelve rows each with 6 or 7 hooks which are 60, 70, 80 and 50 μ long. Embryos 110 μ long by 13 μ broad. This European species has been identified by Van Cleave who showed that it is apparently rare in this country.
From intestine of *Diemyctylus viridescens* taken near Baltimore, Maryland.

16 (15)   Retinacula emerge from lateral walls of proboscis sheath; ganglion distinctly anterior to blind posterior end of sheath.
Echinorhynchus Zoega 1776 . .   17

Neck wanting or very short; proboscis long, cylindrical, bent ventrad. Hooks numerous, much alike throughout except that roots grow shorter and disappear in later rows.
In marine and fresh-water fishes.
Nearly every new species described from this continent has been assigned to this genus, many of them erroneously. Several good species in North America. Abundant in whitefish and lake trout from the Great Lakes.

17 (18)   Embryos from 85 to 108 μ long.

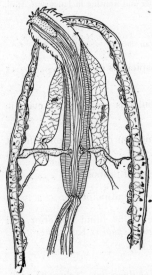

Echinorhynchus thecatus Linton 1892.

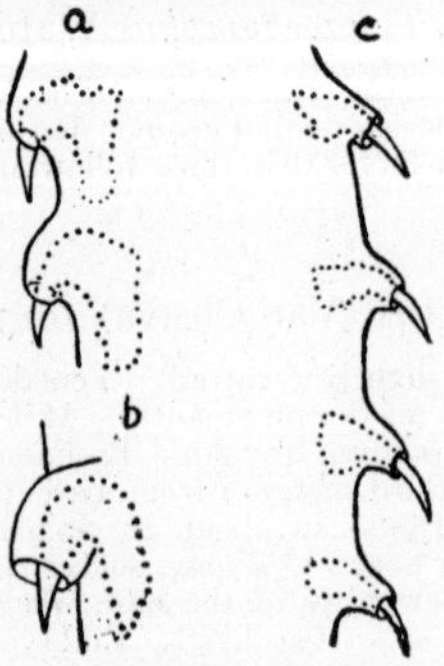

Body cylindrical, slightly curved; proboscis curved also. Female 11 to 26 mm. long; width 0.51 to 0.89, anteriorly 0.8 to 1.4 mm. in maximum, 0.52 to 1 mm. posteriorly. Male 7 to 12 mm. long; width 0.39 to 0.69 anteriorly, 0.59 to 0.95 in maximum, 0.37 to 0.75 posteriorly. Hooks in 24 to 31 transverse and 12 longitudinal rows surrounded by prominent collars. Embryos 85 to 108 μ long by 18 to 22 μ broad. (Graybill.)
In alimentary canal and body cavity of *Micropterus dolomieu, Ambloplites rupestris, Amia calva*, and *Roccus lineatus*. Great Lakes and eastern waters.

Fig. 850. *Echinorhynchus thecatus. a*, hooks from ventral side of proboscis near base; *b*, hook from ventral, i.e., concave side of proboscis; *c*, hooks from dorsal, i.e., convex side of proboscis. × 150. (After Linton.)

18 (17)   Embryos from 115 to 165 μ long. . *Echinorhynchus salvelini* Linkins.

Male 7 to 9 mm. long, 0.82 to 1.27 mm. broad. Female 10 to 17 mm. long, 1.2 to 1.6 mm. wide. Proboscis armed with 26 circular rows of 8 hooks each. Hooks alternate in adjacent rows. Basal hooks 39 to 50 μ long; hooks in middle and anterior regions 44 to 68 μ long, those with basal processes 83 μ long. Embryos 115 to 165 μ long by 20 to 25 μ wide.
From lake trout; Lake Michigan.

Fig. 851. *Echinorhynchus salvelini.* Optical section through anterior region of body. × 60. (After Linkins.)

19 (14)   Spines on body at some point at least, usually at anterior end. .   20

20 (23)   Body tapers regularly towards both ends. Proboscis in line with axis of body. Posterior limit of spines alike on dorsal and ventral surfaces.   21

21 (22)   Cement glands tubular. . . . .   *Polymorphus* Lühe 1911.
Fine spines on skin of anterior body. Just behind the limit of these spines a conspicuous annular constriction. Type species *P. minutus* (Goeze) from various European water birds. At least one species yet undescribed from North American Anseriformes.

22 (21)   Cement glands irregularly ovoid. (Males and some females or young specimens.) . . . .   *Filicollis* Lühe 1911.
Compare number 37 in this key.
The males, the young females and even some adult females of certain species have a proboscis that departs only slightly from the usual type, being a little enlarged but not conspicuously

set off from the neck. In the type species, *Filicollis anatis*, a European form not yet definitely reported for North America, the adult female has the proboscis enlarged to a thin-walled spherical bladder which bears the hooks on its anterior aspect in a series of radiating lines.

Representative North American species.

Filicollis botulus Van Cleave 1916.

This peculiar form found in water birds has been reported from the eider (*Somateria dresseri*) from Maine. Although the range of the bird carries it (rarely) as far west as Colorado, yet the particular parasite may not be native to fresh waters. Acanthocephala of this general type have been reported from North American ducks under the name of "*Echinorhynchus polymorphus.*"

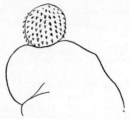

FIG. 852. *Filicollis botulus.* Female with tip of proboscis slightly inturned. × 10. Male, neck retracted, body spines not shown. × 17. (After Van Cleave.)

23 (20)   Body club-shaped, anterior end enlarged. Proboscis bent ventrad, forming an angle with axis of the body. Spines extend further posteriad on ventral surface than on dorsal.

Corynosoma Lühe 1904.

The peculiar form and the unusual distribution of spines on the body serve to identify the members of this genus which is apparently limited in the adult stage to fish-eating birds and mammals, chiefly seal. The genus is mainly marine but Van Cleave has a record of a species from birds at Yellowstone Lake.

24 (13)   Proboscis sheath attached at center of proboscis.

Family CENTRORHYNCHIDAE Van Cleave 1916 . .   25

The proboscis sheath starts from near the center of the proboscis wall. The mature forms are parasitic in the intestine of birds.

25 (26)   Proboscis receptacle two layered: retractors penetrate its posterior rounded tip. . . . .   *Centrorhynchus* Lühe 1911.

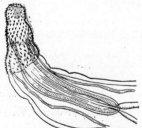

Three long tubular cement glands.

Only North American species.

Centrorhynchus spinosus Van Cleave 1916.

Female 20 mm. long, 0.6 mm. broad anteriorly, 0.5 mm. posteriorly. Proboscis 0.65 mm. long constricted at insertion of proboscis receptacle with hooks of 2 types in 30 longitudinal rows of about 24 hooks each.

In intestine of *Herodias egretta* from District of Columbia (?).

FIG. 853. *Centrorhynchus spinosus.* Proboscis and anterior region of body, showing also insertion of proboscis receptacle and location of the retractors of the receptacle with reference to the wall. × 26. (After Van Cleave.)

26 (25)   Proboscis receptacle single layered; retractors pass through its sides some distance anterior to posterior tip.

Mediorhynchus Van Cleave 1916.

Nerve ganglion near center of proboscis receptacle. In male 8 round or pyriform cement glands. Proboscis hooks distinctly of two types. Proboscis receptacle not cylindrical in form.

Known species mostly in land birds but one record concerns the Carolina rail, *Porzana carolina*, that might have been infected from an aquatic intermediate host.

27 (12)   **Hooks** not alike on ventral and dorsal surfaces of proboscis. . .   **28**

28 (29)   Hooks differ in form, especially of root, but not in size. Body uniformly cylindrical or nearly so.
Rhadinorhynchus Lühe 1911.

Hooks of dorsal surface with much shorter root, also slenderer and less curved than those on ventral surface. In marine fishes almost exclusively, but present in trout from eastern states. Species yet undescribed.

29 (28)   Hooks differ noticeably both in form and size. Body very large and slender, with marked enlargement near anterior end.
Arhythmorhynchus Lühe 1911 . .   30

Body in front of enlargement covered with fine spines. Proboscis very long, enlarged at center, oblique to body axis. Adults in intestine of birds.

30 (31)   Hooks on mid-ventral surface of proboscis conspicuously larger than any others.
Arhythmorhynchus trichocephalus (R. Leuckart) 1893.

Body very slender. Length 5 to 8 cm., diameter 0.5 to 0.8 mm. Ovoid swelling 2.3 to 2.9 mm. behind neck with length of 1.6 to 2.4 mm. and breadth of 0.6 to 1.4 mm. Anterior to swelling many dermal spines 28 to 35 μ long. Proboscis with 20 longitudinal rows and 19 or 20 transverse rows of hooks.
From Florida; host unknown.

31 (30)   Hooks on mid-ventral surface of proboscis not conspicuously larger than others.   32

32 (33)   Large hooks exceed 100 μ in length.
Arhythmorhynchus uncinatus (Kaiser) 1893.

Length 4 to 6 cm., diameter 1 to 1.2 mm. Ovoid swelling about 5 mm. behind neck; 0.6 mm. in front of swelling prominent annular enlargement 1 to 1.4 mm. long, 1.7 to 2 mm. in diameter and covered thickly with small spines. Proboscis with 18 transverse and 18 longitudinal rows of hooks.
From Florida; host unknown.

33 (32)   Large hooks not more than 50 μ long.   34

34 (35)   Eighteen longitudinal rows of hooks.
Arhythmorhynchus brevis Van Cleave 1916.

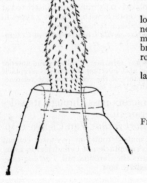

Female 6 to 12 mm. long, 3 mm. wide. Male 5 to 6 mm. long, 1 to 1.5 mm. wide. Neck naked. Body just back of neck with few small spines. Proboscis 0.665 mm. long, 0.23 mm. wide at base, 0.19 mm. at tip, 0.34 mm. at center. Embryos 76 to 100 μ by 24 to 30 μ. Middle shell heavy, with rounded swelling at each pole.
From bittern (*Botaurus lentiginosus*); Baltimore, Maryland.

Fig. 854. *Arhythmorhynchus brevis.* Anterior end of body. × 40.
.(After Van Cleave.)

35 (34) Proboscis with sixteen longitudinal rows of hooks.

> Arhythmorhynchus pumilirostris Van Cleave 1916.

Female up to 30 mm. long, and 1.5 mm. broad. Proboscis 0.45 mm. long, 0.114 mm. wide at base, 0.095 mm. at tip, 0.18 mm. at center. Embryos 65 to 89 μ long, 18 μ broad. Middle shell with evagination at each pole.
From bittern (*Botaurus lentiginosus*); Washington, D. C.

FIG. 855. *Arhythmorhynchus pumilirostris.* Profile, anterior end of body. X 95. (After Van Cleave.)

36 (11) In anterior region of mature specimens prominent bulbous enlargement, separated from body by slender cylindrical neck. 37

The bulb is embedded in the intestinal wall or may even be in the body cavity when the slender region traverses the wall connecting with the body of the parasite in the intestine. In handling such material the proboscis may easily be partly or completely torn off, and the parasite is then difficult to identify as the characteristic bulb at least is gone.

37 (38) Bulb consists of the proboscis. Hooks on the anterior face of the bulb in radial lines. . . (Females of) *Filicollis* Lühe 1911.

Representative North American species.

> *Filicollis botulus* Van Cleave 1916.

In females thus far reported under this name for North America the bulb is wanting; it may be present in older specimens and in fact is described in specimens recorded under the name *E. anatis* which may belong here.
Compare number 22 in key.

38 (37) Bulb consists of anterior part of neck only. Proboscis extends anteriad from bulb. . . . *Pomphorhynchus* Monticelli 1905.

Proboscis long, cylindrical, with many hooks. Neck very long, expanded in anterior region, slender, cylindrical in posterior portion. In intestine of fishes; one of the commonest types in European fresh-water hosts. Not infrequent in North American fresh-water fishes; species not described.

IMPORTANT REFERENCES ON NORTH AMERICAN PARASITIC ROUNDWORMS

GENERAL WORKS

See also list in Chapter XIII, page 452

HAMANN, O. 1891. Die Nemathelminthen. Heft 1, 120 pp., 10 pl. 1895. Heft 2, 120 pp., 11 pl. Jena.

LEUCKART, R. 1876. Die menschliche Parasiten. Vol. 2 [Nematoda, Acanthocephala]. 882 pp., 401 figs. Leipzig.

NEMATODA

DRASCHE, R. von. 1882-3. Revision der in der Nematoden-Sammlung des K. K. zoologischen Hofcabinetes befindlichen Original-Exemplare Diesing's und Molin's. Verh. zool.-bot. Ges. Wien, 32: 117-138, 4 pl.; 33: 107-118, 3 pl.; 33: 193-218, 4 pl.

HAGMEIER, A. 1912. Beiträge zur Kenntnis der Mermithiden. Zool. Jahrb., Syst., 32: 521-612, 5 pl.

HALL, M. C. 1916. Nematode Parasites of Mammals, etc. Proc. U. S. Nat. Mus., 50: 1-258, 1 pl.

LINSTOW, O. von. 1909. Parasitische Nematoden. Süsswasserfauna Deutschlands, Heft 15, p. 47-81.

MAGATH, T. B. 1916. Nematode Technique. Trans. Amer. Mic. Soc., 35: 245-256.

RAILLIET, A. and Henry, A.
    1915. Sur les Nématodes du genre Camallanus Raill. et Henry, 1915 (Cucullanus auct., non Mueller, 1777). Bull. soc. path. exot., Paris, 8: 446-452.

RANSOM, B. H. 1911. The Nematodes Parasitic in the Alimentary Tract of Cattle, Sheep, and other Ruminants. Bur. An. Ind., Bull. 127, 132 pp.

SCHNEIDER, A. 1866. Monographie der Nematoden. 357 pp. 28 pl. Berlin.

SEURAT, L. G. 1916. Contribution a l'étude des formes larvaires des Nématodes parasites hétéroxènes. Bull. sci. France et Belgique, 49: 297-377.

STOSSICH, M. 1896. Il genere Ascaris Linné. 1897. Filarie e Spiroptere. 1899. Strongylidae. Trieste.

WARD, H. B. and MAGATH, T. B. 1916. Notes on Some Nematodes from Fresh-Water Fishes. Jour. Parasitol., 3: 57-64, 1 pl.

GORDIACEA

MONTGOMERY, T. H., Jr. 1898. The Gordiacea of Certain American Collections. Bull. Mus. Comp. Zool. Harvard, 32: 23-59, 15 pl.

1898a. The Gordiacea, etc. Pt. II. Proc. Cal. Acad. Sci., (3) 1: 333-344, 2 pl.

1899. Synopses of North American Invertebrates. II. Gordiacea (Hair worms). Amer. Nat., 33: 647-652.

ACANTHOCEPHALA

LÜHE, M. 1911. Acanthocephalen. Süsswasserfauna Deutschlands, Heft 16, 60 pp., 87 figs.

VAN CLEAVE, H. J. 1913. The Genus Neorhynchus in North America. Zool. Anz., 43: 177-190.

1915. Acanthocephala in North American Amphibia. Jour. Parasitol., 1: 175-178.

CHAPTER XVII

THE WHEEL ANIMALCULES (ROTATORIA)

By H. S. JENNINGS

Professor of Zoology, Johns Hopkins University

THE Rotatoria or Rotifera are perhaps the most characteristic group of fresh-water animals, and at the same time the most attractive and beautiful. They are everywhere abundant in fresh water, but are rare elsewhere. With their varied and fantastic forms, their brilliant colors and lively manners, they have long been the favorites of amateur microscopists. Some of the older observers have expressed themselves with great enthusiasm in regard to these creatures. Eichhorn (1781) who discovered *Stephanoceros* in 1761, calls it the "crown polype," and likens this "incomparable animal" to a pomegranate blossom. Of *Floscularia* he says, "Now I come to a very wonderful animal, which has very often rejoiced me in my observations: I call it the Catcher: extraordinarily artistic in its structure, wonderful in its actions, rapid in capturing its prey." Eichhorn's account of the capture of prey is excellent: "Its head was a widespread net . . . with points which had little round balls on their tips; so it awaits its prey; when a little animal came into this net or hollow basin, then it convulsively drew the neck a little together, as if to find out, as it were, whether it had really gotten its booty; then it suddenly folded the net together and pushed the prey into its body, where one could still see it plainly. . . . And I have often seen it exactly as in [Fig.] *K*; then it looked terrible, no lightning stroke can rush from the clouds into the air so quickly as this little animal fiercely struck together the two hooks when it noticed a prey in its outspread net."

The rotifers are minute, chiefly microscopic animals. Their most characteristic feature is the ciliated area at or near the anterior end of the body, serving as a locomotor organ or to bring food to the mouth. Taken in connection with the lack of cilia on other parts of the body (save in rare cases at the posterior end), this ciliated area or corona serves as a rule to distinguish a rotifer at once from any other many-celled animal living in fresh water.

The extreme diversity of form and organization in different rotifers, though constituting the greatest charm of their study, makes it almost impossible to give a formal definition of the group. Even the most characteristic feature, — the ciliated corona, — is in a few cases lacking. The form of the body varies extremely, from spherical in *Trochosphaera* (Fig. 947) to the excessively attenuated form of *Rotifer neptunius* (Fig. 960), the flower-like shape of *Stephanoceros* (Fig. 937), or the spiny, turtle-like figure of *Polychaetus* (Fig. 905).

Yet one can give a characterization that will be true for the great majority of the rotifers. The body is as a rule somewhat elongated, with the ciliated corona at the anterior end; it is extended at the posterior end, behind and below the cloacal opening, to form a stalk, or tail-like appendage known as the foot. This frequently ends in two small pointed toes. There is a well-developed alimentary canal, with a muscular pharynx, containing complex jaws. There is a simple excretory system, while circulatory and respiratory systems are lacking. The nervous system consists of a prominent brain and of certain nerves and sense organs. The sexes are separate, and the male is usually a minute, degenerate creature, lacking the alimentary canal.

Rotifera may be found wherever there is fresh water. Lakes, ponds, and streams harbor them in immense number and variety. Swamps and marshes swarm with them. Wayside pools, drains, and even the dirty water that stands in barnyard holes about manure heaps, are prolific sources of rotifers. The mud of eave-troughs, the bottoms of funeral urns, the cavities found in the axils of the leaves of certain mosses, — all these are famous collecting grounds for the rotifer hunter. A few rotifers are parasitic, some externally, some internally. A few live in salt water, but they are much less abundant in the ocean than in fresh water.

In giving an account of the structure and life of the rotifers, it will be well to have in mind at first some representative type; then the variations found in other rotifers may be traced. The typical rotifers, as well as the commonest ones, are those belonging to the great family of Notommatidae, and there is much reason to believe that all other rotifers have been derived from forms essentially similar to those found in this family. The different members of the Notommatidae are so much alike that it is hardly necessary to select precisely some one species for a type. But it will be well in following this account to have in mind such an animal as *Proales* (Fig. 856), or *Notommata truncata* (Fig. 857, *A* and *B*), or *Copeus*

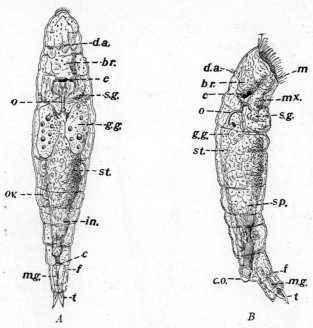

A   B

<small>FIG. 856.   *Proales werneckii* Ehr., a typical notommatoid rotifer.   *A*, Female, dorsal view.   × 400. *B*, Male, side view.   For explanation of letters, see Fig. 857. × 600.   (After Rousselet.)</small>

pachyurus (Fig. 857, *C*). For convenience one can refer to any member of the Notommatidae as a *notommatid*.

The notommatids, though the most abundant, are as a rule the least conspicuous of the rotifers. They have usually a nearly cylindrical body, often somewhat swollen behind, and with a slender posterior foot (*f*) ending in two toes (*t*). Most of them are found swimming about amid vegetation or creeping over its surface. Like all other living things, these rotifers are bundles of activity. They are busily engaged in carrying on many processes, internal and external; in meeting and solving the problems which the world presents. And it is almost surprising to note, when the matter is first examined from such a standpoint, how nearly the objects of the strivings of almost any lower group resemble those of the highest. To get proper food and oxygen; to find or construct a proper place to dwell; to arrange for the production and growth of the young; to protect one's self and one's progeny from ene-

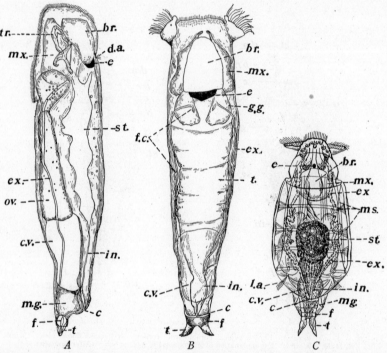

FIG. 857. Notommatoid rotifers. *A*, *Notommata truncata* Jennings, side view. × 300. *B*, same, dorsal view. × 300. *C*, *Copeus pachyurus* Gosse. × 150. The letters in Figs. 856 and 857 have the following signification: *br*, brain; *c*, cloaca; *co*, copulatory organ; *cv*, contractile vacuole; *e*, eye; *ex*, excretory organs; *f*, foot; *fc*, flame cell; *gg*, gastric glands; *in*, intestine; *la*, lateral antennae; *m*, mouth; *mg*, mucous glands of foot; *ms*, muscles; *mx*, mastax; *o*, esophagus; *ov*, ovary; *sg*, salivary glands; *sp*, spermarium; *st*, stomach; *t*, toes. (After Weber.)

mies and from the forces of nature, — these, and the activities growing out of them, form the groundwork of life in the lowest as well as the highest creatures. In studying the rotifers, it will be best to look upon them as living things and to ask: What processes and activities are they carrying on? And what apparatus do they use in these activities? Thus, one is led to take up in order the various systems of organs, to notice their variations and modifications, and the uses they serve.

Perhaps the chief concern of all organisms is to provide material for carrying on the complicated chemical processes that are going on within, — that is, to get food and oxygen. How does the rotifer accomplish these ends?

This is done mainly by the aid of the ciliated surface at the anterior end, — the corona. The cilia of this region are fine, hair-like processes which are in constant motion. They strike backward more strongly than forward, so that they cause a current to pass backward from in front of the animal to its mouth, and thence over the surface of the body (Fig. 858). In the simplest notommatids

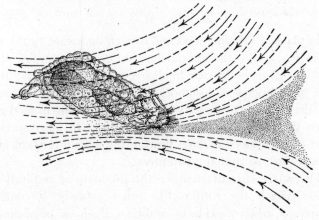

Fig. 858. Currents of water caused by the cilia of a rotifer. The dotted area shows how material lying in front of the rotifer is drawn out in the form of a vortex to its mouth. (The rotifer is *Proales sordida* Gosse, from a figure by Dixon-Nuttall.)

the corona is a mere flattish disk on the ventral side of the anterior end, covered uniformly with short cilia (Fig. 859). In other rotifers there are great variations in the size and arrangement of the cilia; these variations will be taken up later. The water current produced by the corona has a number of different uses:

1. It continually renews the water that bathes the surface of the animal, thus insuring a constant supply of fresh oxygen. The oxygen thus supplied is absorbed by the entire surface of the animal, apparently, for there are no special respiratory organs.

2. The current brings to the mouth any particles of food that

may be floating in the water, or that are easily washed from surrounding objects. The mouth, situated in the posterior part of the corona, opens, and so admits or seizes such food as is adapted to the rotifer. In many rotifers the cilia are the chief direct agents in obtaining food, and in practically all species they are either directly or indirectly of the greatest importance for this function.

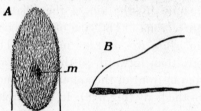

FIG. 859. Corona of *Proales tigridia* Gosse. *A*, surface view, from ventral side. *B*, side view. *m*, mouth. (After Wesenberg-Lund.)

3. In place of bringing food and oxygen backward to the rotifer, the cilia may carry the animal forward to new supplies of these necessities. This is the case in all free-swimming rotifers; the cilia are the main organs of locomotion. In thus moving the animals about, the cilia of course play as important a part in food-getting as when they bring the food to the rotifer. In most species the cilia act in both ways at once, bearing the animal forward and the food backward, so that the two meet.

4. The water currents remove the products of respiration and excretion, which the rotifer, like other animals, is continually giving off. Carbon dioxide is doubtless given off over the whole surface of the body, while other waste products are discharged by the contractile vesicle (see p. 561). If these waste products were allowed to accumulate, they would be most injurious.

While these are the main uses of the cilia, they assist, in a number of rotifers, in other important operations, such as the construction of a tube or nest.

The further course of the food may now be followed. The mouth, situated in the posterior part of the corona (Fig. 859, *m*), leads into a cavity with thick, muscular walls, known as the mastax (Figs. 856 and 857, *mx*). The mastax is armed with a complicated set of jaws, which have little resemblance to jaws found anywhere else in the animal kingdom. They are known as the trophi (Fig. 857, *A*, *tr*).

The trophi consist of a number of pieces, so arranged that two main parts may be distinguished. There is a middle portion, somewhat fork-shaped, which is known as the incus (Fig. 860, *in*), and two lateral parts known as the mallei (*ma*).

In the middle portion or incus may be distinguished a single basal piece, comparable to the handle of the two-tined fork; this basal piece is known as the fulcrum (*fu*, Fig. 860). The two blade-like pieces resting on it, *i.e*, the tines of the fork, are the rami (*ra*).

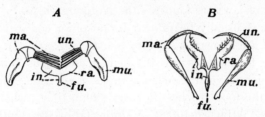

FIG. 860. Trophi or jaws of rotifers. *A*, Malleate type. (From Wesenberg-Lund, after Hudson and Gosse.) *B*, Forcipate type, from *Diglena forcipata* Ehr. (After Gosse.) *fu*, fulcrum; *in*, incus; *ma*, mallei; *mu*, manubrium; *ra*, ramus; *un*, uncus.

The rami are joined to the fulcrum in such a way that they may move back and forth, like the blades of a pair of shears. They often bear teeth.

In the lateral parts or mallei one may likewise distinguish two parts. The basal piece, serving as a sort of handle, is known as the manubrium (Fig. 860, *mu*). Joined to the top of this, but placed nearly at right angles to it, is the piece known as the uncus (*un*); the two unci usually lie across the tops of the rami, their points meeting in the middle. Each uncus may bear one or more points, or a number of sharp ridges serving as teeth. The food passes between the teeth of the unci and rami and is cut and ground by them. The jaws are worked by muscles which are attached to the manubria and to other parts of the apparatus; these muscles make up the main part of the mastax.

In different rotifers the trophi vary much in the form and relative development of the typical parts; this is true even within the Notommatidae. There are two main lines of divergent development: (1) In many rotifers the parts of the trophi become thick and stout; the unci are broad plates bearing a number of ridges. Such jaws are used mainly for grinding, and are said to belong to the malleate type (Fig. 860, *A*), on account of the great development of the mallei.   (2) In other species all parts of the trophi are long and slender; the unci end in a single sharp point, which may be thrust out of the mouth to seize upon living prey.   The two rami like- wise form a pair of strong, blade-like jaws.   Such trophi are said to belong to the forcipate type (Fig. 860, *B*); they are found in active rotifers of predatory habits.   There exist many modifications of these two types, and many jaws intermediate between the two. Both types of jaws are found in the Notommatidae.

The mastax usually bears near its posterior end a pair of small glands that are known as salivary glands (Fig. 856, *sg*).   From the mastax the food passes into the slender esophagus (Figs. 856 and 857, *o*), which leaves the mastax on its dorsal side.   Through the esophagus the food reaches the large stomach (*st*), where digestion takes place.   Attached to the anterior end of the stomach are the two large gastric glands (*gg*).   From the stomach the undigested remnants of the food pass back into the straight slender intestine, and thence to the outside at the cloacal opening (*c*).   This lies on the dorsal side of the body, above the foot.

The body cavity is enclosed by but a single layer of cells, which form the body wall, so that each cell is bathed on its outer surface by the outer water and on its inner surface by the fluid of the body cavity.   By this arrangement the processes of respiration are made very simple.   Oxygen doubtless passes from the surround- ing water through the single layer of cells into the body fluid, while the waste carbon dioxide produced within is given off in the same way to the outside.

The nitrogenous waste products are not so easily eliminated as is the carbon dioxide; for removing these the rotifers have a set of excretory organs.   These consist of fine tubules running through the body cavity at the sides of the alimentary canal (see Fig. 857, *ex*, and Fig. 861).   On each side there are usually two tubes, one with thick walls (*a*), the other with very thin ones (*b*).   These two are usually connected (*c*) in the anterior part of the rotifer.   They commonly bear at intervals along their course certain minute club-shaped organs (Figs. 857, *B*; 861, *fc*).   These are closed at their free ends, and contain within them either a vibrating membrane or a bunch of long cilia. The membrane or the bunch of cilia is always in rapid movement, giving the appearance of a minute flame, so that these structures are called flame cells. The cilia or membrane doubtless serve to propel a current through the tubes. In many rotifers a transverse tube in the head region unites the

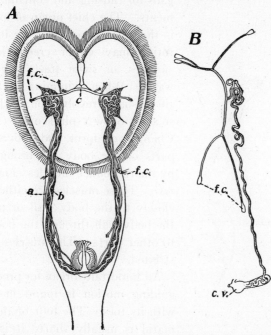

Fig. 861. Excretory organs. *A, Lacinularia socialis* Ehr., showing the thin-walled tube *a*, the thick-walled tube *b*, the transverse connecting tube *c*, and the flame cells *fc*. Modified from a figure by Hlava. *B*, Excretory tubules of right side in *Floscularia campanulata* Dobie. *cv*, contractile vesicle; *fc*, flame cells. (After Montgomery.)

thin-walled tubes of right and left sides. Often all the tubes are convoluted in their course.

There is reason to believe that the walls of the tubes absorb the nitrogenous waste matter from the fluid of the body cavity. This waste matter passes backward, driven by the flame cells, to the region of the cloaca (Figs. 856, 857, *c*). Here is found in most rotifers a small sac into which the tubes from both sides enter. This sac opens along with the intestine into a small cavity known as the cloaca. The sac, or contractile vesicle (*cv*), as it is called, contracts at intervals, expelling to the outside the fluid with which the tubes have filled it. The contractions take place frequently, so that a large amount of fluid is expelled.

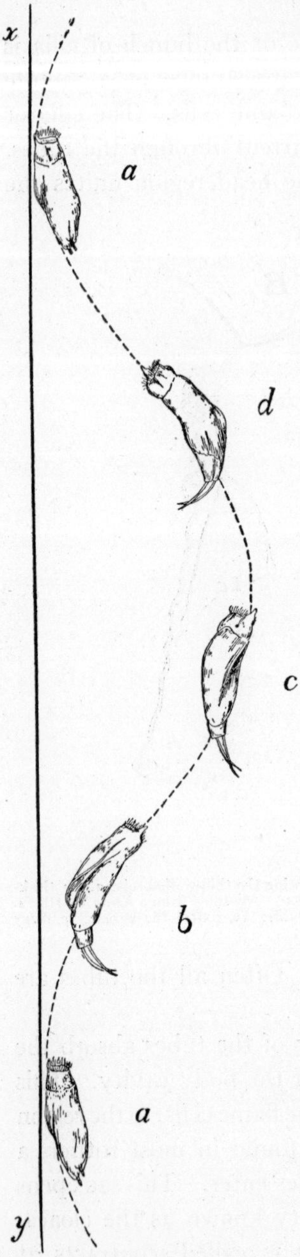

Besides its organs for the nutritive processes, the rotifer has of course organs for causing and controlling movements. The chief organ of locomotion is the ciliated corona. By its aid the rotifer may either creep along over surfaces, or swim freely through the water. When swimming freely the rotifer usually revolves on its long axis, so as to follow a spiral course (Fig. 862). Changes of form and movements of parts of the body are brought about by many slender muscles (Fig. 857, *C*, *ms*). These muscles are either applied closely to the body wall or pass from the body wall through the body cavity to other parts. The muscles are often striated.

An important organ for producing or guiding motion is found in the foot with its toes. The foot of the notommatid is usually short; it is nothing more than that part of the body behind the cloaca. It usually tapers somewhat, but is not clearly marked off from the rest of the body, as it is in some rotifers of other families. At its posterior end it bears side by side the tapering, pointed toes, which are usually small in the Notommatidae. The toes serve as a steering apparatus in swimming, and as points of support and attachment in creeping. For attachment the toes are supplied with

FIG. 862. Spiral path followed by swimming rotifer, as seen in *Diurella tigris* Müller. (After Jennings.)

two glands lying in the foot (Figs. 856 and 857, *mg*); these secrete a sticky, tenacious mucus, which may be discharged either at the tip of the toes, or at their base, so as to flow out over their surface. By this mucus the rotifer may attach itself loosely to objects of various sorts, so that the movements of its cilia may continue to bring food to the mouth without carrying the rotifer away from its anchorage. Often the mucus is drawn out to form a long thread, like that produced by a spider; from this thread the rotifer remains as it were suspended, swinging about from side to side at a distance from the point of attachment, but not breaking away from it completely. At times the rotifer spins out behind it a thread of mucus as it progresses slowly through the water; this thread steadies its course and keeps it connected with its point of departure. The foot and toes are modified in many ways in other groups, as will be seen later.

For controlling motion the rotifer has a nervous system and a number of sense organs. The chief part of the nervous system is a large ganglion known as the brain (*br*), lying on the dorsal side, just above the mastax, at the anterior end. From the brain nerves pass in many directions to the various organs of the body.

Several different kinds of sense organs are found in the rotifers. In some part of the anterior end, usually attached to the brain, there are usually one or two red pigment spots; these are supposed to be organs of light perception, and are known as eye-spots (*e*). In a few cases three or more of these are found. Sometimes the eye-spots are not attached directly to the brain, but are connected with it by nerves (for example, in the genus *Rotifer*). The eye-spots sometimes bear on their anterior surfaces hemispherical crystalline lenses. In some rotifers eye-spots are lacking.

Many rotifers bear sense organs of various kinds on the corona (see for example the corona of *Synchaeta*, Fig. 883, or of *Hydatina*, Fig. 906, *B*). Such sense organs are less common in the Notommatidae than in more specialized rotifers.

Almost all rotifers have a pair of sense organs on the sides of the body behind the middle; these are known as the lateral antennae (Fig. 857, *C*, *la*). Either another antenna, or a pair of them, is found on the dorsal surface of the head, just above the brain; these are known as the dorsal antennae (Figs. 856 and 857, *da*).

The organs of reproduction are still to be considered. Most of the rotifers commonly seen are females, as the males are very minute and rare. In the Notommatidae, as in most other rotifers, there is a single large reproductive body, commonly spoken of as the ovary, or sometimes as the germarium. This lies ventral to the intestine, in the posterior third of the body (Figs. 856 and 857, *ov*). It consists of two portions, of different functions. The large part contains a small number of large nuclei, often just eight; this portion prepares the yolk for the developing egg, so that it is called the vitellarium. At one end or side of this vitellarium is a small mass containing many minute nuclei. From this part the egg develops, the small nuclei becoming each the nucleus of an egg. This part is known as the germarium, since it produces the egg or germ. From the ovary a thin-walled, sac-like passageway, the oviduct, leads backward to the cloaca; by it the egg is discharged. The oviduct can be seen, as a rule, only with great difficulty.

In most rotifers the males are small and degenerate. But in some of the Notommatidae, as well as in a few other species, they are nearly as well developed as the females, and resemble them in structure. In *Proales werneckii* (Fig. 856), which lives within *Vaucheria* filaments, the male is as large as the female, but the alimentary canal is not quite so well developed. In *Rhinops vitrea* (Fig. 863), the male is smaller than the female but not otherwise degenerate, while in the aberrant rotifers known as the Seisonacea males and females are alike, save for the reproductive organs. In most other rotifers the minute males either lack the alimentary canal entirely or have only vestiges of it (see Fig. 864). In all cases in the male in place of the ovary is found a sac, the spermarium (*sp*), in which many spermatozoa are seen swimming about. The sac extends backward as a large tube, ending in a ciliated opening from which the spermatozoa are discharged. That portion of the tube bearing the opening may be protruded as a copulatory organ.

The chief structures of a typical rotifer have now been described, mainly as shown in the Notommatidae. Next, the Rotifera as a whole will be surveyed and the different groups examined rapidly to note how these differ from the notommatids and from one another. Such a survey gives strongly the impression that the other rotifers have been derived by various modifications from rotifers having in general the characteristics of the Notommatidae. Space will not permit setting forth in detail the grounds for this impression, nor will it allow describing the many forms transitional between the Notommatidae and other groups. But in giving an

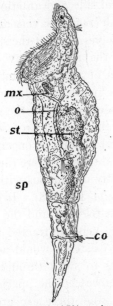

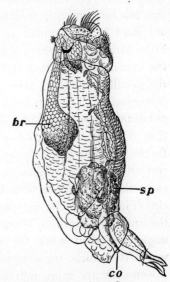

FIG. 863. Male of *Rhinops vitrea*, Hudson, showing presence of the alimentary canal. *co*, copulatory organ; *mx*, mastax; *o*, esophagus; *sp*, spermarium; *st*, stomach. × 400. (After Rousselet.)

FIG. 864. Male of *Copeus pachyurus* Gosse, showing absence of alimentary canal. *br*, brain; *co*, copulatory organ; *sp*, spermarium. × 260. (After Dixon-Nuttall.)

account of the other rotifers, they will be grouped about the Notommatidae in the way which appears to be called for by the facts.[1]

[1] This follows mainly Wesenberg-Lund (1899), who has developed a classification of the Rotifera based on their origin from Notommatoid forms. While this classification has not thus far been commonly employed, the same can be said of any other classification that has been proposed. The writer is convinced that the classification given by Wesenberg-Lund is the only really natural one and that its use is a great aid to an understanding of the Rotifera; he has therefore employed it. It should be noted, however, that the arrangement here given differs in many details from that of Wesenberg-Lund, as the advance of knowledge, or the writer's own experience, seems to require. No scheme of classification can be completely fixed until knowledge of the organisms to be classified is infinitely more complete than is the present knowledge of the Rotifera.

1. *Notommatidae.* It will be helpful first to notice some of the chief variations of type among the Notommatidae themselves. The simplest, most undifferentiated rotifers that exist are those commonly classed in the genus *Proales.* They have small, soft bodies, nearly cylindrical, and obscurely segmented externally (Fig. 856). The foot and toes are short. The corona is a uniformly ciliated, nearly plane surface on the ventral side and anterior end (Fig. 859). These rotifers are small, sluggish creatures, very numerous, but not differing greatly among themselves, so that the species are hard to distinguish and students of the rotifers have paid little attention to them. In other species of the Notommatidae the corona has become differentiated in a peculiar way, forming the so-called auricles; these species are classed mainly in the genus *Notommata.* The auricles are portions of the ciliated area set off prominently on each side of the corona and bearing stronger cilia (Fig. 857, *B*); they serve to enable the animal to move more rapidly. In the simplest cases the auricles are directly continuous with the rest of the ciliated disk, as in *Notommata aurita* (Fig. 878). In other cases there is a space without cilia between the disk and the auricles (Fig. 881). The auricles are commonly kept contracted when the animal is creeping about, so that their existence would not be suspected. But when the animal prepares to swim through the water it unfurls these auricles and sails away. The species of *Notommata* are more active than *Proales,* and there are greater differences among the different members of the genus.

2. *Synchaetidae.* A line of divergence, consisting essentially in a greater development of those characteristics of *Notommata* which give it rapidity of movement, leads to the production of what is commonly classed as a different family, — the Synchaetidae (Fig. 880). In *Synchaeta* the entire corona is very large, occupying the large end of the cone-shaped body, while the auricles are highly developed, forming powerful swimming organs which are set off at a distance from the remainder of the corona. By the aid of these auricles the species of *Synchaeta* dash about with such rapidity that they can hardly be followed with the microscope. (See the monographic study of the Synchaetidae by Rousselet, 1902.)

A further development of this line is seen in *Polyarthra* (Fig. 882). Here powerful swimming organs have developed in the form of appendages along the sides of the body, while the auricles have disappeared. The animal never attaches itself, so that the disappearance of the foot is complete. In *Anarthra* (Fig. 885) we find precisely a *Polyarthra* that has not yet developed the appendages, or that has lost them (?).

Synchaeta and *Polyarthra* are typical open-water rotifers, constituting important elements of the plankton.

To introduce the families of Rotifera next to be considered, it is necessary to return to certain features of the Notommatidae. Many of the species of that family show a very slight tendency to a stiffening of the cuticula, so that the body retains a somewhat definite form, often a little angular. Such notommatids are classed in the genus *Furcularia* (Fig. 870). These are usually more active than *Proales* or *Notommata*, and have longer, stiffer toes. By accentuation of these features of *Furcularia*, and by further specialization, there are formed several families of free-swimming rotifers:

3. *Salpinidae.* The cuticula becomes more hardened, and three or four longitudinal furrows are formed, one in the dorsal middle line, one on each side, and sometimes a weak one in the ventral middle line. Thus there is produced a sort of armor or lorica, composed of three or four plates (Figs. 886, 887). Such loricas are seen in most pronounced form in *Salpina* (Fig. 886). But every possible intermediate gradation exists, leading from *Furcularia* to *Salpina.* The intermediate steps are mostly classed in the genus *Diaschiza* (Fig. 887); here the cuticula is only slightly stiffened, and the longitudinal clefts are little marked. The species of *Diaschiza* are many of them hardly distinguishable from *Furcularia* or even from *Notommata;* they were formerly classed in these two genera. In *Salpina* the lorica is strongly developed and bears long spines or teeth. *Diplois* and *Diplax* stand between *Diaschiza* and *Salpina*, having strong loricas but no teeth. There is thus a continuous series from the Notommatidae to *Salpina*. The Salpinidae are common amid vegetation. (See the Monograph on *Diaschiza* by Dixon-Nuttall and Freeman, 1903.)

4. *Euchlanidae.*   Another line of divergence leads from the Notommatidae, probably likewise through *Furcularia*, to *Distyla*,
Cathypna, *Monostyla*, and *Euchlanis*, — forming the family Euchlanidae.   The first steps in this series are seen in those species of
Distyla in which the body is soft, wrinkled, and only a little flattened (Fig. 890).   In the extended condition these are hardly to be
distinguished from small species of *Furcularia*.   But when retracted there is a tendency to form lateral furrows along the side,
while a sharp edge is seen in front (Fig. 890, *B*).   In other species of
Distyla (Fig. 891) these differentiations are permanent and the cuticula forms an evident lorica, consisting of a dorsal and a ventral plate.
This line of evolution shows its highest development in *Euchlanis*
(Fig. 893).   The Euchlanidae are common among aquatic vegetation.

5. *Coluridae.*   This group resembles the Euchlanidae, but has
probably developed from the Notommatidae separately.   The
hardened cuticula here forms a solid lorica, open at each end for
head and foot; sometimes the cuticula is not hardened on the
ventral surface.   A portion of the lorica extends out over the
head as a sort of hood (Fig. 901).   *Metopidia* (Fig. 901), *Colurus*
(Fig. 900), and *Stephanops* (Fig. 899) are the principal genera; they
are all minute, creeping about among plants and debris.

6. *Rattulidae.*   A fifth line of divergence leads from the Notommatidae to the genera *Diurella* (Fig. 895) and *Rattulus* (Figs. 896, 897).
The cuticula of the nearly cylindrical body becomes hardened over
nearly the entire surface, so as to form a curved, pipe-like structure,
with openings for the protrusion of head and foot.   The less differentiated Rattulidae (*Diurella*, Fig. 895) resemble greatly the lower
Notommatidae, having the cuticula only a little stiffened and toes
differing but little from those of *Furcularia*.   But this line runs into
extremely bizarre forms.   The animals tend to become unsymmetrical, the organs of the right side being smaller, while the body
becomes in some cases twisted into a segment of a spiral.   The
right toe becomes enormously extended to form a long rod-like
structure, while the left toe nearly disappears (Figs. 896, 897).   The
right side of the trophi (Fig. 898) becomes smaller than the left.
The Rattulidae are common among vegetation.   (See the monograph of this family by the present writer (Jennings, 1903).)

7. *Dinocharidae. Scaridium* (Fig. 903) is perhaps essentially a *Furcularia* which has developed a long foot and long toes, for leaping (compare *Furcularia longiseta*, Fig. 871). *Dinocharis* (Fig. 904) and *Polychaetus* (Fig. 905) are perhaps further developments, somewhat divergent, along the same line. All these animals are given to springing about wildly by the aid of powerful strokes of the foot and toes; the same habit is found in various species of *Furcularia*.

Next may be taken up a line of divergence from the central Notommatidae that leads to some extraordinary forms. It produces the great families of the Hydatinidae, the Notopsidae, the Ploesomidae, and the Brachionidae, with their relatives. Here development has proceeded both toward greater strength and activity and toward protective armor, so that the result is to produce some of the most powerful and ferocious rotifers that exist.

8. *Hydatinidae.* The close connection with the Notommatidae is seen in the Hydatinidae. The well-known rotifer *Hydatina senta* (Fig. 906) was formerly classed with the Notommatidae. It has a soft, segmented body, small foot and toes, ventral corona, — all as in the primitive genus *Proales*. But the corona (Fig. 906, *B*) is large and differentiated in a way that is characteristic for the families making up the present group. Around the outer edge of the corona the cilia form a prominent wreath, while about the mouth is another series of cilia so interrupted as to form three groups, one dorsal and two lateral (Fig. 906, *B*). In the region between the outer and inner series of cilia are certain prominences (three in *Hydatina*), on which the cilia have become long, stiff setae, doubtless serving as sense organs. The coronal area between the parts thus far mentioned retains in *Hydatina senta* a portion of the covering of fine cilia primitively found in *Proales;* in most other members of this group these fine cilia have quite disappeared. The jaws are of the peculiar type shown in Figure 906, *C*.

9. *Notopsidae.* The next step in differentiation is seen in *Notops* (or *Hydatina*) *brachionus* (Fig. 909). The cuticula, while still soft, has become a little stiffened, so that the body tends to hold its form; the foot is more prominent.

The next steps seem to be as follows: *Notops clavulatus* (Fig. 912) and *Triphylus lacustris* (Fig. 908) are rotifers showing still the soft body of the Notommatidae, but approaching the definite permanent form found in *Ploesoma*. The corona (Fig. 912, *B*) is much like that of *Hydatina*, save that the fine ciliation of the general surface has disappeared. *Notops pelagicus* (Fig. 910) shows a further step in the same direction; the cuticula is here stiffened to form a thin transparent lorica, of sufficient stiffness to form angles and teeth, though with by no means the thickness and solidity found in *Ploesoma* and *Brachionus*.

From *Notops pelagicus* it is but a short step in one direction to *Gastropus* and *Ploesoma*, in another to *Brachionus*.

10. *Gastropodidae*. The transition from *Notops* to *Gastropus* is shown by *Gastropus hyptopus* (Fig. 915), which was originally considered a species of *Notops*, and which if it stood by itself would still be placed in that genus. The lorica is here soft, the body short and thick. The lorica becomes more marked, and the other peculiarities more pronounced in the other species of *Gastropus*, *Gastropus stylifer* (Fig. 917) forming the extreme in this direction.

11. *Anapodidae*. Probably derived from forms similar to *Gastropus* by a process of reduction are the species of *Anapus* (Fig. 911), in which the foot is lacking, the corona small and simple.

12. *Ploesomidae*. The species of *Ploesoma* (Figs. 918 to 920) are closely related to *Notops* and *Gastropus*. *Ploesoma truncatum* (Fig. 920) shows a lorica only a little stronger than that of *Notops pelagicus*, and resembling that of *Gastropus hyptopus*, though it has many irregular wrinkles. In other species of *Ploesoma* the lorica becomes stronger and marked in very peculiar ways. *Ploesoma lenticulare* (Fig. 918) and *P. hudsoni* (Fig. 919) are among the most active and powerful of the predaceous Rotifera. They tear their way through the water at a furious rate, darting from side to side, and seizing and devouring with their powerful jaws other rotifers with which they come in contact. The Ploesomidae are among the most important plankton organisms.

13. *Brachionidae*. From *Hydatina* and *Notops* to *Brachionus* the step is perhaps still shorter than to *Gastropus* and *Ploesoma*. In *Brachionus* (Figs. 922, 923) the three prominences that surround the mouth in *Hydatina* and *Notops* (see Figs. 906, 910) have become

much developed, so that they stand high above the general surface
of the corona (Fig. 923). They partly enclose a sort of funnel,
open on the ventral side, which leads down to the mouth. In
most species of *Brachionus* the integument has become very thick
and hard, so as to form a stout lorica, often bearing spines or teeth
(Fig. 921). But *Brachionus mollis* Hempel (Fig. 925) marks the
transition in this respect, the integument being merely a little
stiffened and without spines or teeth. In *Brachionus*, as in *Ploesoma*
and *Gastropus*, the stout foot is marked with rings. The jaws are
constructed on much the same plan throughout all these groups.

The Brachionidae are among the most numerous of the rotifers
found in ponds and pools amid vegetation. Some of the species
are extremely variable.

14. *Anuraeidae.* An offshoot of the Brachionidae is found in the
Anuraeidae (Figs. 913, 916). The general organization is the same
as in *Brachionus*, but the foot has been lost, though in the males
(Fig. 913, *C*) it is retained. The lorica shows in some species of
Notholca a tendency to run into bizarre forms (Fig. 916). The
Anuraeidae are among the commonest of the rotifers of the plank-
ton; they vary extremely with seasonal and other changes.

15. *Asplanchnidae.* The group diverging by way of *Hydatina*
is now left, and another offshoot of the Notommatidae taken up.
In the Asplanchnidae the body remains soft, but becomes large and
inflated, while the foot disappears; the jaws are of a remarkable
type known as the incudate (Fig. 929, *B*), and the alimentary canal
loses its posterior opening (see Fig. 929, *A*), the undigested waste
being disgorged through the mouth. But one finds in all these
respects forms transitional between the Notommatidae and the
Asplanchnidae. Thus, *Asplanchnopus* (Fig. 927) retains the foot,
though it lacks the intestine, and has the characteristic jaws of this
family. *Harringia* (Fig. 928) retains not merely the foot, but likewise the intestine. Its corona is like that of *Asplanchna* while its
jaws (Fig. 928, *B*) are squarely intermediate between the usual form
and the incudate type characteristic of *Asplanchna*. The typical
incudate jaws consist mainly of the very large incus (fulcrum and
rami), the mallei having nearly or quite disappeared; but in *Harringia* all the typical parts of the jaws are clearly seen.

The typical Asplanchnas are beasts of prey, the jaws forming a great pair of forceps which can be thrust from the mouth to seize other large animals. *Asplanchna herrickii* de Guerne and *A. priodonta* Gosse (Fig. 929) are important elements of the plankton of lakes. In the Great Lakes they sometimes swarm so densely that a net dipped into the water captures thousands. Other species of the Asplanchnidae live among water plants.

16–18. *Floscularida.* Now come certain groups of rotifers that seem at first view to differ markedly in almost every respect from the notommatids. The Flosculariidae (Figs. 933 to 936) live attached in tubes. The foot has become a stalk for attachment; there are no toes. The corona is immensely large, forming a great lobed net of thin membrane, which can be spread widely and serves to capture living prey; the mouth lies in the center at the bottom of this net. The cilia about the edge of the corona have become enormously long and slender rods or threads, which do not beat as cilia usually do, but may be moved about so as to aid in entangling prey. In connection with the method of feeding on large animals thus captured, the alimentary canal (Fig. 934) has become greatly developed. The upper part of the coronal net forms a great funnel, called the infundibulum (*i*), partly closed off below by a ring-like fold, the diaphragm (*d*), which has about its edge an interrupted circlet of cilia. The opening through the diaphragm leads into a second chamber, the vestibulum (*v*), at the bottom of which is the mouth (*m*). From the mouth there hangs the slender esophageal tube (*o*) ending freely below. The food after passing through this reaches a third large cavity, the proventriculus (*pr*). It is only at the posterior part of this that the mastax (*mx*) and jaws are reached; so that all thus far seen corresponds merely to the short mouth cavity lying in front of the jaws in other rotifers. The trophi (Figs. 934 and 933, *D*) are peculiarly modified, the unci forming a pair of two-tined forks which are the main part of the jaws, though the other typical parts can be distinguished.

The Flosculariidae include two genera, *Floscularia* (Figs. 933 to 936) and *Stephanoceros* (Fig. 937). The numerous species are found abundantly seated in transparent tubes attached to plants; they are among the most attractive objects known to microscopists (cf. p. 553). Of *Stephanoceros* there is but one species (Fig. 937), while of *Floscularia* there are many, varying extremely in the form of the corona. A few species have become free and swim about in the open water (Fig. 935). The fact that they bear their tubes with them shows that the free life has been secondarily acquired, after the animals had become adapted to the attached condition. All young Floscularias swim about for a time by means of moving cilia, just as do other rotifers. The males (Fig. 933, *B*) are free-swimming throughout life.

What relationship have the Flosculariidae to the typical rotifers found in the Notommatidae? It must be remembered that not all Flosculariidae have the extraordinary forms shown in Figs. 933 and 937. In some, the borders of the corona are not drawn out into lobes, but are smooth, as in other rotifers (see Fig. 936). In others the cilia of the coronal edge are all, or partly, short and beat regularly, like those of other rotifers; and about the mouth is the same circlet of cilia found in other rotifers. Such Flosclularias approach much more nearly to the typical Notommatidae than do the extreme developments along this line seen in *Stephanoceros* and certain species of *Floscularia*.

Furthermore, among close relatives of the notommatids are certain rotifers that seem to show transitional stages leading to the Flosculariidae.[1] In *Microcodides* and in *Microcodon* (Fig. 931), the corona is formed on essentially the same plan as in the Flosclularias, and there are other peculiarities that seem to show that these are transitional forms. In *Microcodon*, as in *Floscularia*, the corona is the broadest part of the body; it has elevated edges, approaching the net formation, and the mouth is in its center, with an interrupted circlet of cilia about it. The foot in *Microcodon* as in *Floscularia* forms a sort of long slender stalk, not ending in toes. But in *Microcodon* it ends in a sharp point, while in *Floscularia* it ends in a disk; this is doubtless because the former is still a free animal, while the latter is attached. It is a most suggestive fact that *Microcodon* frequently places itself in the upright position, with the toe attached by a thread of mucus, and thus remains for a time in a certain spot; such habits might readily lead to permanent attachment.

[1] These important considerations are due to Wesenberg-Lund (1899).

All together, *Microcodon* seems to form a link between the Flosculariidae and the Notommatidae. *Microcodon* itself is closely connected with the Notommatidae by the transitional species belonging to the genus *Microcodides* (Fig. 932). These have corona, body, and toes more nearly on the notommatoid plan. The two genera make up the family Microcodonidae.

Specialization going even beyond that in the Flosculariidae is seen in *Apsilus* (Fig. 938) and *Atrochus* (Fig. 939). In these extraordinary rotifers the cilia have been completely lost. The complicated structure of the alimentary canal shows their close relationship to the Flosculariidae. In the young the cilia still exist, and the animals swim about by their aid.

19-22. *Melicertida*. Another group of extraordinary and attractive rotifers is that of which *Melicerta* (Fig. 948) is the representative. These were formerly classified with the Flosculariidae, the two forming the group Rhizota. But it is evident that the two families differ widely, and that the group Rhizota is not a natural one. The Melicertidae are found, like the floscules, attached to aquatic plants, often in great numbers. Many live in tubes, and the species of *Melicerta* manufacture their tubes in a most interesting manner, as is well described in Hudson and Gosse (1889).

The most important peculiarity of the Melicertidae is perhaps the corona. This is a large disk, bare within, but having around its outer edge a series of strong cilia, just as in many other rotifers. But in this group is found a special peculiarity. This outer wreath is differentiated into two series of cilia, running parallel around the disk (Fig. 865). The inner series has much larger cilia than the outer one, and between the two is found, in most cases, a groove. This groove is often lined with fine cilia. Along the groove small food particles are carried to the mouth, situated on the ventral side. In some genera the disk is drawn out to form two, four, or eight lobes, giving the animal an extraordinary appearance (Fig. 950); in other cases it is nearly circular (Figs. 865, 951, 952). Throughout this group the jaws are of a peculiar type (Fig. 866), known as the malleo-ramate. As a rule the animals have two eyes.

The more extreme types of this group seem to stand far from

the typical free-swimming rotifers. Yet again, as in most other cases, free-swimming species form a transition to these extreme types. One finds the same peculiar corona, the same remarkable type of jaws, and various other features in common with the Melicertidae, in a number of free-swimming rotifers. These include the genera *Pterodina* (Fig. 942), *Pompholyx*, *Pedalion* (Fig. 946),

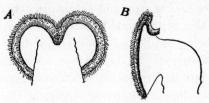

FIG. 865.　Corona of *Lacinularia socialis* Ehr., to show the two wreaths of cilia.　*A*, Dorsal view.
B, Side view.　(After Wesenberg-Lund.)

Triarthra (Fig. 944), and *Tetramastix* (Fig. 945). These rotifers are the only ones that have corona and jaws like those of the Melicertidae, and they agree with them in many other particulars. Thus, all have two eyes, while most other rotifers have but one. In all there is either no foot, or it is a peculiar one, lacking the characteristic toes. In *Pterodina* the foot ends in a bundle of cilia, and this is likewise true of the young of the Melicertidae. In

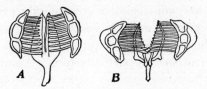

FIG. 866.　Malleo-ramate jaws.　*A*, Jaws of *Melicerta ringens* Schrank.　(After Weber.)　*B*, Jaws
of *Pterodina caeca* Parsons.　(After Rousselet.)

many Melicertidae there is below the mouth a peculiar fold of integument forming the so-called "chin" which plays a part in the formation of the pellets used for building the tubes. This chin is likewise found, in a slightly less developed condition, in *Pedalion* (Fig. 946, *ch*) and in *Triarthra*, while nothing of the sort is found outside the present group. The remarkable similarity of corona, jaws, eyes, and other features seems to demonstrate clearly that all these free-swimming rotifers are closely related to each other and to the Melicertidae.

The free-swimming members of the group have developed a number of striking external peculiarities, due to differences in the mode of life. *Pterodina* (Fig. 942) has a flat body, protected by a hard cuticula forming a lorica; this shape aids it greatly in swimming. *Pedalion* (Fig. 946) has developed six great limbs which likewise aid it in swimming. Similar limbs, but in a simpler condition, are seen in *Triarthra* (Fig. 944) and *Tetramastix* (Fig. 945). In these genera the function of the limbs seems to be mainly to protect the animals from being swallowed by such predatory beasts as *Asplanchna*. One often sees an *Asplanchna* attempt to swallow one of these at a gulp, but the prey at once extends its long appendages in all directions, and these frustrate the attempt. The male of *Pedalion* (Fig. 946, *B*) has simple appendages and bears a striking resemblance to one of the simpler species of *Triarthra* (Fig. 944, *B*).

An extraordinary offshoot of the Meticertidae is seen in the spherical rotifer *Trochosphaera* (Fig. 947). In the corona, the jaws, the lack of a foot, and various other features it agrees essentially with the Melicertidae, though its external form is very different.

23–25. *Bdelloida*. This, the last group of rotifers, includes mainly the genera *Rotifer* (Figs. 958, 960), *Philodina* (Fig. 959), *Callidina* (Fig. 961), *Microdina* (Fig. 962), and *Adineta* (Fig. 957). They are somewhat worm-like animals, often creeping like leeches, and found in great numbers amid aquatic vegetation. They are specially abundant in *Sphagnum* and other wet moss or moss-like plants; an immense number of species particularly of *Callidina* are found in such places.

This group differs widely from the typical rotifers in many points. The typical corona of the Bdelloida is a highly differentiated structure consisting mainly of two flat disks borne on stalks and with cilia about their edges (Fig. 959, etc.). When the cilia are in motion these two disks give the appearance of two revolving wheels. It is to this that the name wheel-animalcule, and the Latin terms *rotifer* and *rotator* are due; the Bdelloida were the first rotifers to attract the attention of microscopists. The base of the stalks bearing the disks is often clothed with short cilia. On the dorsal side of the corona there is a long tentacle.

The foot ends as a rule in three or four minute projections, by which the animals attach themselves; it bears also a pair of "spurs" on its dorsal side, a short distance from the end. These spurs perhaps represent the two toes of other rotifers.

The trophi (Fig. 867) present perhaps the most modified type found in the Rotifera; they show clearly that this group is not a primitive one. In most species the trophi are represented by two pieces shaped like a quarter of a sphere and placed side by side (Fig. 867, *A*). Across the free surface of these pieces extend two or more ridges. These jaws may be opened and closed by the muscular mass in which they are imbedded, the ridges fitting together in such a way as to serve as grinding teeth. The two halves of the

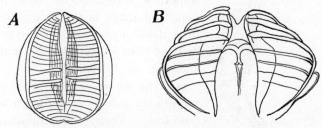

FIG. 867. Jaws of Bdelloida. *A*, Jaws of *Philodina brycei* Weber (typical ramate jaws). *B*, Jaws of *Microdina paradoxa* Murray. (After Murray.)

trophi represent the two rami of other rotifers, the remainder of the apparatus having almost completely disappeared. But transitional forms (Fig. 867, *B*) show clearly how these trophi are derived from the typical structure.

The point in which the Bdelloida differ most from other rotifers is in the fact that they have two ovaries in place of one. This peculiarity is shared with the Bdelloida only by a bizarre group of parasitic marine rotifers, the Seisonacea (Fig. 868) which live attached to the marine crustacean *Nebalia*. On account of this peculiarity the Bdelloida and Seisonacea are commonly classed apart from all other rotifers as the Digononta, the others being called the Monogononta.

The Bdelloida include an immense number of species, the greater part of them belonging to the genus *Callidina*. The difference between species is often only slight, and the animals change form almost continually, so that their systematic study is perhaps more difficult than that of any other group of rotifers; it has been confined mainly to specialists in this particular group.

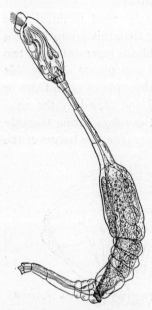

Many species of the Bdelloida possess a remarkable power of withstanding drying. *Philodina roseola* is often found as little pink balls in the dry deposits in the bottoms of urns and eave-troughs. When this material is placed in water, the pink balls quickly swell, take the rotifer form, and continue their interrupted life activities where these were stopped. Many species may be obtained for study in the living condition from dried moss and other vegetation brought from a distance. No males are known in the Bdelloida.

26. The *Seisonacea* (Fig. 868) are extraordinary rotifers parasitic on marine crustacea. Their relationships are uncertain, but, having two ovaries, they are usually placed near the Bdelloida. In the Seisonacea male and female are

Fig. 868. *Seison annulatus* Claus, female. (After Claus.)

similar and of equal size. Since they are exclusively marine, these forms are omitted from the synoptic key.

The studies thus far made of the rotifers of different regions seem to indicate that in general these animals may be said to be potentially cosmopolitan, any given species occurring wherever the conditions necessary to its existence occur. Whether any given rotifer shall be found in a given body of water depends mainly, not upon the locality of this body of water, but upon the precise conditions there found. Studies on the rotifers of Europe, Asia, Africa, America, and Australia show, not different faunas in these regions, but the same common rotifers found everywhere, with merely a new form here and there, and it is an extraordinary fact that when a new rotifer is described from Africa or Australia, its next occurrence is often recorded from Europe or America. In stagnant swamps all over the world appear to be found the characteristic rotifers of stagnant water; in clear lake water are found the characteristic limnetic rotifers; in sphagnum swamps everywhere, the sphagnum rotifers. Variation in the rotifer fauna of different countries is probably due mainly to differences in the conditions of existence in the waters of these countries, rather than to any difficulty in passing from one country to another. The number of different sorts of Rotifera to be found in any given region depends upon the variety of conditions to be found in the waters of this region. Two bodies of water half a mile apart, presenting entirely different conditions, are likely to vary more in their rotifer fauna than two bodies of water 5000 miles apart that present similar conditions. Of course, the tropics will have characteristic species not found in cooler regions, since they present conditions of existence not found elsewhere, and the same may be true of Arctic regions. The problem of the distribution of the Rotifera is then mainly a problem of the conditions of existence rather than of the means of distribution. The ability of the eggs to live in dried mud, which may be carried about on the feet of birds or blown about as dust by the winds, seems to give sufficient opportunities for any species to multiply wherever occur the conditions necessary for existence. Most rotifers seem adapted to a rather narrowly limited set of conditions.

Many species of rotifers vary extremely in the external details of their structure. This is particularly true of loricate rotifers that bear teeth, spines, or other projections. Extreme examples of such variation are seen in *Brachionus bakeri* Ehr. and in *Anuraea cochlearis* Gosse (Fig. 913). Lauterborn shows that the variations of *Anuraea cochlearis* are by no means haphazard, but depend upon the seasons and upon changes in the conditions of existence. In the course of a year this species undergoes a cycle of regular changes from month to month, and this yearly cycle was found to be essentially the same during a period of study of twelve years. In the colder months of the year appear individuals of greater size, with smooth loricas and long prominent spines. As the waters become warmer, in spring and summer, the individuals found are smaller in size, the surface of the lorica becomes roughened, and the spines grow shorter, until the caudal one disappears completely. As cold weather approaches there is a return to the stouter forms. There results an immense number of different forms, many of which have been described as different species. Apparently these changes are adaptive in character. At the higher temperatures of summer the inner friction of the water decreases much (as Ostwald has shown), so that swimming animals tend to sink more readily than before. The decrease in size of the body, with the roughening of its surface, increases greatly the proportion of body surface to body weight, so that the animals sink less readily; the tendency to sink due to the warmth of the water is compensated. The small, rough forms are therefore adapted to warm weather. But the decrease in size of the spines cannot be accounted for in this way; it must depend on other relations.

In the Rotifera the males are usually minute, degenerate creatures, — the race being represented mainly by the females! The males usually have no alimentary canal, and thus during their entire life they never take food. They are, of course, therefore, condemned to an early death. They usually swim about rapidly, often swarming about the females. Fecundation takes place in some cases by the insertion of the copulatory organ of the male into the cloaca of the female; this has been seen in many cases. In other cases apparently the male pierces the body wall of the female, injecting the spermatozoa directly into the body cavity. This takes place in *Hydatina*.

In a few of the Rotifera the males are of the same size and structure as the females (in the Seisonacea). In *Proales werneckii* the male is of the same size and form as the female, but the alimentary canal, while present, is simplified and reduced in size. In other species, various vestiges of the alimentary canal may be present, but they are not functional. In certain groups no male is known to exist; this is true for the entire suborder of the Bdelloida. In the Rattulidae likewise no males have as yet been seen. Much further study of the existence, structure, and activities of the males is needed. If they are actually non-existent in some groups, then of course the reproduction is throughout by parthenogenesis, — fertilization of the egg not occurring even at long intervals.

Most rotifers produce several different sorts of eggs. These are

the following: (1) large eggs, without a thick shell, from which
females are produced; (2) small eggs, similar to the last in appearance but producing males; (3) eggs which have a thick shell,
often armed with spines or projections. These are often spoken
of as "winter eggs" or "resting eggs." They may apparently
live a long time under all sorts of unfavorable conditions, developing when favorable conditions are restored. The relation of
these different sorts of eggs to the appearance of the males, and to
fertilization, has been much discussed and investigated. In *Hydatina*, according to Maupas, and in *Asplanchna priodonta*, according
to Lauterborn, the following is the state of the case. There are
two sorts of females, not distinguishable externally, but one producing large eggs, the others small ones. The large eggs cannot be
fertilized, and they always develop into female rotifers. The small
eggs, if not fertilized, develop into male rotifers, but they may be
fertilized, and if this occurs they become transformed into the
"resting eggs," from which there later develop female rotifers.
In *Hydatina*, according to Maupas, fecundation can occur only
when the female is young, before any of the eggs develop, and the
female so fecundated produces only resting eggs. But in *Asplanchna* and in various other rotifers the same female produces
both male eggs and resting eggs, although only the latter are
fertilized. According to Mrazek, in *Asplanchna herrickii* the same
female bears at the same time ordinary female eggs, male eggs, and
resting eggs. There is apparently much variation in these relations among different rotifers.

Males and resting eggs are as a rule not found at all times of
the year, but appear at certain periods, — the resting eggs of
course following the appearance of males. In the pelagic Rotifera,
Lauterborn has made a study of the periodical appearance of males
and of resting eggs. He finds that these rotifers may be divided
into three classes: (1) perennial rotifers, which occur in greater
or less numbers all the year round; (2) summer species, found
only in summer; (3) winter species, found only in winter. In the
perennial species parthenogenetic reproduction continues throughout the year; but males appear as a rule only twice a year, in
spring and fall. In the summer rotifers, males appear in the fall,

and the species is carried over the winter in the resting eggs resulting from fertilization by the males. In the winter rotifers, the
males appear in the spring, and the species is carried over the summer by the resting eggs.

By the greater number of rotifers the eggs are laid as soon as
they are completely formed, development taking place outside the
body of the mother. But some rotifers are viviparous, the egg
being retained in the mother's body until it is partly or completely
developed. It is remarkable that the viviparous condition is found
in several different groups of rotifers that are not closely related,
so that it must have been developed independently several times
within the Rotifera. *Asplanchna* and *Rotifer* are among the best-
known viviparous genera. *Philodina* and *Callidina*, closely related
to *Rotifer*, as a rule deposit the eggs undeveloped, though certain
species in both these genera produce living young. Thus ovi-

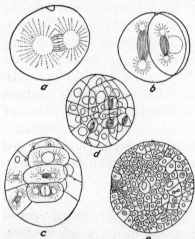

parity and viviparity, which in
some higher animals distinguish
grand classes, are among the
rotifers both found in the limits
of a single genus.

It is a rather remarkable fact
that the cleavage and early development of the rotifer egg does
not resemble that of the animals
to which the rotifers have often
been considered the nearest relatives. In annelids and lower
mollusks the early development
shows a remarkable similarity
even in the details of the spiral
cleavage. But in the rotifers
the cleavage follows a completely

Fig. 869. Developing egg of a rotifer. *Asplanchna
herrickii* de Guerne.   *a*, Single cell stage; *b*, four
cells; *c*, twenty cells; *d*, ninety-four cells; *e*, optical
section through embryo formed of many cells.
(After Jennings.)

different type (Fig. 869). The developing rotifer forms a solid mass,
which contains no cavity until the organs formed within this mass
begin to separate, just before the rotifer takes its final form and
becomes active.

When living the body of the Rotifera is usually transparent and all the organs are sharply defined, so that they are readily seen. After death, the transparency and sharpness are as a rule lost, and most methods of killing the rotifers cause them to become strongly contracted, so that the structure is no longer clear. Direct observation of the living animal will therefore always remain one of the most important methods of studying these forms, for whatever purpose.

By Rousselet's method, however, it is now as easy to preserve most of the Rotifera in natural form as any other lower animals. This method is essentially as follows: The animals are killed uncontracted by the aid of a narcotizing fluid, the essential feature of which is a $\frac{1}{4}$ to 1 per cent solution of hydrochlorate of cocaine. The cocaine may be used in a simple watery solution, but better results are reached by using the following mixture:

Hydrochlorate of cocaine (2 per cent solution).. 3 parts
Methyl alcohol............................. 1 part
Water.................................... 6 parts

The rotifers are brought into a small volume of water, and a little of this narcotizing fluid is mixed with it. The proper amount must be learned by trial, but it is always best to begin with a very small proportion of the fluid, $\frac{1}{10}$ or less, and to add more as required. This fluid causes the rotifers to swim slowly and gradually to sink to the bottom. They will soon die, and if allowed to die unfixed will be quite worthless for study, destructive changes taking place in the tissues at the moment of death. As soon therefore as the ciliary movement has nearly ceased, as much as possible of the water should be drawn off, and a small amount of 0.25 per cent osmic acid introduced, which kills and fixes the rotifers at once. Now the osmic acid should be drawn off at once and water added or the rotifers removed with a capillary pipette to fresh water; they should be washed several times in distilled water. If the osmic acid is allowed to act too long the rotifers will be blackened. The blackening may, however, be later removed, if necessary, with hydrogen peroxide. After washing, the rotifers should be preserved in 3 to 6 per cent formalin. They cannot as a rule be preserved in alcohol without extensive shrinkage, rendering them useless for further study.

If desired, the specimens may be permanently mounted in hollow ground slides. The slides should be thin and the concavities shallow, so that high powers of the microscope may be used. The specimens are transferred to the concavities along with some of the formalin and covered with a circular cover-glass. It is best not to leave any bubbles of air beneath the cover. The superfluous formalin may be withdrawn from the edge of the cover with a bit of filter paper, and the cover is then sealed by the aid of a revolving stage. It is, of course, necessary to use some sealing material that will not allow water to evaporate through it. Rousselet recommends the following for sealing the mounts: After fixing the cover with a layer composed of a mixture of two-thirds gum damar with one-third gold size, there are added two coats of pure shellac, followed by three or four coats of gold size, allowing twenty-four hours for each coat to dry before another is added.

Extensive collections containing many species of Rotifera may be made by travelers and others by the use of the method given above. The rotifers, taken with a net or otherwise, are brought into as small an amount of water as possible, in a watch-glass. Then a considerable quantity of the narcotizing fluid is introduced and the rotifers are watched till most of them have sunk to the bottom. Thereupon the water is removed, so far as possible, and the $\frac{1}{4}$ per cent osmic acid added. This is removed as quickly as can be done without taking up too many of the rotifers; they are then washed and preserved in formalin. It is very desirable to kill a certain proportion of every collection in osmic acid without previous narcotization, as some of the loricate rotifers are more easily determined from contracted specimens than from extended ones.

A method of mounting Rotifera in the ordinary mounting media, such as Canada balsam, has been given by Zograf. It does not give such perfect results, in most cases, as does Rousselet's method, but it is useful for some species. The rotifers are stupefied and killed in the way given above. After they have been in the osmic acid from two to four minutes, this is removed as far as possible, and a considerable quantity of 10 per cent pyroligneous acid is added. This is allowed to act five or ten minutes; then the rotifers are washed several times in distilled water. As a result of the hardening action of the pyroligneous acid, they may now be passed, like other objects, through successively stronger grades of alcohol till absolute alcohol is reached. They may then be cleared in clove or cedar oil, in the usual way, and mounted in Canada balsam, or gum damar, or they may be mounted in glycerine.

In America the systematic work on the Rotifera has consisted largely in the publication of lists of species found in certain regions. While this work undoubtedly has its uses, there are other lines of study which would at the present time be of much greater value even for purely systematic purposes. On account of the very large number of species of Rotifera, their minuteness, and the unsatisfactory work that has been done upon them, it is often almost impossible to determine with certainty even common species. This can best be remedied by studying carefully circumscribed groups, such as single genera and families, collecting them extensively, describing and figuring all the species, and going critically over the literature of the group in such a way as to set the synonymy in order.

Careful comparative studies of certain organs or sets of organs, such as the corona, the trophi, etc., throughout varied groups, would help much in understanding the interrelationships of the Rotifera. If possible a study of the habits should be made in their relation with the structures, since these matters are closely connected. Monographic anatomical studies of certain species are always of value. They would be especially useful if a thorough study of the habit and physiology could be made at the same time.

A most important field, and one little cultivated, lies in the study of the activities by which the rotifers respond to their environment. Thorough studies of the movements and habits, the reactions to stimuli, "tropisms," and the like, would be of great interest. Disconnected observations on these matters are of comparatively little value; definite problems should be taken up and followed to the end.

The variations induced in a single species, and in an entire fauna, by changes in seasons, temperatures, and in other features, have received some study and deserve much more. One of the most interesting lines of work for which the rotifers present opportunity lies in the study of the various problems connected with reproduction and the diversity of the sexes. Few groups of organisms present conditions so favorable for the study of these fundamental matters.

The relationships of the Rotifera to other groups, and their interrelationships among themselves are subjects which have been much discussed and on which there is wide divergence of opinion. As a result, the classification of the group differs greatly with different authors. The classification perhaps most commonly employed is that given in Hudson and Gosse's Monograph of the Rotifera. Wesenberg-Lund's classification, based on that view of the interrelationships of the Rotifera set forth in the foregoing paper, has been little used; yet it appears to be that to which a careful and unprejudiced study of the members of the group leads. Most earlier classifications have found their guiding principles in matters quite extraneous to the Rotifera as such. Led by theoretical considerations, the primitive rotifers have been looked for among highly specialized species. Huxley compared the two ciliary wreaths of *Lacinularia* to the two wreaths of certain larvae of other groups, — of echinoderms, annelids, and the like, — thus indicating a possible close relationship between them. This suggestion was eagerly followed up, and the primitive organization of the Rotifera has been sought in such highly differentiated, untypical forms as the Melicertidae, the Philodinidae, and the like. Even that bizarre side-shoot of one of the most highly specialized families, *Trochosphaera* (Fig. 947), has been considered a primitive rotifer of special significance, from its superficial resemblance to the trochophore larvae of annelids, etc. Less popular, but still enjoying considerable repute, have been the theories which held that such forms as *Pedalion* (Fig. 946) show a close relationship of the Rotifera with the larvae of Crustacea. Careful comparative study of the Rotifera themselves seems to show clearly that *Lacinularia* and the Melicertidae, *Trochosphaera* and *Pedalion* are alike terminal twigs of the rotatorian tree — highly specialized forms, whose origin is to be sought in such rotifers as the primitive Notommatidae.

Note. — For recent changes in the names of many rotifers, in accordance with the strict rules of priority, the paper of Harring ('13) should be consulted.

KEY TO NORTH AMERICAN FRESH-WATER ROTATORIA

1 (138) One ovary. Do not creep like a leech.

Subclass **Monogononta** . . 2

This subclass includes all the rotifers commonly met, save the Bdelloida (q.v.), which are distinguishable by their habit of creeping like leeches.

2 (109) Corona of various types. Where there are two wreaths of cilia, those of outer wreath never shorter than those of inner. . . . 3

3 (97) Mouth not near center of corona. . . . Order **Notommatida** . . 4

Free-swimming or creeping rotifers, but never creeping like a leech; corona ventral or terminal, consisting of a disk which is either uniformly ciliate or has a wreath of cilia about its circumference with usually two or more groups of cilia close to the mouth, or shows some intermediate condition. Where there are two wreaths of cilia, the outer is never shorter than the inner. Mouth not in the center of the disk. Jaws never ramate (Fig. 867, A) nor malleoramate (Fig. 866). Foot usually ending in two toes placed side by side; rarely ending in one; sometimes absent; never forming a disk for attachment nor ending in a bunch of cilia. Lorica present or absent.

4 (90) Jaws not incudate. Intestine and anus present. 5

5 (31, 64) Without lorica. Corona when as broad as other parts of the body, not consisting of an outer wreath, a partial wreath about the mouth and styligerous prominences between.

Suborder **Notommatina** . . 6

Body usually soft and somewhat segmented. (See also family HYDATINIDAE, 66.)

6 (26) Corona without long antenna-like bristles and setigerous prominences. Foot present. . . . . . Family NOTOMMATIDAE . . 7

Soft-bodied rotifers, usually elongated, cuticula more or less distinctly segmented; foot not distinctly marked off from the remainder of the body, usually short and ending in two toes placed side by side, or rarely but one toe. Corona usually not so wide as the remainder of the body. Living mainly amid vegetation of the shores and bottom.

This family cannot be sharply marked off from others; see particularly Hydatinidae. The genera of the Notommatidae are likewise not sharply definable; they are merely more or less convenient subdivisions of a group that would be too unwieldy if taken as a unit.

7 (19) Without auricles. 8

N.B. Auricles are often contracted and are then invisible.

8 (16) With one or more eyes. 9

9 (12, 15) With a single eye only. 10

FIG. 870. *Furcularia forficula* Ehr. ✕ 300. (After Weber.)

FIG. 871. *Furcularia longiseta* Ehr. ✕ 400. (After Dixon-Nuttall.)

FIG. 872. *Diglena rostrata* Dixon-Nuttall. ✕ 320. (After Dixon-Nuttall.)

FIG. 873. *Distemma setigerum* Ehrenberg. ✕ 166. (After Ehrenberg.)

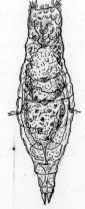

FIG. 874. *Triophthalmus dorsualis* Ehrenberg. ✕ 80. (After Ehrenberg.)

FIG. 875. *Albertia intrusor* Gosse. ✕ 135. (After Gosse.)

FIG. 876. *Pleurotrocha grandis* Western. ✕ 125. (After Dixon-Nuttall.)

FIG. 877. *Taphrocampa annulosa* Gosse. ✕ 14. (After Weber.)

10 (11)   Eye in neck region. . . . . *Proales* Gosse.
Small, slow-moving, soft-bodied species, with partly ventral corona.   Many species.
Representative species(Fig. 856, page 555). *Proales werneckii* Ehrenberg.
(Fig. 858, page 557). . . . *P. sordida* Gosse.
(Fig. 859, page 558). . . . *P. tigrida* Gosse.

11 (10)   Eye near front . . . . *Furcularia* Ehrenberg.
Cuticula a little stiffer, so that the form is retained; shape at times a little prismatic; toes longer and stiffer than in *Proales;* active.   Species numerous.
Representative species (Fig. 870). . *Furcularia forficula* Ehrenberg.
(Fig. 871). . . . . . *F. longiseta* Ehrenberg.

12 (9, 15)   With two eyes. 13

13 (14)   Eyes near front. . . . . *Diglena* Ehrenberg.
Strong predacious species with forcipate jaws; toes usually large.   One or two species.
Representative species (Fig. 872). . *Diglena rostrata* Dixon-Nuttall.
(Fig. 860, *B*, page 559). . *D. forcipata* Ehrenberg.

14 (13)   Eyes in neck. . . . . *Distemma* Ehrenberg.
Representative species (Fig. 873). . *Distemma setigerum* Ehrenberg.

15 (9, 12)   With three eyes in a transverse row. . *Triophthalmus* Ehrenberg.
One species only (Fig. 874). . . . . . . *Triophthalmus dorsualis*.

16 (8)   Without eyes. 17

17 (18)   Internal parasites. . . . . *Albertia* Dujardin.
Few species.
Representative species (Fig. 875). . . . . . *Albertia intrusor* Gosse.

18 (17)   Free, or external parasites. . . . . *Pleurotrocha* Ehrenberg.
Few species.
Representative species (Fig. 876). . . *Pleurotrocha grandis* Western.

19 (7)   With auricles. 20
N.B.   Auricles invisible when contracted.

20 (25)   With one eye. 21

21 (24)   Smaller, soft-bodied forms. 22

22 (23)   Cuticula with many transverse folds. . . . . *Taphrocampa* Gosse.
Representative species (Fig. 877). . *Taphrocampa annulosa* Gosse.

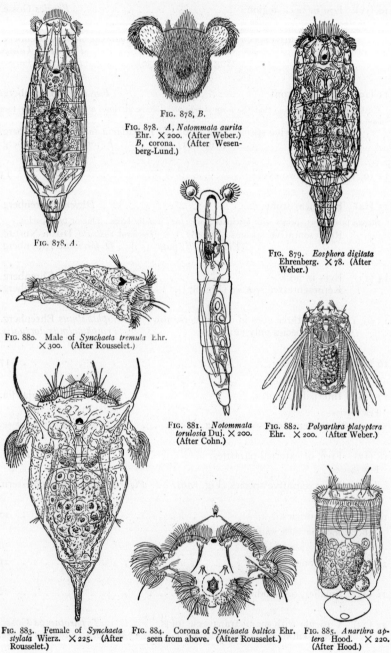

Fig. 878, B.

Fig. 878. *A, Notommata aurita*
Ehr. × 200. (After Weber.)
B, corona. (After Wesen-
berg-Lund.)

Fig. 878, *A*.

Fig. 879. *Eosphora digitata*
Ehrenberg. × 78. (After
Weber.)

Fig. 880. Male of *Synchaeta tremula* Ehr.
× 300. (After Rousselet.)

Fig. 881. *Notommata*
torulosia Duj. × 200.
(After Cohn.)

Fig. 882. *Polyarthra platyptera*
Ehr. × 200. (After Weber.)

Fig. 883. Female of *Synchaeta*
stylata Wierz. × 225. (After
Rousselet.)

Fig. 884. Corona of *Synchaeta baltica* Ehr.
seen from above. (After Rousselet.)

Fig. 885. *Anarthra ap-*
tera Hood. × 220.
(After Hood.)

23 (22) Cuticula without many transverse folds. . *Notommata* Ehrenberg.

Many species.

> Representative species (Fig. 878). . . *Notommata aurita* Ehrenberg.
> (Fig. 881). . . . . . *N. torulosia* Dujardin.
> (Fig. 857, *A* and *B*, page 556).
> *N. truncata* Jennings.

24 (21) Very large, thick-bodied forms. . . . . *Copeus* Gosse.

Corona extending far on ventral surface. Few species.

> Representative species (Fig. 857, *C*, page 556, and Fig. 864, page 565).
> *Copeus pachyurus* Gosse.

25 (20) With three eyes. . . . . *Eosphora* Ehrenberg.

One large eye on brain; others small, in front. Few species.

> Representative species (Fig. 879). . . *Eosphora digitata* Ehrenberg.

26 (6) Two or four long bristle-like antennae on corona. Foot present or
absent. . . . . Family SYNCHAETIDAE . . 27

Open-water rotifers; bodies short; foot short or absent; corona as broad as the broadest
part of the body, consisting mainly of a row of large cilia about the circumference.

27 (28) Auricles present. . . . . *Synchaeta* Ehrenberg.

Body usually conical, largest at the head; foot short, rarely absent. About a dozen species.

> Representative species (Fig. 883). . . *Synchaeta stylata* Wierzejski.
> (Fig. 880). . . . . . *S. tremula* Ehrenberg.
> (Fig. 884). . . . . . *S. baltica* Ehrenberg.

28 (27) Auricles absent. No foot. 29

29 (30) With lateral oar-like swimming appendages. . *Polyarthra* Ehrenberg.
One species only (Fig. 882). . . . *Polyarthra platyptera* Ehrenberg.

30 (29) Appendages lacking. . . . . *Anarthra* Hood.
One species only (Fig. 885). . . . . *Anarthra aptera* Hood.

31 (5, 64) Lorica always present. Corona small, not so broad, as a rule, as
the broadest part of the lorica. Suborder **Loricatina** . . 32

Foot present, short, not ringed; ending in two toes, or rarely one.

32 (47) Lorica divided into plates by longitudinal furrows. 33

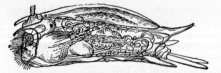

Fig. 886. *Salpina spinigera* Ehr. × 200.
(After Weber.)

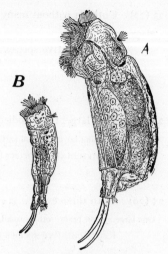

Fig. 887. *Diaschiza hoodii* Gosse.
A, Female. *B*, Male. × 300.
(After Dixon-Nuttall and Free-
man.)

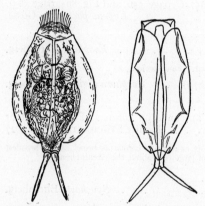

Fig. 888. *Diplois daviesiae* Fig. 889. *Diplax videns*
Gosse. × 87. (After Levander. × 267. (After
Weber.) Lucks.)

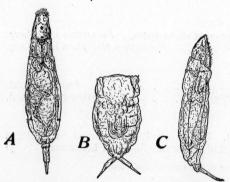

Fig. 890. *Distyla inermis* Bryce. *A*, Dorsal view; *B*, contracted; *C*, side view. × 225. (After Dixon-Nuttall.)

Fig. 891. *Distyla ohioensis* Herrick.
× 420. (After Jennings.)

33 (40) Lorica of three or four plates. Furrows are one mid-dorsal, two lateral; sometimes one mid-ventral.

Family SALPINIDAE . . 34

34 (35) Lorica with teeth or spines in front, or behind, or both.

Salpina Ehrenberg.

Representative species (Fig. 886). . . *Salpina spinigera* Ehrenberg.

35 (34) Lorica without teeth or spines. 36

36 (39) One eye present. 37

37 (38) Lorica not strongly marked, the furrows and plates noticeable only on close examination. . . . . *Diaschiza* Gosse.

Representative species (Fig. 887). . . . . *Diaschiza hoodii* Gosse.

38 (37) Lorica distinct and strong. . . . . *Diplois* Gosse.

Two species.

Representative species (Fig. 888). . . . . *Diplois daviesiae* Gosse.

39 (36) No eye; lorica distinct. . . . . *Diplax* Gosse.

Representative species (Fig. 889). . . . . *Diplax videns* Levander.

40 (33) Lorica of two plates. Furrows lateral. Family EUCHLANIDAE. . 41

One plate dorsal, the other ventral.

41 (46) Two toes. 42

42 (45) The two plates connected by a membrane which folds into the lateral furrow. 43

Small species, not specially clear, lorica often marked in various ways.

43 (44) Lorica narrower. . . . . *Distyla* Eckstein.

Many species.

Representative species (Fig. 890). . . . . . *Distyla inermis* Bryce.

Representative species (Fig. 891). . . . . . *D. ohioensis* Herrick.

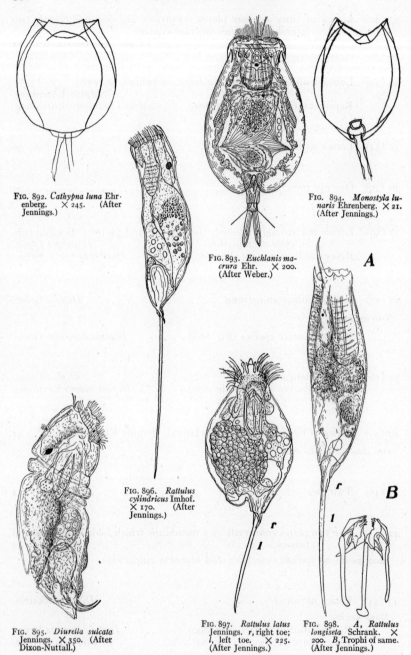

FIG. 892. *Cathypna luna* Ehrenberg. × 245. (After Jennings.)

FIG. 893. *Euchlanis macrura* Ehr. × 200. (After Weber.)

FIG. 894. *Monostyla lunaris* Ehrenberg. × 21. (After Jennings.)

FIG. 895. *Diurella sulcata* Jennings. × 350. (After Dixon-Nuttall.)

FIG. 896. *Rattulus cylindricus* Imhof. × 170. (After Jennings.)

FIG. 897. *Rattulus latus* Jennings. *r*, right toe; *l*, left toe. × 225. (After Jennings.)

FIG. 898. A, *Rattulus longiseta* Schrank. × 200. B, Trophi of same. (After Jennings.)

44 (43) Lorica broader. . . . . *Cathypna* Gosse.
Several species.
Representative species (Fig. 892). . . . *Cathypna luna* Ehrenberg.

45 (42) The two plates not connected by membrane. . *Euchlanis* Ehrenberg.
Large, conspicuous, clear species; lorica not sculptured or otherwise marked. Many species.
Representative species (Fig. 893). . *Enchlanis macrura* Ehrenberg.

46 (41) One toe. . . . . *Monostyla* Ehrenberg.
Many species.
Representative species (Fig. 894). . *Monostyla lunaris* Ehrenberg.

47 (32) Lorica undivided, of a single piece. 48

48 (51) Lorica somewhat pipe-shaped, often unsymmetrical.
Family RATTULIDAE . . 49
Lorica closed all around, cylindrical, fusiform, ovate, or conical, with an opening at each end for head and foot; often unsymmetrical and with oblique ridges or furrows. Toes bristle-like; sometimes equal, then short; sometimes very unequal, so that but one is noticeable, this then very long.

49 (50) Toes equal, or, if unequal, the shorter one more than one-third the length of the longer. . . . . *Diurella* Bory.
Many species.
Representative species (Fig. 895). . . . . *Diurella sulcata* Jennings.
(Fig. 862, page 562). . . . . *D. tigris* Müller.

50 (49) Toes unequal. The smaller less than one-third length of longer.
Rattulus Lamarck.
Many species.
Representative species (Fig. 896). . . . *Rattulus cylindricus* Imhof.
(Fig. 897). . . . . *R. latus* Jennings.
(Fig. 898). . . . . . *R. longiseta* Schrank.

51 (48) Lorica not pipe-shaped. Symmetrical. 52

52 (59) Foot and toes not exceptionally long. No spines.
Family COLURIDAE . . 53
Lorica of a single piece, either covering both dorsal and ventral surfaces, or only the dorsal.

53 (58) Head surmounted by a chitinous shield. 54

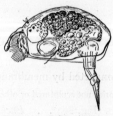

FIG. 900. *Colurus grallator* Gosse. × 375. (After Weber.

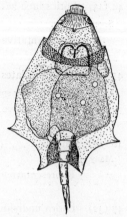

FIG. 899. *Stephanops intermedius* Burn. × 350. (After Weber.)

FIG. 901. *Metopidia ehrenbergii* Perty. × 400. (After Jennings.)

FIG. 902. *Cochlearet urbo* Gosse. × 200. (After Gosse.)

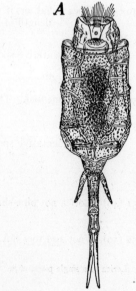

A

B

FIG. 903. *Scaridium longicaudum* Ehr. × 200. (After Dixon-Nuttall.)

FIG. 904. *Dinocharis pocillum* Ehr. *A*, Female. *B*, Male. × 300. (After Weber.)

54 (55) Head shield broad, flat, appearing from above like a halo.
Stephanops Ehrenberg.

Several species.

Representative species (Fig. 899). . . *Stephanops intermedius* Burn.

55 (54) Head shield arched, in side view appearing like a hook. **56**

56 (57) Lorica arched and laterally compressed. . . . . *Colurus* Ehrenberg.
Many species.

Representative species (Fig. 900). . . . . *Colurus grallator* Gosse.

57 (56) Lorica flattened, wider than high. . . . . . *Metopidia* Ehrenberg.
Representative species (Fig. 901). . . . *Metopidia ehrenbergii* Perty.

58 (53) No head shield. . . . . *Cochleare* Gosse.
Lorica shaped like a coat, covering only the anterior half or less of the dorsal surface. One or two species.

Representative species (Fig. 902). . . . . . *Cochleare turbo* Gosse.

59 (52) Foot and toes usually long; if not, upper surface of lorica with long spines. . . . . Family DINOCHARIDAE . . **60**
Lorica entire, covering head as well as body. Movements often of a leaping character.

60 (63) Lorica without spines on dorsal surface. **61**

61 (62) Lorica weak, hardly noticeable. . . . . . . *Scaridium* Ehrenberg.
No sculpturing of any sort; toes very long. Two species.

Representative species (Fig. 903).
Scaridium longicaudum Ehrenberg.

62 (61) Lorica rough. . . . . *Dinocharis* Ehrenberg
Two species.

Representative species (Fig. 904). . *Dinocharis pocillum* Ehrenberg.

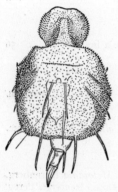

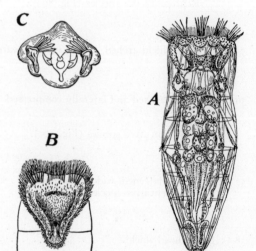

FIG. 905. *Polychaetus collinsii*
Gosse.   × 250.   (After
Jennings.)

FIG. 906.   *Hydatina senta* Ehr.   *A*, Dorsal view of female
× 150.   (After Weber.)   *B*, Corona.   (After Wesenberg
Lund.)   *C*. Trophi.   (After Weber.)

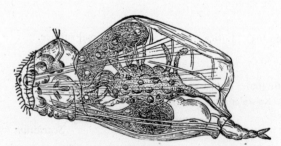

FIG. 907. *Cyrtonia tuba*
Ehrenberg.   × 200.
(After Rousselet.)

FIG. 908.   *Triphylus lacustris* Ehrenberg.   × 134.   (After Western.)

63 (60) Lorica bearing long spines on dorsal surface. . *Polychaetus* Perty.
Lorica turtle-shaped. Two species.

Representative species (Fig. 905). . . . *Polychaetus collinsii* Gosse.

64 (5, 31) With or without lorica. Corona usually as broad as broadest part of body and consisting of an outer wreath of cilia and an inner interrupted wreath about the mouth, with styligerous processes between them.

Suborder **Hydatinina** . . 65

A heterogeneous group in external characters but showing evidence of close relationship throughout. Corona never a perfect circle of two wreaths, with mouth in center. All loricate forms without foot belong here. In all non-loricate forms foot present and ending in two toes, side by side. In loricate forms foot when present ends in two toes, side by side, save in one species, *Gastropus stylifer*, where there is but one toe. The families of this order are greatly in need of a revision based on thorough comparative study of all the species.

65 (73) Without lorica. **66**

66 (70) Foot not sharply separated from body.

Family HYDATINIDAE . . 67

Large rotifers, body soft and segmented, of notommatoid characteristics, not greatly swollen dorsally, nor compressed sidewise. Corona of typical form of suborder, or having a large dorsal proboscis that bears two eyes. Foot lying in the body axis, not ventral; ending in two short toes.

67 (68, 69) No eye. . . . . *Hydatina* Ehrenberg.
Only one species (Fig. 906). . . . . . *Hydatina senta* Ehrenberg.

68 (67, 69) One eye. . . . . *Cyrtonia* Rousselet.
Only one species (Fig. 907). . . . . *Cyrtonia tuba* Ehrenberg.

69 (67, 68) Two eyes; corona with dorsal proboscis. . . . *Rhinops* Hudson.
Only one species (Fig. 863, page 565). . *Rhinops vitrea* Hudson.

70 (66) Foot decidedly set off from remainder of body.

Family NOTOPSIDAE . . 71

Body much swollen dorsally, flatter ventrally; cuticula slightly stiffer so that the body holds its shape, or sometimes forming a weak but evident lorica. Foot forming a prolongation of the ventral surface or extending ventrally; two small toes.

71 (72) Two eyes. . . . . *Triphylus* Hudson.
Only one species (Fig. 908). . . . . *Triphylus lacustris* Ehrenberg.

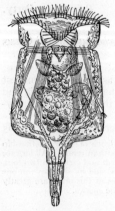

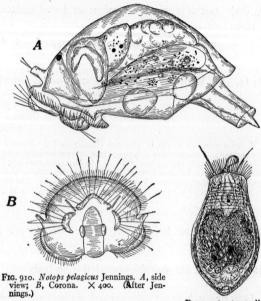

FIG. 909. *Notops brachionus* Ehr. × 100. (After Weber.)

FIG. 910. *Notops pelagicus* Jennings. *A*, side view; *B*, Corona. × 400. (After Jennings.)

FIG. 911. *Anapus ovalis* Bergendal. × 240. (After Weber.)

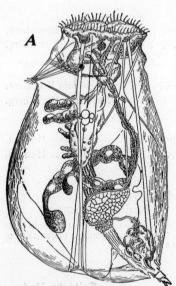

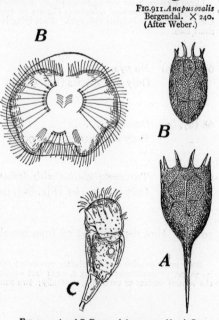

FIG. 912. *A, Notops clavulatus* Ehr. × 100. (After Hudson and Gosse.) *B*, Corona. (After Jennings.)

FIG. 913. *A* and *B*, Forms of *Anuraea cochlearis* Gosse. *A*, variety *macracantha*. *B*, Variety *tecta*. × 300. (After Lauterborn.) *C* Male of *Anuraea brevispina* Gosse.

72 (71)   One eye. . . . .   *Notops* Hudson.
Slight indication of lorica sometimes.   Several species.
     Representative species (Fig. 909). . . *Notops brachionus* Ehrenberg.
          (Fig. 912). . . . . *N. clavulatus* Ehrenberg.
          (Fig. 910). . . . . . *N. pelagicus* Jennings.

73 (65)   Lorica present. 74

74 (81)   No foot. 7

75 (76)   Lorica of two convex plates, placed together at their edges.
          Family ANAPODIDAE.
Lorica ovoid or oval.
     Only one genus. . . . . *Anapus* Bergendal.
One or two species.
     Representative species (Fig. 911). . . . . *Anapus ovalis* Bergendal.

76 (75)   Lorica of a convex dorsal and a flat ventral plate, or sometimes
          irregular. . . . . Family ANURAEIDAE . . 77
Open in front for head and behind for cloaca; usually armed with spines or teeth.

77 (80)   Spines or teeth at the anterior or posterior edges of the lorica, or
          none. 78

78 (79)   Lorica not longitudinally striated. . . . . . . *Anuraea* Ehrenberg.
     Representative species (Fig. 913, *A* and *B*). *Anuraea cochlearis* Gosse.
Many species.   Lorica of convex dorsal and flat ventral plate.
          (Fig. 913, *C*). . . . . . . *A. brevispina* Gosse.

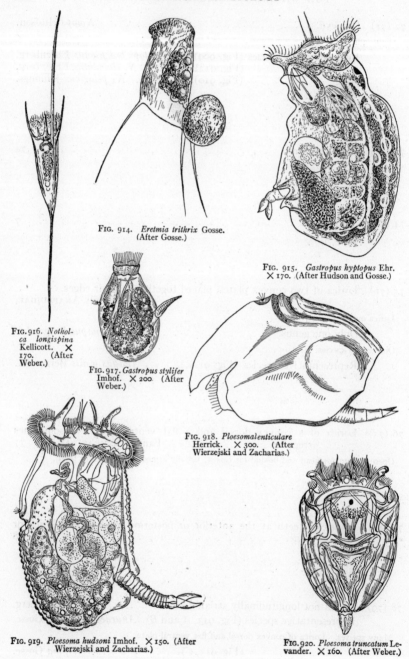

FIG. 914. *Eretmia trithrix* Gosse.
(After Gosse.)

FIG. 915. *Gastropus hyptopus* Ehr.
× 170. (After Hudson and Gosse.)

FIG. 916. *Nothol-
ca longispina*
Kellicott. ×
170. (After
Weber.)

FIG. 917. *Gastropus stylifer*
Imhof. × 200. (After
Weber.)

FIG. 918. *Ploesoma lenticulare*
Herrick. × 300. (After
Wierzejski and Zacharias.)

FIG. 919. *Ploesoma hudsoni* Imhof. × 150. (After
Wierzejski and Zacharias.)

FIG. 920. *Ploesoma truncatum* Levander. × 160. (After Weber.)

79 (78) Lorica longitudinally striated. . . . . *Notholca* Gosse.
Sometimes very long and slender.   Three or four species.

> Representative species (Fig. 916). . . *Notholca longispina* Kellicott.

80 (77) Lorica with long bristle-like outgrowths from its surface but not from anterior or posterior borders. . . . . *Eretmia* Gosse.
Few species, all more or less doubtful.

> Representative species (Fig. 914). . . . . . *Eretmia trithrix* Gosse.

81 (74) Foot present. 82

82 (85) Foot projects from ventral surface. 83

83 (84) Lorica entire, not wrinkled. . . . . Family GASTROPODIDAE.
Lorica flask-shaped with small foot projecting from ventral surface.   Foot ringed, ending in one or two toes.

> One genus only. . . . . *Gastropus* Imhof.
> Several species.

> Representative species (Fig. 915). . *Gastropus hyptopus* Ehrenberg.
> (Fig. 917). . . . . *G. stylifer* Imhof.

84 (83) Lorica open along mid-ventral line; marked with wrinkles or vesicles. . . . . Family PLOESOMIDAE.
Lorica stout, widely open in front for the large head, and open ventrally for the foot.   Foot strong, ringed, ending in two toes.   Strong, active rotifers.

> Only one genus. . . . . *Ploesoma* Herrick.
> Three or four species.

> Representative species (Fig. 920). . *Ploesoma truncatum* Levander.
> (Fig. 918). . . . . . . *P. lenticulare* Herrick.
> (Fig. 919). . . . . *P. hudsoni* Imhof.

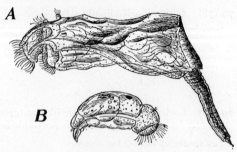

A

B

FIG. 921. *A, Brachionus punctatus* Hempel. × 400. (After Dixon-Nuttall.) *B,* Male of *Brachionus quadratus* Rousselet. (After Marks and Wesché.)

FIG. 922. *Brachionus pala* Ehr. × 160. (After Weber.)

FIG. 923. Corona of *Brachionus angularis* Gosse. (After Wesenberg-Lund.)

FIG. 924. *Schizocerca diversicornis* Daday. × 300. (After Wierzejski.)

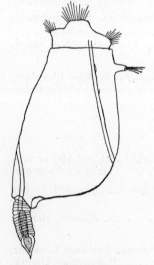

FIG. 925. *Brachionus mollis* Hempel. × 280. (After Hempel.)

FIG. 926. *Noteus quadricornis* Ehrenberg. × 144. (After Hudson and Gosse.)

85 (82)   Foot projects from posterior end. . Family BRACHIONIDAE . .   86

Lorica consisting of a convex dorsal plate and a flat ventral one; usually stout and armed with spines, though not always. Lorica opened behind for the long, strong foot which is often covered with close rings. Foot either ending in two toes or forked at its free end.

86 (89)   Foot not forked.   87

87 (88)   Lorica very convex dorsally. . . . . *Brachionus* Ehrenberg.

Many species.

Representative species (Fig. 922). . . *Brachionus pala* Ehrenberg.
(Fig. 921, *A*). . . . . *B. punctatus* Hempel.
(Fig. 921, *B*). . . . *B. quadratus* Rousselet.
(Fig. 923). . . . . . . *B. angularis* Gosse.
(Fig. 925). . . . . . . *B. mollis* Hempel.

88 (87)   Lorica flat. . . . . *Noteus* Ehrenberg.

Foot not ringed.

Representative species (Fig. 926). . *Noteus quadricornis* Ehrenberg.

89 (86)   Foot forked at its end. . . . . : . . *Schizocerca* Daday.
Only one species (Fig. 924). . . . *Schizocerca diversicornis* Daday.

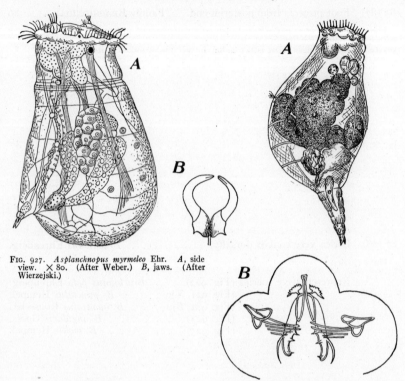

FIG. 927. *Asplanchnopus myrmeleo* Ehr. *A*, side view. × 80. (After Weber.) *B*, jaws. (After Wierzejski.)

FIG. 928. *Harringia eupoda* Gosse. *A*, side view. × 100. (After Western.) *B*, jaws. (After Wierzejski.)

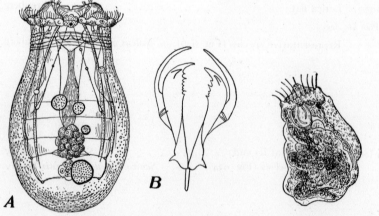

FIG. 929. *Asplanchna priodonta* Gosse. *A*, Dorsal view. × 100. (After Weber.) *B*, jaws. (After Wierzejski.)

FIG. 930. *Ascomorpha ecaudis* Perty. × 200. (After Hudson and Gosse.)

90 (4)   Jaws incudate, save in *Ascomorpha*.   Intestine and anus lacking, save
in *Dinops*. . . . .   Suborder **Asplanchnina**.

Sac-shaped rotifers, usually without a foot, though in some cases a small foot is present on
the posterior part of the ventral surface.

One family only. . . . .   Family ASPLANCHNIDAE . .   91

91 (94)   Foot present.   92

92 (93)   Intestine absent. . . . .   *Asplanchnopus* de Guerne.

Two or three species.

Representative species (Fig. 927)
Asplanchnopus myrmeleo Ehrenberg.

93 (92)   Intestine present. . . . .   *Harringia* Beauchamp.
Only one species (Fig. 928). . . . .   *Harringia eupoda* Gosse.

94 (91)   Foot absent.   95

95 (96)   Large clear rotifers with incudate jaws. . . . .   *Asplanchna* Gosse.

Many species.

Representative species (Fig. 929). . .   *Asplanchna priodonta* Gosse.
(Fig. 869, page 583). .   *A. herrickii* de Guerne.

96 (95)   Very small rotifers, usually colored or opaque;   jaws not incudate.
Ascomorpha Perty.

One or two species.

Representative species (Fig. 930). . . .   *Ascomorpha ecaudis* Perty.

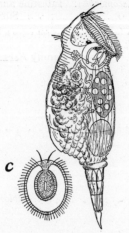

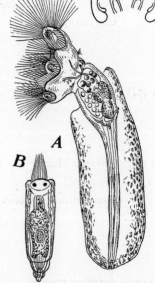

FIG. 931. *Microcodon clavus* Ehr., ventral view. × 260. (After Weber.)

FIG. 932. *Microcodides robustus* Glasscott, with corona (*c*). × 300. (After Rousselet.)

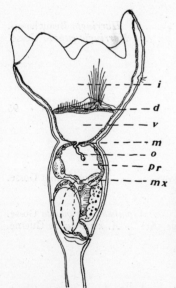

FIG. 933. *A. Floscularia proboscidea* Ehr. Female. × 100. (After Weber.) *B*, Male of the same. *D*, Side view of jaws of Flosculariidae. (After Wierzejski.)

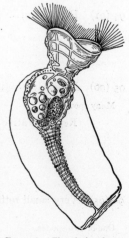

FIG. 934. Alimentary canal of *Floscularia campanulata* Dobie. (Modified from Montgomery.) *d*, diaphragm; *i*, infundibulum; *m*, mouth; *mx*, mastax; *o*, esophagus; *pr*, proventriculus; *v*, vestibulum.

FIG. 935. *Floscularia uniloba* Wierz. × 125. (After Wierzejski.)

FIG. 936. *Floscularia edentata* Collins. × 150. (After Weber.)

97 (3) Mouth nearly in center of large corona. . Order **Floscularida** . . 98

Corona circular or drawn out into lobes, points, or arms. Foot never ending in two toes placed side by side. Mostly attached or tube-bearing rotifers, the foot forming a disk for attachment; a few free-swimming species in which the foot ends in a single toe, sometimes accompanied by a dorsal spur.

98 (101) Free swimming; foot ending in a single toe.
Family MICRODONIDAE . . 99

Corona circular, with mouth in center, an outer wreath of active cilia; cilia about the mouth larger and bristle-like. One eye.

99 (100) Foot as long as body. . . . . *Microcodon* Ehrenberg.

Body slender, corona with raised borders, slightly bilobed; foot slender, straight, ending in a single toe; no dorsal spur.

Only one species (Fig. 931). . . . . *Microcodon clavus* Ehrenberg.

100 (99) Foot not more than half as long as body. . *Microcodides* Bergendal.

Body not so slender; foot ending in one toe which is sometimes accompanied by a dorsal spur.

Representative species (Fig. 932). . *Microcodides robustus* Glasscott.

101 (98) Attached, or bearing tubes if free swimming. 102

102 (105) Cilia around corona. . . . . Family FLOSCULARIIDAE . . 103

Corona large, forming a net for the capture of prey. Cilia about its edge usually forming long threads or bristles which do not beat like those of other rotifers, though they may move rather slowly. Jaws uncinate (Fig. 933, *D*).

103 (104) Corona circular, or drawn into lobes, or pointed; its cilia not in whorls or regular groups. . . . . *Floscularia* Oken

Many species.

Representative species (Fig. 933, *A* and *B*).
Floscularia proboscidea Ehrenberg.
(Fig. 934 and 861, *B*, page 561).
F. campanulata Dobie.
(Fig. 935). . . . . . *F. uniloba* Wierzejski.
(Fig. 936). . . . . . . *F. edentata* Collins.

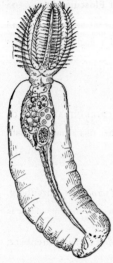

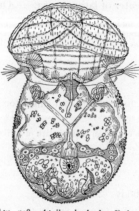

FIG. 938. *Apsilus bucinedax* Forbes. Ventral view. ✕ 65. (After Stokes.)

FIG. 937. *Stephanoceros eich-hornii* Ehr. ✕ 60. (After Weber.)

FIG. 939. *Atrochus tentaculatus* Wierz. ✕ 35. (After Wierzejski.)

FIG. 940. *Pompholyx complanata* Gosse. ✕ 245. (After Hudson and Gosse.)

A

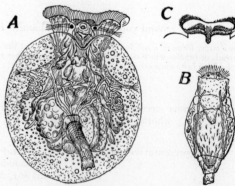

C

B

FIG. 941. *Acyclus in-quietus* Leidy. ✕ 12. (After Leidy, from Hudson and Gosse.)

FIG. 942. *Pterodina patina* Ehr. *A*, Dorsal view of female. ✕ 225. (After Weber.) *B*, Dorsal view of the male. (After Marks and Wesché.) *C*, Corona, showing the two wreaths of cilia. (After Wesenberg-Lund.)

104 (103)   Corona drawn out into long pointed arms, which bear cilia arranged
in whorls. . . . . *Stephanoceros* Ehrenberg.
One species only (Fig. 937). . *Stephanoceros eichhornii* Ehrenberg.

105 (102)   No cilia on corona. . . . . Family APSILIDAE . . 106

106 (107, 108)   Body short, sac-like. . . . . *Apsilus* Metschnikoff.
Corona a large sac or chamber; no foot; attached by an adhesive disk.   Two or three species.
Representative species (Fig. 938). . . . *Apsilus bucinedax* Forbes.

107 (106, 108)   Body longer, fusiform, a narrowed neck separating off a
conical anterior part. . . . . *Atrochus* Wierzejski.
Corona a membranous ring with five short lobes bearing tentacles.
Only one species (Fig. 939). . *Atrochus tentaculatus* Wierzejski.

108 (106, 107)   Body long, with a long, slender, tapering stalk.
Acyclus Leidy.
Corona with but one large dorsal lobe.   Living in colonies of *Megalotrocha alboflavicans*.
Representative species (Fig. 941). . . . . *Acyclus inquietus* Leidy.

109 (2)   Corona surrounded by two parallel wreaths of cilia with a furrow between.   Cilia of outer wreath always shorter than those of
inner.
Order **Melicertida** . . 110
The furrow between the wreaths of cilia sometimes clothed with short cilia.   Jaws malleo-
ramate (Fig. 866).   Foot never ending in two toes side by side; sometimes lacking.   Eyes two,
rarely absent.   Fixed or free swimming; the free-swimming species often without foot and
frequently bearing appendages on the body.

110 (121)   Free swimming and not in tubes or in colonies. 111

111 (120)   Not spherical. 112

112 (115)   With a lorica.   Without appendages.
Family PTERODINIDAE . . 113

113 (114)   Foot present, long, ringed, ending in a bunch of cilia.
Pterodina Ehrenberg.
Lorica more or less flattened dorso-ventrally.   Many species.
Representative species (Fig. 942). . . *Pterodina patina* Ehrenberg.
(Fig. 866, *B*, page 575). . *P. casca* Parsons.

114 (113)   No foot. . . . . *Pompholyx* Gosse.
Lorica not flat.   Two or three species.
Representative species (Fig. 940). . . *Pompholyx complanta* Gosse.

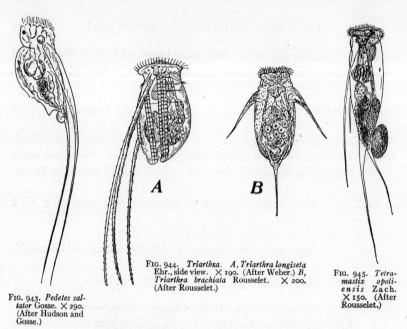

FIG. 943. *Pedetes sal-
tator* Gosse. × 290.
(After Hudson and
Gosse.)

FIG. 944. *Triarthra*. *A*, *Triarthra longiseta*
Ehr., side view. × 190. (After Weber.) *B*,
Triarthra brachiata Rousselet. × 200.
(After Rousselet.)

FIG. 945. *Tetra-
mastix opoli-
ensis* Zach.
× 150. (After
Rousselet.)

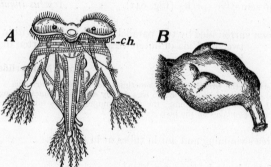

FIG. 946. *Pedalion mirum* Hudson. *A*, Ventral view of female, *ch*, "chin." × 70. (After Weber.)
B, Male. (After Wesenberg-Lund.)

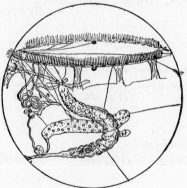

FIG. 947. *Trochosphaera solstitialis* Thorpe. × 80. (After Rousselet.)

115 (112) Without lorica. With spine-like or limb-like appendages. No
           foot. . . . .   Family PEDALIONIDAE . .   116

116 (117, 118, 119) Appendages, two, very long. . . . . .   *Pedetes* Gosse.
           Representative species (Fig. 943). . . . . .   *Pedetes saltator* Gosse.

117 (116, 118, 119) Appendages, three, spine-like.   .   *Triarthra* Ehrenberg.
Two or three species.
           Representative species (Fig. 944, *A*). . *Triarthra longiseta* Ehrenberg.
                              (Fig. 944, *B*). . . . .   *T. brachiata* Rousselet.

118 (116, 117, 119) Appendages, four; spines or bristles.
                                        Tetramastix Zacharias.
           One species only (Fig. 945). . . *Tetramastix opoliensis* Zacharias.

119 (116, 117, 118) Appendages, six, branching, somewhat crustacean-like.
                                        Pedalion Hudson.
Two species.
           Representative species (Fig. 946). . . . *Pedalion mirum* Hudson.

120 (111) Body spherical, no foot. . . . . .   Family TROCHOSPHAERIDAE.
           One genus only. . . . .   *Trochosphaera* Semper.
           Representative species (Fig. 947). . *Trochosphaera solstitialis* Thorpe.

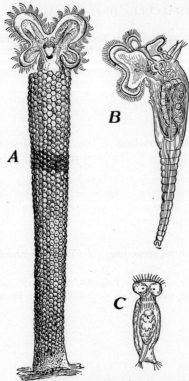

FIG. 948. *Melicerta ringens* Schrank. *A*, Animal in its tube. × 60. (After Hudson and Gosse.) *B*, Side view of animal removed from its tube. (After Weber.) *C*, Male. × 45. (After Joliet, from Weber.)

FIG. 949. *Limnias ceratophylli* Schrank. × 87. (After Hlava.)

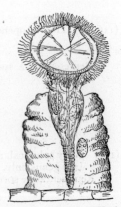

FIG. 950. *Octotrocha speciosa* Thorpe. × 40. (After Thorpe.)

FIG. 951. *Oecistes brevis* Hood. × 200. (After Rousselet.)

121 (110) Fixed by the tip of the stalk-like foot, or with tubes, or in colonies.
Secondarily free in a few cases, then distinguishable by the
soft elongated body, without lorica or appendages.
Family MELICERTIDAE . . 122

122 (130, 133) Individuals attached, separate, or in branching, non-spherical
colonies of few specimens (1–30). 123

123 (124, 125) Corona four lobed. . . . . *Melicerta* Schrank.
Two lobes in one species. Living in tubes. Several species.

Representative species (Fig. 948 and Fig. 866, *A*, page 575).
Melicerta ringens Schrank.

124 (123, 125) Corona eight lobed. . . . . *Octotrocha* Thorpe.
Representative species (Fig. 950). . . . *Octotrocha speciosa* Thorpe.

125 (123, 124) Corona more or less two lobed. ,. 126

126 (129) Dorsal antenna minute or absent. 127

127 (128) Corona broad, of two lobes, with a wide dorsal gap.
Limnias Schrank.

Dorsal antenna minute, ventral antennae long; living in tubes not made with pellets. Several species.

Representative species (Fig. 949). . . *Limnias ceratophylli* Schrank.

128 (127) Corona a wide oval or nearly circular, indistinctly two lobed.
Dorsal gap minute. . . . . *Oecistes* Ehrenberg.

Dorsal antenna inconspicuous or absent. Ventral antennae obvious. Living attached in tubes. Many species.

Representative species (Fig. 951). . . . . . *Oecistes brevis* Hood.

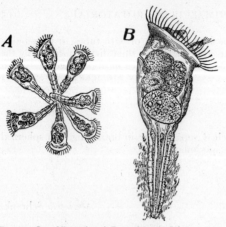

FIG. 952. *Conochilus unicornis* Rousselet. *A*, Colony. ×40.
B, Single animal isolated. ×150. (After Weber.)

FIG. 953. *Conochiloides natans*
Seligo. ×87. (After Hlava.)

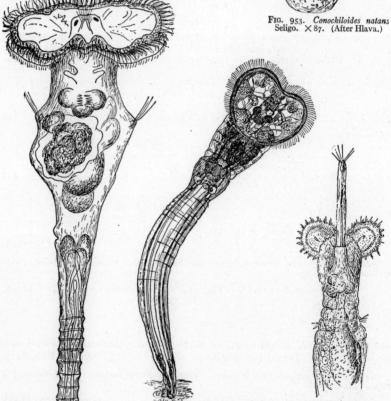

FIG. 954. *Pseudoecistes rotifer* Stenroos. ×150. (After Stenroos.)

FIG. 955. *Megalotrocha alboflavicans*
Ehrenberg. Single individual.
×87. (After Hlava.)

FIG. 956. *Cephalosiphon
limnias* Ehrenberg. ×280.
(After Dixon-Nuttall.)

129 (126) Dorsal antenna very large, with two projections or hooks at its side. . . . . *Cephalosiphon* Ehrenberg.

Corona nearly circular with a distinct dorsal gap. Ventral antennae small or absent.

Representative species (Fig. 956). . *Cephalosiphon limnias* Ehrenberg.

130 (122, 133) Not attached nor forming colonies, save that one adult may be grouped with its young. **131**

131 (132) Not forming tubes. . . . . *Pseudoecistes* Stenroos.

In other respects like *Cephalosiphon*. One or two species.

Representative species (Fig. 954). . . *Pseudoecistes rotifer* Stenroos.

132 (131) Inhabiting a tube. . . . . *Conochiloides* Hlava.

Individuals separate or one grouped with its young. One or two species.

Representative species (Fig. 953). . . . *Conochiloides natans* Seligo.

133 (122, 130) In clusters of many individuals, forming usually a spherical colony appearing to the naked eye as a yellowish ball. . **134**

134 (137) Clusters attached. **135**

135 (136) No tubes. . . . . *Megalotrocha* Ehrenberg.

Colonies often several millimeters in diameter, attached to plants. Individuals not imbedded in a gelatinous mass; corona broad, kidney shaped. Body usually with two or four opaque warts. Several species.

Representative species (Fig. 955).
Megalotrocha alboflavicans Ehrenberg.

136 (135) Dwelling in transparent gelatinous tubes. . *Lacinularia* Schweigger.

Colony, a mass of some mm. in diameter, often appears to be imbedded in a mass of jelly. Corona heart shaped (Figs. 861, *A*, and 865). Several species.

Representative species (Fig. 861, *A*, page 561, and Fig. 865, page 575).
Lacinularia socialis Ehrenberg.

137 (134) Clusters or colonies free swimming. . . . *Conochilus* Ehrenberg.

Two or three species.

Representative species (Fig. 952). . *Conochilus unicornis* Rousselet.

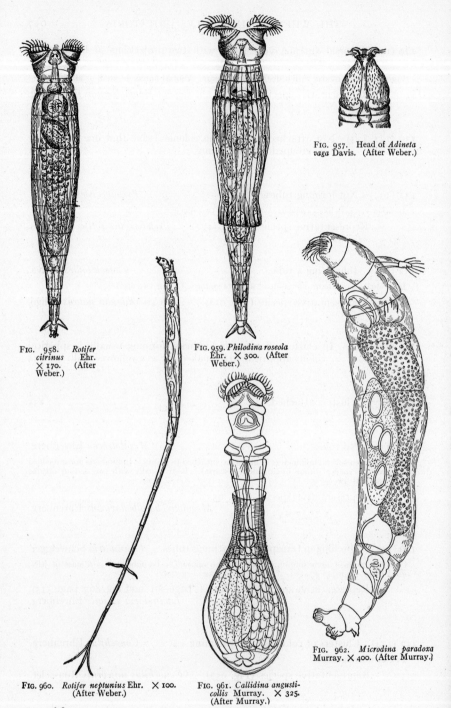

FIG. 957. Head of *Adineta*
vaga Davis. (After Weber.)

FIG. 958. *Rotifer*
citrinus Ehr.
× 170. (After
Weber.)

FIG. 959. *Philodina roseola*
Ehr. × 300. (After
Weber.)

FIG. 962. *Microdina paradoxa*
Murray. × 400. (After Murray.)

FIG. 960. *Rotifer neptunius* Ehr. × 100.
(After Weber.)

FIG. 961. *Callidina angusti-*
collis Murray. × 325.
(After Murray.)

138 (1)   Two ovaries. . . . .   Subclass **Digononta.**
In fresh water; only one group.   . . . .   Order **Bdelloida** . .   139

Free-living. Swimming with the corona or creeping like a leech, or both. Body without lorica, usually nearly cylindrical, dorsal and ventral surfaces not being conspicuously differentiated, and composed of rings which may be drawn one within the other in telescopic fashion. A dorsal proboscis behind the corona; jaws ramate (Fig. 867).

139 (146)   Corona present.   140

140 (145)   Corona of two nearly circular disks raised on short stalks, presenting the appearance of two wheels.
Family PHILODINIDAE . .   141

141 (144)   Eyes, two.   142

142 (143)   Eyes in the dorsal proboscis. . . . .   *Rotifer* Schrank.

Several species.

Representative species (Fig. 958). . .   *Rotifer citrinus* Ehrenberg.
(Fig. 960). . . .   *R. neptunius* Ehrenberg.

143 (142)   Eyes in the neck, directly over the brain, just above the jaws.
Philodina Ehrenberg.

Several species.

Representative species (Fig. 959). . .   *Philodina roseola* Ehrenberg.
(Fig. 867, *A*, page 577). . .   *P. brycei* Weber.

144 (141)   Eyes, none. . . . .   *Callidina* Ehrenberg.

The genus *Callidina* when revised will be broken into several genera. Many species.

Representative species (Fig. 961). .   *Callidina angusticollis* Murray.

145 (140)   Corona a flat surface covered with cilia on the ventral side of the anterior end. . . . .   Family ADINETIDAE.
One genus only. . . . .   *Adineta* Hudson.
Representative species (Fig. 957). . . . . . ,   *Adineta vaga* Davis.

146 (139)   No corona. . . . .   Family MICRODINIDAE.
The mouth has a group of cilia about it.

One genus only. . . . .   *Microdina* Murray.
Representative species (Fig. 962 and Fig. 867, *B*, page 577).
Microdina paradoxa Murray.

IMPORTANT REFERENCES ON FRESH–WATER ROTATORIA

DIXON–NUTTALL, F. R., and FREEMAN, R. 1903. The Rotatorian Genus *Diaschiza;* a Monographic Study. Jour. Roy. Micr. Soc., 1903: 1–14, 129–141.

HARRING, H. K. 1913. Synopsis of the Rotatoria. U. S. Natl. Museum, Bull. 81. 226 pp. (Changes some of the generic names here employed.)

HUDSON, C. T., and GOSSE, P. H. 1889. The Rotifera or Wheel Animalcules. 2 vols. London.

JENNINGS, H. S. 1900. Rotatoria of the United States with especial reference to those of the Great Lakes: Bull. U. S. Fish Com., 1899: 67–104.

1901. Synopsis of North American Invertebrates XVII. The Rotatoria. Amer. Nat., 35: 725–777; 171 figures.

1903. Rotatoria of the United States, II. A monograph of the Rattulidae. Bull. U. S. Fish Com., 1902: 273–352.

1904. Reactions to Stimuli in certain Rotifera. Carnegie Institution, Publ. 16: 73–88.

MONTGOMERY, T. H. 1903. On the Morphology of the Rotatorian Family Flosculariidae. Proc. Acad. Nat. Sci., Phila., 1903: 363–385.

ROUSSELET, C. F. 1902. The Genus *Synchaeta;* a Monographic Study. Jour. Roy. Micr. Soc., 1902: 269–290.

SURFACE, F. M. 1906. The Formation of New Colonies of the Rotifer *Megalotrocha alboflavicans* Ehr. Biol. Bull., 11: 182–192.

WESENBERG–LUND, C. 1899. Danmarks Rotifera I. Grundtraekkene i Rotiferernes Okologi, Morfologi og Systematik. Kobenhavn.

CHAPTER XVIII
GASTROTRICHA

By HENRY B. WARD

Professor of Zoology, University of Illinois

AMONG the microscopic animals common in fresh water and limited in distribution to that environment are certain minute organisms known as the Gastrotricha. Though limited in variety of species they are so abundant, so widely distributed, and so striking in appearance as to command the attention of every student of aquatic life. They live in numbers among algae and debris and in almost every bottom collection appear in company with the rotifers and protozoans. In movements and habits they resemble closely the ciliate Protozoa, and are easily confused with them. Ehrenberg, who first described in detail the structure of these organisms, placed them among the Rotifera and many later investigators have followed this suggestion. Others incline to regard them as Nematoda from which they differ most strikingly in possessing cilia which are not known in other worms of that group. In size they are strictly microscopic, varying from 0.54 mm. in maximum length to only one-eighth of that. They constitute a distinctly uniform group not closely related to any other existing types of animal life. Our knowledge of the anatomy of these organisms is due principally to the investigations of Stokes in this country and Zelinka in Germany.

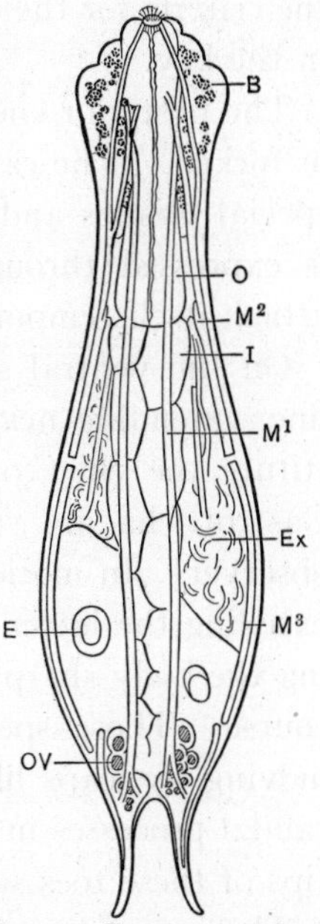

The general structure of the group is well illustrated in the figure of *Chaetonotus maximus* taken from Zelinka's monograph (Fig. 963). While the form of the body approaches a cylinder, there is usually an expanded area in front known as the

FIG. 963. *Chaetonotus maximus* in ventral view. *Ex*, kidney; *M*, muscles; *B*, brain; *E*, egg; *O*, esophagus; *I*, intestine; *Ov*, ovary. × 400. (After Zelinka.)

"head," a narrower part just behind it called the "neck" and the larger "rump," or body proper, which constitutes the major portion of the animal. These regions are not sharply limited and sometimes can not be distinguished at all. They do not correspond to any internal structures. The ventral surface is more or less flattened and the dorsal surface arched as is conspicuously seen in side view.

The head bears at its tip an opening, the mouth, surrounded by a row of delicate oral bristles which point forward. The sides of the head are often lobed and carry two circles or series of groups of fine sense hairs; those of the anterior series point outward and forward while the others are usually directed backward. Sometimes the entire body is smooth, or it may be partly or entirely covered with plates, spines, or hooked bristles. These furnish the criteria for the distinction of species and are carefully described in the key.

The posterior end of the body may be bluntly rounded, pointed, or forked. The caudal processes, often spoken of as "toes," carry special bristles and contain cement glands, the secretion of which is expressed through terminal pores and enables the animal to attach itself temporarily to objects in the water.

On the ventral surface are two bands of cilia near the median line, extending nearly the entire length of the body. These constitute the chief organs of locomotion. The movements of the Gastrotricha are so graceful as to elicit admiration from every observer. In motion they recall the long-necked infusoria, though excelling the latter in speed and variety of movement. By bending the body sharply on itself the animal may instantly reverse its course. Those species possessed of long bristles utilize them in moving by leaps like jumping rotifers. Other species employ the caudal processes in movement, looping the body and attaching the tips of these toes successively in different places.

The internal anatomy is simple. From the mouth (Fig. 964, A), a straight alimentary canal traverses the length of the animal terminating in a simple anal orifice just above the posterior end of the body. One can distinguish an anterior muscular region, the esophagus and a posterior portion, the intestine (Fig. 964, C), which is lined by large digestive cells, rich in protoplasm. Small gland

cells on the esophagus are designated as salivary in character
and other gland cells in a fringe at the beginning of the intestine
have been regarded as hepatic or liver cells. The food of the
Gastrotricha consists mainly of unicellular algae, the tests of which
can often be recognized in the intestine.

Six pairs of delicate longitudinal strands constitute the entire
muscular system as there are neither circular nor oblique muscles.
One pair of muscles extends nearly
the entire length of the body;
the others occupy only the anterior or the posterior region meeting
near the center. They lie in the
body cavity which is devoid of
any special lining epithelium. The
head region of the body cavity
is almost completely filled by a
saddle-shaped mass (Fig. 964,*B*) of

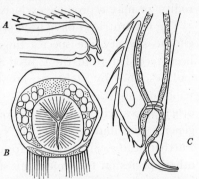

nerve cells dorsal and lateral to
the esophagus which constitutes
the brain. From it nerve fibers
go out to the anterior sense hairs
and lateral strands follow the
alimentary canal to the posterior
end of the body. Minute pigment

Fig. 964. *Chaetonotus maximus.* *A*, optical longitudinal section through anterior tip of the body
showing mouth, oral bristles, frontal plate, and
esophagus. × 535. *B*, cross section through
posterior extremity of *A*, showing tripartite
esophagus and above it the saddle-shaped brain
while below are the two ventral cilian bands.
× 690. *C*, longitudinal section through the posterior region of the body showing below the intestine, rectum, and anus; above in the ovary a
single ripe egg; on the upper surface fine
bristles, and at the posterior tip one of the toes
with its adhesive gland. × 430. (After Zelinka.)

spots which may be designated as eyes certainly occur in some
species despite the doubts expressed by Zelinka.

Excretory organs are present in the form of a pair of lateral
much coiled tubes near the center of the body. The inner end of
each tube is closed by a long flame cell and the outer end opens
on the ventral surface near the median line and just behind the
center of the body. Just behind these coils, in the mature females,
lie the large eggs that mark the anterior limit of the simple ovary.
These eggs become so large that they extend over one-third to
one-half the length of the entire body and increase its normal
transverse diameter noticeably so as to modify greatly the form of
the gravid female. The large, oval eggs are laid on algal threads
or empty shells of other animals. When deposited they have a

tough thick shell, often covered with hooks and knobs, that seem to anchor them in place. When the embryo has reached its full development its vigorous movements burst the shell and a full-grown animal emerges.

No one has yet described a male and it is uncertain that any other type than the female exists. This form may have a sperm-producing organ yet undiscovered and thus be in reality hermaphroditic or may reproduce exclusively by parthenogenesis.

The Gastrotricha have been studied but little in North America. Of the seventy-five species thus far described only sixteen have been recorded from the United States. Most of these were found and described by Stokes at Trenton, New Jersey. While this distribution appears highly local there is no doubt that search in other places will demonstrate for American species the same wide general distribution that has been shown for European forms. Further study will doubtless result also in the discovery of many other species on this continent, since the evidence thus far secured indicates that, like most minute aquatic organisms, these forms, too, are cosmopolitan in distribution.

KEY TO NORTH AMERICAN FRESH-WATER GASTROTRICHA

1 (31)　Caudal end prolonged into two prominent lateral processes.
Suborder **Euichthydina** . . 2
Each caudal process encloses a glandular apparatus and bears a pore at the tip.

2 (11)　Body naked, scaled, or covered with rugosities or papillae, but never
bearing spines. . . . . . . Family Ichthydiidae . . 3

3 (6)　Body without scales; cuticula smooth.
Ichthydium Ehrenberg 1830 . . 4
Seven or eight species described; only two reported from North America.

4 (5)　Surface of body entirely smooth, no constant furrows or ridges.
Ichthydium podura O. F. Müller 1786.

Total length 0.075 mm.; esophagus 0.0188 mm., caudal process 0.00875 mm. long. Breadth of anterior region 0.0163 mm. The cuticula is thin and is often laid in deep wrinkles, but these are entirely inconstant. The lateral margins show no trace of being flattened. The caudal processes are sharply set off from the body. Eggs smooth.

Fig. 965. *Ichthydium podura* in dorsal view. × 360. (After Zelinka.)

5 (4)   Dorsal and lateral surface with deep transverse furrows.   Posterior
        region of body narrow and elongated.
                                            Ichthydium sulcatum Stokes 1887.

Total length 0.107 to 0.187 mm.; esophagus not more than one-sixth the
entire length.   The body is unusually soft and flexible.   The lateral margins
are so flattened that they impart to the body the effect of wings.   The posterior region is narrow and very much longer than in other species.

FIG. 966.   Posterior region of *Ichthydium sulcatum* in dorsal aspect.   × about 600.
(After Stokes.)

6 (3)   Body covered with smooth scales or with rounded papillae, but without
        spines. . . . .   *Lepidoderma* Zelinka 1889 . .   7

Six species described; three reported from North America.

7 (10)   Minute soft scales present.   8

8 (9)   Scales shield-shaped. . . .   *Lepidoderma squamatum* (Dujardin) 1841.

Length of body from 0.119 to 0.2 mm., of esophagus 0.042 to 0.044 mm.; breadth of anterior
region 0.033 mm., of posterior body also 0.033 mm.   Large smooth scales near the posterior
end seen in profile simulate curved bristles or spines.   Scales on body and neck in seven alternating longitudinal rows; on posterior region eight rows present.   New Jersey.

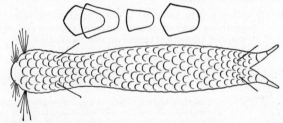

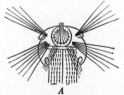

FIG. 967.   *Lepidoderma squamatum* in dorsal aspect with characteristic dorsal scales of head, neck, and
trunk.   × 375.   (After Zelinka.)

9 (8)   Scales rhombic, pointed. . . .   *Lepidoderma rhomboides* (Stokes) 1887.

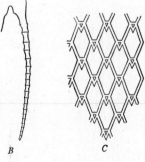

FIG. 968.   *Lepidoderma rhomboides.*   *A*, ventral
view of head.   *B*, caudal branch.   *C*, portion of the
scale pattern.   × 350.   (After Stokes.)

Length 0.295 mm.; breadth of anterior region
0.036 mm.   Body long, slender.   Esophagus
short, "not over one-sixth total length."   Scales
0.00506 mm. long, thickened along the margins.
Posterior margin of each scale appears to carry
a small triangular supplementary scale.   Caudal process remarkably long, marked by about 20
delicate rings.   New Jersey.

10 (7)   Body covered with hemispherical papillae.

Lepidoderma concinnum (Stokes) 1887.

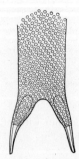

Length 0.096. Body cylindrical. Back and sides covered with small half-round papillae arranged in thick-set oblique rows. Egg smooth, 0.055 mm. long. New Jersey.

Fig. 969.   Posterior region of *Lepidoderma concinnum* in dorsal view.
X about 525.   (After Stokes.)

11 (2)   Body provided with spines either attached to the dermal scales or springing directly from the surface.

Family CHAETONOTIDAE . .   12

12 (30)   Caudal process simple; spines attached to dermal scales.

Chaetonotus Ehrenberg 1830 . .   13

A large and complicated group; more than forty species already described; ten species reported from North America by Stokes.

13 (20)   Dorsal spines nearly uniform in length, at most twice as long on posterior region as on anterior region, and without any marked transition from one size to another.   14

14 (15)   Dorsal spines with accessory barbs or points. Anterior region sharply set off from so-called "neck."

Chaetonotus similis Zelinka 1889.

Length of body 0.12 to 0.22 mm., of esophagus 0.05 mm. Body covered dorsally and laterally with triangular scales carrying spines with accessory point. Oral funnel plicate. Originally described from Trenton, New Jersey, as *Ch. maximus* which it closely resembles in head and body. Under a high magnification differences in the spines appear. All of them are forked and have a fine lateral point near the tip.

A

Fig. 970.   *Chaetonotus similis* in dorsal view.   X 375.   *A*, body spine from the side.   X 1600.   (After Zelinka.)

15 (14)   Dorsal spines simple; *i.e.*, without lateral barbs or points. . . .   16

16 (17)   Anterior region sharply set off from narrow "neck" region.
Chaetonotus formosus Stokes 1887.

Length 0.169 mm. Oral ring minutely beaded. Head three lobed. Dorsal and lateral aspects of body covered with short, fine recurved spines with slight basal enlargements (but without scales?). Spines all subequal, in length 0.0292 mm., or less. Trenton, New Jersey. No figure published.

17 (16)   Transition from anterior region to body gradual, not sharply marked
at any point.   18

18 (19)   Head rounded. . . . . . .   *Chaetonotus brevispinosus* Zelinka 1889.

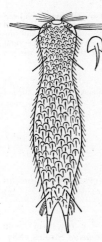

Length of body 0.095 to 0.149 mm., of esophagus 0.0223 mm. Spines somewhat curved, remarkably short, slightly larger poste-riorly, arranged in eleven rows. Head circular in front, with four eye-spots. The only American species reported more than once. Orono, Me., and Trenton, New Jersey. It is the *C. larus* of Stokes, also of Fernald.

FIG. 971. *Chaetonotus brevispinosus* in dorsal view, × 460, with spinose scale more highly magnified. (After Zelinka.)

19 (18)   Head five lobed. . . . .   *Chaetonotus acanthodes* Stokes 1887.

Length 0.1411 mm. Body covered with scales which bear each a small supplementary scale; the latter in the anterior region possesses a short, curved spine; just behind the middle of the body these termi-nate in a cross row of larger spines. On each side near the caudal processes are two larger curved spines. Trenton, New Jersey.

FIG. 972. Posterior end of *Chaetonotus acanthodes* in dorsal view. × about 570. (After Stokes.)

20 (13) Certain dorsal spines of much greater length than others. . . . 21

All species in this group thus far reported from North America have large bifurcate spines. A number of European species have simple spines without a lateral point near the tip. Grünspann classes the next species among the latter despite Stokes' positive statement that the spines are bifurcate.

21 (26) Head and neck free from covering of small spines. Large spines on
　　　　　body proper. 22

22 (23) Large dorsal spines in longitudinal rows and of approximately equal
　　　　　length. . . . . *Chaetonotus octonarius* Stokes 1887.

Length 0.0862 to 0.1034 mm. Breadth of distinctly five-lobed head 0.0206 mm. Large spines unequally furcate arranged in two lateral rows of three spines each and a median row with one anterior and one posterior spine. The figures and descriptions given by Stokes and Grünspann do not agree fully and may belong to separate species. Rare; Trenton, New Jersey.

Fig. 973. *Chaetonotus octonarius* in dorsal view. X about 580. (After Stokes.)

23 (22) Large dorsal spines in two distinct transverse rows, with spines in
　　　　　one row clearly longer than those of the other. 24

24 (25) Eight (rarely fewer) large spines in two transverse rows set close
　　　　　together. . . . . . *Chaetonotus longispinosus* Stokes 1887.

Length 0.0736 mm. Large spines usually eight, four in each row, or five in one and three in the other; sometimes only four spines in all (the others lost?); longer spines in posterior row. The figure in Grünspann is really the next species. The European form identified as this species is twice as large. Trenton, New Jersey.

Fig. 974. *Chaetonotus longispinosus* in dorsal view. X 610. (After Stokes.)

25 (24)   Seven (rarely fewer) large spines in two widely separated transverse
rows. . . . . *Chaetonotus spinulosus* Stokes 1887.

Length 0.0675 to 0.089 mm. Usually four large spines in anterior
row and three in posterior. Some may be suppressed (or lost?), leaving three in front and only one in the center behind. Spines of
anterior row distinctly longer. Egg 0.0339 mm. long, covered on
one side with short hairs. The embryo escapes in thirty hours and
thirty hours later the young individual shows an ovarian egg in which
the nucleus becomes conspicuous six hours later.

FIG. 975.   *Chaetonotus spinulosus* in dorsal view.   X 665.   (After Stokes.)

26 (21)   Spines present on head and neck much smaller than those on
body. 27

27 (28, 29)   Four transverse rows of large dorsal spines on posterior region
of body.   Also one large lateral spine on each side at caudal
process. . . . . .   *Chaetonotus acanthophorus* Stokes 1887.

Length 0.108 mm. Head and neck covered with short spines.
Large spines on body in four cross rows of five each, not alternating
so that they appear also as five longitudinal rows of four spines each.
The last lateral spine at the base of the caudal process is large and much
like those in the dorsal rows. Trenton, New Jersey.

FIG. 976.   *Chaetonotus acanthomorphus* in dorsal view.   X 415.   With dorsal
spine.   X about 1165.   (After Stokes.)

28 (27, 29)   One transverse row of large spines just in front of the caudal end
of the body. . . . . . .   *Chaetonotus spinifer* Stokes 1887.

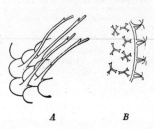

Length 0.1954 mm. Back and sides covered by
rounded imbricated scales, each with stout recurved
spine minutely furcate at tip. The four spines in a
single series immediately in front of the caudal process
are much larger and stouter than those on the rest of
the body. Egg ornamented with processes varying
in length and shape in different specimens. Stokes
distinguishes eggs with three separate patterns, respectively, 0.0705, 0.0736, and 0.0793 mm. long. Trenton,
New Jersey.

FIG. 977.   *Chaetonotus spinifer.*   *A*, spinose scales.   *B*, portion of egg, showing trifid and quadrifid spines in profile
and surface aspects. Highly magnified. (After Stokes.)

A   *B*

29 (27, 28) Five transverse rows with thirteen large spines. Also two conspicuous lateral spines on each side near the end.

Chaetonotus enormis Stokes 1887.

Length 0.0846 mm. Of the thirteen large spines three stand in the anterior row, four in the next, one at the extreme on each side in the next, three in the fourth row, and one at the center in the fifth row. On each side near the caudal process are two forked spines easily confused with those of the five rows which they much resemble. Trenton, New Jersey.

FIG. 978. *Chaetonotus enormis* in dorsal view. X 530. (After Stokes.)

30 (12) Caudal process branching or notched. A transverse row of large spines near its base. Body surface rough.

Chaeturina Ward.

Only one species known.

Chaeturina capricornia (Metchinkoff) 1864.

A swamp animal not yet reported from North America.

31 (1) No caudal processes. Posterior end simply rounded or lobed, in the latter case provided with long fine spines.

Suborder **Apodina.**

Reported from North America . . . . Family DASYDYTIDAE.

Two genera described for Europe.

Single North American genus. . . . . . . *Dasydytes* Gosse 1851.

Several species listed from Europe.

Only species reported from North America.

Dasydytes saltitans Stokes 1887.

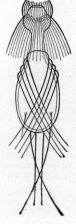

Length 0.085 mm. Head three lobed, distinctly separated from body by slender neck, provided with two rows of cilia which vibrate alternately. Four long heavy spines arise on each side near the neck and cross the back obliquely. Two long straight spines, and two others long and curved, project from the posterior end. This species swims rapidly but also moves by sudden leaps to one side or the other, covering a distance equal to double its length or more in a single jump. Trenton, New Jersey.

FIG. 979. *Dasydytes saltitans* in dorsal view. X 410. (After Stokes.)

IMPORTANT PAPERS ON NORTH AMERICAN GASTROTRICHA

FERNALD, C. H. 1883. Notes on the *Chaetonotus larus*. Amer. Nat., 17: 1217–1220; 2 figs.

Interesting biological study on *Ch. brevispinosus*.

GRÜNSPANN, TH. 1910. Die Süsswasser-Gastrotrichen Europas. Ann. Biol. Lacustre, 4: 211–365; 61 figs.

STOKES, A. C. 1887. Observations on *Chaetonotus*. The Microscope, 7: 1–9, 33–43; 2 pl. Translated in Jour. Microg., 11: 77–85, 150–153, 560–565; 2 pl.

1887a. Observations on a New *Dasydytes* and a New *Chaetonotus*. The Microscope, 7: 261–265; 1 pl. Translated in Jour. Microg., 12: 19–22, 49–51; 1 pl.

1896. Aquatic Microscopy for Beginners. Third edition (Gastrotricha, pp. 178–193).

ZELINKA, C. 1889. Die Gastrotrichen. Zeit. f. wiss. Zool., 49: 209–384; 5 pl.

CHAPTER XIX
AQUATIC EARTHWORMS AND OTHER BRISTLE-BEARING WORMS (CHAETOPODA)

By FRANK SMITH
Professor of Systematic Zoology and Curator of the Museum of Natural History, University of Illinois

EARTHWORMS, with their flexible segmented bodies and four double rows of bristles, or setae, are objects familiar to all students of animal life. Although most species are terrestrial there are also aquatic ones and these are abundantly represented in our fresh waters. Closely related to the earthworms and similar in structure are numerous other worms which are essentially aquatic. These also, with certain exceptions, are provided with setae and are included with earthworms in the group Oligochaeta. The setae-bearing worms of the sea (Polychaeta) commonly bear the setae on lateral muscular outgrowths of the body wall, the parapodia. The Oligochaeta and Polychaeta collectively are often referred to as the Chaetopoda.

The Chaetopoda, Hirudinea (leeches), and certain strictly marine worms which are not under consideration here, are included in the phylum Annelida.

FRESH-WATER POLYCHAETA

Although the Polychaeta are essentially marine in habit, a few species in various parts of the world have become adapted to fresh-water conditions. *Manayunkia speciosa* Leidy is found in the Schuylkill River and in other fresh-water situations near Philadelphia, and Johnson has described two fresh-water species from the western coast region, — *Nereis limnicola* Johnson from Lake Merced, near San Francisco, and *Lycastoides alticola* Johnson from Lower California.

These are stray intruders from the rich, marine fauna of this group in adjacent salt water, and none have yet been discovered at any great distance from the sea. Further, more careful study of the life in brackish water estuaries and fresh-water bodies in close contiguity with the ocean is likely to reveal the presence of such forms in other localities.

FRESH-WATER OLIGOCHAETA

The Oligochaeta, including the earthworms and related aquatic forms, are segmented worms which have a somewhat extensive and well-defined body cavity separating the alimentary tract from the body wall. They are hermaphroditic, with the reproductive organs limited to a few definite segments or somites. The bristle-like setae in the body wall aid in locomotion, but such setae are absent in the family Discodrilidae which are parasitic on the external surfaces of crayfishes. The majority of the species are terrestrial, and the aquatic forms are nearly all confined to fresh water. Seven families of aquatic Oligochaeta are found in the northern hemisphere and are all abundantly represented in the United States.

Morphological Relations. The general plan of structure of the aquatic forms agrees essentially with that of the earthworm. External metamerism is indicated by the transverse grooves and by the segmentally arranged setae, and the corresponding internal metamerism is recognizable in the septa, nephridia, transverse blood vessels, and in the ganglia of the ventral nerve chain. The prostomium — the dorsal part of the anterior somite extending anterior to the mouth — is very flexible and sensitive, and is an important tactile organ which in some species is prolonged into a proboscis (Fig. 984.) The somites are numbered consecutively from the anterior end, and are designated in these pages by Roman numerals in accordance with a common practice. The boundary between two somites is indicated thus: X/XI.

The setae are usually conspicuous and are of taxonomic importance. They are commonly grouped into dorsal and ventral bundles, the most anterior ventral pairs being always on the second somite. Figure 991 illustrates some of the more usual types of setae.

The nephridia are the segmental excretory organs, which typically are paired and are usually present in all somites of the body

except a few anterior ones and one at the posterior end.   Not infrequently some of the nephridia may fail to develop, when a more or
less irregular and asymmetrical distribution results.

The reproductive organs of the fresh-water Oligochaeta are similar to those of the terrestrial earthworms.   One or two pairs of
male gonads (spermaries or testes) are attached to the anterior
septa of certain somites and extend freely posteriad into the cavities
of the somites.   One or two pairs of ovaries are correspondingly
situated in somites posterior to those which contain the spermaries.
The sperm ducts of most species have their internal openings or
spermiducal funnels in the somites which contain the spermaries,
and the external openings, or spermiducal pores, on some somite
posteriad; but in a few species both openings may be in the same
somite.   In many species the sperm ducts are modified in various
ways, giving rise to prostates, atria and storage chambers (Fig.
990).   The internal openings of the oviducts, the oviducal funnels,
are in the ovarian somite, and the oviducal pores are either at the
posterior boundary of the same somite or, more commonly, on
the following one.   Accessory reproductive organs are commonly
present.   Evaginations of the septa of the somites which contain
spermaries form sperm sacs in which the sperm cells may complete
their development and be temporarily stored before they pass out
through the sperm ducts during copulation.   Evaginations of the
posterior septa of the ovarian somite form ovisacs.   Invaginations
of the body wall of certain somites produce spermathecae, usually
paired, which serve for storage of the sperm cells received during
copulation, from another individual.

Sexual reproduction occurs in all families of fresh-water Oligochaeta at more or less definite seasons of the year.   In the two
families Naididae and Aeolosomatidae, asexual reproduction by
budding is the mode by which the majority of new individuals
are produced.   Figure 980 exhibits the main features of the process
and renders an extended description unnecessary.   The body wall
thickens anterior to the middle of the budding somite and forms a
budding zone, the anterior half of which gives rise to an indefinite
number of new somites which form the posterior part of the anterior daughter-worm.   The posterior half of the budding zone

gives rise to a definite number of new somites (five in most species of Naididae), which form the anterior part of the posterior daughter-worm. The daughter-worms, before separation, may in turn develop budding zones, and in some cases even a third series of these zones may appear and thus give rise to chains of incipient individuals, or zooids. In some species chains of eight zooids are of ordinary occurrence. In the genus Chaetogaster the plane of division is in a septum between two somites.

Although many aquatic Oligochaeta have the power to regenerate

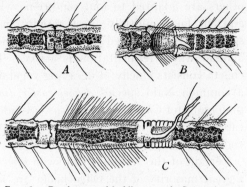

Fig. 980. Development of budding zones in *Stylaria lacustris.* *A*, An early stage. *B*, A later stage. *C*, Still later stage with a second budding zone well started. ×25. (After Leuckart.)

missing parts, greatly developed, there is lack of evidence that it is of much importance in normal reproduction.

Environmental Relations. The well-known investigations of Darwin and others, on the action of terrestrial earthworms on the soil and its organic contents, have led to a general appreciation of the importance of the relations of these animals to their surroundings. It is less generally understood that their aquatic relatives play a very important part in reducing the great masses of aquatic vegetation to a finely-comminuted condition. Oligochaeta of various species abound in the mud at the bottom and along the shores of most bodies of fresh water, and an almost continuous stream of this mud with its decaying organic contents is passing through their bodies and being still further subdivided and deprived of organic material and its available energy. Numerous other species swarm in the decaying leaves and stems of coarse vegetation of swampy areas and materially aid in their disintegration, while still other kinds populate the floating masses of algae, which they rapidly devour as decay progresses. Since under favorable conditions it requires but two or three days for Naidiform worms to reproduce by budding, they multiply with such rapidity that they can extensively populate large masses of moribund algae in a very short time, and their activity accounts in part for the speedy disappearance of such masses in the autumn. Although many of these worms will not thrive in polluted water, others are adapted to foul conditions where fermentation is rife, and, in fact, multiply most rapidly in such situations. Some species of this sort feed extensively on the zoogloeic masses which abound where fermentation is active. The food of most Oligochaeta consists chiefly of decaying vegetable matter, but worms of a common Naid species, *Chaetogaster diaphanus*, have a marked preference for *Chydorus sphaericus*, a Cladoceran species which they capture and devour in large numbers. Worms of the family Discodrilidae are parasitic on crayfishes.

Certain of the Naididae can swim effectively in open water, but a great majority of the Oligochaeta are limited to crawling movements for locomotion.

Striking structural adaptations are not numerous in the group, but the peculiar modification of the posterior end in *Aulophorus* and *Dero* for purposes of respiration, deserves mention. These worms live chiefly in tubes of their own making or with their bodies almost wholly buried in masses of vegetable material, and respiration is aided by well-developed gill structures (Fig. 985). The Discodrilidae in adaptation to their peculiar mode of life, have become so leech-like in action and external appearance that formerly it was usual to treat them as belonging to the Hirudinea rather than to the Oligochaeta.

Collection and Preservation. The larger specimens may be obtained by carefully screening mud from bottoms and shores and from about the roots of coarse plants through fine-meshed nets or sieves. Others may be obtained by carefully pulling to pieces decaying rushes and masses of algae. Smaller specimens often may be obtained from the sides of aquaria in which mud and vegetable material have been allowed to stand for a few days. During the fermentation of such masses large numbers of small worms appear in the surface layers and about the margins.

The most successful methods of preservation vary with different species, and must be gained by experiment, but some general hints may be given here. Specimens intended for sectioning must be kept in water and material which is free from grit until the alimentary tract is cleansed from mud and sand. The methods necessary for securing straight and well-extended specimens for fixation vary greatly with the species. Dilute solutions of the fixing agent when of the right strength will often cause the worms to die in a properly extended condition, and this is especially true of some of the Tubificidae when corrosive sublimate is used. Commonly some means of narcotization is required to secure the relaxation necessary for the preparation of well-extended specimens. Good results are often obtained by the gradual addition of a solution of chloretone until the worms no longer respond to stimuli and fail to contract excessively when placed in the fixing fluid. Another common expedient used with success for some species is to immerse the worms in water within a closed vessel and there subject them to the action of the vapor of chloroform, which is put into the same closed vessel but in a separate container. Only the vapor should be allowed to reach the water that contains the worms.

When properly narcotized the specimens may be immersed in the fixing agent and kept straight by holding them against any convenient straight edge until they have become sufficiently rigid. A rectangular glass candy-tray is a convenient vessel for fixation purposes since the angles formed by the sides and the bottom furnish good opportunities for keeping the worms straight. It is often advantageous to use a small amount of fixing fluid at first and to keep the worms only partially submerged until they have become stiffened and then completely immerse them. Small specimens like tubificids and enchytraeids may be conveniently fixed on a glass plate with the aid of square-edged toothpicks which have been soaked in the fixing agent. A toothpick with the adhering fluid is placed on the glass, an anesthetized worm stretched along one edge of the toothpick, another toothpick placed against the other side of the worm and a second worm stretched along the free edge of the second toothpick. A repetition of this process will enable one to prepare a considerable number of specimens in a brief time. Subsequent treatment is like that for other material of similar nature.

KEY TO NORTH AMERICAN FRESH–WATER OLIGOCHAETA

1 (45)　Well-developed setae present on most somites.　. . . . . . . **2**

2 (24)　Reproduction chiefly asexual, by budding; sexual reproduction less frequent. Clitellum, when present, on some somites of V–VIII. Length less than 25 mm. in most species.　. **3**

3 (4)　Setae of ventral bundles as well as dorsal setae capilliform; septa imperfectly developed; prostomium broad and ciliated ventrally; integument of most species contains conspicuous colored bodies of some shade of red, green, or yellow. Usually 1–2 mm. long.　. . . . . . Family AEOLOSOMATIDAE.

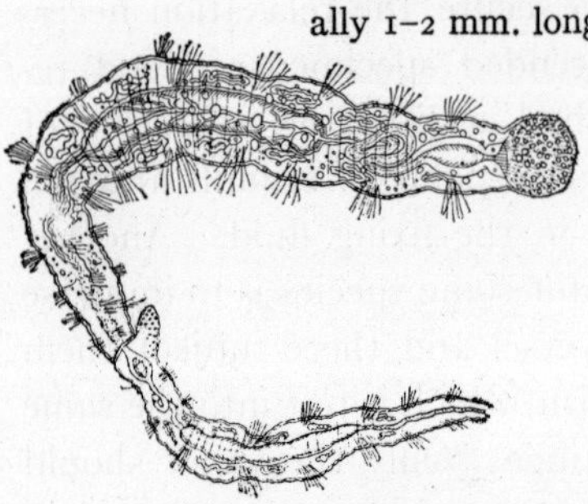

Aeolosoma Ehrenberg is the only North American genus and the species of the U. S. have not been much studied. *A. tenebrarum* Vejdovsky has pale yellow or greenish integumental bodies. One or two species with colorless bodies are known. *A. hemprichi* Ehrenberg has salmon-colored bodies. This last named species thrives exceptionally well in hay infusions and in similar cultures from wheat and thus large numbers are readily obtained for experimental purposes.

FIG. 981. *Aeolosoma hemprichi.* X 20. (After Lankester.)

4 (3)　Ventral setae all uncinate (Fig. 991); septa well developed; **no** brightly colored integumental bodies.

Family NAIDIDAE . . **5**

5 (8)　No dorsal setae **6**

6 (7)　Ventral bundles of setae on III–V as on other somites.

Schmardaella Michaelsen 1900.

The South American species *S. filiformis* (Schmarda) has recently been reported from Lake St. Clair (Moore, 1906).

7 (6)　No setae on III–V. Somite III much elongated.

Chaetogaster K. von Baer 1827.

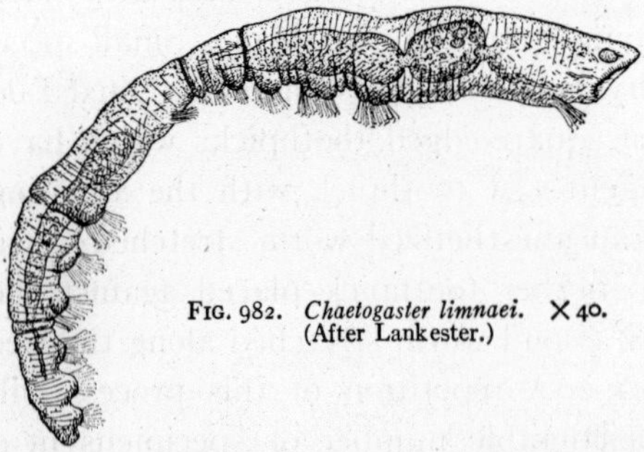

Several species are known from North America, of which *C. limnaei* K. von Baer, which lives in mollusks, and the large transparent *C. diaphanus* (Gruithuisen), 10–15 mm. long, are easily recognized.

FIG. 982. *Chaetogaster limnaei.* X 40. (After Lankester.)

8 (5)　Setae in both dorsal and ventral bundles. **9**

9 (12)　No capilliform setae in dorsal bundles. **10**

10 (11)   Setae of dorsal bundles all uncinate. . *Paranais* Czerniavsky 1880.

P. litoralis (Müller) reported as abundant on the New England coast and may occur in adjacent fresh waters.   The first dorsal setae are on V.

11 (10)   Dorsal setae nearly straight, slightly toothed or simple-pointed.
Ophidonais Gervais 1838.

O. serpentina (Müller) may be easily recognized by the small irregularly distributed dorsal setae; by the four large transverse pigmented areas on the anterior region, and by the relatively large size.   Length 25–30 mm.

FIG. 983.   Anterior end of *Ophidonais serpentina*.   X 40.   (After Piguet.)

12 (9)   Capilliform setae present in dorsal bundles. 13

13 (21)   First anterior dorsal setae on V or VI. 14

14 (18)   Posterior end not modified into a gill-bearing respiratory organ; first anterior dorsal setae on VI. 15

15 (16, 17)   One or more capilliform setae of VI much longer than those of other somites and equal to three or four times the diameter of the body. . . . . *Slavina* Vejdovsky 1883.

S. appendiculata (d'Udekem), common in some parts of the United States, has body surface studded with sensory papillae and with foreign bodies.

16 (15, 17)   Prostomium elongated to form a proboscis; dorsal setae of VI similar in length to those of other somites.   *Stylaria* Lamarck 1816.

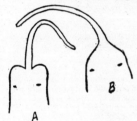

S. lacustris (Linnaeus) has proboscis flanked by prominent lateral prostomial lobes (Figs. 980 and 984).   *S. fossularis* Leidy lacks the lateral prostomial lobes (Fig. 984). The former is abundant and widely distributed in the United States while the latter is reported only very infrequently.

FIG. 984.   Prostomium and proboscis, *Stylaria*.   *A, S. lacustris; B, S. fossularis*.   X40.   (Original.)

17 (15, 16)   Without proboscis; dorsal setae of VI similar in length to those of other somites. . . . . *Nais* Müller 1774.

Several species without conspicuous differences are reported from the United States.   *N. elinguis* Müller is one of the best-known species and *N. communis* Piguet is very common.

18 (14)   Posterior end modified into a gill-bearing respiratory organ, the branchial area. 19

19 (20)   Ventral margin of the branchial area with a pair of long processes.
Aulophorus Schmarda 1861.

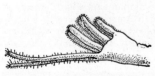

A. furcatus (Oken) has the first dorsal setae on V and has two pairs of well-developed gills.
A. vagus Leidy crawls or floats about in a tube made from bryozoan statoblasts and bits of vegetation.   It has the first dorsal setae on VI and has only slightly developed gills.

FIG. 985.   Posterior end of *Aulophorus furcatus*.   X 40.   (After Bousfield.)

20 (19)   Ventral margin of the branchial area without long processes.

Dero Oken 1815.

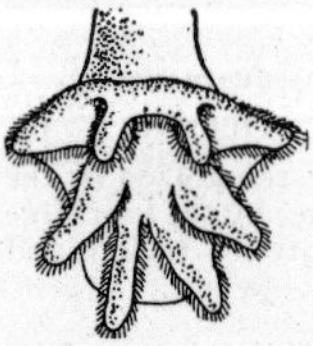

D. limosa Leidy is abundant and the best known of the North American species. *D. obtusa* d'Udekem and a species which probably is *D. perrieri* Bousefield are of frequent occurrence, but a careful study of the North American representatives of this genus, as well as of *Nais*, is necessary before we can be sure of their exact relation to European species.

Fig. 986. Posterior end of *Dero limosa*.   × 25. (After Bousefield.)

21 (13)   First anterior dorsal setae on II.   22

22 (23)   Dorsal setae of two kinds: capilliform and shorter needle-form setae which commonly have cleft distal ends.

Naidium O. Schmidt 1847.

N. osborni Walton has been described from Lake Erie (Walton, 1906). This genus is united with *Pristina* by some writers.

23 (22)   Dorsal setae all capilliform, mostly with very fine teeth on convex side; prostomium commonly elongated into a proboscis.

Pristina Ehrenberg 1831.

P. longiseta var. *leidyi* Frank Smith has the capilliform setae of III greatly lengthened (.700 mm.) and without serrations. The typical form of this species as found in Europe has extremely minute inconspicuous serrations on the capilliform setæ of dorsal bundles of somites other than III. In the variety *P. l. leidyi*, which is found in the United States and certain other parts of the world, the serrations are coarser and more easily seen.

Fig. 987. *Pristina longiseta* var. *leidyi*.   *v. s.*, ventral seta; × 300.   *d. s.*, part of seta from dorsal bundle.   × 450. (After Smith.)

d.s.   v.s.

P. flagellum Leidy has a very characteristic posterior end. Specimens of this species have been met with by the writer but once and when there was no opportunity for study beyond enough to convince him of the general accuracy of Leidy's description and that the species really belongs to *Pristina*. Representatives are sometimes found of certain species in which the dorsal setae of III are not especially elongated but their exact relationship to European species is uncertain.

Fig. 988. Posterior end of *Pristina flagellum*.   × 16. (After Leidy.)

24 (2)   Reproduction sexual, never by budding; clitellum ordinarily posterior to VIII.   25

25 (34, 35) Ordinarily more than two well-developed setae in each of some or all of the bundles; ventral setae ordinarily cleft (exc. *Telmatodrilus:* see below); clitellum ordinarily on X or XI and one or more adjacent somites; ♂ pores ordinarily on XI, exceptionally on XII; spermathecal pores on somite anterior to one bearing ♂ pores (in North American species); length commonly more than 25 mm.; blood vessels usually with conspicuous red contents. . . . Family TUBIFICIDAE . .   26

Accurate identification of species in this family usually requires the aid of careful dissections or of serial sections, and depends largely on a careful study of the reproductive organs. (Fig. 990.)

26 (27) Sperm-ducts without definite prostate glands and opening into a common median chamber with single ventral median opening on XI; spermathecal pores on X; setae of dorsal bundles all cleft. . . . . *Rhizodrilus* Frank Smith 1900.

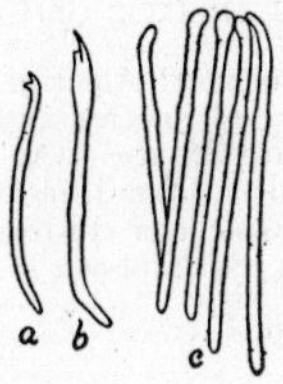

One species thus far known in North America, *R. lacteus* Frank Smith, found in roots of *Sagittaria* in Illinois. Has two kinds of genital setae on IX and XI; length 75–100 mm.; whitish in appearance (Smith, 1900). Michaelsen includes this species in *Monopylephorus* Levinsen.

FIG. 989. *Rhizodrilus lacteus.* *a*, ordinary uncinate seta; *b* and *c*, genital setae from IX and XI. × 150. (After Smith.)

27 (26) Sperm-ducts with definite prostate glands. 28

28 (29) Ten or more small definite prostates on each sperm-duct; no capilliform setae; setae indistinctly cleft and sometimes simple-pointed. . . . . *Telmatodrilus* Eisen 1879.

Two species, *T. vejdovskyi* Eisen and *T. mcgregori* Eisen, are found in California.

29 (28) Sperm-ducts each with one definite prostate gland (Fig. 990). . 30

30 (31) Dorsal setae all uncinate and similar to ventral setae; penis with chitinous sheath. . . . . . *Limnodrilus* Claparède 1862.

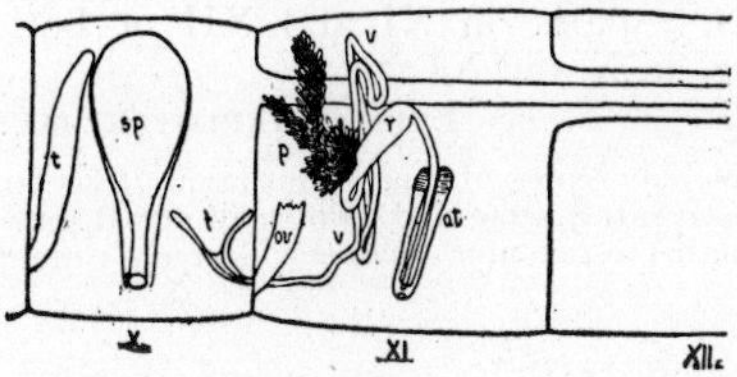

Several species have been described from California (Eisen, 1885).

L. gracilis Moore has recently been described from Lake Erie (Moore, 1906). In *L. claparedianus* Ratzel, an abundant species of wide distribution, the length of the chitinous penis sheath is 8–30 times its diameter.

FIG. 990. Reproductive organs of *Limnodrilus gracilis.* *t*, spermary; *sp*, spermatheca; *f*, spermiducal funnel; *v, v*, sperm-duct; *p*, prostate gland; *r*, atrium; *at*, penis and penis sheath; *ov*, ovary. × 20. (After Moore.)

31 (30) Dorsal bundles ordinarily contain capilliform setae and also pectinate or palmate setae. (Fig. 991.) 32

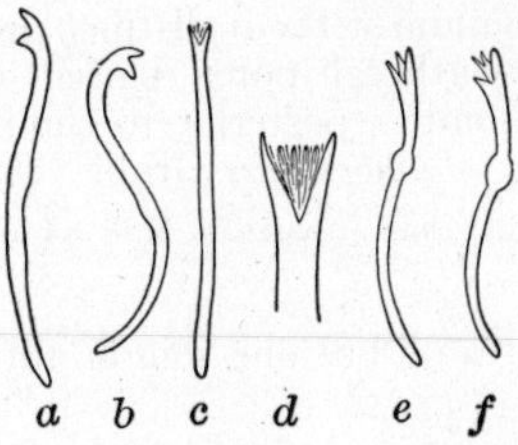

FIG. 991. *a* and *b*, uncinate setae from *Tubifex multisetosus; c* and *d*, palmate setae, *T. multisetosus; e* and *f*, pectinate setae, *T. tubifex.* *a, b,* and *c,* × 150. (Original.)

a   b   c   d   e   f

32 (33) Length of atrium and penis combined, at least two-thirds that of the remainder of the sperm-duct. . *Ilyodrilus* Eisen 1879.

Three species described from California (Eisen, 1885).

33 (32)   Atrium and penis combined, much shorter than the remainder of
the sperm-duct. . . . .   *Tubifex* Lamarck 1816.

Several species have been described from North America.
T. tubifex (Müller) is a widely distributed species and
abundant both in Europe and the United States. Another species, *T. multisetosus* (Frank Smith) from Illinois
has large integumental papillae and conspicuous clusters
of capilliform setae (Smith, 1900). (Figs. 991 and 992.)

FIG. 992.   Anterior somites of *Tubifex multisetosus*. × 13. (Original.)

34 (25, 35) Ordinarily with more than two setae in each of some or all the
bundles; setae simple-pointed and usually nearly straight;
clitellum on XII and on more or less of adjacent somites;
♂ pores ordinarily on XII; spermathecal pores on IV/V.
Ordinarily whitish in appearance and seldom more than
25 mm. in length. Both terrestrial and aquatic species
abound. . . . .   Family ENCHYTRAEIDAE . . 35

There are numerous species of this family represented in the fresh waters of North America,
which have only recently received attention from the systematists of the group. Eisen
(1905) has described several fresh-water species from the Pacific Coast states belonging
to *Mesenchytraeus* Eisen, *Enchytraeus* Henle and *Lumbricillus* Oersted. Smith and Welch
(1913) have described *Marionina forbesae* from Illinois and Welch (1914) has described
Lumbricillus rutilus from Illinois.

35 (25, 34) Ordinarily with not more than two well-developed setae per bundle,
or eight more or less separated setae per somite. . . . 36

36 (37, 42) Setae simple-pointed; ♂ pores, 2 pairs on XI and XII or both
pairs on XII; spermaries in X and XI.
Family HAPLOTAXIDAE.

Haplotaxis (Phreoryctes) emissarius (Forbes) is the only representative of this family thus far
known in North America. Has two large isolated ventral setae and two small dorsal setae
per somite; many somites without dorsal setae; length 150–200 mm.; diameter, scarcely 1 mm.;
subterranean habit.

37 (36, 42) Setae either simple-pointed or cleft; ♂ pores on one or more somites
anterior to XII, with spermiducal funnels in same somites;
cecal diverticula of the dorsal vessel or its branches, in the
mid-body region. . . . .   Family LUMBRICULIDAE . . 38

38 (39)   Setae cleft at distal extremities; prostomium without distinct proboscis; spermathecae and spermathecal pores paired or
asymmetrical in three or more somites posterior to somite
bearing ♂ pores. . . . .   *Lumbriculus* Grube 1844.

L. inconstans (Frank Smith), common in the Mississippi Valley, has ♂ pores on X or XI and
spermathecae in XI–XV or XII–XVI (Smith, 1905).

39 (38)   Setae simple-pointed; spermathecal pores on but one somite anterior to ♂ pores. 40

40 (41)   Large median spermathecal sac with numerous tubular diverticula
in VIII; with single median external opening.
Sutroa Eisen 1888.

Two species, *S. rostrata* Eisen and *S. alpestris* Eisen, each with distinct proboscis, are
found west of the Rocky Mountains.

41 (40)   Spermathecae without diverticula, paired or two unpaired ones opening separately; long, highly muscular, ejaculatory chamber forms part of each otherwise highly differentiated sperm-duct. . . . . *Eclipidrilus* Eisen 1881.

A genus of peculiar North American Lumbriculidae which includes *E. frigidus* Eisen from California, with paired ♂ pores on X; *E. asymmetricus* (Frank Smith) from Illinois, with single median ♂ pore on X; and *E. palustris* (Frank Smith) from Florida, with paired ♂ pores on IX (Smith, 1900a).

42 (36, 37) Earthworms, essentially aquatic in habit. Setae simple-pointed and paired in each of four bundles per somite; ♂ pores exceptionally on XII or XIII, commonly further posterior; spermaries in X and XI; ovaries in XIII. 43

43 (44)   Clitellum beginning on XIV to XVI and extending over 10–12 somites; ♂ pores on XVIII/XIX or on XIX, recognizable only in sections; few or no dorsal pores; without well-developed gizzard. . . . . *Sparganophilus* Benham 1892.

Several North American species, of which *S. eiseni* Frank Smith is found in the Mississippi Valley, Great Lakes region, and Florida; *S. smithi* Eisen and subspecies occur in California; *S. benhami* Eisen and subspecies in Mexico and Central America (Eisen, 1896).

44 (43)   Clitellum beginning on XVIII–XXIII and extending over 4–6 somites; ♂ pores on XII, XIII, or XV, conspicuous; gizzard limited to XVII; first dorsal pores on IV/V.
           Helodrilus Subgenus *Eiseniella* Michaelsen 1900.

The highly variable species, *H. (E.) tetraedrus* (Savigny), is represented in North America by several of the subspecies indicated in the diagram from Michaelsen (Fig. 993).

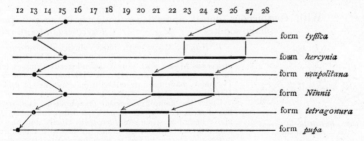

12 13 14 15 16 17 18 19 20 21 22 23 24 25 26 27 28

form *typica*

form *hercynia*

form *neapolitana*

form *Ninnii*

form *tetragonura*

form *pupa*

FIG. 993.   Different forms of *Helodrilus (Eiseniella) tetraedrus* (Savigny). The diagram shows the positions for the spermiducal pores and the tubercula pubertatis. (After Michaelsen.)

A specimen which is presumably the type of *Helodrilus tetraedrus* forma *pupa* (Eisen) was deposited in the United States National Museum and has been studied by the writer. It is almost certainly a regenerated individual and is highly abnormal and hence the form presumably has no systematic status except in synonomy. References in paragraphs 42 and 44 of the above key and in Fig. 993, to spermiducal pores on XII, have therefore lost their significance.

Beside these essentially aquatic forms, several species of *Diplocardia* and *Helodrilus* live in bottomlands and low-lying banks of streams which are subject to overflow for prolonged intervals.

45 (1)   Without setae; pharynx with two chitinous jaws, dorsal and ven-
           tral. Small leech-like worms, parasitic or symbiotic, on
           crayfishes. . . . . Family DISCODRILIDAE . . 46

The family name Branchiobdellidae is preferred by some writers.

46 (49)   Two pairs of spermaries and two pairs of sperm-ducts in the fifth
           and sixth post-cephalic somites. 47

47 (48)   Without conspicuous dorsal appendages on post-cephalic somites.
                                              Bdellodrilus Moore 1895.

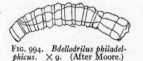

FIG. 994. *Bdellodrilus philadel-phicus.* ✕ 9. (After Moore.)

B. *philadelphicus* (Leidy) and B. *illuminatus* (Moore)
resemble each other in having the anterior pair of nephridia
open to the exterior through a common pulsatile vesicle on
the mid-dorsal line of the third post-cephalic somite and in
having the dorsal and ventral jaws quite dissimilar. The
former has the head much broader than the anterior body
somite and enjoys a wide distribution in the eastern half of
the United States. The latter has nine pairs of conspicuous
lateral glands, the head narrower than the following somite and is less common.

FIG. 995. *Bdellodrilus instabilis.* ✕ 9. (After Moore.)

B. *pulcherrimus* (Moore) and B. *instabilis* (Moore) resemble each other in having the anterior nephridia open
separately and in having the dorsal and ventral jaws similar. The former has all post-cephalic somites evidently
biannulate; alimentary canal straight; jaws small, each
bearing three teeth. The latter has biannulation conspicuous on only anterior four post-cephalic somites; alimentary canal with transverse loop in seventh somite;
and dark-brown jaws, each bearing four teeth. They have been described from North Carolina
and Pennsylvania (Moore 1893).

Under the name *Cambarincola macrodonta*, Ellis (1912) has described a species from Colorado
which is closely allied to B. *philadelphicus* but which has the head narrower than the greatest
width of the body and different shaped jaws. It also lacks the conspicuous glands of B.
illuminatus.

48 (47)   With conspicuous dorsal appendages on each of several post-
           cephalic somites. . . . . *Pterodrilus* Moore 1894.

FIG. 996. *Pterodrilus alcicornus.* ✕ 50. (After Moore.)

P *distichus* Moore, with simple cylindrical dorsal appendages on each of post-cephalic somites II to VIII, and P.
alcicornus Moore, with dorsal appendages of complex form
on post-cephalic somites III and VIII and simple ones on
IV and V, have been described from crayfishes of eastern
United States (Moore 1894).

Under the name *Ceratodrilus thysanosomus*, Hall (1914)
has described a species from Utah which resembles the
above described species of *Pterodrilus* closely, but has the
antero-dorsal border of the head furnished with a membranous border deeply incised to form four tentacular append-
ages. The dorsal appendages are transverse bands with edges bearing six to eight points.

49 (46)   But one pair of spermaries and one pair of sperm-ducts and these
           in the fifth post-cephalic somite.
                                              Branchiobdella Odier 1823.

B. *americana* Pierantoni has the prostomium entire and the jaws dissimilar. It has been
collected in Texas and North Carolina. B. *tetrodonta* Pierantoni has the prostomium divided
into dorsal and ventral lobes and the jaws similar. It is found in California (Pierantoni 1912).

LITERATURE ON FRESH-WATER OLIGOCHAETA

EISEN, G. 1885. Oligochaetological Researches. Rept. U. S. Fish Com. for 1883, 11: 879–964; 19 pl.

1896. Pacific Coast Oligochaeta II. Mem. Calif. Acad. Sci., 2: 123–198; 12 pl.

1905. Enchytraeidae of the West Coast of North America. Harriman Alaska Expedition, 12: 1–166; 20 pl. New York.

ELLIS, M. M. 1912. A New Discodrilid Worm from Colorado. Proc. U. S. Nat'l Mus., 42: 481–486.

GALLOWAY, T. W. 1911. The Common Fresh-Water Oligochaeta of the United States. Trans. Amer. Micr. Soc., 30: 285–317; 14 figs.

HALL, M. C. 1914. Descriptions of a New Genus and Species of the Discodrilid Worms. Proc. U. S. Nat'l Mus., 48: 187–193.

MICHAELSEN, W. 1900. Oligochaeta. Das Tierreich. No. 10. Pp. xxix and 575.

MOORE, J. P. 1893. On Some Leech-like Parasites of American Crayfishes. Proc. Acad. Nat. Sci. Phila., 1893: 419–428; 1 pl.

1894. Pterodrilus, a Remarkable Discodrilid. Proc. Acad. Nat. Sci. Phila., 1894: 449–454; 1 pl.

1906. Hirudinea and Oligochaeta Collected in the Great Lakes Region. Bull. Bur. Fish., 21: 153–171; 1 pl.

PIERANTONI, U. 1912. Monografia dei Discodrilidae. Ann. Mus. Zool. Univ. Napoli, n.s., 3, No. 24, 28 pp.; 1 pl.

SMITH, FRANK. 1900. Notes on Species of North American Oligochaeta III. Bull. Ill. State Lab. Nat. Hist., 5: 441–458; 2 pl.

1900a. Notes on Species of North American Oligochaeta IV. Bull. Ill. State Lab. Nat. Hist., 5: 459–478; 1 pl.

1905. Notes on Species of North American Oligochaeta V. Bull. Ill. State Lab. Nat. Hist., 7: 45–51.

SMITH, F., and WELCH, P. S. 1913. Some New Illinois Enchytraeidae. Bull. Ill. State Lab. Nat. Hist., 9: 615–636; 5 pl.

WALTON, L. B. 1906. Naididae of Cedar Point, Ohio. Amer. Nat., 40: 683–706.

WELCH, P. S. 1914. Studies on the Enchytraeidae of North America. Bull. Ill. State Lab. Nat. Hist., 10: 123–212; 5 pl.

CHAPTER XX

THE LEECHES (HIRUDINEA)

By J. PERCY MOORE

Professor of Zoology in the University of Pennsylvania

THE Hirudinea or leeches are predatory or parasitic annelids with terminal suckers serving for attachment and locomotion. Quite nearly related to the Oligochaeta and closely resembled by the semi-parasitic Discodrilidae in the possession of suckers, jaws, and median genital orifices and in the absence of setae, they are characteristically modified for procuring and digesting their peculiar food, consisting typically of blood and other animal juices.

The body of a leech is generally constituted of thirty-four metameres (designated I to XXXIV), each represented in the central nervous system by a ganglion usually consisting of six capsules or groups of nerve cells. Externally superficial furrows divide each fully developed somite into from two to sixteen rings or annuli. One of these, lying at the middle of the somite, contains the ganglion and usually bears three or four dorsal pairs and three ventral pairs of eye-like sense organs or sensillae and is termed the neural or sensory ring. Segments having the full number of annuli characteristic of the genus are termed complete, and are always found in the middle region. Incomplete or abbreviated segments occur at the ends of the body and may have any number of annuli less than the complete somites into which they grade. Recognizing the triannulate somite as basic for most leeches and considering that more complex somites may be derived by repeated binary division of its annuli the following symbols are employed for the precise designation of particular rings. Counting from the head end the rings of the triannulate somite are A^1, A^2, and A^3, where A^2 is the neural or sensory annulus. These, bisected, give collectively the secondary annuli B^1 to B^6. Repeated subdivisions give tertiary annuli C^1 to C^{12} and quaternary annuli D^1 to D^{24}. But the full theoretical number of the fourth order is never developed and the neural annulus is usually less divided than the others.

Setae are always absent, except in *Acanthobdella*, and suckers always present, except in a few exotic, chiefly burrowing, genera. The oral sucker surrounds the mouth, sometimes forming mere lips and being widely expanded only in Ichthyobdellidae and a few Glossiphonidae. The caudal or subanal sucker is larger, discoid or, more rarely, deeply cupped, and widely expanded beyond its constricted central pedicle. There is a powerful and elaborate muscular system, consisting of circular, oblique, and thick, longitudinal coats, as well as vertical and radial sheets and fibers.

The digestive tract is divided into buccal chamber, pharynx, esophagus, stomach or crop, intestine and rectum. In the jawed leeches the mouth is large; in the proboscis leeches a mere pore in the disk of the sucker. In the former the buccal chamber usually contains three compressed muscular jaws bearing serial teeth on the ridge. The pharynx is a muscular bulb, a straight tube, or a slender, exertile proboscis moving within a sheath. Salivary glands may open into the short esophagus or on the jaws. The large stomach or crop varies with the nature of the food and may be a straight tube, or complicated by from one to twenty pairs of simple or branched lateral ceca, of which the posterior pair is largest and most constant. Generally short and simple, the intestine may bear four pairs of simple ceca (Glossiphonidae). A short, narrow rectum opens by a small dorsal anus usually behind XXVI or XXVII, but rarely behind XXIII.

Leeches are hermaphroditic. The genital orifices are median, with the male pore preceding the female. The testes (really coelomic sacs enclosing the testes) vary from one elongated pair in *Acanthobdella* to usually six (five to nine) pairs in the Rhynchobdellae, nine or ten (five to nineteen) pairs in the Hirudinidae, and very numerous small ones in the Herpobdellidae. A vas deferens on each side continues into an epididymis and an ejaculatory duct which may be provided with a sperm sac and a glandular region for forming the horny spermatophores. The two ejaculatory ducts open into an unpaired genital bursa or a more complex atrium which may be elongated into a highly muscular sheath enclosing a penis and provided with a prostate gland. The ovaries, also coelomic sacs, are a single pair, usually elongated and folded and opening directly into a small median bursa. In the Hirudinidae they have special ducts provided with an unpaired albumen gland and a muscular vagina. Accessory copulatory glands may occur.

A most striking characteristic of leeches is the great reduction of the body cavity which, besides the ovarian and testicular coelom, is represented only by a system of sinuses, the extent and arrangement of which vary in the several families. In addition there is a true blood vascular system consisting of dorsal and ventral longitudinal trunks and a peri-intestinal sinus united by transverse loops and in the caudal sucker by a circle of radiating loops. Except in some Ichthyobdellidae, which have lateral gills or pulsating vesicles, leeches respire solely by virtue of the capillary network underlying or even penetrating the hypodermis.

The nephridia in general resemble those of the Oligochaeta, but the funnels especially are more complex and variable, being sometimes branched and sometimes having the opening occluded. Not more than seventeen pairs usually occur, they being absent from both ends of the body and often from one or more clitellar segments.

Pigment occurs in the form of excreted matter contained in wandering cells and reserve cells and is usually deposited along the line of muscle bundles in either metameric or non-metameric spots or bands. The eyes are highly developed sensillae, several of which are sometimes united in a common pigment mass. They occur rarely on the caudal sucker as well as on the head.

Leeches are among the most interesting and beautiful of the invertebrate inhabitants of our fresh waters. They abound in ditches, pools, ponds and lakes, few species occurring in swift, cold streams. In the small lakes of our northern borders they fairly swarm.

They are predatory hunters or scavengers, temporary or nearly permanent parasites, or they may change from one mode of life to another. The few fresh-water Ichthyobdellidae attach themselves chiefly to the fins and gills of fishes. Several Glossiphonidae have similar habits and one remarkable species is a nearly permanent parasite on the sheepshead of the lakes of Minnesota, its sucker becoming fixed into deep pits in the inflamed tissues of the isthmus. Many of this family are temporary parasites on turtles, frogs, salamanders, etc., but also live free and subsist upon aquatic worms, mollusks, etc. Because of the nature of their food the smaller species are known as snail leeches. The Herpobdellidae are voracious destroyers of aquatic worms, larvae, insects, and even of their own kind. Many of the Hirudinidae have similar habits but also burrow into mud. Some even habitually leave the water in quest of earthworms and one, *Haemopis lateralis terrestris*, inhabits garden soil several miles from water.

While most species will partake of vertebrate blood, especially just before the breeding season, *Macrobdella* is our only native true sanguivorous jawed leech. While young it feeds upon larvae and worms and attacks vertebrates only when mature, and even then varies the blood diet with an occasional meal of frogs' eggs. This and other jawed leeches painlessly make a trifid incision in the skin and quickly extract more than their own weight of blood, the flow of which is facilitated by a ferment which prevents coagulation. As the blood fills the gastric ceca its fluid constituents are drawn off through the walls and exude in droplets from the nephropores. The solid parts remain and, protected from decay by a preservative secretion, may not be completely digested for upwards of a year.

The short, flat triannulate Glossiphonidae are poor swimmers but sometimes active creepers. When disturbed they roll into a ball, pill-bug-like, and fall to the bottom, soon to creep hastily to shelter. Species with longer, more complex segments are better swimmers and the elongated and muscular Herpobdellidae and Hirudinidae swim powerfully, moving rapidly with graceful undulations in either the vertical or horizontal plane. Their resting attitudes are varied and characteristic. Probably in order to facilitate respiration many species attach one or both suckers and wave the body with an undulatory motion. Most leeches are nocturnal and except when stimulated by hunger and the proximity of food they avoid the light by hiding beneath stones, among plants or in the mud.

Reproduction takes place in the spring and summer, some species continuing to produce batches of eggs for five or six months. In the Rhynchobdellae and Herpobdellidae copulation consists in the implanting by one individual of a horny, usually two-chambered spermatophore on the skin of another. From this the spermatozoa issue in a stream and, by a process that Professor Whitman has aptly termed hypodermic injection, penetrate the tissues to the ovarian sac where impregnation occurs. Among the Hirudinidae a more definite act of copulation and reciprocal fertilization takes place during which the filamentous penis of one individual deposits a spermatophore within the vagina or at the genital orifice of the other.

The Glossiphonidae carry their eggs in several membranous capsules attached to the venter, maintaining an undulatory movement for their aeration. The young also remain for a time fixed by a sort of byssus thread and later by the sucker, and are said to be partly nourished by an albuminous secretion of the parent. All other leeches form chitinoid cocoons or egg capsules from the secretion of the deeper glands of the clitellum which hardens on exposure to the water. The Ichthyobdellidae deposit a single ovum in a small stalked capsule, the Herpobdellidae and Hirudinidae several in an albuminous mass within a larger capsule, which in the case of the former is a flat pouch attached by one side and in the latter an ellipsoidal case with a thick, spongy, vesicular wall buried in wet earth.

Leeches have rather dull senses which arise in three sets of cutaneous organs. Numerous goblet cells located in the lips are taste organs and guide the leech on the trail of its prey. Tactile organs are scattered all over the skin but are especially numerous on the lips. Wave movements and light stimuli appear to affect all parts of the body. The eyes are strongly sensitive and the sensillae much less so to changes in the intensity of light.

Leeches may readily be found by searching in the situations indicated above. Sanguivorous species are easily collected by stirring the mud in their haunts with one's bare feet and removing them from the skin as they become attached, or by attracting them with fresh blood placed in the water. They may be kept and studied indefinitely in aquaria. For examination alive under a microscope they should be stupefied and relaxed by placing a little carbon dioxide (as soda water), chlorotone, or cocaine in the water.

For preservation they should always be first relaxed with similar reagents and extended before fixing. Chromic acid in one-quarter to one-half per cent solutions, picro-sulphuric acid, Gilson's fluid, corrosive-sublimate-acetic mixture and Fleming's fluids are all good fixatives, but great care should be taken to wash out the acids in order to prevent swelling of the connective tissues. Formalin is a good preservative for general purposes.

KEY TO NORTH AMERICAN FRESH-WATER LEECHES

1 (36) Mouth a small pore in oral sucker from which a muscular proboscis may be protruded; no jaws.
Suborder **Rhynchobdellae** . . 2

2 (33) Body not divided into two regions; usually much depressed; eyes near median line; stomach usually with well developed lateral ceca. . . . . Family GLOSSIPHONIDAE . . 3

3 (28) Complete somites essentially triannulate. 4

4 (13) Epididymis and ejaculatory duct forming a long, open, backward loop; salivary glands diffuse; eyes simple; size small; chiefly under stones and on plants in ponds and lakes.
Glossiphonia Johnston 1816 . . 5

5 (10) Eyes one pair, well separated. Genital pores separated by one annulus. 6

6 (7) A brown chitinoid plate and underlying nuchal gland on dorsum of VIII. . . . . . *Glossiphonia stagnalis* (Linnaeus) 1758.

7 (6) No nuchal gland or plate. 8

8 (9) Greatly elongated, slender and nearly terete; without papillae; very transparent; colorless; gastric ceca one pair.
Glossiphonia nepheloidea (Graf) 1899.

9 (8) Relatively short, broad and flat; cutaneous papillae absent or in 1 to 5 series, small or large, often double; deeply pigmented in narrow longitudinal lines, or diffusely with metameric white spots on neural annuli; gastric ceca six pairs, simple. *Glossiphonia fusca* Castle 1900.

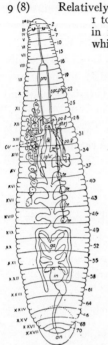

This species is very variable, especially in the character of the dorsal cutaneous papillae which may be scarcely evident and limited to a median series on a few segments, or large and conspicuous and arranged in five series extending for the entire length, or in any intermediate condition. Those of the median series are formed of a pair of papillae more or less completely coalesced. Usually they are deeply pigmented and contrast strongly with the clear white spots flanking them. The eyes are unusually large and conspicuous. It lives in ponds but also in colder waters than most species of the genus, even in springs, and attaches itself to the larger water snails and more rarely to leeches. The eggs, like those of *Glossiphonia complanata*, are laid in a few large gelatinous capsules borne on the venter of the parent leech and breeding is continued to midsummer. *Glossiphonia fusca* is much less active than *Glossiphonia complanata* and feeds less frequently upon worms and larvae, preferring snails.

FIG. 997. *Glossiphonia fusca*. General anatomy showing external outline, segmentation and annulation, alimentary canal, reproductive organs, etc. I–XXVII — somites; 2–70, annuli; *pro*, proboscis; *po* ♂, male orifice; *po* ♀, female orifice; *ov*, ovary; *oe*, esophagus; *iglv*, stomach or crop; *te*, testes; *ga* and *in*, intestine; *an*, anus; *dt. ej*, ductus ejaculatorius. × 10. (Modified from Castle.)

10 (5) Eyes three pairs. 11

11 (12) Genital pores separated by one annulus; eyes in three groups of two, in a triangular figure; body transparent, with little pigment; no papillae; gastric ceca six pairs, nearly or quite unbranched. . . *Glossiphonia heteroclita* (Linnaeus) 1758.

12 (11) Genital pores separated by two annuli; eyes in two nearly parallel rows; body rather thick and opaque, usually deeply pigmented, a pair of dorsal and ventral dark, narrow lines running for nearly entire length; gastric ceca seven pairs, slightly branched. . *Glossiphonia complanata* (Linnaeus) 1758.

13 (4) Epididymis more or less complexly and compactly folded in vicinity of atrium; salivary glands usually compact. . . 14

14 (27) One pair of anterior compound eyes; gastric ceca seven pairs, usually much branched; salivary glands compact; size moderate to large. Temporary parasites on water turtles, frogs and fishes; most species also free-living.
Placobdella R. Blanchard 1893 . 15

15 (16) Somites I–V distinctly widened to form a discoid "head." Somites I and II biannulate; dorsum with three strong papillated keels. On fishes and frogs. . *Placobdella montifera* Moore 1912.

16 (15) Somites I–V not especially widened. 17

17 (18) • Anus at XXIII–XXIV and following somites forming a narrow sucker pedicle. Gastric ceca branched once; very contractile; no cutaneous papillae. Nearly permanent parasite on fishes in Minnesota lakes.

Placobdella pediculata Hemingway 1908.

18 (17) Anus behind XXVII; posterior segments normal.

Placobdella (s. str.). . . . 19

19 (22) Cutaneous papillae smooth and round. 20

20 (21) Integuments opaque, deeply pigmented in a conspicuous pattern of olive green and yellow; annulus a^3 without trace of a secondary furrow; size large. Common on *Chelydra*, etc.

Placobdella parasitica (Say) 1824.

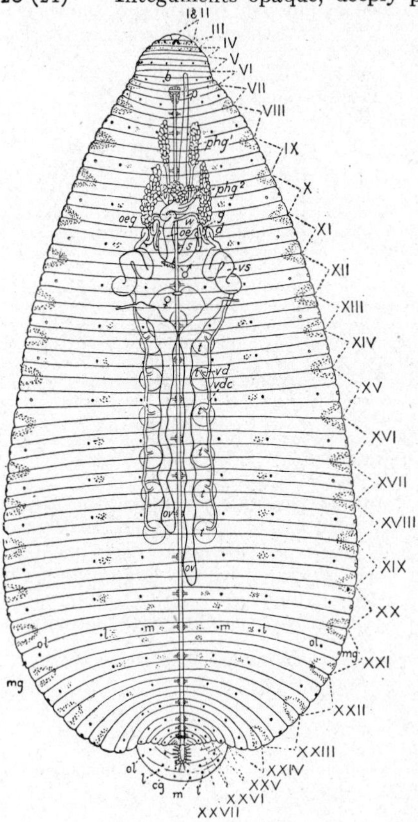

One of the best known of our leeches, most often found clinging in large numbers to the naked skin at the base of the hind legs of the snapping turtle whose blood they suck. Large individuals measure from 3 to 4 inches long in partial extension and are very broad, thin, and foliaceous. When bearing eggs or young they often leave the host and for a time lead a free life in ponds and streams, feeding on worms and larvae. Eggs and young are borne in large numbers and it is an interesting sight to observe the crowded family of youngsters actively bending and turning on the venter of the parent, the thin margins of whose body are inrolled to form a protecting fold. The color pattern is rich and striking, the ground color of dull green or olive green standing in sharp contrast to the bold and characteristic markings of yellow by which it is replaced to a varying degree.

FIG. 998. *Placobdella parasitica.* External metamerism, central nervous system, reproductive organs, etc. I–XXVII — somites; *mg, ol, l, m,* marginal, outer lateral, lateral and median sensillae respectively; *phg.*[1–2], pharyngeal glands; *oe,* esophagus; *s,* atrium or spermatophore sac; *d,* ductus ejaculatorius; *vs,* vesicula seminalis; ♂ and ♀, male and female pores; *vdc,* vas deferens; *t,* testes; *ov,* ovary. × 2. (Redrawn from Whitman.)

21 (20) Integuments translucent, brightly but not deeply pigmented with green, orange, and white; a^3 of complete somites with a distinct secondary cross-furrow; size medium.

Placobdella picta (Verrill) 1872.

22 (19) Cutaneous papillae prominent and rough or pointed. 23

23 (26) No marginal papillae on caudal sucker. 24

24 (25) Much depressed; papillae numerous; no accessory eyes; size large.
Placobdella rugosa (Verrill) 1874.

25 (24) Moderately depressed; papillae less numerous; neural annulus with much dark pigment; several pairs of simple accessory eyes succeeding compound eyes; size medium.
Placobdella hollensis (Whitman) 1892.

26 (23) Numerous minute papillae around margin of caudal sucker. Moderately depressed; dorsal papillae usually in a median and two paired series, small, acute and pale yellow or brown; a very conspicuous and constant pale band across somite VI; size small. . . . . *Placobdella phalera* (Graf) 1899.

27 (14) Eyes four pairs, all simple; gastric ceca nine or ten pairs; salivary glands diffuse; body very soft and almost oedemous; genital pores at XI–XII and XII a^2/a^3; color green with three series of pale yellow spots. On fishes and free in streams.
Protoclepsis occidentalis (Verrill) 1874.

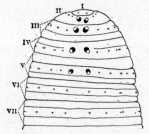

This leech and others of the genus are noteworthy among the members of their family for their transparency and activity. No other glossiphonids creep with any approach to the same speed and none swim so well. So far as has been observed the eastern species is exclusively sanguivorous, pursuing and attacking frogs and fishes. Nothing is known of the breeding habits beyond the fact that spermatophores are formed and attached to the skin.

Fig. 999. *Protoclepsis occidentalis.* Dorsal view of anterior seven segments, showing annuli, eyes, and sensillae. × 20. (Original.)

28 (3) Complete somites not triannulate. 29

29 (30) Complete somites of two annuli, the anterior much the larger. Salivary glands compact; gastric ceca seven pairs; epididymis a short, wide, U-shaped sperm-sac; eyes one pair, united; genital pores separated by the large annulus of XII; size small. On salamanders, North Carolina.
* Oligobdella biannulata (Moore) 1900.

(* *Oligobdella* nom. nov. for *Microbdella* Moore preoccupied.)

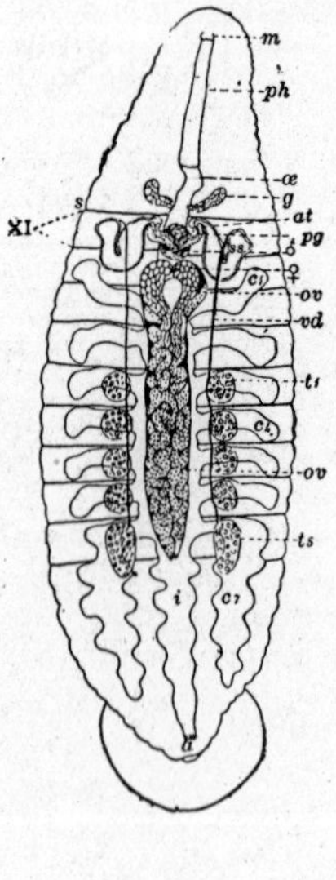

An interesting and little known leech taken on only one occasion in a cold mountain stream. Nothing known of breeding habits. Color green.

Fig. 1000. *Oligobdella biannulata.* General anatomy: boundaries of middle somites indicated; *g,* salivary gland; *at,* atrium; *ps,* spermatophore sac; *ss,* sperm sac; ♂ male and ♀ female orifices; c_1 to c_7, gastric ceca; *ov,* ovary; *vd,* vas deferens; t_1 to t_5, testes; *i,* intestine; *a,* anus. × 10. (After Moore.)

30 (29)   Complete somites of six unequal annuli; salivary glands diffuse; gastric ceca seven pairs; caudal sucker with marginal circle of glands and papillae; eyes one pair, united; size small. Probably fish parasites. . *Actinobdella* Moore 1901 . . 31

31 (32)   Sucker papillae and glands about 60; five series of dorsal papillae. *Actinobdella annectens* Moore 1901.

32 (31)   Sucker papillae and glands about 30; median dorsal series of papillae alone developed.

Actinobdella inequiannulata Moore 1905.

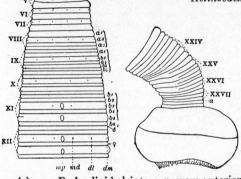

FIG. 1001. *Actinobdella inequiannulata.* Annulation, sensillae and dorsal cutaneous papillae of anterior twelve somites. Posterior end with sucker from the side. × 20. (After Moore.)

33 (2)   Body divided into a narrow anterior and a wider posterior region; little depressed; eyes when present usually well separated; stomach usually with only a posterior pair of more or less coalesced ceca. . . . Family ICHTHYOBDELLIDAE . . 34

34 (35)   Complete somites of 12–14 very short annuli; no distinct lateral vesicles; eyes one or two pairs; size small. Parasitic on small fishes. . . . . . *Piscicola punctata* (Verrill) 1871.

35 (34)   Complete somites of six annuli; strongly divided into two regions; lateral pulsating vesicles in somites XII to XXIII; eyes two pairs; size medium. Parasitic on *Fundulus* in fresh and salt water. . . . . . . *Trachelobdella vivida* (Verrill) 1872.

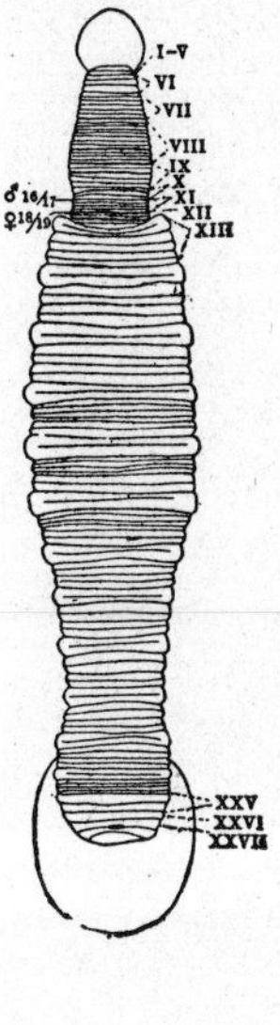

The anterior region is formed of eleven somites of which the first five comprise the head and the last three the clitellum, which is somewhat sunken into the widened posterior region. A little known leech which has been taken only in southern New England.

FIG. 1002. *Trachelobdella vivida.* Annulation from dorsum. Somites at the ends of the body are numbered and the annuli between which the male and female orifices lie are indicated. × 3. (After Moore.)

36 (1)   Mouth large, occupying entire cavity of sucker; pharynx not
          forming a proboscis; jaws often present.
                                    Suborder **Gnathobdellae** . . 37

37 (54)   Eyes typically five pairs on somites II–VI, arranged in a regular sub-
          marginal arch; complete somites five-ringed; toothed jaws
          usually present; genital ducts complex, usually with a pro-
          trusible penis and muscular sheath (atrium) and a vagina
          of corresponding length; testes strictly paired, usually nine or
          ten pairs; stomach with at least one pair of spacious ceca;
          size generally large. . . . . Family HIRUDINIDAE . . 38

38 (43)   Jaws prominent, teeth numerous, in one series; ceca along entire
          length of stomach. True blood-suckers. 39

39 (42)   Copulatory gland pores on somites XIII and XIV; penis conical;
          dorsum with metameric median red and lateral black spots.
                                    Macrobdella Verrill 1872 . . 40

40 (41)   Genital orifices separated by five annuli.
                                    Macrobdella decora (Say) 1824.

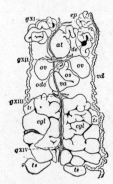

The species of *Macrobdella* are the nearest approach in our
fauna to the medicinal leech of Europe but at times vary the
diet of blood with frogs' eggs and worms. *M. decora* is well-
known as a voracious infester of swimming holes and of drinking
places for cattle and has received the name of "blood-sucker."
After coitus, during which the copulatory glands function,
spongy cocoons are formed and deposited to hatch in the mud
by the side of ponds and streams. Widely distributed; reported
from Maine to Minnesota and from Pennsylvania to Kansas,
northward into Canada.   Frequently used by physicians instead
of imported leeches for blood-letting. Said to be equally effica-
cious of the smaller capacity, about 5 gm. It is so powerful that
serious results have followed its attacks on legs of children wading
in its haunts.

FIG. 1003. *Macrobdella decora*. Reproductive organs (in part) dissected.
at, atrium; *cgl*, copulatory glands; *de*, ductus ejaculatorius; *ep*, epididymis; *gXI–XIV*, ganglia XI to XIV; *os*, ovisac; *od* and *odc*, oviduct;
ov, ovary; *t₁* and *t₂*, first and second pairs of testes; *vd*, vas deferens.
× 3. (After Moore.)

41 (40)   Genital orifices separated by two and one-half annuli.
                                    Macrobdella sestertia Whitman 1886.

42 (39) No copulatory glands; penis filamentous; colors variable, dorsum usually green with six or four brown stripes, sometimes broken. European medicinal leech; introduced.
Hirudo medicinalis Linnaeus 1758.

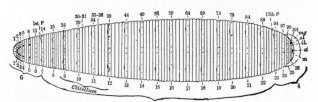

FIG. 1004. *Hirudo medicinalis.* External morphology from the dorsum. The numerals on the right indicate the annuli, those on the left the somites, the index lines running to the neural annuli; *1st P.* and *17th P.*, first and last nephridiopores. Natural size. (After Whitman.)

43 (38) Jaws variable, sometimes rudimentary or absent; teeth when present all or partly in double series; gastric ceca one large posterior pair only. Chiefly predaceous. 44

44 (47) Jaws short and high; teeth small, only partly in two series; no penis; genital orifices separated by three or four rings, surrounded by systems of gland pores. . *Philobdella* Verrill 1874. . 45

45 (46) Denticles about 35; narrow median dorsal and broader marginal yellow stripes and a few brown spots.
Philobdella gracile Moore 1901.

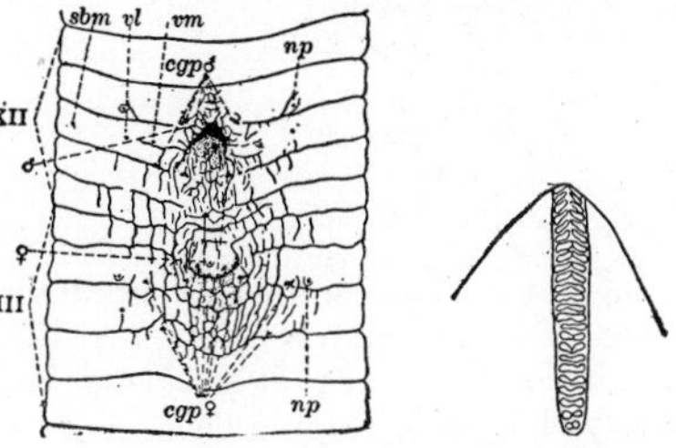

Philobdella takes the place of *Macrobdella* in the Gulf States and has singular habits. It is the native "blood-sucker" of that region.

FIG. 1005. *Philobdella gracile. A,* external genital orifices (♂, ♀) with their respective systems of gland pores (cgp ♂ and cgp♀); *np,* nephridiopores; *sbm, vl, vm,* submarginal, lateral, and median sensillae. × 3½. (After Moore.) *B,* outline of a jaw with teeth. × 35. (After Moore.)

46 (45) Denticles about 20; no median dorsal stripe and no spots; two faint stripes of reddish brown separated by a narrow line of blackish on each side of dorsum.
Philobdella floridana Verrill 1874.

47 (44) Jaws rather small and retractile into pits or absent; teeth when present coarse and all in double series; penis filamentous; genital orifices separated by five rings; no copulatory glands.
Haemopis Savigny 1820 . . 48

48 (51) Jaws and teeth present. 49

49 (50)   Teeth 12–16 pairs; annuli VII a^3 and VIII a' enlarged, but only
            slightly subdivided; color variable, usually blotched.
                                        Haemopis marmoratis (Say) 1824.

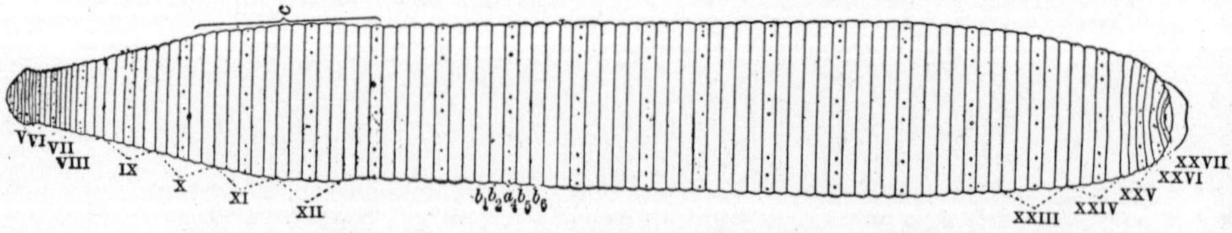

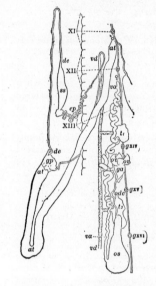

FIG. 1006. *Haemopis marmoratis.* External morphology,
showing sensillae, annulation, and limits of somites.
c, clitellum; V–XXVII, somites; b_1, b_2, a_2, b_5, b_6, the five
annuli of somite XV. × 1¼. (Original.)

FIG. 1007. *Haemopis marmoratis.* Reproductive organs,
dissected. *at*, atrium or penis sheath; *de*, ductus ejaculatorius; *ep*, epididymis; *g*XI–XVI, ganglia XI–XVI;
ga, albumin gland; *gp*, prostate gland ; *os*, ovisac; *odc*,
common oviduct; *ov*, ovary; *ss*, sperm sac; *t1–3*, testes;
va, vagina; *vd*, vas deferens; ♂ male orifice; ♀ female
orifice. × 2. (After Moore.)

50 (49)   Teeth 20–25 pairs; annuli VII a^3 and VIII a', completely subdivided;
            color gray or plumbeus with no or few spots, usually a
            median black and marginal orange stripes; size very large.
            An aquatic and a terrestrial variety.
                                        Haemopis lateralis (Say) 1824.

51 (48)   Jaws absent or rudimentary; no teeth. 52

52 (53)   Upper lip relatively narrow and arched; ♂ orifice XI b^5/b^6, ♀
            XII b^5/b^6; protruded penis very slender and straight; ven-
            tral ground color paler than dorsal; dark blotches always
            present; size very large. . *Haemopis grandis* (Verrill) 1874.

53 (52)   Lip relatively broad and flat; genital pores near middle of XI b^6
            and XII b^6; protruded penis very long, rather thick and
            twisted; ground color nearly uniform; dark blotches fre-
            quently absent or few; size moderate.
                                        Haemopis plumbeus Moore 1912.

54 (37)   Eyes three or four pairs (rarely absent), usually one or two pairs on II and two pairs at sides of mouth on IV; no jaws, no gastric ceca; genital ducts relatively simple, with small atrium produced into a pair of dorsal cornua and no penis; testes numerous, not paired. Predaceous.

Family HERPOBDELLIDAE . . 55

55 (56)   Somites strictly five-ringed, none of the annuli obviously enlarged or subdivided. Eyes three pairs, the first largest; genital pores separated by two annuli; atrial cornua simply curved; vasa deferentia reaching forward to ganglion XI.

Herpobdella punctata (Leidy) 1870.

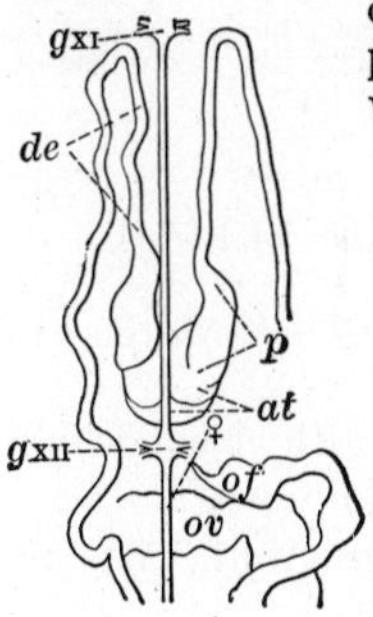

The largest, best known and most widely distributed member of the family in North America. The color varies considerably according to the amount of black pigment present. A very active leech which feeds voraciously on small worms, other leeches, and aquatic insect larvae. It will take human blood when opportunity offers. Egg capsules found abundantly attached to stones, etc.

FIG. 1008. *Herpobdella punctata.* Atrium and neighboring parts of reproductive organs. *at*, atrium; *de*, ductus ejaculatorius; *g*XI, ganglion XI; ♀, female orifice; *of*, fundus of ovary; *ov*, ovary; *p*, atrial horn. × 7½. (After Moore.)

56 (55)   Annulus *b* obviously enlarged and subdivided. 57

57 (58)   Atrial cornua spirally coiled, vasa deferentia with anterior loops reaching to ganglion XI; eyes four pairs; genital orifices separated by two annuli; colors plain or irregularly blotched.

Nephelopsis obscura Verrill 1827.

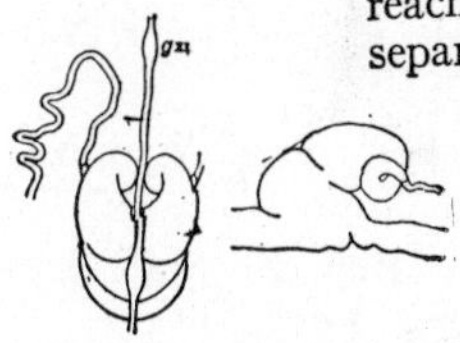

FIG. 1009. *Nephelopsis obscura.* Dorsal and lateral aspects of atrial region. × 3. (Original.)

58 (57)   Atrial cornua not spirally coiled, but short and merely curved.

Dina R. Blanchard 1892 . . 59

59 (62)   Vasa deferentia with anterior loops reaching to ganglion XI. . 60

60 (61)   No pigmented eyes; genital pores separated by two annuli; longitudinally striped. California. . *Dina anoculata* Moore 1898.

61 (60)   Eyes four pairs; genital pores separated by three to three and one-half annuli; nearly pigmentless. . *Dina parva* Moore 1912.

62 (59)   Vasa deferentia not extending anterior to atrium 63

63 (64)   Eyes, three pairs; genital pores separated by three annuli; atrial cornua very small; pigment nearly absent.

Dina microstoma Moore 1901.

64 (63) Eyes, three or four pairs; genital pores separated by two annuli; atrial cornua prominent; pigment absent or in scattered flecks. *Dina fervida* (Verrill) 1871.

Fig. 1010. *Dina fervida.* Reproductive organs except testes. *at*, atrial cornua; *de*, ductus ejaculatorius; *g*XI–XVIII, ganglia XI to XVIII; *of*, closed end of ovary; *ov*, ovary; *ss*, sperm sac; *vd*, vas deferens. × 3½. (After Moore.)

IMPORTANT PAPERS ON NORTH AMERICAN LEECHES

BRISTOL, C. L.   1899.   The Metamerism of Nephelis.   Journ. Morph., 15: 17–72.

CASTLE, W. E.   1900.   Some North American Fresh-water Rhynchobdellidae and their Parasites.   Bull. Mus. Comp. Zool. Harv., 36: 18–64.

1900.   The Metamerism of the Hirudinea.   Proc. Amer. Acad., Arts and Sci., 35: 285–303.

FORBES, S. A.   1890.   An American Terrestrial Leech.   Bull. Ill. State Lab. Nat. Hist., 3: 119–122.

GRAF, A.   1899.   Hirudineenstudien.   Nova Acta Leop. Carol. Akad. Natw., 72: 215–404.

HEMINGWAY, ERNEST E.   1908.   Placobdella pediculata n. sp.   Amer. Nat., 42: 527–532.

LEIDY, JOSEPH.   1868.   Notice of Some American Leeches.   Proc. Acad. Nat. Sci., Phila., 20: 229–230.

MOORE, J. PERCY.   1901.   The Hirudinea of Illinois.   Bull. Ill. State Lab. Nat. Hist., 5: 479–546.

1905.   Hirudinea and Oligochaeta collected in the Great Lakes Region. Bull. U. S. Bur. Fish., 25: 153–171.

NACHTRIEB, HEMINGWAY, and MOORE.   1912.   Report on the Leeches of Minnesota.   Geological and Natural History Survey of Minnesota, Zoological Series No. V.   Part III., Classification of the Leeches of Min-nesota, by J. Percy Moore, pp. 65–150.   Frontispiece and Plates I–VI.

VERRILL, A. E.   1874.   Synopsis of the North American Fresh-Water Leeches. Report U. S. Comm. Fish., 2: 666–689.

CHAPTER XXI

THE FAIRY SHRIMPS (PHYLLOPODA)

By A. S. PEARSE

Associate Professor of Zoology, University of Wisconsin

PHYLLOPOD crustaceans are among the most graceful and attractive of the inhabitants of fresh-water pools. A familiar example is the fairy shrimp (*Eubranchipus*) that is a harbinger of spring throughout the eastern and central United States. No phyllopods are of great size, the largest usually not exceeding a couple of centimeters in length, though one species of *Apus* reaches seven. Certain genera of this group[1] of crustaceans existed in Devonian times but recent species were first described by scientists early in the eighteenth century, and were, with the cladoceran *Daphnia*, made the subject of a series of remarkable memoirs by J. C. Schäffer (1752–1756). Up to the present time forty-one species have been described from North America and a large number from other continents, for phyllopods occur in every part of the world and are found from sea-level to altitudes of more than 10,000 feet. But the animals that are to be discussed in this chapter are interesting not only on account of their ancient lineage and wide distribution. Their primitive structure has been much studied by those who sought to solve the riddle of the origin of the arthropods, and their remarkable ability to withstand striking changes in temperature and humidity, as well as the various forms that some species assume under different conditions, have made them equally attractive to naturalists and those interested in the experimental side of zoology.

The different suborders of phyllopods present considerable diversity in general shape. Such diversity is due largely to differences in the development of the carapace, which may form a shell-fold, and these differences are curiously correlated with variations

---

[1] Calman rejects the suborder Phyllopoda and divides his subclass Branchiopoda into four orders: Anostraca, Notostraca, Conchostraca, Cladocera. There is much in favor of such a system.

in the position of the eyes. In the Anostraca (Fig. 1011) there is no shell-fold and the body, composed of many distinct somites, has an almost worm-like aspect; the Notostraca (Fig. 1012) are also elongated and composed of numerous somites, but are flattened, and their anterior portion is covered dorsally by a broad arched carapace; the bodies of the Conchostraca (Fig. 1013) tend to be laterally com · pressed and are enveloped in a bivalve shell that makes them look like a small clam. The shell-fold is not attached to the trunk somites which it envelops. It may be more or less corneous but is never calcified. The eyes are elevated on movable peduncles in the Anostraca but are sessile in all other phyllopods. A peculiar

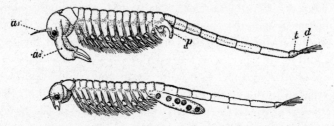

Fig. 1011. *Branchinecta paludosa*, male and female. a1, first antenna; a2, second antenna; d, cercopods or furcal rami; p, penis; t, telson. × 3. (After Packard.) ;

structure, the frontal (or haft) organ, is variously developed in the different groups; in some it is only a sensory area and in others it has a knob-like pediculated form.

The head is distinct from the trunk and the number of trunk-somites is variable. Some notostracans have as many as forty-two trunk-somites; the Conchostraca have from thirteen to twenty-eight, and the number in the Anostraca ranges from nineteen to twenty-three. Apart from the head, the trunk of phyllopods shows no differentiation into distinct regions. The terms "thorax" and "abdomen" have been variously used to designate the pre- or post-genital, or the limb-bearing or limbless, regions respectively. But the limits of these regions do not coincide, even approximately, except in the Anostraca; and "thoracic" and "abdominal" are therefore not applicable to the group. The last segment, or telson, usually bears a pair of appendages, the furcal rami or cercopods.

The appendages are fairly uniform in character, except as they are modified by sexual dimorphism. The first antennae are always small and often unsegmented. The second antennae are vestigial or absent in the Notostraca; in the male anostracans they form variously modified clasping organs; and in the Conchostraca they are biramous swimming appendages. Male Anostraca often bear frontal organs which may arise from the bases of the second antennae or from the front of the head. The trunk-limbs are leaf-like in form (hence the name Phyllopoda) and are remarkable for having gnathobases, or "chewing bases," far removed from the mouth. The first or the first and second pair are modified in male Conchostraca for clasping the female. In female Notostraca the limbs of the eleventh trunk somite are modified to form brood-pouches, or "oostegopods," for carrying eggs. The females of some Conchostraca have the flabella of two or three limbs near the genital aperture enlarged and the egg masses are attached to these. In the Anostraca the appendages of the somites on either side of the genital opening are modified for reproduction in both sexes.

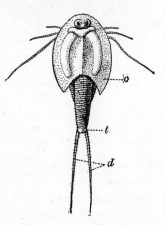

In addition to the various appendages which serve as accessory reproductive organs, the oviducts unite to form an external uterine chamber in the Anostraca, and the males of the same suborder have a copulatory organ

FIG. 1012. *Apus aequalis. c*, carapace; *t*, telson; *d*, cercopods or furcal rami. × 3. (After Packard.)

formed by the fusion of the extremities of the vasa deferentia. All phyllopods are of separate sexes. Males are much less common than females, in fact some species are known only from female specimens, and the development of several is believed to be usually parthenogenetic. The gonads are paired and have a simple tubular structure, except in the Notostraca where they are much ramified. In the Anostraca the eggs are carried in the female's brood-pouch, the uterine portion of the oviduct, sometimes until they hatch. The Notostraca bear the eggs in the special receptacles formed by the eleventh pair of trunk-limbs, and the Conchostraca carry them enclosed in the valves of the shell.

The alimentary canal of phyllopods consists of a large masticatory and glandular atrium produced by an overhanging labrum

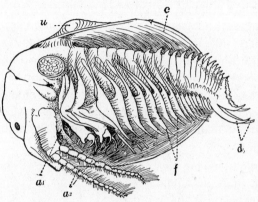

in front of the mouth; this is followed by a buccal cavity, a vertical esophagus and a small globular stomach within the head; and, behind these, is a long straight intestine which terminates in a short rectum at the posterior end of the body. The heart is greatly elongated in the Anostraca, oc-

FIG. 1013. *Estheria morsei*, with left valve of shell removed. × 9. *a₁*, first antenna; *a₂*, second antenna; *c*, carapace; *d*, cercopods or furcal rami; *f*, flabella; *u*, umbone. (After Packard.)

cupying nearly all the trunk-somites, with a pair of ostia opening in each somite. In the Notostraca and Conchostraca it is more restricted — and extends through only three or four segments in the latter. There are no definite blood vessels. A maxillary gland (consisting of an end-sac, glandular coiled tube, and short terminal duct) serves as an excretory organ in phyllopods. The ladder-like structure of the ventral nerve chain shows the primitive character of the nervous system.

After leaving the egg, all American phyllopods begin their development as a free swimming nauplius or metanauplius (Fig. 1014). Some differences exist even in closely allied forms in regard to the stage of development reached at hatching. The larvae of the Notostraca and Anostraca are typical metanauplei at the time

FIG. 1014. Metanauplius of *Apus cancriformis*, just hatched. (After Claus, from Lankester's Treatise on Zoology.)

of hatching, with an oval body that shows the beginning of several trunk-somites posteriorly and sometimes the rudiments of their appendages. The first antennae are well developed but uniramous, the second antennae have a movable masticatory process and the mandibles are but feebly developed. The earliest conchostracan larva has no trace of trunk-somites; the first antennae are greatly reduced and the labrum is very large. The trunk-somites and their appendages become differentiated in regular order from before backwards. The single median eye of the larva persists in adult phyllopods.

All Phyllopoda, except *Artemia*, live in small fresh-water pools, especially those that are formed during spring rains and dry up during the summer. In such situations they often occur in enormous numbers. The writer once saw in Nebraska nearly half a bushel of dead *Apus* bodies on the bottom of a shallow dried-up depression about twenty feet in diameter. The eggs of most genera can resist prolonged desiccation; indeed it seems necessary for the development of many species that eggs should first be dried and afterwards immersed in water. Many eggs float when placed in water and development takes place at the surface. The mud of dried pools often contains large numbers of eggs that may be carried long distances by winds, birds, or by other means. Many exotic species have been reared from dried mud brought home by travelers.

On account of the rapid evaporation of the pools in which they live, phyllopods are able to withstand considerable changes in the amount of mineral salts in the water. It is remarkable that, though none of these crustaceans are marine, *Artemia salina* lives in salt lakes and salt evaporating basins where the salinity far exceeds that of the ocean. One instance has been recorded where the salts in solution were 271 grams per liter, and where the water was of the color and consistency of beer. *Artemia salina* is subject to marked form variations that are more or less correlated with salinity, and both Kellogg and Artrom have observed that this species tends to assume a reddish color as the water about it grows denser.

Phyllopods usually swim on their backs with the ventral surface uppermost. *Eubranchipus* swims easily about when it is not resting on the bottom; *Apus* is a graceful swimmer but often creeps on its ventral surface over the bottom and upon vegetation; *Estheria* commonly burrows in the mud. Food is collected in the ventral food-groove between the post-oral limbs whose gnathobases drive it forward to the mouth. It consists of suspended organic debris, together with diatoms, other algae, and Protozoa. Large species, however, are able to gnaw objects, and *Apus* is said to nibble insect larvae and tadpoles. No parasitic phyllopods are known.

The distribution of all species is apt to be local and irregular. A certain pool may swarm with phyllopods, while others near at hand will not possess a single individual. A particular species may be extremely abundant for one season and then be infrequent or entirely absent for several years, or it may appear regularly in a certain spot season after season. No Notostraca have been found in eastern United States and none of the genus *Estheria* in the Conchostraca are found east of the Mississippi River. The greater part of the North American species are found on the great plains.

Collecting phyllopods is usually a simple matter. They are easily captured with a hand net or picked up with the fingers. For ordinary purposes 70 per cent alcohol is a satisfactory preservative; specimens may be kept for future reference by dropping them into it and keeping them in a tightly stoppered bottle. Dilute formol may also be used, but is not as satisfactory as alcohol because it often makes specimens so brittle that they break up easily. These crustaceans are admirable aquarium animals and make attractive objects for a school room or private study. With a few water plants for company they may live for weeks. They should not be put in aquaria with predaceous animals for usually they will be quickly devoured.

KEY TO NORTH AMERICAN FRESH-WATER PHYLLOPODA

1 (36)   Body elongated, without carapace (Fig. 1011) . Suborder **Anostraca** . 2
2 (5)   Seventeen to nineteen pairs of pregenital ambulatory limbs.
                                                Family POLYARTEMIIDAE.
      Only one genus in America. . . . . *Polyartemiella*. . . 3
3 (4)   Male frontal appendage tuberculiform; male clasping antenna quadri-
             ramose. . . . . . *Polyartemiella hanseni* (Murdoch) 1874.

Described from Alaska. This and the following species are remarkable for the large number of ambulatory limbs which exceeds that of any other anostracan. Apparently common in portions of Alaska and Yukon Territory that border on the Arctic Ocean.

FIG. 1015. *Polyartemiella hanseni*. Side view of head of male. X 6.
(After Daday.)

4 (3) Male frontal appendage wanting; male clasping antenna triramose.

Polyartemiella judayi Daday 1909.

The copulatory appendages of this form are thick, spiny, and shaped like a fish-hook; the female has a long median finger-like appendage on the dorsal surface above the egg sac.
Pribyloff Islands and Alaska. The genus to which this species belongs is entirely arctic in its distribution.

FIG. 1016. *Polyartemiella judayi.* Dorsal view of head of male. X 5. (After Daday.)

5 (2) Eleven pairs of pregenital ambulatory limbs. 6

6 (33) Clasping antenna of male biarticulate. 7

7 (16) Head of male unarmed in front, basal segment of clasping antenna without a laminar appendage. . Family BRANCHINECTIDAE . . 8

8 (15) Post-genital region 9-segmented, apical article of male clasping antenna triangular and falciform. . . . . *Branchinecta* . . 9

9 (10) Basal segment of male clasping antenna serrate on inner margin.

Branchinecta paludosa (O. F. Müller) 1788.

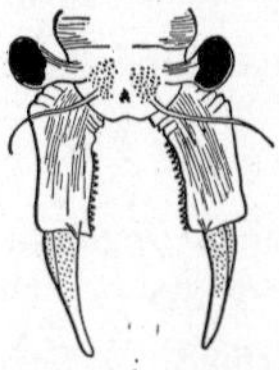

The egg sac of the female is very long and slender. The copulatory appendage of the male is thick and arcuate.
This is an arctic species and occurs in northern Europe as well as in Greenland, Labrador, and Alaska, in North America. See also Fig. 1011.

FIG. 1017. *Branchinecta paludosa.* Head of male, dorsal view. X 5.
(After Daday.)

10 (9) Basal segment of male clasping antenna not serrate on inner margin. 11

11 (14) Basal segment of ·male clasping antenna with a spiny area on
       ·   inner margin. 12

12 (13) Inner margin of basal segment of male clasping antenna with a rounded tubercle near base and a swollen spiny area just proximal to middle.

Branchinecta coloradensis Packard 1874.

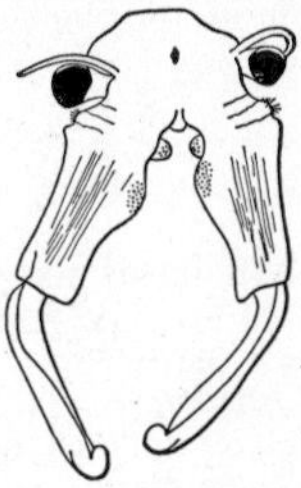

The segmentation and early development take place under the ice in Alpine Lakes. The eggs of this species are much larger than those of others in the genus. This fact may account for the ability to develop so early.
Reported from Colorado where it occurs at an altitude of 11,000 ft. The larvae appear as soon as the ice melts in the spring.

FIG. 1018. *Branchinecta coloradensis.* Head of male, front view. X 7.
(After Shantz.)

13 (12) Basal segment of male clasping antenna armed with a large spiny process, one third as long as the segment, which arises just distal to the middle of the inner margin and projects proximally, a prominent finger-like process with a tuberculated tip near inner proximal angle.

Branchinecta packardi Pearse 1913.

The five pregenital segments of female produced laterally into strong spinous processes; these grow larger posteriorly. Collected at La Junta, Colorado.

FIG. 1019. *Branchinecta packardi.* Basal segment of second antenna of male.

14 (11)   Inner margin of basal segment of male clasping antenna without a tubercle but with a spiny area near proximal end.
Branchinecta lindahli Packard 1883.

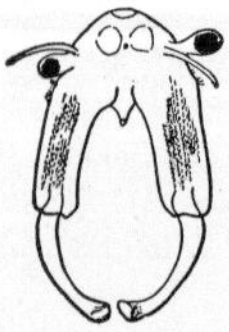

The body is robust; the caudal appendages are comparatively long; the eggs are small, and the ovisac usually contains about fifty of them. A plains species recorded from Kansas, Nebraska, Colorado, and Wyoming. It is known to occur as high as 7500 ft. above sea level.

FIG. 1020. *Branchinecta lindahli*. Head of male, front view. × 3. (After Shantz.)

15 (8)   Post-genital region 8-segmented, apical article of male clasping antenna compressed. . . . . *Artemia*.
Only one species. . . . *Artemia salina* (Linnaeus) 1851.

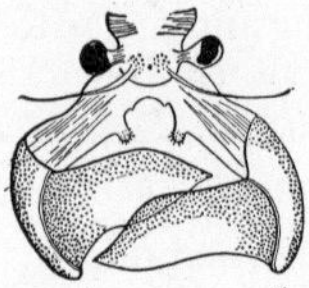

Connecticut, Utah, California, Lower California. This species is remarkable for its ability to live in extremely saline water. It is frequently found in salt evaporating basins. The form is variable, and several varieties have been described.

FIG. 1021. *Artemia salina*. Head of male, dorsal view. × 4. (After Daday.)

16 (7)   Head of male often bearing a frontal appendage or a laminar appendage on the basal segment of the clasping antenna.
Family CHIROCEPHALIDAE . . 17

17 (30) Frontal appendage of male variable, rather short; terminal segment of copulatory organ smooth. . . . . *Eubranchipus* . . 18

18 (25) Body segments of male and female all superficially unarmed. . . 19

19 (20) Frontal appendage of male short, about as long as basal joint of second antenna; lanceolate, margin denticulate.
Eubranchipus vernalis Verrill 1869.

Massachusetts, New Jersey, Indiana, Michigan. This species appears in small quiet pools soon after the snow disappears in spring, or even in mid-winter, but has not been observed during the summer months.

FIG. 1022. *Eubranchipus vernalis*. Head of male, side view. × 4. (After Packard.)

20 (19) Frontal appendages of male when extended longer than basal joint of second antenna. 21

21 (22) Frontal appendages of male attenuate, middle fourth serrate.
Eubranchipus holmani (Ryder) 1879.

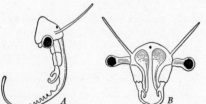

This species was first discovered in New Jersey and has since been observed on Long Island, New York. Packard ('83) confused this species with *Branchinella gissleri* Daday.

FIG. 1023. *Eubranchipus holmani*. Head of male; *A*, side view; *B*, front view. × 4. (After Daday.)

22 (21) Frontal appendages of male broad, lanceolate, lobate on margins. 23

23 (24) Terminal segment of male clasping antenna with a small process near base that is one-eighth as long as the segment.

Eubranchipus ornatus Holmes 1911.

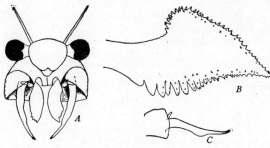

This species was described from specimens taken in Wisconsin. The frontal appendages are remarkably broad. In the left-hand figure the male frontal appendages are rolled up.

FIG. 1024. *Eubranchipus ornatus.* Male. *A*, posterior view of head; *B*, frontal organ; *C*, second antenna. × 10. (After Holmes.)

24 (23) Terminal segment of male clasping antenna armed with a process near its base that is half as long as itself.

Eubranchipus dadayi Pearse 1913.

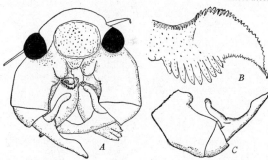

Recorded from eastern Nebraska and Missouri. Some specimens are remarkably transparent. This species appears in small pools during April and May. The females are more reddish than the translucent males.

FIG. 1025. *Eubranchipus dadayi.* Male. *A*, posterior view of head; *B*, frontal organ; *C*, second antenna. ×8.

25 (18) Some body segments produced into lateral processes. 26

26 (27) Body segments 9 and 10 of female produced into lateral processes; post-genital segments unarmed.

Eubranchipus gelidus (Hay) 1889.

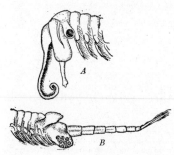

Records from New York, Massachusetts, Indiana, Alaska, and Yukon Territory, Canada. Usually abundant where it is found. The processes on the somites just in front of the egg sac on the female distinguish this species from all others in the genus. The Hay's ('89) hatched the eggs of this anostracan from dried mud, without freezing, and described developmental stages. The wide range is remarkable for a member of this genus.

FIG. 1026. *Eubranchipus gelidus.* *A*, side view of head of male; *B*, side view of posterior portion of female. × 4.

27 (26) Body segments 9 and 10 of female not produced laterally; post-genital segments acutely produced on both sides. . . . 28

28 (29)   Post-genital region 8-segmented; cercopods ensiform.
 Eubranchipus serratus Forbes 1876.
Described from specimens taken in Illinois.

29 (28)   Post-genital region 9-segmented; cercopods dilated with obtuse
apices. . . . . *Eubranchipus bundyi* Forbes 1876.
Described from specimens collected in Wisconsin.

30 (17)   Frontal appendage of male either vertical or extending out from the
middle of front of head; terminal segment of copulatory
organ spiny. 31

31 (32)   Post-genital segments distinct in both sexes, cylindrical, cercopods
always distinct. . . . . *Branchinella.*
Only one species in North America. . *Branchinella gissleri* Daday 1910,

This interesting phyllopod has been recently described
from specimens collected in New York. Packard ('83)
confused it with *Eubranchipus holmanii* (Ryder). The
male frontal appendages are usually twisted, and coiled
together.

Fig. 1027. *Branchinella gissleri.* Dorsal view of head of male.
× 5. (After Daday.)

32 (31)   Post-genital segments fused in both sexes; cercopods confluent.
Thamnocephalus.
Only one species. . . . . *Thamnocephalus platyurus* Packard 1879.

A peculiar species that has been recorded from Ellis,
Kansas, where it frequented temporary pools in the
bottoms of ravines, and from La Junta, Colorado,
where it was found in a "cattle pool."
Fig. 1028. *Thamnocephalus platyurus.* Dorsal view of
male. × 1. (After Packard.)

33 (6)   Clasping antenna of male triarticulate. Family Streptocephalidae.
Only one genus in America. . . . . *Streptocephalus* . . 34

34 (35)   Anterior digit of male clasping antenna broad, undulate, bifid at tip.
Streptocephalus texanus Packard 1871.

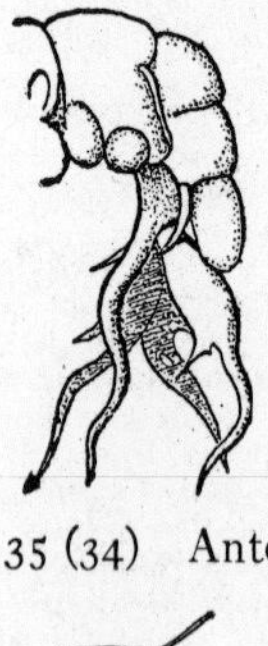

The second antennae of the female scarcely exceed the first in length;
her cercopods are stouter than those of the male.
The appendages beneath the head of the male are root-like and give the
animal a very peculiar appearance.
Texas, Kansas, Colorado, Nebraska. This species occurs in the spring or
fall in pools on the open prairie.

Fig. 1029. *Streptocephalus texanus.* Head of male. × 4. (After Packard.)

35 (34)   Anterior digit of male clasping antenna nearly straight, linear.
Streptocephalus sealii Ryder 1879.

New Jersey. This species has been known to appear twice in the same pool
during a summer, in June and August, following rains.
Packard described another species, *S. floridanus,* but the description was
not definite enough to differentiate it from other American species.

Fig. 1030. *Streptocephalus sealii.* Head of male. × 3. (After Packard.)

36 (1)   Body with a well-developed carapace. 37

37 (52) Body depressed, covered dorsally by a depressed shield.
Suborder **Notostraca** . . 38

38 (45) Telson ending in a long, paddle-shaped outgrowth. . *Lepidurus* . . 39

39 (40) Telson short, obtusely pointed, spiny on edge.
Lepidurus glacialis Kroyer 1847.

An arctic species recorded from Greenland and Labrador. The carapace is very large and regularly ovate; twelve segments are exposed behind it.

FIG. 1031. *Lepidurus glacialis.* Telson. X 6. (After Packard.)

40 (39) Telson spatulate. 41

41 (42) Telson carinate dorsally; carapace large, leaving only five body segments and telson uncovered.
Lepidurus couesii Packard 1875.

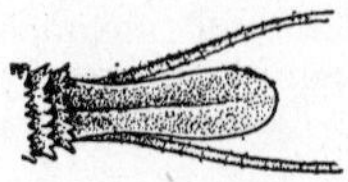

This species occurs in Utah where it frequents prairie pools of various sizes.

FIG. 1032. *Lepidurus couesii.* Telson. X 6. (After Packard.)

42 (41) Telson not carinate dorsally. 43

43 (44) Telson long bilobed; carapace short, without spinous crest.
Lepidurus bilobatus Packard 1877.
This species has not been recorded since the Hayden survey, when it was taken in Colorado.

44 (43) Telson long, not carinate, sometimes bilobed; carapace with a median spinous crest. . . . . . *Lepidurus lemmoni* Holmes 1894.
California.   The cercopods are very long in this species.

45 (38) Telson short, cylindrical, simple. . . . . *Apus* . . 46

46 (47) Carapace as long as the portion of the abdomen projecting beyond it; telson short with two median and two lateral spines on its dorsal median third. . . . *Apus aequalis* Packard 1871.

A widely distributed species occurring in Mexico, Lower California, Texas, Nebraska, and Kansas. It has 23 segments exposed behind the carapace. Fig. 1012 shows the form of this species.

FIG. 1033. *Apus aequalis.* Telson. X 6. (After Packard.)

47 (46) Carapace shorter than the portion of the abdomen exposed behind it. 48

48 (49) Telson long, with three median and two lateral spines on its dorsal median third; 29 segments exposed behind carapace.
Apus newberryi Packard 1871.

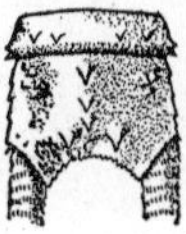

Recorded from Utah and Colorado. The hairs along the cercopods are said to be remarkably fine.

FIG. 1034. *Apus newberryi.* Telson. X 6. (After Packard.)

49 (48) More than 30 segments exposed behind carapace. 50

50 (51)   Carapace short, three-fifths as long as exposed abdomen; telson with
          one (or two) median and two lateral spines on its dorsal
          median third. . . . . . .   *Apus lucasanus* Packard 1871.

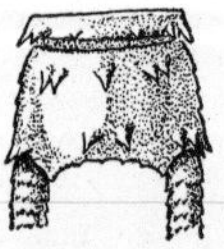

          An abundant and widely distributed species; reported from Lower Cali-
          fornia and Kansas.

          FIG. 1035. *Apus lucasanus.* Telson. X 6. (After Packard.)

51 (50)   Carapace even shorter than in *A. lucasanus;* telson very short with
          one median and four lateral spines on dorsal median third.
                                        Apus longicaudatus Leconte 1846.

          This form occurs in Colorado, Nebraska, Texas, and along the Yellowstone
          River.

          FIG. 1036. *Apus longicaudatus.* Telson. X 6. (After Packard.)

52 (37)   Body compressed, carapace forming two lateral valves which enclose
          the body. . . . .   Suborder **Conchostraca** . . 53

53 (60)   Only the first post-cephalic limbs prehensile in the male; carapace
          spheroidal, without lines of growth; head not included
          within carapace-chamber. . . . . . Family LIMNETIDAE.
          Only one genus . . . .   *Limnetis* . . 54

54 (57)   Shell subspherical. 55

55 (56)   Length, 3 mm.; front of male's head narrow; second antenna 16-seg-
     A   B   mented; flabellum very large. . *Limnetis gouldii* Baird 1862.

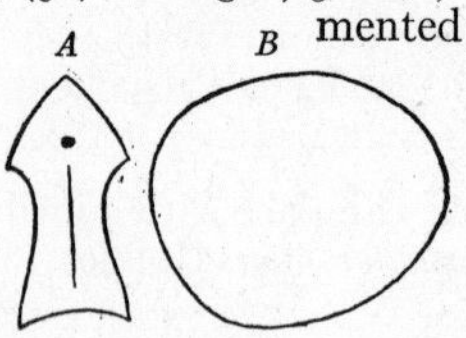

               A form widely distributed through Massachusetts, New
               Hampshire, Rhode Island, New York, Illinois, and Canada.
               It is very hardy and will live for months in aquaria.

               FIG. 1037. *Limnetis gouldii.* A, head of male, dorsal view. X 21;
               B, shape of shell. X 7. (After Packard.)

56 (55)   Length, 4.2 mm.; front of male's head very broad; antenna 20-seg-
          mented. . . . . . .   *Limnetis gracilicornis* Packard 1871.

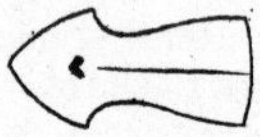

               This species was described by Packard from specimens collected
               at Waco, Texas.

               FIG. 1038. *Limnetis gracilicornis.* Head of male, dorsal view. X 18.
               (After Packard.)

57 (54)   Shell suboval. 58

58 (59)   Length, 4 mm.; front of male's head broad and square; second an-
     A   B   tenna 14- and 17-segmented; flabellum very narrow.
                                        Limnetis mucronatus Packard 1875.

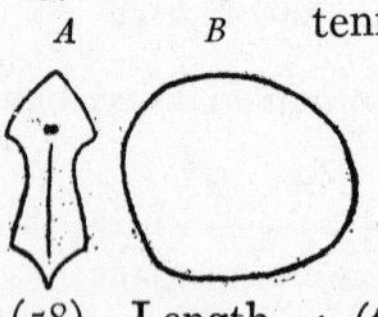

               This species has been reported from Montana and Kansas.
               It is easily recognized by the mucronate, tridentate front.

               FIG. 1039. *Limnetis mucronatus.* A, head of male, dorsal view. X 20;
               B, shape of shell. X 4. (After Packard.)

59 (58)   Length, 4 (to 6) mm.; front of male's head rather broad; second
     A   B   antenna 29-segmented; flabellum short and broad.
                                        Limnetis brevifrons Packard 1877.

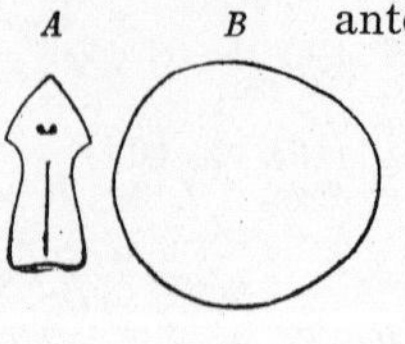

               This is the largest known species of this genus in North
               America. It has been observed only at Ellis, Kansas.

               FIG. 1040. *Limnetis brevifrons.* A, head of male. X 8. B, shape
               of shell. X 3. (After Packard.)

60 (53)   First and second post-cephalic limbs prehensile in the male; carapace
          distinctly bivalve, enclosing head, with concentric growth
          lines around a more or less prominent umbo.
                                         Family LIMNADIIDAE . . 61

61 (66)   With pediculated dorsal organ on front of head. 62

62 (63)   Shell broad oval, much flattened, subtriangular, with about 18 lines
          of growth; flagella of second antenna 12- to 13-segmented;
          18 to 22 pairs of limbs. . . . . *Limnadia.*
          Only one species . . . . *Limnadia americana* Morse 1875.

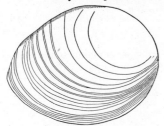

This species was described from specimens collected
at Lynn, Massachusetts.
Another possible species, *Limnadia coriacea* Haldeman, was collected at Cincinnati and in ditches along
the Susquehanna river, but it has not been sufficiently
described so that its relationships can be determined.
See Packard (1883, pp. 313, 314).

FIG. 1041.   *Limnadia americana.*   Side view.   × 3.
(After Packard.)

63 (62)   Shell narrow-ovate, rather prominent behind the umbones with 4 to
          5 lines of growth; flagella of second antennae 9- to 10-seg-
          mented; 18 pairs of limbs. . . . . . . *Eulimnadia* . . 64

64 (65)   Shell narrow-ovate, with 4 lines of growth; telson with 12 pairs of
          dorsal spinules not including the terminal spine.
                                  Eulimnadia agassizii Packard 1874.

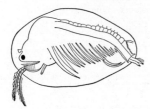

This small crustacean has only been observed on
Penikese Island, Massachusetts.   The figure shows
the large dorsal organ projecting above the eye.   The
valves of the carapace are whitish and very transparent.   Their shape is regularly oval.

FIG. 1042.   *Eulimnadia agassizii.*   Side view.   × 4.
(After Packard.)

65 (64)   Shell narrower than that of *Eulimnadia agassizii,* with 5 lines of growth;
          telson with 16 fine teeth above.
                                  Eulimnadia texana Packard 1871.

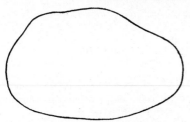

The valves of the carapace are whitish and
rounded oval in shape.
This species has been collected in Kansas,
Nebraska, and Texas.   It is said to be common in the last locality in early spring.   The
figure shows only the shape of the shell.

FIG. 1043.   *Eulimnadia texana.*   Shape of shell,
side view.   × 7.   (After Packard.)

66 (61)   Shell oval, more or less globose, with 18 to 22 lines of growth, amber
          colored; no pediculated dorsal-organ on front of head;
          flagella of second antennae 11- to 17-segmented; 24 to 28
          pairs of limbs. . . . . *Estheria* . . 67

67 (70)   Umbones one-sixth length of shell from anterior end. 68

68 (69)   Shell large (16 mm. long), flat; umbones small; flagella of second
antenna 13- and 15-segmented.

Estheria californica Packard 1874.

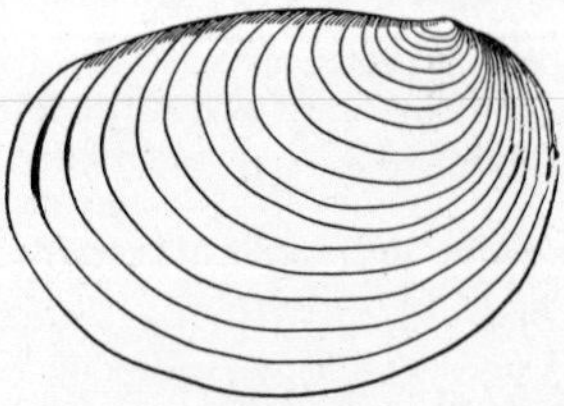

Thus far this species has been collected at two
localities in California. The small size of the umbones
is remarkable. Length of shell, 16 mm.; height,
10 mm.; breadth, 4 mm.

Fig. 1044. *Estheria californica.* Shell, side view. × 3.
(After Packard.)

69 (68)   Like *Estheria californica* but umbones more prominent and dorsal
edge of shell sloping down to posterior end.

Estheria newcombii Baird 1866.

Possibly the same as the last species but as Packard's and
Baird's figures appear to differ somewhat the two are separated.
It is found only in California.

Fig. 1045. *Estheria newcombii.* Shell, side view. × 2. (After Baird.)

70 (67)   Umbones more than one-sixth length of shell from anterior end. . 71

71 (72)   Shell long and narrow; umbones small, one-fifth length of shell from
anterior end; telson armed with small fine teeth; hands of
male short and thick; flagella of second antenna 15- and
14-segmented. . . . *Estheria compleximanus* Packard 1877.

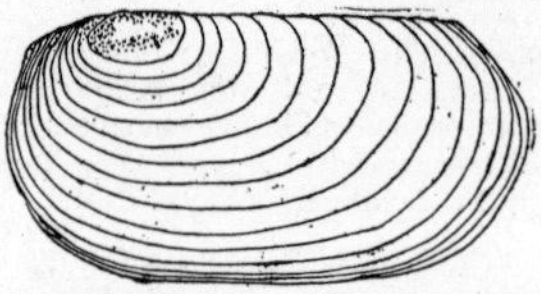

Packard reported this species from two localities in
Kansas and more recently Richard discovered it in a
collection from Lower California. Length of shell,
11 mm.; height, 5.5 mm.

Fig. 1046. *Estheria compleximanus.* Shell, side view.
× 3. (After Packard.)

72 (71)   Shell more or less swollen or globose; umbones prominent. . . . 73

73 (74)   Shell globose, wider than high; umbones prominent and oblique
one-fourth length of shell from anterior end, lines of growth
not sharply marked. . . . . . *Estheria digueti* Richard 1895.
Described from Lower California.

74 (73)   Lines of growth well marked; shell not wider than high. 75

75 (78)   Flagella of second antennae 15- and 14-segmented. 76

76 (77)   Shell globose with 24 lines of growth; umbones large and prominent,
two-fifths length of shell from anterior end.

Estheria belfragei Packard 1871.

This fine species was described by Packard from specimens collected
in the month of April at Waco, Texas.

Fig. 1047. *Estheria belfragei.* Shell, side view. × 4. (After Packard.)

77 (76) Shell globose with 13 lines of growth; umbones prominent, one-third length of shell from anterior end.

Estheria setosa Pearse 1913.

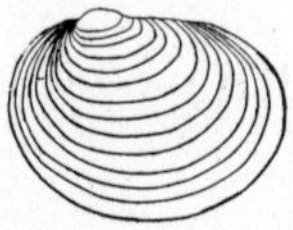

This species resembles *Estheria belfragei* in many respects but is easily distinguished by the smaller number of lines of growth and the length of the dorsal setae at the anterior edge of the telson. Collected in eastern Nebraska from small pools.

FIG. 1048. *Estheria setosa.* Shell, side view. × 3.

78 (75) Flagella of second antenna 17- and 16-segmented. 79

79 (80) Shell swollen; umbones rather prominent, one-fourth length of shell from anterior end; dorsal margin short, suddenly sloping at posterior end; telson with larger teeth interpolated between the smaller ones. . . . . . *Estheria mexicana* Claus 1860.

A species of very wide range extending from Lake Winnipeg through Kansas, Nebraska, Kentucky, Ohio, and New Mexico into Mexico. It is rather variable in its structure.

FIG. 1049. *Estheria mexicana.* Shell, side view. × 4. (After Packard.)

80 (79) Shell somewhat globose; umbones more prominent than in *Estheria mexicana*, slightly nearer the anterior end than in *Estheria belfragei*. . . . . *Estheria morsei* Packard 1871.

South Dakota, Nebraska. Fig. 1049 shows the general structure of this species.

IMPORTANT PAPERS ON FRESH-WATER PHYLLOPODA

CALMAN, W. T. 1909. Crustacea. Lankester's Treatise on Zoology, Pt. VII, Fasc. 3: 29–55. London and New York.

DADAY, E. 1910. Monographie systématique des Phyllopodes Anostracés. Ann. Sci. Natur., (9) 11: 91–492, 84 figs.

HAY, O. P., and W. P. 1889. A contribution to the knowledge of the Genus Branchipus. Amer. Natur., 23: 91–95.

PACKARD, A. S. 1883. A Monograph of the Phyllopod Crustacea of North America, with Remarks on the Order Phyllocarida. 12 Ann. Rept. U. S. Geol. Surv.: 295–590, 39 pls., 1 Map.

PEARSE, A. S. 1913. Notes on Phyllopod Crustacea. 14 Rept. Michigan Acad. Sci.: 191–197, 3 pls.

SHANTZ, H. L. 1905. Notes on North American Species of Branchinecta and their Habits. Biol. Bull., 9: 249–264; pls. 10–12.

CHAPTER XXII

THE WATER FLEAS (CLADOCERA)

By EDWARD A. BIRGE

Dean, University of Wisconsin

WHEN men began to study nature by the aid of the microscope in the seventeenth century the "insects" were among the first objects to be examined. In 1669, the Dutch physician, Swammerdam, described in his history of insects the "*pulex aquaticus arborescens*" — the water-flea with branching arms. This was one of the Cladocera, still called *Daphnia pulex*, the commonest species in shallow pools. These creatures he described and figured, giving an account of their structure and habits and speaking of their sudden appearance in enormous numbers, and their equally sudden disappearance. So the Cladocera made their début into science along with the microscope.

For nearly a century little was added to the knowledge of the group. In 1755, the German, Schaeffer, gave the first really good account of their structure. In 1785, O. F. Mueller, the Danish naturalist, issued the first general systematic work upon Entomostraca. This described many of the species as we now know them and gave a firm scientific basis for further knowledge of the Cladocera. In the rapid advance of science during the latter half of the nineteenth century the systematic work of the group was substantially done, the Norwegian, G. O. Sars, having contributed more than any other one man. This work showed that the Cladocera constitute the largest group of fresh-water crustacea in number of species; the most diversified in size, in structure, and in habits.

During the opening years of the present century the scientific study of fresh-water life has advanced rapidly and the biology of the Cladocera is receiving much attention. The conditions of variation and the nature of the variants are examined, as well as the conditions of sexual reproduction, the centers of origin and dispersal of species, and other similar matters.

The Cladocera are particularly well suited for study by those persons who are interested in observing animals with the microscope and who cannot command the resources of a university laboratory. They are easily collected and preserved and the species may be readily identified, since little or no microscopic dissection is needed to make out the specific characters. Many of the Cladocera are so transparent that the internal organs can be studied in detail when the animal is viewed from the side under the microscope. Many of the forms can readily be kept alive in small aquaria, and their habits observed. There is still a great amount of work to be done in this country in finding out the local geographical distribution of the species and the variation of the variable forms.

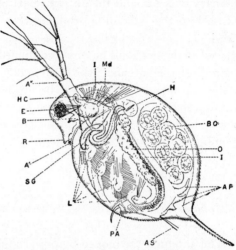

The suborder is divided into two sections so different that few statements can be made of them in common. The first, and by far the larger section, the Calyptomera, have a large, bivalve shell, which covers the body and legs.

FIG. 1050. *Daphnia longispina.* *A'*, antennule; *A''*, antenna; *AP*, abdominal processes; *AS*, abdominal setae; *B*, brain with optic ganglion and ocellus; *BC*, brood case with developing ova; *E*, eye, with three eye muscles of left side; *H*, heart with venous opening on side and exit in front; *HC*, hepatic cecum; *I*, intestine; *L*, legs; *Md*, mandible; *O*, ovary; *PA*, post abdomen with anal spines and terminal claw; *R*, rostrum or beak; *SG*, shell gland. (After Sars.)

The second section, the Gymnomera, includes two species in our fresh waters. These retain the shell only as a brood sac; the body and legs being free. In the account which follows, the Calyptomera are kept in mind. The animals belonging to this group range in size from about 0.2 mm. to 3.0 mm., or even more. All have a distinct head, and a body covered by a fold of the skin, which extends backward and downward from the dorsal side of the head and constitutes a bivalve shell. The junction of head and body is sometimes marked by a depression, the cervical sinus or notch (Figs. 1051, 1073, 1091).[1]

[1] The figures referred to are designed to give the specific characters rather than the anatomy, which is shown only incidentally.

In the head is the large compound eye (Fig. 1050). This has numerous or few lenses (Figs. 1059, 1076, 1169), and is capable of being rotated by three muscles on each side. It is a most conspicuous organ, by its size, its dark pigment, and its constant motion during life. In the head are also the brain, the optic ganglion, with its numerous nerves to the eye, the ocellus, or pigment spot, the antennary muscles, and the anterior part of the digestive tract. The head bears two pairs of appendages: (1) The antennules (Figs. 1051, 1079, 1114, 1152), which carry sense-rods, the olfactory setae, usually placed at the end, and have also ordinarily one or more lateral sense hairs; (2) the antennae, the main organs of locomotion, large swimming appendages, with a stout basal joint bearing two branches or rami, which, in turn, carry long plumose setae. The number of the antennary setae may be expressed by a formula which shows the number of the setae on each joint of each branch of the antenna; the numbers for the dorsal branch occupying the place of the numerator of a fraction. The formula thus constructed reads

Daphnia (Fig. 1050), $\dfrac{0-0-1-3}{1-1-3}$; that for *Sida* (Fig. 1051), $\dfrac{0-3-7}{1-4}$.

The antennae are moved by powerful muscles, which may occupy a great part of the interior of the head (Fig. 1050). On the size of the antennae, the length and number of the setae, and on the size of the muscles operating them, depends the type of locomotion. *Latona* (Fig. 1052) leaps suddenly from point to point by single powerful strokes of its broad antennae. The smaller Daphnidae (Fig. 1079) hop, rather than leap, by more numerous and less vigorous strokes. The heavier forms of this family (Fig. 1075), with smaller antennae, have a rotating, unsteady motion, produced by rapid strokes. *Drepanothrix* (Fig. 1104), whose antennae bear saber-like setae, scrambles and pushes itself about, and the mud-haunting *Ilyocryptus* (Fig. 1110) crawls and pulls itself about among the weeds, rather than swims. The members of the large family of the Chydoridae have small antennae and move them very rapidly; while their progress varies from a rapid whirling-motion, as in *Chydorus* (Fig. 1150), to a slower wavering and tottering progress, as in *Acroperus* (Fig. 1121). In the Macrothricidae and Chydoridae the post-abdomen is often an efficient aid to locomotion. It may push the animal along, as in *Ilyocryptus* (Fig. 1110) and *Camptocercus* (Fig. 1119). In *Dunhevedia* (Fig. 1134) it is peculiarly effective, broad and stout, covered with numerous small spines and setae, and by its aid the animal may execute sudden and vigorous jumps.

The head also bears the mouth parts: (1) The mandibles (Figs. 1050, 1068, 1099, and others); stout, strongly chitinized organs, made in one piece and without a palpus. Their opposing faces are toothed and ridged and they grind the food very perfectly. (2) The maxillae, a pair of very minute organs, lying concealed on the ventral surface of the body, just behind the mandibles. Each is a small, pointed structure, bearing several curved setae. They work like a pair of hands to push the food between the mandibles. (3) The labium, an unpaired structure, attached to the rear of the head and closing the mouth from below. In many of the Macrothricidae and Chydoridae this structure bears a keel or projection which is of systematic value (Figs. 1051, 1060, 1106, 1135).

The axis of the head may continue that of the body (*extended*, Fig. 1100), or it may be bent downward (*depressed*, Fig. 1087). That part in front of the eye is known as the vertex. There is usually a sort of beak in front of, or between, the antennules, which is known as the rostrum, whose size and shape have systematic value. There is commonly a ridge above the insertion of the antenna, which helps to stiffen the side of the head and to support the pull of the antennary muscles. This is the fornix, whose shape and extent may form an important systematic character (Figs. 1063, 1083).

The shell, though called bivalve, is really in one piece, bent along the back, but never showing a division or joint at this place. It has very different forms, as seen from the side, nearly square, oval, or round. It may be marked in the most various fashions. It may bear hairs, or spines, along the ventral edge. There may be a single spine on the dorsal side, prolonging the junction of the valves, as in *Daphnia*, or each valve may have one or more spines at the lower posterior part, the infero-posteal angle (Fig. 1076). This angle in the Chydoridae may be acute or rounded, smooth or toothed, and its characters are of systematic value. The shell is always a duplicature of the skin. Its inner wall is far more delicate than the outer, and between the walls the blood circulates and the inner surface serves as a respiratory organ.

Just back of the head, on the dorsal side, lies the heart, an oval or elongated sac (Figs. 1050, 1051, 1089), whose rapid pulsations are easily seen in the living animal. It receives the colorless or yellow blood by one opening on each side and expels it in front. There are no blood vessels, but the circulation passes along definite courses through a complex series of passages all over the body. The movements of the blood corpuscles may be readily seen in transparent Cladocera.

Respiration is not served by any single organ. The legs and the inside of the valves are the main surfaces for the exchange of gases.

In the anterior part of the valves lies an organ whose structure is not readily made out. This is the shell gland (Figs. 1050, 1051, 1056), a flattened glandular tube in several loops, which probably serves the function of a kidney.

The body lies free within the valves and is divided into the main portion, bearing the feet, which is not plainly segmented, and a single unjointed portion, the post-abdomen. Through it runs the intestine, and along the sides of the body lie the simple reproductive organs. To the ventral side are attached the feet, ordinarily five pairs, sometimes six. These are mainly leaf-like structures, each with several parts, bearing numerous hairs and long setae (Figs. 1050, 1142). Their structure is too complex to describe here. In the first two families all the feet are similar and foliaceous. Their use is to create a current of water through the valves, bringing in oxygen for respiration and particles of food. The latter consists chiefly of algae, though nothing edible is rejected that the current brings in. The food particles collect below the body between the bases of the feet and are fed forward into the mouth. The maxillae push them between the jaws as the labrum opens, the mandibles grind them up, and they pass on into the esophagus. Cladocera are normally eating all of the time.

In the Daphnidae and remaining families the feet differ in structure; the first pairs being more or less prehensile and having other functions besides the main one of drawing in water. These animals live chiefly among the weeds, and the hooks and spines of the first foot aid them in clinging to plants and also may help to pull off attached algae, etc., for food.

In the more transparent species the digestive tract may be seen throughout its full extent. The narrow esophagus (Figs. 1050, 1051, 1096) widens suddenly into the stomach, which lies in the head and whose posterior end passes insensibly into the intestine. Attached to the stomach in many species are two sacs, often long and curved (Figs. 1050, 1053, 1060, 1064, 1100). These are the hepatic ceca, which no doubt function as a digestive gland. The stomach and intestine have a muscular wall and a lining of dark-colored, glandular cells. The cavity is ordinarily filled with food. The intestine has a direct course in the first four families. In the Macrothricidae it is sometimes direct (Fig. 1106), and sometimes convoluted (Figs. 1100, 1103). In the Chydoridae it is always convoluted and there is often a cecum attached to the ventral side near the posterior end (Figs. 1121, 1141). The terminal part of the intestine, the rectum, is always transparent and the muscles which open and close it can easily be seen. The anus lies either at or near the end of the post-abdomen, as is usually the case in the first five families, or in the Chydoridae and in some forms of the other families (Figs. 1089, 1091, 1100, 11c9), on the dorsal side.

The post-abdomen is ordinarily jointed to the body and is bent forward; hence its dorsal side may come to be the lower one. On the dorsal side it bears two sensory hairs, often very long (Fig. 1090), the abdominal setae. At the end of the post-abdomen are two terminal claws, which, in turn, may have spines at their base, the basal spines (Figs. 1123, 1144), or, when numerous, the pecten (Fig. 1066), and the concave side may also have a row of very fine spinules (denticulate). The post-abdomen almost always has more or fewer spines, or teeth, the anal spines. In the Chydoridae there are frequently two rows on each side behind the anus, the marginal and lateral denticles (Fig. 1147). These spines and teeth may have the most diverse shape and structure (squamae, fascicles, etc.), and furnish important systematic characters. Their main use seems to be to comb the legs and keep them clean and free from foreign matters and from parasites which might otherwise readily attach themselves.

Little study has been given to the senses of the Cladocera, except that of sight. As special organs of touch there are the abdominal setae, which are sometimes very long (Fig. 1090); sensory hairs on the basal joint of the antenna near the body (Fig. 1075), or near the apex (Figs. 1051, 1053, 1089); the lateral sense hair of the antennule (Figs. 1089, 1117, 1154); the flagellum on the antennule of the Sididae (Figs. 1051-1057), which is often fringed with fine hairs; and the frontal sense hair of *Bosmina* (Fig. 1096). Any of the innumerable hairs and setae may also serve this sense, though not specially modified for that purpose. There is no auditory organ. Whether the olfactory setae really give sensations of smell and taste is doubtful, although the structure of the sense rods is such that they may well serve a chemical sense. They lie at the entrance of the valves in the current of water which is coming in under the impulses of the feet, and may take cognizance of the particles of food, etc., which come along with the water. The Cladocera are certainly able to discriminate between different kinds of particles brought in by the legs, eating some and rejecting others. They have decided tastes in the matter of diet, preferring some forms of algae to others. In general, the diatoms are eaten in preference to the blue-green algae. In the selection of food, the Cladocera are aided also by sensations which arise in the mouth, since they may reject particles which have been brought into the mouth and partially chewed.

The eye is obviously the visual organ. It is sensitive to light and can no doubt distinguish objects by the shadows which they produce, although its lenses are by no means numerous enough, or perfect enough, to give sensations of form. The constant motions of the eye are for the purpose of moving the lenses so that they will cover the entire field of vision, and the animal no doubt directs its movements by sensations which it receives through the eye. The Cladocera respond differently to light of different intensities and various colors. Most of them react positively to a weak light and negatively to a strong one. There is, however, much difference in this respect. *Drepanothrix*, for example, is vigorously repelled by the light of a lamp, which will attract all the other Cladocera in the vessel with it. Newly hatched Cladocera are attracted by light which will repel older forms. On a bright, calm day a few inches

of water at the surface of a lake may be deserted by the Cladocera. A little deeper may be found young forms, and still deeper,
perhaps one or two meters below the surface, the adult animals.
The temperature of the water also has much influence on the reaction to light. In cold water Cladocera are attracted by a light
which will repel them at higher temperatures. The limnetic forms
of *Daphnia pulex* ordinarily remain during the daytime in the cool
water immediately beneath the thermocline, though they may rise
into the warm water during the night. In the winter, when the lake
is skimmed with ice, the same animals may be seen in the bright
sunshine immediately below the ice. Practically all of the Cladocera
react negatively to the blue rays of the spectrum, are nearly un-
influenced by the rays at the red end, and find the yellow rays the
most attractive.

The ocellus is rarely absent (*Diaphanosoma, Daphnia retrocurva,
longiremis*); sometimes rudimentary (many forms of *Daphnia*);
sometimes larger than the eye (*Leydigia, Dadaya*); and rarely the
sole organ sensitive to light (*Monospilus*). It is not known in what
respects its function differs from that of the eye.

This imperfect sketch shows how complex the structure of the
Cladocera is, — wonderfully complex, when their small size is considered. The smallest of them are hardly more than one one-
hundredth of an inch in length. Yet these have ten complicated
legs, besides the numerous other structures named and many which
have not been mentioned. Probably no other animals of so small
size have so complex a structure, yet they must suffer the disgrace
of being eaten by *Stentor* and so being among the few Metazoa
which are swallowed whole by one-celled animals.

The reproduction of the Cladocera is noteworthy. During the
open season the females produce eggs which develop without being
fertilized. These may number only two, the usual number in the
Chydoridae, or, in the larger Daphnidae, there may be more than
twenty. These eggs are deposited in the cavity bounded by the
dorsal part of the valves and the upper side of the body — the
brood case. Here they develop and hatch in a form quite like
that of the parent and are well grown before they are set free.
Hence there are no free-living larval forms of Cladocera, such as

are so abundant in the Copepoda. The young are nourished in the brood-cavity, not only by the yolk of the egg, but also by a secretion from the dorsal wall of the sac. The brood case may be closed behind by extensions of the body — the abdominal processes — which have some systematic importance. This parthenogenesis goes on regularly through the favorable season for growth, closing when the pools begin to dry or other unfavorable conditions arise. Several successive broods of females are ordinarily produced in this way, although in *Moina*, which lives in temporary pools, the second generation may be sexual. Sooner or later true females and males are hatched from the eggs. These females produce one or two eggs, large and opaque, with abundant yolk and thick shell, and which must be fertilized by the male before developing. These eggs pass into the brood sac, whose walls have usually acquired a peculiar structure. In the Chydorinae (Fig. 1159) they are merely thickened and darkened. In the Daphnidae (Figs. 1073, 1079, 1093), a semi-elliptical portion of the dorsal region of each valve becomes greatly altered to form the ephippium, so called from its resemblance to a saddle. In the Chydorinae the sexual egg is deposited in the brood sac and the whole shell is then molted; the egg remaining enclosed in it. Where the ephippium is developed, this separates during the molt from the rest of the shell and closes about the one or two eggs deposited in it. In either case the eggs lie over to the next favorable season before they develop.

This process of sexual reproduction occurs at different times in various species. Like the blossoming of flowers, it cannot always be directly correlated with any definite conditions of food or temperature. In those species which live in the open waters of lakes, sexual reproduction is often greatly reduced or wholly absent and the species is carried on from year to year by asexual generations. In many species the males are very rarely seen and in none are they abundant.

The males are smaller than the females and usually of similar form. They are distinguished by larger antennules; the post-abdomen is usually somewhat modified (Fig. 1144); the first foot is frequently armed with a stout hook which serves to clasp the females. In *Moina* this function is performed by the very large antennules (Fig. 1092).

Little is known regarding the length of life of the individual Cladocera. It doubtless varies from a few weeks to several months. Limnetic forms probably have a longer life than the littoral, as the food supply and other conditions of life are more constant. Individuals from the broods of *Daphnia longispina* (*hyalina*) which are born late in October and in November may survive through the winter and produce one or more broods of young in the spring. The last survivors die in June, weakened by old age and attacked by parasitic fungi. This is probably about the maximum length of life.

The Cladocera are found in all sorts of fresh waters. Lakes and ponds contain a much larger number of forms than do rivers. The shallow, weedy backwaters of a lake whose level is fairly permanent harbor a greater variety of species than does any other kind of locality. Here are found almost all of the Chydoridae and Macrothricidae, as well as most of the representatives of the other families. In such localities are found the best conditions for the life of these animals: warmth, shelter from enemies, and abundant food. It must not be supposed, however, that each square rod of such waters harbors a like population. On the contrary, anyone who collects frequently in one lake will come to know certain places as especially favorable to these creatures, which are present in greater number and variety than in places apparently quite similar and closely adjacent. While by far the greater number of species belong to the littoral region, living among the weeds and feeding on algae and similar organisms, a few species live near the bottom. Several species are commonly found in or near the mud, although not specially adapted to a life in the mud; such are *Alona quadrangularis* and *Drepanothrix*. The genera *Ilyocryptus* and *Monospilus* live regularly on the bottom; their structure is adjusted to a life in the mud and their shells are often overgrown by algae. These forms may and do swim, but more often scramble about on the bottom, pulling with their antennae and pushing with the postabdomen. In both forms the old shell is not cast off in molting, the new and larger shell appearing beneath it (Figs. 1110, 1168).

The species of *Moina* are found most commonly in muddy pools, such as those in brick-yards, though not confined to such waters.

With them are frequently associated members of the *Daphnia pulex* group. These last are also found in temporary pools of clear and weedy water, and, less frequently, in lakes. *Daphnia magna* in Europe is found in waters which are slightly brackish and very possibly does not disdain slightly alkaline waters in this country.

The limnetic region of the inland lakes has a cladoceran population, large in number of individuals but not rich in species. *Chydorus sphaericus* is almost the only Chydorid which is ever abundant here, though any species may be present as an accidental visitor. The regularly limnetic species belong chiefly to the genera *Bosmina, Diaphanosoma, Daphnia,* and *Holopedium.* These forms are transparent — an obviously protective character. *Chydorus* is an exception and the size of this species is so small that transparency may be unnecessary. Apart from transparency and a general lightness of build, the limnetic forms have generally no peculiar characters. *Holopedium* forms a marked exception to this statement, as its globular gelatinous case is wholly unique in the group and indeed in the crustacea.

Certain forms are intermediate in character between the limnetic and the littoral forms. Such is *Ophryoxus gracilis* (Fig. 1100), which paddles about in the open waters between weeds, and such also is *Sida crystallina* (Fig. 1051). Both of these forms are transparent, but they are never present in large numbers in the open water, nor are they likely to be found far out from the weedy margin.

In southern waters, where are found masses of floating plants such as the water hyacinth, the distinction between the littoral and limnetic species quite disappears.

The Gymnomera differ widely in structure and habits from the Calyptomera. The section includes two species in our fresh waters: *Polyphemus pediculus* (Fig. 1169), and *Leptodora kindtii* (Fig. 1170). In both forms the shell is reduced to an egg case and the feet are free, jointed, and provided with stout spines and hairs. In *Leptodora* the body is long and jointed, while in *Polyphemus* it is very short. Both animals are predacious, feeding on protozoa, rotifers, and minute crustacea. *Polyphemus* lives chiefly in marshes and in the weedy margins of ponds and lakes, but may also be found in the limnetic region and in the Great Lakes. *Leptodora* is always limnetic in its habits. It is almost perfectly transparent; the dark eye and yellow stomach alone being visible when the animal is viewed by transmitted light. It is by far the largest of the Cladocera, reaching a length of 18 mm. Its winter eggs hatch as nauplii and this is the only species of Cladocera in which this characteristic crustacean larva appears.

The Cladocera have great economic value. Together with the Copepoda they constitute the chief agency for converting the smaller algae of fresh water into a form edible by the carnivorous aquatic animals. They are the prey of insect larvae, which are in turn an important item in the bill of fare of the larger fishes. Cladocera are themselves of great value as food for young fishes and there is a period in the life of almost every fish when it feeds exclusively on Entomostraca. Even the larger fishes do not disdain these animals. The great spoonbill (*Polyodon*) fills its stomach with Bosminae, or other tiny inhabitants of the water from which it strains its food.

The geographical distribution of Cladocera offers little of interest that can be stated in a brief sketch, chiefly because the species are so widely distributed. Some species, like *Chydorus sphaericus*, are cosmopolitan. A majority of the species found in this country are found also in Europe. Where a species is peculiar to this region it is often but slightly different from the European form. The student of Cladocera should presume that any species is probably intercontinental, though it may prove to be more restricted in its range. The study of our forms has not gone far enough to enable us to speak of the local distribution of each species within the general area which it covers, but it is known that the rare species are very irregularly distributed. On the whole, the fauna of the various regions of the country is strikingly similar, but with some forms peculiar to each region. The southern states contain numerous species which are common to them and to South America, but are not found in the northern states.

The student of Cladocera will find the cone net (p. 68) the best agent for collecting the littoral forms. The catch should be put into a cup, which should be filled with water, and the debris allowed to settle before pouring off the water and the crustacea through the funnel. As little as possible of the weed and debris should be included in the catch, since it is a wearisome task to search for the various species in a catch which contains great masses of weed with but few crustacea. It is well to retain a part of the weed in a separate bottle, so that species which go to the bottom may not be overlooked. It is also well to cover the cup with one's hat, or otherwise, while the debris is settling so that species which fly from the light may not go into the weed at the bottom. Numerous hauls of the net should be made and concentrated so as to give abundant material. Considerable experience with collections sent me by students of Cladocera has shown me that the chief faults of the collector are including too much debris in the catch and taking too few hauls of the dredge.

The best preservative I have found to be strong, 95 per cent, alcohol. This keeps the shape of the species as well as or better than anything else. Certain soft-bodied forms with strong muscles may be distorted by any fluid which kills and hardens quickly. Such are *Pseudosida, Latona*, and *Latonopsis*, and, to a less degree, *Moina* and *Diaphanosoma*. For these also we have nothing better for field use than alcohol. If their forms are to be well preserved they should be killed individually by some poison like osmic acid, or chloral hydrate, and then hardened gradually, according to regular microscopic methods. Formalin distorts many species.

I have found no better mounting fluid than pure glycerine. I place the animal with a small drop of glycerine in the center of the slide and support the cover glass by three bits of paper thick enough to permit the cover to press slightly on the specimen. The cover glass is put on carefully so that the glycerine occupies its center only. A bit of soft paraffin (melting point about 50° C.) is placed at the edge of the cover glass, and, on warming the slide, the paraffin melts and runs in, sealing the mount. The cover may afterwards be cemented down by any microscopic cement, and this should be done if the preparation is to be kept; but for purposes of study it is well not to do so, since an advantage of the method is the ease with which the specimen can be unmounted for study or dissection.

KEY TO NORTH AMERICAN FRESH-WATER CLADOCERA

1 (248)   Body and feet covered by a bivalve shell.   Feet in general foliaceous, not plainly jointed. . . .   Section A. **Calyptomera** . .   2

2 (21)   Six pairs of feet, all similar, except the last, and all foliaceous.
Tribe I. **Ctenopoda** . .   3

3 (18)   Shell of ordinary type.   Antenna biramous in female, rami flattened, the dorsal with numerous setae, both lateral and terminal.
Family SIDIDAE Baird . .   4

Head large; cervical sinus present. Antennules large, movable. Antennae with terminal setae only on ventral ramus. Eye large, with numerous lenses; ocellus small or absent. Intestine simple, usually with more or less distinct median cecum or enlargement at anterior end; rarely with 2 hepatic ceca. Heart elongated. Male usually with characteristic antennule; the flagellum united with the base into one structure, long, tapering, with a row of fine spinules toward apex; usually with grasping organ on first foot and copulatory organs on post-abdomen.

4 (5)   Dorsal ramus of antenna 3-jointed, rostrum present.
Sida Straus 1820.

Head with large gland on dorsal side; pointed rostrum; no fornices. Antennules of ♀ attached to side of rostrum, short, truncate, with short flagellum. Ventral ramus of antennae 2-jointed. Antennules of ♂ very long; no copulatory organ; first foot with hook.

Only one American species. . . *Sida crystallina* (O. F. Müller) 1785.

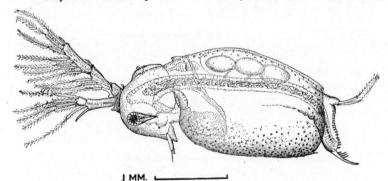

|_ MM. |_____|

FIG. 1051.   *Sida crystallina*.   (Unless otherwise indicated all figures were drawn especially for this chapter.)
Color yellowish-hyaline, sometimes with brilliant blue spots. Length, ♀, 3.0–4.0 mm.; ♂, 1.5–2.0 mm.
Common in lakes and ponds among weeds.

5 (4)   Dorsal ramus of antenna 2-jointed.   6

6 (9)   With lateral expansion on basal joint of dorsal ramus of antenna.
Latona Straus 1820 . .   7

Large, tongue-shaped projection on ventral side of head, its ventral surface concave. Ventral ramus of antennae 3-jointed. Long setae on posterior margin of valves. Eye dorsal, far from optic ganglion. ♂ with copulatory organ; no hook on first foot.

7 (8)   Antennary expansion very large; no hepatic ceca.

Latona setifera (O. F. Müller) 1785.

Antennules of both sexes alike, bent, with large, hairy flagellum set on at angle, looking like continuation of base.   Color yellow; not transparent; old ♀ often with brilliant colors in late autumn.   Length, ♀, 2.0–3.0 mm.; ♂, ca. 1.5 mm.   Widely distributed, but never abundant, among weeds in ponds and lakes.

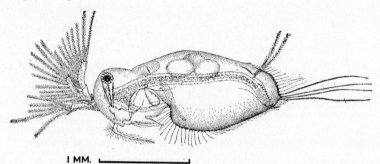

.I MM.

FIG. 1052.   *Latona setifera.*

8 (7)   Antennary expansion small; hepatic ceca present.

Latona parviremis Birge 1910.

Antennule of ♀ with basal part and long slender flagellum, like *Latonopsis;* of ♂ very long, like other Sididae.   Color yellow.   Length, ♀, to 2.5 mm.; ♂, 0.8 mm.   Northern Wisconsin, Michigan, Maine; in weedy waters of lake .

0.5 MM.

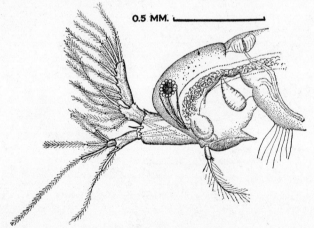

FIG. 1053.   *Latona parviremis.*

9 (6)   Without lateral expansion of antenna. 10

10 (13)   No spines on post-abdomen. .   *Diaphanosoma* Fischer 1850 . . 11

No rostrum, fornix, or ocellus.   Antennule small, truncated; olfactory setae terminal, with slender flagellum.   Dorsal ramus of antennae 2-jointed; ventral 3-jointed.   Claws with 3 basal spines.   ♂ with long antennule; copulatory organ; hook on first ʾoot.

11 (12) Reflexed antenna not reaching posterior margin of valves.
Diaphanosoma brachyurum (Liéven) 1848.

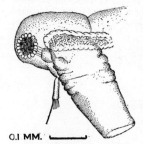

Eye pigment large; eye filling end of head. Color yellowish-transparent.   Length, ♀, 0.8–0.9 mm.; ♂, ca. 0.4 mm.   Common in marshes and weedy margins of lakes. Very probably the next species is merely a limnetic variety of this.

Fig. 1054. Diaphanosoma brachyurum.

0.1 MM. ⊢━━━⊣

12 (11) Antenna when reflexed reaches or exceeds posterior margin of valves.
Diaphanosoma leuchtenbergianum Fischer 1850.

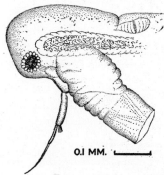

Eye not filling end of head, pigment small. Color hyaline. Length, ♀, 0.9–1.2 mm.; ♂, to 0.8 mm. Common in open waters of lakes.

Fig. 1055. Diaphanosoma leuchtenbergianum.

0.1 MM. ⊢━━━⊣

13 (10) Spines on post-abdomen. 14
14 (17) Eye dorsal, far from insertion of antennule and optic ganglion. No rostrum. . . . . Latonopsis Sars 1888 . . 15
No tongue-shaped process on ventral side of head, or antennary expansion. Otherwise much like Latona parviremis. Posterior margin of valves with very long setae (often lost). ♂ with long antennule, copulatory organ, and hook on first foot.
15 (16) Shell gland drawn out into very long posterior loop.
Latonopsis occidentalis Birge 1891.
Post-abdomen with about 9 small anal spines. Color yellowish-transparent. Length, ♀, to 1.8 mm.; ♂, ca. 0.6 mm. New England to Colorado and Texas; in weedy pools and lakes.

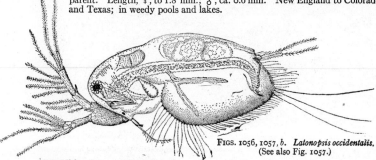

Figs. 1056, 1057, b. Latonopsis occidentalis. (See also Fig. 1057.)

0.5 MM. ⊢━━━━━⊣

16 (15)   Shell gland of ordinary form. . . *Latonopsis fasciculata* Daday 1905.

Post-abdomen with projections on dorsal (posterior) margin and 12–14 clusters of 2–3 lancet-shaped anal spines. Color yellowish. Length, ♀, to 2.0 mm.; ♂, to 1.0 mm. Louisiana, Texas; in weedy pools and lakes.

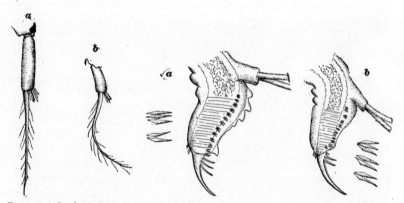

FIG. 1057. *a, Latonopsis fasciculata;*   FIG. 1058.   *a, Latonopsis fasciculata; b, Pseudosida bidentata.*
b, Latonopsis occidentalis.

17 (14)   Eye ventral or in middle of head.   Rostrum present.
                                       Pseudosida Herrick 1884.
       Only one American species. . . *Pseudosida bidentata* Herrick 1884.

General form like *Sida* but head more depressed and dorsum more arched. Rostrum present; no fornix or cervical glands. Antennules attached as in *Sida*, long basal part with olfactory setae on side, and long flexible flagellum. Dorsal ramus of antennae with 2, ventral with 3, joints; setae very unequal in length. Post-abdomen with about 14 clusters of spinules; claws with 2 large basal spines and a very small spine proximal to them.

♂ with antennule of standard form; copulatory organs. Complex grasping apparatus on first foot.

Color yellowish, semi-transparent. Length, ♀, to 1.8 or 2.0 mm.; ♂, 0.9 mm. Southern states, in pools and lakes.

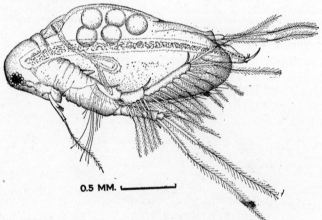

0.5 MM. L⎯⎯⎯⎯⎯⎯⎯⎯⎯

FIGS. 1059, 1058, *b.*   *P. bidentata.*   (After Foster.)   (See also Fig. 1058.)

18 (3)   Enclosed in gelatinous mantle.   Antennae simple in female, **cylindrical,**
with 3 terminal setae. . . . . Family HOLOPEDIDAE Sars.

Animal enclosed in a large, globular, transparent, delicate but tough, gelatinous case, open ventrally and forming 2 valves. Body much compressed, shell of head and body very thin and high, as seen from side, leaving uncovered the mouth parts, the ends of the feet, and the hind part of body. Antennule small, fixed; with 5–6 olfactory setae and lateral sense-hair, but no flagellum. Antennae in ♀ long; basal joint curved, annulated; the single ramus 2-jointed; antennae of ♂ biramous. Post-abdomen large, fleshy, not bent forward; with rather long, curved anal spines and clusters of very fine spinules; abdominal setae long, set on single, long, conical projection. Claws large, curved, denticulate, not set off from body by distinct joint. Eye small, with numerous lenses; ocellus small. Intestine simple with 2 hepatic ceca. Branchial sac on second to fifth feet. Color transparent. Swims on its back.

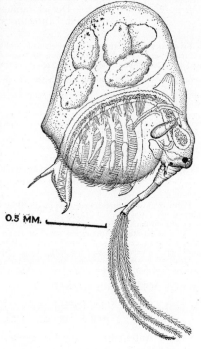

Sole genus with characters of family.
Holopedium Zaddach 1855 . . 19

19 (20)   Ventral margins of valves
with fine spines.
Holopedium gibberum Zaddach 1855.

Post-abdomen elongated (ca. one-third length of body) and tapering; anal spines numerous, up to 20.   Claws with 1 basal spine.   Length, ♀, 1.5–2.2 mm.; ♂, 0.5–0.6 mm.

0.5 MM.

This remarkable and beautiful species is not uncommon in open water in northern lakes; has been found in the Great Lakes, and in many inland waters, both lakes and smaller bodies of water.

FIGS. 1060, 1061, *a.   Holopedium gibberum* (gelatinous case not shown).   (See also Fig. 1061.)

20 (19)   Ventral margin of valves smooth.
Holopedium amazonicum Stingelin 1904.

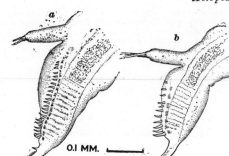

a

b

Post-abdomen short, blunt (ca. one-fourth of body in length), with 7–8 anal spines, the row continued forward by 3–4 very small spinules.   Claws without basal spine.   Abdominal setae very long and 3-jointed.   ♂ unknown.   Length, ♀, 1.0 mm. Lake Charles, Louisiana.

FIG. 1061.   *a, Holopedium gibberum.*
b, Holopedium amazonicum.

0.1 MM.

21 (2)   Five or six pairs of feet.   First and second pairs more or less prehensile, others foliaceous. . . .   Tribe II. **Anomopoda** . .   22

22 (117)   Antennules attached to ventral side of head, not covered by fornices.   23

23 (76, 83)   Antennules of female usually small, sometimes rudimentary; if large, never inserted at anterior end of ventral surface of head.   Dorsal ramus of antenna 4-jointed, ventral ramus 3-jointed.   Intestine simple with 2 hepatic ceca.
                                          Family DAPHNIDAE Straus . .   24

Five pairs of feet, the first two prehensile and without branchial lamella; the fifth with large recurved seta, extending around branchial sac.   Antennules in general small or rudimentary, and when large not at the anterior extremity of the head.   Antennae long, not strong, cylindrical, setae $\frac{0-0-1-3}{1-1-3}$.   Post-abdomen distinctly set off from body, usually more or less compressed, always with anal spines.   Abdominal setae not borne on distinct projection or papilla.   Claws sometimes pectinate; always denticulate, unless worn by use; never with basal spine.   Intestine not convoluted, with 2 hepatic ceca.   Eye large; ocellus usually small, sometimes wanting.   Summer eggs ordinarily numerous; typical ephippium formed, containing 1 or 2 eggs. ♂ usually with hook on first foot.

24 (48)   Rostrum present.   25

25 (39)   No cervical sinus.   Valves with polygonal, usually rhomboidal, marking, and with a posterior spine.   Crest on dorsal side of head.
                                          Daphnia O. F. Müller 1785 . .   26

. Form oval or elliptical, except as modified by crest of head (helmet) in some species.   Body always compressed, often greatly so.   Valves reticulated; dorsal and ventral margins rounding over toward each other and provided with spinules along posterior part.   Rostrum well-marked in ♀ and pointed.   Antennules small or rudimentary, not movable, placed behind rostrum.   Abdominal processes 3-4, all ordinarily developed; the anterior especially long, tongue-shaped and bent forward.   Ephippium with 2 eggs.   Summer eggs often very numerous.
Head of ♂ without rostrum; antennules large, movable, ordinarily with long, stout, anterior seta or flagellum; first foot with hook and long flagellum.

26 (34)   Claws with pecten.   27

27 (30)   Heavy, thick-bodied forms.   Fornix and secondary fornix (Fig. 1063) well developed.   Distal pecten with more than 12 teeth. .   28

28 (29)   Antennules large for genus; post-abdomen with deeply sinuate margin. . . . .   *Daphnia magna* Straus 1820.

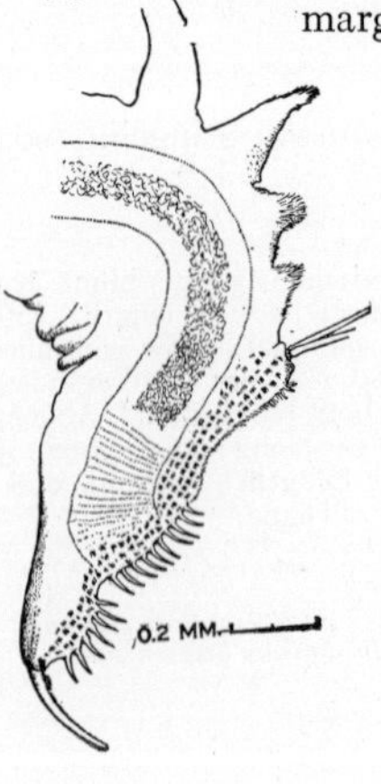

Form rounded or oval, body thick and heavy, not transparent.   Post-abdomen long, with deep indentation behind anus, breaking through row of anal spines.   These are about 12 in proximal and 8–10 in distal set.   Claws with two pectens of numerous teeth.   Ephippium characteristic; dorsal margin of valves separates with it both behind and before; 2 eggs, placed obliquely.   Summer eggs numerous.   Length, ♀, to 5.0 mm.; ♂, 2.0 mm. or more.   The largest of the family.   Maine, Colorado, Nebraska, N. Dakota, California.

0.2 MM

FIG. 1062. *Daphnia magna,* post-abdomen,

29 (28) Rostrum and antennules *pulex*-like; post-abdomen tapered, not sinuate. . . . . *Daphnia psittacea* (Baird) 1850.

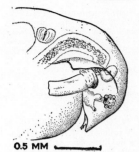

General form like *D. magna* but smaller and more transparent. Post-abdomen tapering, not sinuate, with about 10 anal teeth and many clusters of short, fine hairs. Claws with two pectens, the distal having about 15 teeth. Length, ♀, to 2.8 mm. besides spine of 0.8 mm.; ♂, to 1.8 mm. Nebraska, in pools.

FIG. 1063. *Daphnia psittacea*, note small secondary fornix behind primary.

0.5 MM

30 (27) Secondary fornix rudimentary or very small. Teeth of distal pecten rarely exceeding 10, usually fewer. 31

31 (32, 33) Ocellus present; head not helmeted.

Daphnia pulex (de Geer) 1778.

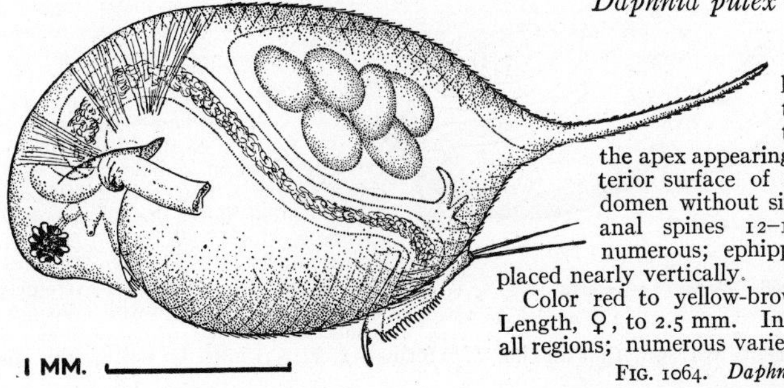

Body stout and heavy; usually not transparent. Antennules very small, the apex appearing as papillae on posterior surface of rostrum. Post-abdomen without sinus; anus at end; anal spines 12–17. Summer eggs numerous; ephippium with two eggs placed nearly vertically.

Color red to yellow-brown, very variable. Length, ♀, to 2.5 mm. In pools and lakes in all regions; numerous varieties.

I MM.

FIG. 1064. *Daphnia pulex.*

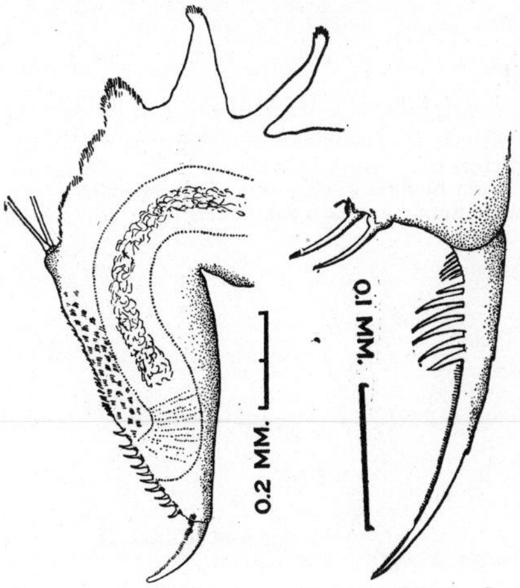

D. pulex includes a great number of varieties, many of which have been described as distinct species. The student will be safe in assigning to *pulex* all opaque, heavy-bodied forms with pectinate claws. In many cases the identification of the variety is more important than that of the species, but the varieties have not been worked out for this country. A few may be noted:

FIGS. 1065, 1066. *Daphnia pulex*, post-abdomen and claw.

Var. *pulicaria* Forbes. A semi-transparent limnetic form, very close to *pulex*, but more slightly built. Long spine. Common in lakes.

Var. *clathrata* Forbes. Only 12 anal spines. Pecten with 3–4 large teeth. Yellowstone.

Var. *minnehaha* Herrick. Slight angle over heart in adult ♀; strong tooth in ♂ and young. Minnesota and elsewhere.

Var. *obtusa* Kurz. Spine very short or

0.1 MM.

0.2 MM.

absent. 9–10 anal spines. Rostrum long and pointed. Maine, Wisconsin, southern states.

Var. *curvirostris* Eylmann. Rostrum very long and continued backward, lying close to valves. Nebraska, California.

32 (31, 33) Ocellus present; head helmeted. . *Daphnia arcuata* Forbes 1893.

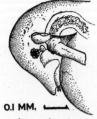

Very transparent. Vertex rounded, rostrum extending backward and applied to margin of valves. Slender spine projecting from middle of valves. Anal spines about 10–12; claws with distal pecten of some 6 teeth. Length of ♀ to 2 mm., besides spine of about 0.5 mm. Wyoming, Wisconsin; in open waters of lakes.
This species forms a transition to the *retrocurva* forms.

FIG. 1067. *Daphnia arcuata.*

0.1 MM.

33 (31, 32) Ocellus absent; head helmeted. . *Daphnia retrocurva* Forbes 1882.
Body much compressed, pellucid. Eye small, with numerous projecting lenses and little pigment; no ocellus. Spine ordinarily above middle of valves, directed upward. Crest very variable, often enormous. Claws with two pectens, the distal of 7–9 teeth. Anal spines 7–12. Summer eggs ordinarily 2; sometimes as many as 6. Length, ♀, to 2.0 mm., besides spine, which may reach 0.5 mm.

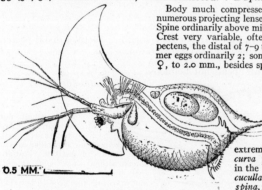

Widely distributed in limnetic region of lakes. Shape of head extremely variable; all forms from var. *breviceps* B i r g e, where the crest is hardly visible, to the extreme of extension shown by *retrocurva* proper. This species replaces in the United States the European *D. cucullata*, which is related to *D. longispina*, much as this form is to *D. pulex*. *D. retrocurva* never has the extremely acuminate form of head which *cucullata* sometimes shows.

0.5 MM.

FIG. 1068. *Daphnia retrocurva.*

Very probably study will show that all the *pulex* forms (31, 32, 33) must be united into one polymorphic species.

34 (26) Claws without pecten. 35
35 (38) Ocellus present, though small.

Daphnia longispina (O. F. Müller) 1785 . . 36

Spine long; claws without pecten. Male without long papilla on posterior part of body. This species is so variable that almost no characters can be given for it. It is less robust than the *pulex* forms, ordinarily fairly transparent; often hyaline. This part of the species divides at once into 2 sections or subspecies, each with numerous varieties which have never been thoroughly studied in the United States.

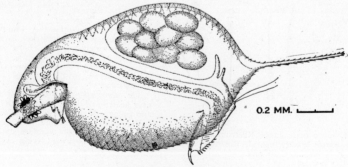

0.2 MM.

FIG. 1069. *Daphnia longispina.* (See also Fig. 1050, p. 677.)

36 (37) Head not helmeted; eye close to margin. . *Daphnia longispina* proper.
There are numerous varieties of *D. longispina* proper; depending on proportion of valves, etc.
The head may be large or small, its ventral margin straight, concave, or convex. The eye may
have a large pigment with few lenses embedded in it, or it may be smaller with numerous pro-
jecting lenses.
Found in all regions of the United States.

37 (36) Head helmeted and eye therefore removed from margin. Usually
more delicate and transparent than 36.
Daphnia longispina var. *hyalina* Leydig 1860.

D. *longispina* var. *hyalina* varies conspicuously and greatly in the form and size of the crest
and of the ventral and dorsal margins of the head, which may be concave, convex, or straight
with any form of crest. The crest may be small and rounded (var. *hyalina typica*); extended
into a broad semi-elliptical form (form *mendotae*); more or less triangular, with an acute point
in front (form *galeata*); which may be extended into a short spine. An indefinite number of
other forms are present, some of which have been studied and described, but not named by
Entemann. The form of the crest in specimens from any one lake is fairly uniform (though
2 varieties may be present), changing with the season, being larger in summer than in spring.
Adjacent lakes may vary greatly. Deep water forms usually have smaller crests than those
from the shallow surface water. All varieties found in open water of lakes, in all parts of the
country.

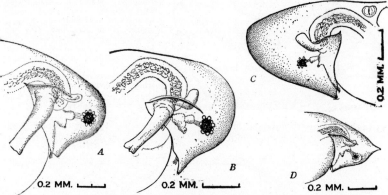

Figs. 1070, 1071. *Daphnia longispina* var. *hyalina.* A and B, form *typica.* C, form *mendotae.*
D, form *galeata.*

38 (35) Ocellus absent; head helmeted.
Daphnia longispina var. *longiremis* Sars 1861.

Valves broadly oval; spine long and slender. Head small and rounded with crest. Antennae
very long, reaching well toward posterior margin of valves when reflexed. Length, ♀, to 1.5 mm.
This is the only representative of the European *cucullata* group as yet seen in this country. No
doubt other forms will be discovered. Indiana; Wisconsin, in deep water of lakes in southern
part of state; in surface waters in northern part.

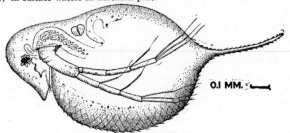

FIG. 1072. *Daphnia longiremis.*

39 (25) Cervical sinus present. No crest. 40

40 (45) Valves transversely striated. Post-abdomen broad, with indentation in which anus opens.

Simocephalus Schoedler 1858 . . 41

Body large and heavy; shell thick. Head and rostrum small. Valves large, somewhat quadrate, with rounded angles and sometimes a posterior spine; marked with oblique striae, anastomos:ng irregularly and with cross-connections. Two abdominal processes developed, placed far apart. Post-abdomen large, broad, truncate, posterior end emarginate and bearing the anal spines. Claws rather straight, always denticulate, sometimes pectinate. Summer eggs numerous; ephippium large, triangular, with one egg. Antennules of ♂ like ♀ but with 2 lateral sense-hairs. First foot without flagellum and with small hook. Poor swimmer; swims often on its back. Color yellow to yellow brown.

41 (44) Vertex rounded, smooth. No posterior spine on valves. 42

42 (43) Ocellus elongated. Vertex rounded over. Claws denticulate.

Simocephalus vetulus (O. F. Müller) 1776.

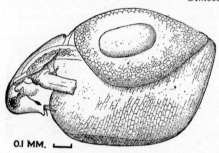

Ocellus large, elongated, rarely rhomboidal. No spine on valves, though there may be a blunt posterior angle. Post-abdomen very broad, deeply emarginate; anal spines about ten, decreasing from the claws; the larger bent and ciliate at the base. Claws long, slender, little curved, denticulate only. Length, ♀, to 3.0 mm.; ♂, ca. 1.0 mm.

Not very abundant, but found everywhere in weedy water.

Fɪɢ. 1073. *Simocephalus vetulus*, with ephippium.

0.I MM.

43 (42) Ocellus rhomboidal or round. Vertex with obtuse or rounded angle. Claws pectinate. . . *Simocephalus exspinosus* (Koch) 1841.

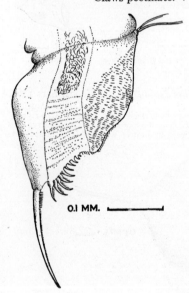

Valves much as in *vetulus*, but striae do not anastomose so freely. Post-abdomen slightly narrower toward apex; anal spines up to 12, evenly curved, not bent; claws with pecten of 8–12 teeth and denticulate. Color and general appearance much as preceding species. Length, ♀, to 3.0 mm.; ♂, to 1.3 mm.

Not common; reported from Massachusetts, Wisconsin, and the southern states.

0.I MM.

Fɪɢ. 1074. *Simocephalus exspinosus*.

44 (41) Vertex angulated, spinous. Blunt, rounded posterior spine on
valves in old individuals. Ocellus rhomboidal or triangular,
rarely elongated. . . *Simocephalus serrulatus* (Koch) 1841.

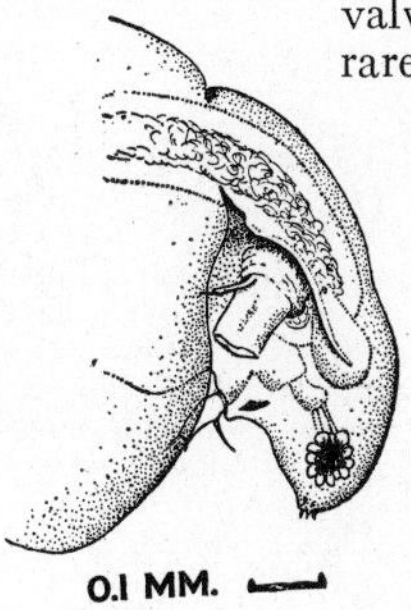

> Anal spines 8–12, the larger bent and ciliate. Claws with fine
> denticles. Color yellow or brownish. Length, ♀, 2.8–3.0 mm.;
> ♂, to 0.8 mm.
> Common everywhere among weeds; the most abundant spe-
> cies. Very variable in outline of head.

FIG. 1075. *Simocephalus serrulatus.*

0.1 MM. ⊢——⏘

45 (40) Valves obscurely reticulated and with some striae. Posterior and
ventral margins straight, the latter extended into a point or
spine. . . . . . . *Scapholeberis* Schoedler 1858 . . 46

Body not compressed; shape more or less quadrate. Cervical sinus deep. Fornices and
rostrum well developed. Head small, depressed. Valves almost rectangular, the infero-
posteal angle of each produced into a longer or shorter spine; ventral margin with short, fine
setae. Claws denticulate, not pectinate. One abdominal projection developed. Antennules
small, about alike in both sexes, borne behind the rostrum. Summer eggs numerous; one
ephippial egg. ♂ much like ♀; hook on first foot.

46 (47) Color usually dark, often nearly black.
Scapholeberis mucronata (O. F. Müller) 1785.

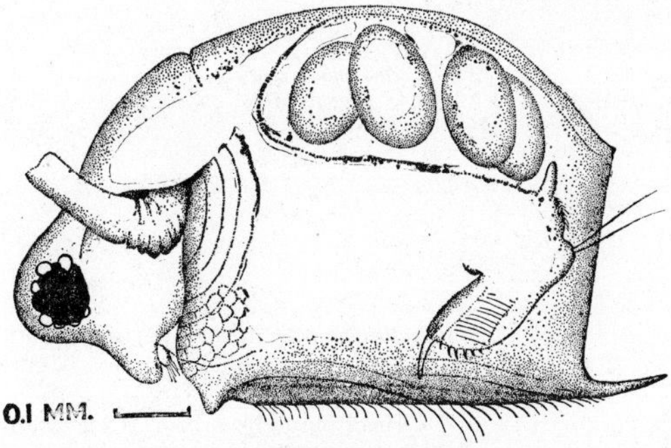

Valves arched dorsally in old
specimens; posterior and ventral margins straight; at their
junction a spine often short,
but often very long; in var.
armata Herrick as long as ventral margin of valve. Antennules very small, almost immovable, set behind beak.
Post-abdomen short and broad,
rounded at posterior end; 5–6
anal teeth. Length, ♀, 0.8–1.0
mm.; ♂, ca. 0.5 mm.
The form with frontal spine
has never been found in the
United States. Common everywhere in pools and lakes in
weedy water, or swimming on
its back near or at the surface.

0.1 MM. ⊢——⏘

FIG. 1076. *Scapholeberis mucronata.*

47 (46) Color whitish or greenish; transparent or opaque, not black.
Scapholeberis aurita (Fischer) 1849.

Head larger than in *mucronata*, rostrum long, lying against
margin of valves. Antennules behind rostrum, conical, large, and
movable; sense-hair about middle. Valves with blunt projection
at infero-posteal angle, obscurely striate and reticulate in front,
and with small elevations elsewhere. Length, ♀, ca. 1.0 mm.;
♂, 0.5 mm.
Not common; in weedy pools and margins of lakes. Northern
states.

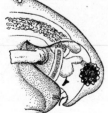

FIG. 1077. *Scapholeberis aurita.*

0.1 MM. ⊢——⏘

48 (24)   No rostrum.   Cervical sinus present. **49**

49 (65)   Head small and depressed.   Antennules small.   Valves oval or round.   No post-anal extension of post-abdomen.
Ceriodaphnia Dana 1853 . . 50

General form rounded or oval; size small, rarely exceeding 1 mm.   Vertex a rounded or angular projection, usually nearly filled by eye.   Valves oval or round to subquadrate, usually ending in a sharp dorsal angle or short spine.   Antennules not very freely movable.   One abdominal process ordinarily developed.   Post-abdomen of various forms, large.   Ephippium triangular, with one egg placed longitudinally.   Antennules of ♂ with long, stout seta, modification of flagellum; first foot with hook and long flagellum.   Free swimming; motion saltatory.

50 (51)   Head with a short spine or horn.
Ceriodaphnia rigaudi Richard 1894.

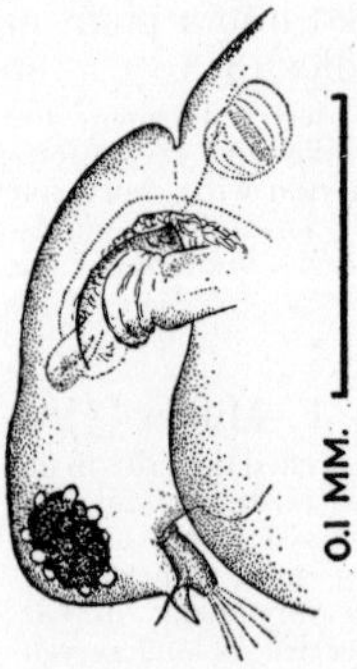

Valves reticulated.   Head produced in front of antennules into a short, conical, sharp-pointed, hornlike process.   Two abdominal processes.   Post-abdomen with 5–6 anal spines.   Claws smooth or denticulate.   Antennules rather slender; lateral sense-hair somewhat distal to middle.   Length of ♀, 0.4–0.5 mm.; ♂ (South American), 0.38 mm.
Pools; Louisiana, Texas.
The form with horn on vertex also is found in South America, mingled with typical *C. rigaudi*.   Probably both forms should be included in *C. cornuta* Sars.

FIG. 1078.   *Ceriodaphnia rigaudi.*

0.1 MM.

51 (50)   Head without horn. **52**

52 (53)   Claws pectinate. . . . . . . *Ceriodaphnia reticulata* (Jurine) 1820.

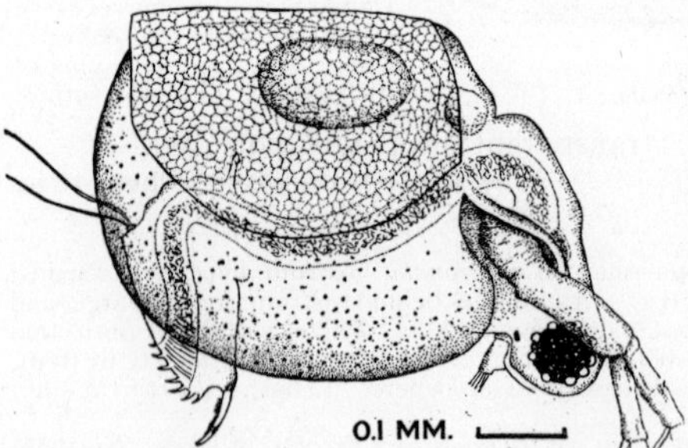

Head obtusely, or not at all, angulated in front of antennules.   Valves reticulated, ending in spine or angle.   Antennules small, with sense-hair near apex.   Anal spines 7–10.   Claws with pecten of 6–10 teeth and denticulate.   Color variable, shades of red and yellow.   Length of ♀, 0.6–1.4 mm.; of ♂, 0.4–0.8 mm.
Common, widely distributed.

FIG. 1079.   *Ceriodaphnia reticulata*, with ephippium.

0.1 MM.

53 (52)   Claws not pectinate. **54**

54 (55) Head and valves strongly reticulated and covered with numerous
short spinules. . . . . *Ceriodaphnia acanthina* Ross 1897.
General shape rotund with well-developed spine. Head much depressed, not angulated in
front of antennules or at vertex. Antennules short and thick with sense-hair near apex. Post-
abdomen narrow, much like *quadrangula*, with 7–9 anal spines. Claws denticulate, the denticles
in the proximal two-fifths of the claw obviously longer than the remainder. Color whitish-
transparent to very dark. Length, ♀, to 1.0 mm., ♂ unknown.
Manitoba, in weedy slough.

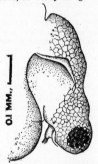

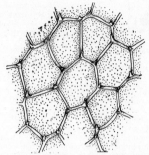

Fig. 1080. *Ceriodaphnia acanthina.*   Fig. 1081. Details of valve, much enlarged.

55 (54) Valves not spinulated. 56

56 (57, 62) Post-abdomen abruptly cut into near apex, serrate above,
spines below. . . . . . *Ceriodaphnia megalops* Sars 1861.

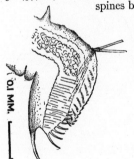

Head angulated before antennules; valves striated. Antennules with sense-hair near apex. Post-abdomen broad, with
an angle near apex, cut into below angle, finely serrate above
and with 7–9 slender anal spines below. Claws not pectinate.
Length, ♀, 1.0–1.5 mm.; ♂, 0.6–0.8 mm.
Widely distributed but not common.

Fig. 1082. *Ceriodaphnia megalops.*

57 (56, 62) Post-abdomen not cut into; of ordinary form. 58

58 (59) Fornices projecting into spinous processes. Eye small.
Ceriodaphnia lacustris Birge 1893.

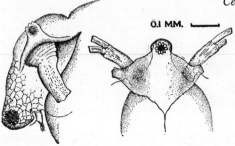

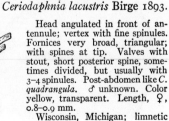

Head angulated in front of antennule; vertex with fine spinules.
Fornices very broad, triangular;
with spines at tip. Valves with
stout, short posterior spine, sometimes divided, but usually with
3–4 spinules. Post-abdomen like *C.
quadrangula*. ♂ unknown. Color
yellow, transparent. Length, ♀,
0.8–0.9 mm.
Wisconsin, Michigan; limnetic
in lakes.

Fig. 1083. *Ceriodaphnia lacustris.*

59 (58) Fornices of ordinary form; eye large. 60

60 (61) Head inflated in front of antennules. Small form not exceeding
          0.7 mm. . . . . *Ceriodaphnia pulchella* Sars 1862.

Form of ordinary type. Head rounded in front; inflated in region behind eye, angulated in front of antennules. Valves reticulated but not plainly so. Post-abdomen not sinuate above anal spines, which number 7–10. Length, ♀, 0.4–0.7 mm.; ♂, 0.5 mm.
Found among weeds and limnetic in lakes and in pools; reported from all regions. Forms agreeing perfectly with this description may be found, as also *quadrangula* forms, but other varieties occur which are difficult to assign to either species, but which so closely agree with them as to render it impossible to make a new species for them.

FIG. 1084. *Ceriodaphnia pulchella.*

61 (60) Head angulated but not inflated in front of antennules.   Length to
          1.0 mm. . . *Ceriodaphnia quadrangula* (O. F. Müller) 1785.

General form like *reticulata*. Valves reticulated, often not plainly marked. Antennules with lateral sense-hair near apex. Post-abdomen narrowing toward apex, often, but not always, sinuate above anal spines; these number 7–9. Claws large, denticulate. ♂ antennules with long flagellum, hook-like at tip. Color transparent to pinkish opaque. Length, ♀, to 1.0 mm.; ♂, to 0.6 mm.
Common in all regions; found both among weeds and limnetic. *C. scitula* Herrick seems to be a large variety of this species.

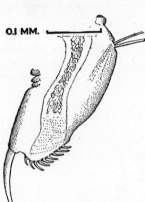
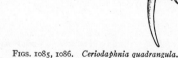

FIGS. 1085, 1086. *Ceriodaphnia quadrangula.*

62 (56, 57) Post-abdomen very broad, obliquely truncate. 63

63 (64) Vertex evenly rounded, without spines. Antennules moderate.
          Ceriodaphnia laticaudata P. E. Müller 1867.

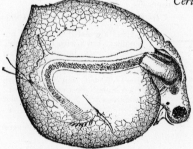

General form round. Valves ventricose below. Post-abdomen large, dilated near middle, obliquely truncated and bearing 8–11 spines on lower margin. Claws long, denticulate. Color transparent or opaque, through red and red-brown to nearly black. Length, ♀, to 1.0 mm., but not seen larger than 0.7 mm. in United States; ♂, to 0.7 mm.
Wisconsin and Minnesota to Florida, Louisiana, and Texas.
This species is *C. consors* Birge.

FIG. 1087. *Ceriodaphnia laticaudata.*

64 (63)   Vertex angulated, with spines.   Antennules long.
Ceriodaphnia rotunda Sars 1862.

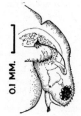

General form much like preceding.   Head angled at vertex, with spines.   Antennules long and slender.   Post-abdomen somewhat enlarged, but not so much as in *laticaudata*, tapering toward apex, obliquely truncate, with 7–9 slender anal spines. Color yellowish or brown, not transparent.   Length, ♀, to 1.0 mm.; ♂, to 0.6 mm.

Rare, Wisconsin.   Both this species and the preceding live among weeds.

FIG. 1088.   *Ceriodaphnia rotunda*.   (After Lilljeburg.)

65 (49)   Head large and usually extended.   Antennules large and freely movable.   Post-abdomen with post-anal extension. . .   66

66 (67)   Body compressed.   Valves elliptical, crested dorsally, completely covering body.   Ocellus present.   Fornix and abdominal process well developed. . . . *Moinodaphnia* Herrick 1887.

Cervical sinus present; no cervical gland.   Valves tumid in postero-dorsal region; crested; minute spines on ventral margin; sharp angle, not spine, at junction of dorsal and ventral margins; marked with oblique striae, usually invisible in preserved specimens.   Antennules attached on ventral surface of head, sense-hair about middle; olfactory setae small.   One large abdominal process, broad, concave in front, somewhat saddle-shaped, forming a transition to the condition in *Moina*.   Post-abdomen as in *Moina*, with slender post-anal projection bearing about 10 finely ciliate spines and a much longer distal spine with 2 unequal prongs, the *bident* (Fig. 1094).   Claws denticulate.   Summer eggs numerous.   Male (South America) much like *Moina*, with large curved antennules.

Only one certain species. . *Moinodaphnia macleayii* (King) 1853.

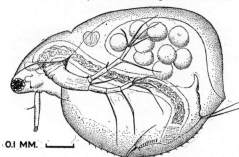

Color yellowish, transparent. Length, ♀, ca. 1.0 mm.
Louisiana.   In weedy pools and lakes.
Herrick's *M. alabamensis* is reported as larger (1.68 mm.) and may possibly be a different species.   Herrick had only King's very imperfect description for comparison with his form, and his own description is correspondingly imperfect.   Sars' figures of *M. macleayii* from Brazil show a form identical with that from New Orleans.

FIG. 1089.   *Moinodaphnia macleayii*.

67 (66)   Body thick and heavy.   Valves somewhat rhomboidal, not wholly covering body.   Fornix small.   Ocellus absent.   Abdominal process represented by horse-shoe shaped fold.
Moina Baird 1850 . .   68

Cervical sinus present.   Valves thin, obscurely reticulated or striated; no posterior spine. Head large, thick, rounded in front; sometimes with deep depression above eye; no rostrum. Antennules long, spindle-shaped, freely movable; lateral sense-hair about middle.   No regular abdominal projection, but in old ♀ a horse-shoe shaped ridge which closes the brood-cavity. Post-abdomen extended into conical post-anal part, bearing ciliated spines and bident.   Claws small; abdominal setae very long.   Summer eggs numerous; ephippium oval, with 1 or 2 eggs. Antennule of ♂ very long and stout, modified into clasping organ; denticulate, with small recurved hooks at apex.   First foot with hook.

The species of *Moina* ordinarily inhabit muddy pools and similar places.   They are soft-bodied, weak creatures; liable to be much distorted by preserving fluids.   The species are much alike and often hard to distinguish unless ♂ and ephippial ♀ are present.

68 (69)   Post-anal spines fewer than 8.   Animal small, about 0.5 mm. long.
Moina micrura Kurz 1874.

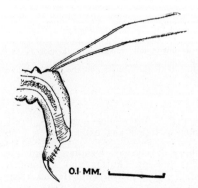

Small, transparent; head relatively very large; deep cervical sinus; supra-ocular depression small or absent. Terminal portion of post-abdomen small with 4–6 spines and a much longer bident. Claws pectinate. Male unknown. Length, ♀, 0.5–0.6 mm. Illinois, Arkansas, Louisiana.

FIG. 1090.   *Moina micrura.*

0.1 MM.

69 (68)   Post-anal spines 8 or more. Animal larger, about 1.0 mm. or more. .   70

70 (75)   Supra-ocular depression present;   claws pectinate;   no flagellum on first foot of male. 71

71 (72)   Two ephippial eggs;   antennules of male with sense seta in middle.
Moina brachiata (Jurine) 1820.

Body stout, heavy; greenish, not transparent. Head ordinarily much depressed, so that vertex often lies almost on level of ventral margin of valves. Deep supra-ocular depression. Valves faintly reticulated. Post-anal spines 7–11 besides bident; claws pectinate. Antennules of ♂ with 4 hooks; first foot without flagellum. Length, ♀, to 1.5 mm.; ♂ unknown in United States.
Wisconsin, Nebraska, Missouri; no doubt widely distributed. In pools.

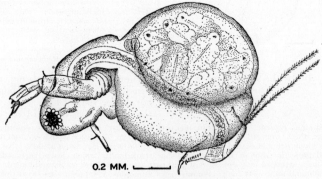

0.2 MM.

FIG. 1091.   *Moina brachiata*

72 (71)   One ephippial egg. . . . . , ... **73**

73 (74)　Valves smooth; ephippium reticulated around edges, smooth in middle; antennules of male with sense seta near middle.

Moina rectirostris (Leydig) 1860.

Colorless, or with bluish cast.　Head extended or little depressed; deep cervical and supra-ocular depressions.　Post-abdomen with long projection and 10–15 post-anal spines and bident.　Claws pectinate.　Antennules of ♂ with 5–6 hooks at apex.　Length, ♀, 1.0–2.0 mm.;　♂, 0.4–0.6 to 1.0 mm.

Widely distributed; in muddy pools.

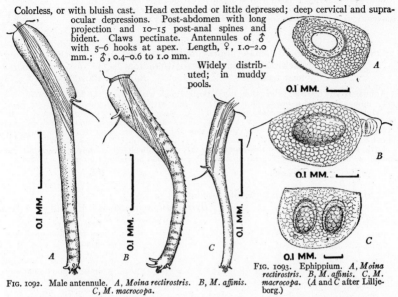

0.1 MM.

A

B

0.1 MM.

C

0.1 MM.

Fig. 1093.　Ephippium.　*A*, *Moina rectirostris.*　*B*, *M. affinis.*　*C*, *M. macrocopa.*　(*A* and *C* after Lilljeborg.)

0.1 MM.

A

B

C

Fig. 1092.　Male antennule.　*A*, *Moina rectirostris.*　*B*, *M. affinis.*　*C*, *M. macrocopa.*

74 (73)　Valves striate; ephippium reticulated all over; antennules of male with sense seta near base. . . .　*Moina affinis* Birge 1893.

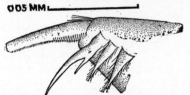

0.05 MM.

Much like *M. rectirostris*, from which the young ♀ are hardly distinguishable.　Antennules of ♂ broad, fringed with fine hairs on inner margin; 4–6 hooks at end.　Length, ♀, 0.8–1.0 mm.;　♂, 0.3–0.6 mm.

Wisconsin to Louisiana.

M. rectirostris, *affinis*, and *brachiata* have been often confused in faunal lists.

Fig. 1094.　*Moina affinis*, apex of post-abdomen.

75 (70)　No supra-ocular depression; claws not pectinate; antennules of male with sense seta in middle or below; first foot of male with long flagellum. .　*Moina macrocopa* Straus 1820.

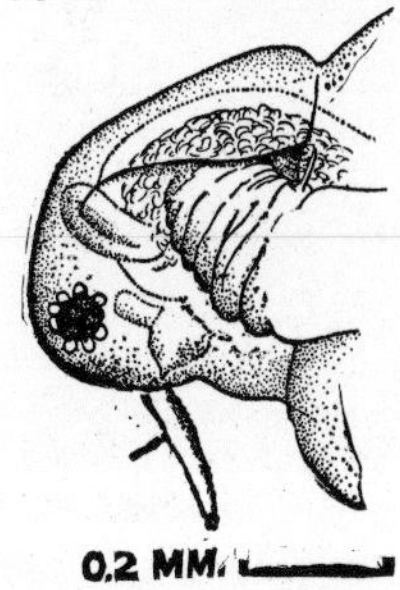

Not very transparent; yellowish or greenish.　Head extended.　Terminal part of post-abdomen long, with 10–12 spines besides bident.　Two ephippial eggs.　♂ with elongated head; 5–6 hooks on antennule.　Length, ♀, to 1.8 mm.;　♂, 0.5–0.6 mm.

Pools, Wisconsin, Nebraska, Colorado, N. Dakota; doubtless widely distributed.

This species is *M. paradoxa* Weismann and *M. flagellata* Hudendorf.

Fig. 1095.　*Moina macrocopa.*

0.2 MM.

76 (23, 83)   Six pairs of feet. Antennules of female large, fixed. Intestine simple; no ceca. . . . . . Family BOSMINIDAE Sars . .   77

Body short and high often oval or round. Valves cover body and abdomen. Antennules of ♀ long, immovably fixed to head. No abdominal process or ocellus. Intestine without convolutions or ceca. Animals small, rarely exceeding 0.5 mm.

77 (82)   Antennules of female approximately parallel to each other, curving backward, fixed to head; olfactory setae on side, usually near base. . . . . *Bosmina* Baird 1845 . .   78

Animal usually hyaline; valves thin; infero-posteal angle with spine — the *mucro*. Antennules of ♀ immovably fixed to head; olfactory setae on side, with small triangular plate above them; distal position of antennules looks segmented. Antennae with 3- and 4-jointed ramus. Post-abdomen somewhat quadrate; anus terminal; spines small and inconspicuous; claws set on a cylindrical process. ♂ smaller than ♀, with short, blunt rostrum; large free antennules; hook and long flagellum on first foot.

Little work has been done in this country on this very difficult genus; but it is certain there are not so many species nor so great an amount of variation here as in Europe.

78 (79)   Claws with two series of spinules.

         Bosmina longirostris (O. F. Müller) 1785.

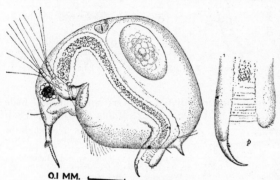

Two series of spinules on claws, the basal increasing in length distally, continued by very fine denticles to tip of claw. Frontal sense-hair about midway between eye and junction of antennules. Antennules moderate or short (var. *brevicornis*); sometimes recurved at apex (var. *cornuta*). Transparent or clear yellowish. Length, ♀, 0.3–0.5 mm.; ♂, 0.25–0.4 mm.

Very common and very variable. In open water of lakes, in weedy margins, in pools and marshes.

0.1 MM.

p

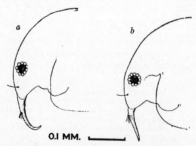

0.1 MM.

FIG. 1096. *Bosmina longirostris*, typical specimen; *p*, post-abdomen more highly magnified. Rostrum; *a*, var. *cornuta*: *b*, var. *brevicornis*.

79 (78)   Claws with basal series of spinules only. 80

80 (81)   Mucro shorter than claws and process bearing them.

Bosmina obtusirostris Sars 1861.

Frontal sense-hair near junction of antennules.   Antennules shorter than length of valves.
Shell reticulated or smooth.   Length, ♀, 0.3–0.5 mm.
In pools and lakes; not rare; very variable.

FIGS. 1097, 1097, *a*.   *Bosmina obtusirostris.*

81 (80)   Mucro longer than claws and process.

Bosmina longispina Leydig 1860.

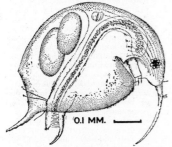

Frontal sense-hair near junction of antennules.
Mucro and antennules long.   Shell striated, marks
especially plain on head.   Transparent.   Length,
♀, ca. 0.4 mm.
Rare, in lakes.

FIG. 1098.   *Bosmina longispina.*

82 (77)   Antennules united at base, and diverging at apex; numerous long
olfactory setae on their ventral side.

Bosminopsis Richard 1895.

Sole American species. . . . .   *Bosminopsis deitersi* Richard 1895.

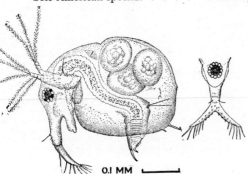

In general much like *Bosmina.*   Basal part of antennules united with each other
and head to form very long
rostrum; diverging laterally
near apex, with long, straggling, olfactory setae.   Antenna with 3-jointed rami.   Post-
abdomen tapering to point at
claws; 1 large spine near
claws and several very minute spinules anterior to it.
♂ with large movable an-
tennules; short rostrum; first
foot with hook and flagellum.
Length, ♀, ca. 0.35 mm.; ♂,
0.25 mm.
Lake Charles and Calcasieu
River, La.

FIG. 1099.   *Bosminopsis deitersi.*

83 (23, 76)   Antennules of female long, freely movable, usually inserted at
anterior end of ventral surface of head. Rami of antennae
3- and 4-jointed. Intestine simple or convoluted. Hepatic
ceca usually wanting. Five or six pairs of feet.
Family MACROTHRICIDAE Norman and Brady . .   84

Abdominal process usually absent; rarely present (*Ilyocryptus*). Feet, 5 or 6 pairs, the
first two prehensile; the last, if present, rudimentary. Post-abdomen marked off from body,
usually large, often bilobed; anus terminal or lateral. Labrum usually with keel or marked
projection. Valves often crested   Fornices well developed.
The members of this family are so various in form that it is hard to find many common
characters; yet the general appearance is always characteristic. The size and position of the
antennules will show the membership of every genus except *Ilyocryptus;* and there is no trouble
in recognizing that genus as belonging to the family.

84 (95)   Intestine convoluted.   85

85 (86)   Valves with spine at supero-posteal angle. Small hepatic ceca.
Ophryoxus Sars 1801.

Sole species. . . . .   *Ophryoxus gracilis* Sars 1861.

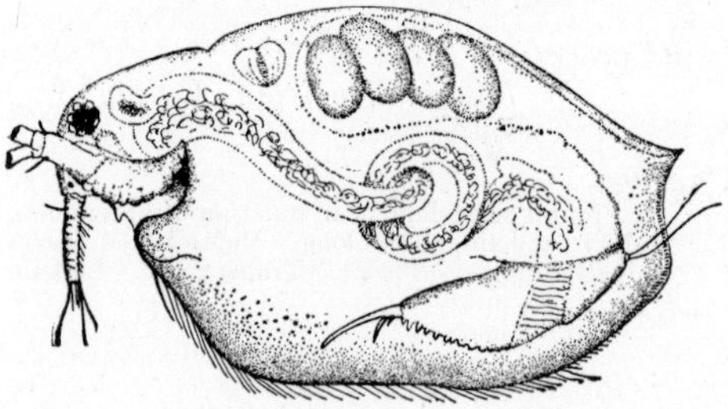

General form elongated, somewhat daphnid. Antennules long,
slender, fringed with numerous
hairs behind, lateral sense-hair
near base; olfactory setae unequal.
Antennae long, weak. Six pairs of
feet. Post-abdomen long, tapering at apex, anus dorsal, post-anal
portion large with numerous short,
blunt, ciliated spines, the proximal
mere elevations bearing fine spinules. Claws straight, with (usually) two stout basal spines. Intestine with convolution in middle
of body; 2 small hepatic ceca.
Antennules of ♂ longer than ♀;
sense-hairs longer. Vasa deferentia open on ventral (anterior) side
of post-abdomen about middle.

O.I MM. ⌐⎯⎯⌐

FIG. 1100. *Ophryoxus gracilis.*

Strong hook on first foot. Color transparent, last foot often purple in old ♀. Length, ♀, to
2.0 mm.; ♂, 1.0 mm.
Widely distributed in lakes among weeds. Swims with constant but rather feeble paddling
motion. Spine longer in young than adult.

86 (85)   No such spine.   87

87 (92)   Hepatic ceca present.   88

88 (89)   Antennary setae ♀, $\frac{o-o-o-3}{o-o-3}$; ♂, $\frac{o-o-o-3}{1-1-3}$; valves narrowed behind and
prolonged into short tube. .   *Parophryoxus* Doolittle 1909.
Sole species. . . . .   *Parophryoxus tubulatus* Doolittle 1909.

Form elongated oval; narrow crest on head and valves. Head rounded, rostrum well
marked; cervical sinus present. Valves thin, transparent; unmarked or faintly reticulated;
prolonged behind into a sort of tube, best seen from above; ventral margin with moderate
setae. Post-abdomen elongated, triangular; post-anal part long and slender, narrowed toward
apex somewhat as in *Ophryoxus;* bearing a few very small spines. Claws long, rather straight;
with 2 basal spines. Antennules cylindrical, slender; with basal sense-hair and three conspicuously long olfactory setae. Antennae long, slender; basal joint annulated; setae not conspicuously dissimilar. Feet, 6 pairs; the last rudimentary. Eye moderate, with few lenses; ocellus

large, some distance from apex of rostrum. Intestine convoluted, with small hepatic ceca.
♂ with hook on first foot; vas deferens opens near claws. Length, ♀, to 1.2 mm. Color
transparent-yellowish.
Maine, New Hampshire; among weeds in lakes. The difference in antennary setae of ♂ and
♀ holds for all specimens hitherto seen.

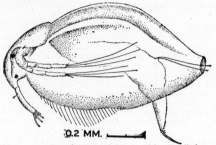

FIG. 1101. *Parophryoxus tubulatus.* (After Doolittle.)

89 (88)   Setae $\dfrac{0\text{–}0\text{–}1\text{–}3}{1\text{–}1\text{–}3}$; animal small, spherical. . *Streblocerus* Sars 1862 . . 90

Body round-oval, not compressed or crested. Labrum with large, serrate, acute process.
Antennules large, flat, bent, or rather twisted, broadened in distal part; with lateral sense-
hair near base, several hairs on posterior face, rows of fine hairs, and subequal minute olfactory setae.
Post-abdomen bilobed; the pre-anal part compressed, semi-circular; the anal part rounded,
with fine spines or hairs. Claws small, curved, with several equal minute denticles on concave edge. Five pairs of feet. Intestine convoluted, with small hepatic ceca. ♂ (European,
of *S. serricaudatus*) small, triangular, much like ♀; first foot without hook.

90 (91)   Dorsal margin of valves smooth.

Streblocerus serricaudatus (Fischer) 1849.

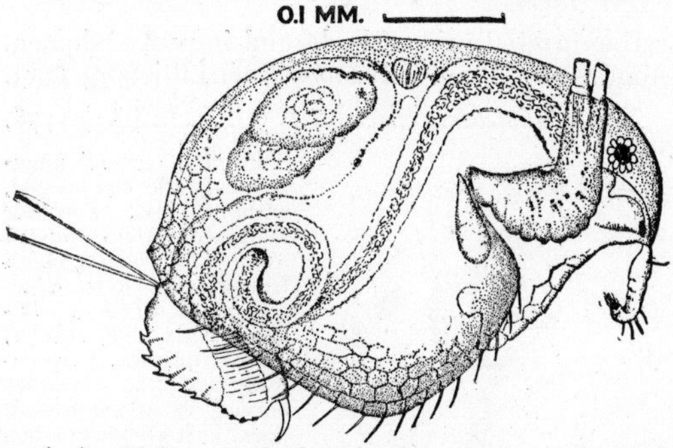

Pre-anal part of post-abdomen with serrate margin and
bearing rows of fine hairs.
Anterior margin of antennule
somewhat toothed. Color
whitish-opaque to yellowish.
Length, ♀, ca. 0.5 mm.; ♂,
ca. 0.25 mm.
Rare but widely distributed
in weedy pools and margins of
lakes. Reported from New
England, Wisconsin, Nebraska,
Louisiana, Colorado, California.

FIG. 1102. *Streblocerus serricaudatus.*

91 (90)   Valves reticulated, the edges of the reticulations making scale-like
ridges, which give the dorsal margin a serrate appearance.

Streblocerus pygmaeus Sars 1901.

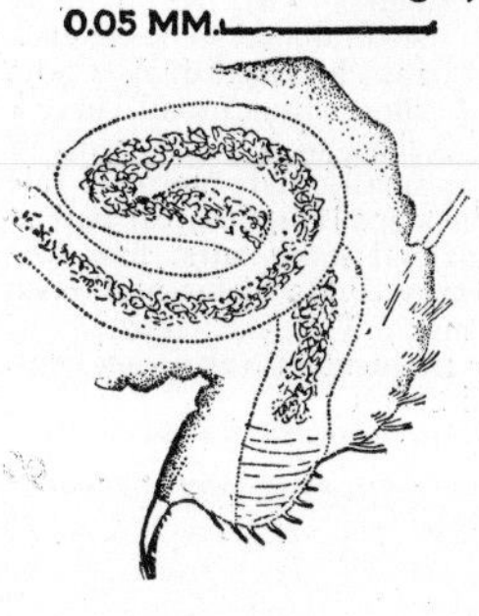

Pre-anal part of post-abdomen not serrate, with 4–5 rows
of fine hairs. Color grayish white, opaque, to nearly black
in ephippial ♀. ♂ unknown.
Length, ♀, 0.2–0.25 mm. The smallest member of the
family and one of the smallest of the group. Louisiana, in
weedy pools, with *S. serricaudatus.*

FIG. 1103. *Streblocerus pygmaeus.*

92 (87)   No hepatic ceca; setae $\dfrac{\text{o-o-o-3}}{\text{1-1-3}}$ **93**

93 (94)   Convolution of intestine in middle of body. Valves crested, with
strong tooth on crest. . . . . . *Drepanothrix* Sars 1861.

Sole species. . . . . *Drepanothrix dentata* (Eurén) 1861.

Valves reticulated; dorsal margin arched, crested, with conspicuous, short, backward-pointing tooth about middle. Antennules broad, flat, twisted, though not so much as in *Streblocerus;* post-abdomen compressed but not extended into a thin edge; almost quadrate as seen from side. Margin with 2 rows of small spines, about 20, and with several rows of hairs besides scattered groups; apex truncate, emarginate, with anus in depression. Claws short, broad, crescentic, smooth, or denticulate; 5 pairs of feet. ♂ much like young ♀; hook on first foot; post-abdomen without spines; vasa deferentia open in front of claws. Color whitish to yellowish; opaque or transparent. Length, ♀, ca. 0.7 mm.; ♂, ca. 0.4 mm. Not commonly collected though widely distributed and probably not very rare in shallow waters of lakes, on bottom or among weeds. Maine, Michigan, Wisconsin, Minnesota, Colorado.

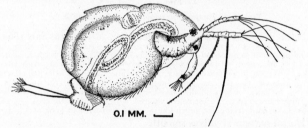

0.I MM. ⊢───

Fɪɢ. 1104. *Drepanothrix dentata.*

94 (93)   Convolution of intestine in hind part of body and in post-abdomen.
No dorsal tooth. . . . . . *Acantholeberis* Lilljeborg 1853.

Sole species. . . . . *Acantholeberis curvirostris* (O. F. Müller) 1776.

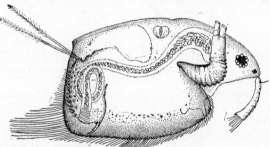

0.5.MM. ⊢────────

Fɪɢ. 1105. *Acantholeberis curvirostris.*

Form in general angular-oval, not compressed, without crest. Posterior margin of valves rounded over into ventral, both fringed with long, close-set, plumose setae. Labrum with long, slender, conical process. Antennules large, flat, somewhat curved, expanded toward apex. Post-abdomen large, moderately broad, not compressed or divided, hairy, with 20 or more small dorsal spines in each row; anus terminal. Claws short, stout, broad, curved, denticulate, and with 2 small basal spines set side by side. Six pairs of feet. Intestine without ceca, convoluted, the loops lying in great part in post-abdomen. ♂ resembling young ♀; antennules with 2 proximal sense-hairs; first foot with small, inconspicuous hook; post-abdomen emarginate dorsally; vasa deferentia open behind claws. Color yellow, not transparent. Length, ♀, to 1.8 mm.; ♂, 0.5–0.7 mm.

In pools and margins of lakes among weeds; reported especially frequent in *Sphagnum* bogs. Maine, Wisconsin, Louisiana; probably in all regions of the United States.

95 (84)   Intestine simple. **96**

96 (99)   Hepatic ceca present; post-abdomen bilobed; antennary setae
$\dfrac{\text{o—o—1—3}}{\text{1—1—3}}$ 97

97 (98)   Post-abdomen very large, with few spines. . *Grimaldina* Richard 1892.
Sole species. . . . . *Grimaldina brazzai* Richard 1892.

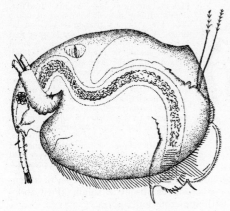

Body compressed, somewhat quad-rangular, with all margins of valves slightly convex. Post-abdomen enor-mous, much compressed, roughly semi-elliptical in form; the pre-anal portion divided by a notch into two parts, of which the anterior is the smaller; a long spine in the notch which marks junction of anal and pre-anal parts; on anal part two lateral rows of small, slender spines, about 7 in anterior, and 5 in posterior row. Claws small, denticulate, with 1 small basal spine. Ephippium rounded-quadrangular; egg-chambers reniform with concave sides toward each other. ♂ (South America) small, like immature ♀; an-tennules with 2 basal sense-hairs; small hook on first foot. Color reddish-brown. Length, ♀ to 0.9 mm.; ♂, 0.5 mm. Louisiana; weedy pools of clear water.

FIG. 1106. *Grimaldina brazzai.*

98 (97)   Post-abdomen moderate; numerous small spines on pre-anal part, clusters of hairs on anal part. . . *Wlassicsia* Daday 1903.
Sole American species. . . . . *Wlassicsia kinistinensis* Birge 1910.

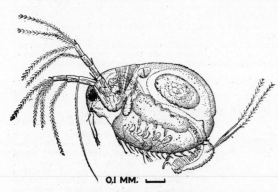

Form oval, not com-pressed. Valves crested; with spines on ventral mar-gin; marked by very deli-cate transverse striae which anastomose, forming fine vertical meshes. Olfactory setae subequal. Two rounded projections at base of labrum on ventral sur-face of head. Labrum with strong conical projection pointing backward and a second projection just in front of small terminal lobe. Post-abdomen with fine spines and hairs. Ab-dominal setae very long, not set on projection. Claws with very small basal spines. Five pairs of feet; branchial sacs on all legs.

0.1 MM.

FIG. 1107. *Wlassicsia kinistinensis.*

♂ with large antennule; small keel on labrum; hook on first foot. Color yellow. Length, ♀, 0.8 mm.; ♂, 0.4 mm. Marsh at Kinistino, Manitoba.

99 (96)   No hepatic ceca; post-abdomen various. 100

100 (107, 116) Antennary setae $\dfrac{\text{o--o--o--3}}{1-1-3}$ 101

101 (102) Wide crest on dorsal margin of valves. Antennules at apex of head. Post-abdomen bilobed, of moderate size.

Bunops Birge 1893.

Sole American species. . . . . Bunops serricaudata (Daday) 1888.

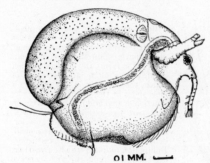

General form rounded, much compressed; high keel on dorsal side. Front of head flat, somewhat kite-shaped, with boss or umbo over eye. Strong triangular keel on labrum. Valves faintly reticulated, produced behind into rounded projection; ventral margin gaping in front, inflexed behind, fringed with rather long straggling hairs or weak setae. Antennules with basal sense-hair and two pairs of sense setae near apex; olfactory setae somewhat unequal. Post-abdomen much like Streblocerus; bilobed, pre-anal portion flattened, semi-circular, with 7–8 notches or teeth on the dorsal margin and 3–4 rows of fine hairs; anal portion with fine hairs and 3–4 spines. Color transparent, tinged with yellow. ♂ unknown. Length of ♀ to 1.0 mm. Maine, Wisconsin; very local in distribution, but not rare when present.

OI MM. ⊢——⊣

FIG. 1108. Bunops serricaudata.

102 (101) Vertex of head forming sharp angle in front of insertion of antennules. Dorsal crest of valves absent or small. Post-abdomen very large, with numerous long spines.

Ilyocryptus Sars 1861 . . 103

General form oval-triangular, the head forming the apex of the triangle, while the enormously dilated ventral and posterior edges of the valves round into each other; these have long, close-set, fixed setae, usually branched and fringed. Antennules short, freely movable, 2-jointed, basal joint very small, attached to ventral side of head behind vertex; olfactory setae unequal. Antennae short, powerful; basal joint annulated nearly to apex; with long sense setae; motor setae not plumose, smooth, or with sparse hairs. Abdominal process long, tongue-shaped, hairy. Post-abdomen large, broad, compressed; anus on side or near apex; many spines on dorsal margin; numerous, long, curved, lateral spines and setae; fine spinules near base of claws. Claws long, straight, denticulate, and with 2 slender basal spines. Intestine simple, no ceca, but enlarged near rectum. Six pairs of feet. ♂ with larger antennules than ♀, bearing 2 sense-hairs; no hook on first foot.

In most species the old shells are not cast off in molting but overlie the youngest in several layers. The species live in mud, creep about among weeds, though they can and do swim; are often greatly loaded with mud and vegetable growths, nearly concealing structure.

103 (106) Anus opening on dorsal margin of post-abdomen; molting imperfect. 104

104 (105) Eight or more pre-anal spines; antennary setae short.

Ilyocryptus sordidus (Liéven) 1848.

O.I MM. ⌐——————

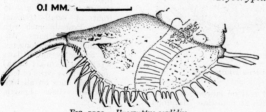

Post-abdomen emarginate where anus opens; 8–14 pre-anal marginal spines; lateral post-anal spines about 8–10; marginal row of numerous smaller spines. Ocellus nearer base of antennule than eye. Six to eight summer eggs.

Color red, but often so loaded with debris as to be opaque. Length, ♀, ca. 1.0 mm.; ♂, 0.42 mm.

FIG. 1109. Ilyocryptus sordidus.

Not very common but widely distributed in weeds on muddy bottoms.

105 (104) Five to seven pre-anal spines; antennary setae ordinarily very long. *Ilyocryptus spinifer* Herrick 1884.

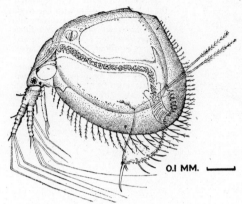

Anus opens in depression on dorsal margin of post-abdomen; 5–7 pre-anal spines; 4–8 post-anal lateral spines in outer row. Antennary setae usually long, sometimes equaling length of valves; in some specimens they are short, apparently because of wear. Eight to ten summer eggs; true ephippium formed and cast off (Sars). ♂ unknown. Color yellow or reddish. Length, ♀, to 0.8 mm.

This species is *I. longiremis* Sars; *I. halyi* Brady. Not uncommon; Maine to Lake Superior and Gulf of Mexico. Probably in all regions of United States.

0.1 MM.

Fig. 1110. *Ilyocryptus spinifer.*

106 (103) Anus at end of post-abdomen; molting complete. *Ilyocryptus acutifrons* Sars 1862.

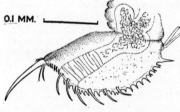

0.1 MM.

Fig. 1111. *Ilyocryptus acutifrons.*

Post-abdomen not emarginate; about 8 small spines near claws, shortest next claw; about 6 long, curved, lateral spines, about 8 marginal spines corresponding to pre-anals of other species; the proximal two directed forward; from distal spine of this set a series of very small marginals to anus. Antennule club-shaped, hairy. Ocellus nearer eye than insertion of antennules. Claws as in *I. sordidus.* Three to four summer eggs. ♂ unknown. Color reddish or yellowish. Length, ♀, ca. 0.7 mm.

Rhode Island, Colorado

107 (100, 116) Antennary setae $\frac{0-0-1-3}{1-1-3}$; basal seta of 3-jointed ramus stout and stiff. . . . . *Macrothrix* Baird 1843 . . 108

Shape oval or rotund, somewhat compressed, with dorsal crest. Head large, ordinarily not depressed; vertex evenly or abruptly rounded; rostrum short. Ventral margin of valves ordinarily with long, stout, movable spines, which project in several directions. Antennules large; lateral sense-hair near base. Antennae large; the proximal seta of 3-jointed ramus long, stiff, and spinous; the others sparsely plumose or partly spinous. Five pairs of feet. No abdominal process. Post-abdomen large; often bilobed. Claws small. Intestine simple, no ceca. ♂ with large antennules; hook on first foot.

108 (115) Dorsal margin of head evenly rounded. 109

109 (114) Head extended; rostrum far from margin of valves. Antennules enlarged near distal end. 110

110 (111) Post-abdomen not bilobed. . *Macrothrix laticornis* (Jurine) 1820.

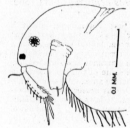

Form round-ovate. Valves crested, the dorsal edge serrate with fine teeth. Head evenly rounded. Labrum with large triangular process. Antennule broader distally; a setiferous projection on posterior margin near apex; anterior margin with several fine incisions and clusters or rows of hairs; olfactory setae conspicuously unequal. Post-abdomen with numerous fine spines and hairs; anus terminal. Claws small. Color grayish white or yellowish. Length, ♀, 0.5–0.7 mm.; ♂, 0.3–0.4 mm.

Widely distributed; found in all parts of the country but nowhere very abundant.

O.I MM.

FIG. 1112. *Macrothrix laticornis.*

111 (110) Post-abdomen bilobed. 112

112 (113) Conspicuous fold or folds of shell of head at cervical sinus. *Macrothrix montana* Birge 1904.

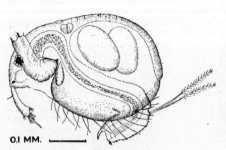

Form ovoid. Head large; dorsal margin evenly rounded; the shell extended into collar-like folds in front of cervical sinus. Antennules stout, large, enlarged near apex, about 6 anterior cross-rows of hairs, and 3–4 stouter posterior setae; olfactory setae unequal. Post-abdomen bilobed. Claws hardly larger than spines. Color transparent, in preserved specimens. ♂ unknown. Length, ♀, ca. 0.55 mm. Colorado.

0.1 MM.

FIG. 1113. *Macrothrix montana.*

113 (112) No such folds. *Macrothrix hirsuticornis* Norman and Brady 1867.

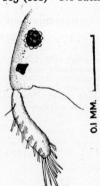

Form broadly ovate, not very different from *M. laticornis.* Antennules broad, flat, bent, varying in form but always enlarged distally; with 6–8 rows of stiff hairs on anterior side; sometimes stout setae on posterior side; olfactory setae unequal. Post-abdomen large, broad, bilobed; pre-anal part not flattened nor with projection for abdominal setae; numerous small spines and hairs on both anal and pre-anal parts. ♂ unknown. Length, ♀, 0.55 mm.

New England, Colorado.

0.1 MM.

FIG. 1114. *Macrothrix hirsuticornis.*

114 (109)   Head much depressed; rostrum close to margin of valves.   Antennules slender, not enlarged near distal end.

Macrothrix borysthenica Matile 1890.

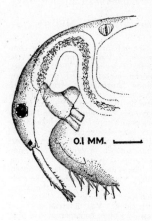

Dorsal margin of head evenly rounded over into that of valves without sinus. Front of head recurved so that rostrum is very close to valves. Antennules with a few scattered fine hairs; olfactory setae small, equal. Post-abdomen elongated, bilobed; with numerous fine spinules and hairs on both lobes. Claws small. Eye moderate; ocellus at rostrum. Color transparent. Length, ♀, to 1.1 mm. Albuquerque, New Mexico (Herrick).

Fig. 1115.   *Macrothrix borysthenica*.   (After Matile.)

115 (108)   Dorsal margin of head curved abruptly in front of eye.   Antennules slender. . . . .   *Macrothrix rosea* (Jurine) 1820.

Form broadly ovate. Valves reticulated, crested, not serrate. Head large; its dorsal margin rounding over abruptly into anterior margin. Antennules long, slender, not enlarged near apex; lateral sense-hair near base on small elevation; olfactory setae unequal. Post-abdomen extended into blunt process, on which abdominal setae are borne; pre-anal part semi-elliptical, with numerous spinules along convex edge and many fine hairs; anal part with several small spines. Claws small, smooth. Summer eggs numerous; ephippium well-developed, with 2 eggs. Antennules of ♂ long, curved. Post-abdomen terminating in long, fleshy projection on which the vasa deferentia open. Hook of first foot serrate at tip. Color transparent to yellowish or sometimes a ruddy tinge. Length, ♀, ca. 0.7 mm.; ♂, 0.4 mm. Common everywhere in marshy pools and margins of lakes.

M. tenuicornis Kurz is a variety of this species. All ♂ ♂ found in America agree with *M. elegans* Sars.

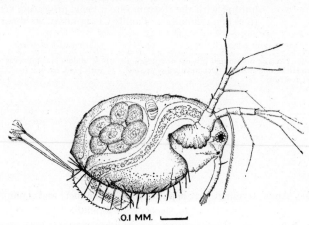

0.1 MM.

Fig. 1116.   *Macrothrix rosea*.

116 (100, 107)   Antennary setae $\dfrac{0-1-1-3}{1-1-3}$; all similar and plumose.

Lathonura Lilljeborg 1853.

Sole species. . . . . . . Lathonura rectirostris (O. F. Müller) 1785.

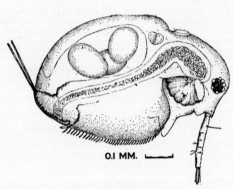

FIG. 1117.   Lathonura rectirostris.

O.I MM. ⌊_____⌋

General form long-oval, not compressed. Valves unmarked; the ventral margin with short, close-set, smooth, lancet-shaped, or spatulate spines. Antennules straight, with sense-hair near base; 2 pairs of sense setae in distal half. Post-abdomen very small, extended behind into a long conical process, which bears the very long abdominal setae; covered with fine spines and setae. Claws small, smooth, or denticulate. Summer eggs, 2 to 10; 1 ephippial egg. ♂ like young ♀, with larger antennules; 2 lateral sense-hairs, the additional one — the distal — the larger; olfactory setae longer. First foot with hook. Vas deferens opens at claws. Color transparent to clear yellow or greenish. Length, ♀, to 1.0 mm.; ♂, ca. 0.5 mm.
Widely distributed in weedy margins of lakes but nowhere common.

117 (22)   Fornices extended so as to cover antennules in whole or in part, and uniting with the rostrum into a beak, projecting ventrally in front of antennules. . Family CHYDORIDAE Stebbing . . 118

Antennae small, rami 3-jointed; setae $\dfrac{1-1-3}{0-0-3}$ or $\dfrac{0-1-3}{0-0-3}$. Labrum with large keel. Five or six pairs of feet. No true abdominal process or ephippium. Post-abdomen compressed, jointed to body. Intestine convoluted. Ocellus always present. ♂ with hook on first foot; large antennule; short rostrum.

118 (119)   Anus terminal. 2 hepatic ceca. Summer and ephippial eggs numerous. . . . . Subfamily EURYCERCINAE Kurz.

Sole genus. . . . . Eurycercus Baird 1843.

Only one American species.

Eurycercus lamellatus (O. F. Müller) 1785.

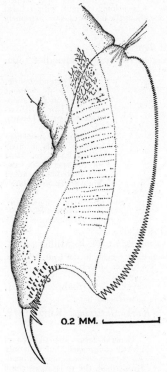

Body stout, heavy. Post-abdomen very large, flattened, general form quadrangular; anus terminal, in depression; dorsal margin, with very numerous — over 100 — saw-like teeth. Claws on spiniferous projection, with 2 basal spines and denticulate. Six pairs of feet. Intestine with hepatic ceca and convolution. ♂ like young ♀; hook on first foot; vas deferens opens at base of claw on ventral (anterior) side. Color yellowish-brown, opaque. Length, ♀, to 3.0 mm. or more; ♂, to 1.4 mm. The largest member of the family. Found everywhere; in permanent pools or margins of lakes among weeds.

Fig. 1118. *Eurycercus lamellatus*. Post-Abdomen.

0.2 MM.

119 (118)   Anus on dorsal side of post-abdomen, whose post-anal portion bears denticles. No hepatic ceca. Two summer eggs; one ephippial egg. ♂ with strong hook on first foot.

Subfamily CHYDORINAE . . 120

120 (247)   Eye present. 121

121 (246)   Eye and ocellus of ordinary size; antennules do not project beyond rostrum, though olfactory setae may. 122

122 (171)   Posterior margin of valves not greatly less than maximum height. 123

No species of *Pleuroxus* belong in this section, though some individuals of 195 and 199 may seem to do so.

123 (135)   Body compressed; claws with secondary tooth in middle. . . 124

124 (129, 132)   Crested; post-abdomen narrow,[1] with marginal and lateral denticles. 125

[1] Terms denoting relative size are to be understood with reference to the section in which they occur.

125 (128)   Crest on head and valves.   .   *Camptocercus* Baird 1843 . .   126
Form oval; greatly compressed, with crest on head and back.   Valves with angles rounded;
small teeth at infero-posteal angle; longitudinally striated.   Post-abdomen very long, slender,
with numerous marginal denticles and lateral squamae.   Claws long, straight, with 1 basal
spine; a series of small denticles, terminating in a larger one about the middle of claw; extremely
fine teeth thence to apex.   Five pairs of feet.

126 (127)   Post-abdomen with 15–17 marginal denticles.
                                    Camptocercus rectirostris Schoedler 1862.

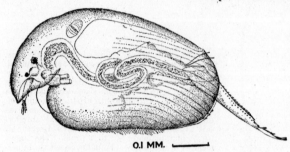

Head extended or de-
pressed.   ♂ without
denticles on post-abdo-
men.   Color yellow-
transparent.   Length,
♀, to 1.0 mm.
Common everywhere
among weeds in mar-
gins of lakes, etc. Most
of the specimens from
the United States are of
the variety *biserratus*.

0.1 MM.

Fig. 1119.   *Camptocercus
rectirostris.*

127 (126)   Post-abdomen with 20–30 marginal denticles.
                                    Camptocercus macrurus (O. F. Müller) 1785.
Much like the preceding.   Very rare, but reported from most regions in the United States.
Undoubtedly the preceding species has been mistaken for this by some observers.

128 (125)   Crest on valves only.   .   *Kurzia* Dybowski and Grochowski 1894.
     This genus is *Alonopsis* (part) of older authors; *Pseudalona* Sars,

Sole American species. . . . . . .   *Kurzia latissima* (Kurz) 1874.

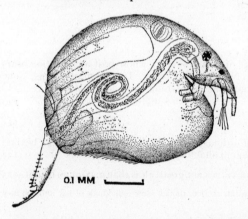

General form subquadrate;
greatly compressed; but with only
slight crest on back, none on head.
Head small, the rostrum reaching
not much below middle of valves,
though longer than antennules.
Post-abdomen long, slender;
lower angle usually produced into
a lobe; 10–12 marginal denticles.
Claws of *Camptocercus* type.   ♂
like ♀; rostrum shorter; post-
abdomen with small denticles; vas
deferens opens on ventral (upper)
side; strong hook on first foot.
Color yellowish, transparent.
Length, ♀, 0.6 mm.; ♂, 0.4 mm.
Found in all regions among
weeds in pools or lakes.

0.1 MM

Fig. 1120.   *Kurzia latissima.*

129 (124, 132)   Crest on head and valves; post-abdomen broad, without
                 marginal denticles. . . .   *Acroperus* Baird 1843 . .   130
Body thin, compressed; crest on head and back.   Valves subquadrate, obliquely striated;
infero-posteal angle rounded or acute, usually with teeth.   Post-abdomen large, compressed;
without marginal denticles but with lateral row of squamae.   Claws long, straight, with 1 basal
spine and secondary denticles, much as in *Camptocercus*.   Intestine with large intestinal cecum.
Eye larger than ocellus.   Color yellow-transparent.

130 (131)   Dorsal margin much arched. . . . *Acroperus harpae* Baird 1835.

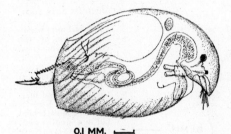

Eye and ocellus near margin. Rostrum acute. Eleven to twelve groups of fine spinules on post-abdomen. Length, ♀, to o.8 mm.; ♂, to o.6 mm.
Common everywhere, among weeds, in relatively open water; not in muddy pools.

FIG. 1121.   *Acroperus harpae.*

0.1 MM. |———|

131 (130)   Dorsal and ventral margins nearly straight.
Acroperus angustatus Sars 1863.

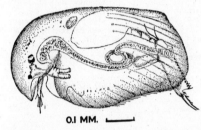

Crest larger than in *A. harpae;* eye and ocellus removed from margin and rostrum obtuse. Length, ♀, to o.9 mm.; ♂, o.6 mm.
Common in similar situations to preceding species. Transition forms between these species may be found and very probably they should be united.

FIG. 1122.   *Acroperus angustatus.*

0.1 MM. |———|

132 (124, 129)   No crest. 133

133 (134)   Valves not tumid; post-abdomen broad.
Alonopsis Sars 1862 . . 133*a*

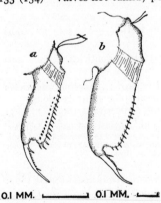

General form resembling *Acroperus* but less compressed and without crest. Keel of labrum moderate or small, almost triangular. Valves obliquely striated but striae often inconspicuous. Post-abdomen long, broad; with well-developed marginal denticles. Six pairs of feet, the last very small. ♂ with usual characters. Color yellow.

FIG. 1123.   *a, Alonopsis elongata; b, Alonopsis aureola.*
(After Doolittle.)

0.1 MM. |———| 0.1 MM. |———|

133*a* (133*b*)   15–17 marginal denticles. . . . . *Alonopsis elongata* Sars 1861.
Minute tooth at infero-posteal angle of valves.   Post-abdomen with lateral fascicles.   Length, ♀, ca. o.8 mm.

133*b* (133*a*)   About 11 marginal denticles. . *Alonopsis aureola* Doolittle 1912.
No lateral fascicles or infero-posteal tooth.   Length, ♀ ca. 1.9 mm.; ♂ unknown.   Both species in margins of lakes and ponds among weeds.   Rare; reported only from Maine.

134 (133) Valves tumid in anterior part; post-abdomen narrow.

Euryalona Sars 1901.

Sole American species. . . . . . *Euryalona occidentalis* Sars 1901.

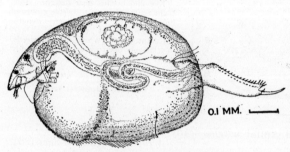

General form resembling *Kurzia*, but less compressed; no crest. Valves gaping in front, tumid in infero-anterior region; marked obscurely with concentric lines; dorsal margin arched. Keel of labrum angled behind but not prolonged. Post-abdomen very long, slender, lobed at apex; with about 20 marginal and very fine lateral denticles. Claws straight, armed about as in *Campto-*

FIG. 1124. *Euryalona occidentalis* Sars.

cercus. Five pairs of feet; hook on first foot of ♀. ♂ with strong hook; vas deferens opens on upper (ventral) side of post-abdomen about middle. Color dark brown-yellow. Length, ♀, to 1.0 mm.; ♂ 0.7 mm.
Florida, Louisiana, Texas; not uncommon in weedy pools and lakes.

135 (123) Body not greatly compressed; claws with 1 basal spine, or rarely none. 136
For all species with two spines on terminal claw, see 171 ff.

136 (168) Rostrum not greatly exceeding antennules. 137

137 (167) Rostrum pointed. 138

138 (150) Infero-posteal angle rounded, without teeth. 139

139 (144, 147) Post-abdomen with marginal and lateral denticles. . . . 140

140 (143) Post-abdomen relatively long and narrow; marginal denticles numerous, longer distally. Basal spine stout and long.
Oxyurella Dybowski and Grochowski 1894 . . 141
In general like *Alona*. Post-abdomen long, slender; with marginal and lateral denticles, the former numerous and ending in a group of large denticles at angle of post-abdomen. Terminal claw straight, with one large basal spine, attached some way distal to base of claw. Color yellow or yellow-brown. This genus is the same as *Odontalona* Birge.

141 (142) 12–15 marginal denticles. . . . *Oxyurella tenuicaudis* (Sars) 1862.

Marginal denticles very small near anus; the distal 4–5 much larger; the penultimate largest. Length, ♀, ca. 0.5 mm.; ♂, 0.4 mm.
Widely distributed but not abundant anywhere. New England and Wisconsin to Gulf of Mexico. This species is *Alona tenuicaudis* Sars.

FIG. 1125. *Oxyurella tenuicaudis.* Apex of post-abdomen. (See also Fig. 1129, *b*.)

142 (141)   About 16 marginal denticles. . *Oxyurella longicaudis* (Birge) 1910.

Between *Alona* and *Euryalona* in form. Valves with concentric marking. About 16 marginal denticles, larger distally; the penultimate much larger, and the ultimate larger still and serrate on concave side. Basal spine stout, attached about one-third way from base of claw. ♂ unknown. Length, ♀, 0.5–0.6 mm.
Rather rare among weeds, Lake Charles, La.

Fig. 1126. *Oxyurella longicaudis.*

143 (140)   Post-abdomen not noticeably narrow; distal denticles not conspicuously larger. Basal spine small. *Alona* (most species). . 151
Take up the key at the number indicated where the genus is discussed as a unit.

144 (139, 147)   Post-abdomen with marginal denticles only. 145

145 (146)   Post-abdomen large, denticles very small. *Alonella diaphana*. . 236
Turn to the key at the number indicated where the species named is discussed.

146 (145)   Post-abdomen of moderate size; denticles of usual size.
Alona guttata . . 156
Turn to the key at the number indicated where the species named is discussed.

147 (139, 144)   Post-abdomen with numerous clusters of large spines.
Leydigia Kurz 1874 . . 148
General shape oval, much compressed but not crested. Head small, extended; keel of labrum rhomboidal with angles blunt or rounded. Post-abdomen very large, compressed, semi-elliptical in form; much-anal part much expanded, with numerous clusters of spines; spines in distal clusters very long. Claws long and slender. Eye smaller than ocellus. ♂ with blunt rostrum; process on upper (ventral) side of post-abdomen on which vas deferens opens; post-abdomen with spines. Color yellow.

148 (149)   Valves without markings. *Leydigia quadrangularis* (Leydig) 1860.
Keel of labrum with minute setae. Claws with basal spine. Length, ♀, to 0.9 mm.; ♂, ca. 0.7 mm.
In all regions of the country; not common; found singly among weeds.

149 (148)   Valves striated longitudinally.
Leydigia acanthocercoides (Fischer) 1854.
Keel of labrum with long cilia. Claws without basal spine. Length, ♀, to 1.0 mm. or more; ♂ (European), 0.7 mm.
Rare; Louisiana.

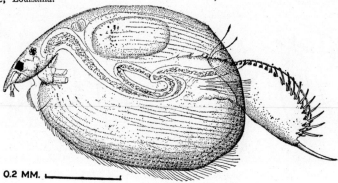

0.2 MM.

Fig. 1127. *Leydigia acanthocercoides.*

722   FRESH–WATER BIOLOGY

150 (138)   Infero-posteal angle rounded, with small tooth or teeth.   151

151 (166)   Valves with longitudinal striae. . . .   *Alona* Baird 1850 . .   152
General form subquadrate; compressed, not crested. Valve with supero-posteal angle
rounded or well marked; infero-posteal angle rounded, almost always without teeth. Fornices
broad; rostrum short and blunt, little exceeding the apex of the antennules. Antennules
short, thick; olfactory setae equal. Keel of labrum large, ordinarily rounded; the posterior
angle not acuminate. Feet, 5 pairs, rarely 6; the 6th, if present, rudimentary. Post-abdomen
broad, compressed, with various armature. Claws with 1 basal spine and denticulate. Color
yellow in some shade, varying from light to dark, with shade of brown in large species. All
species littoral.

152 (153)   Infero-posteal angle with 1–3 small teeth.
                                        Alona monacantha Sars 1901.

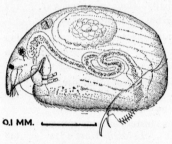

In general form and appearance not unlike *A.
intermedia.* Valves distinctly striated; infero-
posteal angle rounded and with 1–3 small teeth.
Post-abdomen with 9–10 denticles; claws with
very long basal spine. Keel of labrum angled
behind. Length, ♀, 0.35–0.4 mm.
This species may be confused with *Alonella
karua* (232). The length of the basal spine on
terminal claw offers a ready distinction.
Louisiana; in weedy pools.

0.1 MM.

Fig. 1128.   *Alona monacantha.*

153 (152)   Infero-posteal angle unarmed.   154

154 (155)   Post-abdomen long, narrow; distal marginal denticles very long.
                                        See *Oxyurella* . .   140

155 (154)   Post-abdomen not notably long.   156

156 (157)   Post-abdomen with marginal denticles only.
                                        Alona guttata Sars 1862.
Form much like *A. costata*, but usually smaller and dorsal margin less arched. Valves
smooth, striate, or tuberculate (var. *tuberculata* Kurz). Post-abdomen short, broad, slightly
tapering toward apex; truncate, angled, with longest marginal denticles at angle; denticles
8–10, pointed, small; no squamae. Claws with small basal spine. Post-abdomen of ♂ without
spines; vas deferens opens behind claws, without any projection. Length, ♀, ca. 0.4 mm.;
♂, 0.3–0.35 mm. See Fig. 1129, *d.*
Not uncommon everywhere.

Fig. 1129.   *a, Alona quadrangularis; b, Oxyurella tenuicaulis; c, Alona costata; d, Alona guttata; e, Alona
rectangula; f, Alona rectangula* var. *pulchra; g, Alona intermedia.*
These figures are not drawn to the same scale.

157 (156) With marginal and lateral denticles. 158

158 (161) Size large; 14 or more marginal denticles. 159

159 (160) Cluster of fine spinules at base of claw.
Alona affinis (Leydig) 1860.

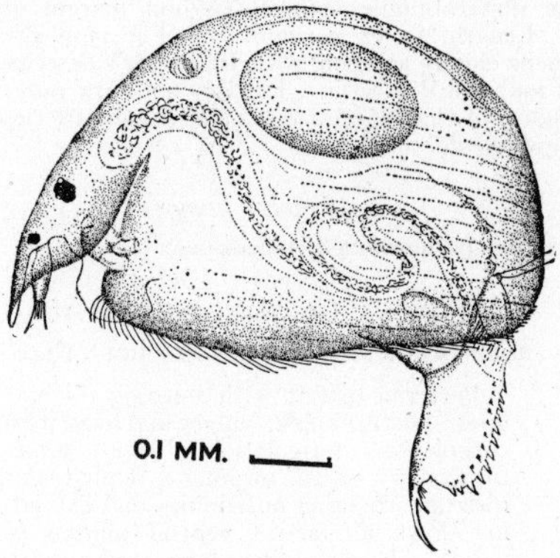

Greatest height usually near middle of valves. Valves longitudinally striated or reticulated, often not plainly marked. Labrum with rhomboidal keel; its corners often angulated, sometimes rounded. Post-abdomen large, not widened behind anus; with 14–16 serrate marginal denticles and a lateral row of small squamae. Claws long, denticulate; with long basal spine and 4–5 spinules inside of basal spine. Six pairs of feet, the last rudimentary. Length, ♀, to 1.0 mm.; ♂, to 0.7 mm.

The largest species of the genus; very abundant in all regions, in margin of ponds and lakes, among weeds.

0.1 MM.

FIG 1130. *Alona affinis.*

160 (159) No spinules at base of claws.
Alona quadrangularis (O. F. Müller) 1785.

Greatest height usually posterior to middle of valves. Valves usually plainly striated, sometimes conspicuously so, with a reticulated area in infero-anterior region (var. *lepida* Birge). Labrum with large keel of variable form; often quadrate or with rounded angles. Post-abdomen large, flattened, dorsal margin dilated; with 15–18 serrate marginal denticles and a row of lateral squamae. Claws large, with long basal spine; no spinules on inside of basal spine. Length, ♀, to 0.9 mm.; ♂, to 0.6 mm. See Fig. 1129, *a*. In similar localities to preceding species; also on bottom of open water.

161 (158) Size moderate or small. Fewer than 14 denticles. 162

This section of the genus needs much additional study. There are species and numerous varieties beside those listed.

162 (163) Lateral fascicles or squamae do not extend beyond dorsal margin of post-abdomen. . . . . *Alona costata* Sars 1862.

Evenly arched or greatest height behind middle; posterior margin convex. Valves striated or smooth. Post-abdomen short, broad; with straight dorsal (lower) margin, tapering toward apex; with about 12 subequal denticles and a row of fine squamae. Post-abdomen of ♂ tapering; no marginal denticles; very fine squamae; vas deferens opens at apex of process extending out ventral to (above) claws; claws without basal spine. Length, ♀, 0.5 mm. or more; ♂, 0.4 mm. See Fig. 1129, *e*.
Found everywhere and very abundant.

163 (162) Lateral fascicles long, extending beyond dorsal margin. . . . 164

164 (165) Post-abdomen not broadened toward apex.
Alona rectangula Sars 1861.

Body evenly arched; general form like *A. guttata.* Valves striated, reticulated, or smooth, rarely tuberculate; ventral margin usually somewhat convex. Post-abdomen short, slightly enlarged toward apex, angle rounded; with 8–9 marginal denticles or bundles of setae and about as many fascicles, the distal long enough to project beyond margin of post-abdomen. Intestine without cecum, enlarged at junction of intestine and rectum, somewhat as in *Ilyocryptus.* Length, ♀, 0.35 to 0.42 mm. See Fig. 1129, *e, f*.
Common everywhere. Most specimens found belong to var. *pulchra* Hellich.

165 (164)   Post-abdomen broader toward apex.   *Alona intermedia* Sars 1862.

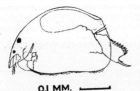

Body evenly arched but not very high. Post-abdomen long, broad, enlarged toward apex, with rounded angle; the 8–9 marginal denticles rather small and thick; the lateral denticles or fascicles much more conspicuous, consisting of bundles of fine setae. The distal seta in each bundle is the largest and the size of setae increases toward apex of post-abdomen. The distal bundles project beyond margin of post-abdomen. Length, ♀, ca. 0.4 mm. See Fig. 1129, g.

Rare; specimens closely agreeing with Lilljeborg's description and figures found in Wisconsin. Possibly not Sars' *intermedia*, as his figure of that species resembles some varieties of Lilljeborg's *rectangula*.

0.1 MM.

FIG. 1131. *Alona intermedia.*

166 (151)   With oblique striae. . . . . *Alonella karua* . . 232
Turn to the key at the number indicated where the species named is discussed.

167 (137)   Rostrum broad, semicircular. . . . . . *Graptoleberis* Sars 1863.
Sole species. . . . . . . *Graptoleberis testudinaria* (Fischer) 1848.

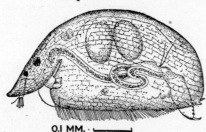

Posterior margin with 2 strong teeth at infero-posteal angle; valves and head with conspicuous reticulation. Head large; fornix very broad, forming a semicircular rostrum, covering antennules and extending down as far as ventral margin of valves. Post-abdomen bent at the sharp pre-anal angle; tapered toward claws, so that form is nearly triangular; marginal spines small; lateral fascicles minute, sometimes wanting. Claws small, with 1 minute basal spine, sometimes wanting (var. *inermis* Birge); ♂ with long, slender post-abdomen, without spines; vas deferens opens on ventral side; claws very minute; hook of first foot slender.

0.1 MM.

FIG. 1132. *Graptoleberis testudinaria.*

Color gray to yellow-white; sometimes opaque. Length, ♀, 0.5–0.7 mm.; ♂, 0.5 mm. or less.
Common among weeds or on bottom of pools and margin of lakes.

168 (136)   Rostrum considerably exceeding antennules. 169

169 (170)   Post-abdomen with marginal denticles only. *Alonella.* . 240, 241
Turn to the key at the numbers indicated where two species are discussed.

170 (169)   Two to four marginal denticles; long series of lateral denticles.
Rostrum very long, recurved. . . . *Rhynchotalona* Norman 1903.
Sole species. . . . . *Rhynchotalona falcata* (Sars) 1861.

General form of body like *Alona*. Rostrum very long, slender, and recurved under the head. Post-abdomen stout, thick, bent at anus, truncate at apex; with about four rather stout marginal denticles near apex, and a lateral series, continued nearly to anus, of very fine spinules in an unbroken row. Intestine with cecum. ♂ (European) with long rostrum, bilobed at apex; post-abdomen tapering and armed with hairs only; ordinary hook on first foot. Color yellow or greenish. Length, ♀, 0.5 mm.; ♂, 0.4 mm.
Maine, Michigan.

0.1 MM.

FIG. 1133. *Rhynchotalona falcata.*

171 (122)   Posterior margin of valves considerably less than maximum height.
            172
All species of *Pleuroxus* belong here; also *Alonella excisa* and *exigua.*

172 (204)   Body elongated, form not spherical. 173

173 (174, 175)   Lower part of posterior margin excised or crenulated.
                        Alonella excisa, A. exigua . . 244, 245
Turn to the key at the numbers indicated where two species are discussed.

174 (173, 175)   Posterior margin with numerous teeth along whole length.
                        Pleuroxus procurvatus, P. truncatus . . 188, 191
Turn to the key at the numbers indicated where two species are discussed.

175 (173, 174)   Teeth (if any) only at infero-posteal angle. 176

176 (179)   Infero-posteal angle well marked, ordinarily with teeth. . . 177

177 (178)   Rostrum long. . . . . *Pleuroxus* most species . . 186
Take up the key at the number indicated where the genus is discussed as a unit.

178 (177)   Rostrum short. . . . . *Alonella dentifera* . . 233
Take up the key at the number indicated where the genus is discussed as a unit.
N.B.   If the rostrum is broad, semi-circular at end, see 167.

179 (176)   Infero-posteal angle rounded. 180

180 (185)   With well-marked tooth or teeth. 181

181 (182)   Rostrum long, recurved. . . . . . . *Pleuroxus striatus* . . 195
Turn to the key at the number indicated where the species named is discussed.

182 (181)   Rostrum short. . . . . *Dunhevedia* King 1853 . . 183
General shape rounded. Valves tumid, gaping below; obscurely reticulated; infero-posteal
angle rounded, with 1 or 2 teeth on ventral margin in front of angle. Post-abdomen bent
abruptly behind anus; post-anal part thick, somewhat foot-shaped as seen from side, its dorsal
(lower) margin lying parallel to ventral margin of valves; with many fine denticles and setae.
Claws short, curved, with 1 basal spine. ♂ with usual characters; post-abdomen same shape
as ♀, with fine hairs only.

183 (184)   Form short and high, as dorsal margin is much arched.
                        Dunhevedia setigera (Birge) 1877.

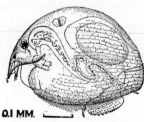

Keel of labrum produced into a somewhat tongue-like
form, its ventral margin smooth. Color yellow. Length,
♀, to 0.5 mm.; ♂, ca. 0.36 mm.
New England and Wisconsin to Colorado, Louisiana,
and Texas. Not common; among weeds. Perhaps identical with *D. crassa* King.

FIG. 1134. *Dunhevedia setigera.*

0.1 MM.

184 (183)   Form more elongated, as dorsal margin is little arched.
Dunhevedia serrata Daday 1898.

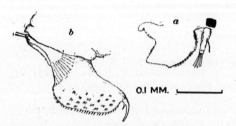

Usually 2 teeth at infero-posteal angle, a very small posterior and a larger anterior one. Keel of labrum serrate in anterior part, smooth behind; about 10–12 serrations, pointing backward. ♂ unknown. Color yellow. Length, ♀, ca. 0.7 mm.
Louisiana, Texas; in pools and lakes among weeds; not abundant.

0.I MM.

Fig. 1135. *Dunhevedia serrata.* a, labrum; b, post-abdomen.

185 (180)   Infero-posteal angle without teeth, or tooth very small; rostrum long or short. 186

186 (203)   Claws with 2 basal spines. . . . *Pleuroxus* Baird 1843 . . 187

Rostrum long and pointed, rarely bent forward. Dorsal margin much arched; posterior margin short, usually less than one-half height, rarely toothed along entire length; infero-posteal angle rarely rounded, usually sharp and toothed. Keel of labrum large, usually tongue-shaped; posterior angle prolonged. Post-abdomen with marginal denticles only. ♂ smaller than ♀, with usual characters; post-abdomen varies in different species.
Three types of form are distinguishable in the genus: (1) relatively long and low species: *striatus* type (*P. striatus, hastatus, hamulatus*); (2) short, high-arched forms: *denticulatus* type (*P. denticulatus, aduncus, trigonellus, truncatus*); (3) the second form with rostrum bent forward: (*P. procurvatus, uncinatus*). All species littoral.

187 (190)   Rostrum bent up in front. 188

188 (189)   Rostrum bent sharply into hook; teeth along whole posterior margin of valves. . . . . *Pleuroxus procurvatus* Birge 1878.

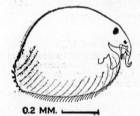

General form and markings like *P. denticulatus.* Posterior margin of valves with 7–8 teeth along the whole length. Post-abdomen like *P. denticulatus* but slightly more broadened behind anus. ♂ unknown. Color yellowish, transparent or opaque. Length, ♀, ca. 0.5 mm.
Northern states, common in weedy waters.

Fig. 1136. *Pleuroxus procurvatus.*

0.2 MM.

189 (188)   Rostrum merely curved forward; teeth at infero-posteal angle only.
Pleuroxus uncinatus Baird 1850.

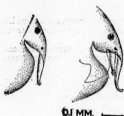

Infero-posteal angle with 2–4 rather long, curved teeth, sometimes branched. Rostrum long, acute, bent forward. Post-abdomen like *P. trigonellus*, broad, somewhat tapered toward apex; about 13 good-sized marginal denticles. Color dirty gray, or with green or yellow tinge. Length, ♀, 0.7–0.9 mm.; ♂ (European), 0.56 mm.
Nebraska (Fordyce). The species is very close to *P. trigonellus*, separated by procurved rostrum and large teeth at infero-posteal angle.

0.I MM.

Fig. 1137. *Pleuroxus uncinatus.* European specimens.

190 (187) Rostrum not bent forward. 191

191 (192) Numerous teeth along whole posterior margin.
           Pleuroxus truncatus (O. F. Müller) 1785.

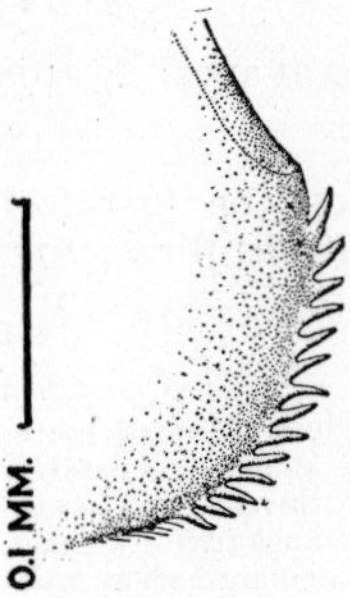

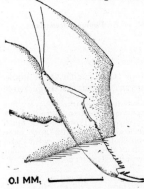

Posterior margin with numerous (more than 20) close-set teeth; valves striated, the striae on middle of valves nearly longitudinal, the others oblique. Post-abdomen much like *P. trigonellus*, slightly tapering toward apex, angle rounded; 12–14 marginal denticles, increasing in size distally. Color yellow-brown. Length, ♀, ca. 0.6 mm.; ♂ (European), 0.45 mm. Nebraska (Fordyce).

FIG. 1138. *Pleuroxus truncatus.* (European specimen.)

192 (191) Teeth at infero-posteal angle only. 193

193 (196) Post-abdomen long, slender, convex on ventral (upper) side. . 194

194 (195) Supero-posteal angle sharp but not projecting; infero-posteal angle a sharp point. . . . . *Pleuroxus hastatus* Sars 1862.

Infero-posteal angle a sharp point, with a very small tooth; valves reticulated, longitudinal marks often more distinct, giving appearance of striation. 16–18 marginal denticles. Color yellow, transparent or opaque; not black unless ephippial. Length, ♀, ca. 0.6 mm.; ♂, ca. 0.45 mm.

Rather rare; New England, Wisconsin, Nebraska, California.

FIG. 1139. *Pleuroxus hastatus.*

0.1 MM.

195 (194) Supero-posteal angle overhanging; infero-posteal angle rounded, with small tooth in front of it.
           Pleuroxus striatus Schoedler 1863.

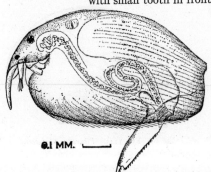

General shape much like *P. hastatus* but never so high arched as this may be. Valves obviously striated. Post-abdomen long, slender, with 20, or more, marginal denticles. Color dark, especially opaque on dorsal side, often nearly black. Length, ♀, ca. 0.8 mm.; ♂, ca. 0.6 mm.

In all parts of United States; common among weeds.

This species is *P. gracilis* Hudendorf; *P. unidens* Birge.

0.1 MM.

FIG. 1140. *Pleuroxus striatus.*

196 (193) Post-abdomen of moderate length; ventral (upper) margin straight, or nearly so; greatest width behind anus. 197

197 (200) Angle of post-abdomen sharp, with cluster of spines at apex. . 198

198 (199) Teeth at infero-posteal angle of valves; no hook on first foot of female. . . . . . . *Pleuroxus denticulatus* Birge 1877.

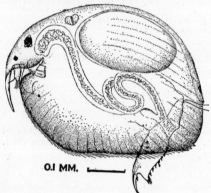

Infero-posteal angle with small tooth-like spines. Post-abdomen moderately long, straight, very little narrowed toward apex; length of post-anal part 1.5 times, or more, that of anal emargination; apex truncate; with cluster of fine, straight denticles at apex and 8–12 anterior to these. Color greenish or yellowish, usually transparent. Length, ♀, 0.5–0.6 mm.; ♂, 0.36 mm.
Common everywhere in weedy water.

0.1 MM.

FIG. 1141. *Pleuroxus denticulatus.*

199 (198) Infero-posteal angle rounded; first foot of female with stout hook.
Pleuroxus hamulatus Birge 1910.

Infero-posteal angle rounded, without teeth; valves reticulated; also marked by very fine striae, which run nearly longitudinally. Rostrum long, recurved. Keel of labrum small, rounded, prolonged. Post-abdomen much like *P. denticulatus*, but with apex more rounded and denticles not so crowded there. Denticles about 12–14. ♂ unknown. Color horn-yellow, often dark on dorsal side like *P. striatus*. Length, ♀, ca. 0.6 mm.
New England and southern states; probably a coastal form; not reported from north central region. Common in pools and weedy waters.

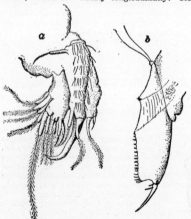

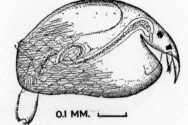

FIG. 1142. *Pleuroxus hamulatus.* a, first foot; b, post-abdomen.

0.1 MM.

FIG. 1143. *Pleuroxus hamulatus.*

200 (197) Angle of post-abdomen rounded. 201

201 (202) Series of marginal denticles longer than anal emargination; post-abdomen of male broadened in middle of post-anal part with crescentic dorsal margin.
Pleuroxus trigonellus (O. F. Müller) 1785.

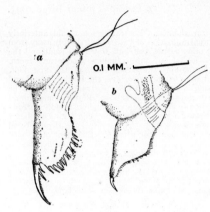

Form of *P. denticulatus* type. Infero-posteal angle with 2 or 3 small teeth, often minute, sometimes wanting. Post-abdomen much as *P. denticulatus;* but dorsal margin slightly convex, broader behind anus; apex rounded; 14–16 marginal denticles, longer toward apex, but not distinctly clustered there. ♂ post-abdomen is characteristic; broadened behind anus into a semi-elliptical plate, bearing thick-set hairs, no spines; greatly narrowed toward apex, forming a slender prolongation. Color yellowish, transparent; post-abdomen often dark. Length, ♀, 0.6 mm.; ♂, 0.4 mm.
Not common; Maine, Wisconsin, Nebraska; doubtless widely distributed.

Fig. 1144. *Pleuroxus trigonellus.* Post-abdomen: *a,* ♀; *b,* ♂.

202 (201) Row of marginal denticles about equals anal emargination; male post-abdomen not crescentic.
Pleuroxus aduncus (Jurine) 1820.

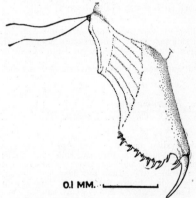

♀ very closely resembling *P. trigonellus,* but differing as follows: valves striated; infero-posteal angle usually without teeth. Post-abdomen shorter, the length of post-anal part hardly exceeding anal emargination; dorsal margin slightly arched, with 9–12 marginal denticles; apex rounded. ♂ post-abdomen very different from *P. trigonellus;* narrower than ♀, tapered toward claws; no dorsal enlargement or apical prolongation. Color horn-yellow, sometimes opaque. Length, ♀, ca. 0.6 mm.; ♂, ca. 0.45 mm.
Colorado, California. Among weeds or in pools.

Fig. 1145. *Pleuroxus aduncus.*

203 (186) Claws with 1 basal spine. . . . *Alonella* (most species) . . 230
Take up the key at the number indicated where one subgenus is discussed as a unit.

204 (172) Body spherical or broadly ellipsoidal. 205

205 (208) Well marked or small spine at infero-posteal angle. 206

206 (207) Valves conspicuously striated. . . . . . *Alonella nana* . . 242
Turn to the key at the number indicated where the species is discussed.

207 (206) Valves reticulated or not plainly marked. *Chydorus barroisi*
Chydorus hybridus . . 226, 227
Turn to the key at the numbers indicated where the two species are discussed.

208 (205) No spine at infero-posteal angle. 209

209 (210) Valves with conspicuous projection on antero-ventral margin.
Anchistropus Sars 1862.
Sole American species. . . . . Anchistropus minor Birge 1893.

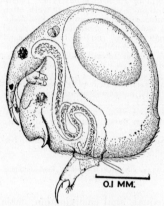

Form globular. Ventral region tumid anteriorly
and ventral margin of valves bent sharply away from
each other about one-third way from front and the
valve folded out into a hollow groove and tooth,
which contains the strong hook of the first foot.
Head large, bulging over eye, the fornices broad and
forming a sort of flap-like rostrum, which can be
closely pressed to the valves. Post-abdomen broad
at base, pre-anal angle overhanging; rapidly narrowing toward apex, which is prolonged into a lobe; a
few marginal spines. Claws with long, slender basal
spine, denticulate or smooth. First foot of ♀ with
strong hook, toothed on concave side, which lies in
groove formed by folding of valves.

In *A. minor*, groove for hook of first foot near
anterior part of valves; hook not large. Color brown-
yellow. ♂ unknown. Length, ♀, ca. 0.35 mm.
Maine, Michigan, Wisconsin, Louisiana.

FIG. 1146. *Anchistropus minor.*

0.1 MM.

210 (209) No such projection. 211

211 (229) Post-abdomen ordinarily short with prominent pre-anal angle.
Chydorus Leach 1843 . . 212
Shape spherical or ovate. Posterior angles little marked; infero-posteal angle usually unarmed. Antennules short and thick. Rostrum long and acute. Post-abdomen usually short,
broad, rarely long and narrow (*C. globosus*); apex rounded; with marginal denticles only or
(*C. globosus*) with very fine lateral fascicles. Claws with 2 basal spines, the proximal often very
minute, rarely absent. ♂ with short rostrum, thick antennule, hook on first foot, post-abdomen
often very narrow.

212 (213) Post-abdomen, long, narrow, *Pleuroxus*-like.
Chydorus globosus Baird 1850.

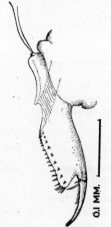

Almost spherical; valves smooth or reticulated, sometimes
striated in front. Post-abdomen with small pre-anal angle;
numerous marginal denticles and very fine lateral fascicles.
Claws with 2 basal spines, the distal very long and slender.
Color bright yellow to dark brown, usually with dark spot in
center of valve. Length, ♀, to 0.8 mm.; ♂, 0.6 mm.
Everywhere; in lakes and ponds, among weeds, but never
present in very large numbers.

C. globosus might well be type of a separate genus. The other
species fall into 3 groups: (1) The *sphaericus* group or *Chydorus*
proper (*C. sphaericus, gibbus, piger, latus, ovalis*); (2) The
javiformis group, similar to (1) but with greatly developed cuticular structures (*C. javiformis, bicornutus*); (3) The *barroisi*
group, with toothed labrum; denticles of post-abdomen shortest
in middle of row (*C. barroisi, hybridus, poppei*).

FIG. 1147. *Chydorus globosus.*

0.1 MM.

213 (212) Post-abdomen short, broad; pre-anal angle marked. 214

214 (215, 216) Shell covered with deep polygonal cells.

Chydorus faviformis Birge 1893.

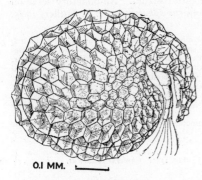

Much like *sphaericus* in form and size. ♂ unknown. Color yellow to light brownish. Length, ♀, 0.5–0.6 mm. New England, Wisconsin, Michigan, Louisiana; not common.

Fig. 1148. *Chydorus faviformis*, cast shell.

0.1 MM.

215 (214, 216) Shell with deep polygonal cells and cuticular ridges.

Chydorus bicornutus Doolittle 1909.

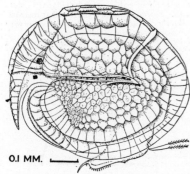

Like *faviformis* in having deep polygonal cuticular cells; but distinguished by the development of an extraordinary and complex system of thin cuticular ridges, which extend far beyond the ordinary cells. A long horn extends laterally from the middle dorsal region of each valve, from which radiate some of the ridges. ♂ unknown. Color yellow. Length, ♀, to 0.7 mm. Maine, New Hampshire, and New Jersey.

Fig. 1149. *Chydorns bicornutus.* (After Doolittle.)

0.1 MM.

216 (214, 215) Shell of ordinary type. 217

217 (225) Ventral edge of keel of labrum smooth. 218

218 (219) Antero-dorsal surface of valves and head flattened.

Chydorus gibbus Lilljeborg 1880.

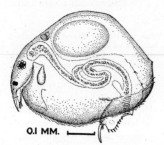

The curve of the dorsal surface somewhat flattened, both in front and behind, making a sort of hump in center of dorsal margin. Valves reticulated. Head small; rostrum projects from valves in characteristic way. Post-abdomen with 8–10 marginal denticles. Color yellowish to brown. Length, ♀, 0.5 mm. Lake Superior, Wisconsin, Michigan; rare. This species is *C. rugulosus* Forbes.

Fig. 1150. *Chydorus gibbus.*

0.1 MM.

219 (218)　Dorsal surface not flattened; form usually spherical or broadly
　　　　　ovate. 220
220 (223, 224)　Small forms not exceeding 0.5 mm., usually less. . . . 221
221 (222)　Fornices gradually narrowing into rostrum. All olfactory setae on
　　　　　end of antennule. *Chydorus sphaericus* (O. F. Müller) 1785.

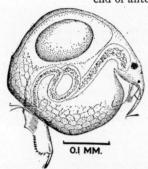

Spherical or broadly elliptical. Shell usually reticulated,
sometimes smooth (var. *nitidus* Schoedler), sometimes
punctate (var. *punctatus* Hellich), or with elevations (var.
coelatus Schoedler). Post-abdomen with 8–9 marginal
denticles. Claws small; proximal basal spine very minute.
♂ with post-abdomen much emarginate. Color light
yellow to dark brown. Length, ♀, 0.3–0.5 mm.; ♂,
0.2 mm. Small limnetic forms constitute var. *minor*
Lilljeborg.
　The commonest of all Cladocera; found all over the
world.

0.1 MM.

Fig. 1151.　*Chydorus sphaericus.*

222 (221)　Fornices abruptly narrowed into rostrum. Two olfactory setae
　　　　　on side of antennule. . . . . . *Chydorus piger* Sars 1862.
General form much like *C. sphaericus.* Ventral margin of valves densely ciliated; valves
ordinarily marked by oblique striae, sometimes smooth. Fornices abruptly narrowed at rostrum.
Antennule with usual lateral sense seta and two olfactory setae on side. Post-abdomen with
8–9 rather long marginal denticles. Claws with 2 basal spines, the proximal one minute. ♂
post-abdomen narrow, but not excavated. Color light to dark yellow. Length, ♀, ca. 0.4
mm. Rare; reported only from Maine.

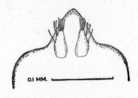

0.1 MM

Fig. 1152.　*Chydorus piger.* Entire specimen and lower side of rostrum with antennules.

223 (220, 224)　Larger forms, to 0.8 mm. Antennules short and thick with
　　　　　all olfactory setae terminal. . . . *Chydorus latus* Sars 1862.

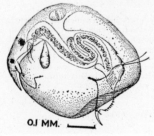

Much like *sphaericus*, but larger. Mandible attached
some way back of junction of head and valve. Denticles of post-abdomen 10–12. Claws sometimes with
only 1 basal spine. Color dark yellow-brown. Length,
♀, to 0.7–0.8 mm.
　Rare; Canada, near Lake Erie.

Fig. 1153.　*Chydorus latus.*

0.1 MM.

224 (220, 223)   About 0.5 mm.   Antennule with one olfactory seta proximal
to cluster at end. . . . . . .   *Chydorus ovalis* Kurz 1874.

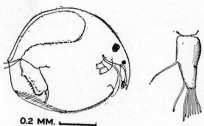

Form round or broad oval. Post-
abdomen with rounded apex; 12–15
marginal denticles. Claws with 2 basal
spines, the proximal minute. Color
yellow, transparent. Length, ♀, to
0.6 mm.; ♂ (European), 0.5 mm.
Rare; Nebraska.

0.2 MM.

FIG. 1154. *Chydorus ovalis.*   Entire specimen and
antennule.

225 (217)   Ventral edge of keel of labrum with one or more teeth.   226

226 (227, 228)   With several teeth; short spine at infero-posteal angle of valves.
Chydorus barroisi (Richard) 1894.

Form and size much like *sphaericus*, though
ventral margin is less curved. Keel of labrum acuminate behind; serrate, with four or
more teeth. Post-abdomen with well-developed pre-anal angle; 10–12 marginal denticles,
shortest in middle of row. Color brown-yellow. Length, ♀, ca. 0.4 mm.
Rare; Lake Charles, Louisiana.

FIG. 1155. *Chydorus barroisi.*

0.1 MM.

227 (226, 228)   With one tooth; infero-posteal spine present.
Chydorus hybridus Daday 1905.

Similar to *barroisi* but with only one tooth on keel of labrum.
Rare; Wisconsin, Michigan, Louisiana, Texas.

FIG. 1156. *Chydorus hybridus.*

228 (226, 227) With one tooth on labrum; no spine on valves.
Chydorus poppei Richard 1897.

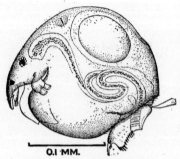

Like *hybridus* but without spine at infero-posteal angle. Tooth on labrum sometimes small or obsolescent.
Louisiana, California; rare.

Very probably the last two species should be listed as varieties of *barroisi*. These species were first placed in *Pleuroxus*, but have no very close affinity with either *Pleuroxus* or *Chydorus;* might well be made a separate genus.

FIG. 1157. *Chydorus poppei.*

0.1 MM.

229 (211) Post-abdomen large, pre-anal angle ordinarily not prominent.
Alonella Sars 1862 . . 230

This genus consists of a heterogeneous assemblage of forms; not assignable elsewhere and not easily separable. There are 3 sections which might well constitute separate genera:
(1) *Alonella* proper. Rostrum long, slender, recurved; usually conspicuously so; post-abdomen with marginal denticles only; claws with 1 basal spine. *A. rostrata, dadayi, nana*. (2) *Paralonella*. Rostrum short, hardly exceeding antennules; post-abdomen with very small marginal denticles, with or without lateral fascicles; claws with 1 basal spine. *A. karua, dentifera, diaphana, globulosa*. (3) *Pleuroxalonella*. Rostrum moderate; post-abdomen with marginal denticles only; claws with 2 basal spines. *Pleuroxus*-like. *A. excisa, exigua*.

230 (235) Rostrum short; post-abdomen with marginal and lateral denticles.
231

231 (234) Valves with infero-posteal angle toothed. 232

232 (233) About 3 fine teeth; valves striated. . Alonella karua (King) 1853.

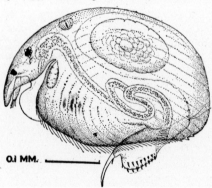

General shape like *Alona* and easily taken for a member of that genus. (See 152.) Valves with oblique striae; infero-posteal angle with 1–4 minute teeth. Post-abdomen broad, expanded behind anus; apex rounded; with about 8 minute marginal denticles and as many lateral fascicles, much larger. Claws with 1 small basal spine. Color yellow, transparent. Length, ♀, 0.45 mm; ♂ (South America), 0.23 mm.
Louisiana, Texas, Arkansas; not rare, in pools and lakes.

0.1 MM.

FIG. 1158. *Alonella karua.*

233 (232) One to three rather strong teeth, valves reticulated.
Alonella dentifera Sars 1901.

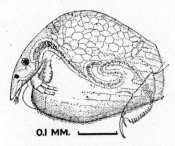

Back high arched; infero-posteal angle acute, with 1–3 fairly strong teeth. Rostrum reaches nearly to ventral margin of valves. Post-abdomen large, broad, somewhat expanded behind anus; apex rounded; with about 12 minute marginal denticles, and as many very minute lateral fascicles. Claws with 1 very long basal spine. Color yellow-brown. Length, ♀ ca. 0.4 mm.; ♂, 0.35 mm.
Louisiana and Texas; not rare in pools and lakes.

FIG. 1159. *Alonella dentifera*, with developing ephippium.

0.1 MM.

234 (231) No infero-posteal teeth; form rotund.
Alonella globulosa Daday 1898.

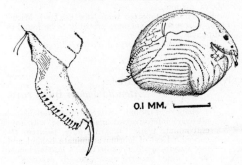

Small; shape oval-rotund; head reaching about to middle of valves. Valves striated; all margins rounded and without teeth. Post-abdomen long, narrow; broadest near anus; about 12 minute marginal denticles and as many slender lateral fascicles. Keel of labrum with 2 notches. Color yellow-brown. Length, ♀, 0.30–0.4 mm.
Lake Charles, Louisiana, among weeds.
This species is *A. sculpta* Sars.

0.1 MM.

FIG. 1160. *Alonella globulosa*.

235 (230) Post-abdomen with marginal denticles only. 236

236 (237) Denticles minute; post-abdomen large, bent behind anus; no infero-posteal tooth on valves. *Alonella diaphana* (King) 1853.

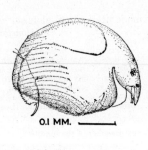

Head short, rostrum not reaching more than two-thirds distance toward ventral margin. Valves striated, sometimes passing into reticulation, often inconspicuous; infero-posteal angle rounded, without teeth. Post-abdomen long, slightly enlarged behind anus; with numerous very minute marginal denticles and no other spines. Claws long; 1 basal spine. Length, ♀, 0.5 mm.; ♂, 0.4 mm. Color yellow, transparent.
Louisiana, Texas; in pools and lakes; rare.

0.1 MM.

FIG. 1161. *Alonella diaphana*.

237 (236) Denticles of ordinary size; infero-posteal tooth present. . . 238

238 (243) Claws with one basal spine. 239

239 (242) Rostrum long, recurved. 240

240 (241) Shape elongated oval; valves striated.

Alonella rostrata (Koch) 1841.

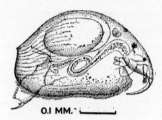

0.1 MM.

FIG. 1162. *Alonella rostrata.*

General form not unlike a *Pleuroxus* of the *striatus* type. Valves striated or reticulated; infero-posteal angle rounded and with minute tooth, sometimes absent. Rostrum long, slender, recurved. Post-abdomen moderately long, somewhat tapering toward apex; angle rounded; 9–12 small marginal denticles. Claws with 1 minute basal spine. Color yellow or brown, usually rather dark. Length, ♀, ca. 0.5 mm.; ♂, ca. 0.4 mm.

Rather rare; reported from New England, Michigan, Wisconsin, Minnesota; probably to be found in all regions.

This species is *Pleuroxus acutirostris* Birge.

241 (240) Shape short oval; valves strongly reticulated.

Alonella dadayi Birge 1910.

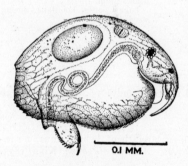

0.1 MM.

Shape oval-rotund. Valves strongly reticulated all over; infero-posteal angle rounded, with several minute teeth. Rostrum long, pointed, recurved. Keel of labrum acuminate behind and its margin with 1 projection. Post-abdomen short, wide; pre-anal angle strongly marked, as in *Chydorus;* with numerous small denticles; apex rounded. Claws with 1 basal spine. Color yellow to brown, often opaque. Length, ♀, 0.25–0.3 mm.; ♂ (South America), 0.2 mm.

Louisiana, Texas; not rare in weedy pools.

This species is *Leptorhynchus dentifer* Daday, whose specific name has to be changed on removing to *Alonella,* as Sars' species *A. dentifera* preoccupies the name.

FIG. 1163. *Alonella dadayi.*

242 (239) Rostrum short or moderate; shape globose; valves conspicuously striated. . . . . *Alonella nana* (Baird) 1850.

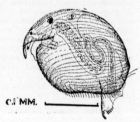

0.1 MM.

Very minute; *Chydorus*-like. Valves coarsely and conspicuously striated; minute tooth in infero-posteal region. Rostrum varies, usually rather long, recurved, considerably exceeding antennules. Post-abdomen short; pre-anal angle strongly projecting; apex rounded; about 6 marginal denticles. Claws with 1 small spine. Color brownish, usually opaque. Length, ♀, 0.2–0.28 mm.; ♂, 0.25 mm.

New England, Wisconsin, Minnesota; rare. The smallest member of the family.

FIG. 1164. *Alonella nana.*

243 (238) Claws with 2 basal spines; posterior margin of valves excised near infero-posteal angle. 244

244 (245) Post-abdomen fairly long; angled at apex; valves reticulated and with fine striae. . . . . . *Alonella excisa* (Fischer) 1854.

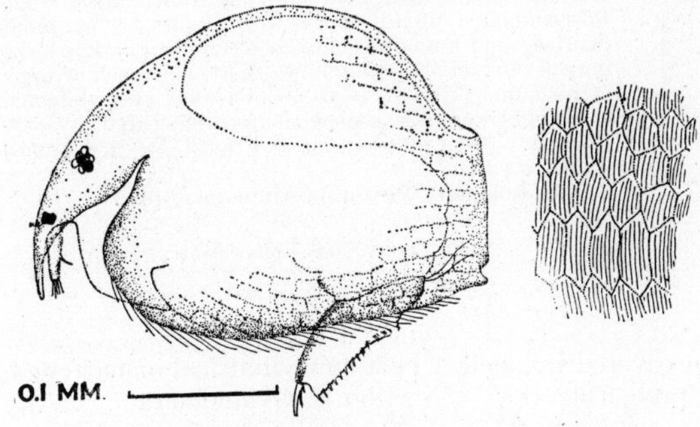

General appearance *Pleuroxus*-like. Rostrum moderate to long, never as prolonged as in *A. rostrata* nor recurved; longer in southern forms. Infero-posteal angle marked, sometimes produced into a point; posterior margin above it excised, sometimes crenulated. Post-abdomen long, narrow, not narrowing much toward apex; apex angled; with about 9–10 small marginal denticles. Color yellow to brown. Length, ♀, to 0.5 mm.; ♂, 0.28 mm.

0.I MM.

Not uncommon in all localities; in weedy pools and lakes.

Fig. 1165. *Alonella excisa.* Entire specimen and details of markings of valve.

245 (244) Post-abdomen short; rounded at apex; valves without fine striae.
Alonella exigua (Lilljeborg) 1853.

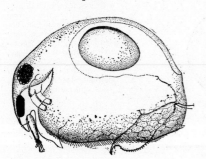

Much like preceding species but smaller. About 6–8 small marginal denticles. Color yellow, not very transparent. Length, ♀, 0.35 mm.; ♂, 0.28 mm. Maine, Wisconsin, Michigan; rare.

Fig. 1166. *Alonella exigua.*

0.I MM.

246 (121) Eye and ocellus very large; antennules project far beyond rostrum.
Dadaya Sars 1901.

Sole species. . . . . *Dadaya macrops* (Daday) 1898.

Form rounded-oval; not compressed. Head small, much depressed; tumid above eye; rostrum short and broad. Antennules long, moderately stout, projecting far beyond rostrum. Post-abdomen of moderate size, compressed, somewhat broadened behind anus, slightly narrowing toward apex; angle rounded; about 14–18 marginal denticles. Claws small, one small basal spine. Eye very large, with few lenses; ocellus nearly as large, crowded down into rostrum. ♂ unknown. Color dark brown. Length, ♀, ca. 0.3 mm.

A single specimen of this species was found in a collection from a weedy pool at Smithville, Texas.

Fig. 1167. *Dadaya macrops.*

247 (120) No eye; ocellus only. . . . . *Monospilus* Sars 1861.
Sole species. . . . . *Monospilus dispar* Sars 1861.

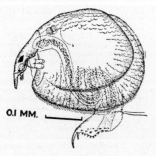

Form oval or round. Shell not cast in molting, as in *Ilyocryptus*. Valves nearly round with fine setae along ventral edge. Head very small, depressed, movable. Keel of labrum with about 4 scallops on ventral edge. Post-abdomen broad, short, with about 5–7 marginal denticles and numerous clusters of fine hairs. Eye lacking; ocellus large. Antennules short, not reaching apex of rostrum. ♂ with hook on first foot; post-abdomen tapering, triangular, somewhat resembling that of *Graptoleberis*. Color brown-yellow. Length, ♀, ca. o.5 mm.; ♂, ca. o.4 mm.

0.I MM.

New England, Wisconsin, Minnesota; rare.

Fig. 1168. *Monospilus dispar.*

248 (1) Body and feet not covered by shell. Feet subcylindrical or flattened, jointed, prehensile. . . . Section B. **Gymnomera** . . 249
No fornices. Rami of antennae 3- to 4-jointed. Feet, 4 to 6 pairs, jointed, prehensile.

249 (250) Four pairs of feet, stout, compressed, with claw-like spines and branchial appendages.

Tribe I. **Onychopoda.**
Sole family. . . . . POLYPHEMIDAE Baird.
Body very short. Shell converted into large globular brood-sac. Caudal process long, slender, with 2 long caudal stylets or setae. Rami of antennae with 3 and 4 joints. Eye very large; no ocellus. Labrum large. Two small hepatic ceca.

One genus. . . . . *Polyphemus* O. F. Müller 1785.
Sole species. . . . . *Polyphemus pediculus* (Linné) 1761.

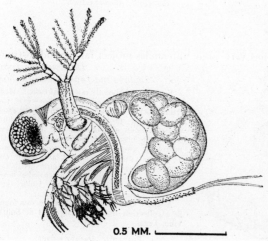

Brood-sac globular, with 20–25 young in full grown specimens. Antennules very small, on ventral surface of head. Head large, filled in front by huge movable eye. Antennae with 7 setae on each ramus. Feet stout, with strong claws, and branchial appendage; fourth pair, very small. Length, ♀, measured to back of brood-sac, to 1.5 mm.; ♂, o.8 mm. Common in northern United States in lakes, pools, and marshes.

Fig. 1169. *Polyphemus pediculus.*

0.5 MM.

250 (249)   Six pairs of feet, cylindrical, first pair very long; without branchial
appendages. . . . .   Tribe II. **Haplopoda.**

Sole family. . . . .   LEPTODORIDAE Lilljeborg.

Head elongated, slender; eye filling anterior end. Body 4-jointed, the first part bearing the 6 feet and dorsal brood-sac; the 3-jointed abdomen ends in 2 short stylets or claws. Antennules small, freely movable. Antennae with very large basal joint; rami 4-jointed, with numerous setae. Mandibles long, slender, pointed, with 3 spines near apex. Esophagus very long, stomach in last abdominal segment. ♀ with very long antennules. The young from winter eggs hatch as a nauplius.

Sole genus with characters of family. . . . .   *Leptodora* Lilljeborg.

Sole species. . . . .   *Leptodora kindtii* (Focke) 1844.

This beautiful, transparent creature is the largest of the Cladocera, the ♀ reaching a length of 18 mm. Rapacious, though its weak mandibles prevent it from being formidable to the harder shelled entomostraca; nocturnal in coming to the surface.

Limnetic in Great Lakes and small lakes in northern United States; not rare.

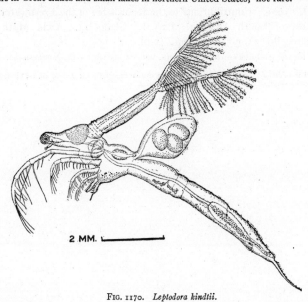

2 MM.

FIG. 1170. *Leptodora kindtii.*

IMPORTANT REFERENCES ON NORTH AMERICAN CLADOCERA.

BIRGE, E. A.   1891.   Notes on Cladocera II.   List of Cladocera from Madison, Wis.   Trans. Wis. Acad., 8: 379–398; 1 pl.

1893.   Notes on Cladocera III.   Descriptions of new and rare species. Trans. Wis. Acad., 9: 275–317; 1 pl.

1910.   Notes on Cladocera IV.   Descriptions of New and Rare Species Chiefly Southern.   Trans. Wis. Acad., 16: 1018–1066; 5 pl.

HERRICK, C. L.   1895.   Synopsis of the Entomostraca of Minnesota.   Second Report of State Zoologist; 337 pp., 81 pl.

Contains much information and many figures, original and from various sources; but the material is not very carefully or critically handled.

KEILHACK, L. 1910. Phyllopoda. In Brauer's Süsswasserfauna Deutschlands, pt. 10; 112 pp., 265 text figs.

An admirable account of the Cladocera of Germany, most of which are found in this country
also. It should be the first book procured by any one who can read German.

LILLJEBORG, W. 1900. Cladocera Sueciae. Upsala. 701 pp., 87 pl.

Latin keys and diagnoses; otherwise German. Indispensable for a critical study of the
group.

RICHARD, J. 1894. Révision des Cladocères. Part I. Sididae. Ann. Sci.
Nat., Zool., (7) 18: 279–389, 2 pl.

1896. Part II. Daphnidae. Ann. Sci. Nat., Zool. (8) 2: 187–363; 6 pl.

Invaluable for the families which they cover.

SARS, G. O. 1901. Contributions to the Knowledge of the Freshwater Entomostraca of South America. Part I. Cladocera. Arch. Math. Nat.
Kristiana, Bd. 23, no. 3, 102 pp., 12 pl.

Necessary for the study of southern cladocera, but not needed for the northern states.

NOTE. — All illustrations for this chapter have been drawn especially for it, and all are made from the
actual specimens, except in a few cases, which are indicated.

CHAPTER XXIII

COPEPODA

By C. DWIGHT MARSH

United States Department of Agriculture

Of all animals encountered in fresh water, perhaps none are more likely to arouse interest than the Copepoda. While many of them are large enough to be seen and watched with the naked eye, yet they are so small that a microscope is needed to get a clear understanding of their form and structure. In company with the Cladocera, they are almost universally distributed, and can be collected in nearly any body of water. Unlike the Cladocera, which show many erratic and bizarre species, the Copepoda are graceful and symmetrical in their forms, with a beauty of structure that is very attractive to the amateur student. Some are wonderfully transparent, while others are strikingly and in some cases gorgeously colored.

Copepoda have been studied ever since the microscope was first used. It is said that the first mention of these animals was made by Stephen Blankaart in 1688. O. F. Müller in 1785 is credited with having given the first scientific description of this group. In 1820 Jurine published his famous "Histoire des monocles qui se trouve aux environs de Genève." Some of the species which he described are still recognized as valid, largely, however, by the courtesy of succeeding writers; for Jurine made his distinctions on insufficient grounds like color, and it is only through his figures that one can conjecture what species he had in hand. No really serious study of this group was made until the middle of the nineteenth century, when the publication of Baird's "Natural History of the British Entomostraca" in 1850 and the various papers of Claus a few years later were the beginning of exact work on these forms. The work of Claus was of first importance. In North America articles were published regarding some forms in the early part of the century, but nothing recognizable appeared until S. A.

741

Forbes commenced his series of papers. Although these papers were not extensive, they were exact and carefully worked out, and to Forbes may be given the credit of laying the foundation for all subsequent work in this country.

Though attractive in form, the Copepoda are complex in their structure, and accurate classification can only be attained by careful and laborious dissection, so that study of the order has been neglected.

With the exception of the Harpacticidae, all the free-swimming Copepoda are characterized by a distinct division of the body into cephalothorax and abdomen, the former being composed of five or six segments and the latter of from three to five. The appendages are as follows, commencing with the front of the animal:

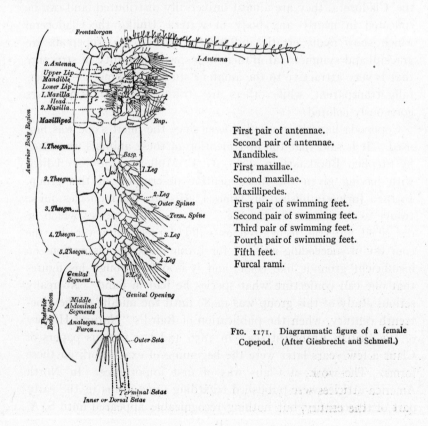

First pair of antennae.
Second pair of antennae.
Mandibles.
First maxillae.
Second maxillae.
Maxillipedes.
First pair of swimming feet.
Second pair of swimming feet.
Third pair of swimming feet.
Fourth pair of swimming feet.
Fifth feet.
Furcal rami.

FIG. 1171. Diagrammatic figure of a female Copepod. (After Giesbrecht and Schmeil.)

All of these appendages are built on the same plan, which is typically represented in the swimming feet of *Cyclops* (Fig. 1221). Each foot consists of two basal segments, and attached to the outer or distal of these are two branches or rami, each of three segments. The outer ramus is known as the exopodite and the inner as the endopodite. This typical plan may be very much modified but, in most cases the fundamental structure can be recognized.

Of these appendages, the first antennae are very characteristic. They are so modified that one of the rami has entirely disappeared, and the one remaining is made up of a considerable number of segments, varying from six to twenty-five. In the same species the number of segments in the antennae is ordinarily invariable. In some of the species of *Cyclops* the antennae are very short, in others they may exceed the length of the cephalothorax, while in the other genera they may equal or exceed the length of the whole body. The segments of the antennae are armed with hairs which are definite in number and location. They have also sensory structures arranged in definite places on the segments. The club-shaped sensory appendage of the twelfth antennal segment of some of the species of *Cyclops* is one of the important means of identification. Some of the species of *Cyclops* have circlets or crowns of spines on certain antennal segments which give them a peculiarly ornate appearance. In some of the species of *Cyclops* there is a thin hyaline lamella extending longitudinally along certain of the segments, being especially marked on the last two. This is particularly noticeable in *Cyclops fuscus* (Fig. 1223).

In the Cyclopidae the antennae are symmetrical and, in the male, are modified to form grasping organs. In the Centropagidae it is only the right antenna of the male that is so modified.

In many of the species of *Diaptomus* the antepenultimate segment of the right antenna of the male has a distinctive form. This may be a hyaline lamella extending the length of the segment, or it may be an extension of one side of the segment in a process which varies from a blunt projection to a hook or, in some cases, a long, slender digitiform extension. The armature of this segment is constant and is one of the important characteristics used in distinguishing species.

The fifth feet in *Cyclops* are very rudimentary structures.

In *Diaptomus* the fifth feet take on interesting forms. In the female they are symmetrical, but not so well developed as the preceding swimming feet. But in the male, the right fifth foot differs from the left, and is modified so as to make a grasping organ. The figures in the synoptical key show the form of these appendages. The modifications are constant in a given species, so that the fifth feet in this genus furnish the most important means of specific identification.

In *Epischura* the fifth feet are modified more profoundly, and this modification is accompanied by a peculiar development of the segments of the abdomen, which also serves as a grasping organ.

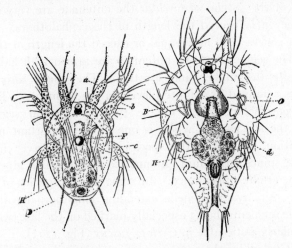

FIG. 1172. Nauplius of *Cyclops*. The fourth pair of appendages are represented by two setae. (After Claus.)

FIG. 1173. Second Stage of *Cyclops*, in which are seen four pairs of appendages. (After Claus.)

In their growth from the egg up, the Copepoda pass through a complicated series of forms. On issuing from the egg the young animal is a flat, oval creature, without any division of the body into cephalothorax and abdomen, and with only three pairs of appendages, the first three of the mature animal, namely, the first and second antennae and the mandibles. These are all used, in this stage of the animal, as swimming organs. This is known as the *nauplius* stage (Fig. 1172). A series of molts follows. In the second stage (Fig. 1173) a fourth pair of appendages is added, which later are known as the maxillae. In a later stage three more pairs of appendages are added, — the maxillipedes, and the first two pairs of swimming feet: this is known as the *metanauplius* stage. The following stage is the first *Cyclops* stage; in this there is a distinct division of the body into cephalothorax and abdomen, and the third and fourth swimming feet are present in a rudimentary form. In this stage, too, the anterior appendages have developed into forms more similar to those in the mature animal.

The process of development is thus accompanied by a continued increase in the number of appendages beginning at the anterior extremity, in the number of segments of the cephalothorax and abdomen, and in the complexity of the appendages, until the mature forms are reached.

Some of the parasitic forms do not pass through all these stages. There are some that never acquire the third and fourth swimming feet; in others, by a progress of regression, the first and second feet may disappear. Some parasitic forms jump the whole series of nauplius stages and almost immediately after leaving the egg appear in the first *Cyclops* stage.

Hardly any body of water is without its copepod inhabitants, although running waters have a less abundant population than lakes. Frequently standing pools swarm with the individuals of one or a few species of this order. Temporary pools in the spring, which are formed in the same place in successive years, will sometimes be almost literally filled with Copepoda, which are strictly seasonal in their life habits; for, as the pools disappear, the copepods disappear, their eggs sink in the mud of the bottom, and remain until the waters of the next season bring about favorable conditions for their generation.

The lakes produce an exceedingly abundant copepod fauna, which has an important practical interest, for the ultimate food of fish is composed almost entirely of these organisms; that is, the small fish of our most abundant species feed entirely upon Entomostraca, of which Copepoda form the greater part, and, in many cases, the mature fish also feed entirely on these same minute creatures.

Similar conditions prevail in the ocean, where Copepoda form an essential part of the plankton, which there, too, is an important element in the food, not only of fishes, but of some of the great ocean mammals. Our fresh-water Copepoda are descendants of salt-water forms, and the elucidation of the lines of descent forms a most interesting problem, towards the solution of which very little has been done.

The distribution of the Copepoda in our lakes is a matter of great interest. Certain species are characteristic of distinct regions of the lakes. For example, *Cyclops bicuspidatus*, *Diaptomus sicilis*, *Diaptomus minutus*, and *Diaptomus ashlandi* are characteristic of the limnetic regions of the Great Lakes. *Cyclops prasinus* is especially characteristic of limnetic regions, *Cyclops albidus* and *Cyclops fuscus* are more commonly littoral, while *Cyclops bicolor* and *Cyclops phaleratus* are more usually found in pools. Others, especially at certain seasons, may be found only in the deeper waters, or are "abyssal" in habitat. This is true of *Limnocalanus macrurus*, which is rarely found at the surface in the summer season, but almost entirely in the region below the thermocline. Generally speaking, the Diaptomi in lakes are characteristic of the limnetic regions, but it does not follow that all Diaptomi are limnetic; for there are many species that confine themselves strictly to the extremely shallow waters of pools, like *Diaptomus sanguineus*, which occurs widely through the temperate regions in the temporary pools of spring. It should not be inferred, however, that these distinctions between littoral, limnetic, abyssal, etc., are absolute. In many cases, species commonly littoral may adapt themselves to a limnetic habitat, or those commonly found in limnetic regions may become littoral, and flourish in those regions, thus forming part of what is sometimes known as the *tycholimnetic* or *tycholittoral* fauna. *Cyclops bicuspidatus*, for example, while ordinarily limnetic, may become a part of the littoral fauna. In other cases, species like *Diaptomus oregonensis* and *Diaptomus minutus* may seem to live equally well in deep or shallow waters. Deep lakes and shallow lakes have their characteristic copepod faunas, but this distinction does not always hold rigidly; for frequently the species show a great deal of elasticity in adapting themselves to changed conditions.

There is a marked difference in form and structure between the Copepoda living in the open water and those that are limnetic in their habit. Those that live among the weeds alongshore, or in pools, are relatively short and stout, and frequently deeply colored. A good example of this is *Cyclops ater*, which has received its name because of its dark color. It is to be presumed that *Cyclops viridis* also received its name from its color, for many of these shore forms show a distinctly green coloration. These colors, doubtless, are protective, for, because of them, the animals are almost invisible when stationary upon a background of bottom mud or of the stems of aquatic plants.

The limnetic species have long and slender bodies, *Limnocalanus macrurus* being an especially good type. Some species of *Cyclops* live either as limnetic or as littoral inhabitants; in these cases one finds the same differences in form, the littoral variety being short and stout, and the limnetic long and slender. This is especially well shown in the varieties of *Cyclops viridis* and *Cyclops serrulatus*. The figures in the systematic discussion of these species show these differences which are especially well marked in the furcal rami (Figs. 1214, 1215). The littoral species have short and stout furcal rami, whereas in the limnetic species these structures are long and slender. The limnetic species are ordinarily colorless, their transparent bodies making beautiful objects for examination under low magnifying powers; for much of the internal anatomy of the animal can be observed, while the animal is still alive: the movements of the alimentary canal can be followed, and the beatings of the heart observed. This lack of color is doubtless an adaptation to the environment, for in open waters colorless animals are much less conspicuous.

Occasionally the Copepoda are of a marked red color. This is sometimes due to oil globules, and is especially marked in some of the species appearing in the early spring, or living in the cold waters of lakes at great altitudes. In other cases, and this is markedly true of some of the Diaptomi, the integument may be deeply colored in reds, blues, and purples. *Diaptomus shoshone*, a large species found in the mountain regions of the West, is an especially good example of a highly colored copepod.

As already noted, certain species appear in temporary pools only in the spring season. In those that occur in lakes, there is sometimes a pronounced seasonal distribution. For example, in Green Lake, Wis., on which extended studies have been made, *Diaptomus sicilis* is common in the winter, but rarely found in the summer, while most forms, as would be expected from the favorable food conditions, are more abundant in the summer months.

Excepting the few winter forms, the maximum numbers of any species occur in the months from May to September or early November. Sometimes there are two maxima, one in the spring and one in the fall. Generally speaking, the maximum development occurs when the waters reach their highest temperature, but other factors may modify the time. Generally speaking, also, the maximum development in numbers is somewhat later in deep lakes than that in shallow lakes, corresponding to the general law for the development of the total plankton.

The great controlling factor in the distribution of the Copepoda is, without doubt, temperature. That *Diaptomus sicilis* should be found in Green Lake only in the winter is a matter of temperature, for it is found in the cold waters of the Great Lakes throughout the summer. *Limnocalanus macrurus*, which, in small, deep lakes, is found during the summer only below the thermocline, comes to the surface in the winter months when the surface water is colder. In Wisconsin, *Cyclops bicuspidatus* is a common limnetic species in the deeper lakes, but is rarely found in the shallower lakes except in the winter season. It is evident that it prefers the colder waters. On the other hand, *Epischura lacustris* and *Diaptomus oregonensis* are distinctly summer forms, disappearing, for the most part, in the winter months.

Partial studies have been made which have disclosed some very interesting facts in regard to the vertical distribution of Copepoda in our lakes. In general it may be said that most of these forms are confined to the upper waters, above the thermocline, some having very distinct vertical migrations, caused by changing conditions of light and temperature. It has long been known that not only are the open waters of our lakes peopled with myriads of these minute creatures, which can readily be collected by a townet dragged behind a boat, but that collections made in the night were much more successful than those in the daytime. It was at first inferred from these collections that the animals shunned the light, and sank beneath the surface during the day, to rise again at night. Careful studies of the subject, however, show that the migration of these animals is by no means so simple a matter as had been thought, and that very complex forces are at work controlling their movements. While some of them are sensitive to the influence of light, it appears that temperature is much the stronger factor, and that, generally speaking, they move up or down as the result of changes of temperature rather than because they seek or avoid the light. This, without doubt, explains the fact that *Limnocalanus* remains in the deeper waters in the summer and gradually rises higher as the waters cool off in the fall. On the other hand, *Cyclops prasinus* has a marked preference for warmer waters. During the summer it is found in the upper layers of water, but in the winter it is inclined to avoid the immediate surface and seek the deeper and warmer waters.

Epischura lacustris is a very interesting species in its vertical distribution; for it is large and a strong swimmer, and changes its location from hour to hour during the day. It likes warm water, but dislikes the light, and its vertical migrations both daily and seasonal are the resultant of these two forces, so that its movements sometimes seem quite erratic.

It is a curious fact that the Copepoda differ in the character of the habitat they like best at different times of their lives. Most of the larval forms are found close to the surface in the daytime, while the maturer animals are found at a greater or less depth.

It seems probable that the movements of the nauplii and larval Copepoda are caused by comparatively slight changes of temperature, and that a somewhat elaborate determination of the changes of temperature in the upper layers of water may explain their movements, which now seem rather strange.

Through the study of the geographical distribution one may hope to get some knowledge of the evolution of the species and genera of the Copepoda, and it is on this account that this phase of the study of any group of animals is especially interesting to the zoologist. Many of the species of the Cyclopidae are almost if not quite cosmopolitan in their distribution; for example, *Cyclops leuckarti* not only occurs all over North America, but in Europe, Asia, and Africa, and without any variations that are characteristic of the different regions. It seems very remarkable that an animal as delicately organized as *Cyclops* should not show the effect of change of location in its structure. Most of the recognized American species of *Cyclops* are identical with those found in other continents; and it is even possible that, when the genus is known more thoroughly than at present, many of the species which are now considered peculiar to our continent may be found to be either identical with foreign species or at most only variations of those forms. So our common species of *Limnocalanus*, *L. macrurus*, is identical with the European form. On the other hand, not only the species but the genera of *Osphranticum* and *Epischura* are peculiar to North America. The genera of the Harpacticidae have never been thoroughly worked over, and, while some of our species are undoubtedly European, it seems probable, from what we now know, that many of them are peculiar to this continent. *Eurytemora* is world-wide in its distribution.

Of the Diaptomi there are now recognized thirty-nine species in North America, and all of these are peculiar to this continent. Not only are they peculiar to the continent, but many are peculiar to certain regions. In a broad way, they illustrate very forcibly what has been said before,—that Copepoda are controlled in their distribution by temperature conditions. This can well be illustrated by a brief discussion of the geographical distribution of the more common species. *Diaptomus minutus* is found from Greenland and Iceland south to the northern tier of states in the United States, but does not occur south of 42° to 43° N. L. *Diaptomus sicilis* is confined to the northern tier of states. *Diaptomus siciloides* is found in a band farther to the south, being limited roughly to the region between the thirty-sixth and forty-third parallels. These three species are closely related to each other in structure, and presumably are of the same line of descent. It will be seen that their distribution, taken in a broad way, is one of latitude.

A similar relation exists between *Diaptomus oregonensis*, *Diapto-*

mus mississippiensis, and *Diaptomus pallidus*. *Diaptomus orego-nensis* is the more northern species. It is found from one side of the continent to the other, as far north as the Saskatchewan region, and as far south as Illinois and Indiana. *Diaptomus pallidus* is a Mississippi Valley species, having been found from Minnesota to Louisiana, and as far west as Colorado. *Diaptomus mississippiensis* is a strictly southern species, being confined, so far as known, to the Gulf States. It is evident that this distribution again is controlled by temperature conditions.

The group which centers around *Diaptomus albuquerquensis* is confined to the south, the most southern species being limited to the island of Cuba. The group centering about *Diaptomus signicauda* is confined to the mountain regions of the West, where a number of rather closely related species have been developed. Probably the greatest number of species is found in this mountain region of the West, where the lakes are separated from each other, and isolation has led to the development of new species. It will thus be seen that the one great controlling factor in the distribution of the Diaptomi is temperature.

It may perhaps be assumed that most of our North American species are descended from the same ancestors as those of the other continents; that as the result of the glacial period the northern forms were forced far to the south; and that, on the retreat of the ice, some followed after the ice, while others remained behind, but changed their form as the result of the changed environment. Thus the more primitive forms would be found to the north. In the south we would find specialized forms due to the various factors which have come into play in the evolution of these animals. It is a peculiar fact that in this change of conditions the Cyclopidae should have succeeded in adapting themselves without change of structure, while the Diaptomi all suffered changes. The difference in the behavior of these two families is a matter that is not at all understood, but it seems possible that the Cyclopidae have more efficient means of distribution, so that the development of new species from isolation would not be as probable as in the case of the Diaptomi. As a matter of fact, very little is known of the life histories of these animals.

Mention has been made of the fact that new species may arise because of isolation. But the question arises, how do the ancestors of any form first reach a given body of water? By what means are these animals distributed from one place to another? Certain species occur in bodies of water from one side of the continent to the other; in some cases the same forms are found even in widely separated continents. How have they reached these places? Eggs are formed which fall into the mud of the floor of the lakes and pools and retain their vitality, sometimes from one season to another, even if the bodies of water disappear and the mud becomes dry. Many species have been seen for the first time by rearing them from eggs found in dried mud. It is natural to infer from this that anything that would move the mud would also move the eggs of the animals. Dried mud, in the form of dust, may be widely disseminated, and thus the eggs might be carried to very distant places. Water birds, too, carry mud on their feet from one body of water to another, and in this way may easily transport the eggs of Copepoda and possibly the living animals. Inasmuch as these birds sometimes make long flights, it is clear that the species of Copepoda may be planted in places far apart. There is no doubt that in both these ways the distribution of the Copepoda has been effected, but these are not the principal ways. It seems evident, for many reasons, that they go from one place to another mainly by direct water carriage. For example, *Diaptomus sici-loides* has been found in only one lake in Wisconsin. If it were readily carried by birds, one would expect to find it in other bodies of water which seem to have the same kind of an environment. On the other hand, in Lake St. Clair, although it is a very shallow body of water, occur the Copepoda that are characteristic of the deeper waters of the Great Lakes. In this case there seems to be no doubt that these deep-lake forms have been carried into an environment where one would not expect to find them. It is noticeable that in connecting bodies of water we find the same forms of Copepoda. Irrigating ditches and ponds are almost entirely without Copepoda. They are peculiarly unprofitable collecting places although the environment would seem to be favorable for the propagation of these forms. For some reason, it is evident that the animals are not planted there. If the eggs of Copepoda were disseminated to any extent with the dust by winds, conditions would seem to be unusually favorable; for such ponds are found in dry regions subject to heavy winds. "Dust storms" are very common, and in them large quantities of dust are moved from one place to another. Ducks, too, frequent these ponds in enormous numbers, and are continually on the wing, moving from one place to another. It would seem, then, that in the arid and semi-arid regions conditions were as favorable as possible for these two methods of transportation. Yet the fact remains that the ponds are frequently almost entirely devoid of copepod life, and one must conclude that these methods of dissemination are of minor importance. It apparently follows from these facts that, when once a form has reached a mountain lake, it may remain in undisturbed possession for a long time, and thus, by the ordinary processes of evolution, one may expect to find in mountain regions a great variety of species. As a matter of fact, in parts of the country where water communication is easy, as in the Mississippi Valley, there prevails great uniformity in the species, while in the mountain regions of the West one finds a greater variety of species.

The ordinary means of collecting other forms of small water animals and plants will serve for the Copepoda. The Birge net is the most useful form of collecting apparatus. Inasmuch as Copepoda are extremely common in open and clean waters, the wire-netting cap of the Birge net (p. 68) can frequently be dispensed with, and the apparatus thus simplified. A conical net of fine muslin with the opening stiffened by a wire ring will serve admirably for making collections. This can be dragged behind a boat, or, if weighted, can be thrown from the shore to a distance of from thirty to forty feet, care being taken, as it is drawn in, to collect as little as possible of floating debris or of mud if it strikes the bottom near shore. The material collected in the end of the net can, by inverting the net, be washed into a wide-mouthed bottle or tumbler or tin fruit can, and then transferred to the homeopathic vials in which it is stored. An easy way to make this transfer is to pour the condensed material on little squares or circles of fine muslin, two or three inches in diameter, and then place cloth and all in the preservative fluid.

For preservative fluid either 5 per cent formol or 75 per cent alcohol can be used. Alcohol preserves the animals in a little better shape, as formol is apt to make them brittle. Dissection is best performed in a drop of glycerin on a slide. The transfer from alcohol to glycerin should be made gradually, through mixtures of alcohol and glycerin. The larger forms of Copepoda can be dissected under lenses magnifying from five to fifteen diameters; but, for the smaller individuals, powers as high as one hundred diameters must be used, and the work is very tedious. The dissected material is best mounted for examination in Farrant's solution, and the cover must be ringed with a good cement, — Brunswick black, for instance.

If one wishes to make a serious study of the animals, the structures to be separated and studied are the following: the antennae, male and female; the abdomens, male and female; the fifth feet, male and female. In addition, the general form of the cephalothorax must be noted, and, in some cases, the structure of the other appendages of the cephalothorax. The Copepoda are so widely distributed and their forms are so characteristic of biological conditions that it is very desirable that every student of water forms, even if his work is only of an amateur character, should be able to make a separation into genera, and, in most cases, make at least a provisional specific determination. Fortunately, the generic distinctions of our American forms are very easily made, and it is not difficult to recognize some of the more common species.

Especially confusing to the beginner is the large number of immature forms. Many of the larval stages of the more highly developed species resemble closely the mature forms of the simpler species, so that the tyro is apt to think that he has a large number of species, when he may have only several stages of one. It is safest for the beginner to make no attempt at identification except in the cases of evidently mature forms, such as egg-bearing females.

The Copepoda are an order of Crustacea, belonging to the subclass Entomostraca. This subclass cannot be easily defined, but it is sufficient for our purposes to say that they are the most simply organized Crustacea. The Copepoda may be defined as those Entomostraca which do not have a shell-like covering of the body (in distinction from many of the Phyllopoda), with four or five two-branched swimming feet on the thorax and an abdomen without appendages. The Copepoda are divided into two suborders, — the Eucopepoda and the Branchiura.

The Eucopepoda do not have compound eyes, and the eggs develop in one or two brood pouches or ovisacs attached to the abdomen. The Branchiura have two compound eyes. The females do not have ovisacs, but the eggs are laid on stones or other convenient hard surfaces. The body is flattened. The Eucopepoda may be considered in two divisions, — Gnathostomata, and Parasita or Siphonostomata. The Gnathostomata include the free-swimming Copepoda; they have appendages about the mouth adapted to mastication and the full number of body segments. The Siphonostomata are parasitic; they have the appendages about the mouth adapted for piercing or sucking, and generally also a reduced number of body segments. The following table shows this classification:

```
Branch: Arthropoda
    Class: Crustacea
        Subclass: Entomostraca
            Order: Copepoda.
                Suborder: (a) Eucopepoda
                    Group 1. Gnathostomata
                    Group 2. Siphonostomata
                Suborder: (b) Branchiura
```

KEY TO NORTH AMERICAN FREE-SWIMMING COPEPODA (GNATHOSTOMATA)

1 (104)   Cephalothorax and abdomen distinctly separated. 2

2 (76)   Antennae long, commonly nearly or quite as long as the whole animal, and composed of 23, 24, or 25 segments. Antennae of male asymmetrical, the right geniculate and modified as a grasping organ. The fifth feet are unlike in the two sexes, and in the male the right and left fifth feet are dissimilar.
Family CENTROPAGIDAE . . 3

3 (8, 73)   Endopodites of first swimming feet composed of one segment. . 4

4 (7)   Endopodites of second, third, and fourth swimming feet composed of one segment. Each furcal ramus armed with three large setae. Abdomen of male asymmetrical, and armed on right side with a peculiar grasping arrangement.
Epischura . . 5

5 (6)   Abdomen of female not distinctly flexed to the right.   Terminal
             setae of furcae equal.

                                          Epischura nevadensis Lilljeborg 1889.

                              Found in the mountain lakes of the western United States.
                              Length of female, 2 mm.
                              Length of male, 1.7 mm.

                   FIG. 1174. Abdomen of male *Epischura nevadensis.* × 24.   (Original.)

6 (5)   Abdomen of female distinctly flexed to the right, the external
             furcal setae much larger than the others.

                                          Epischura lacustris Forbes 1882.

                              Common in the Great Lakes and other large bodies of water in
                              the central and eastern United States.
                              Length of female, 1.78 mm.
                              Length of male, 1.38 mm.

                   FIG. 1175. Abdomen of male *Epischura lacustris.* × 49.   (Original.)

7 (4)   Endopodites of second, third, and fourth feet composed of two
             segments.   Furcal rami elongated.

                                          Eurytemora affinis Poppe 1880.

     Really a salt-water form, and commonly found in fresh water only when it is more or less
closely connected with the sea.   Only one species is known in America in fresh waters and that
has been found in waters connected with the Gulf of Mexico and the Atlantic Ocean.
                              Length of female, 1.5 mm.
                              Length of male, 1.5 mm.

8 (3, 73)   Endopodites of first swimming feet composed of two segments, of
             third and fourth swimming feet composed of three segments.
             Furcal rami short.   Right fifth foot of male terminates in
             a more or less sickle-shaped hook. . . . *Diaptomus.* . 9

9 (22)   Antepenultimate segment of the male right antenna without dis-
             tinct appendage. 10

10 (11)   Right and left fifth feet of male nearly equal in length, terminal
             hook of right foot symmetrical.
                              Diaptomus oregonensis Lilljeborg 1889.

The most widely distributed of all North American species, and the one most likely to be collected in the northern part of the United States. It is found from one side of the continent to the other. The most noticeable characteristic is the equal length of the fifth feet of the male.
Length of female, 1.5 mm.
Length of male, 1.4 mm.

A

B

FIG. 1176. *Diaptomus oregonensis. A*, fifth feet of male. X 193. *B*, fifth foot of female. X 200. (Original.)

11 (10)   Left fifth foot of male shorter than right. 12
12 (15)   Left fifth foot reaching beyond first segment of right exopodite. . 13
13 (14)   Terminal hook of right exopodite uniangular, right endopodite
             equal in length to first segment of exopodite.
                              Diaptomus reighardi Marsh 1895.

This has been found in only four localities, — Intermediate Lake and Crooked Lake in northern Michigan, a lake on Beaver Island in Lake Michigan, and Sodus Bay, N. Y.
Length of female, 1.14 mm.
Length of male, 1.02 mm.

FIG. 1177.   Fifth feet of male *Diaptomus reighardi*. X 145.   (Original.)

14 (13)   Terminal hook biangular, right endopodite large, longer than first
             segment of exopodite.
                              Diaptomus mississippiensis Marsh 1894.

The most common form of the Southern States; it is abundant all through the states bordering on the Gulf.
Length of female, 1.2 mm.
Length of male, 1.1 mm.

FIG. 1178.   Fifth feet of male *Diaptomus mississippiensis*. X 145.
(Original.)

15 (12)   Left fifth foot of male, reaching end of first segment of right expodite, or only slightly exceeding it. 16

16 (17)   Antepenultimate segment of right antenna of male produced at distal end into a blunt point, first segment of right expodite of fifth foot with marked quadrangular hyaline appendage. . . . . *Diaptomus birgei* Marsh 1894.

FIG. 1179.   *Diaptomus birgei*, male.   *A*, terminal segment of right antenna.   × 191.
          B, fifth feet.   × 109.   (Original.)

Common in Indiana and has been found in Wisconsin and on Long Island.
Length of female, 1.3 mm.   Length of male, 1.2 mm.

17 (16)   Antepenultimate segment of right antenna of male not produced into blunt point on distal end. 18

18 (19)   Inner process of the terminal segment of exopodite of left male fifth foot falciform, no hyaline appendage of first segment of right exopodite. . . . . *Diaptomus pallidus* Herrick 1879.

Occurs in Mississippi Valley, as far west as the foothills of the Rocky Mountains, but is comparatively rare north of Iowa and Illinois.
          Length of female, 1.2 mm.
          Length of male, 1.04 mm.

FIG. 1180.   Fifth feet of male *Diaptomus pallidus*.   × 190.   (Original.)

19 (18)   Inner process of terminal segment of left exopodite of male fifth
           foot digitiform, hyaline appendage on internal distal angle
           of first segment of right exopodite.   20

20 (21)   Lateral spine of second segment of right exopodite nearly straight,
           no blunt spine on posterior surface of this segment.
                                        Diaptomus tyrelli Poppe 1888.

Widely spread in the mountain lakes of the West.
Length of female, 1.2 mm.
Length of male, 1.15 mm.

FIG. 1181.   Fifth feet of male *Diaptomus tyrelli.* × 190.
(Original.)

21 (20)   A second hyaline appendage on dorsal side of distal margin of first
           segment of right exopodite, lateral spine of second segment
           of right exopodite strongly curved, and a blunt spine on
           posterior surface of this segment.
                                   Diaptomus coloradensis Marsh 1911.

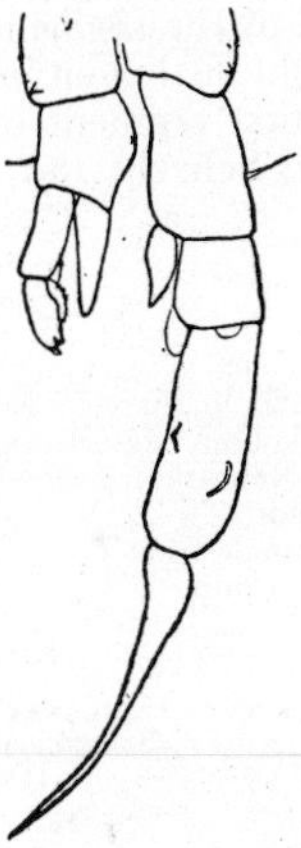

In the Rocky Mountains in Colorado *D. tyrelli* is replaced by this closely
allied species which is, apparently, the characteristic species of the mountain lakes of Colorado.
Length of female, 1.38 mm.
Length of male, 1.32 mm.

FIG. 1182.   Fifth feet of male *Diaptomus coloradensis.* × 120.   (Original.)

22 (9)   Antepenultimate segment of male right antenna with lateral lamella
           or terminal process.   23

23 (26, 42) Antepenultimate segment of right antenna of male with hyaline
           lamella.   24

24 (25)   Hyaline lamella broad, extending beyond the end of the segment,
second basal segment of right exopodite of male fifth foot
armed on the posterior surface with small hook.

Diaptomus leptopus Forbes 1882.

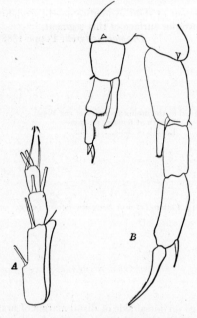

Found generally distributed through the
Mississippi Valley, and extending into Canada.
The variety piscinae occurs in some of the
more northern collections and as far west as
Flathead Lake, Montana. This differs from
typical leptopus mainly in the greater length
of the endopodites of the male fifth feet and
in the fact that in the female fifth feet the
third segment of the exopodite is indistinctly
separated and armed with two spines with a
third one present on the second segment.
This third spine is absent in leptopus.
Length of female, 1.5 to 1.89 mm.
Length of male, 1.4 to 1.83 mm.

FIG. 1183. Diaptomus leptopus, male. A, terminal segments of right antenna. × 185. B,
fifth feet. × 83. (Original.)

25 (24)   Hyaline lamella narrow, extending beyond the end of the segment
slightly, if at all; first basal segment of right fifth foot of
male armed with hook equal in length to first segment of
exopodite. . . . . . .   Diaptomus clavipes Schacht 1897.

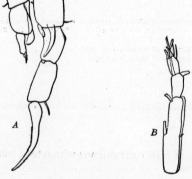

Has been found in three localities, in West Okoboji Lake, Iowa,
near Lincoln, Nebraska, and at
Greeley, Colorado.
Length of female from 1.37
to 2.5 mm.

FIG. 1184. Diaptomus clavipes, male.
A, fifth feet. × 83. B, terminal
segments of right antenna. × 141.
(Original.)

26 (23, 42) Antepenultimate segment of right antenna of male bears a slender
straight process.   **27**

27 (32, 35) Process much shorter than penultimate segment. 28
28 (31)   Right endopodite of male fifth foot rudimentary. 29
29 (30)   Lateral spine of second segment of right exopodite of male fifth
          foot terminal. . . . . . . *Diaptomus lintoni* Forbes 1893.

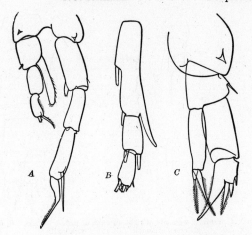

Found in Yellowstone Park and in the valley of the Gallatin River, Montana.

Fig. 1185. *Diaptomus lintoni.* A, fifth feet of male. × 110. B, terminal segments of right antenna of male. × 220. C, fifth foot of female. × 258. (Original.)

30 (29)   Lateral spine of second segment of right exopodite of male fifth foot
          near the proximal end. . *Diaptomus trybomi* Lilljeborg 1889.

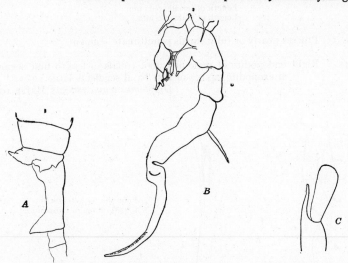

Fig. 1186. *Diaptomus trybomi.* A, abdomen of female. × 70. B, fifth feet of male. × 120. C, terminal segments of right antenna of male. × 100. (After De Guerne and Richard.)

The antennal process is dentate on the outer margin and the abdomen of the female asymmetrical. Has been found only in Oregon.

Length of female, 1.5 mm.
Length of male, 1.4 mm.

31 (28)   Right endopodite of male fifth foot about equal in length to first segment of exopodite. . . *Diaptomus judayi* Marsh 1907.

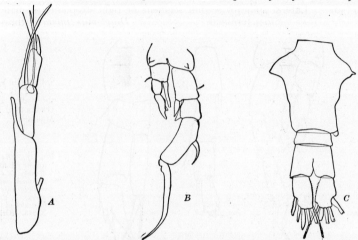

FIG. 1187. *Diaptomus judayi.* *A*, terminal segments of right antenna of male. ✕ 290. *B*, fifth feet of male. ✕ 145. *C*, abdomen of female. ✕ 165. (Original.)

Lateral spine of the second segment of the right exopodite is median, first segment of the female abdomen has a process on the posterior margin on the right side. Has been found only in the mountains of Colorado.

Length of female, 0.93 mm.
Length of male, 0.9 mm.

32 (27. 35) Process nearly or fully equals penultimate segment. 33

33 (34)   Right endopodite of male fifth foot equals in length first segment of exopodite, spines of first basal segments large.

Diaptomus tenuicaudatus Marsh 1907.

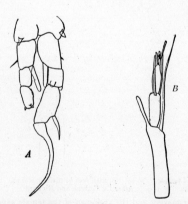

Found in Saskatchewan.
Length of male, 1.195 mm.

FIG. 1188. *Diaptomus tenuicaudatus*, male. *A*, fifth feet. ✕ 145. *B*, terminal segments of right antenna. ✕ 194. (Original.)

34 (33)   Right endopodite of male fifth foot exceeds length of first segment
of exopodite, spines of first basal segments small.

Diaptomus sicilis Forbes 1882.

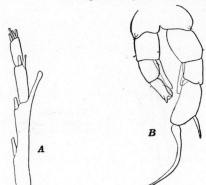

Found in the Great Lakes, being
the most abundant form taken in
limnetic collections; found to some
extent in other lakes in the same
general region. It is, as a rule,
confined to the larger and deeper
lakes. It is frequently found associated with *D. minutus* but is readily distinguished by the slender,
symmetrical, sickle-shaped hook
terminating the exopodite of the
right fifth foot of the male; this is
not a characteristic, however, that
will distinguish it from species
found in other localities.

Length of female, 1.25 mm.
Length of male, 1.15 mm.

FIG. 1189. *Diaptomus sicilis,* male. *A,* terminal segments of
right antenna. × 194. *B,* fifth feet. × 194. (Original.)

35 (27, 32) Process exceeds in length penultimate segment. 36

36 (39)   Large. Lateral spine of second segment of exopodite of right fifth
foot of male terminal or nearly so. 37

37 (38)   Process of antepenultimate segment of right antenna of male only
slightly longer than penultimate segment, antennae equal in
length to cephalothorax.

Diaptomus shoshone Forbes 1893.

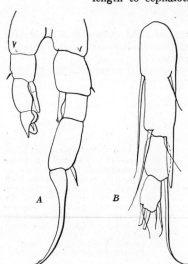

Rocky Mountains. Not so widespread
or characteristic of the mountain lakes as
D. Tyrelli Poppe, although this giant species is by no means uncommon, and is especially striking because commonly colored a
bright red.

Length of female, 2.9 mm.
Length of male, 2.5 mm.

FIG. 1190. *Diaptomus shoshone,* male. *A,* fifth feet.
× 108. *B,* terminal segments of right antenna.
× 180. (Original.)

38 (37)   Antennal process of male exceeds ultimate segment, antennae
reach furca. . . . . *Diaptomus wardi* Pearse 1905.

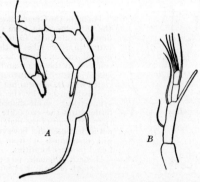

Washington.
Length of female, 2.9 mm.
Length of male, 1.6 mm.

FIG. 1191. *Diaptomus wardi*, male. *A*, fifth feet.
×173. *B*, terminal segments of right antenna.
×112. (After Pearse.)

39 (36)   Small. Lateral spine of second segment of right exopodite of
male on proximal half of segment, antennae reach beyond
furca. . . . . , 40

40 (41)   Lateral spine of second segment of right exopodite of male fifth
foot short, right endopodite rudimentary, endopodites of
female fifth feet rudimentary.
Diaptomus minutus Lilljeborg 1889.

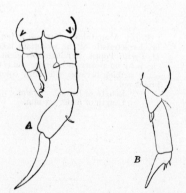

Northern United States and north
to Greenland and Iceland. It is one
of the most easily recognized species
because of the broad, saber-like hook
on the right fifth foot of the male and
the rudimentary endopodites of the
fifth feet of both sexes. It is common
in the waters of the Great Lakes, but
that is as far south as one may expect
to find it.
Length of female, 1 to 1.1 mm.
Length of male, 1 mm.

FIG. 1192. *Diaptomus minutus. A*, fifth foot
of male. ×154. *B*, fifth feet of female.
×200. (Original.)

41 (40)   Lateral spine of second segment of right exopodite of male fifth
foot long, right endopodite equals in length first segment
of exopodite. . . . . . *Diaptomus ashlandi* Marsh 1893.

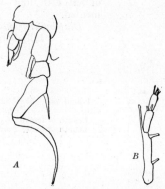

Found in the Great Lakes and some
lakes immediately connected with them
and west to the State of Washington.
Length of female, 0.97 mm.
Length of male, 0.89 mm.

FIG. 1193.   *Diaptomus ashlandi*, male.   *A*, fifth
feet. ✕ 145.   *B*, terminal segments of right
antenna.   ✕ 145.   (Original.)

42 (23, 26) Antepenultimate segment of right antenna of male bears curved
process. 43

43 (46)   Process equals or exceeds in length penultimate segment. . . 44

44 (45)   Process about equals in length last two segments, second basal
segment of right fifth foot of male dilated on inner margin,
endopodites of fifth feet in both sexes indistinctly two-
segmented. . . . . . *Diaptomus eiseni* Lilljeborg 1889.

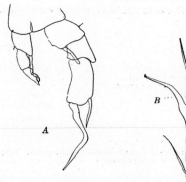

Has been found only in California
and Nebraska.
Length of female, 4 mm.
Length of male, 3.5 mm.

FIG. 1194.   *Diabtomus eiseni*, male.   *A*, fifth feet.
✕ 38.   *B*, terminal segments of right antenna.
✕ 133.   (Original.)

45 (44) Process slightly exceeds in length penultimate segment, second basal segment of right fifth foot of male not dilated on inner margin, endopodite of left fifth foot one-segmented.

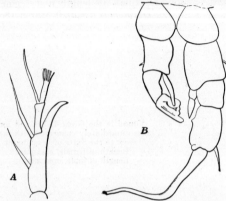

Diaptomus franciscanus Lilljeborg 1889.

B

Found only near San Francisco.
Length of female, 2.3 mm.
Length of male, 2 mm.

A

FIG. 1195. *Diaptomus franciscanus*, male. *A*, terminal segments of right antenna. X 200. *B*, fifth feet. X 200. (After De Guerne and Richard.)

46 (43) Process shorter than penultimate segment. 47

47 (66) One or both terminal processes of last segment of left exopodite of male fifth foot distinctly falciform. 48

48 (56, 63) Right endopodite of fifth foot of male small, shorter than first segment of exopodite. 49

49 (53) Terminal segment of right exopodite of fifth foot of male elongate. 50

50 (51, 52) In fifth foot of male right endopodite rudimentary, left endopodite two-segmented and spatulate in form.

Diaptomus spatulocrenatus Pearse 1906.

Found in New England.
Length of female, 1.52 mm.
Length of male, 1.31.

FIG. 1196. Fifth feet of male *Diaptomus spatulocrenatus*. X 84. (After Pearse.)

51 (50, 52) Terminal segment of right exopodite of fifth foot of male much broader at distal end, lateral spine nearly terminal and straight, left endopodite elongate.

Diaptomus conipedatus Marsh 1907.

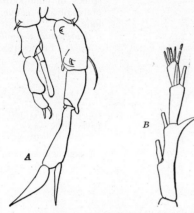

Found in Louisiana.
Length of female, 1.49 mm.
Length of male, 1.325 mm.

FIG. 1197. *Diaptomus conipedatus*, male. *A*, fifth feet. × 126. *B*, terminal segments of right antenna. × 193. (Original.)

52 (50, 51) Terminal hook of right exopodite of fifth foot of male falciform, lateral spine at distal third of segment, second basal segment of right foot broad at distal end with process at external distal angle.

Diaptomus sanguineus Forbes 1876.

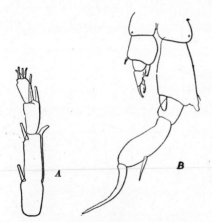

Mississippi Valley. Occurs in spring, in stagnant pools.
Length of female, 1.4 to 2.12 mm.
Length of male, 1 to 2 mm.

FIG. 1198. *Diaptomus sanguineus*. *A*, terminal segments of right antenna of male. × 193. *B*, fifth feet of same. × 110. (Original.)

53 (49)   Terminal segment of right exopodite of male fifth feet of usual
length, lateral spine terminal. 54

54 (55)   Inner surface of left endopodite of male fifth foot rugose, terminal
spines of endopodites
of female fifth feet very
long.
Diaptomus stagnalis
Forbes 1882.

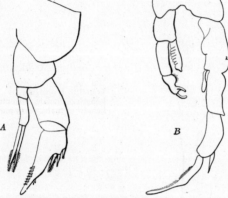

A very large species
found in the Mississippi
Valley in the spring.
Length of female, 4 to
4.5 mm.
Length of male, 3.5 to
4 mm.

FIG. 1199. *Diaptomus stagnalis.* A, fifth foot of female. (After Forbes.)
B, fifth feet of male.   (After Herrick and Turner.)

55 (54)   In male, segments of right fifth foot short and broad, terminal hook
long and strongly curved, lateral spine long and straight;
in female, dorsal process on fifth cephalothoracic segment,
endopodites of fifth feet short and one-segmented.
Diaptomus saltillinus Brewer 1898.

Found in Nebraska.   Length of female, 1.5 mm.   Length of male, 1.25 mm.

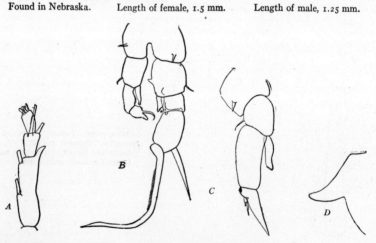

FIG. 1200. *Diaptomus saltillinus.* A, terminal segments of right antenna of male. × 193. B, fifth
feet of same.   × 126. C, fifth foot of female. × 193. D, dorsal process of same. × 193.
(Original.)

56 (48, 63) Right endopodite of fifth foot of male distinctly longer than first
segment of exopodite. 57

57 (60)   Second segment of right exopodite of male fifth foot has oblique
ridge on posterior surface. 58

58 (59)   First segment of right exopodite of male fifth foot has transverse
ridge on the posterior surface.
                                    Diaptomus asymmetricus Marsh 1907.

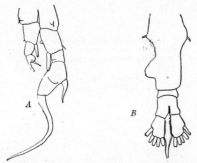

In the male fifth foot the lateral
spine of the terminal segment is
about one-half as long as the segment; the first segment of the female
abdomen has a prominent swelling on
the right side.   Found in Cuba.
  Length of female, 1.39 mm.
  Length of male, 1.16 mm.

FIG. 1201. *Diaptomus asymmetricus.* A, fifth feet of
male.   × 103.   B, abdomen of female.   × 79.
(Original.)

59 (58)   First segment of right exopodite of male fifth foot has two curved
processes on posterior surface.
                                    Diaptomus dorsalis Marsh 1907.

In the male fifth foot the lateral
spine of the terminal segment equals
or exceeds in length the segment; the
fifth cephalothoracic segment of the
female is armed with two dorsal
processes.   Found in Louisiana and
Florida and probably in other states
bordering on the Gulf of Mexico.
  Length of female, 1.13 mm.
  Length of male, 1.069 mm.

FIG. 1202. *Diaptomus dorsalis.* A, fifth feet of male.   × 145.
B, profile dorsal surface of cephalothorax of female.   × 38.
(Original.)

60 (57)   Second segment of right exopodite of fifth foot of male does not
             have oblique ridge on posterior surface. 61

61 (62)   Lateral spine of terminal segment of right exopodite of male fifth
             foot terminal, endopodites distinctly two-segmented.
                                        Diaptomus bakeri Marsh 1907.

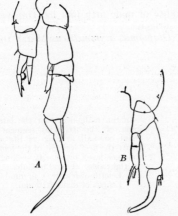

In the female fifth foot the exopodites are
distinctly three-segmented, the endopodites
distinctly two-segmented. Found in California.
      Length of female, 1.27 mm.
      Length of male, 1.124 mm.

FIG. 1203. *Diaptomus bakeri.* *A*, fifth feet of male.
× 110. *B*, fifth foot of female. × 193. (Original.)

62 (61)   Lateral spine of terminal segment of right exopodite of male fifth
             foot situated on distal third of segment, right endopodite
             indistinctly two-segmented, left one-segmented.
                                 Diaptomus washingtonensis Marsh 1907.

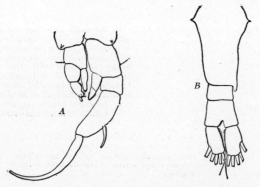

The first abdominal
segment of the female
has a digitiform process
on the right posterior
border.   Found in
Washington.
      Length of female,
         1.187 mm.
      Length of male,
         1.137 mm.

FIG. 1204. *Diaptomus washingtonensis.* *A*, fifth feet of male. × 126.
       B, abdomen of female. × 110. (Original.)

63 (48, 56) **Right** endopodite of fifth foot of male equals or only slightly exceeds first segment of exopodite. 64

64 (65) Terminal segment of right exopodite of male fifth foot has oblique ridge on posterior surface, lateral spine exceeds segment in length. . . . . . *Diaptomus albuquerquensis* Herrick 1895.

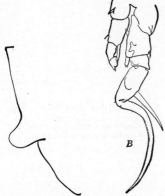

B

The fifth cephalothoracic segment of the female has a dorsal process, and the endopodites of the fifth feet are commonly two-segmented. Found in New Mexico and Colorado. As the name indicates, this form was originally described by Herrick, from material collected in Albuquerque, N. M. It is found, however, from Colorado to the City of Mexico, and seems to be a typical form of the Southwest.

Length of female, 1.76 mm.
Length of male, 1.58 mm.

FIG. 1205. *Diaptomus albuquerquensis.* *A*, dorsal process of female. × 180. *B*, fifth feet of male. × 49. (Original.)

65 (64) Terminal segment of right exopodite of male fifth foot does not have oblique ridge on posterior surface; lateral spine short, about one-half length of segment. ·
Diaptomus novamexicanus Herrick 1895.

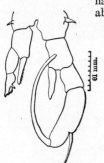

Found in New Mexico.
Length of female, 1.1 to 1.2 mm.

FIG. 1206. Fifth feet of male *Diaptomus novamexicanus.* (After Herrick and Turner.)

66 (47) Terminal processes of left exopodite of fifth feet of male digiti form, right endopodite shorter than first segment of exopodite. 67

67 (70) First segment of exopodite of male fifth foot without hyaline appendage. 68

68 (69) Right endopodite of male fifth foot triangular in form, first abdominal segment of female has digitiform process on right posterior border. . . . . . *Diaptomus nudus* Marsh 1904.

Found in lakes near Pike's Peak, Colorado.
Length of female, 1.132 mm.
Length of male, 1.115 mm.

A   *B*

FIG. 1207. *Diaptomus nudus.* *A*, fifth feet of male. × 105. *B*, abdomen of female. × 105. (Original.)

69 (68) In male fifth foot, second basal segment with hyaline appendage on inner margin, first segment of right exopodite with transverse ridge, second segment with oblique ridge and hyaline process near the outer margin.
Diaptomus purpureus Marsh 1907.

Found in Cuba. This is a conspicuous species, both on account of the large size and the purple color of the furcae, furcal setae, and distal ends of the antennae.
Length of female, 2.56 mm.
Length of male, 2.24 mm.

FIG. 1208. Fifth feet of male *Diaptomus purpureus.* × 76. (Original.)

70 (67)   First segment of right exopodite of male fifth foot has hyaline
           appendage. 71

71 (72)   Hyaline appendage of first segment of exopodite of male fifth foot
           at inner distal angle, endopodite of right foot about equals
           first segment of exopodite.
                                    Diaptomus signicauda Lilljeborg 1889.

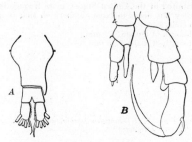

FIG. 1209. *Diaptomus signicauda.* *A*, abdomen
of female. × 118. *B*, fifth feet of male.
× 174. (Original.)

The first segment of the abdomen of
the female has a digitiform process on
the right posterior border. Found in
mountain regions of western United
States. It represents a group of species
that are found in the mountain regions
of the western part of the United States.
The peculiar appendage of the first segment of the female abdomen has given
the name to the species, and is characteristic of the group. Collections in the
Rocky Mountains and farther west are
likely to contain this or allied species.
Length of female, 0.93 mm.
Length of male, 0.9 mm.

72 (71)   Hyaline appendage of first segment of exopodite of male fifth foot
           on inner distal half, endopodite of right fifth foot much
           shorter than first segment of exopodite.
                                    Diaptomus siciloides Lilljeborg 1889.

FIG. 1210.   Fifth feet
of male *Diaptomus
siciloides.*   × 122.
(Original.)

Found in the Mississippi Valley and west to California. As *D. oregonensis* is typical of the Northern States, so *D. siciloides* may be considered
as typical of a region a little farther to the south. It has been found from
Long Island on the east to the Rocky Mountains on the west, and, while
not the exclusive form, is more apt to be seen than any other, especially
along the Ohio River.
Length of female, 1.06 to 1.225 mm.
Length of male, 1.01 to 1.1125 mm.

73 (3, 8)   Endopodites of first swimming feet composed of three segments.   74

74 (75)   Endopodites of all swimming feet composed of three segments,
           antennae of 23 segments (according to Herrick 24), furca
           short.   Only one species.
                              Osphranticum labronectum Forbes 1882.

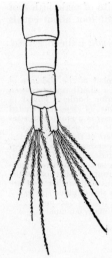

Found widely distributed in the United States, more frequently
in the Mississippi Valley but never in large numbers, so that it is
comparatively rare in collections.
                    Length of female, 1.7 mm.
                    Length of male, 1.36 mm.

Fig. 1211.   Abdomen of female *Osphranticum labronectum.*   × 51.
                              (Original.)

75 (74)   Endopodites of all swimming feet composed of three segments,
           antennae of 25 segments, furca long.
                              Limnocalanus macrurus Sars 1862.

Found only in deep lakes.   It is especially interesting, as it is the only
species of the Centropagidae found in both Europe and America.   It is
widely distributed in northern Europe and Asia and is found in salt water
as well as in fresh.   It is considered a representative of the "fauna relicta," that is, it is a salt water form which has become adapted to the
environment of fresh water.
                    Length of female, 2.4 mm.
                    Length of male, 2.2 mm.

Fig. 1212.   Abdomen of female *Limnocalanus macrurus.*   × 37.   (Original.)

76 (2)   Antennae short, never longer than cephalothorax, generally much
           shorter, and composed of from six to seventeen segments;
           antennae of male symmetrically geniculate; fifth feet rudi-
           mentary, composed of from one to three segments.
                              Family CYCLOPIDAE.
           Only one genus. . . . . *Cyclops* . . 77

The main points to be noted in the specific determination of the genus are:
length and number of segments in the antenna of the female;
armature of the antennal segments, especially of the terminal segments;
form of the abdomen, especially the form and armature of the furcal rami;
form and armature of the rudimentary fifth feet;
structure of the second antennae, of the maxillipedes, and of the swimming feet.
These last structures are of less importance.

77 (98)   Antennae composed of twelve or more segments. 78

78 (92, 93) Antennae composed of seventeen segments. 79

79 (80)   Fifth feet composed of one segment armed with one spine and
           two long setae. . . . . *Cyclops ater* Herrick 1882.

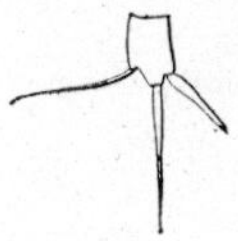

It is a large dark-colored species, rather rare, probably distributed very
widely, and growing in shallow water. In spite of its wide distribution,
however, it is a rare form.
Length of female, 1.77 to 2.88 mm.

FIG. 1213. Fifth foot of *Cyclops ater*. × 296. (Original.)

80 (79)   Fifth feet composed of two segments. 81

81 (84, 89) Second segment of fifth feet armed with seta and short spine.   82

82 (83)   Spine of second segment of fifth feet small and near end of seg-
           ment; last three segments of female antenna without hya-
           line membrane. . . . . *Cyclops viridis* Jurine 1820.

FIG. 1214. Abdomen of fe-
male *Cyclops viridis*, var.
americanus. × 77. (Original.)

FIG. 1215. Abdomen of
female *Cyclops viridis*,
var. *brevispinosus*. ×
66. (Original.)

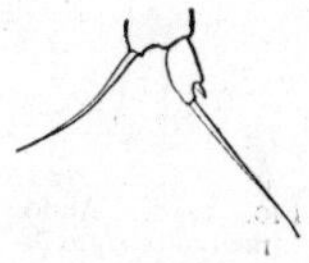

FIG. 1216. Fifth foot of
Cyclops viridis. × 218.
(Original.)

A widely distributed species, being found both in pools and lakes. It varies greatly in its
form and general appearance, so that it has received a number of different specific names,
which are now reduced to varieties, since it has been found that there are intermediate forms
showing all the stages between the extremes. When living in pools it is apt to be deeply
colored, while its relatives living in the open waters of our lakes are colorless and almost transparent. Especially noticeable is the difference in the form of the furcal rami, as shown in
Figs. 1214 and 1215. The forms found in pools generally have comparatively short and stout
furcal rami; on the other hand, the forms in deep waters have long and slender furcal rami.
Even in the limnetic forms there is wide variation. In typical *viridis* there is a short seta on
the outer angle of the furcal ramus. This is replaced in the form which Herrick called *brevispinosus* by a short broad spine. This variety is a common limnetic form in some classes of
lakes; a form with the furca armed at its outer angle with a seta like typical *viridis*, but differing
from *viridis* in the structure of the swimming feet and of the fifth feet, called *americanus*, is
common in shallow waters, and is the variety that is most frequently seen in the waters of the
United States. Wherever a collection is made one is likely to get some form of *viridis*, and
generally it will be *americanus*.
Length of female, 1.25 to 1.5 mm.

83 (82)   Spine of second segment of fifth foot stout, located at about middle
           of segment; last three segments of female antenna with
           delicate pectinate hyaline membrane.

                                        Cyclops strenuus Fischer 1851.

It is one of the most common forms on the continent of Europe, but has
been found in America in only one locality, — a pond in the Adirondacks. It
is probable, of course, that it will be found in other localities, but it is a curious fact that hitherto it has been found only in a single collection. In its
general form it closely resembles *viridis*.

                     Length of female, 1.35 mm.

FIG. 1217. Fifth foot of *Cyclops strenuus*. × 358. (Original.)

84 (81, 89) Second segment of fifth feet armed with two setae.   85

85 (86)   Second segment of fifth feet elongate, inner setae spine-like, much
             shorter than outer. . . .   *Cyclops bicuspidatus* Claus 1857.

FIG. 1218. Abdo-   FIG. 1219.   Abdo-   FIG. 1220. Fifth foot
men of *Cyclops bi-*   men of *Cyclops bi-*   of *Cyclops bicuspi-*
cuspidatus. × 76.   *cuspidatus*, var.   *datus*.   × 227.
(Original.)   *navus*.   × 62.   (Original.)
                        (Original.)

The furca of this species is very characteristic. It not only has a lateral seta at a little more
than one-half its length, but it has a little depression armed with minute spines on its outer
margin at a little less than one-fourth of its length. These characteristics — the position of the
lateral seta, the lateral depression with the elongated furca — are presumptive evidence that a
species with seventeen segmented antennae is *bicuspidatus*. If, in addition, one can make out
the two terminal setae on the second segment of the fifth feet, he can be pretty certain of his
identification. *Cyclops bicuspidatus* is most commonly a limnetic species, and is the *Cyclops*
which may be considered as characteristic of the Great Lakes. While the form described and
figured is the common one, this species has varieties similar to those noted for *viridis*, and we
sometimes find in pools a form agreeing in general structure with the typical forms, but with a
short furca. This modification was named *navus* by Herrick, and the name can be well retained
as a varietal distinction. *Navus*, however, is not so common in pools as the corresponding
variety of *viridis*. Fig. 1218 shows the typical form of furca in *bicuspidatus*, and Fig. 1219 the
form in the variety *navus*.

                     Length of female, 1.1 mm.

86 (85)   Second segment of fifth feet short, armed with two nearly equal
           setae.   87

87 (88) Setae of fifth feet very elongate, last antennal segment armed with serrate hyaline plate; common.

Cyclops leuckarti Claus 1857.

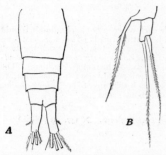

This species is easily recognized from the form of the furcae. No other species with seventeen segmented antennae has this characteristic form of short rami, with the lateral setae placed at about midway of its length. If one can make out the structure of the fifth feet (Fig. 1221), he can be quite sure of the identification; for no other American species has this form, with the exception of *tenuis*, and, so far, *tenuis* has been found in only one locality. This species, as has been noted in another place, is peculiarly interesting; for it is almost world-wide in its distribution, having been found in all continents. Moreover, the little variations which are found in details of structure are also world-wide, so that change of location seems to have no effect on the species.

Length of female, 1.14 mm.

A

B

FIG. 1221. *Cyclops leuckarti.* *A*, abdomen of female. × 69. *B*, fifth foot of same. × 232. (Original.)

88 (87) Setae of fifth feet of moderate length, last antennal segment without hyaline plate. . . . . . . *Cyclops tenuis* Marsh 1910.

It has been found in Arizona and in the Isthmus of Panama.
Length of female, 1.1 mm.

FIG. 1222. Fifth foot of *Cyclops tenuis.* × 272. (Original.)

89 (81, 84) Second segment of fifth feet armed with three setae. 90

90 (91) With sensory club on twelfth antennal segment, hyaline plate of seventeenth antennal segment smooth or serrate, egg sacs standing out from abdomen. . *Cyclops albidus* Jurine 1820.

A

B

C

FIG. 1223. *Cyclops albidus.* *A*, abdomen of female. × 66. *B*, fourth foot of same. × 147. *C*, fifth foot of same. × 227. (Original.)

91 (90)   With sensory hair on twelfth antennal segment, hyaline plate of seventeenth antennal segment deeply notched, egg sacs lying close to abdomen. . . .   *Cyclops fuscus* Jurine 1820.

Cyclops fuscus and *C. albidus* resemble each other very closely, and it is only by a careful examination that they can be distinguished.   They are very common, especially in pond collections, *Cyclops albidus* being found much the more frequently.   They are much larger than *C. leuckarti* and the furcal armature differs in that the lateral seta is placed near the end of the ramus (Fig. 1223).   The form of the fifth feet and of the furcal rami will readily serve to show when we have one of these two species, and in most cases it will prove to be *Cyclops albidus*. Length of female, about 2 mm.

FIG. 1224.   Antennal segments of female *Cyclops fuscus*.   ✕ 137.   (Original.)

92 (78, 93) Antennae composed of sixteen segments, fifth feet of three segments. . . . .   *Cyclops modestus* Herrick 1883.

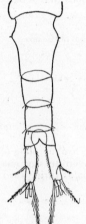

This species is comparatively rare altho it has been found in a considerable number of places.   It occurs as far east as Pennsylvania, as far west as Wyoming, while its northern and southern limits are Wisconsin and Alabama.
Length of female, 1.2 to 1.25 mm.

A

B

FIG. 1225.   *Cyclops modestus*.   *A*, abdomen of female.   ✕ 179.   *B*, fifth foot.   ✕ 448.   (Original.)

93 (78, 92) Antennae composed of twelve segments, fifth feet of one segment.
94

94 (97)   Fifth feet armed with three setae, swimming feet composed of three segments. 95

95 (96) Furcae of variable length, armed externally with a row of fine spines; very common. . . *Cyclops serrulatus* Fischer 1851.

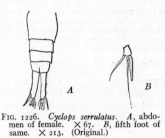

FIG. 1226. *Cyclops serrulatus.* *A*, abdomen of female. ✕ 67. *B*, fifth foot of same. ✕ 213. (Original.)

The long twelve-segmented antennae and the serrate margined furcal rami serve to distinguish this species. The figure of the abdomen shows the characteristic structure of the furcal rami. There is a good deal of variation in the form of the furca. When *serrulatus* is limnetic in habitat, the furcal rami are long and slender; this form is known as variety *elegans* Herrick. When it lives in pools or littoral waters, the furcal rami are short and stout; this form is known as variety *montanus* Brady. The abdomen figured may be considered as typical of *serrulatus, elegans* being much longer, and *montanus* correspondingly shorter. Found everywhere the world over. Length of female, 0.8 to 1.25 mm.

96 (95) Furcae short, without lateral row of spines.
Cyclops prasinus Fischer 1860.

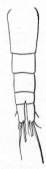

It is a minute limnetic form. It resembles *serrulatus* in its long twelve-segmented antennae, but its abdomen is very different. The furcal rami resemble *leuckarti* in the fact that the lateral seta is placed at about midway of the length, but the species is distinguished at a glance, not only by its smaller size, but by the fact that the antennae are composed of twelve segments. *Cyclops prasinus* is widely distributed, especially in the larger bodies of water. It is common in the Great Lakes. Length of female, 0.48 mm.

FIG. 1227. Abdomen of female *Cyclops prasinus.* ✕ 137. (Original.)

97 (94) Fifth feet armed with one seta, swimming feet of two segments.
Cyclops varicans Sars 1862.

Cyclops varicans occurs in Panama and Guatemala, but there are no authentic records of its occurrence in the United States.

98 (77) Antennae composed of eleven segments or less. 99

99 (102, 103) Antennae composed of eleven segments. 100

100 (101 Rami of swimming feet composed of three segments.
Cyclops phaleratus Koch 1838.

This stout, dark-colored species is not uncommon in shallow lakes and stagnant pools, and is readily recognized by the characters given in the key. Length of female, 1.2 mm.

FIG. 1228. Abdomen of female *Cyclops phaleratus.* ✕ 69. (Original.)

101 (100)   Rami of swimming feet composed of two segments.

Cyclops bicolor Sars 1863.

It is not common, but is occasionally seen. The only species with which it is likely to be confused is *phaleratus*, and the difference in the segmentation of the swimming feet makes the distinction easy, as the rami have only two segments, while in *phaleratus* they have three. The fifth foot consists of a single segment and bears one spine.
Length of female, 0.5 mm.

Fig. 1229.   Fifth foot of *Cyclops bicolor*.   × 450.   (Original.)

102 (99, 103)   Antennae composed of eight segments.

Cyclops fimbriatus Fischer 1853.

Is the only species with antennae of eight segments, and, if found, can easily be recognized by this characteristic if one is sure that he is examining mature forms.
Length of female, 0.7 to 0.84 mm.

103 (99, 102)   Antennae composed of six segments.

Cyclops aequoreus Fischer 1860.

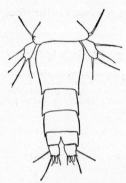

Found only in brackish water. It has been found in America in waters connected with the Gulf of Mexico, and those connected with the Pacific Ocean in Panama.

Fig. 1230.   Abdomen and fifth feet of female *Cyclops aequoreus*. × 73.   (Original.)

104 (1)   Cephalothorax and abdomen not distinctly separated, so that the whole body is somewhat worm-like; antennae short, never composed of more than eight segments.

Family Harpacticidae   .   105

All species of Harpacticidae are very minute. Only a few species have been described and those very inadequately. Probably there are many undescribed species and other genera than those mentioned.

105 (108)   Antennae composed of six segments, endopodites of all swimming feet composed of two segments, segments of endopodite of fourth foot fused so as to appear as one, endopodite of first foot slightly elongate; found in fresh and brackish waters, in New Mexico. . . . . *Marshia* . . 106

106 (107)   Furca of female two and one-half times as long as broad, furca of male four times as long as broad, median furcal setae fused at base.

Marshia albuquerquensis Herrick 1895.

107 (106)   Furcae of female and male twice as long as broad, median furcal setae not fused at base. . *Marshia brevicaudata* Herrick 1895.

108 (105)   Antennae composed of eight segments, endopodites of swimming feet composed of two or three segments, endopodite of third foot usually much longer than exopodite, endopodite of male fifth foot always of three segments.

Canthocamptus . . 109

109 (120) Anal plate without spines, or spines are simple, i.e., do not have
two points. 110

110 (113) Sides of last abdominal segment have spine-like prolongation
caudad. 111

111 (112) Spines of anal plate few in number, not exceeding five or six.
Canthocamptus staphylinoides Pearse 1905.

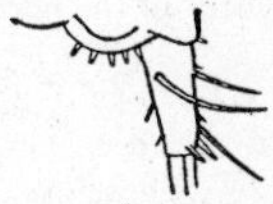

FIG. 1231. Anal plate and furca of *Canthocamptus staphylinoides.* X 153.
(After Pearse.)

112 (111) Spines of anal plate numerous.
Canthocamptus staphylinus (Jurine) 1820.

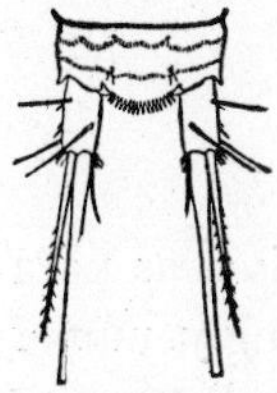

FIG. 1232. Last segment and furcae of male *Canthocamptus staphylinus.*
(After Schmeil.)

113 (110) Sides of last abdominal segment do not have spine-like prolongation
caudad. 114

114 (115) Furca long and slender, nearly four times as long as wide.
Canthocamptus idahoensis Marsh 1903.

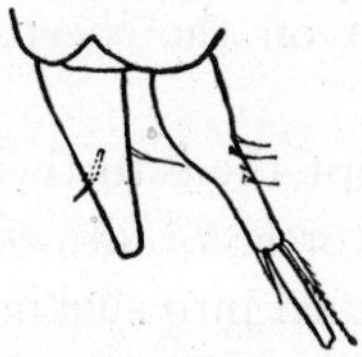

FIG. 1233. Furcae of female *Canthocamptus idahoensis.* X 120. (Original.)

115 (114) Furca short, its length not exceeding twice its width. . . . 116

116 (119) Furca with two setae. 117

117 (118) Anal plate with spines. . *Canthocamptus illinoisensis* Forbes 1876.

118 (117) Anal plate without spines. . *Canthocamptus hiemalis* Pearse 1905.

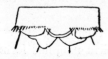

FIG. 1234. Anal plate of female *Canthocamptus hiemalis.* X 144.
(After Pearse.)

119 (116)   Furca with three setae. . *Canthocamptus northumbricus* Brady 1880.

This is probably, next to *minutus*, the most widely distributed species in North America.

120 (109)   Spines of anal plate bifid. . . *Canthocamptus minutus* Claus 1863.

This is the most common species and is found everywhere in the northern continents.

FIG. 1235.   The last segment and furcae of male *Canthocamptus minutus.*
(After Schmeil.)

SIPHONOSTOMATA

THE parasitic Copepoda pass all or a part of their lives as parasites upon fish and other animals. They are exceedingly numerous in both salt and fresh water, and very interesting because of the strange forms which many of them assume, — forms which would appear to be in no way related to the structure of a copepod. Many of them would be taken for worms. Some bore into the tissues of their hosts, others dwell in the gills, and still others in the nasal cavities. One species is very abundant on the sheepshead of the Central States.

The appendages are profoundly modified to adapt them to their parasitic existence. The swimming feet are more or less rudimentary. The appendages about the mouth are modified into sucking or prehensile organs. The antennae are similarly modified. In some the second antennae are armed at the end with hooks to enable the animal to retain its hold on its host. In some that are semiparasitic, the appendages from the opposite sides are joined together in a sucker. Sometimes the segmentation of the body disappears entirely. The appendages in some are reduced to mere protuberances, or may be like roots penetrating the body of the host.

And yet all these forms are free-swimming in their early stages. When hatched from the egg they have the typical nauplius form of the true copepods, and go through a process of degeneration later. In some the male dies immediately after reaching the *Cyclops* stage; in others, the male, while highly organized, is very small and lives as a parasite on the body of the female.

The parasitic Copepoda are much more numerous in salt water than in fresh. In an ordinary examination of fresh-water collections one is not apt to find them, although the male of *Ergasilus* is occasionally seen. An examination of almost any group of fish, however, will show that they are not at all rare.

It is a most fascinating study to compare the structure of these degenerate forms with the highly organized free-swimming species, thus finding evidence of the true copepod structure in animals that at first sight would seem to be far removed from the copepods. The structural relationships of these peculiar forms are only imperfectly understood, so that no satisfactory classification has been made, and, pending more thorough knowledge, all are grouped together, in a somewhat unscientific way, under the term " Siphonostomata." Although it is well known that these forms are very numerous in the fresh waters of America, the family of the Ergasilidae is the only one which has been studied from a systematic standpoint. Almost total ignorance prevails in regard to the species of the other families. From the studies in other countries something is known of these families, and it may be assumed that representatives of all of them can be found in American waters. For the sake of completeness of record these families, six in all, will be characterized briefly.

1. *Ergasilidae.* These resemble very closely the free-swimming copepods, the general form being much like that of the Cyclopidae. The second antennae are armed at the ends with hooks. On the ventral side of the body of the male there are ordinarily patches of pigment of a deep steel-blue color. The males are free-swimming through the whole period of their lives. The synopsis of the Ergasilidae is adapted from C. B. Wilson.

Ergasilus is the only genus of this family, and specimens are not unfrequently taken in limnetic collections. They have been found in nearly all parts of the United States.

2. *Caligidae.* The body is flat, the caudal part of the abdomen

much reduced. The antennae of the second pair are armed with hooks at the ends, but they are much shorter than in the Ergasilidae.

3. *Dichelestidae.* The body is elongated, the thoracic segments distinct, the abdomen rudimentary except for the elongated genital segment. At least the last two pairs of swimming feet are rudimentary. The maxillipedes are armed with hooks.

4. *Lernaeidae.* The body is worm-like and unsegmented, and the abdomen rudimentary. Processes growing from the head serve to attach the animal to the host. The four swimming feet are

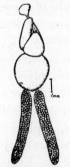

either very small or entirely lacking. A representative of this family is found on the sheepsheads of the Mississippi Valley.

5. *Lernaeopodidae.* The head is distinct, the rest of the body sac-shaped, and generally unsegmented. The second maxillipedes are very large, and, arching over the head, are joined together to form an organ for attachment to the host. The swimming feet are entirely lacking.

6. *Chondracanthidae.* The body is indistinctly

FIG. 1236. *Lernaeopoda beani* Wilson, found on rainbow trout and Quinnat salmon. (After Wilson.)

segmented, and the abdomen rudimentary. The first two pairs of swimming feet are rudimentary, the others lacking. The second antennae bear hooks. The male is small, distinctly segmented, and lives as a parasite on the female.

KEY TO NORTH AMERICAN FRESH-WATER ERGASILIDAE

1 (8)   Head completely fused with first thoracic segment, with no indication of union; carapace elongate, much longer than wide, and more than half entire length. 2

2 (5)   Anterior margin of carapace evenly rounded, first antennae hardly reaching end of first segment of second pair. . . . . ._. 3

3 (4)   Second antennae one-third entire length.
                                                    Ergasilus funduli Kröyer 1863.

Basal segment of second antennae much swollen and widened distally; second segment with a large process on its outer border. Found on the gills of *Fundulus ocellaris.*

4 (3)   Second antennae half the entire length.

Ergasilus labracis Kröyer 1863.

The two basal segments without swellings or processes; found on the striped bass, *Roccus lineatus*.

FIG. 1237. *Ergasilus labracis*. (After Wilson.)

5 (2)   Anterior margin of the carapace projecting strongly at the center in a rounded knob, first antennae much longer than in 2. .   6

6 (7)   Terminal claw of second antennae simple.

Ergasilus centrarchidarum Wright 1882.

Both rami of fourth feet three-segmented. Found on the family Centrarchidae, the redeye, *Ambloplites rupestris*, small-mouth black bass, *Micropterus dolomieu*, etc.

FIG. 1238. *Ergasilus centrarchidarum*. (After Wilson.)

7 (6)   Terminal claw toothed on the inner margin.

Ergasilus caeruleus Wilson 1911.

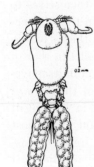

Exopodites of fourth feet two-segmented. Found on the bluegill, *Lepomis pallidus*.

FIG. 1239. *Ergasilus caeruleus*. (After Wilson.)

8 (1)   Head fused with first thoracic segment, but fusion indicated by
             distinct indentations on lateral margins; carapace half en-
             tire length and violin-shaped. 9

9 (10)   Second antennae as long as carapace.
                                    Ergasilus versicolor Wilson 1911.

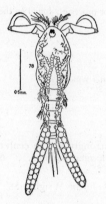

Found upon species of catfish.

Fig. 1240.   *Ergasilus versicolor.*   (After Wilson.)

10 (9)   Second antennae only one-half length of carapace.
                                    Ergasilus chautauquaensis Fellows 1887.

Suborder Branchiura

THERE is but one family in this suborder, — the Argulidae. They
are ectoparasites upon fish, and are commonly known as fish lice.
They have compound eyes, four or five pairs of swimming feet, and
the first maxillipedes are modified into a pair of sucking disks. In
connection with the mouth is a true stinging organ which penetrates the skin of the host. They are found most abundantly in
the branchial chamber of the host, but may attach themselves to
other parts of the body. It is a matter of interest in this connection, as has been noted by Wilson, that they attach themselves in
such a way as to place the long axis of the body parallel to that of
the host, so that they will be less likely to be brushed off in its movements. To this end, too, the under side of the body of the *Argulus*
is armed with backward-pointing spines, which aid in keeping it
in place. *Argulus* is strictly dependent on the blood of its host
for food, but can and does frequently swim about freely. Inasmuch as the eggs are laid attached to stones and similar objects, it
must leave the host at the breeding season. They are not con-

fined to a single species of fish for a host, but seem able to make use of a great variety, and may even attach themselves to other aquatic animals, like tadpoles. Some of them can live almost equally well in both salt and fresh water.

The following key to the species of *Argulus* which have been described from the fresh waters of America is adapted from Wilson's paper on the Argulidae.

KEY TO NORTH AMERICAN FRESH-WATER ARGULIDAE

1 (4, 9)   Carapace lobes overlap base of abdomen. 2

2 (3)   Diameter of sucking disks 0.25 mm.
                    Argulus catostomi Dana and Herrick 1837.

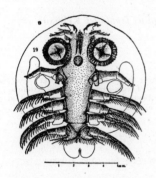

Spines on antennae reduced in number, small and weak; abdomen small and orbicular; found on sucker, *Catostomus commersoni,* and chub sucker, *Erimyzon sucetta oblongus.*

FIG. 1241. *Argulus catostomi.* (After Wilson.)

3 (2)   Diameter of sucking disks 0.15 mm.
                    Argulus americanus Wilson 1903.
Spines on antennae large and strong, reenforced; abdomen large and broadly cordate. Found on mudfish, *Amia calva.*

4 (1, 9)   Carapace lobes just reach base of abdomen. 5

5 (8)   Carapace orbicular, wider than long. 6

6 (7)   Anal sinus narrow and slit-like. *Argulus versicolor* Wilson 1903, male.

7 (6)   Anal sinus broadly triangular. . *Argulus maculosus* Wilson 1903.
Anal papillae lateral; bases of antennae widely separated; found upon the muscallonge, *Lucius masquinongy.*

8 (5)   Carapace orbicular, longer than wide.
                    Argulus appendiculosus Wilson 1907.
Found upon a sucker.

9 (1, 4)   Carapace lobes do not reach abdomen. 10

10 (16)   Swimming legs with flagella. 11

11 (13)   Carapace orbicular, wider than long. 12

12   Abdomen medium, oval, anal sinus short, slit-like, papillae subterminal. . . . . *Argulus versicolor* Wilson 1903, female.

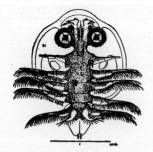

Anal papillae subterminal; bases of antennae close to mid-
line of carapace; found on the common pickerel, *Lucius
reticulatus.*

Fig. 1242. *Argulus versicolor*, female. (After Wilson.)

13 (11)   Carapace elliptical, longer than wide. 14

14 (15)   Flagella on anterior swimming legs.
Argulus lepidostei Kellicott 1877.

Carapace elliptical, longer than wide, its lobes very short,
barely covering two pairs of legs; abdomen broad, triangular, cut to the center or beyond with acute lobes; found on
the gar pike, *Lepidosteus osseus.*

Fig. 1243. *Argulus lepidostei.* (After Wilson.)

15 (14)   Flagella on all four pairs of swimming legs.
Argulus ingens Wilson 1912.

Male 16 mm., female 21 to 25 mm. long. By far the largest American species. From the
alligator gar, *Lepidosteus tristoechus*, in Moon Lake, Miss.

16 (10)   No flagella on swimming legs. . . *Argulus stizostethi* Kellicott 1880.

Carapace elliptical, longer than wide; abdomen elongate, cut to the center or beyond; the
lobes lanceolate-acuminate; found on the blue pike, *Stizostedion canadense.*

IMPORTANT PAPERS ON FRESH–WATER COPEPODA

Van Douwe, C., and Neresheimer, E. 1909. Copepoda. Die Süsswasserfauna Deutschlands. Heft 11.

Forbes, Ernest B. 1897. A Contribution to a Knowledge of North American Fresh-water Cyclopidae. Bull. Ill. State Lab. Nat. Hist., 5: 27–82;
13 pl.

GIESBRECHT, W., and SCHMEIL, O. 1898. Copepoda. I. Gymnoplea. Das Tierreich, 6 Lief.

GUERNE, J. DE, ET RICHARD, J. 1889. Révision des Calanides d'eau douce. Mém. Soc. Zoöl. France, 11: 53–181; 4 pl.

HERRICK, C. L., and TURNER, C. H. 1895. Synopsis of the Entomostraca of Minnesota. Geol. and Nat. Hist. Survey Minn., Zool. Series II; 525 pp., 81 pl.

MARSH, C. D. 1893. On the Cyclopidae and Calanidae of Central Wisconsin. Trans. Wis. Acad., 9: 189–224; 5 pl.

1895. On the Cyclopidae and Calanidae of Lake St. Clair, Lake Michigan, and certain of the inland lakes of Michigan. Bull. Mich. Fish Com. No. 5; 24 pp., 9 pl.

1897. The Limnetic Crustacea of Green Lake. Trans. Wis. Acad., 11: 163–168; 10 pl.

1903. The Plankton of Lake Winnebago and Green Lake. Bull. Wis. Geol. and Nat. Hist. Survey, 12: 1–94; 22 pl.

1907. A Revision of the North American Species of Diaptomus. Trans. Wis. Acad., 15: 381–516; 15 pl.

1910. A Revision of the North American Species of Cyclops. Trans. Wis. Acad., 16: 1067–1135; 10 pl.

SCHACHT, F. W. 1897. The North American Species of Diaptomus. Bull. Ill. State Lab. Nat. Hist., 5: 97–207; 15 pl.

1898. The North American Centropagidae belonging to the Genera Osphranticum, Limnocalanus, and Epischura. Bull. Ill. State Lab. Nat. Hist., 5: 225–269.

SCHMEIL, OTTO. 1892. Deutschlands freilebende Süsswasser-Copepoden. I. Cyclopidae; 192 pp., 8 pl.

1893. Deutschlands freilebende Süsswasser-Copepoden. II. Harpacticidae; 100 pp., 8 pl.

1896. Deutschlands freilebende Süsswasser-Copepoden. III. Centropagidae; 144 pp., 12 pl.

WILSON, C. B. 1903. North American Parasitic Copepods of the Family Argulidae. Proc. U. S. Nat. Mus., 25: 635–742; 20 pl.

1911. North American parasitic Copepods Belonging to the Family Ergasilidae. Proc. U. S. Nat. Mus., 39: 263–400; 20 pl.

CHAPTER XXIV

THE OSTRACODA

By R. W. SHARPE

Instructor in Biology, Dewitt Clinton High School, New York City

AN early author says of the Ostracoda, "these little creatures are enclosed in a bivalve shell of lime and seem to be very lively in their native element, being almost constantly in motion by the action of their antennae, or walking upon plants and other solid bodies floating in the water." Also "by opening and closing their valves, they enjoy light and move at their will, sometimes burying themselves in the mud, sometimes darting through the water, the humid air of their sphere. If they meet with any unforeseen object, they conceal themselves all at once in their shells and shut the valves, so that force and address seek in vain to open them."

The Ostracoda are found abundantly in all kinds of fresh and salt waters. They owe their name to the possession of a two-valved limy shell, which is hinged dorsally, and encloses the entire body. They are commonly more or less bean-shaped (Fig. 1244), and seen from above (Fig. 1255 b) are usually oval or egg-shaped. In many cases the shells overlap each other, or there may be a ventral flange present. They average about 1 millimeter in length.

The body of these little creatures is not segmented, and is completely enclosed in its bivalved shell, which is hinged along the dorsal margin by means of a hinge ligament, somewhat as with the molluscan bivalves. These valves are kept closed by adductor muscles, their points of attachment being indicated by a number of lucid spots about the middle of each valve (Fig. 1255 a). These are called "muscle impressions" and may often be of systematic value. At the anterodorsal end of the body is a single eye, although it may occasionally be double. Most commonly the shells of the sexes are of the same size and shape, although secondary sexual characters may appear here. For instance, the males of the genus *Candona* are larger and of a different shape (Fig. 1300), while in *Cypris* and *Notodromas* the females are the larger.

790

Baker, in 1753, is said to be the first author who sufficiently described any of these small forms so that the description could be recognized as referring to a *Cypris*. In the work "Employment for the Microscope" an anonymous correspondent describes an insect with a bivalve shell, somewhat resembling a fresh-water mussel, and gives a figure of it lying on its back.

Linnaeus, in his "Systema Naturae," in 1748, mentions a species under the name "Monoculus concha pedata." For many years the general term "Monoculus" was in use for all entomostraca until finally, in 1776, O. F. Müller, in his "Zoologiae Danicae Prodromus," first established the genus *Cypris*, as well as a number of other genera of the entomostraca.

In 1894 G. W. Müller published his masterly work on the Ostracoda of the Gulf of Naples. His descriptions and figures are most carefully and accurately made, and in connection with his similar work on the fresh-water Ostracoda of Germany, published in 1900, may well form the best published basis for future work. He describes about 125 species from the Gulf of Naples and some 65 for Germany.

Structure. — It is not uncommon for the extremities and ventral edges of the shell of *Cypris* to exhibit a number of subparallel canals (Fig. 1271) which radiate outwards, and are called "pore canals." The same regions may be tuberculate, the right valve alone with tubercles as in the subgenus *Cyprinotus* (Fig. 1270), or the left valve alone similarly tuberculate as with the subgenus *Heterocypris*. Various species of other groups may thus be similarly marked. Occasionally the shell may show a series of longitudinal markings, as *Ilyodromus* (Fig. 1259) or a network of anastomosing and parallel lines, as *Cypria exsculpta*.

Exclusive of the abdominal appendages, called the furca, there are seven pairs of appendages in the Cyprididae. These may be enumerated as follows: first antenna, second antenna, mandible, first maxilla, second maxilla, first leg, and second leg, naming one of each pair (Fig. 1244).

The anterior lip or labrum (Fig. 1244) forms a prominence projecting between the bases of the second antennae and anteriorly covering the oral orifice. The posterior lip or labium (Fig. 1245) forms a thin membrane, reenforced by a pair of very strong chitinous rods, each expanded into a transverse plate armed at their extremities with a series of about seven strong teeth. Posteriorly the lip joins a sternumlike vaulted plate, carinated along the middle, and placed between the bases of the first pair of maxillae.

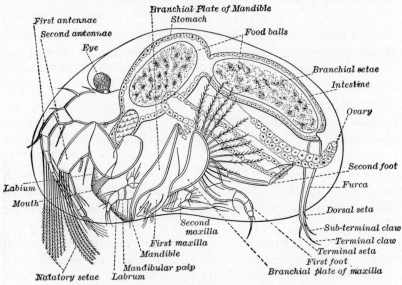

FIG. 1244. General anatomy of *Cypris virens* Jurine. (After Vavra.)

The mandibles (Fig. 1245) are each composed of a chitinous elongate body, and a well-developed pediform palp (Fig. 1245 b^1). They are located on either side of the body immediately behind the base of the second antennae with its upper acuminate extremity (Fig. 1245 b^2) articulated to the inner surface of the corresponding valve just in front of the adductor muscle impressions, whereas the lower incurved extremity is wedged in between the lips. The greater part of the body (Fig. 1245 b^3) is hollowed to receive the powerful adductor biting muscles. The cutting edge (Fig. 1245 b^4) is divided into several strong, bifurcate teeth. The palp (Fig. 1245 b^1) forms a thick, fleshy, somewhat pediform jointed stem, curving downwards, and bears on its outer side a narrow plate, a so-called branchial appendage (Fig. 1245 b^5) which is provided with a number of plumose setae.

The first pair of maxillae (Fig. 1245 c) is formed of a thick, muscular, basal part, from the extremities of which four digitiform processes originate. The larger of these prominences (Fig. 1245 c^1) is jointed and movable and must evidently be regarded as a palp, whereas the three remaining form the immediate continuation of the basal part and are the true masticatory lobes. The first one of these is usually armed with two strong spines (Fig. 1245 c^2 and Fig. 1270 e) which may or may not be toothed, and are regarded as of specific importance. To the outer side of the basal part a large

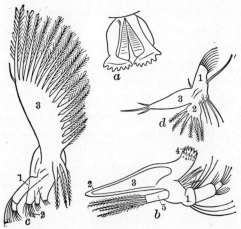

FIG. 1245. (a) Lower lip or labium; (b) Mandible with palp; (c) First maxilla with branchial plate; (d) Second maxilla of female with palp (*Cypris incongruens*).

semilunar lamella (Fig. 1245 c^3) is attached, which is generally called the branchial plate. This plate may be seen to move rhythmically in the living animal, and is for the purpose of renewing the supply of fresh oxygen-laden water within the shell cavity. It is directed obliquely upwards and exhibits along the posterior edge a series of dense and regular finely plumose setae, from 16 to 20 in number.

The second pair of maxillae (Fig. 1245 d) consists of the same principal parts as the first, though different in appearance. The basal part (Fig. 1245 d^1) is much smaller, not divided at the end, and terminating in a single masticatory lobe. The branchial lamella (Fig. 1245 d^2) are usually semicircular and provided with a few plumose setae, while the palps (Fig. 1245 d^3 and Fig. 1299 d–e) are of

different shapes in the sexes. In the female they are conical
(Fig. 1245 d^3), while with the male (Fig. 1299 e) they are converted in a peculiar manner into powerful prehensile organs which
serve for grasping the female during copulation. The palps of
the right and left sides in the male are different in size and shape
(Fig. 1246 e–f). The form of these palps is regarded as of specific
importance.

The two pairs of antennae are found in the head region, and in
most cases are provided with long natatory setae, which aid in
swimming (Fig. 1268 e). The mandibles and first maxillae serve
as mouth parts. The fifth pair may be modified in some cases, as
in the Limnicythere, serving as legs — in most cases as maxillipeds
or second maxillae. The fifth pair is known as the first legs
(Fig. 1260 d), and the sixth pair is known as the second legs (Fig.
1285 d). The second legs are commonly not ambulatory, but are
bent backwards within the shell. They are often called the
"cleaning feet" on account of their observed use in cleaning the
valves of any foreign matter. The mouth parts commonly carry
a number of setae which create a current of water between the
valves for respiratory purposes.

The general color of the surroundings seems to have some relationship to the general color of the forms present. For instance,
all those living in algae-rich habitats are notably green, as many
species of *Cypris*, while those creeping about on the bottom amongst
dead leaves and ooze, are commonly devoid of any especial pigment, as are most species of *Candona*. The color of the various
forms varies from yellowish white to yellow, green, blue, and violet
to purple. The species of *Candona* are commonly of a pearly
to yellowish white, while *Cypris*, *Cypridopsis*, and *Cypria* — forms
that inhabit algae-rich regions — commonly show a greenish color.

The food canal begins with a mouth, which is bounded by upper
and lower lips. It is interesting here to observe that the marine
forms belonging to the genus *Pyrocypris* are provided with phos-
phorescent glands in the upper lip, which cause much of the
phosphorescence of the sea. From the mouth the food passes
through a short esophagus to a stomach, which is commonly
followed by a short constriction separating it from the short

stomach-like intestine (Fig. 1244). The intestine opens at the origin of the furcal appendages.

Propagation. — The male sexual organs are usually large, of complex structure, and may consist of a whorled sack or spiny cylinder, the ejaculatory duct (Fig. 1246 *b*), connecting with the testes and vas deferens, which may lead to a more or less chitinous plate or penis (Fig. 1246 *a*). The testes usually consist of glands which are partly extended within the shell proper and the shell membrane, and may show through the shell as three or four granular bands (Fig. 1271 *b*), as in *Candona* and *Cypris*. The arrangement of these testes may constitute a good generic character, as in *Spirocypris* (Fig. 1267), where the testes originate in the anterior part of the shell in parts of circles or circles.

The ovaries may show through the shell in its posterodorsal part, and are arranged somewhat as the testes (Fig. 1244). They usually lead to a chitinous plate by a vaginal canal or oviduct, which retains the semen and undeveloped eggs as with *Cypris*, and commonly lie between the two lamellae of either valve, and extend diagonally to the posterior extremity, where they curve up to form a nearly semicircular band. Here the true germinal layer is found, which forms the ovicells. These ovicells are poured from the ovary into the body cavity, where they generally accumulate in its posterior part on either side of the intestine. Here they attain their full development and are fertilized, after which they are laid.

The inner genital organs of the male are more complicated (Fig. 1246). As the ovaries, they are situated between the lamellae of the valves, and commonly consist of a number of narrow and elongate bands on either side, which are generally to be found filled with numerous fine, thread-like bodies (Fig. 1246 *d*), the spermatozoa, which may occasionally be curled up in spiral groups. In addition there are present a number of large nuclear cells (Fig. 1246 *g*). These are the germinal cells, or spermatocysts, from which the spermatozoa develop.

The efferent or ejaculatory apparatus (Fig. 1246 *b*) consists of the spiny cylinder already mentioned. It seems to be composed of an inner tube (Fig. 1246 *c*), supported by a complicated chitinous skeleton of whorled radiating spines. The efferent duct leads to a tube, the vas deferens, which in turn leads to the penis (Fig. 1246 *a*).

These forms may also be propagated from unfertilized eggs, *i.e.*, by parthenogenesis. In such cases there may be a sexual generation followed by a number of such parthenogenetic generations. Again, in some forms males have never been discovered, even after as many as 18 years of continuous observation by very care-

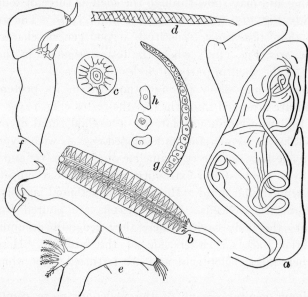

FIG. 1246. *Cyprinotus dentata* Sharpe. (*a*) Penis, × 210; (*b*) Efferent or ejaculatory apparatus; (*c*) Cross-section of same, × 293; (*d*) Part of a spermatozoon, × 525; (*e*) Right maxillary palp of male, × 158; (*f*) Left palp of same; (*g*) Extremity of testicular tube, showing spermatocysts, × 120; (*h*) Mature spermatocysts, × 120.

ful observers. *Herpetocypris reptans* is a good example. Thus some authors distinguish four types of the method of propagation, as follows:

    1. Always sexual as in *Notodromas monacha, Cyclocypris laevis, Cypria ophthalmica.*

    2. Temporarily parthenogenetic, as in *Candona candida, Cypridopsis vidua.*

    3. Locally parthenogenetic, as in *Cypris incongruens.*

    4. Always parthenogenetic, as in *Herpetocypris reptans.*

The method of propagation has been much used as a generic character, but much more must be known of its constancy before it can be finally accepted as at all reliable. The form of the penis and of the vaginal plate, however, may both be accepted as constant characters.

The eggs are provided with small limy shells, and commonly develop in from 5 to 14 days. They are laid in characteristic ways. For example, the eggs of *Candona candida* are whitish, and are laid singly, without being fastened together; those of *Cypris incongruens* are orange red, while those of *Cypridopsis vidua* are dark green. Both are laid in packets on the leaves and stems of water plants, especially the under sides of Lemna leaves. The eggs of *Notodromas monacha* are first white and later yellowish. They are oval-elongate, and are laid in rows, pole to pole, on the roots of Lemna. The eggs of *Herpetocypris reptans* are spherical and of a yellowish color, which deepens later — indeed, when freshly laid, they may be almost white.

Bottom forms, such as *Candona* and *Herpetocypris*, laboriously contrive by creeping and crawling to reach Lemna and other surface plants. They first reach the roots, and later the upper surfaces, where they appear to scrape a place with their antennae, and then deposit and fasten their eggs with fine threads. All this must be quite an acrobatic feat for them, as they must balance themselves meantime. After finishing, they permit themselves to fall to the bottom. It is here worthy of remark that these biological distinctions such as habitat, means of locomotion, food, means of propagation, and egg laying, all have their value in specific distinctions.

Their eggs also have remarkable vitality. An instance is on record of samples of dried mud being sent to England from Jerusalem and entomostraca being raised therefrom (*Cypris* and *Daphnia*) after a lapse of from 24 to 30 years. G. O. Sars, of Norway, has reported raising them from dried mud sent him from Australia and China. In fact, he has described many new species from material sent to him in this way.

The eggs hatch into nauplii, which resemble the adult, although varying much in the shape of the shell and internal structure.

They molt many times before reaching maturity. The change that takes place is most complete. The shell falls off, and all the internal parts are shed, even to the minutest hairs.

The nervous system is composed of a so-called brain or supra-esophageal ganglion, and several other ganglia and connecting nerve structures. The most important branches lead to the eyes, which are either double as in *Notodromas* (Fig. 1247), or, more commonly, as a single median-dorsal pigment spot.

The most common sense organs other than the eyes are found on the second antennae (Fig. 1290 *c*). These resemble a club and hence are often called "sense clubs." Other sense organs appear on the second antennae of the male, especially such forms as *Candona, Cypria,* and *Notodromas* (Fig. 1298 *c*).

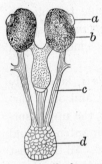

FIG. 1247. *Notodromas monacha* (O. F. M.). (*a*) Lens; (*b*) Eyeball; (*c*) Optic nerve; (*d*) Forebrain.

Most Ostracoda are omnivorous. Decaying vegetation and small animals form a large part of their diet. *Cypridopsis* has been observed forming skeleton leaves. Some will eat their own kind, if opportunity offers. While in captivity most forms will eat from thin slices of potato. *Notodromas* is an exception to most others, as it has the curious habit of swimming back down and clings to the surface film in an endeavor to obtain food. Some forms may also attack living or dying animals. Instances are also on record of their having attacked *Melicerta ringens*, a common fixed rotifer. Thus they act principally as scavengers, as their greediness and oftentimes great numbers would constitute them no inefficient agent in the work of purifying standing waters.

The fresh-water Ostracoda entirely lack any such organ as a heart. The respiratory process therefore takes place through the entire upper surface of the body, and through the inner cell layers of the shell. A number of respiratory plates are fastened to the mouth parts, the motions of which keep up a continuous stream of fresh oxygen-laden water pouring through between the valves.

It is self evident that favorable or unfavorable life conditions exert a striking influence on the distribution of Ostracoda in isolated waters, although this fact has not received the attention it should. Even though in general they seem to be no more sensitive to their surroundings than the Cladocera or the Copepoda, yet there is no doubt that the amount of light, of pressure, of variations in temperature and composition of the water, the rate of flow of the same, the nature of the bottom, and the presence or absence of algae, etc., must certainly exert a real or intrinsic influence on the prosperous development of all these Entomostraca. Direct or intense light certainly accelerates all their life processes, as may be evidenced in the fact that all free and actively swimming forms are quite likely to turn towards a source of light, or, in other words, are positively heliotropic. Shady areas in pools are not nearly so likely to contain the free swimming forms such as *Cypris*, *Cypria*, *Cyclocypris*, and *Notodromas* except occasionally or sporadically, while the lighter and sunnier areas of the same body will contain them in abundance; in other words, the more uniform the distribution of light, the more nearly uniform becomes the distribution of any certain form. On the other hand, it seems a general rule that the less able these forms are to swim, the greater the certainty that they are confined to the deeper and darker areas, in the ooze and slimy debris of the bottom. It also appears that some species may be affected but little by depth, and therefore light and pressure; *Cypridopsis vidua* has been found in all depths from 1 centimeter to fully 300 meters.

Experience teaches that practically no forms are found in pure spring water or in well water. Even so, we find practically none in waters that have been polluted with dyes, or by chemical means, although many different degrees of power of resistance in this regard may be found. Some species may be enclosed in the smaller glass aquaria and live almost indefinitely without change of water, even though the water becomes quite foul. For example, *Cypria opthalmica* has been known to survive in such aquaria long after the larger forms have died. *Cyclocypris laevis* will also live many months in water that has not been freshened. Some few forms have been known to exist in sulphur waters, others in hot springs and even in sewer drains. *Cypris incongruens* has been found in a pond fed by the drainage from a barnyard manure heap. This species really seems to be indifferent to any variation in the pollution of the swampy water in which they normally live, variations and situations that would be fatal to most other Ostracoda. These forms have also been found in more or less permanent ponds fed in part from the drainage from cesspools and from leaky sewers.

Many bodies of water of different degrees of swiftness are likewise determinative of different forms. Brooks and rivers are not especially good habitats, as plant life there is not abundant, and most free-swimming Ostracoda seemingly delight to hang to such supports. However, most forms may be occasionally or adventitiously found in such waters, as well as in quieter waters. *Notodromas* is typically an inhabitant of pure, fresh pools, although it is a good swimmer, and has the curious habit of trying to support itself on the surface film.

Among those forms depending upon the Ostracoda in part for food, one must certainly include the young of many fishes, and even the adult *Coregonus* or whitefish has been found with *Candona* in the stomachs. Some of the larger marine fishes seek Ostracoda in the mud. Even aquatic birds may include them in their bill of fare, as, for example, the shoveler or spoonbill duck has been found with *Ilyodromus* and *Cypria* in its stomach.

Owing to the variations in habitat, and the vicissitudes to which most fresh-water Ostracoda are subject, and because of the variable and inconstant nature of their surroundings, it is almost impossible to work out their exact distribution. *Cyclocypris laevis*, *Cypria opthalmica*, *Cypria exsculpta*, and *Cypridopsis vidua* seem to be cosmopolites in temperate zones, and the most indifferently distributed of any, as they are found in all pools, ponds, swamps, lakes, and rivers of both mountainous and level areas. Their small size permits them to be readily carried about, and their power of adaptation and scavenger habits permit them to thrive in almost any apparently adverse situation. *Notodromas*, as already stated, appears only in pure standing waters, and mostly in immense numbers. Less abundantly, but still very widely distributed, may be found various species of *Candona, Cypris fuscata*, and *Herpetocypris reptans*.

The vertical distribution of these forms has not been fully worked out. Various species of *Candona*, *Ilyocypris*, as well as *Cypridopsis vidua* and *Cyclocypris laevis* have been found at depths of at least 300 meters, while a few have been reported from depths of fully 2500 meters.

The constancy of color, form, and size of most of these species is still an open question, and yet requires much careful work. Because of differences in methods of measuring and the chance that undeveloped or sexually immature individuals become described, it is certain that there exist many discrepancies as to published descriptions, and therefore of reports on distribution.

Despite these discrepancies and uncertainties, it is likely that local varieties exist in many quite restricted areas, that in many cases are so far divergent that one would be disposed to ascribe them to different species. On this account, if for no other, it is advisable to be very careful concerning the establishment of new species. In all cases the appendages should be very critically examined, and if these show differences and the shells are constant in general markings and form, then only should a new species be created. Of course, very exact and minute descriptions are indispensable.

The distribution of Ostracoda seems to be both actively and passively brought about. The creeping forms may be said to be actively distributed, while the free-swimming forms are passively distributed. Those that creep must actively exert themselves if in deep water, often against the force of the stream, to prevent themselves from being buried in the mud. Passively, the swimmers may be distributed by high water or by direct means of transport. The amount of water is of more consequence than the flow of water. Even though the amount of water is great, they still can remain in the place of their temporary abode, while in brooks or rivers they are carried away by the force of the current, and may become lost. In rainy seasons, therefore, the natural increase may be very scanty, while in drier periods many individuals of both sexes find one another, and the eggs deposited always have a sufficient opportunity of finding necessary moisture for development.

Migration from one region to another may be brought about by swimming beetles such as *Belostoma, Gyrina*, etc. *Cyclocypris* has been observed hanging to the legs of such beetles, even though the beetles were actively using their legs. Birds may also be of great importance as carriers of both the minute flora and fauna of a region. The eggs of Ostracoda, and even the animals themselves, may be carried about on the bills and feet of aquatic birds, and even fishes may act as a means of transport from one region to another.

The Ostracoda belong to the plankton. In common with certain other organisms, such as Rhizopods, Diatoms, *Hydra*, etc., they appear in the plankton under certain conditions of temperature and food, and hence are said to belong to the adventitious planktonts, in distinction to such forms as *Cyclops*, which are always in the plankton, and therefore called continuous planktonts, or those that appear periodically, as *Daphnia* and some *Rotifera*, when they are called periodic planktonts. For evident reasons the creeping or burrowing forms rarely occur in ordinary plankton catches.

According to their habitat and mode of locomotion, the ostracod adventitious planktonts may be classified as follows:

A. Free swimming.
  1. Limnetic, with surface habits, as *Notodromas monacha.*
  2. Free swimming, below the surface, as *Cypris laevis, C. incongruens, C. vidua,* etc.

B. Creeping or burrowing.
  1. Creeping *on* water plants or ooze, as *Herpetocypris reptans.*
  2. Burrowing *in* the slime or ooze, as *Candona candida,* and *Limnicythere.*

Little is surely known of the duration of life of special forms. Some species are present the entire year. They live over the winter, and are also found in different developmental stages under the ice. It is an easy matter to collect mud under ice in midwinter, place it in a small aquarium jar and set in a moderately warm place, and very shortly find plenty of *Cypris, Cypria,* and *Candona.*

Notodromas appears purely as a summer form. It winters in different "egg stages," develops in April or May, and by September has entirely disappeared. *Cypridopsis vidua* and *Cypris incongruens* appear in early spring and last until late autumn. The spring forms appear to have a much shorter life history.

These forms may be collected in great variety and abundance by drawing a Birge or cone net through submerged plants present in ponds, slow streams, and lakes, and by stirring up the bottom ooze and slime, and drawing the weighted net to and fro over the bottom.

In this manner not only the free-swimming forms may be captured, such as *Cypris*, *Cypridopsis*, etc., but typically bottom forms such as *Candona*, *Herpetocypris*, etc., may also be included. By emptying the mud and all other accumulations in a beaker of water, and stirring well, it will usually result in many of the Ostracoda getting air caught between their valves, thus causing them to float on the surface, from which they may be readily removed with a "medicine dropper" or pipette. The use of a small hand lens is advisable in determining whether or not Ostracoda are surely present. In any case, the "catch" may now be concentrated by carefully pouring off the contents of the beaker from the sediment in the bottom into a small dip net made of Swiss or bolting cloth.

After washing out as much of the soluble or other matter as is possible, the remainder may be emptied into a Syracuse watch glass or other shallow vessel containing but a small quantity of water. Thus the catch is condensed to such bulk as may now be easily transferred to small vials of preservative fluid such as 90 per cent alcohol, or a mixture of 80 per cent alcohol and glycerin in about the proportion of 10 to 1. However, killing had better be done in about 70 per cent alcohol, which should be gradually increased in strength, as in this manner the shells are more likely to remain open than when killed in alcohol of a higher percentage.

If a large quantity of living forms should be desired, the entire catch of a locality may be poured into a special pint strainer jar (Fig. 1248).

This may be made out of a common pint fruit jar, by inserting
a funnel through one side of the cover for pouring in the catch,
and so arranged that the excess water may run off through an
overflow tube, after passing through a cloth strainer
made of the same material as the dip net, and which
is distended and held in place by two narrow wire
loops soldered to the inner end of the overflow tube.
The strainer cloth is made in the form of a bag nearly
as long as the depth of the jar, with its upper end held
in contact with the inner end of the overflow tube by
a couple of rubber bands.

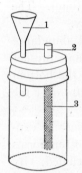

FIG. 1248. Diagram
of strainer jar;
(1) Funnel intake;
(2) Overflow tube;
(3) Cloth strainer.

In many cases it is recommended that the collected
material be allowed to stand in a shallow vessel after
reaching the laboratory, when the creeping forms will
appear on the surface of the ooze and slime, and others
will collect about the edges of the vessel, commonly on
the side nearest the source of light, or the opposite.

If it is thought desirable, small portions of the ooze and slime
may be examined under the low power of the compound microscope. Even the creeping Cyprididae are easier to find than the
Cytheridae, such as *Limnicythere*, as they are more active and
readily gather about the edges of any shallow vessel.

No satisfactory work in identification can be accomplished in
most cases until the body with its appendages is removed from the
shell. It is not necessary to place the specimens in weak acid so
as to decalcify the shell, as a little practice with dissecting needles
and microscope will soon enable one to remove the parts from the
shell without destroying them.

After a preliminary examination, place the specimen in a small
drop of Farrant's medium or in glycerin. The shell may now be
opened with a pair of No. 12 needles, which are mounted in handles,
or by the flexible probing needles used by dentists. Free the body
from the shell entire, if possible, and afterwards separate the appendages, beginning with the antennae and taking them in order to
the furca at the posterior extremity. This is not an especially
difficult process, excepting possibly the maxillae, which are commonly very small and securely joined in place, so that even the

finest needle is scarcely efficient as a dissecting instrument. Either of the above two mounting media bring out to view even the finest hairs or ciliated structures. Alcohol or water are not advisable as dissecting media and should be risked with few specimens. Furthermore, Farrant's medium makes a very good permanent mount, providing there is not too much on the slide. Either medium should be added to the slide in small drops, then spread out in a thin layer before attempting to dissect therein. It is commonly best to make a preliminary examination of the dissection with a $\frac{2}{3}$-inch objective, to see that the mount has been well prepared and arranged. If so, add a small additional amount of the medium, cover with cover glass, and the mount is permanent, provided the work is neatly done, too much medium is not added, and the mounts are kept stored in a horizontal position when not in use.

The valves should be preserved entire, if possible, and removed to one side of the slide for further study. It is often desirable that they be removed to a separate slide and mounted in balsam; especially if the slides are to be permanent and subject to much handling.

Drawings as well as study of a side view should always be made from *one* of the valves, rather than from the entire specimen, as otherwise a distorted view is likely to result.

The dorsal view is more difficult to get — indeed, it is often advisable not to attempt it. Unless this view is obtained directly above the specimen, it is worthless. Sometimes one valve alone may be used by fastening it to a needle or similar object, and then studying while covered with glycerin, or, if the valves are dissimilar the entire animal may thus be mounted so that an exact profile may possibly be obtained. It is indeed often possible to get very good dorsal profiles from many specimens while they are in alcohol and glycerin in a syracuse watch glass.

The following characters have been retained as of most value in the following key: presence and length of natatory setae of the second antennae, segmentation of the second antennae, form and number of spines of the first maxillary process, armature of the second leg, arrangement of the spermatic glands, and armature and shape of the furca.

KEY TO NORTH AMERICAN FRESH-WATER OSTRACODA

1 (2) Second antenna two-branched; one branch rudimentary, immobile, the other elongate, flexible, with long natatory setae (MYODOCOPA); or both branches well developed, movable, and natatory (CLADOCOPA); or both branches flattened, similar to feet of the Copepoda (PLATYCOPA). . . MARINE TRIBES.

These groups are not represented in fresh water so far as known.

2 (1) Second antenna simple, subpediform, clawed at apex. Mostly fresh-water forms. . . . . Tribe PODOCOPA . . 3

3 (4) Three nearly similar pairs of legs. Furca rudimentary. Second antenna with flagellum (Fig. 1251 d^1), and little adapted for swimming. . . . . Family CYTHERIDAE . . 5

4 (3) Two dissimilar pairs of legs. Furca commonly well developed. Second antenna without flagellum and commonly with natatory setae. 9

5 (6) Parasitic on gills of crustacea. Terminal claws of legs with four large teeth (Fig. 1249 a). . . . . . *Entocythere* Marshall 1903. Only one species of this genus known.

Entocythere cambaria Marshall 1903.

Length 0.60 mm. Males abundant. Shell thin, fragile and transparent. First antenna six-segmented. Second antenna four-segmented. Flagellum unsegmented. Caudal rami short and thick. Parasitic on gills of crayfish (*Cambarus*). Wisconsin. A most remarkable form, in that Ostracoda rarely adopt parasitic habits.

FIG. 1249.
Entocythere cambaria. (a) End of third leg; (b) Side view, × 50. (After Marshall.)

6 (5) Not parasitic. Crawlers or burrowers. Terminal claws of legs with not more than two teeth, or plain (Fig. 1260 d).
Limnicythere Brady 1868 . . 7

7 (8) Shell decidedly reticulate, with two lateral furrows. Furca blunt, about three times as long as wide (Fig. 1250 a).
Limnicythere reticulata Sharpe 1897.

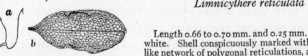

Length 0.66 to 0.70 mm. and 0.25 mm. wide. Grayish white. Shell conspicuously marked with a honeycomb-like network of polygonal reticulations, and deep lateral furrows (Fig. 1250 b). Furca (Fig. 1250 a) cylindrical, thick and blunt, about three times as long as wide, with two small setae. Posterior dorsal part of carapace tapers to a point. Muddy bottom of ponds. Illinois, April.

FIG. 1250.
Limnicythere reticulata. (a) Furca; (b) Dorsal view; (c) Side view, × 54.

8 (7)   Shell faintly reticulate, with one lateral furrow.   Furca tapering to a
        seta like extremity (Fig. 1251 *b*).
                              Limnicythere illinoisensis Sharpe 1897

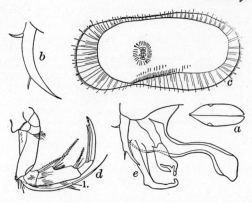

Length 0.88 mm., height 0.40 mm., and width 0.29 mm. Dark grayish white. Flagellum two-segmented. Furca cylindrical, about seven times as long as wide (Fig. 1251 *b*). Male grasping organs unusually well developed. Terminal claw of second antenna of male armed with 3 or 4 strong teeth at tip. Sandy bottoms, Illinois River, bayous, and lake shores. May.

FIG. 1251.
Limnicythere illinoisensis. (*a*) Dorsal view; (*b*) Furca; (*c*) Side view, ✕ 54; (*d*) Second antenna showing flagellum, *d* 1; (*e*) Sexual organs of male.

9 (10)   Abdomen without furca.   Second legs not backwardly directed.
                                  Family DARWINULIDAE.
         Darwinula stevensoni Brady and Robertson 1870.

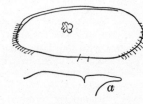

Length 0.70 to 0.80 mm. Right shell overlapping the left. Abdomen ending in a cylindrical unpaired process (Fig. 1252 *a*). Sandy or muddy bottoms. Georgia. (*D. improvisa* Turner 1895, is a synonym.)

FIG. 1252.
Darwinula stevensoni. (*a*) Tip of abdomen, ✕ 166.

10 (9)   Abdomen with furca.   Second legs backwardly bent.
                                  Family CYPRIDIDAE . .   11

11 (12)   Furca rudimentary, with a long seta at tip (Fig. 1253).   13

12 (11)   Furca band-like, with claws and setae at tip (Fig. 1258 *a*). . .   16

13   Natatory setae of second antennae long, reaching at least to tips
           of terminal claws.   Second foot beak-shaped at tip, with a
           terminal claw. . . .   Subfamily CYPRIDOPSINAE . .   14

14 (15)   Shell broad from above, tumid.   Second antenna five-segmented.
                                  Cypridopsis Brady 1868.
           Only one species in North America.   The most common North
           American ostracod. . . *Cypridopsis vidua* O. F. Müller 1785.

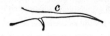

Length 0.60 to 0.70 mm., plump.   Marked dorsally and laterally with three prominent dark bands.   Very common, wherever algae are present.

FIG. 1253.   *Cypridopsis vidua.* Furca, ✕ 180.

15 (14) Shell rather narrow from above, compressed (Fig. 1254 *b*). Second
antenna four-segmented. . . . . *Potamocypris* Brady 1870.
Only one species in North America.

Potamocypris smaragdina (Vavra) 1891.

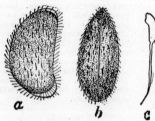

Length 0.65 mm. Shell grass green, nearly crescent-shaped, and thickly covered with long, closely appressed hairs. Pools and ditches, July, August, and September. Eggs vermilion red. Ponds and ditches, April, July, August. South Chicago, Mexico.

FIG. 1254.
Potamocypris smaragdina. (*a*) Side view, × 40;
(*b*) Dorsal view; (*c*) Furca, × 150.

16 (17) With two distinct eyes (Fig. 1255 *b*). 18

17 (16) With eyes fused, or none apparent (Fig. 1258 *c*). 22

18 (19) First maxillary process with six spines. Furca with three long setae
and no spines (Fig. 1255 *c–d*). 20

19 (18) First maxillary process with six spines. Furca with four long setae
and no spines (Fig. 1256 *c*). 21

20   Second antenna six-segmented in both sexes. Second leg terminating in three setae, one of which is reflexed.

Notodromas Lilljeborg 1853.
Only one species in North America.

Notodromas monacha (O. F. Müller) 1785.

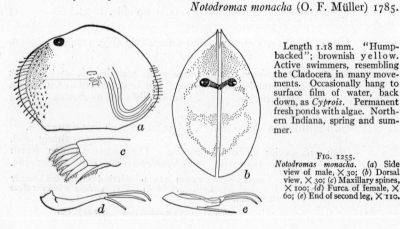

Length 1.18 mm. "Hump-backed"; brownish yellow. Active swimmers, resembling the Cladocera in many movements. Occasionally hang to surface film of water, back down, as *Cyprois.* Permanent fresh ponds with algae. Northern Indiana, spring and summer.

FIG. 1255.
Notodromas monacha. (*a*) Side view of male, × 30; (*b*) Dorsal view, × 30; (*c*) Maxillary spines, × 100; (*d*) Furca of female, × 60; (*e*) End of second leg, × 110.

21   Second antenna five-segmented in both sexes. Second leg terminating in one claw and one reflexed seta (Fig. 1256 *b*).

Cyprois Zenker 1854.

Only one species found in North America.

Cyprois marginata Strauss 1821.

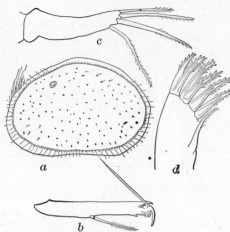

Length 1.53 mm., breadth 0.75
mm., height 0.96 mm. Uniformly
yellowish in color. An active, restless swimmer, and at times tries
hanging to the surface film of
water. Somewhat resembling *N.
monacha* in its swimming movements. May also creep on bottom debris. Grassy pools which
later dry up. Sexual. Furca stout,
slightly curved; dorsal seta uncommonly long. April to July. Chicago, Ill. (Jackson Park), April,
May, June.

Fig. 1256.
Cyprois marginata. (*a*) Side view of
female, × 25; (*b*) End of second leg,
× 75; (*c*) Furca of female, × 60;
(*d*) Maxillary spines, × 75.

22 (23)   Natatory setae of the second antennae entirely lacking (Fig. 1298 *c*).
Subfamily CANDONINAE . . 91

23 (22)   Natatory setae of the second antennae very evident, usually extending at least to tips of terminal claws (Figs. 1268 *e* and
1290 *c*). 24

24 (25)   Terminal segment of second leg with three long setae and no claws,
— one seta reflexed (Fig. 1258 *b*).
Ilyocypris Brady and Norman 1889 . . 26

25 (24)   Terminal segment of second leg with at least one claw (Fig.
1268 *b*), — and usually beak-shaped. 28

26 (27)   Shell with many prominent tubercles, knobs, and furrows. Natatory setae reaching to tips of terminal claws, or slightly
beyond. . . . . *Ilyocypris gibba* Ramdohr 1808.

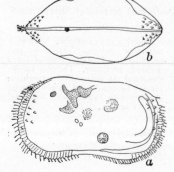

Length 0.85 to 0.95 mm. Shell much tuberculate
anteriorly and posteriorly, and decidedly furrowed
anterodorsally. Two prominent tubercles just back
of the eye-spot. Poor swimmers. Furca nearly
straight, its terminal claws nearly equal in length, and
plain. Terminal seta of furca about two-fifths length
of terminal claw. Swampy regions, in mud, during
the spring months. In company with *I. bradyi*, usually. Colorado, March.

Fig. 1257.
Ilyocypris gibba. (*a*) Side view, × 45;
(*b*) Dorsal view, × 45.

27 (26) Shell with weak tubercles, knobs, and furrows. Natatory setae reaching scarcely to tips of terminal claws.

Ilyocypris bradyi Sars 1890.

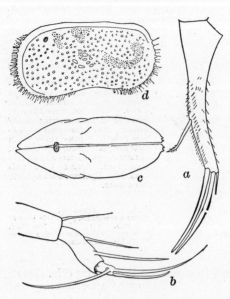

Length about as *I. gibba*. Height of female 0.45 to 0.5 mm., breadth 0.32 to 0.5 mm. Male slightly larger. Scarcely free swimming, but creeps or burrows. Shell weakly tuberculate and not furrowed posterodorsally. Habitat and occurrence as *I. gibba*. Furca strong curved, and much broadened at base. About ten times as long as width in middle. Dorsal seta plumose and bent near tip. Distal half of dorsal part of furca ciliate. These two species are quite variable, thus causing much confusion in diagnosis. Both species are also found in Britain and Germany.

FIG. 1258.
Ilyocypris bradyi. (a) Furca, X 200; (b) End of second leg, X 150; (c) Dorsal view, X 45; (d) Side view, X 45.

28 (29) Natatory setae of the second antenna shortened, no swimmers. Second leg with a beak-like end segment and a claw (Fig. 1268 b). . . . . Subfamily HERPETOCYPRIDINAE . . 30

29 (28) Natatory setae of the second antenna long, reaching at least to tips of terminal claws. Second leg as above.

Subfamily CYPRIDINAE . . 42

30 (31) Furca abnormal, with three claws, — the usual dorsal seta being replaced by a claw. Shell faintly longitudinally striated (Fig. 1259). . . . . *Ilyodromus* Sars 1894. Only one species known in America.

Ilyodromus pectinatus Sharpe 1908.

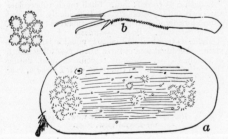

Length 1.10 to 1.18 mm. Shell with reticulate patterns anteriorly and posteriorly. Posterior edge of furca decidedly pectinate. The only known species of the genus with a pectinate furca. In ponds and slowly flowing streams, with *Typha, Iris, Chara,* etc. South Carolina.

FIG. 1259.
Ilyodromus pectinatus. (a) Side view, X 45; (b) Furca, X 140.

31 (30) Furca normal, with two spines and two setae (Fig. 1264 *b*). . . . 32

32 (33) Second segment of first leg with two setae on anterior margin (Fig. 1260 *d*). Three spines on first maxillary process.
Chlamydotheca Saussure 1858 . . 34

33 (32) Second segment of first leg with one seta on anterior margin (Fig. 1277 *b*). Two spines on first maxillary process.
Herpetocypris Brady and Norman 1889 . . 38

34 (35) Shell plain, no special markings of any sort. Seen from above, the shell is decidedly wedge-shaped anteriorly (Fig. 1260).
Chlamydotheca azteka Saussure 1858.

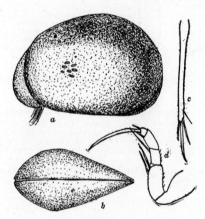

Length 3.30 mm., height 2.00 mm., breadth 1.80 mm. Yellowish gray. One of the largest species of the genus known. Natatory setae of the second antennae reach to tips of terminal claws. No males known. Seen from above, the shell is much more wedge-shaped anteriorly than *C. mexicana*. It also lacks the greenish stripes in the shell. Furca almost straight, about 18 times as long as wide, and faintly pectinate on the dorsal margin. Texas, Mexico. Ditches and pools, October.

FIG. 1260.
Chlamydotheca azteka. (*a*) Side view, × 15; (*b*) Dorsal view; (*c*) Furca, × 150; (*d*) First leg, × 125.

35 (34) Shell with semicontorted and radially arranged colored bands. Shell more tumid from above (Fig. 1261). 36

36 (37) Shell with at least six sinuous radiating dark-green bands on its sides . . . . *Chlamydotheca herricki* Turner 1895.

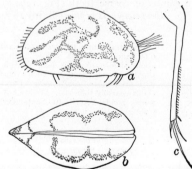

Length 3.00 mm., height 1.70 mm., width 1.43 mm. Light ground color with sinuous and radially arranged dark-green bands. Claws of first mandibular process, smooth. Terminal claw of first leg almost as long as entire leg. Furca straight, one-half the dorsal margin pectinate, about twenty times as long as wide. Shallow canal basin. Ohio.

FIG. 1261.
Chlamydotheca herricki. (*a*) Side view, × 25; (*b*) Dorsal view; (*c*) Furca, × 100.

37 (36)   Shell with but three such bands.

Chlamydotheca mexicana Sharpe 1903.

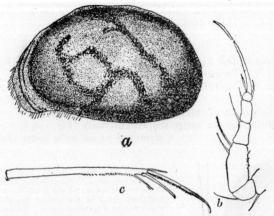

Length 2.75 mm., height 1.55 mm., width 1.60 mm. No males yet found. Two or three narrow greenish bands irregularly arranged on sides of shell. Furca straight, about twenty-three times as long as wide and faintly toothed on about one-half of dorsal margin. Ponds; September. Durango, Mexico.

FIG. 1262.
Chlamydotheca mexicana.
(a) Side view, × 25;
(b) First leg, × 100;
(c) Furca, × 125.

38 (39)   Length about four mm. . . . . . Herpetocypris barbatus Forbes 1893.

Width 1.60 mm., height 2.00 mm. Shell fairly full, but not plump. Large, hairy, yellowish brown in alcohol, with reddish patches on either side. One of the largest of the fresh-water ostracoda. Valves equal. Furca about twenty times as long as wide, slightly sinuate. Yellowstone River, Wyoming. July, August.

FIG. 1263.
Herpetocypris barbatus.   (a) Side view with shell removed; (b) Furca.   (After Forbes.)

39 (38)   Length less than three mm. 40

40 (41)   Dorsal edge of furca with five combs of coarse teeth (Fig. 1264 b).

Herpetocypris reptans Baird 1850.

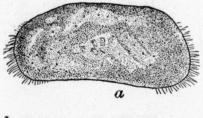

Length 2.00 mm. to 2.50 mm., height 0.80 mm. Brownish yellow. Furca about sixteen times as long as wide, slightly curved; its dorsal edge armed with *five combs of coarse teeth*. Furca claws coarsely toothed. Muddy bottoms, ponds; April to September. California.

FIG. 1264.
Herpetocypris reptans.   (a) Side view;
(b) Furca.

41 (40) Dorsal edge of furca plain (Fig. 1267 b).

Herpetocypris testudinaria Cushman 1908.

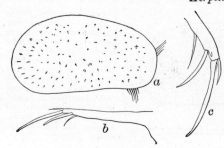

Length 2.10 mm., height 1.00 mm., width 0.80 mm. A small extra spine by subterminal claw. Furca about fourteen times as long as wide, its claws plain. Ponds. Newfoundland. May.

FIG. 1265.
Herpetocypris testudinaria. (a) Side view; (b) Furca; (c) End of furca, showing small spine by claw.

42 (43) Natatory setae of second antenna reach to tips of terminal claws, or slightly beyond. Second leg with a beak-like end segment and a claw (Fig. 1268 b, e). . Subfamily CYPRIDINAE . . 44

43 (42) Natatory setae of the second antenna reach beyond tips of terminal claws by about one-half their length. Second leg with three terminal setae of different lengths, two of them reflexed, the other short and claw-like (Fig. 1290 c, f).

Subfamily CYCLOCYPRIDINAE . . 75

44 (45) Testes, if present, originating in anterior part of shell in form of concentric circles or half circles (Fig. 1266).

Spirocypris Sharpe 1903 . . 46

45 (44) Testes, if present, not originating in anterior part of shell in form of concentric circles or half circles (Fig. 1271 b).

Cypris O. F. Müller 1785 . . 48

46 (47) Shell not tuberculate, excessively hairy (Fig. 1266 a).

Spirocypris passaica Sharpe 1903.

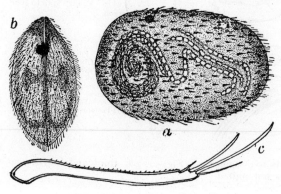

Length 1.60 mm., height 0.80 mm., breadth 0.82 mm. Brownish with dark-blue patches laterally and dorsally. Natatory setae reach slightly beyond tips of terminal claws. Terminal claw of second leg one and one-half times length of terminal segment. Furca about one-half length of shell, about twenty-three times as long as wide, and its dorsal margin weakly pectinate. Weedy ponds; spring months. Massachusetts, New Jersey.

FIG. 1266.
Spirocypris passaica. (a) Side view, × 30; (b) Dorsal view; (c) Furca.

47 (46) Shell **very** tuberculate, sparsely hairy and unusually plump (Fig. 1267 c). . . . . . . *Spirocypris tuberculata* Sharpe 1908.

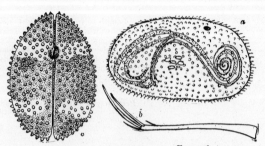

Length 0.93 mm., height 0.53 mm., width 0.70 mm. Purplish brown, with one or two dorsal transverse lighter bands. Right valve slightly overlaps the left anteriorly. Natatory setae extend but slightly beyond the terminal claws. Furca about thirty-two times as long as wide. Shallow, weedy, and s w a m p y ponds; spring. Chicago and northern Indiana.

FIG. 1267.
Spirocypris tuberculata. (a) Side view, × 43; (b) Furca; (c) Dorsal view.

48 (49) First leg four-segmented, third and fourth segments united (Fig. 1268 c). . . Subgenus *Eurycypris* G. W. Müller 1898. Only one species in this subgenus.
　　　　　　　　Cypris (*Eurycypris*) *pubera* O. F. Müller 1785.

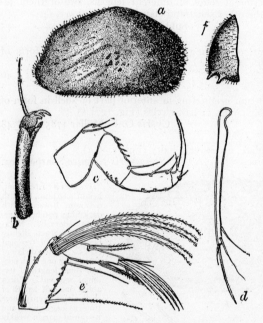

Length 2.10 mm., height 1.25 mm., breadth 1.20 mm. Greenish in color. A dark patch at its highest and central part as seen from the side. Shell sparsely hairy. Anterior and postero-ventral margins with prominent external tubercles. Two prominent tubercles at postero-ventral part of shell. This character alone is sufficient to identify this species of cypris. First leg four-segmented. Furca nearly straight, about twenty-four times as long as wide. Ponds; April to June. Oregon.

FIG. 1268.
Cypris (*Eurycypris*) *pubera.*
(a) Side view, × 10;
(b) End of second leg;
(c) First leg;
(d) Furca;
(e) Second antenna;
(f) Posteroventral part of shell.

49 (48) First leg plainly five-segmented (Fig. 1277 b), third and fourth segments not united. 50

50 (51) Inner anterior edge of right shell thickly tuberculate (Fig. 1270 a). Subgenus *Cyprinotus* Brady 1885 . . 52

51 (50)   Inner anterior edge of right shell plain (Fig. 1278 c). 62

52 (53)   Dorsal seta of furca more than one-half length of subterminal claw
          (Fig. 1270 c). 54

53 (52)   Dorsal seta of furca not more than one-half length of subterminal
          claw (Fig. 1273 c). 58

54 (55)   Left shell larger than the right, and its edges not tuberculate (Fig.
          1270 b). 56

55 (54)   Left shell smaller than the right, and with a row of scattered tubercles
          along the inner margin (Fig. 1269 b, e).
                        Cypris (Cyprinotus) pellucida Sharpe 1897.

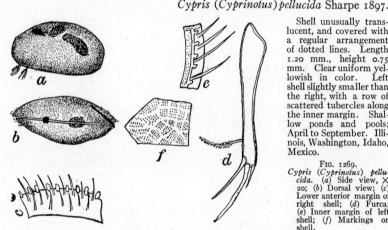

Shell unusually trans-
lucent, and covered with
a regular arrangement
of dotted lines. Length
1.20 mm., height 0.75
mm. Clear uniform yel-
lowish in color. Left
shell slightly smaller than
the right, with a row of
scattered tubercles along
the inner margin. Shal-
low ponds and pools;
April to September. Illi-
nois, Washington, Idaho,
Mexico.

Fig. 1269.
*Cypris (Cyprinotus) pellu-
cida.* (a) Side view, ×
20; (b) Dorsal view; (c)
Lower anterior margin of
right shell; (d) Furca;
(e) Inner margin of left
shell; (f) Markings on
shell.

56 (57)   Right-shell margin tuberculate only at anterior and posteroventral
          margins. Shell about four-sevenths as high as long (Fig.
          1270 a). . *Cypris (Cyprinotus) incongruens* Ramdohr 1808.

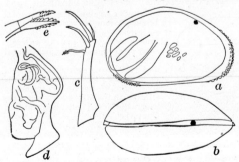

Shell densely pigmented to quite
translucent yellowish in alcohol.
Smooth. Length 1.40 to 1.70 mm.
Left valve overlaps right. Furca
curved, about ten times as long as
wide. Spines of first maxillary
process toothed. Quite common,
even in temporary ponds and
watering troughs. Florida, Ohio,
Pennsylvania.

Fig. 1270.
Cypris (Cyprinotus) incongruens.
(a) Right shell, × 22½; (b) Dorsal view
of female, × 22½; (c) Furca of female, × 55; (d) Penis, × 100; (e)
Spines of first maxillary process, ×
190.

57 (56) Right-shell margins unusally tuberculate, as in Fig. 1271 *b*. Shell not more than one-half as high as long (Fig. 1271 *a*).

Cypris (Cyprinotus) dentata Sharpe 1910.

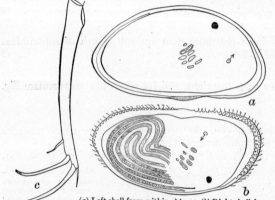

Shell brownish yellow and translucent in alcohol. Length 1.35 to 1.60 mm., and height not more than one-half as great. Shell pointed posteriorly, and anterior half of ventral margin slightly sinuate in the male, but nearly straight with the female. Natatory setae reaching well beyond the terminal claws. Males common. Furca gently curved, about sixteen times as long as wide. Spines of first maxillary process toothed. Temporary ponds. Stamford, Nebraska.

Fig. 1271.
Cypris (Cyprinotus) dentata.
(*a*) Left shell from within, × 30; (*b*) Right shell from within, × 30; (*c*) Furca, × 105.

58 (59) Dorsal seta of furca less than width of furca from subterminal claw (Fig. 1272*c*). . *Cypris (Cyprinotus) burlingtonensis* Turner 1894.

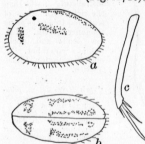

Length 1.50 mm., height 0.70 mm., width 0.70 mm. Yellowish brown with bluish black longitudinal stripes on dorsum and sides. Hairy. Natatory setae extend slightly beyond tips of terminal claws. Maxillary spines toothed. Furca slender and straight, about eighteen times as long as wide. Dorsal seta close to subterminal claw. Shallow, temporary, grassy pools. Ohio, Georgia, Delaware.

Fig. 1272.
Cypris (Cyprinotus) burlingtonensis. (*a*) Side view, × 16; (*b*) Dorsal view; (*c*) Furca.

59 (58) Dorsal seta of furca more than width of furca from subterminal claw. 60

60 (61) Shell with no markings, translucent. Right valve the larger.

Cypris (Cyprinotus) americanus Cushman 1905.

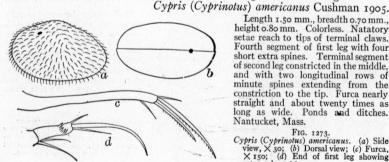

Length 1.50 mm., breadth 0.70 mm., height 0.80 mm. Colorless. Natatory setae reach to tips of terminal claws. Fourth segment of first leg with four short extra spines. Terminal segment of second leg constricted in the middle, and with two longitudinal rows of minute spines extending from the constriction to the tip. Furca nearly straight and about twenty times as long as wide. Ponds and ditches. Nantucket, Mass.

Fig. 1273.
Cypris (Cyprinotus) americanus. (*a*) Side view, × 30; (*b*) Dorsal view; (*c*) Furca, × 150; (*d*) End of first leg showing extra spines, × 150.

61 (60)   Shell reticulated, thin, the spermaries showing through.   Equivalve.
Cypris *(Cyprinotus) crena* Turner 1893.

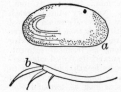

Shell equivalve from above, wedge-shaped anteriorly. Hinge line sinuate. Length 1.14 to 1.23 mm., height 0.60 to 0.65 mm., width 0.59 to 0.60 mm. Yellowish green. Maxillary spines smooth. Fourth segment of first leg not with four extra short spines. Furca curved, about eighteen times as long as wide. Males common. Abundant in small weedy ponds and canal basins. Ohio.

Fig. 1274.
Cypris *(Cyprinotus) crena.*   (a) Side view, X 15;   (b) Furca of male.

62 (63)   Furca normal, with two spines and two setae (Fig. 1278 d).
Subgenus *Cypris* . .   64

63 (62)   Furca abnormal, the terminal seta missing (Fig. 1280 c).
Paracypris New Subgenus . .   73

64 (65)   Both spines of first maxillary process smooth.   66

65 (64)   Both spines of first maxillary process toothed (Fig. 1270 e). . .   68

66 (67)   Shell bluish black, with two yellowish areas in region of eye-spot
(Fig. 1275 a). . . . .   Cypris *(Cypris) virens* Jurine 1820.

Length 1.70 to 2.00 mm., height 0.90 to 1.00 mm. Shell covered with short hairs, and left valve slightly overlapping the right. Ventral edge flanged anteriorly. Natatory setae reach to tips of terminal claws. Dark to yellowish green. Furca weakly S-shaped to straight and from eighteen to twenty times as long as average width, and its dorsal margin smooth. Very variable. Weedy ponds; April to July. Massachusetts, Mexico, Ohio, Wisconsin.

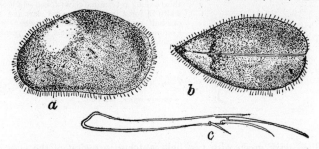

Fig. 1275.
Cypris *(Cypris) virens.*   (a) Side view, X 18;   (b) Dorsal view;   (c) Furca.

67 (66)   Shell bright, deep green, smooth, with minute punctures.
Cypris *(Cypris) altissima* Chambers 1877.

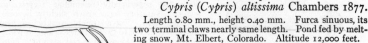

Length 0.80 mm., height 0.40 mm. Furca sinuous, its two terminal claws nearly same length. Pond fed by melting snow, Mt. Elbert, Colorado. Altitude 12,000 feet.

Fig. 1276. Cypris *(Cypris) altissima.* Furca.

63 (69)   Terminal three segments of first leg longer than two-thirds of its
terminal claw (Fig. 1277 b).   70
69 (68)   Terminal three segments of first leg shorter than two-thirds of its
terminal claw.   72

70 (71)   Shell thin, and dirty to ocherous yellow.

Cypris (Cypris) testudinaria Sharpe 1897.

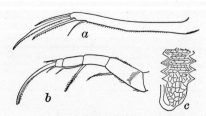

FIG. 1277.
Cypris (Cypris) testudinaria. (*a*) Furca; (*b*) First leg; (*c*) Part of ejaculatory duct of male, and origin of vas deferens.

Length 1.15 mm., height 0.75 mm., width 0.65 mm. Natatory setae just reach tips of terminal claws. Terminal claw of first leg one-sixth longer than the last three segments. Terminal claw of second leg one-third as long as terminal segment. Furca slightly curved, its dorsal edge serrate two-thirds its length, and sixteen to eighteen times as long as wide. Dorsal seta two-thirds as long as terminal one, and width of ramus from subterminal claw. Terminal seta fully one-half as long as the terminal claw. Ejaculatory duct five times as long as wide, with spines thickly set over the entire surface (Fig. 1277 *c*), instead of in wreaths, as is common. Ponds in woods. Illinois.

71 (70)   Shell dark green to chestnut brown with transverse lighter patches dorsolaterally (Fig. 1278 *a–b*).

Cypris (Cypris) fuscata Jurine 1820.

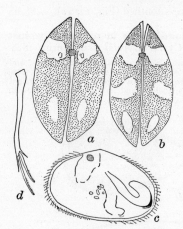

Length 1.30 mm., height 0.80 to 0.95 mm., width 0.80 to 0.85 mm. Right shell overlaps left. Sparsely hairy. Terminal claws of first leg less than one-third longer than the last three segments. Furca weakly S-shaped to nearly straight, and from eighteen to twenty times as long as wide. Terminal seta of furca weak, not more than one-third as long as terminal claw; dorsal seta less than width of furca from subterminal claw and about one-half as long as the terminal seta. Sexual. Common everywhere in shallow, grassy ponds and swamps; April to June.

FIG. 1278.
Cypris (Cypris) fuscata. (*a*) Variety *major,* dorsal view, × 20; (*b*) Variety *minor,* dorsal view; (*c*) Side view variety *major;* (*d*) Furca, × 125.

72   Shell dark green with two light patches in region of the eyes (Fig. 1279 *a*). . . . . *Cypris (Cypris) reticulata* Zaddach 1844.

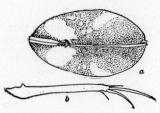

Length 1.10 to 1.30 mm., height 0.72 mm., width 0.65 mm. Shell usually reticulate or tesselated. Somewhat superficially resembling *Cypris fuscata major.* Natatory setae reach slightly beyond the terminal claws. Furca straight, weakly bent near the end, and from ten to twelve times as long as wide, and faintly toothed along the dorsal margin. Terminal seta slender and of the same length as the dorsal one, which is situated about width of furca from subterminal claw. Abundant in small, temporary grassy pools. Illinois, Massachusetts, New York, New Jersey.

FIG. 1279.
Cypris (Cypris) reticulata. (*a*) Dorsal view, × 27½; (*b*) Furca, × 132½.

73 (74) Posterior margin of furca pectinate (Fig. 1280 c).
Cypris (Paracypris) perelegans Herrick 1887.

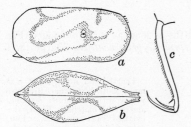

Length 3.60 mm., height 1.72 mm., width 1.40 mm. Color clear pale yellow, with a sigmoid pattern in clear brown. Seen from above, the shell is acutely wedge-shaped anteriorly. From the side the upper and lower margins are nearly parallel, with a large projecting tooth postero-ventrally. Terminal segment of second leg with two small claws and one seta. Dorsal seta spine-like. Weedy ponds. Alabama.

Fig. 1280.
Cypris (Paracypris) perelegans. (a) Side view, × 9; (b) Dorsal view; (c) Furca.

74 (73) Posterior margin of furca plain (Fig. 1281 c).
Cypris (Paracypris) grandis Chambers 1877.

Length 3.60 mm., height 2.09 mm., width 1.39 mm. From above, shell regularly elliptical. Bluish white to pale greenish. Ponds along the Arkansas River, Colorado. Altitude 8000 feet. A doubtful form.

Fig. 1281.
Cypris (Paracypris) grandis. (a) Side view, × 4; (b) Dorsal view; (c) Furca; (d) Maxillary palps of male. (After Chambers.)

75 (76) Terminal segment of second leg small, with two short claws, and a long reflexed seta (Fig. 1282 d). Second antenna of male with two sense organs on fourth segment.
Cypria Zenker 1854 . . 77

76 (75) Terminal segment of second leg long and narrow, with short claw, and two long reflexed setae (Fig. 1290 f). Second antenna of male without sense organs on the fourth segment.
Cyclocypris Brady and Norman 1889 . . 89

77 (78) Right-valve margin not crenulate anteriorly. Valves about the same size (Fig. 1284 a–b). . . . Subgenus Cypria . . 79

78 (77) Right-valve margin crenulate anteriorly. Valves of decidedly different sizes (Fig. 1287 a–b).
Subgenus Physocypria Vavra 1891 . . 87

79 (80) Terminal claws of second leg approximately equal (Fig. 1282 d). . 81

80 (79) Terminal claws of second leg evidently unequal (Fig. 1285 d). . . 85

81 (82)   Terminal claws of furca not more than one-half as long as furca
          (Fig. 1283 *b*).   83

82 (81)   Terminal claws of furca three-fifths as long as furca or longer (Fig.
          1282 *c*). . . . . . .   *Cypria (Cypria) dentifera* Sharpe 1897.

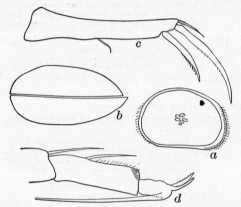

Length 0.69 mm., height 0.38 mm., width 0.26 mm. Brownish yellow, with dark brown markings and reddish blotches. Right valve overlaps l e f t anteriorly. Left-valve margins crenulate, anteriorly. Natatory setae reach length of antennae beyond tips of terminal claws. Terminal short claws of second leg approximately equal and as long as the terminal segment. Furca stout, ten times as long as wide, its subterminal claw with a comb of remarkably long teeth. Males common. Algae-rich ponds. Illinois, Ohio, New York, New Jersey.

FIG. 1282.
Cypria (Cypria) dentifera. (*a*) Side view of left valve, × 30; (*b*) Dorsal view; (*c*) Furca; (*d*) End of second leg.

83 (84)   Shell covered with a close reticulum of longitudinally subparallel
          lines (Fig. 1283 *c*).   Abdomen without processes.
                    Cypria (Cypria) exsculpta Fischer 1855.

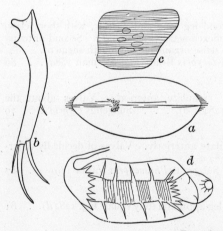

Length 0.60 to 0.75 mm., height 0.38 to 0.42 mm., width 0.25 to 0.28 mm. Shell thin, covered with anastomosing subparallel lines. Color clear chestnut brown. Common in streams and ponds everywhere. Also common in bottom tows in river channels, lake and river shores. Caudal rami short, stout and much curved; both terminal claws smooth; dorsal setae situated slightly beyond middle of ramus. Distribution world wide. This species may be at once identified by means of the reticulum of anastomosing subparallel lines on the valves. These may be readily seen with a two-thirds-inch objective.

FIG. 1283.
Cypria (Cypria) exsculpta. (*c*) Dorsal view, × 45; (*b*) Furca; (*c*) Striations on shell; (*d*) Spiny cylinder of ejaculatory duct, in sack.

84 (83) Shell plain, with small puncta. Abdomen with two cylindrical
processes. . . . . *Cypria (Cypria) opthalmica* Jurine 1820.

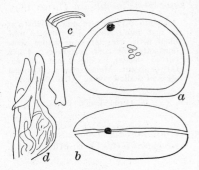

Length 0.56 to 0.60 mm., height 0.36 to 0.40
mm., width 0.32 to 0.36 mm. Shell compressed,
clear brown, with dark-brown patches anteriorly and posteriorly and just back of eye-spot.
Natatory setae very long, reaching beyond
terminal claws by more than the entire length
of the antenna. Furca about eight times as
long as wide. Surface and bottom tows in
river channels and lakes, and their shores;
February to October. Also common in ponds
and ditches where there is little or no vegetation. Georgia, Illinois, Minnesota, Oregon.

FIG. 1284.
Cypria (Cypria) opthalmica. (*a*) Side view, × 49;
(*b*) Dorsal view; (*c*) Furca, × 137½; (*d*) Penis,
× 190.

85 (86) Shell clear to brownish yellow, with a few scattered puncta.
Cypria (Cypria) obesa Sharpe 1897.

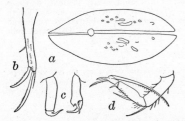

Length 0.78 mm., height 0.48 mm., width
0.33 mm. Plump. Furca bent, about nine
times as long as wide, its dorsal seta three
times width of ramus from subterminal claw,
and as long as the terminal seta. Males common. In tow of sandy lake shore; May.
Illinois.

FIG. 1285.
Cypria (Cypria) obesa. (*a*) Dorsal view, × 45;
(*b*) Furca; (*c*) Maxillary palps of male; (*d*) Second
leg.

86 (85) Shell white, smooth, and shining, with numerous almost confluent
puncta. . . . . . *Cypria (Cypria) mons* Chambers 1877.

Length 0.70 mm. A doubtful form, not well described.
Colorado, Mt. Elbert. Altitude 11,000 feet.

FIG. 1286.
Cypria (Cypria) mons. (*a*) Dorsal view; (*b*) Side view, × 16.
(After Chambers.)

87 (88) Left shell higher than right. Terminal short setae of second leg
about twice as long as the terminal segment (Fig. 1287).
Cypria (Physocypria) pustulosa Sharpe 1897.

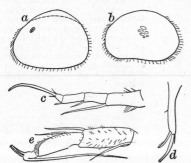

Length 0.51 mm., height 0.39 mm., width
0.22 mm. Clear brownish with dark patches.
Extremities of shell hairy. A decided dorsal
flange on left valve (Fig. 1287 *a*). Natatory
setae three times as long as the distance between the place of their insertion and tips of
terminal claws. Furca two and two-fifths
length of terminal claw. Dorsal seta weak and
situated about middle of furca. Bottom tows
in river channels, surface and bottom tows in
lakes, and lake and river shores; April to
September. Illinois.

FIG. 1287.
Cypria (Physocypria) pustulosa. (*a*) Left valve, ×
36; (*b*) Right valve; (*c*) First leg; (*d*) Furca;
(*e*) Second leg.

88 (87)   Left shell same height as right, but longer.   Terminal short setae of
second leg about as long as terminal segment.

Cypria (Physocypria) inequivalva Turner 1893.

Length 0.42 to 0.55 mm., height 0.35
to 0.38 mm., width 0.26 to 0.28 mm.
Shell with irregular cross-shaped spots
dorsoanteriorly and posteriorly. Furca
curved, slender, its dorsal seta rudimentary or absent. Males common. Amongst
algae of shallow ponds. Ohio, Georgia.

FIG. 1288.
Cypria (Physocypria) inequivalva.   (a) Side view, × 44; (b) Dorsal view; (c) Furca.

89 (90)   Dorsal seta of furca rudimentary or absent (Fig. 1289 c).

Cyclocypris laevis O. F. Müller 1785.

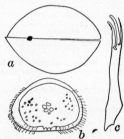

Length 0.45 to 0.48 mm., width 0.24 to 0.28 mm.,
height 0.30 to 0.35 mm. Color lemon yellow to chestnut
red or horn brown. Plump, and left shell overlapping the
right anteriorly. Furca stout, nearly straight, six times
as long as wide. Terminal seta more than one-half length
of terminal claw. Common in weedy streams, ponds, and
swampy regions; April to November. Delaware, Indiana, Illinois, New York, New Jersey.

FIG. 1289.
Cyclocypris laevis.   (a) Dorsal view, × 60; (b) Side view, × 45;
(c) Furca.

90 (89)   Dorsal seta of furca plainly well developed.   Terminal claws of furca
strong, and much bent at tip (Fig. 1290 e).

Cyclocypris forbesi Sharpe 1897.

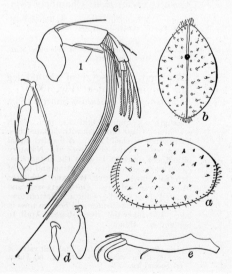

Length 0.55 mm., width 0.36
mm., height 0.39 mm. A small
form. Plump and sepia brown in
alcohol. Natatory setae four times
length of terminal claws. Penultimate segment of second antenna
with but one seta. Terminal segment of second leg three-eighths
as long as the preceding segment
(Fig. 1290 f). Furca about eight
times as long as wide. Both terminal claws strongly bent at tip,
nearly smooth. Right palp of second maxilla of male larger than
the left one. Terminal seta about
as long as width of furca. Males
common. Ponds in woods; April.
Illinois.

FIG. 1290.
Cyclocypris forbesi.   (a) Side view, ×
60; (b) Dorsal view; (c) Second
antenna; (d) Maxillary palps of
male; (e) Furca; (f) Second leg.

91   Terminal segment of second leg with three unlike setae, one of which
              is reflexed (Fig. 1291 d). . Subfamily CANDONINAE . .   92

92 (94)   Shell reticulate, very tumid.   Small, plump forms, not more than 0.80
              mm. long.   Second antenna of both sexes five-segmented.
                                Paracandona Hartwig 1899 . .   93

93   Shell profusely ornamented with polygonal areas and tubercles
              (Fig. 1291 a).
                                Paracandona euplectella Brady and Norman 1889.

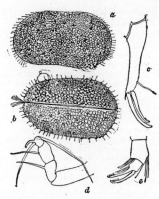

Length 0.56 to 0.58 mm., height 0.32 to 0.36
mm., width 0.32 to 0.34 mm.   Male somewhat
larger.   One terminal claw of mandibular palp
fused to terminal segment (Fig. 1291 e).   Furca
stout, six times as long as wide.   Dorsal seta about
length of subterminal claw.   Terminal seta weak,
scarcely evident.   No other Candona-like ostracod shows the ornamentation of polygonal areas
and tubercles.   The specific name very happily
refers to the striking external appearance.   Shallow, swampy regions, in mud and debris of the
bottom; spring months.   New Jersey.

FIG. 1291.
Paracandona euplectella. (a) Side view, × 50; (b) Dorsal view; (c) Furca; (d) Second leg; (e) Mandibular
palp.

94 (92)   Shell plain, at least not reticulate or excessively tuberculate or
              tumid. - 95

95 (96)   Furca abnormal, terminal seta absent (Fig. 1292 b).
                                Typhlocypris Vejdovsky 1882 . .   97

96 (95)   Furca normal, with 2 claws and 2 setae (Fig. 1294 b).
                                Candona Baird 1850 . .   99

97 (98)   Furca nearly straight.   Dorsal-valve margins evenly curved. (Fig.
              1292 a–b). . . . .   Typhlocypris peircei Turner 1895.

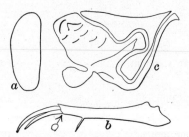

Length 0.70 to 0.79 mm., width 0.22 to 0.31
mm., height 0.33 to 0.37 mm.   Color white,
tinged with yellow.   Shell smooth, much
compressed.   Furca nearly straight, and about
twelve times as long as wide.   Subterminal
claw more than two-thirds length of terminal
one.   Sexual.   Ejaculatory duct of seven whorls
of chitinous spines.   Shallow, weedy ponds;
June.   Georgia.

FIG. 1292.
Typhlocypris peircei. (a) Side view of female, × 28;
(b) Furca of male; (c) Penis.

98 (97) Furca decidedly curved. Dorsal-valve margins "humped" (Fig. 1293 a). . . . *Typhlocypris delawarensis* Turner 1895.

Length 0.95 mm., width 0.43 mm., height 0.54 mm. Color greenish yellow with brown blotches. Maxillary spines plain. Terminal claws of furca slender and plain. Furca slender and much curved. Creeks; March. Delaware. (A doubtful form, not well described.)

FIG. 1293.
Typhlocypris delawarensis. (a) Side view, × 15; (b) Furca.

99 (100) Shorter seta of terminal segment of second leg outwardly flexed (Fig. 1294 a1). . . . . . . *Candona reflexa* Sharpe 1897.

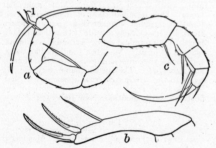

Shell twice as long as high, cinereous. Second leg five-segmented, its terminal segment as wide as long, and about one-third as long as the penultimate segment. Furca eight times as long as wide and slightly curved. Dorsal seta as long as subterminal claw. This is the only *Candona* known with the peculiar, partly reflexed seta of the second foot, and it may be a characteristic of a young stage. Tows along lake shores along the bottom; April to November. Illinois.

FIG. 1294.
Candona reflexa. (a) Second leg; (b) Furca; (c) First leg.

100 (99) Shorter seta of terminal segment of second leg not outwardly flexed (Fig. 1296 b). 101

101 (102) Length of shell more than 1.50 mm.

Candona crogmani Turner 1894.

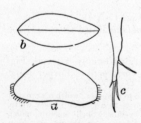

Length 1.52 mm., height 0.76 mm., width 0.58 mm. Shell thin, pellucid, inequivalve, greenish yellow. Maxillary spines plain. Second leg indistinctly segmented. Furca straight, ten times as long as average width, its terminal claws pectinate. Dorsal seta one-third length of furca from subterminal claw. Shallow, temporary ponds; December. Georgia.

FIG. 1295.
Candona crogmani. (a) Side view, × 15; (b) Dorsal view; (c) Furca.

102 (101) Length of shell not more than 1.50 mm. 103

103 (104) Length of shell less than one mm. 105

104 (103) Length of shell more than one mm. 108

105 (106) Subterminal claw of furca decidedly S-shaped (Fig. 1296 *d*).
Candona simpsoni Sharpe 1897.

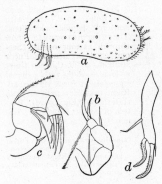

Length 0.73 mm., height 0.31 mm., width 0.29 mm. Yellowish white. Left valve overlaps the right. Upper and lower valve margins nearly parallel. Furca curved, stout, seven times as long as wide with the subterminal claw decidedly S-shaped — a marked character. Dorsal seta twice width of furca from subterminal claw, and two-thirds its length. Bottom forms of lakes and river shores, and ponds; spring and autumn. Illinois.

FIG. 1296.
Candona simpsoni. (*a*) Side view, × 47; (*b*) Second leg; (*c*) Second antenna; (*d*) Furca.

106 (105) Subterminal claw not S-shaped (Fig. 1297 *c*).   107

107 Shell with dorsal and ventral margins nearly parallel (Fig. 1297 *a*).
Candona parallela G. W. Müller 1900.

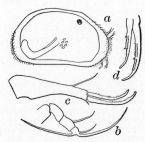

Length 0.78 to 0.85 mm., height 0.42 to 0.46 mm., width 0.35 to 0.42 mm. Height to length about as 1 to 18. Furca straight, about seven times as long as wide, its terminal seta rudimentary, and its terminal claws doubly pectinate with unusual teeth. Dorsal seta about twice width of furca from subterminal claw. Second leg five-segmented. Swampy ponds; May. Colorado.

FIG. 1297.
Candona parallela. (*a*) Side view, × 37½; (*b*) Second leg; (*c*) Furca; (*d*) Terminal claws of furca.

108 (109) Furca plainly curved (Fig. 1301 *b*).   112

109 (108) Furca not plainly curved, approximately straight (Fig. 1298 *d*).   110

110 (111) *Both* claws of furca plainly S-shaped (Fig. 1298 *d*).
Candona sigmoides Sharpe 1897.

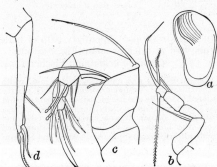

Length of male 1.25 mm., height 1.63 mm. Second leg five-segmented. Furca long and straight, about twelve times as wide as average width. Dorsal seta about four times width of furca from subterminal claw. Female not known. Lake and river shores; May and October. Illinois.

FIG. 1298.
Candona sigmoides. (*a*) Side view of male, × 15; (*b*) Second leg; (*c*) Second antenna; (*d*) Furca.

111 (110)   Both claws of furca not S-shaped — gently curved (Fig. 1299 a).
Candona recticauda Sharpe 1897.

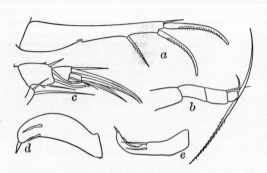

Male 1.18 mm. long, 0.70 mm. wide. Shell curved with scattered papillar elevations. The spermatogonia show through as four bands. Second leg six-segmented. Furca straight, about thirteen times as long as wide, with a dorsal sinus base of furca very broad. Right maxillary palp of male club-shaped (Fig. 1300d). Bottom of ponds; February. Illinois.

FIG. 1299.
Candona recticauda. (a) Furca; (b) Second leg; (c) End of second antenna; (d) Right maxillary palp of male; (e) Left maxillary palp of male.

112 (113)   Second leg six-segmented. 114

113 (112)   Second leg less than six-segmented. 116

114 (115)   Shell with fine longitudinal striations when in glycerin. Maxillary palps of male enormously thickened, their fingers fully as thick as the stem (Fig. 1300 d).
Candona fabaeformis Fischer 1854.

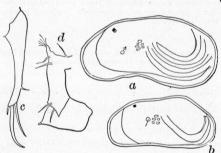

Length 1.00 to 1.26 mm., height 0.47 to 0.50 mm., width 0.49 to 0.51 mm. Shell yellowish transparent, strongly compressed, the left valve overlapping the right at both extremities, and also with dorsal flanges. Furca ten times as long as wide, straight. Abundant in small pools in March, April, and September. Georgia, Illinois.

FIG. 1300.
Candona fabaeformis. (a) Side view of male, × 30; (b) Side view of female, × 30; (c) Furca; (d) Right maxillary palp of male, × 75.

115 (114)   Shell without fine longitudinal striations. Maxillary palp of male with finger about one-half as thick as stem (Fig. 1301 c).
Candona acuminata Fischer 1854.

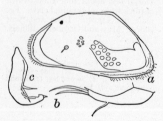

Length 1.20 to 1.50 mm., height 0.60 mm., width 0.46 to 0.50 mm. Posterior extremity of shell sharply pointed. Dorsally about as *Candona fabaeformis*, but less compressed, and dorsal flanges weaker. Furca eight times as long as wide, decidedly curved, and much the broader at its base. River shores and ponds with rich vegetation; April, May, and September. Texas.

FIG. 1301.
Candona acuminata. (a) Left shell of female, × 20; (b) Furca; (c) Left maxillary palp of male.

116   Shell decidedly arched dorsally, much the highest in the middle
         (Fig. 1302 a). . . .   *Candona candida* O. F. Müller 1785.

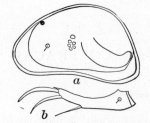

Length 1.05 to 1.20 mm., height 0.60 mm. Second leg
four or indistinctly five-segmented. Furca five times as
long as average width, decidedly curved. Males uncommon. Shallow, temporary ponds and ditches; April and
September. Massachusetts.

FIG. 1302.
Candona candida.   (a) Side view of female, X 29; (b) Furca of
female, X 75.

REFERENCES ON NORTH AMERICAN FRESH–WATER OSTRACODA

BRADY and NORMAN. 1889. A Monograph of the Marine and Fresh-Water
Ostracoda of the North Atlantic and North-western Europe. Sci. Trans.
Royal Dublin Soc., Ser. 2, 4 : 63–270.

HERRICK, C. L. 1887. Contribution to the Fauna of the Gulf of Mexico
and the South. Memoirs of Denison Sci. Ass'n, 1 : 1–56.

MARSHALL, W. S. 1903. *Entocythere cambaria.* A Parasitic Ostracod.
Trans. Wis. Acad. of Sci. Arts and Letters, 14 : 117–144.

MÜLLER, G. W. 1894. Die Ostracoden des Golfes von Neapel. Monogr. 21.
Fauna und Flora des Golfes von Neapel. Berlin.

1900. Deutschlands Süsswasser-Ostracoden. Zoologica, Heft 30, 112 pp.

SHARPE, R. W. 1897. Contributions to a Knowledge of the North American Fresh-Water Ostracoda included in the Families Cytheridae and
Cyprididae. Bull. Ill. State Lab. of Nat. Hist., 4:414–484.

1903. Report of the Fresh-Water Ostracoda of the United States National
Museum, including a Revision of the Subfamilies and Genera of the
Family Cyprididae. Proc. U. S. Nat. Mus., 26:969–1001.

1908. A Further Report on the Ostracoda of the United States National
Museum. Proc. U. S. Nat. Mus., 35 :399–430.

1910. On some Ostracoda, mostly new, in the Collection of the United
States National Museum. Proc. of the U. S. Nat. Mus., 38:335–341.

TURNER, C. H. 1893. Additional Notes on the Cladocera and Ostracoda of
Cincinnati, Ohio. Bull. Sci. Lab. Denison Univ., 8, pt. 1 : 1–18.

1894. Notes on American Ostracoda, with Descriptions of new Species.
Bull. Sci. Lab. Denison Univ., 8, pt. 2, 13–26.

1895. Fresh-Water Ostracoda of the United States. Geol. and Nat. Hist.
Survey of Minn., Zool. Ser., 2: 277–337.

VAVRA, W. 1891. Monographie Ostracoden Böhmens. Archiv. der naturw.
Landesforschung von Böhmen, Bd. VIII, no. 3.

CHAPTER XXV

HIGHER CRUSTACEANS (MALACOSTRACA)

By A. E. ORTMANN

Curator of Invertebrate Zoology, Carnegie Museum, Pittsburgh.

To the higher Crustaceans (subclass Malacostraca) belong such forms as the sow-bugs, scuds, shrimps, prawns, crayfishes or craw-fishes, and crabs. These popular names are not sharply defined, but it appears convenient to restrict the name sow-bugs to the Isopods, that of the scuds to the Amphipods. For the Mysidacea, the term opossum-shrimps has been introduced, while the names shrimps and prawns belong to certain Decapods, and are almost synonyms: the former is now used chiefly for the smaller forms, the latter for the larger ones. Crayfishes and Crawfishes are the Decapods of the genera *Cambarus* and *Potamobius*. Often for these also the name crabs is used, but this is a misnomer, and it should be restricted to marine forms of the type of the common edible blue crab.

The great majority of the Malacostraca belong to the sea, occurring in all regions, near the shore as well as on the bottom of the deep sea, and floating and swimming on the surface. But a considerable number have entered the fresh water, and are found in rivers, creeks, ponds, lakes, etc. A few forms are known, which live parasitic upon other aquatic creatures.

They are omnivorous, feeding on vegetable and animal matter, both living and dead, but dead and decaying matter is preferred by most of them. *Asellus* (of the Isopods) distinctly prefers de-caying vegetable matter, while *Palaemonias* (of the Decapods) seems to be specialized as a mud-eater: at any rate, the peculiar hair-tufts on the claws probably serve the same purpose as in the allied tropical forms, where it has been observed that they are used in gathering mud, like a small brush.

Generally, the fresh-water Malacostraca are not very conspicu-ous, some because they are rather small and easily escape detec-tion, while others, which are larger, keep in hiding, under stones and logs, in holes, or among vegetation. But they are present practically everywhere, and in most bodies of water, even small ones, one or several forms may be expected to occur. Certain forms (burrowing crayfishes) do not live in open water, but burrow in the ground, going down to the ground-water; their presence is indicated by piles of mud, brought out of the holes.

Fresh-water Malacostraca are found, with exception of the Antarctic regions, practically all over the world, including the Arctic, but naturally are most abundant in the tropics. A number of groups are distinctly characteristic of temperate climates, and at least one group (genus *Cambarus*, crayfish) has reached its highest development in North America. Here Malacostraca are found everywhere, but chiefly in the interior basin with its great and diversified river systems. They become rather scarce on the western plains and in the arid regions, but are not entirely missing there. The various forms are adapted to different surroundings; some prefer large rivers, others creeks or ponds, or small pools, springs, and even subterranean waters.

They belong to very different groups of the subclass Malacostraca. The latter has been divided, in the more recent systems, into ten orders, and of these four possess representatives in our fresh waters: Isopoda, Amphipoda, Mysidacea, and Decapoda. These differ very much in their outer features, in general shape of body, size, color, and details of morphology, so that it is hard to give a short general account of their characters.

The body may be only a few millimeters long, up to one or two centimeters (Isopods, Amphipods), or it may be somewhat longer (Mysidacea and some Decapods), while in other cases (prawns and crayfishes among the Decapods) it may reach the considerable length of ten centimeters and over. In the smaller forms, the color is generally inconspicuous, whitish or grayish, often more or less transparent. The larger forms have more distinct colors, which may become quite brilliant in certain parts of the body: the large claws of the genus *Palaemon* (prawns) are, in the male sex, often red, blue or purple. The crayfishes are, in general, of greenish or brownish olive tints, but as a rule adult males are more vividly colored, and in some species the adult male assumes a color entirely different from the greenish female and young: lighter or darker red.   At least two species are remarkable for their striking color in both sexes: one is red, the other is beautifully blue.

The morphological characters of the Malacostraca are the following:

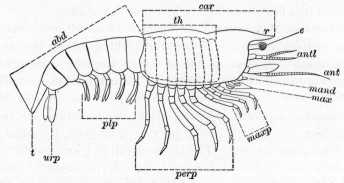

FIG. 1303.   Diagram of a higher Crustacean.   (After Calman.)

The body is enclosed in a comparatively hard shell, which is articulated, forming a number of successive segments or somites, which have a very constant number.   Each somite may be compared to a ring, which, however, is not completely circular, but the upper part, called tergum or tergite, is convex, while the lower, sternum or sternite, is rather flat.   The two unite on each side, the tergite projecting over the sternite, and this projecting part is called the pleuron.   All these parts (as well as the appendages) consist of a hornlike substance, called chitin, very often reinforced by a considerable amount of calcareous matter.

In the anterior part of the body we have a headpiece, to which are added several more or less obscure somites that are chiefly indicated by their appendages.   As the foremost appendage we may regard the eyes (*e* in Fig. 1303).   These, however, may not be true appendages.   Then follow two pairs of feelers, called antennulae (*antl*) and antennae (*ant*); one pair of mandibles (*mand*), and two pairs (first and second) of maxillae (*max*).

Behind these parts the segmented body begins, including fifteen somites, which all (barring reductions) bear appendages, with the exception of the last, the telson (*t*).   According to the appendages, the body is distinctly divided into two parts: the anterior, thorax or trunk (*th*), comprising the first eight somites; the posterior, abdomen (*abd*), with the six following (to which the telson is added).

The appendages of the thorax are called thoracic limbs. Some or all of the first three of them are in many cases specialized as maxillipeds (*maxp*), and in this case the following five are called peraeopods (*perp*). The abdominal appendages are called pleopods (*plp*), but those of the last (sixth) pair are often differentiated in a peculiar way, so as to form with the telson a caudal fan, and in this case the name uropods (*urp*) is used for them.

The detail-structure of the appendages of the different regions of the body is very different. The eyes (only doubtfully regarded as appendages) may be entirely sessile, or may be elevated upon short, subcylindrical, more or less movable eye-stalks. The antennulae have an articulated base, with one or two terminal, articulated branches (flagella). The antennae have an articulated basal part, with one terminal, articulated flagellum, and often the basal part has a lateral scalelike process: the antennal scale or scaphocerite.

The mandible consists of a more or less solid part, to which an articulated palpus may be attached. The maxillae are of various shapes, and are probably to be regarded as modified anterior thoracic appendages. They consist of an inner and an outer branch (endopodite and exopodite), which, however, are often augmented by certain parts belonging originally to the gill apparatus.

The most marked difference is between the thoracic and the abdominal appendages. The former consist originally of a larger, seven-jointed inner branch (endopodite), and a smaller, articulated outer branch (exopodite), but the latter may be absent. The seven joints of the endopodite are rather constant, although some of them may become united, or others may be subdivided. They have received separate names, which are, from the proximal to the distal end: coxa, basis, ischium, merus, carpus, propodus, dactylus (or coxopodite, basipodite, etc.). In certain thoracic limbs, the last two joints (propodus and dactylus) assume a peculiar position, forming a chela (pinchers, claws).

The typical pleopods consist of a simple basal part, with two sub-equal, terminal, articulated branches. But in many cases differentiations and reductions are observed, the most important being that of the uropods, referred to above, and the transformation of certain pleopods into copulatory organs in the male.

In certain forms (Mysidacea and Decapoda) the dorsal shell of the most anterior part of the body (head) is produced backward, and covers more or less the thoracic somites in the shape of a shield, curved down over the sides, which is called the cephalothorax or carapace (car). Very often the carapace has a median anterior projection, called the rostrum (r).

The branchial apparatus of the Isopods is formed by the pleopods. In all other groups special appendages (gills) of the thoracic somites assume this function; they may be attached to the sides of the thorax, or to the basal parts of the thoracic limbs.

The genital openings of the male are always originally on the coxopodite of the eighth trunk-leg (or fifth peraeopod), those of the female on the sixth (or third peraeopod), but in certain cases either one of these may shift to the sternite.

All Malacostraca of the fresh water have separate sexes, and very often the males are distinguished by secondary sexual characters (size, color, development of claws). Copulation, or rather conjugation, seems to take place in all of them, although this has been observed in detail only in very few forms: it is best known in the crayfishes.

Propagation is by eggs. In the smaller forms (Isopoda, Amphipoda, Mysidacea), very little is known about propagation and development, and with regard to the North American forms of these groups investigations are altogether lacking. But from what is known of exotic, chiefly European, forms it is probable that in all the eggs are carried by the female for a certain period, before the young are set free. In the Isopods, the female develops during the breeding season peculiar lamellae at the base of some thoracic legs (four pairs in *A sellus*), which serve to cover and to hold the eggs. In the Amphipods and Mysidacea similar, but greatly variable, devices are present. In the Decapods, no such apparatus is known, but here the eggs are attached to the pleopods and are carried under the abdomen of the mother till the young are ready to hatch.

Within these brood-pouches the embryonal development takes place. After the young have reached a more or less advanced stage, they leave the egg, but always remain a certain time in the brood-room of the mother. In the Isopods (*Asellus*) the young leave the egg at a rather early stage, and they have yet to undergo considerable changes; in the other groups the larva hatches in a more advanced stage, and the subsequent changes are slight. In none of our fresh-water crustaceans are free swimming larvae known, but these might be present in the families Atyidae and Palaemonidae, in which such have been observed in their allied marine forms.

Of the life history of the Isopods, Amphipods, Mysidacea, and most of the Decapods, practically nothing is known. However, in the Decapod-genus *Cambarus* (crayfishes) more complete information is at hand.

After hatching, the young crayfishes remain for a short time with the mother, but soon leave her, and grow in the beginning at a rather rapid rate, each increase in size being connected with a moulting of the shell. Later, they grow less rapidly, and, after the first summer, we may distinguish, in general, a spring and an autumn moult. The total length of life seems to be several years: four, five, or even more. Sexual maturity may be reached within the first year, at least in some species. Males and females attain about the same size, but in most species (except the burrowing) the male possesses much stronger chelae than the female.

A very peculiar difference is found among the males, which at first was believed to be dimorphism, but has now been recognized as alternating conditions in the life of the same individual. Males of the first form have been distinguished from males of the second form; the former is the fully developed and sexually potent form, while the latter is an impotent form. Generally speaking the first form is assumed by the male in autumn, and lasts through the winter (copulating season), while the other is assumed in spring, and lasts through the summer. Young males, in their first summer, are always of the second form. The difference between these two forms is seen in the sexual organs: in the males of the second form these organs are softer, the horny tips are undeveloped, and the copulatory hooks on the ischiopodites of the peraeopods are small.

According to the general rule, that the males assume the first form in autumn, the copulating season falls in the autumn, and copulation may be repeated in the winter months. The male seizes the female and holds it, sternites against sternites, chiefly by the aid of the hooks of the ischiopodites of the peraeopods. The sperm is discharged and stored in the female's *annulus ventralis*, a pocket on the thoracic sternum, which thus serves as receptaculum seminis. Oviposition takes place later, generally in spring.

This seasonal cycle, as described, is not observed in all species, but there are some, in which the alternation of the two forms of the male is irregular and not connected with the seasons, and where copulation and oviposition are also irregular. It has been found that regularity of the annual cycle is connected with a habitat in water which is subject to regular and considerable seasonal changes of temperature (species living in rivers and ponds), while irregularity of the life-cycle is found among those which live preferably in water with slight temperature changes and that at the same time is rather cool (species of mountain streams and of cool springs or groundwater).

The fresh-water Malacostraca depend entirely upon the presence of water, and cannot leave the water as a rule. This holds good for the Isopoda, Amphipoda, and Mysidacea, and also for the Atyidae and Palaemonidae among the Decapoda. In the water, the Isopods (except the parasitic forms) crawl around on the bottom, under stones, or climb among water weeds, but do not move by swimming. The Amphipods are very lively in their movements, which consist chiefly of swimming, often lying upon the side. The swimming is often done in jerks, by curving and stretching the compressed body. They move also by climbing among water weeds, but hardly ever by crawling. All Mysidacea are distinctly swimming forms, and so are the Atyidae and Palaemonidae among the Decapods, while the movements of the crayfishes are of various kinds, but fall under two main heads: crawling and swimming. The first is the general mode of locomotion. It is not very rapid and may take place in all three directions: forward, backward, and sideward. More rarely the crayfishes move by swimming, and chiefly so when alarmed and trying to escape; this swimming is always backward, and is effected by quickly repeated strokes of the abdomen. This kind of locomotion, however, is kept up only for short distances.

With regard to the habitat, not much detail is known in the isopods and amphipods. They seem to prefer more quiet bodies of water, small streams and springs, to the larger rivers. Some of them are not very particular as to their habitat, and consequently possess a very wide geographical distribution, while others are very restricted, possibly on account of special habitat preferences. The only Mysidacean found in North America (*Mysis relicta*) inhabits the Great Lakes to a considerable depth (as do two species of the Amphipod-genus *Pontoporeia*). The genus *Palaemon* of the Decapods is known only from our largest rivers (Mississippi and Ohio).

In the genus *Cambarus*, very complex conditions are observed and the different species differ considerably in their ecology. Although they all need water for their existence, it is a general rule that all crayfishes are able to leave the water temporarily, and some may stay out of the water for a considerable time, and do so habitually. Of course, in order to moisten their gills, they always have to return to the water.

In the water, the crayfishes try to hide, either under rocks, logs, water weeds, etc., or they construct artificial hiding places (holes and burrows). The latter tendency is, as will be seen, especially developed in certain ecological groups. In connection with this tendency to hide probably is the fact that the crayfishes seem to be more or less nocturnal.

With regard to their ecological preferences, different types have been distinguished in the genus *Cambarus*. These are the following:

1. Species living in quiet waters: slowly running, large rivers, ponds, lakes. To this group belongs chiefly the subgenus *Cambarus*, and its distribution over the coastal plains and the interior basin expresses this ecological habit, since here such conditions are pre-eminently found. But certain species of the subgenus *Faxonius*

also prefer these surroundings. These species are content with hiding under other objects, and make holes only incidentally.

2. Species living preferably in water with a rather strong current.

(a) Species of the larger rivers. The subgenus *Faxonius* is typical for this habitat, and the location of its center of distribution in the central basin with its large rivers expresses this.

(b) Species living in small streams of the uplands. The representatives of this habitat belong chiefly to the subgenus *Bartonius*, and its distribution over the Appalachian Mountains and the Allegheny and Cumberland Plateau clearly indicates this.

Of course, there are all transitions between habitats (a) and (b), as many of the river species go well up into the head-waters, and vice versa. Yet the original differentiation in the habitat of the subgenera *Faxonius* and *Bartonius* is very evident. All these species in running water are good burrowers, and they generally excavate holes under protecting stones, etc. In some of the species from the mountain streams this faculty of burrowing is rather highly developed, and leads us to the next ecological type.

3. Burrowing species ("chimney builders"). These species have retired from the open water into the ground water, and one may understand the origin of this peculiar habit by imagining that forms in the small upland streams, with well-developed burrowing faculties, were forced, in periods of draught, when the streams inhabited by them began to dry up, to dig down in the bed into the gravel and mud, to reach the water. Or one may imagine, that they ascended in the streams up to the sources, and went under ground, where the water appears in the shape of springs. In a number of species this tendency has been carried to an extreme, and it is known that these live habitually under the surface of the earth, in the ground-water, where they excavate more or less complex systems of holes, burrows, or tunnels, which open upon the surface in one or more openings. These burrows are built by the crayfish, by using the chelae in digging (hence the similarity of the chelae in both sexes), and the material removed, mud, clay, etc., is carried to the surface, where it is piled up around the mouth of the burrow in irregular or regular piles, generally known by the name of "mud chimneys." These burrows and chiefly the mud

chimneys have attracted much attention, and the idea has been advanced that the chimneys are constructed by the crayfish for a certain definite (useful) purpose. But recent investigations seem to point to the conclusion that the regular shape of the chimneys, when present, is accidental, and the mud piles are nothing but the natural product of the burrowing, disposed of in the most convenient way (around the mouth of the hole). The burrows themselves are rather irregular, more or less complex, and consist of simple tunnels, often branching, and one or more pockets, or widenings of the tunnel. They go down into the ground from one to several feet, but always deep enough as to contain ground-water, at least at the bottom.

Burrowing species are found chiefly in the subgenus *Bartonius*, and form a very well defined morphological group, and it is just this group of this subgenus, which has spread out from the original territory (the mountains), and has descended into the plains. On the western and southwestern plains is found another group of burrowers which belong to the subgenus *Cambarus*.

Another special ecological group should not be forgotten. These are the cave species. With the exception of the Mysidacea, all our fresh-water Malacostraca have developed certain forms which are adapted to the life in subterranean waters, and live in caves, springs, artesian wells, etc. This peculiar habitat has affected their structure greatly, and the most important and interesting feature is the loss of the eyes. Some of these forms are entirely blind, having lost the visual elements of the eyes (cornea and pigment), while in others the reduction is only partial.

Among the Isopods, the only North American fresh-water form, belonging to the Cirolanidae, is a blind subterranean form (*Cirolanides texensis*, Fig. 1304). Of the Asellidae, some live in caves and have suffered the loss of the eyes. This is especially true of the genus *Caecidotea*, the species of which have been found in caves of Virginia, Georgia, Tennessee, Kentucky, Indiana, Illinois, and in subterranean waters in Texas. *Mancasellus*, which possesses eyes, has often been found in caves or in streams issuing from caves; it also lives in the Great Lakes.

The fresh-water Amphipods are remarkable for the development of eyeless cave forms; in fact, there is a strong tendency among them toward underground life. Of the 20 species known, 10 or 11 seem to be inhabitants of caves, wells, or springs. Not all of them have the eyes reduced, but the species of the genera *Crangonyx*, *Stygonectes*, and *Apocrangonyx* are actually blind, and there is a blind species in each of the genera *Eucrangonyx* and *Gammarus*, while the other species of these two genera show all transitional stages from well-developed eyes to more or less reduced eyes. The correlation between subterranean life and reduction of the eyes is very evident in this group.

The only species of the decapod-family Atyidae found in the United States, *Palaemonias ganteri* (Fig. 1311), is a blind cave-form, and it was discovered only recently (1901) in the waters of Mammoth Cave in Kentucky. This form has eye-stalks, but the visual elements of the eye are gone. This is an extremely interesting form on account of its primitive structure as well as its geographical relations. Most of the members of this family, which is strictly a fresh-water group, are found in the tropical and subtropical regions of both hemispheres, but a form very closely allied to the American is known from caves in Carniola, Austria.

In the family Palaemonidae is included *Palaemonetes antrorum*, which was discovered in an artesian well in Texas. Also this species is provided with eye-stalks, but the eyes themselves are obliterated.

Within the genus *Cambarus* of the family Potamobiidae, five cave species are known. They are all blind, but the eye-stalks remain. These species belong to different subgenera, and the best known is the famous blind crayfish of Mammoth Cave in Kentucky (*Cambarus pellucidus*), which is also found in other caves in Kentucky and in Indiana. It belongs to the subgenus *Faxonius*, and represents a rather ancient type, so that we are justified in regarding it as an old immigrant into the subterranean waters. Three species (*C. hamulatus*, *C. setosus*, and *C. ayersi*) belong to the subgenus *Bartonius*, representing a primitive section of it. The first of these is found in Nickajack Cave in eastern Tennessee, while the two others are from caves in the Ozark region in Missouri. These three species also must be old immigrants into

the caves.   The fifth of the blind species is *C. acherontis*, found in
caves in Florida.   This belongs to the subgenus *Cambarus*, and is
a member of a rather highly advanced section of the subgenus
which is common on the coastal plain, and is to be regarded as a
more recent addition to the cave fauna.

The economic value of the fresh-water Malacostraca is very
different in the different groups.   While the isopods, amphipods,
and Mysidacea are small, the decapods are larger, but also of these
the Atyidae and certain Palaemonidae attain only a medium
size.   These groups naturally have only an inferior value for man,
and are generally overlooked and neglected.   Of the larger forms,
certain species of *Palaemon* (prawns, also called shrimps), and the
crayfishes have attracted attention, and are used by man, primarily as food.   Although this is generally the case in Europe and
with a number of tropical forms, in North America they are not
very popular, and are only occasionally eaten; yet there is no
doubt that *Potamobius* and *Cambarus* are to be regarded as part
of the natural food supply of this country.   Other uses, for instance
as fish bait, should be mentioned incidentally.

On the other hand, some kind of damage or injury done to man
or man's work has also been noticed in so far as certain burrowing
species are liable to damage dams or levees, or to interfere with
farming operations.   The latter species are also reported to be
injurious to crops, chiefly to sprouting plants.

In the general economy of nature, all the higher crustaceans
perform a twofold task.   First, on account of their general habit
of devouring masses of decaying vegetable and animal matter,
they are to be counted among the scavengers, and second, they
themselves serve as food for other animals.   They are most important as fish-food, and even the larger forms are eaten by the larger
fishes.   In addition, a number of other creatures feed upon them
(amphibians, water snakes, birds, and certain mammals).

Collecting Malacostraca is comparatively easy: the chief thing
is to ascertain their whereabouts.   This is done along the banks
of streams, ponds, or lakes by turning over stones or logs, by
investigating overhanging banks, or examining bunches of water

weeds. The smaller forms may be taken in numbers by transfer-ring water weeds, dead leaves or other rubbish found on the bottom into tubs or dishes, and picking out the specimens with a pair of pincers. The larger forms must be caught by hand, or with a small dip-net (minnow netting). For many forms the seine is a very successful implement.

In collecting the burrowing crayfishes special efforts are neces-sary. It sometimes happens that the crayfish can be induced to come to the mouth of its hole by destroying the entrance. But generally the collector should not hesitate to go after the crayfish by digging it out. Of course, a spade or shovel is most efficient, although often too heavy to be carried along, but a strong garden-ers' trowel is very convenient: the best tool is a so-called pioneers' bayonet. With this the ground should be loosened around the hole, and the dirt be taken out with the hands, care being taken always to follow the direction of the hole. By digging deep enough (1 to 3 feet), finally the pocket will be reached, in which the cray-fish lives, and then it may be taken out.

Preservation should always be in alcohol. Formalin should be avoided, except in cases of necessity. Even then the specimens should never be left in the formalin for a long time: it hardens them too much, makes all the appendages brittle, and renders them unfit for safe handling. The best results are obtained by killing them in weak alcohol and transferring them into stronger (2 to 3 changes), until they finally are in 75 to 80 per cent alcohol: when so treated all appendages remain soft and flexible as in life.

For scientific study no special work is required in the case of the larger forms, and all systematic characters may be seen with the bare eyes or by the use of a hand-lens. In the smaller forms it is necessary to study the appendages separately. They should be teased out under a dissecting microscope (using two pairs of pincers) and mounted in the usual way upon microscopic slides. Care should be taken that the appendages are taken out in the proper order, so that they do not become mixed. For the micro-scopic investigation a very low power is sufficient.

KEY TO NORTH AMERICAN FRESH–WATER MALACOSTRACA

1 (26) Without carapace, but first thoracic somite coalesced with the head. Eyes (when present) sessile. Thoracic limbs without exopodites, first pair modified as maxillipeds. 2

2 (11) Body depressed. Pleopods biramous, uniform in shape, with exception of the uropods and the anterior pairs of the male.

Order **Isopoda**. . 3

3 (4) Uropods lateral, forming with the telson a tail-fan.

Family CIROLANIDAE.
Only one genus and one species in the United States.
Cirolanides texensis Benedict 1896.

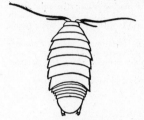

This is a blind form, which has been found in an artesian well in Texas. All other representatives of this family are marine. Many of them are ectoparasites on fishes.

FIG. 1304. *Cirolanides texensis* Benedict. ✕ 4.
(After Richardson.)

4 (3) Uropods inserted at the posterior end of the telson, not forming a tail-fan. 5

5 (10) Pleopods covered by a thin opercular plate, the modified first pair. Body symmetrical. Free living. Family ASELLIDAE. . 6

This is a typical fresh-water family.

6 (7) Mandibles without a palp. Last six pairs of thoracic legs with dactylus biunguiculate. . . . . *Mancasellus* Harger.

Five species, living in springs and caves, some in rivers and lakes. Eyes present in all, but small.

7 (6) Mandibles with a three-jointed palp. Last six pairs of thoracic legs with dactylus uniunguiculate. 8

8 (9) Eyes present. Head narrower than the first thoracic segment. Telson not longer than broad. . . . . *Asellus* Geoffroy.

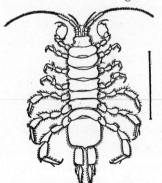

Seven species in rivers, creeks, ponds, ditches, springs, lakes. Some (as *Asellus communis* Say) widely distributed, others more local. Common in ponds, ditches, etc., living among decaying vegetable matter.

FIG. 1305. *Asellus communis* Say. ✕ 2. (After Smith.)

9 (8) Eyes wanting. Head not narrower than the first thoracic segment. Telson much longer than broad. . . *Caecidotea* Packard.

Four species, in caves, springs issuing from caves, and artesian wells.

10 (5) Pleopods not covered by an opercular plate. Body of female peculiarly deformed, unsymmetrical, that of the male more or less normal and symmetrical. Parasitic upon higher crustaceans. . . . . Family BOPYRIDAE.
Only one genus in the North American fresh waters.
Probopyrus Giard and Bonnier.

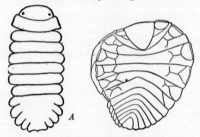

Chiefly a marine group; the only genus known from the fresh water of North America, enters with its hosts, being found parasitic upon the gills and in the gill cavities of Decapods of the genera *Palaemonetes* and *Palaemon*. Three species are known, and are found along the Atlantic coast from New Hampshire to Florida, and in the Mississippi River in Louisiana.

FIG. 1306. *Probopyrus pandalicola* Packard. *A*, Male; × 30. *B*, Female; × 3. (After Richardson.)

11 (2) Body compressed. Pleopods divided into two sets, the first three pairs with multiarticulate rami, the last two pairs generally similar to the uropods, with unsegmented rami. No sexual modification of pleopods in the male.
Order **Amphipoda** . . 12

12 (25) Antennulae with secondary flagellum. Telson cleft or entire. . . 13

13 (14) Fifth peraeopods shorter than the preceding. Second maxillipeds smaller than the first. Uropods with two nearly equal rami. . . . . Family LYSIANASSIDAE.
Only one fresh-water genus in North America. . *Pontoporeia* Kroyer.

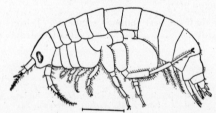

This family is chiefly marine; two species live in rather deep water of the lakes Superior and Michigan. These species are closely allied to certain European fresh-water forms, and probably immigrated into the lakes at the close of the glacial time.

FIG. 1307. *Pontoporeia hoyi* Smith. × 4. (After Smith.)

14 (13) Fifth peraeopods longer than the preceding. Second maxillipeds generally larger than the first. Uropods with two unequal rami or without rami. . . . Family GAMMARIDAE. . 15

A family represented both in the sea and in fresh water, and containing a great number of forms.

15 (20) Telson cleft. Uropods biramous. 16

16 (19) Inner ramus of uropods rudimentary. Telson cleft not more than three-fourths the distance to the base. 17

17 (18) Outer ramus of third uropods uniarticulate.

Eucrangonyx Stebbing.

Five species are known, living in ponds, springs, and wells. Eyes either well developed or more or less rudimentary. One species is blind.

18 (17) Outer ramus of third uropods biarticulate. . . . . Niphargus Hay.

A single species in caves in Tennessee, with the eyes wanting or very rudimentary.

19 (16) Inner ramus of uropods not rudimentary, one-half or three-fourths as long as the outer. Telson cleft to the base or nearly so.

Gammarus Fabricius.

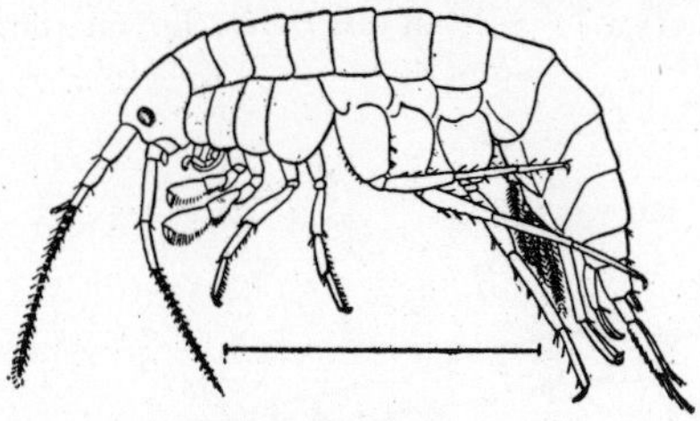

Six species, two of them (G. fasciatus Say and G. limnaeus 'Smith), rather abundant in rivers, lakes, and smaller bodies of water. The other species are more local. Eyes present, but one species is a blind cave-form of Cuba.

FIG. 1308. Gammarus limnaeus Smith. X 2. (After Smith.)

20 (15) Telson entire. 21

21 (24) Third uropods with rami. 22

22 (23) Third uropods uniramus. Telson short and broad. Crangonyx Bate.

Three species are known, all without eyes, living in caves and wells, and with very local distribution (Kentucky, Indiana, Connecticut, Wisconsin).

23 (22) Third uropods biramous, inner ramus rudimentary, outer uniarticulate. Telson long. . . . . Stygonectes Hay.

Only one blind species, found in an artesian well in Texas.

24 (21) Third uropods without rami. . . . . . . Apocrangonyx Stebbing.

One species, blind, from a well in Illinois.

25 (12) Antennulae without secondary flagellum. Telson entire. Third uropods uniramous. . . . . Family ORCHESTIIDAE.

This family is abundantly represented in the sea.

Only one genus and species in the fresh water of North America.

Hyalella knickerbockeri (Bate) 1862.

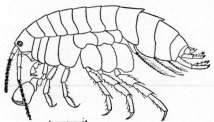

This species possesses a very wide range, and is found in rivers, ponds and lakes from Maine to Florida and California (and extends southward into Central America). This genus (Hyalella) is remarkable for the fact that all its species are found exclusively in fresh water and are restricted to North and South America.

FIG. 1309. Hyalella knickerbockeri Bate. X 5. (After Smith.)

26 (1) With a carapace. Eyes upon movable eye-stalks. Thoracic limbs with or without exopodites, one, two, or three of the anterior pairs modified as maxillipeds. 27

27 (28) Carapace coalesced dorsally with not more than three of the thoracic somites. Thoracic limbs with natatory exopodites, first pair modified as maxillipeds. Pleopods more or less reduced and greatly different in the two sexes. Eggs carried in a brood pouch at the base of the thoracic legs.

Order **Mysidacea.**

This order forms part of the old division Schizopoda. The Mysidacea live chiefly in salt water. The system of this group needs a thorough revision, and no satisfactory division into larger groups (families) has been published.

Only species in North America. . . . . *Mysis relicta* Lovén 1862.

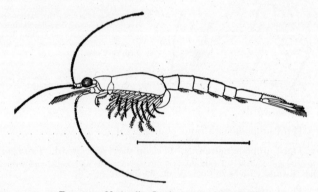

FIG. 1310. *Mysis relicta* Lovén. × 2. (After Smith.)

Very few Mysidacea are known from the fresh water, and the present is identical with a species living in lakes in northern Europe (Ireland, Scandinavia, Russia). It is found, in North America, under similar conditions, in the lakes Superior and Michigan, down to a considerable depth (150 fathoms).

In Europe, this form has been much discussed, and, as the name indicates, was supposed to point to a former connection between the sea and the lakes in which it lives. It was believed that these lakes were cut off from the sea and became fresh-water lakes, but retained part of the original marine fauna adapted to the fresh-water conditions: these animals were called "marine relics," and *Mysis relicta* was taken for one of the most prominent examples of this kind. However, this theory has been greatly shaken recently, and, as far as it concerns the North American stock of *Mysis relicta*, there is no reason to assume that it is a marine relic, but we are to regard it as an immigrant into the Great Lakes in glacial times (as *Lysianassa*).

28 (27) Carapace coalesced dorsally with all of the thoracic somites. Thoracic limbs rarely with exopodites, the first three pairs modified as maxillipeds. Pleopods not much reduced, and not very different in the two sexes, except the anterior ones. Eggs carried under the abdomen, attached to the pleopods.

Order **Decapoda** . . 29

29 (34) Body and rostrum compresssed. Pleura of second abdominal somite overlapping those in front. First two pairs of peraeopods chelate. Anterior pleopods of the male not transformed into copulating organs. 30

30 (31)   Chelae of peraeopods weak, subequal, fingers with terminal hair-tufts. . . . . Family ATYIDAE.
Only species in North America. . . *Palaemonias ganteri* Hay 1903.

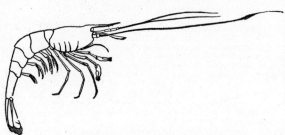

A typical and characteristic fresh-water group, abundant in the tropics, but certain forms are found in temperate regions, and their distribution is quite peculiar, they being found at rather isolated localities, remote from each other. This discontinuity is a mark of antiquity of the group. One of these isolated forms is found in North America, *Palaemonias ganteri*

FIG. 1311. *Palaemonias ganteri* Hay. × 1. (After Hay.)

Hay, and is blind, living in Mammoth Cave in Kentucky. The nearest place where related forms are found is in the West Indies.

31 (30)   Chelae of peraeopods inequal, the second pair larger, often much larger, than the first, and very strong. Fingers without terminal hair-tufts. . . . Family PALAEMONIDAE . . 32

A family abundant in the sea, but also of great importance in the fresh water. All transitional stages between life in the sea and in fresh water are found here.

32 (33)   Mandible without palpus. Second pair of peraeopods only slightly larger than the first, both of them rather weak. Size of body medium. . . . . *Palaemonetes* Heller.

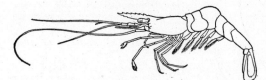

Contains a number of species which live in salt and brackish water. One of them (*P. vulgaris* Say) is found along our Atlantic coast. Other species have become true fresh-water forms: Two have been described from the United States: *P. paludosa* Gibbes and *P. exilipes* Stimpson, both from Carolina, but they are supposed to be identical.

FIG. 1312. *Palaemonetes exilipes* Stimpson. × 1. (After Smith.)

This form has also been found in Florida, in the Illinois River, and in Lake Erie.

33 (32)   Mandible with palpus. Second pair of peraeopods, in the male, excessively developed, very long (often longer than the whole body), with strong chelae. Size of body considerable.
Palaemon Fabricius.

This genus (sometimes, but erroneously, called *Bithynis*) is extremely abundant in the fresh water of the tropics. Only one species is recorded from the United States: *P. ohionis* Smith, which is found in the Mississippi and lower Ohio Rivers (up to Cannelton, Ind.). Little more is known about this species than that it exists and that it is locally used as food. (Not even a figure of it has been published.)

34 (29)   Body subcylindrical in its anterior part, abdomen depressed. Rostrum depressed. Pleura of second abdominal segment not overlapping those in front. First three pairs of peraeopods chelate, the first pair much larger than the others.

Family POTAMOBIIDAE . . 35

An exclusive fresh-water family of old age, and the most important group of higher crustaceans in the fresh waters of North America. Its general distribution includes Europe, northeastern Asia, North and Central America. In the United States two genera are found: one, containing a few species, is believed to be identical with the European genus (*Potamobius*); the other (*Cambarus*) is restricted to America, and has very many species. The differences of these genera are found chiefly in the sexual apparatus.

In the southern hemisphere, in Australia, New Zealand, South America, and Madagascar this family is represented by an allied one, Parastacidae while in the tropical belt similar forms are missing. This peculiar distribution has given origin to much speculation, and chiefly the close affinity of the southern forms has been introduced as evidence for the former connection of the southern continents.

Through Huxley's book (1880) this family has become a standard group for biological study.

35 (36)   Male copulatory organs rather simple. Peraeopods of male without hooks on the ischiopodite. Female without receptaculum seminis. A pleurobranchia present on the last thoracic somite. . . . . *Potamobius* Leach.

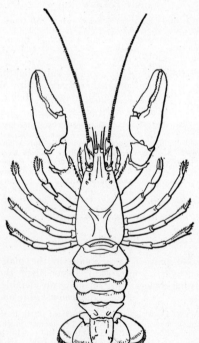

This is the genus which includes the European crayfishes, frequently, but incorrectly, called *Astacus*. It possesses five species in North America, the range of which is on the western Pacific slope, from California to British Columbia. One species (*P. gambeli* Girard), has crossed the continental divide in the region of Yellowstone Park, and is found on both sides in the drainages of the upper Columbia River and of the upper Missouri.

The European species (about six) have frequently been subjects of systematic, anatomical, biological, and embryological studies. The best known species is the common crayfish of Central Europe, *Potamobius astacus* (Linnaeus).

FIG. 1313. *Potamobius trowbridgei* Stimpson.
× ½. (After Hagen.)

A species found abundantly in the drainage of the lower Columbia River in Washington and Oregon, and of considerable economic value.

36 (35) Male copulatory organs more or less complex. Some peraeopods of the male with hooks on the ischiopodite. Female with receptaculum seminis (annulus ventralis) upon the sternum of the thorax. No pleurobranchiae present.

                                       Cambarus Erichson . . 37

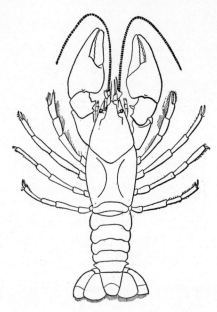

Restricted to North America east of the Rocky Mountains, Mexico, Guatemala, and Cuba. It contains between seventy and eighty species, which fall into six subgenera, four of which are represented in the United States.

The geographical distribution of the species of *Cambarus* is very interesting, and apt to furnish evidence for the geological changes of our river-systems. This genus is also eminently fit for ecological studies on account of the great diversity of the habit-preferences of the single species.

Besides the four subgenera treated here, two others have been distinguished (*Paracambarus* and *Procambarus*), but they do not possess representatives in the United States.

FIG. 1314. *Cambarus bartoni* Fabricius.
     × 1. (After Paulmier.)

The most common species in the eastern United States, found in small streams of the Appalachian chain from Tennessee and the Carolinas to Maine and New Brunswick.

37 (44) Sexual organs of male with more than two tips. 38

38 (43) Third, or third and fourth, peraeopods of the male with hooks on the ischiopodite. Sexual organs of male blunt or truncated, with one soft tip, and several short, horny teeth.

                           Subgenus *Cambarus* Ortmann . . 39

Distribution: Chiefly southern and southwestern in the United States.

39 (42) Male with hooks on third peraeopods. 40

40 (41) Areola narrow. Chelae elongated.

                   Section of *Cambarus simulans* Faxon 1884.

The *areola* is the posterior, median dorsal part of the carapace, included between the lines which bound the lateral (branchial) regions. The areola is " obliterated," when these lines come into contact.

Two species in the southwestern United States and Mexico.

41 (40) Areola obliterated in the middle. Chelae short and broad.

                   Section of *Cambarus gracilis* Bundy 1876.

Three species, burrowing forms, on the coastal plain from South Carolina to Texas, and northwards over the prairie region to Wisconsin.

42 (39) Male with hooks on the third and fourth peraeopods. Chelae elongated. . . . Section of *Cambarus blandingi* Harlan 1830.

About seventeen species, falling into four groups, distributed over the Atlantic
and Gulf coastal plain, and passing up the Mississippi valley into the interior basin.
C. blandingi (Harlan) is the type species of this group and of the whole genus. Its
distribution covers practically all of the range of the section. The other species are
more local, and some of them are probably mere local races. The blind species,
C. acherontis Loennberg, from Florida, belongs here.
Species of lakes, ponds, or sluggish rivers, avoiding strong current.

Fig. 1315. *Cambarus (Cambarus) blandingi* Harlan. Copulatory organ of male. × 4.
(After Faxon.)

In other species, the horny tips of these organs are more or less different, and
furnish important specific characters.

43 (38) Second and third peraeopods of the male with hooks on the ischiopodite. Sexual organs of male with one soft, and two horny,
elongated points. . . . . Subgenus *Cambarellus* Ortmann.

Only one species is found in the United States: *C. shufeldti* Faxon, from Louisi-
ana; a few more species are known from Mexico.
This species appears to be geographically isolated from its related forms (in
Mexico).

Fig. 1316. *Cambarus (Cambarellus) Shufeldti* Faxon. Copulatory organ of male. × 4.
(After Faxon.)

44 (37) Sexual organs of male with two tips, one soft, the other horny. . . 45

45 (50) Sexual organs rather slender, the terminal tips more or less elongated,
straight or gently curved. Ischiopodite of third peraeopods
of male with hooks, rarely also that of fourth.
Subgenus *Faxonius* Ortmann . . 46

Distribution: Pre-eminently in the large rivers of the central basin (Mississippi and Ohio,
and their tributaries). Very few species have reached the Atlantic drainage system.

46 (47) Sexual organs of male with the tips free only for a short distance.
Hooks on third, or on third and fourth, peraeopods.
Section of *Cambarus limosus* Rafinesque 1817.

Five species, of which *C. limosus* (Rafinesque) (very generally called *C. affinis* Say, which
name, however, is a synonym) is the best known: it is found on the Atlantic side of the Alle-
ghenies in rivers, ponds, canals, from New York and Pennsylvania to Virginia. The allied
species are found at a great distance from this, in Kentucky, Indiana, and Missouri, and among
them is the blind cave-species *C. pellucidus* (Tellkampf).

47 (46) Sexual organs of male with the free tips longer. Hooks on third
peraeopods only. 48

48 (49)   Tips of sexual organs rather straight.
               Section of *Cambarus propinquus* Girard 1852.

About ten species belong here, but some of them are mere local races. The most important ones are *C. propinquus* Girard, and *C. rusticus* Girard, both found in the larger and smaller rivers of the interior basin. The other forms also belong to these river systems, but extend also into the lower Mississippi drainage, to the Atlantic side in Georgia and South Carolina, and to the Great Lakes and the St. Lawrence system.

FIG. 1317. *Cambarus (Faxonius) rusticus* Girard. Copulatory organ of male. × 4.
(After Faxon.)

A species characteristic for the lower Ohio and its tributaries. In other species the copulatory organs are more or less different.

49 (48)   Tips of sexual organs gently, but distinctly, curved.
               Section of *Cambarus virilis* Hagen 1870.
Twelve species are known, but again some may be only local forms. *C. virilis* Hagen possesses a wide range in the rivers of the central basin from Arkansas and Kansas to Canada. A very abundant species is *C. immunis* Hagen, which prefers stagnant, often temporary, pools of the western prairies. The other species are found chiefly in the lower Mississippi drainage in Mississippi, Arkansas, Kansas, Oklahoma.

50 (45)   Sexual organs rather stout, terminal tips rather short, strongly recurved. Ischiopodite of third peraeopods of male with hooks. . . . . . . Subgenus *Bartonius* Ortmann . .   51
Distribution: Chiefly in and near the Appalachian Mountains, but some species on the coastal plain and the western plateau.

51 (52)   Eyes rudimentary. Chelae subelongated. Carapace subcylindrical.
               Section of *Cambarus hamulatus* Cope and Packard 1881.
Three cave species belong here (see p. 837).

52 (51)   Eyes present. Chelae subovate. Carapace more or less ovate. .   53

53 (54)   Rostrum with marginal spines.
               Section of *Cambarus extraneus* Hagen 1870.
Three species, rather local in Kentucky, Tennessee, Northern Alabama, and Northern Georgia.

54 (53)   Rostrum without marginal spines.   55

55 (56)   Areola wide, or a little narrower.
               Section of *Cambarus bartoni* Fabricius 1798.

About four species, distributed over the Appalachian Mountains, where they live in mountain streams, descending more or less toward the lowlands. The best-known form is *C. bartoni* (Fabricius) (Figs. 1314 and 1318), which covers the whole range of the section, and has developed a number of more or less well defined local races.

FIG. 1318. *Cambarus (Bartonius) bartoni* Fabricius. Copulatory organ of male. × 4.
(After Hagen.)

In this subgenus, the shape of this organ is rather uniform in all species, which is in strong contrast to the variability seen in the other subgenera.

56 (55)   Areola very narrow, linear, or entirely obliterated.

Section of *Cambarus diogenes* Girard 1852.

Five species, all burrowing forms and chimney builders. Some (the more primitive forms) are found in the Appalachian Mountains and upon the Allegheny and Cumberland Plateau; others have descended to the Atlantic coastal plain, and have spread over the interior basin, and westward to the Rocky Mountains, so, for instance, *C. diogenes* Girard. Again other species are local forms of the lowlands.

IMPORTANT PAPERS ON NORTH AMERICAN HIGHER CRUSTACEA

ANDREWS, E. A.   1904.   Breeding Habits of Crayfish.   Amer. Nat., 38: 165–206.

EMBODY, G. C.   1912.   Distribution, Food and Reproductive Capacity of Same Fresh-Water Amphipods.   Int. Rev. ges. Hydrobiol., Biol. Suppl. III. 27 pp.

FAXON, W.   1885.   A Revision of the Astacidae.   Mem. Mus. Comp. Zool. Harvard, 10: 1–186.

HAGEN, H. A.   1870.   Monograph of the North American Astacidae.   Ill. Cat. Mus. Comp. Zool. Harvard, No. 3; 109 pp.

HARRIS, J. A.   1903.   An Ecological Catalogue of the Crayfishes belonging to the Genus Cambarus.   Kansas Univ. Science Bull., 2: 51–187.

HAY, W. P.   1896.   The Crawfishes of the State of Indiana.   Rep. Indiana Geol. Surv., 20: 475–506.

     1899.   Synopsis of North American Invertebrates.   VI.   The Astacidae of North America.   Amer. Nat., 33: 957–966.

HUXLEY, T. J.   1880.   The Crayfish.   The International Scientific Series. New York.

KINGSLEY, J. S.   1899.   Synopsis of North American Invertebrates.   III. The Caridea of North America.   Amer. Nat., 33: 709–719.

ORTMANN, A. E.   1905.   The Mutual Affinities of the Species of the Genus Cambarus, and their Dispersal over the United States.   Proc. Amer. Philos. Soc., 44: 91–136.

     1906.   The Crawfishes of the State of Pennsylvania.   Mem. Carnegie, Mus., 2: 343–523.

PACKARD, A. S.   1886.   The Cave Fauna of North America.   Mem. Nat. Acad. Sci., 4: 1–156.

PEARSE, A. S.   1910.   The Crawfishes of Michigan.   Mich. State Biol. Surv., 1: 9–22.

RICHARDSON, H.   1905.   A Monograph on the Isopods of North America. Bull. U. S. Nat. Mus., 54; 727 pp.

SMITH, S. I.   1874.   The Crustacea of the Fresh Waters of the United States. Rep. U. S. Comm. Fish., 2: 637–665.

STEELE, M.   1902.   The Crayfish of Missouri.   Bull. Univ. Cincinnati, No. 10; 54 pp., 6 pl.

WECKEL, ADA L.   1907.   The Fresh-water Amphipoda of North America. Proc. U. S. Nat. Mus., 32: 25–58.

CHAPTER XXVI

THE WATER–MITES (HYDRACARINA)

By ROBERT H. WOLCOTT

Professor of Zoology in the University of Nebraska

CONSPICUOUS among aquatic organisms on account of their activity and the brilliance of their coloring are the water-mites, forming the group Hydracarina. These attractive little creatures may be met with in water almost anywhere, but being carnivorous and thus dependent on the presence of much animal life, and having a life-time extending over a number of months, they are found regularly and in abundance only in pools which are moderate in depth, permanent in character, and which possess a considerable plant growth. There in the vegetation of the bottom and the shore they live, clambering about over the surface of the plants, swimming across from one stem or leaf to another, and feeding on crustacea, insect larvae or other animals which they may be able to overpower and capture. A few species are pelagic, spending most of their time in the open water of the lake or pond, while other forms, as *Tyrrellia*, are found wandering over the moss and debris which accumulates along a swampy portion of the shore. *Feltria* is a genus containing small forms that are found only in the mountain streams of Europe; yet in general water-mites are not abundant in flowing streams except in sheltered places where there is a growth of vegetation which protects them from the rapid current. Two genera are parasitic in fresh-water mussels, and the larvae and pupae of others attach themselves to aquatic insects or other animals. Most of them are fresh-water forms, but a very few have been described which are marine and a few others have accustomed themselves in certain localities to life in brackish water.

Hydrachnids are generally distributed over the world but seem to reach the greatest abundance in the clear, cool waters of the spring-fed lakes and pools, rich in plant life, which are so characteristic of all temperate latitudes, and which dot our northern states

851

and Canada. An interesting occurrence was the finding of a species of *Lebertia*, a genus usually found in alpine and more northern waters, in a spring at Omaha, Nebraska, the only record of the genus in a state where bodies of water of that character are almost lacking. At present about seventy genera are known, containing several hundred described species, the number of which is fast increasing.

The water-mites are found at all seasons of the year, even under the ice in winter. Certain ones, especially of the red mites, are abundant in pools in early spring, but the greatest number of species appear as adults during the latter part of the summer or in the fall. They are small forms usually from 1 to 2 millimeters long, rarely exceeding a length of 5 millimeters, but on the other hand, in the adult condition, rarely measuring less than half a millimeter.

The color varies greatly, but is most frequently either some shade of red or green; the same species may at the same locality and at the same time be both red and different shades of green or bluish green. The color is partly due to pigment deposited in the epidermal cells, but from above or beneath blackish, brownish or greenish spots are seen, which vary in size and intensity and are due to the stomach and its blind diverticula seen through other more superficial structures. A whitish, yellowish, or reddish Y-shaped dorsal mark, or markings of various form seen on the dorsal, lateral, or posterior surfaces, are due to the presence of excretory matter in the so-called Malpighian vessels, and thus are very variable in number and extent. Hence while color is a clue to identification which may be of service to the experienced observer, it cannot be relied upon, and is of little or no value in the discrimination of species.

As seen in the water the hydrachnids appear at first glance like small water spiders, possessing, as they do, four pairs of legs and a pair of palpi corresponding to the pedipalps of spiders. But they can at once be referred to the mites when it is noted that there is no trace of segmentation or of division of the body into regions.

The body is compact and usually more or less globular, ellipsoidal, or ovoidal, though in some cases compressed dorso-ventrally or laterally, and in the males of certain species of *Arrhenurus* prolonged posteriorly into a curious handle-like appendage. The form is more definite in the higher forms than in those which seem most primitive. The skin in some forms is soft and the surface smooth, but more usually it is marked by fine striae like the lines on the palm of the hand, and in the lower forms it is often granulated or papillated. Other species possess chitinous plates, which may be few and small or larger and more numerous, and may even completely enclose the body in a sort of armor. These chitinous plates do not seem to mark either higher or lower types and occur in different families. Glands occur here and there on the surface, and also hairs and bristles, which are frequently accompanied by small pieces of chitin.

There is usually a pair of eyes, but each can be seen on close examination to be double, and in some cases the two of each side are separate. They are of only moderate size, but prominent, owing to the presence of dark pigment. There may be also, in some of the lower forms, a "fifth" or median eye, in the median line between the others.

The four pairs of legs are articulated to an equal number of coxal plates, or epimera. These are frequently more or less fused, may even form a single large plate covering the whole ventral surface, and may also extend up on the sides so as nearly to enclose the body, as in *Frontipoda*. Sometimes the body is constricted above this plate, giving to the animal in lateral view the appearance of a broad-crowned cap or flat-based knob, the legs springing from the upper side of the projecting epimeral plate. The legs are each

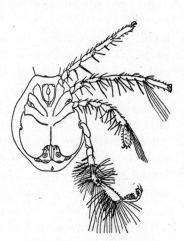

FIG. 1319. *Pionacercus leuckarti* Piersig, a European form, showing extreme modification of the last pair of legs in the male. (Legs shown on one side only; palpi not shown.) (Modified from Piersig.)

composed of six segments, and vary greatly in length, in the form of individual segments, and in the character of the spines, bristles and hairs which they bear. They are usually terminated by two movable claws, but there may be only one, or rarely the leg may end in a spine or bristle. The more active and the pelagic forms have longer legs with fewer and longer spines and bristles, the less active shorter, stouter legs with more thickly set and shorter bristles. In some cases a number of long hairs in a close-set row on the outer segments of the leg seem to aid in swimming and so are called swimming-hairs; while in other cases curiously modified leg segments and spines characterize the male and serve as accessory organs in pairing (Fig. 1319).

The genital opening is situated behind or between the epimera and is usually flanked by plates which bear characteristic cup-like or knob-like structures known as acetabula, the exact nature and function of which is unknown. There may be in addition movable flaps, which may or may not cover the acetabula, and in some cases such flaps, by fusion with the genital plates, seem to have become immovable.

Between the anterior epimera is a plate, which has been termed, from its form, the maxillary shield, and which is the ventral side of a chitinous box called the camerostom, which encloses the mouth-parts. To this are articulated the five-jointed palpi; at its anterior end is the mouth-opening, through which project the stiletto-like or sabre-like mandibles; and on its dorsal surface are the two stigmata, leading by air-tubes into two air-sacs placed above the pharynx, from which a system of tracheal tubes runs throughout the body. In the forms parasitic on the fresh-water mussels these tubes are lacking. The maxillary shield is frequently prolonged posteriorly into a kind of ancoral process, and the anterior ventral angle of the camerostom may be produced into a sort of rostrum. All these structures together are termed the capitulum.

The sexes are separate, sexual dimorphism being a common phenomenon, and all species lay eggs. These may, rarely, be laid free in the water, but are more usually deposited singly or in mass, surrounded by a gelatinous envelope, on water plants or other submerged objects. The embryo undergoes considerable development before escaping from the egg membranes, at which time it becomes an active six-legged larva (Fig. 1320). This larva after a short free existence becomes a parasite either on an aquatic insect which remains habitually in the water or on one which leaves the water and becomes aerial. Other species place the eggs singly in the tissues of fresh water mussels, or in masses between the gills,

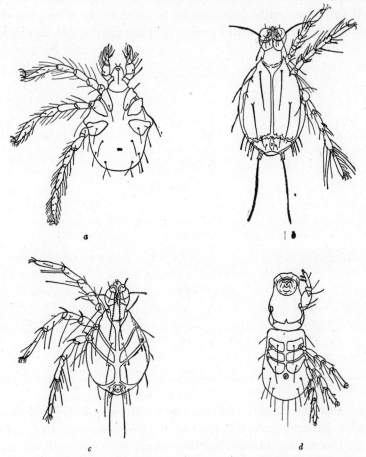

FIG. 1320.   Various types of hydrachnid larvae (each figure showing the legs of one side only). *a, Diplodontus; b, Hygrobates; c, Arrhenurus; d, Hydrachna.*   (Modified from Piersig.)

and still others in the substance of fresh-water sponges or in the gelatinous matrix of a colonial protozoan. In these cases the larva does not become free but remains in the body of the mollusk or other animal in which the eggs were laid. During this parasitic existence the larval appendages drop off and the animal takes on the character of a pupa, which increases greatly in size, drawing nourishment from its host, and beneath the skin of which new appendages are gradually developed. From this quiescent pupa emerges an active, eight-footed nymph (Fig. 1321) possessing legs and palpi frequently quite similar to those of the adult, but with smaller epimera and with a genital field lacking the structures which

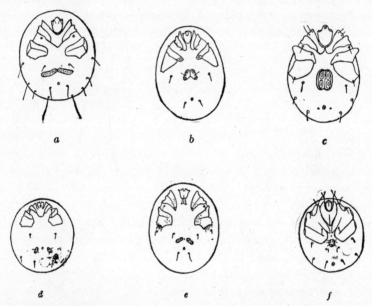

FIG. 1321. Figures showing the ventral surface of the body of the nymphs of several genera of water-mites. (Appendages are similar to those of the adult and not shown here; compare with figures of adults on succeeding pages.) a, *Arrhenurus;* b, *Limnesia;* c, *Sperchon;* d, *Hygrobates;* e, *Piona;* f, *Lebertia.* (Modified from Piersig.)

distinguish the adult. During this nymph stage the mite is not usually parasitic except in the case of the mussel parasites. However, *Unionicola crassipes* has been found by Soar, in all stages, in the fresh-water sponge, and the author has taken the different developmental stages of a species of *Piona* in the gelatinous matrix of a colonial protozoan. Another moult must occur before the mite becomes adult, but this is passed through rapidly and in the forms in which the nymph is free frequently occurs while the animal is clinging to aquatic plants. This moult may or may not be accompanied by the loss of the nymphal appendages and the development of a new set, and the skin may be cast all at once or in several portions. Instances have been described in which the nymph was produced directly from the egg in the egg-mass.

These water-mites, like most aquatic animals, spend much of their time in active motion, swimming with comparative rapidity through the open water or more slowly walking over the bottom or climbing about on plants or other objects. At times they stop and remain stationary, clinging to whatever object they may rest upon, but a touch from another animal sends them whirling on again with rapid leg movements. When prey is secured they stop to suck the juices from the body of the victim, casting aside the carcass when it has been drained. Aside from the sense of touch, which seems quite acute, the senses are poorly developed, or at least appear to be little used. They rarely feign death, but almost invariably attempt to escape a threatened danger by rapid flight. The less uniform rate of motion they exhibit is of aid in distinguishing them from other forms, especially ostracods, with which they may be confused. The leg movement also aids in their discrimination.

Attractive as the hydrachnids are to the student of fresh-water life and to the biologist, they are of economic importance only as they afford an element in the food of fishes. Examinations of the contents of fish stomachs frequently show that they have been eaten, and their abundance at times would seem to indicate that under such circumstances they might make up no inconsiderable portion of the food. But they seem to go to pieces very quickly and so are rarely reported in any numbers in the results of examinations of such stomach contents.

In collecting these little fellows one needs a net, a number of wide-mouthed bottles or jars, a pipette, and, in case he is not to examine his collections within a few hours, a bottle of formalin.

The most serviceable net is the "cone" or "Birge" net (see page 68). The net may be used from boat or shore and the material, after being run into a wide-mouthed bottle or jar, be preserved *in toto* at once by adding directly a little strong formalin and shaking thoroughly, or it may be carried home in the fresh state. Frequently mites may be collected along shore by the use of the pipette, being picked up individually as they swim about in sight.

The material, if preserved in formalin, may be put aside for future examination. If not, it should be poured soon into a flat dish, from which the mites may be picked out by means of a pipette. The dish should be looked over several times, as some tend to hide in the débris at the bottom, and stirring after the material has once settled often reveals hidden specimens.

Five per cent formalin, into which they may be put directly, is likely to make them brittle, and the catch is better preserved in a mixture of glycerine, 2 parts by volume; pure water, 3 parts by volume; 2 per cent acetic acid, 2 parts by volume; absolute alcohol, 1 part by volume.

If the mites are to be kept alive for observation their cannibalistic instincts make it necessary that different genera be segregated and kept in separate dishes, with a small amount of some water plant and a few crustacea or non-predatory insect larvae as food. Crowding should be guarded against.

The activity of water-mites makes them difficult objects to study alive, but by the cautious addition of water saturated with chloroform vapor they may be narcotized, and, after being examined, will come out from under the influence of the chloroform apparently uninjured. The author has subjected specimens to this treatment on several successive occasions without evident harm.

In the study of specimens it is necessary to make use of slide mounts. The mouth-parts may be dissected and mounted separately upon slides, and the palpi and legs may also be removed and mounted. If the specimens have been kept in a solution containing some glycerine an opening may be made in the body-wall through which the contents of the body can be pressed out, and in that way transparent mounts of the complete individual secured. The thickness of the body makes it difficult to secure a transparent mount from material preserved in alcohol or formalin mixtures, but the specimens may be successfully softened in some cases by a weak potash solution or else must be mounted as opaque objects.

In the identification of water-mites care must be used, as the general resemblance between them is close. But the characters also seem to be very constant and few species are subject to marked variation. The accompanying synopsis will aid in placing specimens in the proper genus. The statements as to the numbers of species refer to North America only.

The legs and the corresponding epimera are designated by Roman numerals, beginning with the most anterior, and the palpal and leg segments are referred to by Arabic numerals, numbering from the base outward. Thus, ep. III is the third epimeron, leg seg. IV 4, the fourth segment of the fourth leg, and pal. seg. 5 the distal segment of the palpus. In most illustrations are shown the ventral surface, only the legs of one side, and the palpus, detached and more highly magnified; these are the characters most important and most readily observed.

The arrangement of genera and higher groups here used is the same as adopted in a previous paper (Wolcott, 05). It is not in all respects satisfactory, but such a difference of opinion exists among students of the group in this regard that the author is not willing to accept any other system since proposed without himself working the whole matter over again.

KEY TO NORTH AMERICAN FRESH–WATER HYDRACARINA

1 (6) Lateral eyes of the two sides close together in the median line and borne on a common eye-plate. 2

2 (5) Pal. seg. 5 deeply set into 4, eye-plate long and narrow.
Family LIMNOCHARIDAE . . 3

3 (4) Without swimming-hairs . . . . *Limnochares* Latreille 1796.

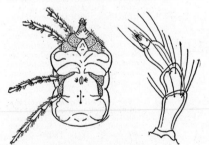

A very large clumsy red mite with soft body, variable in form but in general rectangular, found in pools in bogs and swamps. Length 3.5–4 mm. One species, generally distributed and common at times.

FIG. 1322. *Limnochares aquaticus* (Linnaeus). Ventral surface, female. X 9. Inner surface, right palpus. X 95. (Modified from Piersig.)

4 (3) With swimming-hairs. . . . . *Cyclothrix* Wolcott 1905.

Also red, but oval and more constant in form and recognized at once by the swimming-hairs. One species found also in ponds and lakes with boggy or swampy shores, and known from several northern states. Somewhat smaller than preceding genus.

5 (2)   Pal. seg. 5 free, eye-plate broad, consisting of two lateral portions
        connected by a transverse middle piece. Family EYLAIDAE.
        One genus only. . . . . *Eylais* Latreille 1796.

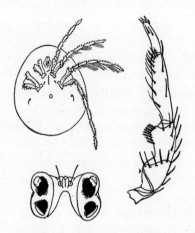

A red mite with body circular in outline and usually smooth; with palpi slender in form and richly supplied with hairs and spines, many of them feathered; hind legs without swimming-hairs and allowed to trail motionless behind in swimming. Several species, very closely allied and generally distributed and often very abundant. Varying in size from about 2 to 5 mm.

FIG. 1323. *Eylais extendens* (Müller), a European species. Ventral surface of female. × 7. Inner side of right palpus. × 69. Eye-plate. × 59. (Modified from Piersig.)

6 (1)   Lateral eyes of the two sides widely separated and in no case borne
        on a common eye-plate. 7

7 (18) Distal extremity of pal. seg. 4 produced beyond the point of inser-
        tion of seg. 5, the two segments together resembling a
        pair of shears. 8

8 (9)   Mandible one-segmented, the terminal portion straight and stiletto-
        like. . . . . Family HYDRACHNIDAE.
        One genus only. . . . . *Hydrachna* Latreille 1796.

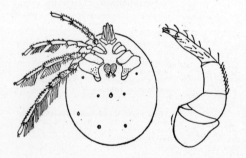

Mites of some shade of red or brown, and sometimes spotted with black, with the body globular, soft, and usually papillated; capitulum produced into a snout. Species numerous, occurring in swamps, lakes and ponds everywhere and usually common. Varying from 1 to even 8 mm. in length.

FIG. 1324. *Hydrachna geographica* (Müller), a European species, also found in New England. The largest described hydrachnid. Ventral surface, female. × 4. Palpus. × 16. (Modified from Piersig.)

9 (8)   Mandible two-segmented, the terminal segment curved and claw-
        like. . . . . Family HYDRYPHANTIDAE. . . 10

10 (11)   Lateral eyes of each side separate and not enclosed in a capsule.
Subfamily DIPLODONTINAE.
One genus only. . . . .   *Diplodontus* Dugès 1834.

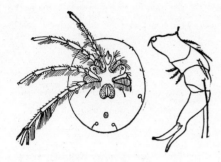

A large, brownish-red mite with body broad, soft, and surface papillated; capitulum forming a snout; palpi very small; legs slender, with long swimming-hairs. One cosmopolitan species, generally distributed in this country and abundant. About 2 mm. long.

FIG. 1325. *Diplodontus despiciens* (Müller). Ventral surface, male. X 15. Outer side, palpus. X 103. (Modified from Piersig.)

11 (10)   Lateral eyes of each side fused and contained in a chitinous capsule.
Subfamily HYDRYPHANTINAE. .   12

12 (17)   Without swimming-hairs.   13

13 (14)   Median eye present . . . .   *Thyas* Koch 1837.

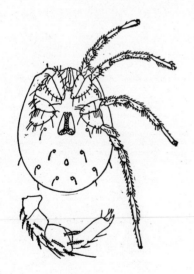

A genus of red mites of moderate size with papillated surface often with chitinous plates; with capitulum forming a snout; legs with only short spines; a bottom and shore form in swampy situations. Varying in size from 1 to 2 or even 2.5 mm. Few species known from the Northern States and Canada and not common.

FIG. 1326. *Thyas venusta* Koch, a European species. Ventral surface, female. X 16. Outer side, left palpus. X 65. (Modified from Piersig.)

14 (13)   Median eye not present   15

15 (16)   Genital flaps present, acetabula 3, knob-like.

Panisus Koenike 1896.

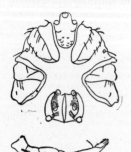

Similar to the preceding in appearance; with chitinous plates more or less developed, in our one described species covering most of the dorsal surface.   One species, *P. cataphractus*, described by Koenike (1895) from Canada, about 1.2 mm. in length.

FIG. 1327.   *Panisus cataphractus* (Koenike).   Epimeral area, genital area and maxillary shield.   × 43.   Outer side, left palpus. × 93.   (After Koenike.)

16 (15)   No genital flaps; numerous stalked acetabula.

Sporadoporus Wolcott, 1905.

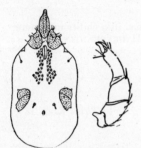

A red mite with body beset by small conical papillae; capitulum produced into a slender snout. One American species, not yet described, known so far only from Yellowstone Park, a little under medium size.

FIG. 1328.   *Sporadoporus invalvaris* (Piersig), a European form.   Ventral surface, female.   × 31.   Palpus.   × 123. (Modified from Piersig.)

17 (12)   With swimming-hairs. . . . . *Hydryphantes* Koch 1837.

A brownish-red mite, with a median eye surrounded by a large chitinous plate; adapted to more open water.   Species several, and occurring frequently.   A little above medium size ranging from 1.2 mm. to about 2.2 mm.

FIG. 1329.   *Hydryphantes ruber* (de Geer), a European species.   Ventral surface, female. × 17.   Outer side, left palpus, of female.   × 42. (Modified from Piersig.)

18 (7)   Distal extremity of pal. seg. 4 slightly or not at all produced beyond the insertion of seg. 5, but the latter free, tapering, the
tip bearing small claws or teeth, or ending in a sharp point.
Family HYGROBATIDAE . .   19

19 (22) Pal. seg. 5 sharply pointed, claw-like, opposable to the projecting
distal flexor margin of seg. 4, forming a sort of pincer.
Body entirely covered by a porous sheet of chitin, divided by
a suture into a smaller dorsal portion and a larger ventral.
Legs with swimming hairs. Subfamily ARRHENURINAE. .   20

20 (21) Genital area lying between epp. IV, the cleft flanked by large valves
each bearing 3 or 4 acetabula.

Krendowskija Piersig 1895.

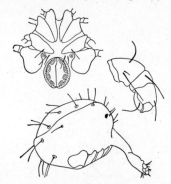

A dark brown mite of medium size, broadly
oval in form; with the capitulum movable and
protrusible, and the camerostom developed into
a long rostrum, sabre-like and curved upward.
One American species, *K. ovata* Wolcott, occurring rarely in Wisconsin and Michigan. Other
species are described from Venezuela and southern
Russia. Each is a little over 1 mm. in length.

FIG. 1330.   *Krendowskija ovata* Wolcott.   Epimeral
area and genital area, female.   × 75.   Inner side, left
palpus, female.   × 250.   Side view of female, showing
proboscis.   × 60.   (After Wolcott.)

21 (20) Genital area lying posterior to epp. IV, the cleft flanked by two
plates forming together an elliptical or circular area, beyond
which are laterally extended, wing-like plates with numerous acetabula. . . . . *Arrhenurus* Dugès 1834.

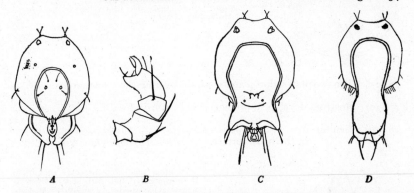

A	B	C	D

FIG. 1331.   *Arrhenurus*. A, *A. forpicatus* Neuman; dorsal surface of female.   × 27.   B, Palpus of
A. albator (Müller), outer side, male.   × 113.   C, *A. maculator* (Müller), dorsal surface, male.   × 30.
D, *A. globator* (Müller), dorsal surface, male.   × 39.   All European species.   (Modified from Piersig.)

The females of this genus are approximately oval in form and possess few characters by
which they may be distinguished, but the males are highly and variously modified in form and
possess complicated accessory sexual structures, including a copulatory organ, the petiole.   Leg

seg. IV 4 is also usually modified in the male by the possession of a peg-like projection and characteristic hairs. The species vary considerably in size, from about 0.55 mm. to nearly 2 mm. One of the most abundant and widely distributed genera, common in clear, shallow, hard waters where plant life is abundant, with about 200 species, all of various shades of bluish or brownish green, or red. There are about 50 species described from North America.

22 (19)   Pal. seg. 5 not opposable to 4, and bearing at the distal end small more or less distinct teeth or claws 23

23 (44)   Epimera in both male and female united and more or less fused into a single epimeral plate. 24

24 (39)   Body more or less compressed dorso-ventrally and completely enclosed in a chitinous covering usually divided into a smaller, elliptical or oval, dorsal plate and a larger ventral plate. Subfamily ATURINAE. . . 25

25 (26)   Four smaller plates, variously shaped, anteriorly, between the dorsal and ventral. . . . . *Torrenticola* Piersig 1897.

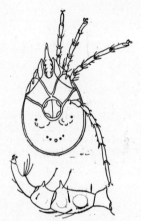

A rather small mite, 0.6 to 0.75 mm. long, of oval form, with the capitulum produced into a sort of snout; no swimming-hairs. One American species, rarely found, and apparently identical with the European *Torrenticola anomala* (Koch).

FIG. 1332. *Torrenticola anomala* (Koch). Ventral surface, female. × 27. Outer side, right palpus, female. × 110. (Modified from Piersig.)

26 (25)   The two plates, dorsal and ventral, covering the whole surface . . 27

27 (30)   Rostrum developed, prolonged and curved upward. 28

28 (29)   Genital area without flaps or valves, with numerous acetabula free in the body surface . . . . . *Tanaognathus* Wolcott 1900.

A rather small mite, strongly compressed dorso-ventrally, and with few swimming-hairs. One species, *T. spinipes* Wolcott, about 0.7 mm. long, known only by a few specimens from Michigan.

FIG. 1333. *Tanaognathus spinipes* Wolcott. Epimeral field and genital area, male. ×42. Outer side, right palpus, male. ×195. (After Wolcott.)

29 (28) Genital cleft flanked by two large movable valves, and also acetabula set free in the body surface. *Koenikea* Wolcott 1900.

A beautiful mite of striking form, being greatly compressed and actually concave dorsally; with swimming-hairs. Brightly and variously colored. One widely-distributed species, *K. concava* Wolcott, adapting itself to varied conditions, and often common. Of small size measuring 0.6 to 0.7 mm. in length.

FIG. 1334. *Koenikea concava* Wolcott. Epimeral field and genital area, male. × 65. Inner side, palpus, male. × 278. Side view, capitulum and rostrum, female. × 277. (After Wolcott.)

30 (27) Rostrum short. 31
31 (36) Suture between the dorsal and ventral plates continuous, completely enclosing the dorsal plate, or open posteriorly. 32
32 (35) Acetabula lying near the genital cleft, no modification of leg IV in the male. 33
33 (34) Ep. IV quadrilateral in form. . . . . . . *Mideopsis* Neuman 1880.

A mite of bright colors, with body almost circular in outline, slightly concave dorsally; a short rostrum; swimming-hairs; 3 acetabula on each side, outside of which are narrow, sickle-shaped flaps. One species, *M. orbicularis* (Müller), common to Europe and America and widely distributed in this country. Of medium size averaging about 1 mm. in length.

FIG. 1335. *Mideopsis orbicularis* (Müller). Ventral surface, female. × 23. Outer side, right palpus. × 123. (Modified from Piersig.)

34 (33) Ep. IV triangular. . . . . : . . *Xystonotus* Wolcott 1900.

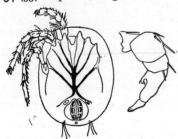

Body elliptical; capitulum small and camerostom slightly developed into a rostrum; no swimming-hairs; 3 acetabula on each side, flanked by movable flaps. The genus containing a single species, *X. asper* Wolcott, known only from two female specimens from Michigan. Of small size, 0.61 mm. long.

FIG. 1336. *Xystonotus asper* Wolcott. Ventral surface, female. × 43. Outer side right palpus. × 195. (After Wolcott.)

35 (32)   Acetabula arranged along the posterior margin of the body, in one
          or more rows, running forward on either side nearly to the
          point of insertion of leg IV, which leg is, in the male, modi-
          fied. . . . . *Aturus* Kramer 1875.

Very small mites, varying in length from 0.33 to
0.38 mm., with the posterior margin of the body
cleft; no swimming-hairs; leg IV of male with
segs. 4 to 6 strikingly modified.   One species,
Aturus mirabilis, is recorded from Canada by
Koenike.   The genus is characteristic of rapidly
flowing streams.

FIG. 1337.   *Aturus scaber* (Kramer), a European species.   Ventral surface of male.   × 61.   Outer side of
palpus, female.   × 150.   (Modified from Piersig.)

36 (31)   Suture open anteriorly, the two ends passing around on to the ven-
          tral surface. 37

37 (38)   Genital area with 4 acetabula on each side . . *Axonopsis* Piersig 1893.

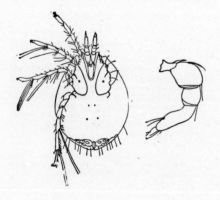

A very small, brightly-colored mite
about 0.45 mm. in length, with a median
cleft in the posterior margin of the oval
body; the anterior epimera extended
beyond the capitulum; few swimming-
hairs.   One North American species,
rare, in northern lakes, apparently the
same as the European *A. complanata*
(Müller).

FIG. 1338. *Axonopsis complanata* (Müller).
Ventral surface of female.   × 50.   Outer
side, right palpus.   × 123.   (Modified from
Piersig.)

38 (37) Genital area with numerous acetabula on each side.

Albia Thon 1899.

A mite of medium size, averaging about 1 mm. in length, with elliptical, strongly compressed body; swimming-hairs present. One North American species, rather rare, in lakes of northern states, frequently pale greenish in color. This is identical with the only European species, *A. stationis* Thon, or very closely related.

FIG. 1339. *Albia stationis* Thon. Ventral surface, female. ✕ 31. Outer side, palpus, female. (After Thon.)

39 (24) Body highly arched, in some cases laterally compressed, with no such dorsal and ventral plate. Subfamily LEBERTIINAE. . 40

Legs with swimming-hairs except in certain species of *Lebertia*.

40 (41) Leg IV with claws at tip, epimera only partly fused.

Lebertia Neuman 1880.

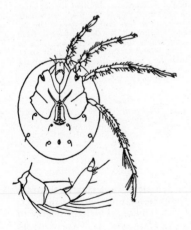

Medium-sized mites, varying in length from 0.8 to 1.5 mm., with ovoidal body, the surface of which is soft or hard, in some cases with small flecks of chitin, usually striate, but rarely papillate; capitulum developed more or less into a short snout. A genus of frequent occurrence in colder waters, represented by several closely allied species which have only been recently recognized as distinct.

FIG. 1340. *Lebertia tau-insignita* (Lebert), of various authors, *L. dubia* Thon. This species was referred to North America by Koenike in 1895, but he has recently identified three species in the material he studied, all of them hitherto undescribed. Ventral surface of female. ✕ 19. Outer side, palpus, female. ✕ 70. (Modified from Piersig.)

41 (40) Leg IV without claws at the tip, ending in a sharp point, epimera completely fused. 42

42 (43)   Body laterally compressed, epimeral plate extending up on the lateral surface, leaving only a dorsal median furrow.

Frontipoda Koenike 1891.

A mite of medium size, somewhat less than 1 mm. long, looking curiously like a very flat elliptical seed, emarginate at the hilum where the legs are bunched together; usually of a greenish color.   One species, frequent in our northern lakes and apparently identical with the one generally distributed European species, *F. musculus* (Müller).

Fig. 1341. *Frontipoda musculus* (Müller). Ventral surface, female.   × 31.   Outer side of palpus, female.   × 93.   (Modified from Piersig.)

43 (42)   Body not so decidedly compressed, epimeral plate not extending upward on the lateral surface. . . .   *Oxus* Kramer 1877.

A form of medium size, different species varying in length from 0.64 to 1.4 mm., with body elongate in form; legs crowded toward the anterior end.   Known in North America only from Wisconsin, where the one species seems to be rare.   This is undescribed, but is similar to *O. ovalis* (Müller) and *O. strigatus* (Müller) the common European forms.

Fig. 1342. *Oxus ovalis* (Müller). Ventral surface, female.   × 30.   *Oxus strigatus* (Müller). Outer side, palpus female.   × 90.   (Modified from Piersig.)

44 (23)   Epimera arranged in groups, in the female always clearly separate from one another, in the male closer together but distinct, only in rare cases in contact or tending in a slight degree to fuse. 45

45 (64)   Epimera in four groups, in the male in some cases only a narrow interval between them. 46

46 (53)   Genital area usually lying far forwards, at least between epp. IV,
          and the epimeral groups often separated by a considerable
          interval, no ancoral process on the maxillary shield.
                              Subfamily SPERCHONINAE   .   **47**

47 (52)   Genital acetabula borne on a plate, no flaps present. **48**

48 (49)   Acetabula numerous. . . . . *Limnesiopsis* Piersig 1897.

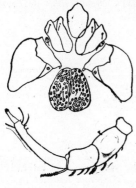

A large hydrachnid, about 2 mm. in length, with
the surface of the body beset with sharp points.   One
species, *L. anomala* (Koenike), described from Canada,
and generally distributed in northern lakes but nowhere common.

FIG. 1343. *Limnesiopsis anomala* (Koenike).   Epimeral
field and genital area, male.   X 25.   Outer side, palpus,
male.   X 49.   (After Koenike.)

49 (48)   Acetabula few, large. **50**

50 (51)   Leg IV with terminal claws, no swimming-hairs.
                              Tyrrellia Koenike 1895.

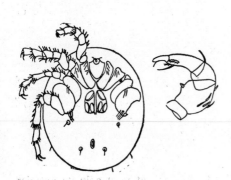

Body almost circular, papillated
with one or two dorsal chitinous
plates; mouth-opening in the middle
of a disk-like surface at the anterior
end of the capitulum, resembling the
condition seen in the Hydryphantidae;
a sluggish, dark-brown mite of medium
size averaging 1.2 mm. in length,
known from Canada and found
abundantly some years since at
Reed's lake, near Grand Rapids,
Michigan, where it was picked up
singly with the pipette in the debris at
the margin of the water in close proximity to a swampy portion of the lake
shore.   Very rare in Birge net hauls
at the same place. Two species taken,
one apparently the same as *T. circularis* Koenike, previously described.

FIG. 1344. *Tyrrellia circularis* Koenike.
Ventral surface, female.   X 26.   Inner side,
palpus, female.   X 49.   (Modified from
Koenike.)

51 (50)   Leg IV ending in a point, a long hair a little back from the tip, swimming-hairs present. . . . . *Limnesia* Koch 1837.

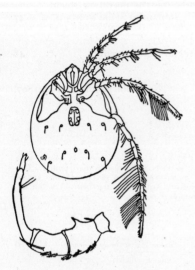

A mite varying from small to large in size,
or from 0.5 to 2 mm. in length, with oval
body, surface striate, sometimes papillose,
and even developing a chitinous meshwork;
two eyes on each side separate. Handsome
mites with bright red spots, very active, and
among the most powerful and voracious of
all. Ten North American species; generally
distributed and found under very varied conditions.

FIG. 1345. *Limnesia histrionica* (Hermann),
the most widely distributed North American species, also found throughout Europe. Ventral surface, female. × 16. Outer side, palpus, female.
× 51. (Modified from Piersig.)

52 (47)   Genital acetabula along the margin of the cleft, covered laterally
by flaps; without swimming-hairs. *Sperchon* Kramer 1877.

Body oval, rarely with small chitinous
plates, smooth, or papillate; capitulum very
movable. A genus found in northern and
mountain lakes and streams. Three species
recorded from Canada. Species small to
medium in size, in length 0.5 to 1.5 mm.

FIG. 1346. *Sperchon glandulosus* Koenike, a
species recorded both from Europe and Canada.
Ventral surface, female. × 24. Outer side of
palpus, female. × 94. (Modified from Piersig.)

53 (46)   Genital area lying posterior to epp. IV, at most only its anterior
end lying between their emarginate posterior angles; an
ancoral process present. . . Subfamily PIONINAE. . 54

54 (61) Posterior margin of ep. IV rounded or transverse 55

55 (58) With swimming-hairs 56

56 (57) Transverse diameter of ep. IV the greater, suture between epp. III and IV complete; no prominent papillae on pal. seg. 4, acetabula very numerous. . . . . . *Neumania* Lebert 1879.

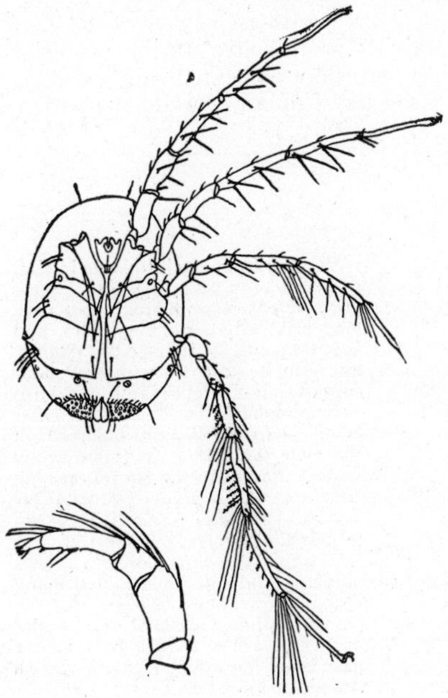

Mites of small to medium size, varying in length from 0.5 to 1.6 mm., with soft body, tending more or less to develop chitinous plates or beset with chitinous points, rarely smooth; leg IV usually with feathered spines. Brightly colored, red or bluish forms, active, but not markedly voracious. Several North American species, common, and widely distributed.

FIG. 1347. *Neumania spinipes* (Müller), a European species represented in this country by a closely allied form. Ventral surface, male. × 40. Outer side, palpus, male. × 70. (Modified from Piersig.)

57 (56) Longitudinal diameter of ep. IV at least equal to the transverse, suture between epp. III and IV incomplete medially; pal. seg. 4 usually with prominent papillae; 5 or 6 acetabula on each side on one or two plates.
(Non-parasitic species) *Unionicola* Haldeman 1842.

58 (55) Without swimming-hairs. 59

59 (60)   Posterior margin of ep. IV rounded; genital area midway between
          epp. IV and the posterior end of the body, genital plates
          elongated transversely.   . . . .   *Najadicola* Piersig 1897.

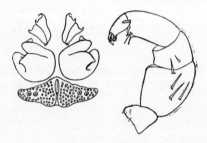

A large mite, 1.5 to 2.5 mm. long,
the gravid female often very large,
reaching a length of even 6 mm., living
in fresh-water mussels and laying eggs
in masses between the gills.   Honey-
yellow in color, more or less distinctly
finely vermiculate with white lines.
One North American species, generally
distributed.

Fig. 1348. *Najadicola ingens* (Koenike).
Epimeral field and genital area, male.
× 23.   (After Koenike.)   Inner side, palpus, male.   × 80.   (After Wolcott.)

60 (59)   Posterior margin of ep. IV straight; genital area at the posterior
          end of the body, genital plates not elongated transversely.
          (Parasitic species) *Unionicola* Haldeman 1842.

Varying from small to large in size,
or from 0.4 to 1.9 mm. in length.   Some
are active, free-swimming mites with
long legs, with swimming-hairs, and
leg I frequently with movable, dagger-
like spines.   Others are mussel parasites, with shorter legs and no
swimming-hairs, leg IV in some cases
being characteristically modified in
the male sex.   In both types strong
spines adjacent to the genital opening
serve together as an ovipositor.   Certain free-swimming forms are regularly
pelagic and very transparent; the parasitic forms are dull-colored.   Species
numerous and widely distributed, many
of them very abundant, especially the
parasitic forms.   The latter are usually
mussel parasites though one species
has been recorded from a South
American univalve.

Fig. 1349.   *Unionicola crassipes* (Müller),
a common and widely-distributed, free-
swimming species, common to North
America and Europe.   Ventral surface,
female.   × 22.   Palpus, outer side, female.
× 63.   (Modified from Piersig.)

61 (54)   Posterior margin of ep. IV with a prominent acute angle. . . . 62

62 (63) Medial margin of ep. IV reduced to merely a medial angle which forms a common angle with the medio-posterior angle of ep. III; leg segs. IV 5 and IV 6 of male modified.

Tiphys Koch 1837.

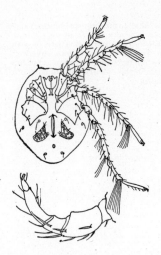

Rather small mites, in length from 0.54 to 1 mm., with swimming-hairs and the hind leg of the male strikingly modified. Few North American species, rare, in our northern lakes, as yet not studied.

Fig. 1350. *Tiphys liliaceus* (Müller), the most common European species. Ventral surface, female. × 28. Outer side, right palpus, female. × 123. (Modified from Piersig.)

63 (62) Medial margin of ep. IV not reduced, and, owing to the angle on the posterior margin, ep. IV more or less clearly five-sided.

Piona Koch 1837.

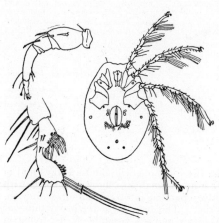

Oval or elliptical forms of various sizes, from 0.45 to 3 mm. long, often brightly colored, with swimming-hairs, and with characteristic modifications of leg segs. III 6 and IV 4 in the male, the latter serving to assist in grasping the female in pairing, the former to carry the semen to the female genital opening. Hardy, active mites, adapting themselves to a great variety of conditions. More than twenty American species, generally distributed over the continent.

Fig. 1351. *Piona rufa* (Koch), a European species. Ventral surface, female. × 22. Outer side, palpus, female.   × 77. (Modified from Piersig.) *Piona constricta* (Wolcott), an American form. Leg segment IV 4, male. × 107. (After Wolcott.)

64 (45) Epimera in three groups, epp. I being fused together behind the capitulum, the groups also often close together in the male.

Subfamily HYGROBATINAE . . 65

65 (66)   Leg segs. I 5 and I 6 modified. . . . . . .   *Atractides* Koch 1837.

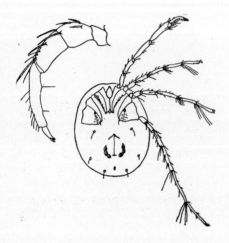

Small to medium-sized mites, varying in length from 0.48 to 1.5 mm.
with surface soft and striate, or with
a flexible or hard porous covering;
swimming-hairs present.   Species
few in this country, rare, in northern
lakes.

FIG. 1352. *Atractides spinipes* Koch, a
species common to Europe and America.
Ventral surface, female. X 25. Outer
side of left palpus, female.   X 103.
(Modified from Piersig.)

66 (65)   Leg segs. I 5 and I 6 normal . . . .   *Hygrobates* Koch 1837.

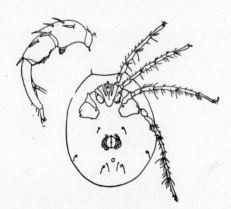

Mites varying in size from small
to even large, or 0.5 to 2.5 mm.,
brightly colored in many cases, without swimming-hairs, but active, and
certain species frequently, if not regularly, pelagic. Several species of general distribution in northern United
States and Canada.

FIG. 1353. *Hygrobates longipalpis*
(Hermann), a species found in North
America, Europe and Western Asia.
Ventral surface, female. X 13. Outer
side, palpus, female. X 125. (Modified
from Piersig.)

In collecting water-mites with the Birge net one will almost always find in
the collection specimens of another mite of small size, brown in color, with
short legs, with the body indistinctly separated into cephalothorax and abdomen and with a horny body-covering.   This belongs to the horny mites or
Oribatidae, probably to the genus *Notaspis*, and is a vegetable feeder living on
aquatic plants beneath the surface of the water.   It can not swim, and will
either cling to objects at the bottom of the dish or float on the surface. Several species occur and are generally distributed.   The species increase in size
and number to the southward.

IMPORTANT PAPERS ON NORTH AMERICAN FRESH-WATER MITES

KOENIKE, F. 1895. Nordamerikanische Hydrachniden. Abh. des Natur-wiss. Ver. zu Bremen, 13: 167–226. Also separate Bremen, 1895.
1912. A Revision of my "Nordamerikanische Hydrachniden." Transl. by E. M. Walker. Trans. Can. Inst., 1912: 281–296.

MARSHALL, RUTH. 1903. Ten Species of Arrenuri belonging to the Subgenus Megalurus Thon. Trans. Wis. Acad. Sci., 14: 145–172.
1904. A New Arrenurus and Notes on Collections made in 1903. Trans. Wis. Acad. Sci., 14: 520–526.
1908. The Arrhenuri of the United States. Trans. Amer. Micr. Soc., 28: 85–140.
1910. New Studies of the Arrhenuri. Trans. Amer. Micr. Soc., 29: 97–110.

PIERSIG, R. 1901. Hydrachnidae. Das Tierreich, Lief. 13.

WOLCOTT, R. H. 1899. On the North American Species of the Genus Atax (Fabr.) Bruz. Trans. Amer. Micr. Soc., 20: 193–259.
1900. New Genera and Species of North American Hydrachnidae. Trans. Amer. Micr. Soc., 21: 177–200.
1901. Description of a New Genus of North American Water-mites, with Observations on the Classification of the Group. Trans. Amer. Micr. Soc., 22: 105–117.
1902. The North American Species of Curvipes. Trans. Amer. Micr. Soc., 23: 201–256.
1903. The North American Species of Limnesia. Trans. Amer. Micr. Soc., 24: 85–107.
1905. A Review of the Genera of the Water-mites. Trans. Amer. Micr. Soc., 26: 161–243.

CHAPTER XXVII

AQUATIC INSECTS

By JAMES G. NEEDHAM

Professor of Limnology, Cornell University

INSECTS are essentially terrestrial animals. Their organization fits them for exposure to the air. On land they are numerically dominant, and it is a comparatively small portion of the group that is to be found in the water. But the lesser portion of a group so large is in itself a host, including a very great variety of forms.

That insects are primarily terrestrial and that they have been secondarily adapted to aquatic life is evidenced in many ways. Their complete armor of impervious chitin and their respiratory apparatus, consisting of internal branching chitin-lined air tubes (tracheae), opening to the outside for the intake of air through spiracles, speak strongly against an aquatic origin. It would be hard to imagine an organization more unsuited to getting air when in the water.

Furthermore, all adult insects, even those that live constantly in the water, have preserved the terrestrial mode of respiration: they all breathe air directly, instead of breathing the air that is dissolved in the water. They have merely acquired means of carrying air from the surface down into the water with them for use there. They are no more aquatic in their mode of respiration than is a man in a diving bell. It is only the more plastic immature stages that have acquired a strictly aquatic type of respiratory apparatus.

Again, it is only isolated and rather small groups of insects that inhabit the water. A few of the smaller orders, like the stone-flies, Mayflies, dragonflies and caddisflies are practically all aquatic in their immature stages; but the larger orders are not so.

There is abundant evidence of the independent adaptation of the various groups. Practically all the adult insects found in the water are either bugs or beetles. Of those aquatic insects having complete metamorphosis, the pupa is strictly aquatic in caddisflies only. The adaptations of the immature stages have chiefly to do with their respiratory apparatus, and this is most extraordinarily diverse. This will be discussed later. Suffice it here to say that gills of several sorts may be developed upon either the outer or inner surfaces of the body, and those on the outside may be dorsal or ventral, and may be developed upon the head or on any segment of the thorax or abdomen: thus they bear all the usual signs of independent and adaptive origin.

Finally, it is to be noted that insects have not invaded the water very far. Nearly all of them have stopped at the shores or in shoal water; only a few have established homes for themselves in deep water. Only the phantom larvae of *Corethra* have become free swimming and are regular plankton constituents; possibly a few others also, for a limited distribution-period immediately following their hatching from the egg. The press of life on land resulting from the evolution of the highly successful hexapod type of organization, with great adaptability, brief life cycle and excellent reproductive capacity, may have resulted in the crowding into the water of those moisture-loving forms whose structures were best adapted to meet the new conditions. The severity of the competition on land is most evident to the careful observer; every nook and corner has its insect inhabitants and every scrap of nutritious food is eagerly sought by a host of competitors. It is easy to conceive that a great variety of forms already accustomed to living by the water side, finding food more abundant in the water than out of it, might, if adaptable, become modified for entering the water for a greater or less depth and for remaining there a greater or less time.

And, as a matter of fact, adaptation of the adults has proceeded only a little way. Some adult insects, as certain caddisflies and damselflies, enter the water only to lay their eggs, and they remain enveloped by a layer of adherent air while beneath the surface. Some live constantly in the water but maintain communication with the surface by means of a long respiratory tube, as does *Ranatra*. The most nearly aquatic of adult insects are the bugs and beetles that have developed oar-like hind feet and have become good swimmers; these enter the water to depths of several feet and spend most of their time near the bottom in shoal waters, but they must come to the surface at intervals for air which they carry down with them beneath their wing covers or adherent to the pile of their bodies. A few adult insects also have taken to walking or running on the surface of the water, but these are naturally the most minute forms, as springtails, or those of slenderer build, like little Diptera and water striders; and of this last-mentioned group, some wander far from shore, even upon the surface of the ocean. But there are few adult insects to be found far from the shelter of vegetation, and it remains true that the great press of insect life is at the shore line.

The case is only slightly different with insect larvae. Most of these have remained near shore. As compared with the adults, their smaller size, less chitinized skin and greater plasticity have allowed much more complete adaptation to aquatic life. There are some larvae, like those of beetles and of many flies, that take air at the surface as do the adult beetles, and there are a few others, that, descending the stems, tap the air spaces of plants far beneath the surface and get oxygen from that unusual source; but there are also very many that are capable of a truly aquatic respiration, being able to utilize the air that is dissolved in the water. Most of these larvae when newly hatched absorb the oxygen directly through their skins; and a few of them, especially such as live in well aerated water, acquire no better means than this during their larval existence, but most of them develop gills of some sort.

These gills are delicate outgrowths of the thinnest integument of the body. Two types of gills are usually distinguishable, blood gills, and tracheal gills. The former are more like the gills of other aquatic animals; the latter are peculiar to insects. The blood gills are simple outgrowths of the body wall into which the blood flows. The interchange of gases which constitutes the respiratory process takes place between the blood within the gill and the water outside it by means of direct diffusion through the thin membranous wall. Such gills are very commonly developed in dipterous larvae as paired and retractile appendages of the posterior end of the alimentary canal, but they also occur on other parts of the body.

Since tracheae are the established channels of air distribution in the bodies of insects, and nearly all insects are hatched from the egg in possession of a number of them, it is natural that tracheal gills should be more commonly developed in the larvae of the group. A tracheal gill differs from a blood gill chiefly in that it is traversed by minute capillary branches of tracheae, and the air is taken up by and distributed through the tracheae. Tracheal gills are usually developed apart from and quite independently of the spiracles or breathing pores. They arise from the thin intersegmental membranes of the body. They may be developed upon the internal walls of the rectum, forming a large and very perfect gill chamber, as in the young of dragonflies. More frequently, they are developed on the outside of the body. They may be flat and lamelliform, as in the three caudal gills of the damselflies and in the paired dorsal abdominal gills of Mayflies, or they may be filamentous, simple, branched or tufted, as in most other forms. Another sort of tracheal gill (the so-called "tube gill") is developed directly from the prothoracic spiracles in certain diptera at the assumption of the pupal stage, in the form of respiratory trumpets (mosquito pupae), combs (black fly pupae), brushes (midge pupae), etc. With the development of gills, insect larvae have become independent of the surface. Many of them remain wholly submerged throughout their entire larval life. A few of them have progressed farther from shore and into deeper water. *Corethra* has been already mentioned as a plankton organism. A few larvae of midges and a few caddis worms are constant denizens of the bottom silt in our deeper fresh-water lakes. This seems indeed considerable progress into a new and totally different environment, when one remembers that they are tied by parentage to the shore.

It is to be noted in passing that only in the Coleoptera and Hemiptera has the adaptation of adults and immature stages been parallel. In the other groups the adults do not live in the water. The possession by a few adult insects (*Pteronarcys*, etc., among stoneflies, and *Chirotonetes*, etc., among Mayflies) of rudimentary gills does not indicate, as was once thought, that this is the primitive condition; it indicates only that, in these relatively primitive forms, structures developed to a considerable extent upon the immature stages have, in the rapid and incomplete transformation these undergo, been carried over in rudimentary form into adult life.

Among aquatic insects are many beautiful and interesting forms. The keys and figures in the following pages should enable anyone who has learned the parts of the body of a grasshopper, or who has mastered such elementary knowledge of insect anatomy as every textbook of zoology or of entomology affords, to identify most of the insects he will find in the water. There are many gaps in our knowledge of all the groups; even the adult insects are not well known except in the showier groups, which have always been more attractive to the collector; and so many immature forms are still unknown, it has been found impracticable to attempt to give keys even to the genera in two orders, Plecoptera and Trichoptera. Limitations of space have compelled restriction to the larger groups among the Diptera. In most of the groups having complete metamorphosis, the characterizations of the immature stages have been adapted from the accounts of European writers, very little having as yet been done on them in America. Here is an attractive field in which the amateur and the isolated student may still find pioneer work to do.

It is the purpose of this chapter to assist the student toward acquaintance with such insects as he may find in the water. The limitations of space allow but brief notice of the natural history of any of the groups and restrict the keys to dealing with families and genera. The aim is to supplement the general works on entomology and not to duplicate any part of them. Keys to the orders of adult insects are available in a number of manuals and textbooks, hence there is need here only to point out the readier recognition marks of those orders which commonly occur in the water, and to give a key to the immature stages.

RECOGNITION CHARACTERS

There are but nine orders of insects commonly found in water in any stage: Plecoptera, Odonata, Ephemerida, Hemiptera, Neuroptera, Trichoptera, Lepidoptera, Coleoptera and Diptera.

The Odonata are distinguished by the venation of the wings, especially by the possession of a distinct nodus and stigma of the type shown in Fig. 1388.

The Ephemerida are distinguished by the venation of the wings (Fig. 1387), and by their proportions and their extensive corrugation.

The Hemiptera are distinguished by the possession of a jointed, sucking proboscis, directed backward beneath the head and thorax.

The Trichoptera are distinguished by the hairy covering of their wings, the absence of jaws and proboscis (palpi are present) and by a type of venation of wings similar to that shown in Fig. 1391.

The Lepidoptera are distinguished by their covering of powdery scales, and by the possession of a *coiled* sucking proboscis.

The Coleoptera are distinguished by the hardened fore wings (elytra) meeting in a straight line down the middle of the back.

The Diptera are distinguished by the possession of a single pair of wings, with very few cross-veins in them (Fig. 1378).

The other two orders, Plecoptera and Neuroptera, lack the above combinations of characters and may be readily recognized by their general likeness to figures published in the following paragraphs devoted to them.

Besides these nine orders, there are three others, of slight importance in the life of the water, that are deliberately ignored. These are:

(1) The Thysanura, or springtails, common on the surface of water, but not living in it. They will be readily recognizable, if collected, by their very minute size, entire absence of wings, mouth parts retracted within the head, and the forked spring beneath the abdomen by means of which they jump freely.

(2) The Orthoptera, of which some of the grouse locusts (family Tettigidae), living by the water side, occasionally jump in and take a swim.

(3) The Hymenoptera, of which a few minute egg parasites, enter the water as adults to find the eggs of their aquatic victims, and these swim with their wings (*Polynema*, etc.).

Stoneflies (Order Plecoptera)

The stoneflies constitute a small and primitive group of insects of inconspicuous coloration and rather secretive habits. They are found almost exclusively about rapidly flowing water. Every spring brook will furnish a few of the smaller grayish or brownish species, and every larger rocky stream is the home of some of the larger forms. During the winter months the small black Capnias appear, often in great abundance on the surface of the snow, *Capnia necydaloides* appearing usually in December, and *Capnia pygmaea*, in March. Several species of *Taeniopteryx* appear also in March, and may often be seen on mild, sunshiny days by the borders of creeks, slowly and laboriously flying along the banks on warm afternoons. Species of *Nemoura* appear in April, emerging from the waters of cold brooks, and making short flights from one gray tree trunk to another. All through the summer the larger species are emerging from rocky streams, but these are very secretive in habits. They may be beaten from the bushes along the stream side, but are oftenest seen in numbers about street lamps and are easiest collected when attracted to lights. The green stoneflies (*Chloroperla*, etc.) fly mainly in midsummer, and frequent the fresh foliage, in the midst of which they are quite inconspicuous.

Rudimentary wings occur in a number of the genera, *Capnia*, *Taeniopteryx*, *Pteronarcella*, *Perla*, etc., and, of course, the wingless species are to be found near the waters from which they emerge on transformation — in fact, not farther therefrom than they are able to run or climb. The males alone are wingless in most cases. The eggs of the females are practically mature at transformation. While there is dearth of observations as to the feeding habits of the adults, it is certain that they will lap up water and other fluid substances, and the small grayish species eat dead grass leaves and other solid food. The mandibles of the larger forms are weak and rudimentary. The adult life, therefore, is probably very brief. Concerning the egg-laying habits also, there is dearth of actual observation. Females of many species may be taken when carrying egg masses extruded at the tip of the abdomen; but just where these are deposited, and when and how, are matters not yet established. One species of *Capnia*, an undetermined, late appearing species that occurs in Lake Forest, Ill. in May, is viviparous.

The nymphs of stoneflies are much easier to find and to collect than are the adults. By lifting stones or other obstructions out of the bed of rapid permanent streams, and quickly turning them over to look on the under side, the nymphs may usually be seen lying flat, outspread, with widely extended legs clutching the sur-

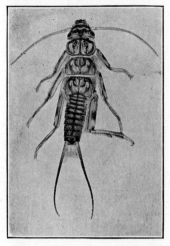

FIG. 1354. The nymph of a stonefly, *Perla*.

face. They are always associated with Mayfly nymphs of similar appearance, but are easily distinguished by the presence of two claws on the tip of each foot, where the Mayfly nymphs have but one, and by the lack of gills upon the dorsal side of the abdomen. The nymphs of larger species, as *Perla* (Fig. 1354), are not easily managed in ordinary aquaria. They cannot live long in still water, and soon after being placed in it, they manifest their discomfort, by a vigorous swaying of the body up and down. This motion brings their tufted gills into better contact with the water. Running water aquaria are essential for their maintenance.

Their transformation may often be easily observed where it occurs naturally out of doors. It always takes place near to the edge of the water. Often rocks that project but a few inches above the surface are favorite places of emergence, and the exposed surfaces of these may sometimes be found covered several layers deep with the skins of the nymphs that have come from the bed of the adjacent parts of the stream. Transformation usually occurs at night, but early and late stragglers may often be found by morning or evening light. The change from nymph to adult is, for insects, comparatively slight: wings and accessory reproductive organs are perfected, and regressive development of gills, external armor, and feeding apparatus occurs, but the change of form and of proportions of the body is slight.

The nymphs of stoneflies are, so far as known, carnivorous: they feed on the nymphs of Mayflies, on the larvae of caddisflies

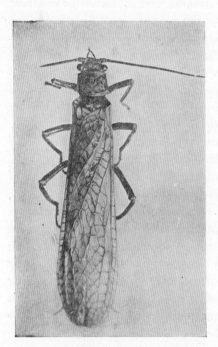 

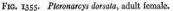

Fig. 1355.　*Pteronarcys dorsata*, adult female.　　Fig. 1356.　*Pteronarcys dorsata*, grown nymph.

and small diptera and perhaps on the young of other stoneflies. They are themselves the food of the trout and of other fishes that frequent swift waters. Hudson has demonstrated the importance of stoneflies as fish food in the mountain streams of New Zealand. Adults and nymphs are equally serviceable for bait in all our mountain streams.

While no keys to the genera of the nymphs of stoneflies have yet been published, if the adults are known, the nymphs may be readily determined by comparison, for the wing venation is fully developed in the wing pads of the nymph and is comparable in close detail with that of the adult. It is only necessary to remove, as with a sharp razor, the wing pads from a well-grown nymph, young enough so that the wings will not be already crumpled within their sheaths, mount, and examine with the microscope. Since, however, it is easier to get nymphs than adults, and nymphs only will often be available, the following hints may be of assistance in their recognition. *Pteronarcys* (Figs. 1355 and 1356) alone has gills upon the first two segments of the abdomen. *Taeniopteryx* alone has three-jointed, telescopic gill filaments attached singly at the base of the coxae. *Peltoperla* alone has conic-pointed gill filaments, in a few small clusters, concealed under the flaring, overarched margins of the thoracic segments. *Perla* and its allies have copious tufts of fine gill filaments before and behind the bases of all legs. *Chloroperla* and its allies, and *Capnia* and *Leuctra* altogether lack gills.

MAYFLIES (*Order Ephemerida*)

The Mayflies constitute a small group of very fragile insects, all of which are aquatic in their earlier stages. They abound in all fresh waters, both swift and stagnant. Some of the larger May-flies are very well known, indeed, from their habit of transforming all at one time and appearing in great swarms along shores of lakes (Fig. 1357) and banks of the larger streams. They fly to lights at night, and sometimes, under the arc lamps in city streets, they accumulate in such heaps as to require removal in wagons. Such concerted appearance of the adults of a single species gives some conception of the abundance of individuals that may live and grow up together in a restricted area; but it is to be borne in mind that there are scores of other species living in the same waters, the adults of which are rarely seen in numbers, of which the individuals are probably quite as numerous. When their period of trans-formation is extended through the summer season and their habits are not gregarious, but solitary and secretive, they may entirely escape the notice of the casual observer.

Mayflies are famed for their ephemeral existence — for living as adults but a day. They are peculiar among insects, in that they moult their external chitinous skin once again after they transform from the nymphal form to that of the adult. It is chiefly these callow and immature adults (known to the books as *sub-imagos*, and to British fishermen as *duns*) that fly to lights. Emerging

Fig. 1357. Mayflies fallen beneath an electric-light post on Lake Erie. (Photograph by Professor O. E. Jennings.)

from a rent in the back of the old nymph skin, they spread their newly expanded wings and rise feebly into the air, and if a light be near, they swarm to it; otherwise they settle upon any conven- ient tree or building, and sit stiffly (Fig. 1358) with uplifted wings until ready for their final moulting. This may occur within a few minutes, as in *Caenis*, or it may be delayed twenty-four hours or more, as in most of our larger species. *Caenis* probably lives but a few hours after leaving the water; but the larger forms live through two days, their transformation from the nymph occurs in one night,

FIG. 1358. A newly-emerged Mayfly, *Hexagenia bilineata*.

their final moult the next night, and their period of adult activity and egg-laying and their death the next evening.

The adults are peculiar in the venation of their wings (Fig. 1387) and in the extent of the longitudinal furrowing of the same, in the lack of functional mouth parts and in the buoyant function assumed by the alimentary canal, which, being no longer used for food, is filled with air. While highly specialized in most respects, one very generalized character has been retained in the group: the openings of the oviducts of the female are paired and separate.

The males of most species indulge in graceful ante-nuptial flights, that to the observer appear most delightful and exhilarating. They assemble in little companies and dance up and down, alternately rising and falling, flying upward and falling down again on outspread wings in long vertical lines. The crepuscular species such as *Ephemera* and *Hexagenia*, that compose the well-known swarms, fly out over the surface of the water, where the females meet the males, and afterwards settle down upon the surface of the water to liberate their eggs. *Caenis* swarms over the edge of the water just as darkness falls. Some of the less nocturnal species, as *Leptophlebia* and *Choroterpes*, swarm out in the sunlight in sheltered places of late afternoons, or dance up and down among the mixed shadows and sunlight beneath the canopied crowns of tall stream-side forest trees. The females of *Baetis* creep beneath stones at the surface of the water and deposit their eggs in single-layered patches just beneath the surface.

The adult life of Mayflies is truly ephemeral and is concerned wholly with reproduction; and the struggle for existence is transferred largely to the immature stages. The nymphs are highly and independently specialized. They are adapted to all sorts of aquatic situations. A few, like *Hexagenia*, *Ephemera*, and *Polymitarcys* (Fig. 1359), are burrowers beneath the bottom silt. A few, like *Caenis* and *Ephemerella*, are of sedentary habits and live rather inactively on the bottom, and on silt-covered stems. Many are

FIG. 1359. The nymph of *Polymitarcys alba.*

active climbers among green vegetation; such are *Callibaetis* and *Blasturus;* and some of these can swim and dart about by means of synchronous strokes of tail and gills with the swiftness of a minnow. The species of *Leptophlebia* love the beds of slow-flowing streams, and all the flattened nymphs of the Heptageninae live in swiftly moving water, and manifest various degrees of adaptation to withstanding the wash of strong currents. The form is depressed, and margins of the head and body are thin and flaring, and can be appressed closely to the stones to deflect the current. So diverse are the nymphs in form that the genera may be distinguished among them by a beginner more easily than among the adult Mayflies.

Mayfly nymphs feed largely on dead vegetable substances — the decaying stems and leaves of aquatic plants. They are of first importance in the food of fishes. But we are as yet largely in ignorance of the conditions that make for their abundance.

The study of this group has been greatly neglected by entomologists and our Mayfly fauna is very insufficiently known. The ecology of the immature stages is especially in need of investigation.

Dragonflies and Damselflies (*Order Odonata*)

This is another isolated group of insects, larger in size and of stronger build. All our representatives of the group are aquatic in their earlier stages, but there are a few Hawaiian damselflies whose nymphs live out of the water, on moist soil under the leaves of liliaceous plants. All members of the order are carnivorous in all stages. They are indeed among the most important of carnivorous forms about the shores of all fresh waters.

The wings of the adults are strongly developed and have a peculiar venation (Fig. 1388). The legs are not used for walking, but only for perching; to facilitate perching on vertical stems, they are set far forward and graduated in length, so that they hold the body when at rest in a more or less horizontal position. This facilitates quick stopping and starting again. Correspondingly the wings are shifted far backward, and tilted upward at their fore margins, and the side pieces of the thorax are askew.

The males are peculiar also among the orders in having the accessory organs of reproduction (copulatory apparatus) developed upon the ventral side of the second abdominal segment, far removed from the opening of the sperm ducts upon the ninth segment. The eyes are very highly developed, and the antennae are minute and setaceous. In this they resembl the preceding order Ephemerida, but the two groups as they exist to-day are highly differentiated from each other, although more or less intermediate fossil forms point to their common origin in the past.

Among the dragonflies are many superb flyers. The speed on the wing of *Tramea* and *Anax* equals, and their agility exceeds, that of swallows. They all capture their prey in flight, and are dependent on their wings for getting a living. But the habit of flight is very different in different groups. Only a few of the strongest forms roam the upper air at will. There is a host of beautiful species, the skimmers or Libellulidae (Fig. 1360), that hovers over ponds in horizontal flight, the larger species on tireless wings, keeping to the higher levels. The stronger flying Aeschnidae course along streams on more or less regular beats: but the Gomphines are less constantly on the wing, flying usually in short sallies from one resting place to another, and alighting oftener on stones or other flat surfaces than on vertical stems.

The damselflies are not such good flyers. The common black-wing *Calopteryx* (Fig. 1361) may usually be seen fluttering gaily about the borders of creeks, but most damselflies are little in

FIG. 1360.   The Blue Pirate dragonfly, *Pachydiplax longipennis*.   (Drawn by Mrs. J. G. Needham.)

evidence, and confine their locomotion to flitting from stem to stem amid the shelter of vegetation.

The dragonflies eat other insects in vast numbers and in great variety. A large part of their food consists of small diptera: and because many of these small diptera are noxious species, mosquitos, etc., an extended inquiry was once made as to the feasibility of using dragonflies to remove these pests: it appeared that dragonflies are not at all discriminating in their feeding, and will as readily eat useful as noxious species. Then, too, they eat other dragonflies, apparently preferring forms that are only a little smaller than themselves. *Hagenius*, for example, eats *Gomphus*, and *Gomphus* eats *Mesothemis*, and *Mesothemis* eats *Lestes*, and *Lestes* eats *Argia*, and *Argia* eats *Ischnura*, and so on from the greatest even unto the least of them.

Many dragonflies are eaten by birds and other animals at their transformation, before they are able to fly and escape; and some of those that are not very strong-flying are eaten habitually by birds — the smaller Libellulines by king-birds, and the smaller damselflies by swallows. But it is doubtful whether anything that flies is able to capture in flight one of the swiftest dragonflies.

There is much diversity of egg-laying habits in the order. All the damselflies and many dragonflies, especially Aeschnidae, are provided with an ovipositor, by means of which punctures are made in the stems of aquatic plants, in logs, in wet mud, etc., for the reception of the eggs. The eggs are placed singly in the punctures, and usually just below the surface of the water; but a few damselflies descend the stems to place them deeper, and some species of *Lestes* place them habitually in the stems above the surface. Here they are subject to the attack of egg parasites. The females of those dragonflies that lack a well-developed ovipositor drop their eggs upon the surface of the water while in flight (usually descending to touch the surface, and thus to wash them free), whereupon the eggs scatter and fall to the bottom; or, they settle on some plant stem at the surface and hang them in gelatinous masses about the stem. In certain of the Cordulinae these masses are long gelatinous strings, containing many hundreds of eggs. It is easy to get the eggs of most Libellulines for study. When a female is seen tipping the surface of the water with her abdomen while in flight, if she be captured uninjured and held by the tips of the fore wings (leaving the hind wings free) and dipped against the surface of the water in a glass, in imitation of her own motion while at large, she will usually liberate eggs in great abundance in the water. These require about three weeks for hatching, and the nymphs begin to eat each other early in life.

There are nymphs of Odonata in all sorts of fresh water. Those of some of the larger active species clamber about freely among

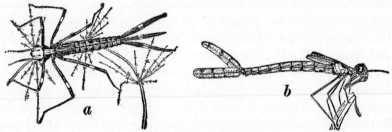

FIG. 1361. Damselfly nymphs; *a, Calopteryx*; *b, Lestes.*

water weeds, and even chase their prey, creeping stealthily upon it until within range. Most damselflies (Fig. 1361) clamber about among green stems, where they are quite inconspicuous. But nearly all dragonfly nymphs get their living by waiting in hiding for the approach of their prey, and comparatively few of them roam freely about in the water. Most of the Libellulidae are bottom sprawlers (Fig. 1362); most of the Gomphines are burrowers beneath

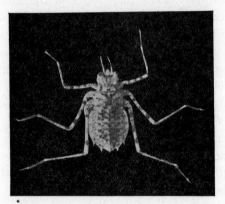

FIG. 1362.   The sprawling nymph of *Didymops transversa*.

the bottom silt, and the nymphs of *Cordulegaster* are expert ambuscaders, scratching a hole in the sand of the bottom and getting into it, kicking the sand up over their backs until covered excepting the tips of the eyes and of the respiratory orifice at the end of the abdomen, and lying in wait until some unsuspecting little animal suitable for food wanders within reach.

The chief organ for capturing prey in the nymphs of all the Odonata is the remarkably developed labium (Fig. 1389 *A*), which has become elongated, hinged in the middle and folded back under the thorax. It has acquired a formidable array of grappling hooks and spines at its tip. It is often longer than the fore legs when extended and possesses muscles capable of extending it with lightning-like speed. It is thrown forward and opened by a single movement, and when it closes on its victim it is withdrawn again instantly, dragging the struggling captive back under the jaws, which then come into play.

The problem of getting air has been solved in two ways in the nymphs of the two suborders of Odonata. In the damselflies

(Fig. 1363), there are developed three more or less leaflike gills upon the tip of the abdomen, and these are traversed by fine tracheae, and doubtless assist in getting air, although not entirely essential to that end. In the larger dragonfly nymphs there is developed

FIG. 1363. The nymph of *Ischnura verticalis*.

within the abdomen a respiratory chamber made out of the hinder portion of the modified alimentary canal. Through the action of the abdominal muscles, the water is alternately drawn into this and expelled again. This chamber is lined with multitudes of tracheal gills, and abundantly supplied with tracheae, constituting the most perfect aquatic respiratory apparatus developed in insects.

Transformation occurs in most Odonata very close above the surface of the water. The larger species transform for the most part at night: the damselflies, at any time. The period of half an hour or more required for drying the wings before sustained flight is possible is a time of great peril in the life of the dragonflies. It is a time of opportunity, however, for the collector of life history material.

WATER BUGS (*Order Hemiptera*)

A small part of this great order is aquatic; a number of families are well adapted for life in the water; a few run over the surface and a few others live habitually on the wet shores and forage in the flotsam and drift of the waves. Adults and nymphs are of similar habits and are generally sufficiently alike in structure for ready identification, the metamorphosis being slight. All are distinguished from the members of other groups by the possession of a jointed puncturing and sucking proboscis that is directed backward beneath the head. The families are so diverse in structure that here again is given evidence of independent adaptation to aquatic life, and nowhere could be found more complete intergradation of habits between terrestrial and shore-loving forms and those that dwell in the water.

The shore bugs (Acanthiidae) and toad bugs (Pelogonidae) are essentially terrestrial; the marsh treaders (Hydrometridae), water

Fig. 1364.　A giant water bug, *Benacus*, clinging to a vertical surface under water.

striders, skaters, etc. (Veliidae and Gerridae), have passed out upon the surface, a few of them having acquired the ability to dive and swim. The Nepidae and Belostomatidae are fairly adapted forms that do not depart far or long from the surface of the water, and only the Corixidae and Notonectidae have acquired very highly specialized apparatus for swimming and for carrying down a copious air supply.

There are no tracheal gills developed in this order. Nymphs and adults alike must come to the surface for air. They are easily collected by sweeping aquatic vegetation with a dip net. The Corixidae stick more closely to the bottom than do other forms.

Transformation occurs in the water, and is only a little more of a change than are the earlier nymphal moults. The adults of many genera fly from one body of water to another, and a few of the largest forms (Fig. 1364) have a habit so well known of flying to electric lights at night that they have been denominated "electric light bugs." These immense bugs are among the most powerful members of the order; the largest of the dragon fly nymphs are no match for them; they will frequently attack and kill frogs, and they have even been found preying on woodpeckers, presumably encountered in flight. Their weapon of offense is the stout beak,

FIG. 1365. A water bug (at the left) and a backswimmer (at the right), resting at the surface of an aquarium.

which is capable of making painful wounds. Even the smaller forms of *Notonecta* (Fig. 1365) can puncture the fingers of the collector if carelessly handled.

The eggs of the more strictly aquatic members of the family are fairly well known. Those of *Benacus* (Fig. 1366) and *Amorgius* are deposited on the vertical stems of *Typha*, etc., above the surface of the water; these are among the largest of insect eggs. Those of the Nepidae, *Nepa* and *Ranatra*, are distinguished by long appendages at the micropylar end, and are inserted into the soft tissues of plants — into rotten, water-soaked wood, or into green herbs. Those of *Notonecta* are deposited singly on the sides of plant stems under water, and those of *Corixa* are deposited in similar places or stuck on to the back of crawfishes.

The surface-haunting forms are characteristically of scavenger habits, eating the insects of all sorts that fall upon the surface of

FIG. 1366 The eggs of the giant water bug, *Benacus*, on the base of a Typha stem.

the water; while the more strictly aquatic bugs are truly predatory with the possible exception of the minute *Plea*, which is believed not to be carnivorous at all. The highly specialized Corixidae are able to remain wholly submerged for long periods. They clamber about amid the debris of the pond bottom, and when they come to the surface for air, they do not remain there, but quickly descend again to the shelter of the bottom trash. Of all Hemiptera these are the ones most commonly eaten by fishes.

Dobsons, Fish Flies, Spongilla Flies (*Order Neuroptera*)

But two families of this great and heterogeneous order, as now commonly restricted, are aquatic, and these in their larval stages only. The larvae of all the members of the small family Sialididae are free-ranging carnivorous, aquatic forms, and in the family Hemerobiidae, there are a few genera whose larvae live in the water. These two families are so very different in every respect that they are better considered separately.

Sialididae. Here belong a few of the most primitive of insects having complete metamorphosis: the orl flies, fish flies, dobsons, etc. They are mostly of large size, and are provided with ample wings, which, however, serve but rather poorly for flight. The dobsons are among the largest of insects, and their larvae, known to the fishermen as hellgrammites, are famous as bait for black bass. They are found in swift streams beneath the stones, where they cling securely by means of their stout legs, aided by a pair of stout-clawed processes at the end of the body. They are provided at the sides of the abdomen with paired lateral fleshy processes, and at the base of each of these there is a large tuft of fine tracheal gills. They are blackish, ugly-looking crawlers, of slow growth, requiring apparently several years to develop. When grown they crawl out on shore and seek a suitable place beneath a log or stone; for the pupae are not aquatic. The adult female lays her eggs in broad flat masses on stones or timbers above the edge of the water, and covers them over with a chalky white incrustation. The eggs are piled several layers deep and are very numerous. On hatching the young fall into the water, and begin at once their predatory existence. But one species of dobson is found in the eastern United States, the common *Corydalis cornuta* L. The fish flies (*Chauliodes*) are insects of similar appearance and habits, about half as large as the dobsons, having an expanse of wing of about one and a half inches. Their larvae usually frequent still water, where they clamber over and under logs. A rotten log on shore furnishes the favorite place for the excavation of a pupal chamber. The eggs are laid above the water in naked patches of one or more layers on either dead wood or green leaves.

The orl flies (*Sialis*) are still smaller having an expanse of wing of an inch or less. They are plain, blackish in color, and rather secretive in habits. Sometimes they occur in such numbers as to blacken the herbage about the pond border. The larvae (Fig. 1367) live among the stones and gravel in the bed of brooks, and in the borders of ponds, and transform in the wet sand on shore. They are readily distinguished from other larvae by the long tail-like prolongation of the last segment of the body. The female lays her eggs (Fig. 1368) in broad, single layered, blackish patches on some stick or timber above the surface of the water. The lateral filaments of the abdomen in *Sialis* are thin-skinned, and contain tracheae, and it is possible that they serve as organs of respiration;

FIG. 1367. The larva of the orl fly, *Sialis infumata*.

there are no additional clusters of fine gills at their bases. Unlike the foregoing, these larvae descend into the bottom silt and burrow through it, and their long abdominal filaments are close laid on the back, as are the gills of the burrowing Mayfly nymphs.

FIG. 1368. The eggs of the orl fly; from a photograph.

There is a striking general similarity between the larvae of the Sialididae and those of the more generalized carnivorous Coleoptera.

HEMEROBIIDAE. Only two genera in this large family of attractive insects are aquatic in our fauna, *Climacia* and *Sisyra* (Fig. 1369). These are small insects, half an inch or less in expanse of wing,

FIG. 1369. A spongilla fly, *Sisyra*.

the former yellow and brown in color, the latter, plain brown. Nothing is known of the feeding habits of the adults. Their larvae

(Fig. 1370) feed upon fresh-water sponges, and live within the osteoles of the same, or in depressions on the exterior of the sponge mass. They puncture the tissue of the sponge with their long decurved sucking mouth parts. The paired appendages of the abdominal segments are bent downward underneath the body, and curiously angulated; they are moved back and forward with a rapid, intermittent, shuttle-like vibration. In the well-grown larvae, the stomach has no posterior opening, and the sponge substance taken up through the slender proboscis appears to be wholly absorbed. Correspondingly, the posterior part of the alimentary canal and its appendages are put to a new use. The malpighian tubules, or nephridia, are metamorphosed in large part into silk secreting organs, the rectum into a silk reservoir, and the terminal aperture into a spinneret. When grown the larva leaves the water and climbs to some suitable supporting surface, and spins with this apparatus first a wide canopy over itself, and then a closer fitting inside cocoon. *Climacia* weaves the outer covering in a beautiful hexagonal mesh; *Sisyra* makes both coverings

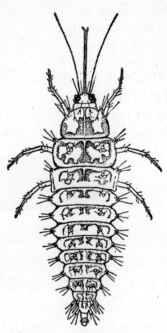

Fig. 1370. The larva of *Sisyra*.

plain and close woven. Nothing is known of the feeding or egg-laying habits of the adult, or of any other particulars except that they are sparingly attracted to lights.

It should be mentioned, perhaps, in passing, that the immature stages of another genus of Hemerobiidae, *Polystoechotes*, the genus containing our largest representatives of the family, are as yet unknown.

THE CADDISFLIES (*Order Trichoptera*)

The caddisflies constitute a large group of insects, nearly all of which are aquatic in their immature stages. Among the adults are many pretty species of soft colors and great elegance of form. Having rudimentary mouth parts they are short-lived. They are chiefly nocturnal in habits and fly to lights, often in great numbers. Some are diurnal and hover over water in long sustained horizontal flight; others dance up and down in companies under the shelter of streamside trees. No insects are more common about the wharf lights on the shores of our great lakes.

The larvae exhibit great diversity of structure and habits. Much excellent work has been done on them in Europe, but our American forms are little known. The most familiar larvae are the well known "caddisworms" that construct portable cases (Fig. 1371),

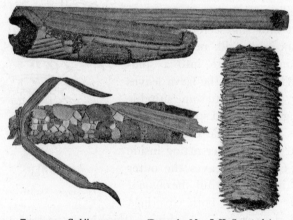

FIG. 1371. Caddisworm cases. (Drawn by Mrs. J. H. Comstock.)

in which to live, and carry them about on their backs. These cases are made out of a great variety of materials: sticks, small stones, sand grains, bits of shell, of leaves or of bark; in short, almost any solid material suitably small and available. In many species the construction of the cases is so uniform in pattern and materials that the larvae may be known by the houses which they drag about. The larvae of the Phrygeaneidae construct cylindrical cases made of bits of stems, grass, etc., placed lengthwise in a continuous spiral band; the larva of *Helicopsyche* builds out of sand grains a spirally coiled case, shaped like a snail shell. The materials of the case are always stuck together by means of the secretion of the salivary glands. Usually the cases are cylindrical but sometimes they are triangular, or square in cross-section. Usually the sticks used are placed lengthwise, but sometimes crosswise, as in stick chimneys, to make the bulky and cumbersome dwellings of some of the Limnophilidae. Sometimes, on the other hand, they are constructed so light and thin as to offer little hindrance to free loco-motion, and a few larvae with well-developed swimming fringes on their long oarlike feet swim freely about. In the cases that are constructed by most larvae of the two families Hydroptilidae (Fig. 1372) and Rhyacophilidae, no extraneous materials are used, but only the secretion of the salivary glands; these cases are therefore thin and parchment-like. Most members of the great family Hydropsychidae make no portable cases at all, but only runways in the crevices between the stones in streams; these they line with silken threads. Some of these larvae, among which are the commonest members of the genus *Hydropsyche*, to be found in every swift stream, spin webs of open mesh, like fishermen's seines, out from the up-stream ends of their tubes or runways; clearly, this is for the purpose of catching any little organisms set adrift in the stream. These are mainly carnivorous larvae; many members of other families have a mixed diet of vegetable and animal food, but a goodly number are characteristically herbivorous.

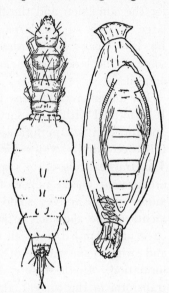

FIG. 1372. Micro-trichoptera. On the left, a larva; on the right, a pupa of another smaller species, within its transparent case.

There are caddisfly larvae for all sorts of waters, and for wet situations, or mossy banks. A few species, accompanying the "blood worms," have migrated far out on the bottoms of our larger lakes into deep water. The gills of the caddisfly larvae are always of the filamentous type, never lamelliform. They are wanting in members of several families, and are variously disposed about the body, singly or in clusters, in many others; their number, form, and arrangement furnish group recognition characters. The more typical caddisworms, having their gill filaments along the sides of the abdomen completely inclosed within the case, keep water flowing through by means of continual undulating motion of the abdomen; three tubercles at the base of the abdomen and a pair of stout prolegs at its apex serve to keep the walls properly spaced for the admission and the flow of the water. The case is always large enough so the larva can entirely withdraw itself inside. By this means it doubtless escapes from many enemies. But some of the larger fishes, as, for example, brook trout, eat case and all.

The pupa of caddisflies is peculiar in that it also is aquatic. It is formed within the larval case or tube, the larva closing the apertures with a perforate web of silk before its final moulting; this web admits water for respiration, but keeps out enemies. True tracheal gills, of the same type as those possessed by the larvae, are present on the pupae of many caddisflies. All the pupae are more or less active; some maintain constant undulating movements of the abdomen to keep the water circulating, and at the close of the pupal stage all work their way out of the larval case, and swim to the surface of the water to undergo their final transformation. In the case of species that inhabit swift waters and transform in the current, this takes place very quickly, the adult emerging instantly on reaching the surface and flying away at once. Although the adults have jaws of the most rudimentary sort, the mandibles of the pupa are often large and conspicuous; they are supposed to be of use in cutting a way out of the larval case.

Fig. 1373. An egg ring of *Phryganea*.

The eggs of caddisflies are laid in various ways and places. Some are dropped in the surface of still pools while in flight. The females of some of the Hydropsychidæ crawl beneath the water and spread their eggs in a single layer over the lee side of stones in the gentler currents. The big forms of *Phryganea* fasten their pretty green eggs in a gelatinous ring (Fig. 1373) on the stem of some aquatic plant.

Aquatic Moths (*Order Lepidoptera*)

Of this great order of insects, only a few moths of the family Pyralidae are aquatic. Many moths live as larvae on plants by the waterside, and a few burrow in the tissues of submerged aquatic plants, obtaining their air from the airspaces of the plant stems. The aquatic caterpillars, like their terrestrial relatives, are distinguished from larvae of other orders by the possession of a brown chitinous shield covering the prothoracic segment, by bristle-bearing tubercles regularly disposed over the body and by fleshy grasping prolegs beneath the abdomen.

There are three types of aquatic larvae found commonly in our fresh waters, two in ponds and one in rapid streams.

The larvae of *Nymphula* (*Hydrocampa*) are destitute of gills, and greatly resemble pale terrestrial caterpillars. They live in flat cases composed of two pieces cut out from green leaves of riverweed or water-lily, and fastened together and lined with silk. They live near the surface of the water. During the pupal stage the cases are often found floating. The eggs are laid on or under floating leaves.

The larvae of *Paraponyx* are provided with abundant branching gills, which surround the body like a white fringe. These larvae live in similar cases or between leaves in sheltering crevices that are lined with silk.

The larvae of *Elophila fulicalis*, as recently described by Lloyd from Ithaca, N. Y., live on the stones in rapid streams, protected by an irregular shelter of thin-spun silk. They are in form strongly depressed, and have unbranched gills arranged in two longitudinal lateral rows. They feed mainly on such green algae as grow near at hand. Each larva when grown fashions a broadly dome-shaped pupal shelter or half-cocoon under some portion of the larval shelter, with a row of marginal openings at either side to permit free circulation of water and air through it.

BEETLES (*Order Coleoptera*)

Of this great group of insects only a few families are wholly aquatic, and a few others are partially so. The order as a whole is predominantly terrestrial, and the aquatic families show unmistakable signs of having been developed from terrestrial ancestors. All the adults and pupae are strictly terrestrial in their mode of respiration, and nearly all the larvae likewise get their air supply from above the surface of the water. The pupae of all are formed either on land, or in direct communication with the air. The families that are strictly aquatic are the Dytiscidae, Haliplidae, Parnidae and Amphizoidae; those that show complete intergradation in habits are the Hydrophilidae and Dascyllidae. The Chrysomelidae are scarcely to be called aquatic at all in any proper sense, although two of the subfamilies live on water plants.

There is such great diversity of habits and structure in water beetles that the families may be best considered separately. We begin with those that are least aquatic in habit.

Two small groups of leaf beetles of the great family Chrysomelidae feed upon water plants; the Galerucellinae, upon the floating leaves of members of the water-lily family. These dingy little beetles lay their yellow eggs in small clusters on the upper surfaces of the leaves, and the black-banded larvae, hatching therefrom, feed upon the tissues, quite as their more familiar relatives feed upon land plants. The other subfamily, the Donaciinae, or long-horned leaf-beetles, is much more interesting. The larvae feed upon the roots of aquatic plants, far beneath the surface of the water. They are provided with a pair of spiracles near the end of the body and these spiracles are armed with sharp corneous processes, capable of being thrust into plant stems, of reaching the air spaces on the inside, and of obtaining the air, rich in oxygen, contained therein. Thus the larvae, while destitute of gills, and strictly air breathers, get their air supply through the medium of the plants, while living always beneath the water. The pupal stage likewise is passed in the place where the larva lived on the roots, but the pupa is inclosed in a water-tight cocoon, attached to the plant tissue and containing air in free communication with that in the air spaces of the plant. The adult beetles spend their lives among the leaves of the plants, flying actively about when disturbed. They are of shining, metallic coloration, blue or green. Those that live on water lilies deposit their eggs through holes eaten in the leaves, arranging them in a curve around the opening on the under side. They are able to place them thus through the possession of a long extensile ovipositor.

The family Hydrophilidae is in part terrestrial and in part aquatic, and the aquatic members show all degrees of adaptation to water life. A few of the larger forms are expert swimmers, but many of the smaller ones are fitted only for dabbling around in the mud at the water's edge. The best-known member of the family is perhaps the big black *Hydrophilus*, with finely fringed swimming legs and with keeled sternum. It is attracted to electric lights in vast numbers in the spring, where it falls beneath them and flounders around in the dust of the street, giving a fine illustration of the uselessness of its specialization when in an unsuitable environment. The larva of this beetle is commonly taken in ponds, not swimming, but clinging to stems at the surface, its squat, hairy body not well fitted for getting through the water, but with immense rapacious jaws, very capable of seizing large Mayfly nymphs and adult *Eubranchipus* when these swim within reach. Another hydrophilid which often swarms into trap lanterns set over streams is *Berosus*, whose aquatic larva is provided with lateral paired abdominal appendages somewhat like those of the neuropterous genus *Sialis*.

The eggs of *Hydrophilus* are laid in a white membranous capsule attached to plant stems and leaves at the surface of the water.

The Amphizoidae and Parnidae are found as adult beetles clinging to logs and stones in clear flowing streams. The former family contains but a few far western species; the latter is widely distributed, and contains numerous genera and species. The name "Riffle beetles" is applied to them to indicate the seat of their greatest abundance. They are mostly of small size and their coloration is usually inconspicuous, although some of them are striped with red or yellow. The adults sun themselves on the stones that protrude from the water, and fly readily from one resting place to another. Many of the larvae, especially the larger ones, are strongly depressed in form, and have flaring lateral margins to the body segments that fit down closely against a stone, limpet-like, to withstand the wash of the current; hence, these are able to maintain a footing in the swiftest waters. The common "water penny," the larva of *Psephenus lecontei*, illustrates the extreme of flattening; this larva has developed abundant tracheal gills from the thin membrane between the body segments, and these are completely covered over by the projecting lateral margins of the body segments. The adult female *Psephenus* crawls down on the lee side of a stone and deposits her yellow eggs in broad one-layered patches on its surface.

The Gyrinidae or whirligig beetles constitute a small group of strictly aquatic forms, very peculiar in structure and habits. They are well known to every one as shining black beetles of oval form, that gather in companies upon the surface of brooks and ponds and glide about in irregular curves with a speed which the eye can hardly follow. When captured they exude a whitish repugnatorial fluid, having a rather disagreeable odor. They hibernate as adult beetles in the mud and in their season of activity they spend much time beneath the water, in which they can dive and swim dextrously. Their fore feet bear hooked claws with which they can cling to the bottom when desiring to remain beneath the surface. They are at once distinguishable from other water beetles by the unusual brevity and peculiar formation of the hind legs, and by the possession of divided eyes, there appearing to be one pair above for vision of objects in air when the beetle lies on the surface, and one below, presumably, for seeing things in the water.

The larva of the gyrinids is elongate and slender, and possesses at the tip of the abdomen two pairs of backwardly directed grappling hooks, and long slender paired filaments arranged segmentally along its sides somewhat like those of the Neuropterous genus *Sialis*. Both larvae and adults are carnivorous. The larvae possess long perforate sickle-shaped mandibles well adapted for puncturing the skins of soft midge or other dipterous larvae, etc., and for sucking out the fluid content of their bodies. The pupae of the Gyrinidae are formed in thin cocoons attached to the side of vertical plant stems above the water.

The little family of Haliplidae contains two genera of pretty little
beetles of brown color spotted with yellow, *Haliplus* and *Peltodytes*. These are easily distinguished from other beetles by the
sternal plates that broadly overlap the bases of the hind legs.
These beetles abound amid thick shore vegetation, and
their larvae adhere very closely to the trash, and are
most commonly found in floating mats of *Spirogyra* and
other filamentous algae. They are among the most
inactive of creatures, and in coloration and in form
show a high degree of protective resemblance. They
are easier overlooked than discovered even by the
collector searching for them. The stick-like larva of
Haliplus is shown in Fig. 1374; *Peltodytes* is strikingly
different superficially, being covered all over its body
by very long jointed slender bristle-like processes.
Matheson has recently shown that the larvae feed upon
filamentous algae, sucking out the contents of the cells,
one by one, and that the eggs are deposited by the
adult beetles within the coarser algal filaments.

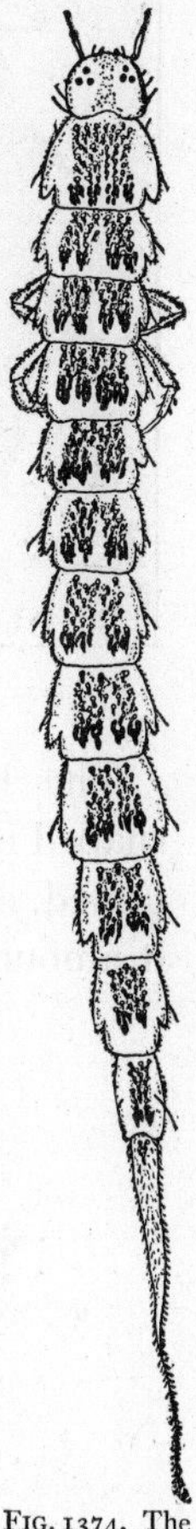

The dominant family of water beetles is the Dytiscidae,
commonly known as diving beetles. These abound in
all fresh-water ponds. All are aquatic in both larval
and adult stages, but all take air at the surface of the
water, with the exception of some of the smaller larvae
which seem to be able to absorb their oxygen from the
water without having developed any special apparatus
therefor. All are carnivorous, and in all the pupa is
formed on shore.

In fitness for swimming, the adult beetles differ
greatly. Some of the larger forms like *Cybister* are
possessed of long oar-like hind legs provided with close-
set swimming fringes, and the long regular synchronous
strokes of the legs drive the body forward with great
ease and swiftness; whereas, some of the lesser and more generalized forms, like *Bidessus*, with scanty swimming fringes, and with
legs otherwise little modified, either in structure or in movement,
from what is useful in walking, swim very poorly. These do more

FIG. 1374. The
larva of *Hali-
plus*. (Drawn
by Miss Edna
Mosher.)

climbing than swimming, and, consequently, they keep nearer to shore and to the shelter of submerged trash. In an aquarium

beetles of the size of *Coptotomus* and *Laccophilus* may be seen feeding in groups on the bodies of dragonfly nymphs and tadpoles much larger than themselves, which they have overpowered. Their own exceedingly hard chitinous armor doubtless protects them from being eaten by the majority of aquatic carnivorous animals.

Egg-laying appears to have been observed hitherto only in *Dytiscus*, which deposits its eggs singly in punctures made in the green stems of aquatic plants.

FIG. 1375. A predaceous diving beetle, *Dytiscus*.

The larvae are voracious creatures, armed with long sickle-shaped mandibles, like those of the larvae of the families just mentioned, each mandible with so deep a groove on the inner side that it amounts to a perforation opening at the tip and the base. The

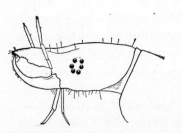

FIG. 1376. Side view of the head of the larva and pupa of the diving beetle, *Hydroporus*. (Drawings by Mrs. Helen Williamson Lyman.)

basal aperture lies just within the mouth-opening when the tips of the mandible are brought together. Nearly all the larvae of this group capture only living prey, but a few like *Hydroporus* (Fig. 1376) will eat pieces of animals that have been killed for them.

Many of the largest larvae are fiercely cannibalistic and will eat their brethren even when other food offers.

Some of the larvae are provided with swimming fringes on the legs, some have them on the tail, and many have them in both places. Some, like the larvae of *Acilius,* are exceedingly lithe and graceful creatures. Others (Fig. 1377) scarcely swim at all, but creep about among the trash at the shore line.

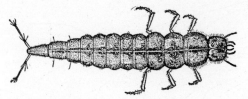

FIG. 1377. The larva of *Coptotomus interrogatus.*

In the present state of our knowledge, it is not possible to give keys that will determine genera of Dytiscid larvae, and the best means of identifying native larvae is by comparison with the beautiful figures of Schiodte, who long ago (1861) described the European representatives of many of our genera.

The Two-winged Flies (*Order Diptera*)

Of this immense order a considerable portion has taken to a more or less aquatic life. A majority of the families have some members that develop in the water, but only a few of the smaller families are wholly aquatic. Those best fitted for life in the water show adaptations of the most diverse sorts, so that here again the families are best considered separately.

Since nearly all the families of the Diptera have some aquatic members, the determination of the adult flies must be left to the aid of the keys in the entomological manuals that are everywhere available. Each of these families has a characteristic type of wing venation, and some aid may be had from comparison with the typical wings shown in Fig. 1378.

It is quite impossible in the space at command to give keys to the genera of Dipterous families, these being very numerous

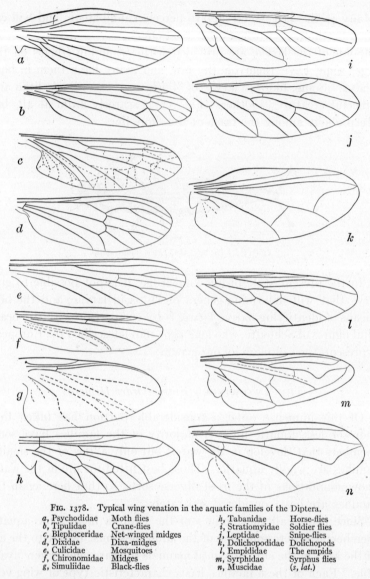

FIG. 1378. Typical wing venation in the aquatic families of the Diptera.

a, Psychodidae	Moth flies	h, Tabanidae	Horse-flies
b, Tipulidae	Crane-flies	i, Stratiomyidae	Soldier flies
c, Blephoceridae	Net-winged midges	j, Leptidae	Snipe-flies
d, Dixidae	Dixa-midges	k, Dolichopodidae	Dolichopods
e, Culicidae	Mosquitoes	l, Empididae	The empids
f, Chironomidae	Midges	m, Syrphidae	Syrphus flies
g, Simuliidae	Black-flies	n, Muscidae	(s, lat.)

in the Chironomidae, Tipulidae, etc., or even to enter into detailed statements as to their habits. A few of the families are comparatively small and unimportant. The moth flies (Psychodidae) are very minute, being among the smallest of flies, and live as larvae in the scum and about the edges of all sorts of fresh water, while their adults swarm in thickets about the shores of pools. The Ptychopteridae inhabit swales, their larvae living in the rotting trash at the edge of the water, and the adults fluttering about the tops of the adjacent herbage. The dixa midges (Dixidae) inhabit spring brooks and clear pools, and their larvae (Fig. 1379), with bodies bent double, slide out upon the surfaces of wet leaves and stones, or edge off into the water and whirl about in short curves; the adults dance in companies above the surface of the water. Some larvae of the Rhyphidae likewise inhabit pools, and the adults sometimes assemble and dance in the shelter of forest trees at some distance from the water. The few known aquatic members of the Leptidae live as larvae in streams and cling with the well-developed claws of their stout muscular abdominal prolegs to the surfaces of stones; the adults flit about the shore, displaying their unusually gaudy colors and velvety textures. These are small and comparatively unimportant families.

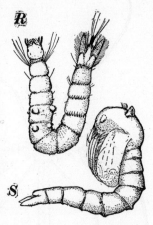

FIG. 1379. Larva (*R*) and pupa (*S*) of the dixa-midge. (After Johannsen.)

Then there are a few large families of which but a small proportion of the members are adapted to aquatic life. The crane-flies (Tipulidae) are essentially terrestrial: most of them live in moist earth or wet leaves. Some are strictly amphibious, like *Epiphragma* (Figs. 1380 and 1381). They possess as larvae the usual terminal spiracles for breathing air, but have these set upon a respiratory disc that can be closed by folding together on the middle line, and they have a bundle of four anal gills that may then be protruded for use under water. There is a fine development of fringes about the respiratory disc of other species, and these fringes spread out upon the surface film, holding the spiracles up to the air, while the larvae are moving about in the water below. A few only of the syrphus flies (Syrphidae) are aquatic, but the larvae of certain of these, the common "rat-tailed maggots" are most peculiar and interesting. A very ordinary sort of white fleshy legless fly larva has the supporting base of the terminal spiracles drawn out into a flexuous slender tube, as long as or longer than the body. The larva lives in the mud in shoal water, and with this tube reaches up to the surface for air. A good many aquatic forms are included among

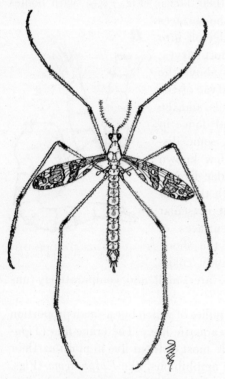

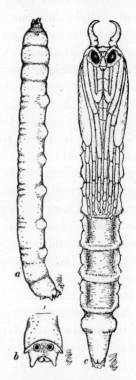

FIG. 1380. The crane-fly *Epiphragma fascipennis*, adult female.

FIG. 1381. *Epiphragma: a,* larva; *b,* end of larva from above; *c,* pupa.

the host of higher diptera that are here dismissed as Muscidae in the broad sense, but the larvae of these (Fig. 1382) differ from their terrestrial relatives by characters of less moment than those just mentioned.

A few small families are most interesting for their fitness for special places in the water, both larval and pupal stages being passed in similar situations. The net-winged midges (Blepharoceridae) live in rapid streams, and are peculiar in the very strongly depressed form of both larva and pupa, and in the row of ventral sucking discs which the larva has developed for hanging fast.

The black-flies (Simuliidae) also live in running water. The larvae adhere to stones and timbers by a single sucking disc at the hinder end of the flask-shaped body, which thus hangs sway-ing in the current with head downstream. Above the mouth on the front of the head there are two processes which bear the name of "fans." These are composed of a very large number of scythe-shaped rays fringed along the side. Set at an angle upon the pedicel, like the fingers of a reaper's cradle upon the handle, together these constitute a net for retaining small organisms adrift in the water, and for holding them up to the mouth.

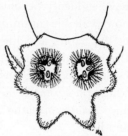

FIG. 1382. The terminal respira-tory disc of a swale-fly larva, *Sepedon.*

This is an aboriginal plankton apparatus. *Simulium* larvae play in the rapids, spinning silken threads in the water, and swinging on them from place to place. Occasionally the threads thus spun in the troughs of fish hatcheries have been sufficiently numerous to entangle and kill newly hatched trout. These threads are spun from the salivary glands; a final use for the secretion of these glands is the making of the open-meshed half-cornucopia-shaped cocoon in which, attached to the sides of the rocks or tim-bers, the pupal stage is passed; a branched prolongation of the tracheal lining of the prothoracic spiracles constitutes the so-called "tube gills," by means of which the black-fly pupa is able to get its air supply while wholly submerged.

The soldier flies (Stratiomyiidae) live as larvae on the surface of still water. They float stiff and rigid and stick-like, with a circlet of water-repellent bristles surrounding the terminal spiracles, keep-ing open the way to the air. The pupa is formed within the larval skin, without further outward indication of the change than a slight angulation of the latter posteriorly. The adult soldier flies hover familiarly about the arrow heads on shore at egg-laying time, and at other times frequent flowers to feed on their nectar.

There remain three large families of the diptera of very great importance. Two of these, the Culicidae and the Tabanidae, are important because of the damage they do, and the other, the Chironomidae, because of the food it furnishes to fishes. The mosquitoes (Culicidae), since the discovery of their importance to man as agents for the dissemination of the germs of malarial and other fevers, have suddenly become well known. A number of good books are now available containing descriptions, figures, and detailed accounts of the habits and life histories of the economic species. Some of the most interesting members of the family are not included in these books among the pests, since the adults do not bite. *Corethra,* whose phantom larvae are a part of the plankton, is one of these, and *Pelorempis,* the large culicid inhabitant of cold springs is another.

The biting adults of the large horse-flies (Tabanidae) are likewise serious pests of the domesticated animals. Their naked

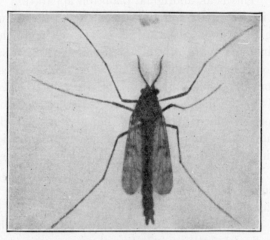

FIG. 1383. The speckled midge, *Tanypus carneus,* male.

translucent larvae, tapering to either end and ringed with fleshy tubercles, are carnivorous, and are found in the trash of the bottom in all shoal fresh waters. But two genera, *Tabanus* and *Chrysops,* are of much importance in our fauna.

The midges (Chironomidae, Fig. 1383) constitute undoubtedly

the largest single complex of aquatic Diptera. They are a host; indeed, the typical genus *Chironomus* is a host in itself. Their larvae (Fig. 1384), with no better apparatus than a few blood gills at the end of the abdomen, and their pupae, with nothing better than "tube gills" protruded from the prothoracic spiracles, are

FIG. 1384.   The larva of *Chironomus*.   (After Johannsen.)

able to live in all waters, from springs to stagnant pools and from rills to deep lake bottoms. They are chiefly herbivorous and are of very great importance in furnishing the food of a multitude of the larger animals, including fishes. The larvae construct for

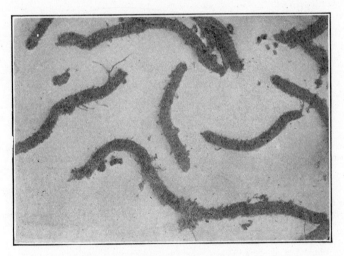

FIG. 1385.   Dwelling-tubes of midge larvae (*Chironomus*) from the lake bottom.
(Photograph by T. L. Hankinson.)

themselves some sort of shelter, fastening the materials their environment offers together with the silk-like secretion of their salivary glands; some in rapid streams build cases on the stones; others, on the lake bottom, build soft flocculent tubes of silt (Fig. 1385).

These latter larvae are red in color and are known as "blood worms." The color is due to haemoglobin in the blood plasma; the capacity of this substance for oxygen gathering seems to enable these blood worms to live in water that is poor in oxygen.

In the preceding pages the principal groups of aquatic insects are briefly characterized, and typical forms are figured. Hints are given for the recognition of the nymphs of Plecoptera on page 885, and of the larvae of aquatic Lepidoptera on page 903. In the following pages keys are given for determining the adults of Trichoptera and Hemiptera, and for both adults and immature stages of the other orders. An understanding of the venation of the wings is essential to the study of adult insects of most orders, and the following figure (Fig. 1386) is given to illustrate the wing venation and explain the terminology used.

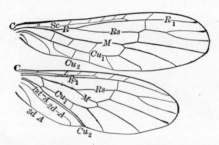

Fig. 1386.   The venation of the wings of a stonefly, *Chloroperla*.   The designation of veins is given here for all succeeding wing figures:

C, Costa	*M*, Media
Sc, Subcosta	*Cu*, Cubitus
R, Radius	*A*, Anal veins.

The radius has a main stem (R_1) and a principal branch (Rs) on the posterior side.

Media is often twice forked, and Cubitus once forked; the recognizable branches are numbered from front to rear: three anal veins are likewise recognized.

KEY TO THE ORDERS OF AQUATIC INSECT LARVAE

1 (8) Larvae with wings developing externally (called *nymphs* in this chapter) and no quiescent pupal stage. 2

2 (7) With biting mouth parts. 3

3 (6) With long, filamentous caudal setae; labium not longer than the head, and not folded on itself like a hinge. 4

4 (5) Gills mainly under the thorax; tarsal claws two; caudal setae two. (Stoneflies; see page 883) . . . **Plecoptera.**

5 (4) Gills mainly on the sides of the abdomen; tarsal claws single; caudal setae generally three. (Mayflies; see page 921). . **Ephemerida.**

6 (3) Caudal setae represented by three broad, leaf-like respiratory plates traversed by tracheae, or by small spinous appendages; labium when extended much longer than the head; at rest, folded like a hinge, extending between the bases of the fore legs. (Dragonflies and damselflies; see page 928) . . **Odonata.**

7 (2) Mouth parts combined into a jointed beak, which is directed beneath the head backward between the fore legs. (Bugs; see page 933) . . . **Hemiptera.**

8 (1) Larvae proper, with wings developing internally, and invisible till the assumption of a quiescent pupal stage. 9

9 (18) With jointed thoracic legs. 10

10 (11) With slender, decurved, piercing mouth parts, half as long as the body; small larvae, living on fresh-water sponges. Family HEMEROBIIDAE (see page 934) of . . **Neuroptera.**

11 (10) With biting mouth parts. 12

12 (15) With a pair of prolegs on the last segment only (except in Sialis, Fig. 1367, which has a single long median tail-like process at the end of the abdomen) these directed backward, and armed each with one or two strong hooks or claws. . . 13

13 (14) Abdominal segments each with a pair of long, lateral filaments. Family SIALIDIDAE (see page 935) of . . **Neuroptera.**

14 (13) Abdominal segments without long, muscular, lateral filaments, often with minute gill filaments cylindric larvae, generally living in portable cases. (Caddisflies; see page 936). . **Trichoptera.**

15 (12) Prolegs, when present, on more than one abdominal segment; if present on the last segment, then not armed with single or double claws (except in gyrinid beetle larvae, which have paired lateral abdominal filaments), often entirely wanting. 16

16 (17) With five pairs of prolegs, and with no spiracles at the apex of the abdomen. . . (Moths; see page 903) . . **Lepidoptera.**

17 (16) Generally without prolegs; never with five pairs of them; usually with terminal spiracles; long, lateral filaments often present on the abdominal segments. (Beetles, adults; see p. 937; larvae; see p. 943) . **Coleoptera.**

18 (9) Without jointed thoracic legs; with abdominal prolegs, or entirely legless. . . . . . (Flies, etc.; see page 943) . . **Diptera.**

KEY TO NORTH AMERICAN MAYFLIES

IMAGOS

1 (13)   The cubital and first anal veins strongly divergent at the base (Fig. 1387).   Venation never greatly reduced. 2

2 (3)   The posterior fork of the median vein very deep, almost reaching the wing base; two long simple intercalaries between the first and second anal veins. . . . . *Campsurus.*

3 (2)   The posterior fork of the median vein (M_3-M_4) forked for not more than three-fourths of its length. 4

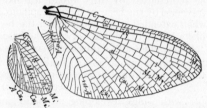

FIG. 1387.   The wings of *Ephemera.*   (Drawn by Dr. Anna H. Morgan.)

4 (5)   Between the first and second anal veins is a bunch of three or four long straight intercalaries, conjoined basally before their attachment to the principal veins; the second anal vein nearly straight and unbranched. . . . . *Polymitarcys.*

5 (4)   Between the first and second anal veins are only shorter, sinuate, and sometimes forking intercalaries, attached directly to the first anal; the second anal vein sinuate and often branched (Fig. 1387). 6

6 (7)   The posterior fork of the median vein forked two-thirds to three-fourths its length; vein Cu_2 not more strongly bent at base than the first anal. . . . . *Euthyplocia.*

7 (6)   This fork of the median vein occupying not more than half its length; vein Cu_2 more strongly bent at base than is the first anal (Fig. 1387). 8

8 (12)   The third anal vein simple, but attached to the hind margin by a number of cross veins; in the narrow posterior fork of the median vein there are one or more cross veins before the origin of the intercalary; male forceps four-jointed. 9

9 (10, 11)   Caudal setae three in both male and female; fore tarsus of female imago three-fourths as long as the tibia. . . . *Ephemera.*

10 (9, 11)   Caudal setae two in the male and three in the female; fore tarsus of the female two-thirds as long as the tibia. . *Pentagenia.*

11 (9, 10)   Caudal setae two in male and female; fore tarsus of female as long as the tibia. . . . . *Hexagenia.*

12 (8) The third anal vein with a simple terminal fork and unattached to the hind margin, although a few isolated short intercalaries lie between; in the wider posterior fork of the median vein there is no cross vein before the origin of the intercalary; male forceps three-jointed . . . . *Potamanthus.*

13 (1) The cubital and first anal veins parallel at base (in a few forms with reduced and scanty venation, appearing a little diverg-ent). 14

14 (15) Hind tarsi with five freely movable segments; eyes of the male simple and remote; venation never greatly reduced; intercalary veins between the first and second anal veins unattached basally and in two pairs, of which the pair nearer the hind angle is the longer. . . . . *Heptagenia.*

15 (14) Hind tarsi usually with but four freely movable segments, the basal segment being more or less completely consolidated with the tibia; eyes of the male enlarged, often approximated on the dorsal side and divided into superior and lateral portions with corneal facets of different size; venation various, sometimes greatly reduced; intercalary veins between the first and second anal never as above. 16

16 (17) The three anal veins nearly parallel to the hind margin of the wing and to each other, ending in the outer margin; in the hind wing the branches of the radial vein are strongly unilateral on the anterior side. . . . . *Baetisca.*

17 (16) Anal veins strongly divergent distally, usually both the second and the third ending in the hind margin; forks of the radial vein in the hind wing more symmetrical. 18

18 (39) The posterior division of the median vein with a normal posterior fork; hind wings, when present, usually but little longer than broad and with a copious venation. 19

19 (32) The intercalaries between the first and second anal veins variable, but usually more or less independent, and not directly dependent from the first anal; three well-developed caudal setae (except in *Blasturus,* in our fauna). 20

20 (31) Hind wings present. 21

21 (28) Bisector of the posterior fork of the median vein and bisector of the cubital fork unattached basally; between the latter and vein Cu_2 no intercalaries; vein Cu_2 in the hind wing rarely preserved; caudal setae generally much longer than the body; penultimate segment of the male forceps shorter than the antepenultimate. 22

22 (27) In the hind wing the subcostal vein reaches nearly to the wing apex; male forceps three-jointed. 23

23 (26) Hind wing with a slight concavity at the middle of costal margin; five to six longitudinal veins between M_1 and M_2; veinlets numerous about the wing margins and cross veins numerous in the hind wings. 24

24 (25) Third anal vein of the hind wing wanting; caudal setae of about equal length. . . . . *Leptophlebia.*

25 (24) Third anal vein of the hind wing present, and often followed by one
          or two additional intercalaries; median caudal seta dis-
          tinctly shorter than the others. . . . . *Blasturus.*

26 (23) Hind wing with an angular lobe projecting forward from the middle
          of the costal margin; four longitudinal veins between M_1 and
          M_2; wing margins free from veinlets, and few cross veins in
          hind wing. . . . . *Habrophlebia.*

27 (22) In the hind wing the subcostal vein terminates in the costa at hardly
          more than half the length of the wing, just beyond the
          obtuse angulation having a thickened margin; forceps of
          male more or less distinctly four-jointed. . . *Choroterpes.*

28 (21) Bisectors of the posterior fork of the median vein and of the cubital
          fork both tending to attach themselves to the posterior
          branch of their respective forks; between the latter and vein
          Cu_2 are generally some short intercalaries (the cubital region
          thus being better developed than in group 21); caudal setae
          about as long as the body; penultimate segment of the male
          forceps longer than the antepenultimate. 29

29 (30) Veins Cu_2 and 1st A separate to base. . . . . *Ephemerella.*

30 (29) Veins Cu_2 and 1st A fused toward the base. . . . . . . *Drunella.*

31 (20) Hind wings absent. . . . . *Caenis.*

32 (19) The intercalaries between the first and second anal veins represented
          by a series of veinlets, often sinuous or forking, extending
          directly from the first anal to the wing margin; costal
          angulation of hind wing close to the base; but two well-
          developed caudal setae, the median one being rudimentary
          or wanting; basal joint of hind tarsi evident but not well
          developed. 33

33 (36) Median caudal seta a distinctly segmented rudiment (Fig. 1354); for-
          ceps of male three-jointed; posterior prolongation of sternum
          of ninth segment of abdomen of female bifid at tip. . . 34

34 (35) Basal segment of fore tarsus of male shortest; claws of each tarsus
          unlike each to each; hind wing with the costal angulation
          acute, and the posterior fork of the median vein occupying
          two-thirds the length of that vein. . . . . . *Coloburus.*

35 (34) Basal segment of fore tarsus of the male longest; claws of each
          tarsus alike; hind wing with the costal angulation obtuse,
          and the posterior division of the median vein forked through
          one-third its length. . . . . *Chirotonetes.*

36 (33) Median caudal seta more rudimentary or wanting; forceps of the
          male distinctly four-jointed; posterior prolongation of the
          sternum of the ninth abdominal segment in the female entire
          at tip. 37

37 (38) Claws of each tarsus alike; caudal setae at least one-half longer than
          the body. . . . . *Siphlurus.*

38 (37) Claws of each tarsus unlike; caudal setae about as long as the body
          in both sexes. . . . . *Ameletus.*

39 (18) Posterior fork of the median vein apparently simple, M_4 being de-
          tached and appearing as an intercalary; hind wings when
          present at least twice as long as wide, and provided with
          but 1–3 longitudinal veins. 40

40 (45)   Hind wings present. 41

41 (42)   Fore wings with numerous costal cross veins before the bulla; hind
          wings with a moderate number of cross veins. . *Callibaetis.*

42 (41)   Fore wings without costal cross veins before the bulla; hind wings
          without cross veins or with but 1–3 of them. 43

43 (44)   Marginal intercalary veinlets in pairs; hind wings oblong, with a
          short costal angulation. . . . . *Baetis.*

44 (43)   Marginal intercalary veinlets of the fore wing single; hind wings
          linear, with a spur-like costal angulation. . *Centroptilum.*

45 (40)   Hind wings absent. . . . . *Cloeon.*

Nymphs

1 (11)   Mandibles with an external tusk-like ramus, visible from above; gills
          on abdominal segments 1–7 (often rudimentary on 1),
          double, flattened, linear, the margins fringed with respira-
          tory filaments. 2

2 (9, 10) Mandibular tusks longer than the head (burrowing species) . . 3

3 (6)   With no frontal prominence. 4

4 (5)   Legs increasing in length posteriorly; gills of the first abdominal seg-
          ment simple; labrum longer than wide; maxillary palpus
          two-jointed. . . . . *Polymitarcys.*

5 (4)   Legs decreasing in length posteriorly; labrum wider than long; maxil-
          lary palpus three-jointed. . . . . *Euthyplocia.*

6 (3)   With a conspicuous frontal prominence. 7

7 (8)   Frontal prominence rounded. . . . . *Hexagenia.*

8 (7)   Frontal prominence bifid at tip. . . . . *Ephemera.*

9 (2, 10) Mandibular tusks shorter than the head, inconspicuous, only their
          tips visible from above. . . . . *Potamanthus.*

10 (2, 9) Unknown . . . . *Campsurus* and *Pentagenia.*

11 (1)   Mandibles without projecting tusk-like ramus; gills not as in 1. 12

12 (13)   Eyes dorsal; body strongly depressed; tarsal claws with lateral teeth;
          dwellers in rapid streams and on wave-beaten shores adapted
          to clinging to flat surfaces of rocks, timbers, etc.
                                                      Heptagenia.

13 (12)   Eyes lateral; claws smooth or toothed below. 14

14 (15)   Gills completely concealed under an enormously enlarged, four-
          spined dorsal thoracic shield. . . . . *Baetisca.*

15 (14)   Gills exposed; thoracic dorsum normal. 16

16 (31)   Outer caudal setae fringed on both sides. 17

17 (24)   Gills on abdominal segments 1–7 double. 18

18 (21)   Gills filamentous. 19

19 (20)   Each a pair of simple filaments. . . . . *Leptophlebia.*

20 (19)   Each a pair of clusters of slenderer filaments. . . . *Habrophlebia.*

21 (18)   Gills lamelliform, at least on the middle segments. 22

22 (23)   Lamellae of each gill similar. . . . . *Blasturus.*

23 (22)   Lamellae of each gill markedly differing in form at tip. *Choroterpes.*

24 (17) Gills absent from one or more of segments 1–7; one pair more or less elytroid, covering those behind it. 25

25 (28) Gills present on the seventh abdominal segment, elytroid on the third or fourth segment; a pair of tubercles on the apical margin of each segment beside the middorsal line. 26

26 (27) Head smooth above. . . . . *Ephemerella*.

27 (26) Head armed above with a pair of erect occipital tubercles. *Drunella*.

28 (25) Gills absent from the seventh abdominal segment, elytroid on the second segment; no dorsal abdominal tubercles. . . . 29

29 (30) Elytroid gill cover subquadrate. . . . . *Caenis*.

30 (29) Elytroid gill cover subtriangular. . . . . *Tricorythus*.

31 (16) Outer caudal setae fringed only on the inner side. 32

32 (37) Posterolateral angles of the hinder abdominal segments prolonged into thin, flat, sharp lateral spines. 33

33 (34) Fore legs conspicuously fringed with long hairs; gill tufts present upon the base of maxillae and front coxae and at bases of lamellae on abdomen. . . . . *Chirotonetes*.

34 (33) Fore legs without conspicuous fringes; no maxillary or coxal gills; no gill tufts at base of lamellae on abdomen. 35

35 (36) Gills double on the basal abdominal segments; end of maxilla fringed with simple hairs. . . . . *Siphlurus*.

36 (35) Gill lamellae all single; end of maxilla fringed with pectinated hooks. *Ameletus*.

37 (32) Posterolateral angles of the hinder abdominal segments hardly more than acute — not prolonged in thin flat lateral spines. . 38

38 (41) Gill lamellae simple. 39

39 (40) Lamellae obtuse at apex; maxillary palpus rounded at the apex. *Baetis*.

40 (39) Lamellae acute at apex; end of maxillary palpus truncated. *Centroptilum*.

41 (38) Gill lamellae double, at least on some of the anterior abdominal segments. 42

42 (43) Antennae shorter than the body; tracheae of gill lamellae pinnately branched. . . . . *Callibaetis*.

43 (42) Antennae longer than the body; tracheae of gill lamellae palmately branched. . . . . *Cloeon*.

KEY TO NORTH AMERICAN DRAGONFLIES

IMAGOS

1 (21) Fore and hind wings similar, usually held vertically in repose (damsel-flies). . . . . Suborder **Zygoptera** . . 2

2 (5) Quadrangle (Fig. 1388) of the wings divided by a number of cross veins; antenodal cross veins numerous; pterostigma lacking a special brace vein; wings rather broad. 3

3 (4) Basal space (space before the arculus) in all wings free from cross veins. *Calopteryx*.

4 (3)   Basal space of all wings traversed by cross veins. . . . . *Hetaerina.*

5 (2)   Quadrangle without cross veins; antenodal cross veins but two in each
        wing; pterostigma with a brace vein at its proximal end in
        the space behind vein R₁; wings narrower. 6

6 (9)   Vein M_3 arising (i.e., separating from vein M_{1+2}) nearer the arculus
        than the nodus. 7

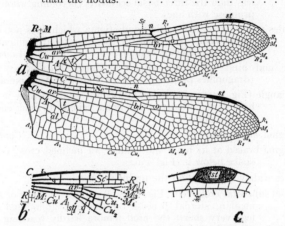

Fig. 1388. Wing venation in the Odonata: (*a*) a dragonfly, *Cordulegaster.* (*b*) a damselfly, *Argia*;
(*c*) the region of the stigma, *st*, with its brace vein, *z*, *ar*, arculus; *al*, anal loop; *br*, bridge; *n*, nodus;
o, oblique vein; *t*, triangle; *t'*, subtriangle; *q*, quadrangle; *sq*, subquadrangle; *v*, basal subcostal cross
veins; *z*, veins as in Fig. 1386.

7 (8)   Vein M_2 separating from vein M_1 at a distance of several cells beyond
        the subnodal cross vein. . . . . *Lestes.*

8 (7)   Vein M_2 separating from vein M_1 close to the subnodal cross vein, less
        than the distance of one cell beyond it. . . *Archilestes.*

9 (6)   Vein M_3 arising nearer the nodus than the arculus. 10

10 (11) Spines on the tibiae very long, twice as long as the intervals between
        them. . . . . *Argia.*

11 (10) Spines of the tibiae hardly longer than the intervals between them.   12

12 (16) No pale postocular spots on the top of the head; sexes similarly
        colored. 13

13 (14, 15) Colors of dorsum blue and black; yellow beneath the thorax.
                                                        Chromagrion.

14 (13, 15) Colors of dorsum red and black; stout species. . *Amphiagrion.*

15 (13, 14) Dorsum bronzy green; slender species. . . . *Nehallennia.*

16 (12) With round or ovoid postocular spots on the head. 17

17 (18) Sexes with a general similarity in color, the female often of a lighter
        shade; the superior abdominal appendages of the male
        not strongly directed downward and inward. . . *Enallagma.*

18 (17) Sexes strikingly unlike in color; a bifid process arising from the apical margin of the 10th abdominal segment in the male and the superior abdominal appendages strongly directed downward and inward. 19

19 (20) Males chiefly green and black, with normal rhomboidal stigma; females with the orange of the abdomen covering something less than the three basal segments (becoming wholly densely pruinose with age). . . . . . , ... *Ischnura.*

20 (19) Males yellow or orange, with ovoid stigma which does not reach the costal vein; females with the four basal segments of the abdomen yellow or orange. . . . . *Anomalagrion.*

21 (1)   Fore and hind wings dissimilar, the latter broader at the base (dragonflies proper). . . . . Suborder **Anisoptera** . . 22

22 (49) Triangle (Fig. 1388) about equally distant from arculus in fore and hind wing; stigma with a brace vein at its inner end (except in *Cordulegaster*). 23

23 (24) Stigma unbraced. . . . . *Cordulegaster.*

24 (23) Stigma braced at its inner end against an inclined cross vein in the space below it (Fig. 1362). 25

25 (36) Eyes widely separated on the top of the head. 26

26 (27) Basal subcostal cross vein (Fig. 1388, *b*) present; a linear or spatulate, median, sternal process on the first abdominal segment; legs very short, the hind femora hardly reaching the apex of the first abdominal segment. . . . . . . *Progomphus.*

27 (26) Basal subcostal cross vein usually wanting; no median sternal process on the first abdominal segment; legs longer, the hind femora reaching or surpassing the middle of the second abdominal segment. 28

28 (31) Hind wings with a distinct anal loop (Fig. 1388, *a*) consisting of several cells. 29

29 (30) Anal loop normally consisting of three cells; first and fifth antenodal cross veins matched in position and hypertrophied; stigma broad with both sides convex; triangles not traversed by cross veins. . . . . *Ophiogomphus.*

30 (29) Anal loop consisting normally of four cells; first and seventh antenodal cross veins matched in position and hypertrophied; stigma long and narrow with parallel sides; each triangle divided by a cross vein. . . . . *Hagenius.*

31 (28) Hind wings with no distinct anal loop, or with one consisting of a single cell. 32

32 (33) Triangle of the fore wing one-third shorter than that of the hind wing; generally a single cell between the bases of veins A_2 and A_3. . . . . *Lanthus.*

33 (32) Triangle of the fore wing less than one-fourth shorter than that of the hind wing; generally, two or more cells between A_2 and A_3 at their origin. 34

34 (35) Hind femora naked, or with numerous short spines. . . *Gomphus.*

35 (34) Hind femora with five to seven long, strong spines. . *Dromogomphus.*

36 (25) Eyes approximated on the top of the head. 37

37 (42) The radial sector (*Rs*, Fig. 1388, *a*) simple. . . . . 3̊

38 (39) But two cubito-anal cross veins; vein M_2 undulate; supratriangle without cross veins; but one cross vein under the stigma.
Gomphaeschna.

39 (38) With three or more cubito-anal cross veins; vein M_2 not undulate; supratriangle divided by cross veins; several cross veins under the stigma. 40

40 (41) Basal space traversed by cross veins. . . . . *Boyeria.*

41 (40) Basal space open. . . . . *Basiaeschna.*

42 (37) Radial sector bearing an apical fork. 43

43 (48) Sectors of the arculus (veins M_{1-3} and M_4) separating from the arculus at or below its middle. 44

44 (47) The radial sector symmetrically forked: between it and the supplementary vein below it, one or two rows of cells. 45

45 (46) Face strongly produced above, the upper margin of the frons very acute; the veins M_1 and M_2 parallel to the level of the stigma; radial sector and the supplementary vein below it separated by a single row of cells. . . . . *Nasiaeschna.*

46 (45) Face vertical, not sharply angulate at upper edge of frons; veins M_1 and M_2 approximated at the stigma; the radial sector and the supplementary vein below it separated by two rows of cells. . . . . *Epiaeschna.*

47 (44) The radial sector strongly deflected toward the stigma at the base of its fork, unsymmetric; between it and the supplementary vein below it, three to seven rows of cells. . . . *Aeschna.*

48 (43) Sectors of the arculus springing from above the middle of the arculus. *Anax.*

49 (22) Triangle in the hind wing much nearer the arculus than in the fore wing; stigma without brace vein. 50

50 (53) The triangle of the hind wing placed considerably beyond the arculus; the anal loop well developed and hardly longer than broad; more than two cubito-anal cross veins. 51

51 (52) Dorsal surface of the head with the occiput larger than the vertex; subtriangle of the fore wings usually divided by a cross vein; four to six cross veins in the space above the bridge (Fig. 1388).
Didymops.

52 (51) Dorsal surface of the head with the occiput much smaller than the vertex; subtriangle of the fore wings generally open; two or three cross veins in the space above the bridge.
Macromia.

53 (50) The triangle of the hind wing retracted to the level of the arculus, or even passing it a little sometimes; the anal loop, greatly elongated (except in *Nannothemis*) and becoming foot-shaped; one or two cubito-anal cross veins. 54

54 (67) Sectors of the arculus (veins M_{1-3} and M_4) distinctly separate at their departure from the arculus; anal loop elongate, but not distinctly foot-shaped, the toe part being little or not at all developed; the last antenodal cross vein extending from the costal to the radial veins (except in *D. lintneri*, in which it generally extends only from the costal to the subcostal); colors often metallic blue or green on thorax and abdomen. 55

55 (56) Veins M_4 and Cu_1 in the fore wing parallel or a little divergent apically, the number of rows of cells between them increasing toward the margin of the wing. . . . . *Neurocordulia.*

56 (55) Veins M_4 and Cu_1 in the fore wing approximated toward the margin of the wing. 57

57 (58) With large brown spots on all wings at nodus and apex.
Epicordulia.

58 (57) No brown spots at nodus and apex. 59

59 (60) Four (rarely five) antenodal cross veins in the hind wing.
Tetragoneuria.

60 (59) Usually more than five antenodal cross veins in the hind wing. . 61

61 (62) Stigma very narrowly diamond-shaped, with the ends of it meeting the sides by an angle of 30° to 35°. . . . . *Helocordulia.*

62 (61) Stigma broader, less pointed. 63

63 (64) Triangle of fore wings open. . . . . *Dorocordulia.*

64 (63) Triangle of fore wings divided by a cross vein. 65

65 (66) Inferior appendage at end of male abdomen bifurcated. *Cordulia.*

66 (65) Inferior appendage simple. . . . . *Somatochlora.*

67 (54) The sectors of the arculus in close apposition or completely fused for a little way beyond the arculus; anal loop generally distinctly foot-shaped, with well-developed "toe"; the last antenodal cross vein often discontinuous at the subcostal vein. 68

68 (69) Triangle of the fore wings four-sided; anal loop poorly developed, not foot-shaped. . . . . *Nannothemis.*

69 (68) Triangle of the fore wing fully differentiated, three-sided; anal loop well developed and foot-shaped. 70

70 (71) Triangle of the fore wing with its front and inner sides meeting by an angle of about 100°; the subtriangle without cross veins; the vein which bisects the anal loop straight. . . *Perithemis.*

71 (70) Triangle of the fore wing with its front and inner sides meeting by an angle of about 90°; subtriangle divided into three or more cells; bisector of the anal loop sinuous. 72

72 (89) Triangle of the fore wing not placed distinctly beyond the level of the apex of the triangle in the hind wing; pterostigma with its ends parallel or not distinctly divergent. 73

73 (84) The sectors of the arculus (veins M_{1-3} and M_4) in the fore wing more or less completely fused for a short distance beyond the arculus; the triangle of the fore wing not greatly produced posteriorly, and (except in *Celithemis*) normally containing but a single cross vein, and followed by two or three rows of cells. 74

74 (79) Vein Cu₁ of the hind wing departing from the triangle at the hind
angle. 75

75 (76) Sectors of the arculus (veins M_{1-3} and M_4) contiguous, but incompletely fused for a distance beyond the arculus; wings generally conspicuously spotted with yellow or reddish brown.
Celithemis.

76 (75) Sectors of the arculus in the hind wing distinctly fused for a distance beyond the arculus. 77

77 (78) Stigma short and thick, about twice as long as wide; anal loop with a big heel, there being generally four cells between the bisector and the heel point; face pure white. . . *Leucorhinia.*

78 (77) Stigma more than three times as long as wide; anal loop generally with but two cells between the bisector and the heel point.
Sympetrum.

79 (74) Vein Cu₁ of the hind wing migrated a little way up the outer side of the triangle, separating itself at a distance from the hind angle. 80

80 (81) With a single cross vein under the stigma, and a long vacant space before that cross vein. . . . . *Pachydiplax.*

81 (80) With two cross veins under the stigma and the adjacent spaces more normal. 82

82 (83) With a single row of cells between veins M_2 and R_s. . . *Mesothemis.*

83 (82) With two rows of cells for a distance between veins M_2 and R_s.
Micrathyria.

84 (73) Sectors of the arculus in the fore wing contiguous, but not completely fused beyond the point of their departure from the arculus; radial sector distinctly undulate (except in Ladona); triangle of the fore wing very much elongated posteriorly and narrow and generally traversed by two or more parallel cross veins, and followed by three to seven rows of cells. 85

85 (86) Vein M_{1a} arising under the proximal fourth of the stigma; fore wings with the subtriangle consisting of three cells, and the triangle followed by three rows of cells. . . . . . . *Ladona.*

86 (85) Vein M_{1a} arising under the middle of the stigma; fore wings with the subtriangle consisting of four to eleven cells, and the triangle usually followed by four to six rows of cells. 87

87 (88) Male with no ventral hooks on the first abdominal segment; female with the hind tibia a little longer than the hind femur; the sexes alike in wing pattern. . . . . *Libellula.*

88 (87) Male with a pair of ventral hooks on the first abdominal segment; female with the hind femur and tibia of equal length; wings dissimilarly colored in the two sexes. . . . . *Plathemis.*

89 (72) Triangle of the fore wing placed beyond the level of the apex of the triangle of the hind wing; stigma with its inner end perpendicular, its outer end very oblique to the bordering veins; wings broad at base and pointed at apex. 90

90 (91) Radial sector regularly curved; hind wings with a broad, basal colored band. . . . . *Tramea.*

91 (90) Radial sector distinctly undulate; hind wings not covered at base by a broad colored band. . . . . *Pantala.*

Nymphs

1 (22) Three large leaflike respiratory plates at the apex of the slender abdomen, and with the body tapering posteriorly from the head (damselflies). . . . . Suborder **Zygoptera** . . 2

2 (5) Basal segment of the antenna very large, as long as the other six together; median lobe of the labium with a very deep cleft; gills thick, the lateral ones triquetral. 3

3 (4) Median cleft of labium very deep, extending far beneath the level of the base of the lateral lobes. . . . . *Calopteryx.*

4 (3) Median cleft of the labium extending only to the level of the base of the lateral lobes. . . . . *Hetaerina.*

5 (2) Basal segment of antenna not longer than succeeding single segments; labium with a very shallow closed median cleft or no cleft at all; gills thin, lamelliform. 6

6 (9) Median lobe of labium with a short, closed, median cleft; lateral lobe trifid at end; movable hook bearing raptorial setae; gills showing transverse segmentation. 7

7 (8) Lateral lobe of the labium terminating in three teeth, between the middle and external of which is situated a truncated and serrated lobe. . . . . *Lestes.*

8 (7) Three teeth only, terminating the lateral lobe of the labium, no truncated and serrated lobe between them. . . . *Archilestes.*

9 (6) Median lobe of labium entire; lateral lobe bifid at end; hook naked; gills various. 10

10 (11) Labium with no raptorial setae on the mentum within; gills broad, thick, dark colored, oval or oblong in shape and obtuse at apex. . . . . *Argia.*

11 (10) Labium with mental setae; gills thinner, more pointed and narrower. 12

12 (15) Hind angles of the head strongly angulate. 13

13 (14) Gills widest beyond the middle; body slender; head half as long as wide. . . . . *Chromagrion.*

14 (13) Gills widest across the middle; body stouter; head nearly as long as wide. . . . . *Amphiagrion.*

15 (12) Hind angles of the head rounded. 16

16 (17) Labium with one mental seta (and a rudimentary second one) each side; antennae six-jointed; lateral lobe of the labium with the distal end above the end hook hardly denticulated.
Nehallennia.

17 (16) Labium with three to five mental setae each side (one may be smaller than the others), and end of lateral lobe denticulated distinctly; antennae seven-jointed (with the possible exception of *Enallagma antennatum*). 18

18 (21) Gills more than half as long as the abdomen, lanceolate; third segment of antennae less than a third longer than the second. 19

19 (20) Labium with four to six lateral setae, generally with five, and with three (rarely four) mental setae each side; gills often with a definite color pattern. . . . . *Enallagma.*

20 (19) Labium with five or six lateral setae, and with four mental setae each side; gills generally with no distinct pattern. . . *Ischnura.*

21 (18) Gills less than half as long as the abdomen, narrower and with a long tapering point; third segment of antenna more than a third longer than the second. . . . . *Anomalagrion.*

22 (1) Without external respiratory plates, but with a respiratory chamber inside the wide abdomen; body less slender, and not widest across the head. (Dragonflies; proper.)

Suborder **Anisoptera** . . 23

23 (47) Labium flat or nearly so (the edges of the lateral lobes slightly upturned in *Tachopteryx*), without raptorial setae. 24

24 (35, 46) Labium with its median lobe entire; antennae four-jointed, the fourth joint rudimentary; fore tarsi two-jointed: burrowing nymphs. 25

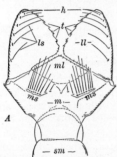 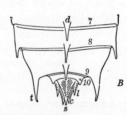

Fig. 1389. Recognition characters of dragonfly nymphs. *A*, inner aspect of the labium; *m*, mentum; *sm*, submentum; *ml*, median lobe; *ll*, lateral lobe; *ms*, mental setae; *ls*, lateral setae; *h*, end hook. *B*, end of the abdomen as seen from above: *7, 8, 9, 10*, abdominal segments; *d*, dorsal hooks; *t*, lateral spines; *s*, superior appendage; *l*, paired lateral appendages; *c*, inferior appendages (cerci).

25 (26) Middle legs more approximate at the base than are the fore legs; fourth segment of the antenna slender, erect, about as long as the third segment is wide; the tenth abdominal segment about as long as the ninth. . . . . *Progomphus.*

26 (25) Middle legs not more (usually less) approximate than the fore legs at base; the fourth segment of the antenna a mere rudiment, orbicular or discoid, much shorter than the third segment is wide; the tenth abdominal segment much shorter than the ninth. 27

27 (28) Wing cases strongly divergent on the two sides; lateral lobe of labium blunt at apex. . . . . *Ophiogomphus.*

28 (27) Wing cases laid closely parallel along the back; lateral lobe of labium ending in a sharp, incurved hook. 29

29 (30) Abdomen very thin and flat, circular in outline as seen from above· third segment of antenna flat and subcircular. . *Hagenius.*

30 (29) Abdomen less depressed, ovate to lanceolate in outline, at least twice as long as wide. 31

31 (32) Third joint of antenna very flat, thin, and in outline circular or broadly oval. . . . . *Lanthus.*

32 (31) Third joint of antenna elongate, linear, little flattened. . . . **33**

33 (34) Dorsum of the ninth abdominal segment rounded, or with a low, obtuse, median longitudinal ridge. . . . . . . *Gomphus.*

34 (33) Ninth abdominal segment with a sharp mid-dorsal ridge, ending in a straight apical spine. . . . . *Dromogomphus.*

35 (24, 46) Labium with a short median cleft; antennae seven-jointed, setaceous; tarsi three-jointed; climbing nymphs, with eyes at sides of head. 36

36 (39) Hind angles of the head, viewed from above, sharply angulate. . 37

37 (38) Lateral lobe of labium squarely truncate on apex. . . . . *Boyeria.*

38 (37) Lateral lobe of labium with taper-pointed apex. . . . *Basiaeschna.*

39 (36) Hind angles of the head obtusely rounded. 40

40 (45) With lateral spines on abdominal segments 4-, 5-, or 6-9. . . 41

41 (44) With lateral spines on segments 4-, or 5-9. 42

42 (43) With dorsal hooks on abdominal segments 7-9. . . *Nasiaeschna.*

43 (42) With no dorsal hooks on abdomen. . . . . *Epiaeschna.*

44 (41) With lateral spines on abdominal segments 6-9. . . . . *Aeschna.*

45 (40) With lateral spines on abdominal segments 7-9. . . . . . *Anax.*

46 (24, 35) Labium with a shallow median cleft; antennae seven-jointed; short; squatting nymphs, with face vertical, and eyes on anterolateral angles; depressed; hairy; tarsi three-jointed. *Tachopteryx.*

47 (23) Labium mask-shaped or spoon-shaped, when closed, covering the face up to the bases of the antennae, armed with raptorial setae. 48

48 (49) The prominent median lobe of the labium cleft into two variously formed teeth at apex. . . . . *Cordulegaster.*

49 (48) The median lobe of the labium entire. 50

50 (53) Head with a prominent pyramidal frontal horn; abdomen flat and almost circular in outline as seen from above; legs long, giving a spiderlike aspect to these big nymphs; the tenth abdominal segment well exposed, not telescoped in the apex of the ninth segment; teeth on the lateral lobes of the labium with deep incisions between them. 51

51 (52) Head hardly as wide across the eyes as across the bulging hind angles; lateral spines not incurved, those of the ninth abdominal segment hardly surpassed by the tips of the appendages; dorsum of the tenth abdominal segment with no trace of a dorsal hook. . . . . *Didymops.*

52 (51) Head widest across the eyes; spines of the ninth abdominal segment shorter, not nearly reaching the level of the apices of the appendages; dorsum of the tenth segment with a very rudimentary dorsal hook. . . . . *Macromia.*

53 (50) Head without pyramidal frontal horn; abdomen less flattened, more elongate; teeth on the lateral lobes of the labium much wider than high. 54

54 (65) Lateral appendages of the abdomen more than half as long as the inferiors; hind femora longer than the head is wide; when the lateral spines are long, then there is a full series of big, cultriform dorsal hooks on the abdomen. 55

55 (56) Lateral setae four or five; mentum about as long as wide.
Epicordulia.

56 (55) Lateral setae seven; mentum of labium longer than wide. . . 57

57 (62) Abdomen with large, laterally flattened, generally cultriform dorsal hooks. 58

58 (59) Lateral spines of the ninth segment longer than half the length of that segment; dorsal hooks on segments 3–9, highest on 6, cultriform, and sharp. . . . . *Tetragoneuria.*

59 (58) Lateral spines of the ninth segment shorter than half of that segment; dorsal hooks less developed. 60

60 (61) Dorsal hooks on segments 4–9 laterally flattened, but not cultriform.
Somatochlora.

61 (60) Dorsal hooks on segments 6–9, longest on 8 and cultriform.
Helocordulia.

62 (57) Abdomen with no dorsal hooks, or with these rudimentary, not flattened laterally or cultriform, but small obtuse or pointed prominences. 63

63 (64) Hind angles of the head rounded; lateral spines of the ninth abdominal segment one-fifth as long as that segment. . . . *Cordulia.*

64 (63) Hind angles of the head angulate superiorly; spines of the ninth abdominal segment one-third as long as that segment.
Dorocordulia.

65 (54) Lateral abdominal appendages generally less than half the length of the inferiors; hind femora generally as long as the head is wide; often when the lateral spines of the abdomen are long the dorsal hooks are wanting or reduced. 66

66 (67) With large, cultriform dorsal hooks on abdominal segments 3–9; eyes small and situated on the mid-lateral margin of the head and directed laterally. . . . . *Perithemis.*

67 (66) With no dorsal hook on the ninth abdominal segment; eyes over-spreading more or less the anterolateral margins of the head. 68

68 (85) Basal segment of the hind tarsus more than half as long as the second segment; lateral appendages of the abdomen not more than half as long as the inferiors (except in *Libellula quadri-maculata*); superior abdominal appendage regularly tapering to a point. 69

69 (70) Abdominal appendages strongly decurved; lateral spines wanting or extremely rudimentary. . . . . *Mesothemis.*

70 (69) Abdominal appendages straight or very slightly declined; lateral spines evident on abdominal segments 8 and 9. 71

71 (74) With no dorsal hooks at all. 72

72 (73)   Abdomen smooth, depressed; head twice as wide as long, with eyes
          very prominent laterally; lateral spines large and straight;
          superior appendage one-third shorter than the inferiors.
                                                          Pachydiplax.

73 (72)   Abdomen hairy at the apex; lateral spines small and sharply in-
          curved; superior appendage as long as the inferiors.
                                                          Nannothemis.

74 (71)   Dorsal hooks present, at least on the middle abdominal segments. 75

75 (80)   Abdomen ovate in outline, rather abruptly narrowed to the posterior
          end; hind margin of the eyes behind the middle of the
          head. 76

76 (77)   Lateral spines long and straight; abdomen not narrowed posteriorly
          before the eighth segment. . . . . *Celithemis.*

77 (76)   Lateral spines shorter and more or less incurvate; the abdomen
          more or less narrowed before the eighth segment. . . . 78

78 (79)   Dorsal hooks as long as the segments which bear them. *Leucorhinia.*

79 (78)   Dorsal hooks shorter than the segments which bear them.
                                                          Sympetrum.

80 (75)   Abdomen lanceolate in outline, slowly narrowed to the pointed
          posterior end; eyes capping the prominent anterolateral
          angles of the head, their hind margin generally before the
          middle of the top of the head; body generally hairy. . 81

81 (82)   The tenth abdominal segment with subcarinate lateral margins;
          appendages very long; lateral setae 0–3. . . . . *Ladona.*

82 (81)   The tenth abdominal segment shorter, cylindric; appendages shorter;
          lateral setae 5–10. 83

83 (84)   Head a little narrowed behind the eyes; front border of the median
          lobe of the labium entire. . . . . *Libellula.*

84 (83)   Head not narrowed behind the eyes to the hind angles; front border
          of the median labial lobe crenulate. . . . . *Plathemis.*

85 (68)   Basal segment of the hind tarsus half as long as the second segment;
          lateral appendages of the abdomen at least three-fourths
          as long as the inferiors; lateral setae 10 or more; superior
          appendage of the abdomen suddenly contracted at its basal
          third, the dorsal two-thirds forming a long slender point. 86

86 (87)   Movable hook of labium long and slender, setiform; teeth much
          broader than high; spines of the eighth segment one-half
          longer than the ninth segment; superior abdominal append-
          age shorter than the inferiors. . . . . *Tramea.*

87 (86)   Movable hook of the labium short, hardly longer than the teeth;
          teeth higher than broad; spines of the eighth segment as
          long as the ninth segment; superior appendage equaling
          the inferiors. . . . . *Pantala.*

KEY TO AQUATIC AND SEMI-AQUATIC HEMIPTERA

1 (8) Antennae longer than the head, free. Forms that walk on the water. 2
2 (5) Last segment of tarsi split, claws inserted before the apex. . . . 3
3 (4) Beak four-jointed; intermediate and posterior legs extremely long and slender; body widest back of the prothorax.
Family GERRIDAE.
4 (3) Beak three-jointed; none of the legs extremely long and slender; body widest across the prothorax. . . . . . Family VELIIDAE.
5 (2) Last segment of tarsi entire, claws inserted at the apex. 6
6 (7) Body linear; head as long as thorax; legs extremely long and slender; beak not reaching anterior coxae. Family HYDROMETRIDAE.
7 (6) Body oval; head shorter than thorax; legs not extremely long and slender; beak reaching intermediate coxae. . Family ACANTHIIDAE.
8 (1) Antennae shorter than the head, nearly or quite concealed beneath the margin of the head, or in a cavity beneath the eyes. . 9
9 (12) Ocelli two; anterior coxal cavities open behind; antennae four-jointed, simple. (Live near the water). 10
10 (11) Fore legs slender, fitted for running; eyes triangular.
Family PELOGONIDAE.
11 (10) Fore legs stout, fitted for grasping; eyes projecting, subglobose.
Family NERTHRIIDAE.
12 (9) Ocelli none; anterior coxal cavities open or closed behind; antennae three or four-jointed, simple or with some of the segments produced into a lateral hook. (Live in the water). . . 13
13 (32) Anterior coxal cavities closed behind; antennae four-jointed, simple or hooked. 14
14 (15) Antennae simple; no caudal appendages; fore legs fitted for grasping, middle and hind legs for walking. . . Family NAUCORIDAE.
15 (14) Second and third (sometimes fourth) joint of antennae produced into lateral hooks; end of abdomen with a pair of caudal appendages; fore legs fitted for grasping, middle and hind legs for walking or swimming. 16
16 (29) Antennae four-jointed; caudal appendages short, strap-shaped, retractile; middle and hind legs flattened, fitted for swimming; tarsi two-jointed. . . . Family BELOSTOMATIDAE . . 17
17 (18) Fore tarsus with two claws. . . . . *Hydrocirius.*
18 (17) Fore tarsus with a single claw. 19
19 (22) Mesothorax with a strong mid-ventral keel. 20
20 (21) An internal tooth borne upon both joints two and three of the antenna; all the ventral surface of the body hairy. *Serphus.*
21 (20) An internal tooth borne upon joints two, three and four of the antennae; venter hairy only in the middle. . . . *Abedus.*
22 (19) Mesothorax without mid-ventral keel; antennae four-jointed. '. . 23
23 (26) Furrow of the membrane of the fore wing regularly curved; an acute internal tooth on antennal segments two and three, the fourth simple and pointed. 24
24 (25) Membrane of the fore wing small; the reentrant angle seen at either side of the front of the head when viewed from above is wholly in the front. . . . . *Pedinocoris.*

25 (24) Membrane large; reentrant angle bordered externally by the eye itself (*Zaitha* of most of our literature). . . . *Belostoma.*

26 (23) Furrow of wing membrane S-shaped; a recurved internal tooth borne on antennal segments two, three and four. . . . 27

27 (28) Front femora grooved internally for the reception of the tibia (*Belostoma* of most of our literature). . . . . *Amorgius.*

28 (27) Front femora not grooved internally. . . . . *Benacus.*

29 (16) Antennae three-jointed; caudal appendages long, filiform, grooved; middle and hind legs fitted for walking; tarsi one-jointed.
Family NEPIDAE . . 30

30 (31) Body oval; legs not extremely long and slender; prothorax much broader than head; anterior femora but little longer than tibiae. . . . . *Nepa.*

31 (30) Body linear; legs extremely long and slender; prothorax but little broader than head; anterior femora more than twice as long as tibiae. . . . . *Ranatra.*

32 (13) Anterior coxal cavities open behind; antennae three or four-jointed, without lateral hooks. 33

33 (38) Head inserted in the prothorax; antennae four-jointed; beak three or four-jointed, not retractile; anterior tarsi one or two-jointed, of the usual form, with two claws.
Family NOTONECTIDAE . . 34

34 (37) Antennae inserted in cavity beneath eyes, second joint thickest; hind legs flattened, ciliated, fitted for swimming; abdomen keeled and hairy. (Size larger). 35

35 (36) Last joint of antenna less than half as long as the third, which is fringed with capitate hairs. Hind tarsi without claws. (Body stouter). . . . . *Notonecta.*

36 (35) Last joint of antenna fringed with capitate hairs, and many times longer than the third, which is very small and inconspicuous. Hind tarsi with claws. (Body more slender). . . *Buenoa.*

37 (34) Antennae inserted beneath the margin of the head, third joint longest and thickest; hind legs like the middle legs, tarsi with claws; abdomen not keeled or hairy. (Size smaller, not over 3 mm. long). . . . . *Plea.*

38 (33) Head overlapping the prothorax; antennae three or four-jointed; beak short, unjointed, retractile; anterior tarsi one-segmented, flattened, with a fringe of hairs on the edge, and without claws. . . . . Family CORIXIDAE.

KEY TO NORTH AMERICAN AQUATIC NEUROPTERA

ADULTS

1 (4) Veins of the wing disc all ending in a succession of symmetrical forks, the terminal forks forming a distinct peripheral zone; antennae moniliform. . . Family HEMEROBIIDAE . . 2

2 (3) The median vein repeatedly forked; some of the branches of vein Cu_1 again forked. . . . . *Sisyra.*

3 (2)   The median vein but once forked; the branches of vein Cu₁ all simple.
Climacia.

4 (1)   Veins of the wing disc extending outward in straighter lines, forks
fewer and less symmetrical; antennae cylindric serrate, or
pectinate. . . . . Family SIALIDIDAE . . 5

5 (6)   Fourth segment of the tarsus bilobed; posterior branch of the radial
sector forked. No ocelli. . . . . *Sialis.*

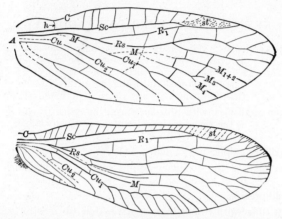

FIG. 1390.   Fore wings of two neuropterous insects, *Sialis* (above) and *Climacia* (below).   *h*, humeral
cross-vein;   *st*, stigma;   designations of principal veins as in Fig. 1386.

6 (5)   Fourth segment of the tarsus simple, cylindric; posterior branch of the
radial sector simple.   Three ocelli. 7

7 (8)   Hind angles of the head rounded;   the median vein two-branched;
antennae with segments enlarged distally.   . . *Chauliodes.*

8 (7)   Hind angles of the head bearing a sharp angulation or tooth;   median
vein three-branched;   segments of the antennae cylindric.
Corydalis.

LARVAE

1 (4)   Mouth parts adapted for piercing and sucking, prolonged to half the
length of the body; living on fresh-water sponges.   . . . 2

2 (3)   Setae on the dorsum of the thorax pedunculate (i.e., the setigerous
tubercles elevated considerably above the level of the integument);   the outer covering of the pupal case spun by the
larva is of a beautiful hexagonal mesh. . . . . . *Climacia.*

3 (2)   Thoracic setae sessile;   the outer covering of the pupal case is close woven.
Sisyra.

4 (1)   Mouth parts adapted for biting. 5

5 (6)   The last abdominal segment produced in a long, median, laterally fringed
tail-like process;   a pair of lateral filaments on abdominal
segments 1–7. . . . . *Sialis.*

6 (5) Last abdominal segment bifurcated, the fleshy forks each bearing a pair of hooks and a minute, external, lateral filament; conspicuous lateral filaments on abdominal segments 1–8. .   **7**

7 (8) Lateral filaments with no tuft of fine tracheal gills at their bases.
Chauliodes.

8 (7) Lateral filaments each with a tuft of fine tracheal gills at its base.
Corydalis.

KEY TO NORTH AMERICAN CADDISFLIES

1 (2) Micro-caddisflies; very small, mothlike, hairy, the fore wings bearing numerous erect clavate hairs; the marginal fringe of the wings longer than their greatest breadth; form of wings narrowly lanceolate; antennae rather stout and not longer than fore wings. . . . . Family HYDROPTILIDAE.

2 (1) Larger caddisflies, with broader wings; marginal fringes never as long as the wings are broad; antennae usually longer than the fore wings. **3**

3 (26) Maxillary palpus five-jointed. **4**

4 (19) Last joint of the maxillary palpus simple, and not longer than the other joints. **5**

5 (10) Ocelli present. **6**

6 (9) Front tibiae with two or three spurs, middle tibiae with four spurs. **7**

7 (8) The first two joints of the maxillary palpus short and thick, the third joint much longer and thinner. . Family RHYACOPHILIDAE.

8 (7) The second joint of the maxillary palpus much longer than the first. Females. . . . . Family PHRYGANEIDAE.

9 (6) Front tibiae with a single spur, or with none; middle tibiae with only two or three spurs. Females. . . . Family LIMNOPHILIDAE.

10 (5) Ocelli wanting **11**

11 (12) A closed cell in the principal fork of the median vein in the fore wings. Family CALAMOCERATIDAE.

12 (11) No closed cell in the median fork. **13**

13 (18) A closed cell in the first fork of the radial sector (R_s). **14**

14 (17) Both branches of the radial sector forked. **15**

15 (16) Veins R_1 and R_2 confluent apically or connected by an apical cross vein in the fore wing. Females. . Family ODONTOCERIDAE.

16 (15) Veins R_1 and R_2 not connected apically.
Family SERICOSTOMATIDAE.

17 (14) Only the anterior branch of the radial sector forked.
Family LEPTOCERIDAE.

18 (13) No closed cell in the first fork of the radial sector.
Family MOLANNIDAE.

19 (4) Last joint of the maxillary palpus usually much longer than the others, twisted, and divided imperfectly into subsegments. . . **20**

20 (21) Ocelli present. . . . . Family PHILOPOTAMIDAE.

21 (20)   Ocelli wanting.   22
22 (23)   Front tibiæ with three spurs. . . . . .   Family POLYCENTROPIDAE.
23 (22)   Spurs of the front tibiae fewer than three.   24
24 (25)   Anterior branch of the radial sector in the fore wing forked.
                                                            Family HYDROPSYCHIDAE.
25 (24)   Anterior branch of the radial sector simple.
                                                            Family PSYCHOMYIIDAE.

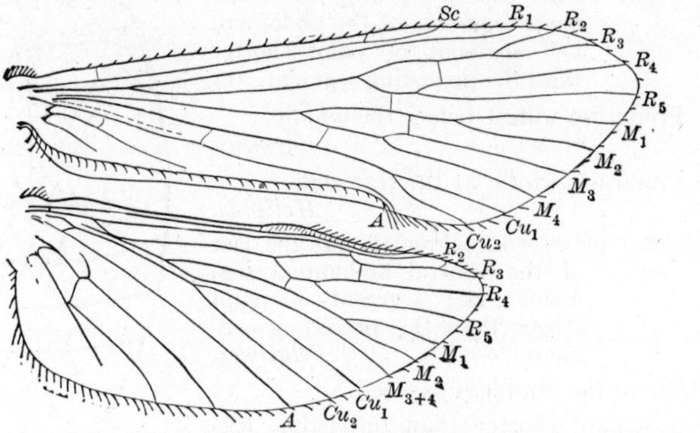

FIG. 1391.   The wings of a caddisfly, *Hydropsyche.*

26 (3)   Maxillary palpi with fewer than five joints.   27
27 (28)   Maxillary palpi with four joints; ocelli present.   Males.
                                                          Family PHRYGANEIDAE.
28 (27)   Maxillary palpi with two or three joints.   29
29 (30)   Maxillary palpi filiform with cylindric smooth joints; fore tibiae with
          a single spur.   Males. . . . . .   Family LIMNOPHILIDAE.
30 (29)   Maxilary palpi hairy or scaly, appressed against and often covering
          the face; fore tibiae with two spurs.   Males.
                                                      Family SERICOSTOMATIDAE.

KEY TO NORTH AMERICAN AQUATIC BEETLES

ADULTS

1 (2)   Hind tarsi with the antepenultimate segment broadly bilobed, and
        receiving the rudimentary penultimate segment (which is
        closely fused with the base of the last segment) in its apical
        notch. . . . .   Family CHRYSOMELIDAE.
2 (1)   Hind tarsi with the last three segments free and similar in form. . . .   3
3 (8)   Hind legs shorter than the fore; eyes four, two above and two on the
        under surface of the head. . . .   Family GYRINIDAE . .   4
4 (7)   Last abdominal segment rounded posteriorly and smooth below. . .   5
5 (6)   Wing of the metasternum (*w*, Fig. 1392) broadly triangular. .   *Dineutes.*
6 (5)   Wing of the metasternum narrow, elongate, widened only at its extreme
        outer end.   *Gyrinus.*

7 (4) Last abdominal segment elongate pyramidal, and furnished with a mid-ventral line of hairs. . . . . *Gyretes.*

8 (3) Hind legs longer than the fore; eyes two. 9

9 (14) Base of the hind legs covered by broad overlapping coxal plates. Family HALIPLIDAE . . 10

10 (13) Coxal plates concealing only the three basal segments of the abdomen; last segment of palpi shorter than the preceding segment. 11

11 (12) Pronotum widest before the middle. *Brychius.*

12 (11) Pronotum widest at the rear end. *Haliplus.*

13 (10) Coxal plates concealing all but the last of the ventral abdominal segments; last segment of palpi longer than the preceding segment. . . . . . . *Peltodytes.*

14 (9) Base of the hind legs exposed. . . . 15

15 (48) Antennae shorter than the palpi; legs usually with swimming fringes. Family HYDROPHILIDAE . . 16

16 (23) Scutellum wanting or indistinct or very small and scalelike. Posterior femora subcylindrical and not noticeably widened in the middle; prothorax narrowed behind, narrower than the elytra. The species are small, elongate, roughly sculptured, greyish or nearly black, and usually tinged with bronze and metallic colors. 17

17 (20) Scutellum indistinct, or apparently wanting; if at all evident it is distinctly triangular and acute. Species from 1–2 mm. long. 18

18 (19) Pronotum without striae; maxillary palpi as long as the head and thorax together, the ultimate segment longer than the penultimate; elytra with more than ten rows of punctures. . . . *Hydraena.*

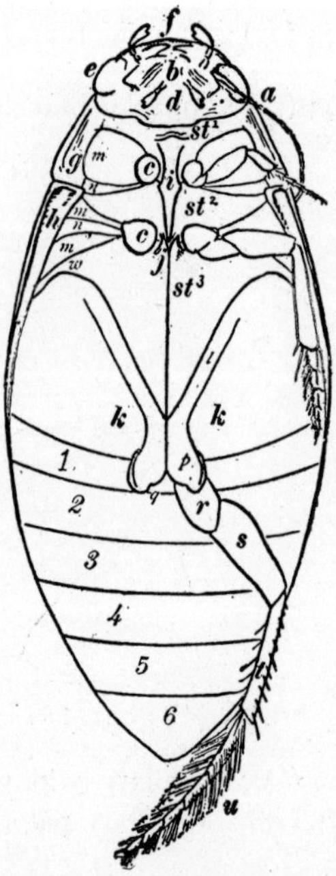

19 (18) Pronotum bearing from one to five longitudinal striae or abbreviated grooves; the maxillary palpi much shorter than the head and thorax together, the ultimate segment shorter than the penultimate; elytra with only ten rows of punctures. *Octhebius.*

FIG. 1392. Diagram of the ventral aspect of a diving beetle, *Coptotomus interrogatus*: *a*, antenna; *b*, mouth; *c, c*, coxal cavities for the fore and middle legs; *d*, labial palpi; *e*, eye; *f*, maxillary palpi; *g*, lateral margin of the prothorax; *h*, epipleuron of the wing cover (elytron); *i*, prosternal process; *j*, metasternal fork; *k*, hind coxa with *l*, the inner lamina; *p*, the coxal process and *q*, the coxal notch; *r*, trochanter of the hind leg; *s*, femur; *t*, tibia; *u*, hind tarsus of five joints; *1, 2, 3, 4, 5, 6*, ventral abdominal segments, st^1, st^2, st^3, sterna of pro-, meso-, and metathorax, respectively; *w*, wing of the metasternum; *m*, episternum, and *n*, epimeron of the successive thoracic segments. The *coxal line* is the line extending between *l* and *k* in the figure, and the *coxal border* is the part of the coxal process, *p*, that is marked off laterally by the posterior end of the coxal line.

20 (17)   Scutellum appearing as a very small but distinct scale, shaped like the last joint of one's thumb; the ultimate segment of labial palpus longer than the penultimate.   Species from 3–6 mm. long. 21

21 (22)   The pronotum bearing five longitudinal striae; labial palpi moderately large. . . . . *Helophorus.*

22 (21)   The pronotum coarsely punctured but without longitudinal striae; labial palpi short. . . . . *Hydrochus.*

23 (16)   Scutellum distinct, moderately large.   Posterior femora flattened and distinctly widened at their middle; prothorax not narrowed posteriorly, as wide as the elytra at their base. The species are small or large, of oval, elliptical or even hemispherical form, with not very coarse sculpture, and are commonly pitchy black, often more or less testaceous, very occasionally with metallic tinges. 24

24 (43)   Metasternum not prolonged into a spine; tarsi not compressed. The species of this group are all smaller than those of the next, less than 9 mm. long. 25

25 (26)   Fifth ventral segment with a deep notch in the middle of its apical border; middle and posterior tibiae and tarsi bearing a close-set fringe of long silky setae; scutellum elongate, acute.
          Berosus.

26 (25)   Fifth ventral segment not notched; tibiae and tarsi not fimbriate. 27

27 (28)   First two ventral segments concealed by whitish translucent plates, one on each side, upon which are a number of long appressed setae.   The species are very convex, have a tendency to partially roll up like a sow-bug, and are from 1–2 mm. in length. . . . . *Chaetarthria.*

28 (27)   No such plates over the first ventral segments. 29

29 (30)   Posterior tibiae incurved, small at base and considerably enlarged at their apex. . . . . *Laccobius.*

30 (29)   Posterior tibiae straight; little or not at all thickened at their apex.   31

31 (32)   Abdomen with apparently eight ventral segments.   The single species is 1½ mm. long; of a black color with pale legs.
          Limnebius.

32 (31)   Abdomen with five ventral segments, the tip of the sixth often visible. 33

33 (40)   Terminal segment of the maxillary palpus rarely as long as, usually shorter than, the preceding segment. 34

34 (35)   Elytra deeply longitudinally striate; tarsi of the middle and posterior legs with only four segments. . . . . . *Helocombus.*

35 (34)   Elytra not striate. 36

36 (39)   Mesosternum with a feeble transverse carina or simple. 37

37 (38)   Mesosternum with a feeble transverse carina; tarsi of the middle and posterior legs with four segments. . . . . . *Cymbiodyta.*

38 (37)   Mesosternum simple; all tarsi with five segments, the first usually triangular. . . . . *Helochares.*

39 (36) Mesosternum with a longitudinal carina; all tarsi with five segments, the first one small. . . . . *Philhydrus.*

40 (33) Terminal segment of maxillary palpi distinctly longer than the penultimate. 41

41 (42) Large species 6.5–8.5 mm.; the elytra distinctly striate or striato-punctate. . . . . *Hydrobius.*

42 (41) Small species 1.5–3.5 mm.; the elytra not striate but with confused punctuation. . . . . *Creniphilus.*

43 (24) Metasternum prolonged into an acute spine; tarsi compressed so as to be oarlike. The color is always pitchy black, occasionally with yellow margins. The size varies from 9 to 35 mm. 44

44 (45) Metasternum produced into a short spine never projecting as far as the posterior margin of the first ventral segment. Prosternum acutely carinate but not grooved for the reception of the mesosternal carina. . . . . *Hydrocharis.*

45 (44) Metatarsal spine very long and acute, extending always beyond the posterior margin of the first ventral segment. Prosternum with a keel-shaped process which is deeply grooved for the reception of mesosternal carina, thus locking pro- and meso-thorax together. 46

46 (47) Length about 10 mm. Terminal segment of maxillary palpi as long as or longer than the preceding; the antepenultimate segment straight; claws simple. . . . . *Tropisternus.*

47 (46) Length about 35 mm. Terminal segment of maxillary palpi much shorter than the preceding; the antepenultimate segment arcuate; claws toothed. . . . . *Hydrophilus.*

48 (15) Antennae longer than the palpi (equaling them in a few riffle beetles).
49

49 (90) Hind coxae broadly flattened out and solidly fused with the meta-sternum. 50

50 (51) Metasternum divided by a transverse suture which separates a short sclerite before the base of the hind coxae.
Family AMPHIZOIDAE.
A single genus from western mountain streams. *Amphizoa.*

51 (50) Metasternum not thus divided.. . . . . Family DYTISCIDAE . . 52

52 (61) Scutellum invisible. 53

53 (54) Third and fourth segments of the fore and middle tarsi not greatly different from the others; prosternal process acute posteriorly.
Laccophilus.

54 (53) Third segment of the fore and middle tarsi deeply bilobed, the fourth segment rudimentary or wanting. 55

55 (56) Base of thorax united to the elytra by a short impressed line on each side, continued without interruption across the border of each; hind margin of the posterior coxae grown solidly coherent with the first ventral segment of the abdomen, which is considerably enlarged; form elongate; very small.
Bidessus.

56 (55) Base of thorax and elytra without a continuous impressed line. . 57

57 (58) Hind margin of the posterior coxae grown solidly coherent with the first segment of the abdomen, which is considerably enlarged; form round and very convex; shining; small.
Desmopachria.

58 (57) Hind margin of the posterior coxae overlapping but not coherent with the first segment of the abdomen, which is not especially enlarged. Form various, but never so round and convex as *Desmopachria,* nor so small and elongate as *Bidessus.* 59

59 (60) Hind coxal processes each divided by a deep posterior notch, the inner ramus appressed against the first abdominal segment.
Hydrovatus.

60 (59) Hind coxal process not so formed. . . . . *Hydroporus.*
(In the broader sense, as used here this genus includes *Coelambus, Deronectes.*)

61 (52) Scutellum visible. 62

62 (63) Clypeal suture entire. . . . . *Dytiscus.*

63 (62) Clypeal suture incomplete. 64

64 (65) More than 30 mm. long; inferior spur of hind tibiae much dilated, bifid, much broader than other spur. . . . . . *Cybister.*

65 (64) Less than 20 mm. long; the two spurs of the hind tibiae of equal or nearly equal breadth. 66

66 (73) Distal margin of each segment of the hind tarsi beset with a transverse row of minute appressed bristles; anterior tarsi of male with dilated segments forming a round disc. . . 67

67 (68) Spurs of hind tibiae acute at tip; claws of hind tarsi unequal, the inner one sometimes obsolete. . . . . *Hydaticus.*

68 (67) Spurs of hind tibiae emarginate at tip; claws of hind tarsi equal or nearly so. 69

69 (70) Elytra closely punctate, usually four-sulcate; female. . . *Acilius.*

70 (69) Elytra not punctate, partly aciculate in female. 71

71 (72) Middle femora beset with elongate setae; female. . *Thermonectes.*

72 (71) Middle femora beset with short and stout setae. . . . *Graphoderes.*

73 (66) Hind tarsi without such appressed bristles; anterior tarsi of female with dilated segments forming an oval disc. 74

74 (79) A linear group of minute setae present upon the postero-external angle of the hind femora. 75

75 (76) Claws of the hind tarsus unequal; the tarsal segments produced posteriorly in overlapping lobes. . . . . *Ilybius.*

76 (75) Claws of the hind tarsus equal and segments simple. 77

77 (78) Wing of the metasternum very narrow and deflexed around the front border of the external lamina of the hind coxa.
Ilybiosoma.

78 (77) Wing of the metasternum wedge-shaped, less noticeably deflexed.
Agabus.

79 (74) No such linear group of setae on the postero-external angle of the hind femora. 80

80 (81, 82, 83) Surface of the elytra reticulate . . . . *Scutopterus.*

81 (80, 82, 83)   Surface of the elytra transversely aciculate. . . *Colymbetes.*

82 (80, 81, 83)   Surface of the elytra with eight to ten longitudinal striae.
                                                     Copelatus.

83 (80, 81, 82)   Surface of the elytra otherwise sculptured or plain. . . 84

84 (85)   Prosternum plainly longitudinally sulcate; species reddish brown.
                                                       Matus.

85 (84)   Prosternum not sulcate. 86

86 (87)   Apical segment of each palpus distinctly emarginate. *Coptotomus.*

87 (86)   Apical segments of palpi obtuse or truncate. 88

88 (89)   Claws of the hind tarsus equal. . . . . *Agabetes.*

89 (88)   Claws of the hind tarsus unequal. . . . . *Rhantus.*

90 (49)   Hind coxae free. 91

91 (110)   Claws large; the three basal ventral segments of the abdomen fused together, obliterating the sutures.
                           Family PARNIDAE . . 92

92 (93)   Ventral abdominal segments (see Fig. 1392) seven in number.
                                          Psephenus.

93 (92)   Ventral abdominal segments five in number. 94

94 (103)   Fore coxae transversely elongated. 95

95 (102)   Sternum of the prothorax prolonged forward beneath the head in a flat rounded lobe; head retracted within the front of the prothorax; the two basal segments of the antennae distinctly enlarged. 96

96 (97)   Body rounded in outline. . . . . *Lutrochus.*

97 (96)   Body oblong, elongate. 98

98 (99)   Antennae approximate, the terminal segments pectinate. *Pelonomus.*

99 (98)   Antennae distant at base. 100

100 (101)   Antennae slender. . . . . *Throscinus.*

101 (100)   Antennae short and thick, the second joint triangularly dilated, the close-set distal segments lamellate. . . . . *Dryops.*

102 (95)   Sternum of prothorax not greatly produced forward; head free; antennae long and serrate (California). . . . . . . *Lara.*

103 (94)   Fore coxae rounded. 104

104 (109)   Sternum of prothorax produced forward in a flat rounded lobe; head retracted within the front of the prothorax. . . . 105

105 (108)   Antennae eleven-jointed. 106

106 (107)   Fore tibiae pubescent internally. . . . . *Elmis.*

107 (106)   Fore tibiae bare internally. . . . . *Stenelmis.*

108 (105)   Antennae six-jointed. . . . . *Macronychus.*

109 (104)   Sternum of prothorax not produced forward; head free.
                                                Ancyronyx.

110 (91)   Claws of moderate size; basal ventral segments free.
                                          Family DASCYLLIDAE.

LARVAE

1 (4) Herbivorous larvae with short, broad inconspicuous mandibles.
Family CHRYSOMELIDAE . . 2

2 (3) Feeding exposed on the floating leaves of water lilies, etc.; elongate brownish larvae of sluggish habits. . . . . . *Galerucella.*

3 (2) Short arcuate grublike larvae, white and translucent, feeding on the submerged roots of aquatic plants. . . . . . . *Donacia.*

4 (1) Carnivorous larvae, with prominent mandibles. 5

5 (12) Mandibles sickle-shaped without internal teeth, but with an internal groove or perforation extending almost from base to apex. 6

6 (7) End of the abdomen with two pairs of strong claws, and the middle segments bearing single pairs of long lateral filaments.
Family GYRINIDAE.

7 (6) No claws at end of abdomen. 8

8 (11) Eyes in groups of five; one claw on each tarsus.
Family HALIPLIDAE . . 9

9 (10) Body nearly smooth, ending in a long tail. . . . . . . *Haliplus.*

10 (9) Body bearing numerous very long and conspicuous bristlelike filaments; no tail. . . . . *Peltodytes.*

11 (8) Eyes in groups of six; two claws on each tarsus.
Family DYTISCIDAE.

12 (5) Mandibles toothed internally, at base or in the middle. 13

13 (14) Tarsi with two claws. . . . . *Amphizoa.*

14 (13) A single claw on each tarsus. 15

15 (16) Antennae as long as or longer than the thorax.
Family DASCYLLIDAE.

16 (15) Antennae shorter than the thorax. 17

17 (18) Larvae depressed; end of the abdomen with short cerci; gills, when present, ventral in position. . . . . . Family PARNIDAE.

18 (17) Body little depressed; cerci wanting; gills rarely present (and then lateral in position, *Berosus*). . . Family HYDROPHILIDAE.

KEY TO NORTH AMERICAN AQUATIC DIPTEROUS LARVAE

1 (65) Head chitinous, free, or retracted within the front of the prothorax. Pupa usually free; when concealed in the old larval skin, that skin splits on emergence of the imago in a longitudinal I- or T-shaped cleft. . . . Suborder **Orthorrhapha** . . 2

2 (58) Mandibles opposed to each other, or inclined obliquely downward and opposed to a strongly chitinized labial border.
Nematocera . . 3

3 (4) Body strongly depressed, and with a row of six ventral suckers for attachment to the rock bed of rapid streams.
Family BLEPHAROCERIDAE.

4 (3) Body cylindric, and usually lacking ventral suckers; when ventral suckers are developed they are more than six. 5

5 (6) Head imperfectly chitinized in the rear, and wholly retracted within the prothorax; posterior spiracles situate upon a respiratory disc. . . . . Family TIPULIDAE.

6 (5) Head fully develcped and usually free. 7

7 (35) No prolegs developed upon the prothorax. 8

8 (11) Prolegs developed upon some of the anterior segments of the abdomen. 9

9 (10) The body terminates in a very long and conspicuous respiratory tube. Family PTYCHOPTERIDAE.

10 (9) Without respiratory tube, body U-shaped in locomotion. Family DIXIDAE.

11 (8) Body without prolegs. 12

12 (31) Thorax thickened, the outline of its constituent segments more or less confluent; a fin of swimming hairs developed beneath the end of the abdomen, and often a respiratory tube on the dorsal side. . . . . . . Family CULICIDAE . . 13

13 (26) The last abdominal segment with a single dorsal breathing tube, through which may be seen a pair of large tracheae. . . 14

14 (15) Antennae fold back against head and terminate in two or three claws. *Corethrella.*

15 (14) Antennae usually only with a few small erect bristles and one or two pointed processes, or pendent and raptorial. 16

16 (23) With brush of hairs projecting forward from the mouth, vibratile. 17

17 (22) Antennae not pendent and raptorial. 18

18 (19) No ventral brush or rudder on last abdominal segment beyond air tube; small species, one of which is found in water in pitcher plant. . . . . *Wyeomyia.*

19 (18) Last segment with ventral brush. 20

20 (21) Head with thick spines; with four blood gills; with stellate hairs on the abdomen. Small species. . . . . *Uranotaenia.*

21 (20) Head without stout spines in addition to the usual setae. *Culex* (sens. lat.).

22 (17) Antennae pendent and raptorial. . . . . : . . . . *Mochlonyx.*

23 (16) Mouth brush folded outward, raptorial, not vibratile. 24

24 (25) A plate on the side of eighth abdominal segment. . . *Megarhinus.*

25 (24) A patch of small scales on the side of the eighth abdominal segment. *Psorophora.*

26 (13) Last segment without long breathing tube. 27

27 (30) Last segment dorsally with a flat area in which may be seen two spiracles. 28

28 (29) Large species with the anal segment bladderlike. Mandibles strongly developed. . . . . *Pelorempis.*

29 (28) Species of medium size with anal segment cylindrical. . . *Anopheles.*

30 (27) Last segment usually with hooks, no spiracles apparent. **Larva transparent.** . . . . *Corethra.*

31 (12) Body cylindric, or depressed fusiform. 32

32 (33, 34) Body ending in two fleshy points. . . . . Family RHYPHIDAE.

33 (32, 34) Body ending in a tapering segment tipped with a tuft or circlet of hairs. . . . . *Ceratopogoniae* of CHIRONOMIDAE.

34 (32, 33) Body ending in a strongly chitinized terminal segment, usually produced in chitinous respiratory tube. . . PSYCHODIDAE.

35 (7) Prothorax with one or two prolegs. 36

36 (57) A pair of prolegs beneath the prothorax, and another pair at the end of the abdomen. . . . . Family CHIRONOMIDAE . . 37

37 (38) Abdomen with prominent rounded elevations or cushions, with rows of teeth on the inferio-anterior angles of the segments.
Psamathiomyia.

38 (37) Abdominal segments without cushions. 39

39 (40) With retractile antennae, the latter often quite long, long stiltlike legs, the caudal tufts of hair mounted on cylindrical processes.
Tanypus.

40 (39) Not with all the above characters. 41

41 (44) With the two caudal hair tufts mounted on cylindrical projections. 42

42 (43) With blood gills on venter of eleventh segment. . . *Hydrobaenus.*

43 (42) With blood gills only at end of twelfth segment. . . *Metriocnemus.*

44 (41) Caudal tufts on small rounded papillae. 45

45 (48) Antennae elongate, at least one-half as long as and often as long as or longer than the head. 46

46 (47) Antenna with one or two sense organs at tip of second segment. (Rendered visible in preserved material by soaking in water). . . . . *Tanytarsus.*

47 (46) Antenna at most with a seta at tip of second segment at side of the third segment. . . . . *Corynoneura.*

48 (45) Antennae short. 49

49 (50) Larvae usually blood red; eleventh body segment with two pairs of blood gills. . . . . *Chironomus* (in part).

50 (49) Larvae greenish, yellowish, or whitish. 51

51 (52) The maxilliary palpus usually noticeably longer than broad. Larva in pools, pond water, or slow streams . . . . *Chironomus.*

52 (51) Palpus about as long as broad. 53

53 (54) Full-grown larva not over 6 mm. long, green or bluish-green in color. Anterior abdominal segments of greater diameter than the posterior ones. Mandibles often transversely wrinkled; the anterior prolegs usually with pectinate setae.
Cricotopus, Orthocladius.

54 (53) Full-grown larva over 6 mm. in length; mandible not transversely wrinkled. 55

55 (56) Labium with teeth all rounded. . . . . *Diamesa.*

56 (55) Labium with middle tooth broadly truncate. . . . . *Thalassomyia.*

57 (36) A single median proleg on the prothorax and a terminal sucking disc upon the abdomen, serving for attachment to stones in rapid streams; abdomen broadened posteriorly.

Family SIMULIIDAE.

58 (2) Mandibles decurved, parallel, their motion vertical, or nearly so.

Brachycera . . 59

59 (64) Posterior spiracles placed together within a terminal cleft. . . . 60

60 (63) Terminal cleft vertical; head retractile.

Family TABANIDAE . . 61

61 (62) Last antennal segment much longer than the one preceding; dorsal areas striated like those of the abdomen. . . . *Chrysops.*

62 (61) Last antennal segment not longer, usually much shorter, than the one preceding; dorsal areas smooth or striated, but those of the thorax nearly or quite free from striae. . . . . *Tabanus.*

63 (60) Terminal cleft transverse; head not retractile.

Family STRATIOMYIIDAE.

64 (59) Posterior spiracles separate. . . . . Family LEPTIDAE.

65 (1) Head membranous, very imperfectly developed, often apparently wanting. Pupa formed in the hardened and contracted larval skin (*puparium*), which opens by a circular cap or lid.

Suborder **Cyclorhapha.**

This group includes many of the higher aquatic Diptera (SYRPHIDAE SCIOMYZIDAE, etc.) still too insufficiently known to admit of the construction of a satisfactory key.

Note: Acknowledgment is hereby made of help generously given in the preparation of the foregoing keys in parts as follows: in Hemiptera by Mr. C. R. Plunkett; in Coleoptera by Dr. J. C. Bradley; in Diptera by Dr. O. A. Johannsen.

IMPORTANT REFERENCES ON NORTH AMERICAN AQUATIC INSECTS.

COMSTOCK, J. H. 1917. Manual for the Study of Insects. 14th Ed. Ithaca.

KELLOGG, V. L. 1905. American Insects. New York.

FOLSOM, J. W. 1913. Entomology, with Reference to its Biological and Economic Aspects. 2d Ed. Philadelphia.

HOWARD, L. O. 1901. The Insect Book. New York.

MIALL, L. C. 1903. Natural History of Aquatic Insects.

CHAPTER XXVIII

MOSS ANIMALCULES (BRYOZOA)

By CHARLES B. DAVENPORT

Director of the Station for Experimental Evolution, Cold Spring Harbor, Long Island, N.Y.

PROMINENT among the animals commonly discovered in fresh water are the Bryozoa, or moss animalcules, also called Polyzoa. They are forms of exceedingly delicate and attractive appearance, often so transparent that under favorable circumstances the entire structure may be made out under the microscope. Almost all species form colonies composed of many individual animals (zooids) united together and the whole mass is not only easily visible but often conspicuous, whereas the separate zooids are so minute that they can ordinarily be detected only with a hand lens. These colonies take the form of branching threads spread on the surface of stones, sticks, submerged plants or other objects in the water. Others produce a thick crust, while still others form solid jelly-like masses which in one species reach the size of the closed fist and not infrequently surpass that (Fig. 1401). The bulk of this mass consists of transparent or faintly tinged gelatinous material from which the individual zooids project into the water as they also do from the filamentous colonies previously mentioned. The expanded "head" (lophophore) of the zooid with its crown of tentacles is difficult to see since the animals are exceedingly timid and respond to the slightest disturbance by retreating instantly within their protective covers where they remain even long after the water has become quiet again. Continuous study of the colony in a dish of fresh water is rewarded by the appearance of

FIG. 1393. *Cristatella mucedo;* colony, natural size. (After Allman.)

the spreading disks or heads, until the surface of the colony blossoms with abundant groups of delicate tentacles. (Fig. 1393.)

All are essentially sessile, but a few, like *Cristatella* and *Pectinatella,* have the capacity for a slight movement of the colony on the substratum. The nature of the colony formation is variable: sometimes close, forming a corm of zooids fused into one mass, as in *Cristatella;* sometimes loose, each zooid being distinct, as in *Urnatella*.

Each zooid has a structure not unlike that of a rotifer. It secretes a resistant outer covering. This is calcareous in some of the marine forms, but is generally chitinous or gelatinous in those of fresh water. So prominent and variable is this cuticula (constituting the "zooecium," or "cell") that its form is frequently used as a means of distinguishing species. The body wall is very thin, having relinquished its protective function in favor of the cuticula. It is separated from the viscera by a relatively enormous body cavity. In the case of species whose zooids are fused together the body cavities are confluent. The alimentary tract is relatively simple. It consists of a U-shaped tube whose only glands are localized in the epithelium of its walls. The mouth end of the tube is furnished with a corona of numerous ciliated tentacles which create a vortex at the mouth. The mouth is, in one order of fresh-water species (Phylactolaemata), provided with an "epistome" or protecting flap. A long esophagus leads to the capacious stomach and this to the flask-shaped rectum. The anus lies near the mouth either outside or inside the corona of tentacles. For protection, the tentacles can be retracted quickly under the shelter of the body cuticula like the proboscis of certain polychaetes. There are numerous long slender muscles effecting the retraction. The nervous system is simple. A brain lies between esophagus and rectum and sends nerves to tentacles and alimentary tract. Circulation is effected by the general fluid of the body cavity. Well defined excretory tubules seem to be missing if we except the doubtful case of certain Phylactolaemata. In the Gymnolaemata the viscera periodically degenerate into a brownish mass, a new alimentary tract regenerates, and the degenerated mass passes through the wall of the gut and is expelled by the anus. Eggs are formed on the body wall and, in Phylactolaemata, the sperm on the mesentery ("funiculus"). In the marine species the embryos early become free-swimming, but in Phylactolaemata they develop in a sort of uterus until they are young colonies.[1] These

[1] The fresh-water form, *Pectinatella magnifica*, produces a small free swimming spherical larva which settles to the bottom almost immediately and there by budding gives rise to a colony.

are then set free, and, after a time, settle and affix themselves. Like other sessile forms, Bryozoa have gained a variety of methods of reproduction. Ordinary sexual reproduction and budding have been already mentioned. In some Phylactolaemata — *Pectinatella* and *Cristatella* — the colonies occasionally undergo fission and move apart, and the same process occurs regularly in *Urnatella*. Statoblast formation, which occurs on the funiculus in Phylactolaemata, is mentioned below.

The fresh-water Bryozoa do not constitute a natural group of animals, but have descended from ancestors belonging to widely distinct families. There can be no question that these ancestors were marine animals. Excepting the suborder Phylactolaemata, all fresh-water Bryozoa belong to groups most of whose representatives are marine. The fresh-water forms seem to have made their way up estuaries and rivers to lakes and ponds. Here they acquired the capacity of forming statoblasts or hibernacula, by virtue of which the species was enabled, on the one hand, to survive the winter and, on the other, to be carried by waterfowl and winds over divides from one drainage basin to another. Thus the fresh-water species have become nearly cosmopolitan. *Plumatella princeps* has been found in North and South America, throughout Europe, in Molucca, Japan, and Australia—i.e., in all but one of the great geographical divisions of the land areas of the globe.

The fresh-water Bryozoa live in all kinds of fresh waters and are indeed among the most ubiquitous of aquatic animals. They are found in stagnant pools and in rushing rivers, although particular species favor special habitats. The different species of *Plumatella* occur in varied habitats. *Paludicella* and *Pectinatella* favor running water and *Lophopus*, *Cristatella*, and *Plumatella polymorpha* favor quiet ponds. The fresh-water Bryozoa feed on microscopic organisms which are caught in the vortex created by their ciliated tentacles. Diatoms are especially conspicuous objects in their alimentary tracts. Since diatoms require light for their constructive metabolism, they are found chiefly in the upper strata of the water, and consequently Bryozoa are usually not found at great depths. However, in a mass of material dredged by Professor H. B. Ward from the Middle Ground, Traverse Bay, Lake Michigan, at a depth of 23 to 36 meters, *Paludicella ehrenbergii* and *Frederi-cella sultana* were abundant.   Although *Cristatella* is usually found on the underside of floating lily pads or in other situations near the surface, I have obtained it from the still waters of Trinity Lake, Westchester County, New York, at a depth of 2 to 3 meters. Asper records dredging *Fredericella sultana* in certain Swiss lakes at a depth of 50 to 80 meters.   Little light penetrates to such a depth, and we may conclude that light is not at all directly neces-sary for the development of fresh-water Bryozoa.   Indeed, masses of *Paludicella* are sometimes obtained from water pipes where they flourish to an alarming extent.

The Bryozoa have become adapted to life in ponds by forming statoblasts at certain seasons of the year.   The entire significance of the statoblasts has not been determined.   Typically, they winter over and one may find the shores strewn with them in the early spring.   They hatch out in New England late in May or early in June.   So the statoblasts have come to be regarded as winter buds, or adaptations to preserve the race from being killed off by freezing of the water.   They often begin to develop early in the summer, and I have observed what has been seen by European observers, that some statoblasts hatch in nature even in September.   Also Fr. Müller has informed Kraepelin that the fresh-water Bryozoa of Blumenbau, Brazil, which experience no winters, nevertheless form statoblasts.   It seems fair to conclude that there are other functions performed by the statoblasts than resistance to winter. For instance, they serve to maintain the species during drought, or they aid in distribution by clinging to the waterfowl or resisting the action of digestive fluids.   The wide distribution of the species of fresh-water Bryozoa indicates the value of the statoblast in the process of dispersion.   For a detailed account of the distribution of the fresh-water species in the United States see Davenport (1904).

Preserving. — The chief difficulties in the way of preserving fresh-water Bryozoa arise, first, from the rapid contraction of the polypides into the corm, and, secondly, in the case of the gelatin-ous forms, from the large amount of water in the body; for, if the specific gravity of the killing or preserving medium is very differ-ent from that of the water, distortion will occur.

To kill expanded it is necessary first to narcotize. Chloral hydrate is used, added slowly in crystals until the polypides do not react to touch. To preserve in the natural form, the animals may be plunged directly into 4 per cent formaldehyde (formalin, 10 per cent).

The classification of fresh-water Bryozoa has been in a state of great confusion owing to the great variability in the form of the colony. The form of the colony depends very largely upon external factors, such as food supply, form of substratum, and crowding. The statoblast has a form that is quite independent of external factors, and upon it, consequently, great stress is laid in systematic work. The form of the statoblast is, however, not wholly uncorrelated with that of the stock, so the form of the stock is to be considered. In the following classification that proposed by Kraepelin has been adopted entire.

KEY TO NORTH AMERICAN FRESH–WATER BRYOZOA

1 (2) Anus opening inside the tentacular corona; tentacles incapable of complete retraction. . . . . Subclass **Endoprocta.**
Only one species known in North America.

Urnatella gracilis Leidy 1851.

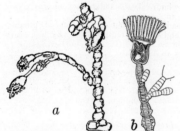

Stock consisting of a basal plate, from which there usually arise two segmented stems terminating in the polypide. More rarely one or more stems arise from the disk. Habit, running water. From Schuylkill River, Pa.; Scioto River, O.; Illinois River, Ill.

Fig. 1394. *Urnatella gracilis.* (*a*) Colony from Illinois River at Havana. ×13. (After Davenport.) (*b*) Single polyp. (After Leidy.)

2 (1) Anus opening outside the tentacular corona, which is capable of being retracted. . . . . Subclass **Ectoprocta** . . 3

3 (6) Zooecia sharply separated from each other; no epistome.

Order **Gymnolaemata** . . 4

4 (5) Stock consists of stolons from which at intervals an erect cylindrical, hyaline single zooid arises, having a terminal aperture.

Pottsiella erecta Potts 1884.

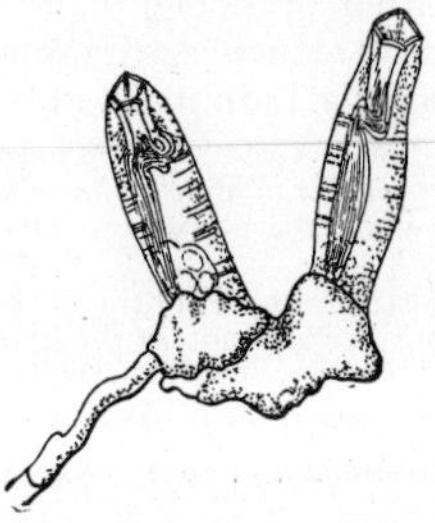

Lophophore circular, 20 (19 to 21) tentacles. Habitat, photophil; on upper surface of stones in rapids; sometimes penetrating incrusting sponges (*Ephydatia leidyi*). From Tacony Creek, Montgomery Co., Pennsylvania.

Fig. 1395. *Pottsiella erecta.* × 25. (From Kraepelin's figure of a Pennsylvania specimen.)

5 (4)   Stock composed of zooids that are sharply separated from one another by partitions; sparsely, usually oppositely branched; with a chitinous cuticula.   The zooids are club-shaped and have a lateral, quadrangular aperture near the larger, distal end.

Paludicella ehrenbergii van Beneden 1848.

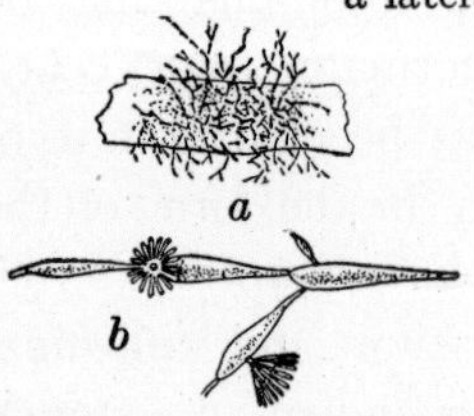

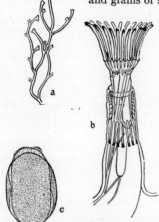

Zooids about 2 mm. long; lateral buds partly repent, partly erect; about 16 tentacles.   Habitat, flowing streams; occasionally in water pipes.   From Massachusetts, Pennsylvania, Illinois, and Lake Michigan.

FIG. 1396.   *Paludicella ehrenbergii.* (a) Colony, half natural size. (b) Portion of same enlarged.   × 5.   (After Kraepelin.)

6 (3)   Zooecia confluent;   epistome   present.   .   Order **Phylactolaemata**.   .   7

7 (14, 15)   Statoblasts without hooks, rounded at ends. 8

8 (9)   Stock branched in form of antlers;   more rarely massed with recumbent and elevated tubes; mostly brown or incrusted with algae and grains of sand;   rarely hyaline.

Fredericella sultana Blumenbach 1774.

Tubes cylindrical, the older ones mostly keeled. Without complete dissepiments.   Apertures terminal at the broadened or bifid ends of tubes.   Polypide very long and slender; tentacles arranged in a nearly circular corona.   Few tentacles, not exceeding 24. Statoblasts dark brown, bean-shaped or elliptical, without float, and with smooth upper surface. Habitat on wood, stones and water plants in standing and slowly flowing waters.   From Maine to Pennsylvania, westward to Wisconsin and even Flathead Lake, Montana.   Common in the Great Lakes.

FIG. 1397.   *Fredericella sultana.*   (a) Portion of branch, natural size.   (b) Polyp magnified.   (After Hyatt.) (c) Statoblast.   (After Kraepelin.)

9 (8)   Colonies consist of cylindrical tubes, which are either branched or form massive clumps or run over the substratum as hyaline, lobed tubes. . . . . *Plumatella* Lamarck. .   10

Partitions rudimentary or absent, cuticula brown to hyaline, often incrusted.   Tentacular corona markedly horseshoe-shaped, with 40 to 60 tentacles.   Intertentacular membrane present. Statoblasts without hooks; either free, elliptical, with broad float, or (in the horizontal tubes) without float, of large size and irregular shape.

The commonest genus of our fresh-water Bryozoa.   Has been reported from all continents except Africa.   Lives in the most diverse habitats, in ponds or streams, usually not in the light.

10 (13)   Colony with vertical as well as horizontal branches. 11

11 (12) Cuticula thick and brown, with a keel that broadens at aperture.
Free statoblasts elongated; proportions 1 : 1.53 to 1 : 2.8.
Plumatella princeps Kraepelin 1887.

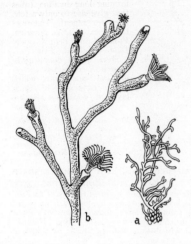

Tubes openly branched, repent, with short lateral branches, antlerlike. . . . . . .Var. α, emarginata.
Colony robust, branched often rising from subtratum. Keel little developed. Statoblasts elongated.
Var. β, fruticosa.
Vertical branches predominate, forming an intertwined mass.
Var. γ, mucosa.
Vertical tubes fused into a mass from which only the aperture rises free. . . . . . . Var. δ, spongiosa.

Fig. 1398. Plumatella princeps, var. α. (a) Portion of colony, two-thirds natural size. (b) Branch much magnified. (After Kraepelin.)

12 (11) Cuticula rarely browned or keeled. Free statoblasts nearly circular,
1 : 1 to 1 : 1.5. . . Plumatella polymorpha Kraepelin 1887.

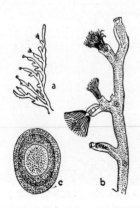

Tubes creeping with short vertical side branches. Cuticula semi-transparent; but variable; keel not evident.
Var. α, repens (=P.-arethusa Hyatt).
Tubes repent, branching or thickly intertwined, covering the substratum. Few or no vertical branches. Cuticula lightly colored to transparent. . . . . Var. β, oppressa.
Tubes repent, with many elongated and branched vertical rami. Cuticula semi-opaque, no evident keel. . . . . . Var. γ, caespitosa.
Tubes repent. Vertical branches close together, even fused, forming great solidness. Cuticula brown, aperture hyaline, slightly elongated. . . . . Var. δ, fungosa.

Fig. 1399. Plumatella polymorpha, var. α. (a) Young colony, two-thirds natural size. (b) Branch much magnified. (c) Statoblast, × 40. (After Kraepelin.)

13 (10) Horizontal branches only. Cuticula delicate, colorless, hyaline. Elevated aperture-cone wrinkled and besprinkled with white. Free statoblasts nearly circular.

Plumatella punctata Hancock 1850.

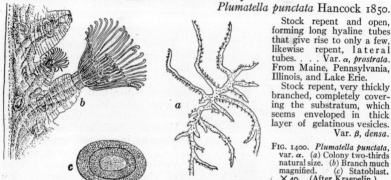

Stock repent and open, forming long hyaline tubes that give rise to only a few, likewise repent, lateral tubes. . . . Var. α, *prostrata*. From Maine, Pennsylvania, Illinois, and Lake Erie.

Stock repent, very thickly branched, completely covering the substratum, which seems enveloped in thick layer of gelatinous vesicles. Var. β, *densa*.

FIG. 1400. *Plumatella punctata*, var. α. (a) Colony two-thirds natural size. (b) Branch much magnified. (c) Statoblast. × 40. (After Kraepelin.)

14 (7, 15) Statoblasts, large, elliptical, but at each end drawn out into a sharp apex; broad float, hooks absent. *Lophopus cristallinus* Pallas 1766.
Colony shaped like a sack; erect, sometimes more or less lobed by indentations of margin, looking then sometimes like a glove. Outer cuticula layer delicate and hyaline, more incrusted at base. Polypides scattered, a group of them rising from each lobe. Lophophores with about 60 tentacles. The colony may divide along the constrictions between the lobes. Habitat, chiefly standing water, such as pools, or, rarely, slowly flowing water. Chiefly attached to plant stems. From Schuylkill and Illinois rivers.

15 (7, 14) Statoblasts with hooks. 16

16 (18) Colonies hyaline, in the form of a rosette, lobed, with horizontal tubes only. . . . . *Pectinatella* Leidy . . 17
They secrete a great gelatinous base which is common to many colonies. Aperture slightly elevated above common coenecium. Statoblasts large and circular to subrectangular, with broad bent float and one marginal row of anchor-shaped hooks.

17 Polypides scattered or in double row along each lobe, the gelatinous base often 10 to 20 centimeters thick. *Pectinatella magnifica* Leidy 1851.

Tentacles 60 to 84 in number. Statoblasts about 1 mm. in diameter, provided with 11 to 22 hooks from 0.15 to 0.25 mm. long. Habitat, submerged branches or twigs of trees, wooden stakes, gates of dams, walls of reservoirs or stones in brooks. Shady situations, such as south walls of reservoirs, or wood-covered streams. From Maine to Mississippi.

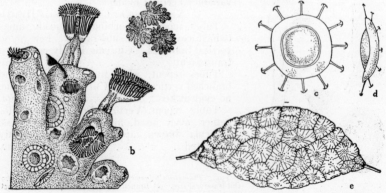

FIG. 1401. *Pectinatella magnifica.* (a) Young colony, natural size. (b) Section highly magnified. (c) Statoblast, ventral view. (d) Statoblast in profile. × 15. (e) Colony on plant stem. × ⅘. (After Kraepelin.)

18 (16) Colony unbranched, gelatinous, with a flat "sole."

Cristatella mucedo Cuvier 1798.

External cuticula lacking, or developed merely as a thin gelatinous layer under the sole. All polypides contract into a common cavity. Statoblast large, circular, with float and a circlet of hooks on both sides. Young corm of circular form later elongated, worm-like, attaining a length of 2 to 5 cm. in summer, to 28 cm. in autumn. Colonies often gregarious in a common gelatinous substance. Eighty to ninety tentacles. Statoblasts with 10 to 34 dorsal hooks, 20 to 50 ventral hooks. Habitat, in standing or slow-flowing water, on submerged branches of dead trees, under side of lily-pads, and on other aquatic plants.

Statoblasts less than 1 mm. in diameter; hooks on dorsal side 10 to 22; on ventral side 20 to 37. . . . . Var. α, *genuina* (= *C. ophidea* Hyatt 1868). From Maine, Massachusetts, New York, Illinois, and Lake Erie. Statoblasts over 1 mm.; hooks on dorsal side 20–34; on ventral side 38–50. Var. β, *idae* (= *C. idae* Leidy 1858; *C. lacustris* Potts 1884). From Rhode Island and Pennsylvania.

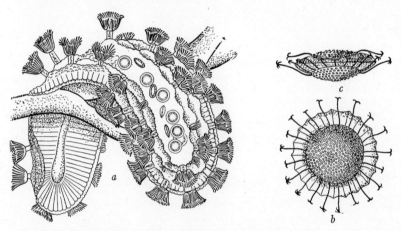

Fig. 1402. *Cristatella mucedo*. (*a*) Colony much enlarged. (*b*) Statoblast ventral aspect. (*c*) Statoblast in profile. × 25. (After Allman.)

IMPORTANT REFERENCES ON FRESH–WATER BRYOZOA

ALLMAN, J. 1856. A Monograph of the Fresh-water Polyzoa. London.

DAVENPORT, C. B. 1890. Cristatella: The Origin and Development of the Individual in the Colony. Bull. Mus. Comp. Zool., Harvard College, 20: 101–152.

1891. Budding in Paludicella and other Bryozoa. Bull. Mus. Comp. Zool., Harvard College, 22: 1–114.

1904. Report on the Fresh-water Bryozoa of the United States. Proc. U. S. Nat. Mus., 27: 211–221.

HYATT, A. 1866–68. Obvervations on Polyzoa, Suborder Phylactolaemata. Communications Essex Institute, 4: 167–228; 5: 97–112, 145–160, 193–232.

KRAEPELIN, K. 1887. Die Deutschen Süsswasser-Bryozoen. Eine Monographie. I, Anatomisch-Systematischer Teil. Abhandl. Naturw. Verein,
Hamburg, 10: 1–168.

LANDACRE, F. 1901. Sponges and Bryozoa of Sandusky Bay. Ohio Nat.,
1: 96–7.

LEIDY, J. 1883. Urnatella gracilis. Jour. Acad. Nat. Sci., Phila., 9: 5–16.

CHAPTER XXIX

THE MOLLUSCA

By BRYANT WALKER, Detroit, Mich.

For the purposes of this treatise and in order to differentiate the group from the other great phyla of the animal kingdom represented in our fresh-water fauna, the Mollusca may be defined as animals with a soft body encased in a hard shell, which may be either in one piece (univalve) or in two pieces (bivalve). In the univalve mollusca or Gastropoda, commonly called snails, the shell may be coiled either obliquely or horizontally or may be a simple uncoiled, conical, tent-shaped secretion on the back of the animal. In this class, the animal possesses a distinct head, with a pair of contractile tentacles, at the base of which are placed the eyes. On the lower side of the head, between the tentacles, is the mouth, which, on its inner, upper margin, is usually provided with a chitinous jaw of from one to three pieces. In the lower part of the mouth is the radula, a muscular ribbon covered with minute teeth.

The fresh-water Gastropoda are divided into two main groups or subclasses according as they breathe the free air by means of a lung or are provided with a gill for subaqueous respiration. As the name implies, these animals progress by crawling on the ventral surface of the body, which is modified to form a flat, muscular disk called the foot.

The bivalve mollusca or Lamellibranchia, usually known as clams or mussels, have the body protected by two symmetrical, opposing valves, which are united above by an elastic tissue called the ligament. They have no head and have, accordingly, been called the Acephala. They have no tentacles, eyes, jaws, or radula. The mouth is simply an orifice at the anterior end of the body, on each side of which is a flap or palpus, which assists in guiding the food to the mouth. The foot is an axe-shaped mass of muscular tissue (hence the name of Pelecypoda often used for the class), which may be extended from the anterior portion of the shell and, by effecting a lodgment in the bottom, drag the animal slowly forward. The lamellibranchs breathe by means of two gills suspended on each side of the body, which are divided into a series of water tubes by septa or lamellae, through which the water circulates by means of cilia. The whole body is enclosed in a soft mantle, which secretes the shell along its outer margins. Posteriorly the mantle has two openings, through the lower of which the water enters the shell, passes forward, aerating the gills and carrying food to the mouth, and then flows out through the upper opening.

A more detailed account of the structure of the two classes represented in our fauna will be found under the head of classification.

THE NORTH AMERICAN FAUNA

As would naturally be expected from the vast extent of the territory included in the United States and British America and the great diversity both in the climatic and physical conditions prevalent in different portions of the continent, the fresh-water fauna of North America is not only one of great abundance, both in species and individuals, but also of great diversity in character; and a very large proportion of the genera represented are peculiar to it. While but one of the eighteen families represented in our fauna is peculiar to the continent, that one, the Pleuroceratidae, is extraordinarily developed both in genera and species and, where found, its members usually occur in great abundance.

On the other hand, of the eighty-six genera recognized at the present time, no less than forty-nine, or five-ninths, are peculiar to North America, while of the many hundred of described species, it is safe to say that more than ninety per cent are not found elsewhere. Indeed, barring the comparatively small number of circumpolar species in the north, and the somewhat larger representation of tropical or subtropical forms found on our southern borders, practically the whole of our molluscan fauna may be said to be distinctively North American.

The distribution of the various families, genera, and species represented in our fauna varies greatly in the different sections of the continent.

Most of the families have representatives in all portions of the country where suitable conditions of environment are to be found. But there are some notable exceptions. Thus the Viviparidae, which form one of the most conspicuous elements of the fauna of the Eastern States, are not found west of the Mississippi Valley. The Ampullaridae, which replace the Viviparidae in the tropics, are only found in Florida and Southern Georgia; while the great family of the Pleuroceratidae, the one family peculiar to our fauna, is not found west of the Mississippi Valley drainage, except for a few isolated species that occur in the northern Pacific states.

Many of the genera have a general distribution in all parts of the continent. That is, some representatives of such genera will be found practically every place where suitable conditions obtain. But it is to be borne in mind that comparatively few species have a general distribution. Many of them have, so far as known, a very limited habitat, while others range over a large extent of territory. Many of the genera are likewise restricted to certain portions of the continent and particularly to certain drainage systems, while others are confined to a very limited area. The Coosa River in Alabama, in this respect, has a most remarkable fauna. No less than six genera and very many species are known to occur only in it and its tributaries.

But while, in a general way, it is true that our fauna as a whole is well known, and its distinctive characters recognized, yet the sum total of our present knowledge, large as it may seem, is very small and inadequate when compared with what we might and would like to know about it.

But a very small portion of the continent has been collected over with any sort of thoroughness, and there are undoubtedly very many new types, both generic and specific, yet to be discovered. While, of course, the mere description of new species is the least important part of the work of the conchologist, yet the accurate knowledge of *all* the species found within our borders is the basis for the solution of the larger problems of distribution and evolution, which are of great importance. The exact range of very few, if any, even of our most common species is exactly known. It is very desirable that lists of the species occurring in all the states and counties of the country should be compiled. Such local lists, when the specimens are correctly determined, are of great value and interest and are always acceptable contributions to scientific literature.[1]

The life history and habits of the different species form a subject of great interest, and as yet but little is known about them. Then, too, very little is known of the internal anatomy of our species, much less, indeed, than of the land mollusca. In all these lines of work and study there is a fruitful and unreaped field of investigation, which cannot fail to yield both pleasure and profit to the student who will undertake to study the common forms of molluscan life, which are to be found so abundantly in all parts of our country.

COLLECTION AND PREPARATION OF SPECIMENS

Nearly every permanent body of water has its mollusks, varying according to its character. Some species are found only in rapidly flowing water, and others only in ponds and still water. Ditches and other stagnant waters are usually good collecting ground for *Pisidia* and other small species. The low places in the woods, which dry up in the summer time, have a number of species that are not found elsewhere, and which bury themselves in the mud when the water disappears. Sand banks in rivers and lakes are favorite resorts of many of the smaller species. The under side of the lily pads should be scrutinized, while the *Ancyli* should be looked for on stones and dead clam shells.

The distribution of the different species in all the states and territories being of prime importance, the collector should always bear in mind:

First, that a dead shell is better than none at all;

Second, that dead shells should not be taken, if live ones can be had, and that careful search will usually discover them in the immediate vicinity.

Third, that all the species are extremely variable in their abundance from year to year, and so it is a safe rule, "when you're getting, to get a plenty."

[1] The writer will gladly aid students in the identification of their specimens without charge. Address 45 Alfred St., Detroit, Mich.

The apparatus for collecting is very simple.

It is necessary to have a dipper and, if possible, a small dredge. The dipper is made from an ordinary tin one by removing the bottom and substituting one of fine wire cloth. By removing the end of the handle, the dipper can be slipped on the end of a cane or pole when in use. This is useful not only for reaching the larger specimens from the shore or boat, but especially for sifting the mud and sand from the bottom, where a multitude of small species live, which otherwise would not be found. It will be found more convenient to empty the contents of the dipper, when thoroughly washed out, into a pail or small bag, and carry the whole mass home before undertaking to pick out the shells. If attempted in the field, many of the smaller and more desirable things are apt to be overlooked. By spreading the mass out in the sun for a short time, it will become dry and friable so that the shells can be easily separated and picked out. An ordinary reading glass is very useful for the detection of the more minute forms in sorting over such material.

Many desirable species live in water too deep for the convenient use of the dipper, and for these it is necessary to have a small dredge. One with an aperture of 9 by 6 inches is as large as can be used satisfactorily by a single person in a boat.

Several small bags and a number of wide-mouthed bottles and small vials should be carried, so that the specimens from different localities may be kept separate. Care must be taken to keep the more fragile species separate from the heavier ones, otherwise they are likely to be damaged in moving about. For the same reason it is better to fill the bottles partially with water while in the field, as the mollusks then attach themselves to the glass and are less likely to be broken. It is not necessary to take alcohol into the field.

Specimens to be kept for anatomical purposes may be preserved in alcohol, which at first should be greatly diluted, not stronger than 25 per cent; after a day or two the specimens should be removed to 50 per cent alcohol, and later to the undiluted. Formaldehyde, 2 per cent dilution, is an admirable preservative for material of this kind. It should not, however, be used when it is desired to keep the shells as specimens, as it destroys those left in it any length of time.

With the exception of the larger species of *Planorbis*, which are more easily cleaned by boiling, it is practically immaterial whether the fluviatile univalves are boiled, or put directly into diluted alcohol for a day or two. In either case there is no difficulty in extracting the animals. The curved points of the collecting forceps are convenient for this purpose, and hooks of various sizes can be made from safety pins. By tying these on small wooden handles very effective instruments can be made. Small hooks or "probes" of various sizes fitting into an adjustable handle are most convenient and can be obtained from any dealer in dental instruments. A small, fine-pointed dental syringe is indispensable for this work. When the animal is completely extracted, the interior of the shell should be thoroughly washed out with the syringe. A small piece of sponge on the end of a fine copper wire, which can be bent in any direction, is very useful for removing the mucus, which is apt to adhere to the interior. This should always be carefully attended to; if not it will greatly disfigure the specimen when dried. The exterior should then be thoroughly scrubbed with a soft tooth or nail brush. When perfectly clean, inside and out, the water should be carefully emptied out and the shell put aside in the air, but not in the sun, to dry.

It is not desirable to attempt to clean the minute species by removing the animal. They should be put directly into 25 per cent alcohol for a day or two. If to be left longer in the alcohol, the strength should be increased. Twenty-four hours, however, in the alcohol is all that is necessary. Then they can be dried in the air without leaving any offensive odor. Either before or after drying they can be cleaned, if necessary, by putting them in a bottle of water, with some fine, clean sand, and shaking them together until all the dirt has been removed by the sand. In the operculate species, it is desirable to retain the opercula of, at least, part of the specimens. While it adds to the labor, it increases the value of the specimen if it is always done. These are easily removed from the animal and, after being cleaned, should be put inside the shell and the aperture plugged with cotton. All the foreign matter both inside and outside of the shell should be removed by thorough washing. All the water species are apt to be more or less incrusted with deposits of lime or oxide of iron. These can be removed by immersing them in oxalic acid. Care should be taken not to prolong the operation, or the texture of the shell may be injured. Elbow grease is the most effective agent for making good specimens. When that fails, use the acid. The Ancyli are always more or less coated in this way, and can easily be cleaned by floating them for a few minutes on the acid, upside down, and then gently brushing them off with a soft brush while held on the tip of the finger.

The larger bivalves should be well washed and, if necessary, scraped off with the knife as soon as taken, care being taken not to injure the epidermis.

They can be boiled, if desired, when the shells will open and the animals easily removed. But, as a rule, it is more convenient, unless collected in large quantities, to cut the muscles, which hold the valves together, with a thin-bladed knife and scrape the animal out. Care should be taken not to break the edge of the fragile species when inserting the knife. All traces of the animal matter should be removed, and after a thorough washing the valves tied together with a string until thoroughly dried. Never use colored twine for this purpose, as it is apt to stain the shells. Any surface incrustation can be removed either with oxalic or muriatic acid. The latter is more convenient for the larger species, and can be applied with a small brush. To avoid trouble, it is safer to wear rubber gloves, if a large quantity of material is to be cleaned. Care must be exercised in using the acid and the specimens frequently washed, lest damage be done to the shell. The smaller bivalves, the Sphaeria and Pisidia, are best treated by putting into diluted alcohol for a day or two and then drying them. If left too long the shells are apt to open, which interferes with the looks of the specimens. The larger species of Sphaerium are better with the animal removed. This can be done after boiling, or a few days in alcohol. As these are usually too small to be easily tied together to keep the valves from gaping, each specimen, while the hinge is flexible, should be closely wrapped up in a small piece of tissue paper until completely dry.

While it is not usually desirable to keep "dead" shells for the cabinet, occasionally it is necessary. In such cases, the color can be in some measure restored by applying a solution of paraffin and gasoline (a cubic inch of the former in half a pint of the latter). "Dead" Unionidae can be improved in appearance and the brilliancy of the nacre measurably restored by applying muriatic acid.

A good collection is characterized by two essentials:

First, the careful selection and preparation of the specimens themselves;

Second, absolute accuracy in the matter of the localities from which they came.

There is little excuse for having poor and ill-cleaned specimens. There is none at all for failure to keep accurate records of the collector's fieldwork. A drawer of any common species, without any indication of whence they came, even if well cleaned, would be absolutely without value. Such a drawer of any of our species from fifty or one hundred different localities, definitely indicated, would be a valuable contribution to the conchology of any state. Specific names can be supplied or corrected any time, but a mistaken or erroneous locality can never be corrected. The collector, therefore, should be careful never to trust to memory for facts of this kind. Both in collecting and cleaning, the specimens from each locality should be kept carefully separated and labeled. Too much importance cannot be given to this point. The study of the geographical distribution of the mollusca is one of the most important branches of conchological work, and, to be of any value, this must be based on absolutely accurate work on the part of the collector.

The manner of casing and arranging the collection is largely one of individual preference. A catalogue, however, is essential, and it is better to begin systematically in this particular and thus avoid the necessity of doing it all over again when the collection begins to assume considerable size. There should be a serial catalogue and a card catalogue. Each addition to the collection should be numbered as soon as received and entered in the serial catalogue, which should be a book ruled in as many columns as the collector desires.

The card catalogue is convenient in a small collection. It becomes absolutely necessary in a large one. The cards should be of uniform size for convenience in handling. If it is desired to have a card for every entry, they can be smaller than if it is desirable for economy of space to have as many entries as possible on one card. In the latter case a convenient size is that of the ordinary library card, which can be ruled to hold twenty entries. The name of the species is written on the top, and the number of each entry of that species and the locality are entered below. Such a card as this enables the collector to see at a glance not only whether any given species is represented in his collection, but also from what localities, and saves a large amount of time which would otherwise be spent in turning over the leaves of a serial catalogue. The cards can be kept in drawers or boxes of proper size and can be arranged alphabetically under the different genera and families. Guide cards slightly higher than the ordinary card, indicating the genera, can be inserted in their proper places.

In collections intended for public exhibition, it is usually necessary to have the specimens mounted on cards or blocks. But in private collections such an arrangement is a mistake, not only on account of the greater room required for the collection, but particularly because it prevents the handling of the specimens for purposes of study.

Specimens under an inch in diameter are most conveniently kept in glass vials. These can be obtained from any wholesale druggist. They should be without a neck and of standard sizes. The length will depend upon the standard size of the tray adopted. For my own collection I use three sizes, $\frac{1}{4}$, $\frac{1}{2}$, $\frac{7}{8}$ inch in diameter. As these vials are rather fragile, the pressure of the cork is apt to break them. The cork should therefore be softened by rolling or crushing. A pair of plumber's burner pliers is useful for this purpose. The serial number should be put on the cork or on a small piece of paper inside. Specimens too large for the vials should have the number on the shell in ink. Then, if a drawer happens to be overturned, the specimens can be sorted out again without difficulty.

When numbered, the vials and specimens should be placed in

trays. For these a standard size should be adopted, so that they will conveniently fit into the drawers of the cabinet. In the National Museum at Washington, the unit is 1 by 2 inches, and the larger sizes are all multiples of that unit. In the Academy of Natural Sciences at Philadelphia, the unit is $1\frac{1}{2}$ by 3. There is one advantage in the use of the larger unit where space is a serious question. For the small species the vials may be used only $1\frac{1}{4}$ inches in length, and two vials can be put into one tray, thus doubling the capacity of the drawer. The trays should be of the same depth. One-half inch is sufficient for most of the univalve species. For the larger species, such as the Unionidae, requiring trays of good size, $\frac{3}{4}$ inch is better. These trays can be had of any paper-box manufacturer, or can be easily cut out of cardboard by the collector, the corners being fastened together by strips of gummed paper. The character of the cases for a collection is determined by the means and inclination of the collector. Any case of shallow drawers will do. If, however, cases are to be made, they should be made of a standard size with interchangeable drawers. Each tray should have a neat label giving the serial number, the name, and the locality of the specimens it contains. A box, bottom side up, can be used for separating the genera and species in every drawer. Small labels of convenient size for designating them can be had, already gummed, at any bookseller's.

In packing shells, small specimens should not be mixed with large ones, as they are apt to get lost; nor should fragile shells be put in with stronger ones, as they are likely to be broken. The minute specimens can be put into gelatin capsules, small vials, quills, or paper tubes made by rolling writing paper around a lead pencil, gumming down the edge and stopping the ends with cotton. Do not mix shells from different localities. Write the locality on a label and wrap it up with each vial or package. Use plenty of cotton in packing fragile shells. Pill boxes and match boxes are convenient for packing purposes. Wrap up each vial or box separately, then, if a smash does occur, there is a fair chance of saving some of the specimens and no danger of mixing the contents of different packages. Do not send paper boxes by mail. Pack in a wooden box.

For purposes of dissection either fresh or alcoholic specimens may be used. Live specimens may be killed by plunging them into boiling water for a few seconds. The animal can thus be removed from the shell in the usual way, using great care not to mutilate it with the hook; or the shell, if not too heavy, can be carefully broken away with the forceps. Preserved specimens are frequently difficult to extract from the shell, in which case the shell must be removed either by breaking or, if too thick, by dissolving it in muriatic acid.

"Two pairs of fine scissors will be necessary, one pair with straight points, the other with curved points; one or more fine scalpels, and two pairs of fine forceps, one straight and the other curved. Dissecting needles are also necessary. These can be made by forcing the heads of fine needles, by means of a pair of pliers, into the end of a round stick of small diameter. The point of one of these needles should be bent so as to form a hook, first heating the end of the needle to a white heat."

"In dissecting the animal, a circular china dish about 4 inches in diameter and 2 in depth will be necessary; also a piece of sheet cork as large as will lie at the bottom of the dish, fastened to a thin sheet of lead with either string or rubber bands. It is best to have the lead of the same size as the cork. This leaded cork is to be placed in the bottom of the dish, and the dish filled with alcohol. If the animal has once been placed in alcohol, all dissections should be made in alcohol, but freshly killed specimens may be dissected in water, and many of the organs at this time present a much more natural appearance than when acted on by alcohol. Place the animal on the cork and fasten it down with small pins, or better yet, with very fine, short needles inserted through the margin of the foot. Then with a fine pair of scissors, commencing at the head, cut through the integument along the center of the back, taking care not to injure any of the organs below. The integument is now to be removed from the dorsal part, turned back and fastened to the cork, removing the needles from the margin of the foot and putting them through the edges of the integument. All the organs of the anterior part of the snail are thus brought into view, and further dissection of the organs can be intelligently made."[1]

The method of preparing the jaws and lingual membrane for examination is as follows:

"On opening the head (of the snail) from above, one readily notices at the extreme anterior part, close against the outer integument, a prominent, oval body. This is called the buccal mass. It is easily cut away from the animal, and will be found to contain both jaw and lingual membrane. These can be removed by fine scissors or knives from the buccal mass in the larger species, but in the smaller species, the method usually employed is putting the whole buccal mass in a watch crystal, full of a strong solution of caustic potash. Allowing it to remain for several hours, the potash will destroy all of the buccal mass, and leave the jaw and lingual membrane perfectly clean and ready for examination. They must be well rinsed in clean water, in another watch crystal, before examination. Another more expeditious process, is to place the whole buccal mass in a test tube with the solution of potash, and boil it for a few seconds over a spirit lamp. Pouring the contents of the tube into a watch crystal, the lingual membrane attached to the jaw will be readily seen by a pocket lens. If the species be small, its whole body may be thrown into the solution. Still more minute species, may be treated in this way; crush the whole shell between the glass slides; wash the particles of broken shell in a few drops of water, still keeping the body of the animal on the slide; when clean, drop on it the caustic potash and boil it by holding the slide itself over the spirit lamp.

"For purpose of examination, the jaw and lingual membrane may be simply mounted in water and covered with thin glass. One must be sure in spreading out the lingual membrane not to have its upper side down, and it is well to cut it transversely in several

[1] No detailed instructions for the dissection of the fresh-water mollusks have been published in this country. For an admirable, fully illustrated paper on the dissection of the land snail, which can be easily adapted for the use of the student, see Simpson, Bull. N. Y. State Museum, viii, p. 241 (1901). The same author has published an excellent study, fully illustrated, of the anatomy of *Anodonta*, which should be in the hands of every student. See Rep. N. Y., State Mus. of Nat. Hist., 35, p. 169.

places, as the teeth are beautifully shown and often stand detached on the edges of the cut.

"For preservation for future study, the glycerin preparations sold by the opticians will be found useful, though they have the great disadvantages of deliquescing in warm weather." [1]

The radula may also be mounted in Canada balsam. In this case it should be stained with carmine or chromic acid, as otherwise the specimens will in time become transparent.

MEASUREMENT AND DESCRIPTIVE TERMS

The length or height of a univalve shell is the distance from the apex to the basal edge of the lip, measured along a line drawn through the axis.

The greater diameter is the greatest width, including the lip, measured on a line drawn at right angles to the axis.

The lesser diameter is measured on the same plane, but on a line at right angles to the greater diameter.

Shells are dextral or sinistral, accordingly as the aperture is on the right or left of the axis, when held, apex uppermost, with the aperture facing the observer.

In bivalve shells, the length is the distance from the anterior to the posterior extremity; the height is the distance at right angles between two parallel lines so drawn as to touch the highest dorsal and lowest basal points; the width is the greatest diameter measured in a line at right angles to the basal line.

The remainder of the terms in common use are sufficiently indicated on the following diagrams.

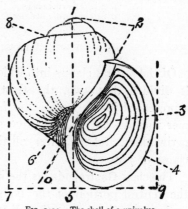

FIG. 1403.   The shell of a univalve.

1. Apex.	6. Umbilicus.
2. Spire.	8. Suture.
3. Operculum.	10. Columella.
4. Lip.	1–5. Height.
7–9. Greatest diameter.	

[1] W. G. Binney, Man. Am. Land Shells, p. 44.   For full instructions in regard to the preparation of the radulae of the minute species, see Beecher, Journal N. Y. Microscopical Society, 1888, p. 7.

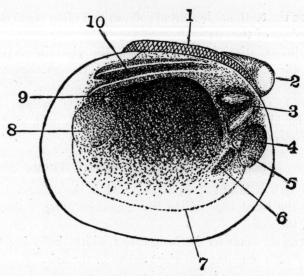

FIG. 1404. The shell of a bivalve.

1. Hinge.   6. Scar of protractor pedis.
2. Beak.   7. Pallial line.
3. Pseudo-cardinals.   8. Scar of posterior adductor.
4. Scar of anterior retractor.   9. Scar of posterior retractor.
5. Scar of anterior adductor.   10. Lateral teeth.

CLASSIFICATION

Of the several classes into which the subkingdom of the Mollusca is divided, but two, the Gastropoda and Lamellibranchia, are represented in the fresh-water fauna of North America. The former includes all the univalve species commonly called snails or periwinkles, and the latter, all the bivalve forms usually known as clams or mussels.

The class **Gastropoda,** as the name implies, are mollusks in which the ventral portion of the body is developed into a fleshy, more or less expanded, creeping disk, called the foot, by the muscular contractions of which the animal progresses.

When fully expanded, the animal is seen to have a distinct head, with a pair of tentacles, at the base of which are placed the eyes. In the center of the head, below and between the tentacles, is the mouth, in which, on the upper surface, are situated the jaws, from one to three, and, on the lower side, the lingual ribbon or radula, the surface of which is covered with numerous rows of small chitinous teeth.

The Gastropoda are either ovoviviparous or oviparous. The sexes are separate in some groups (Dioecia) and united in the same individual in others (Monoecia). All of the fresh-water gastropods are provided with an external shell, which covers the animal completely when retracted, and which is spiral, discoidal, or conical in shape.

Owing to the torsion of the body, caused by the spiral shape of the shell, the animal of all the fresh-water gastropods, while externally bilaterally symmetrical, is internally asymmetrical. There is but one lung or one functional gill, as the case may be, and the terminations of the digestive and genital systems, instead of being posterior and central, corresponding to the mouth, are on the side near the respiratory chamber.

The Gastropoda are further divided into subclasses, accordingly as the torsion of the viscera has or has not been accompanied by a similar twisting of the visceral nerve loop. In the Euthyneura, the visceral nerve loop lies beneath the intestinal canal, and was consequently not affected by the torsion to which that organ was subjected, while in the Streptoneura, the visceral nerve loop lies above the intestines and became involved in the twisting of the viscera and was consequently made to assume the form of the figure 8. The aquatic Euthyneura, which comprise practically all our air-breathing or pulmoniferous fluviatile mollusks, are included in the order Pulmonata; while the Streptoneura comprise all the gill-breathing or branchiferous species, which are furnished with a peculiar chitinous or calcareous structure attached to the upper surface of the posterior extremity called the operculum, and which, when the animal retires within the shell, completely closes the aperture. Species thus provided are termed operculate. The Pulmonata, on the other hand, have no operculum, and are therefore called inoperculate.

The Pulmonata are divided into two suborders: the Stylommatophora, in which the eyes are borne on the extremities of retractile tentacles, and which are all terrestrial species; and the Basommatophora, in which the eyes are placed at the base of contractile tentacles, and which are aquatic or amphibious in habit.

The Basommatophora are subdivided into three superfamilies based mainly on the general character of their habitat:

I. Terrestrial or semiamphibious, living in damp places or near the margin of the sea, but not in the water, — Akteophila.

II. Aquatic, living in fresh water and usually coming occasionally to the surface for air, — Limnophila.

III. Aquatic, living in salt or brackish water along the seashore in the littoral zone, — Petrophila.

The Streptoneura are divided into two orders:

I. The Aspidobranchia, in which the nerve centers are not closely concentrated, and the original bilateral symmetry has not wholly disappeared, there being two auricles to the heart and two kidneys.

II. The Pectinibranchia, in which all trace of bilateral symmetry in the circulatory, respiratory, and execretory systems has disappeared and the nervous system is more concentrated.

The fresh-water aspidobranchs all belong to the suborder Rhipidoglossa, in which the radula has very numerous marginal teeth arranged like the sticks of a fan.

The Pectinibranchia are divided into two suborders, of which only one, the Taenioglossa, in which the radula has but one lateral and two marginal teeth on each side of the central tooth, is represented in our fluviatile fauna. The fresh-water Taenioglossae are all included in the superfamily Platypoda, in which the foot is flattened ventrally for creeping purposes.

The several superfamilies of the Euthyneura and Streptoneura are subdivided into families, of which thirteen are represented in the North American fauna.

The class Lamellibranchia, so called from the form of the gills, comprises all the fresh-water bivalve shells commonly called clams or mussels. The name Pelecypoda is frequently applied to this class from the hatchet-like shape of the foot. The lamellibranchs are aquatic mollusks, without a distinct head and with the mantle divided into two lobes, which secrete a bivalve shell united by a ligament, which covers the entire animal. The lobes of the mantle are united by one or two transverse muscles, which are attached to the inner surface of the valves and by their con-

traction close the shell. They are destitute of jaws or radula, and
the cephalic region is furnished only with a pair of labial palps on
each side. They feed by ciliary action and breathe by gills suspended on each side of the body. The digestive system consists
of a stomach, a liver, and a more or less convoluted intestinal canal
with its oral and anal extremities at the opposite ends of the body.
The edges of the mantle lobes in the fresh-water forms are usually
united between exhalent and inhalent orifices, and in some families
the posterior margins are extended in one or two siphons. The
foot is ventral, usually compressed, hatchet-shaped, and adapted
for burrowing. The nervous system consists of three principal
groups of ganglia (cerebral, pedal, and visceral), united by nerves.
They are monoecious or dioecious.

The following diagram represents the classification of the fresh-
water Gastropoda as thus briefly outlined.

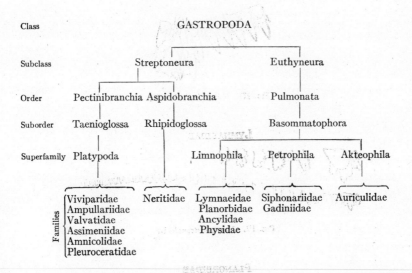

THE RADULA

As the radula of the gastropod mollusca is very important as a
basis for classification, the following series of typical forms is given,
which should be used in connection with the key.

AURICULIDAE

FIG. I. *Carychium exiguum* Say.

SIPHONARIIDAE

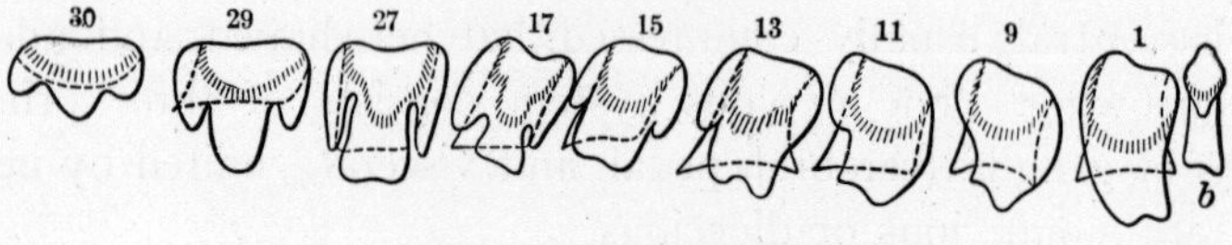

FIG. II. *Siphonaria alternata* Say.

GADINIIDAE

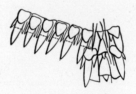

FIG. III. *Gadinia reticulata* Say.

LYMNAEIDAE

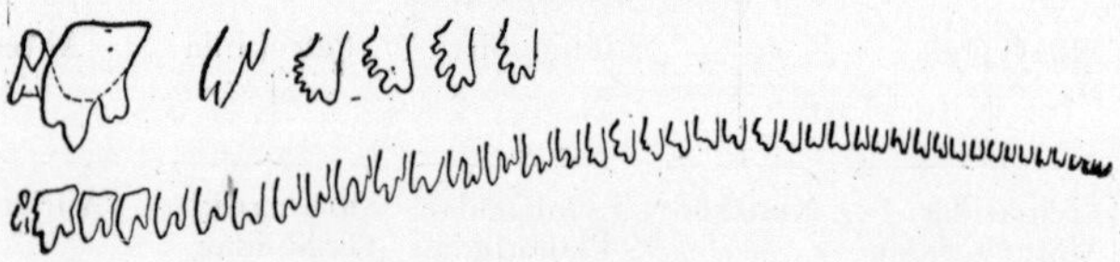

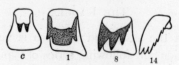

FIG. IV. *Lymnaea stagnalis* L.

PLANORBIDAE

FIG. V. *Planorbis trivolvis* Say.

PHYSIDAE

Fig. VI. *Physa humerosa* Gld.

ANCYLIDAE

Fig. VII. *Gundlachia meekiana* Stimp.

AMPULLARIIDAE

Fig. VIII. *Ampullaria paludosa* Say.

VIVIPARIDAE

Fig. IX. *Viviparus intertextus* Say.

VALVATIDAE

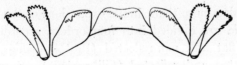

Fig. X. *Valvata tricarinata* Say.

ASSIMENIIDAE

FIG. XI. *Assimenia grayana* Leach.

AMNICOLIDAE

FIG. XII. *Amnicola porata* Say.

PLEUROCERATIDAE

FIG. XIII. *Anculosa dissimilis* Say.

NERITIDAE

FIG. XIV. *Neritina reclivata* Say.

The classification of the Lamellibranchia is based primarily on the structure of the gill. Each gill consists of "a hollow vascular axis bearing on each face a row of more or less flattened filaments which are nothing more than simple expansions of the axis." The Lamellibranchia are divided into four orders, according as these filaments are flat and non-reflected (Protobranchia) or parallel, ventrally directed and reflected (Filibranchia), or are united at regular intervals by vascular junctions (Eulamellibranchia), or are entirely absent (Septibranchia).

All of the North American fresh-water lamellibranchs belong to the order Eulamellibranchia. This order is divided into nine sub-orders, of which only one is represented in our fauna. The suborder Submytilacea consists of "Eulamellibranchia, in which the mantle is only slightly closed, generally there is only a single suture. Siphons absent or very short. Gills smooth. Nearly always dimy-arian (with two adductor muscles). Shell equivalve with an exter-nal ligament."

The Submytilacea are divided into a large number of families of which seven are represented in the North American fauna:

Margaritinidae   Sphaeriidae
Unionidae   Cyrenidae
Dreissensiidae   Cyrenellidae
            Rangiidae.

KEY TO NORTH AMERICAN FRESH- AND BRACKISH-WATER MOLLUSCA.

1 (103)   Animal with a distinct head, bearing, usually, contractile tentacles.
          Shell univalve . . . . Class **Gastropoda** . . 2

2 (63, 100)   Animal inoperculate, pulmoniferous. . Order **Pulmonata** . . 3

3 (17, 22)   Animal terrestrial or semiamphibious.   Shell spiral, columella
          plicate at the base; outer lip usually dentate or lirate.
                         Family AURICULIDAE . . 4

4 (9)   Foot entire, not divided transversely. . Subfamily AURICULINAE . . 5

5 (6, 7)   Shell minute, pupaeform, outer lip thickened, reflected, or expanded.
                         Carychium Müller.

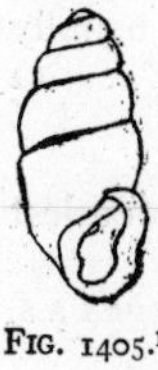

A group of small species of general distribution from the Atlantic to the Pacific. The only genus in the family found at a distance from the seashore. Found in damp places under dead leaves, pieces of bark, etc. They are usually included among the terrestrial species and are included here rather on account of their systematic position than as belonging strictly to the fresh-water fauna. Example, *C. exiguum* Say, (Fig. 1405; × 10), from the Eastern States.

FIG. 1405.[1]

---

[1] Unless otherwise indicated, the figures are of natural size. In other cases, the amount of enlargement or reduction is indicated. To obtain the actual size of any species, divide the length of the figure in millimeters by the index.

6 (5, 7)   Shell oval; lip thickened but not reflected; smooth within; no callous
deposit. . . . . *Auricula* Lamarck.

The typical Auriculae are not represented in our fauna. A single species, *A. pellucens* Mke. (Fig. 1406), belonging to the subgenus *Auriculastrum* Fischer, is found along the southern Florida coast and keys.

FIG. 1406.

7 (5, 6)   Shell oval; lip thickened, with a single strong ridge revolving longitudinally into the aperture. . . . . *Tralia* Gray . . 8

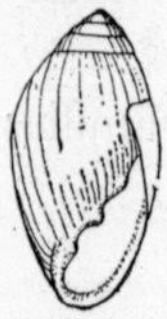

A single species, *T. pusilla* Gmel., (Fig. 1407; × 1 1/10), found along the Florida coast and "easily recognized by its pure brown color, three plaits and the single ridge on the inside of the impressed outer lip" (Dall.).

FIG. 1407.

8   Shell oblong-ovate; lip thickened by a ridge of callus, simple or denticulate,
within the edge; no lirae or longitudinal ridges.
Subgenus *Phytia* Gray.

This group has been usually known as *Alexia* Gray, but that name is preoccupied and inadmissible. A single species, *T. mysotis* Dr., (Fig. 1408; × 2¾), locally intro-duced from Europe on both the Atlantic and Pacific coasts. The west coast form is usually known as *Alexia setifer* Cooper.

FIG. 1408.

9 (4)   Foot divided transversely by a sulcus.   Subfamily MELAMPINAE . . 10

10 (11, 16)   Shell globose-conic; lip sharp, with a dentate or nodulous callus
within . . . . *Pedipes* Adanson.

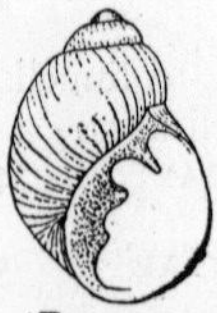

Several species are found on the southern Floridan and Californian coasts and are easily distinguished by their globular form and unusually large parietal tooth. Example, *P. unisulcatus* Cpr., (Fig. 1409; × 2½) from California.

FIG. 1409.

11 (10, 16)   Shell ovate-conic, oblong, or subfusiform; outer lip sharp, usually
lirate within . . . . *Melampus* Montfort . . 12
Four subgenera: 12, 13, 14, 15.

12 (13)   Shell ovate-conoid; spire short; body-whorl very large, broadest
above and tapering to the base; lip lirate within.
Subgenus *Melampus* s.s.

The species of this group are abundantly found in the salt marshes and brackish water of both the eastern and western coasts. The shape of the shell and the apertural armature are eminently characteristic. Example, *M. lineatus* Say, (Fig. 1410; × 1½), from the Atlantic coast.

FIG. 1410.

13 (14) Shell ovate-oblong; spire produced, pointed; outer lip thickened, sometimes with one denticle on the callus.

Subgenus *Ovatella* Bivona.

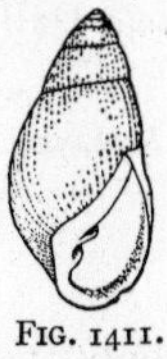

A single European species, *Melampus bidentata* Mont., (Fig. 1411; × 2½), introduced on the coast of New England. "The shell, except for its smoother epidermis and obsolete parietal denticle, is almost exactly like the lighter-colored forms of *Tralia mysotis*, a fact which has led to much confusion" (Dall.). In living examples, this species is easily distinguished by the transversely divided foot.

FIG. 1411.

14 (15) Shell elongated, solid, rounded to a point at both ends; outer lip lirate within. . . . . Subgenus *Detracia* Gray.

A single species, *Melampus bulloides* Mont., (Fig. 1412; × 2⅔), is found along the Florida coast and keys.

FIG. 1412.

15 (12) Shell small, thin, subfusiform; spire elevated; columella twisted to form one strong, spiral ridge entering the volutions; outer lip thin, sharp, without internal lirae, thickening or denticulations. . . . . Subgenus *Sayella* Dall.

Only two minute species are known, both of which occur on the Florida coast. Example, *Melampus hemphilli* Dall. (Fig. 1413; × 5.)

FIG. 1413.

16 (10, 11) Shell small, sinistral, elongate; lip slightly thickened, smooth within . . . . *Blauneria* Shuttleworth.

A single species, *B. heteroclita* Mont., (Fig. 1414; × 3⅔), occurs on the Florida coast. It is easily distinguished by its sinistral shape.

FIG. 1414.

17 (3, 22) Animals marine or semi-amphibious, living on rocks where they are immersed at high tide. Head without tentacles. . . . 18

18 (21) Shell patelliform, with a subcentral apex. Animal with a jaw and both lung and gill. . . . . Family SIPHONARIIDAE.
Only one genus . . . . . *Siphonaria* Sowerby . . 19

19 (20) Shell solid, porcellanous; surface with more or less elevated ribs extending to the margin. . . . . . Subgenus *Siphonaria* s.s.

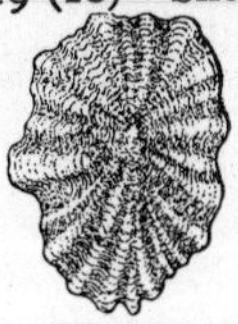

Two species only, found on the east coast of Florida. Example, *S. alternata* Say, (Fig. 1415).

FIG. 1415.

20 (19)   Shell thin, horny, smooth, or with fine radiating lines, which do not
interrupt the margin. . . . . . . Subgenus *Liriola* Dall.

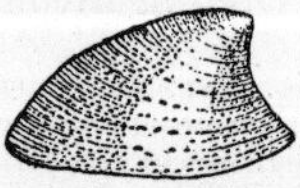

Two species are represented on the west coast.   Example, *Siphonaria
peltoides* Cpr., (Fig. 1416; × 1½).

FIG. 1416.

21 (18)   Shell patelliform, obliquely conical.   Animal with a lung only; no
gill; no jaw. . . . . Family GADINIIDAE.
Only one genus. . . . . *Gadinia* Gray.

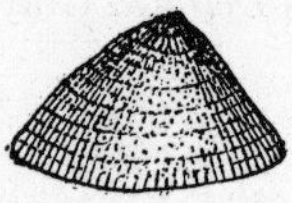

Two species occur on the southern California coast.   Another, described from Cuba, may be looked for on the Florida keys.   Example,
G. reticulata Sby., (Fig. 1417.)

FIG. 1417.

22 (3, 17)   Animal aquatic, inhabiting fresh water. 23
Four families: 23, 32, 50, 53.

23 (32)   Shell spiral, dextral; spire more or less elongated; tentacles flattened,
triangular. . . . . Family LYMNAEIDAE.
Only one genus. . . . . *Lymnaea* Lamarck . . 24
Eight subgenera: 24, 25, 26, 27, 28, 29, 30, 31.

24 (25)   Shell large, thin; spire slender and acute; body-whorl large, inflated;
columella strongly twisted; axis pervious.
Subgenus *Lymnaea* s.s.

The typical species, *L. stagnalis* L., is circumboreal, but the typical form is
not found in America.   The common American form is known as *L. stagnalis
oppressa* Say, (Fig. 1418; × ⁵⁄₇).

FIG. 1418.

25 (26)   Shell large, solid, bulimiform; spire short; body-whorl large, inflated;
axis impervious. . . . . Subgenus *Bulimnaea* Haldeman.

The typical and only species, *Lymnaea megasoma* Say, (Fig. 1419; × ¾),
inhabits the northern United States and Canada, west to Manitoba.
Minnesota and Iowa.

FIG. 1419.

26 (27) Shell thin; spire short, acute; body-whorl large, inflated; lip expanded.
Subgenus *Radix* Montfort.

The typical species, *Lymnaea auricularia* L. (Fig. 1420), is European, but has been locally introduced in several of the Eastern States.

FIG. 1420.

27 (28) Shell thin; spire short; body-whorl large, elongated, not inflated; surface sculptured with spiral incised lines.
Subgenus *Pseudosuccinea* Baker.

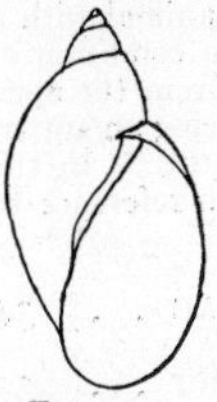

The typical species, *Lymnaea columella* Say, (Fig. 1421), has a general distribution throughout the eastern United States and Canada.

FIG. 1421.

28 (29) Shell very long and slender; spire elongated, acute; body-whorl long and narrow; columella smooth. Subgenus *Acella* Haldeman.

A single species, *Lymnaea haldemani* "Desh." W. G. Binn., (Fig. 1422), occurs in the St. Lawrence drainage system and the upper part of the Mississippi River.

FIG. 1422.

29 (30) Shell varying from elongate to short ovate; outer lip (usually) somewhat thickened within; columella somewhat twisted and plicate; surface with strong, spirally impressed lines.
Subgenus *Stagnicola* Leach.

The typical species, *Lymnaea palustris* Mull., (Fig. 1423), is a circumboreal and is usually the most common species in the Northern States and Canada.

FIG. 1423.

30 (31) Shell as in *Stagnicola*, but with the surface longitudinally costate.
Subgenus *Polyrhytis* Meek.

The only recent species known, *Lymnaea utahensis* Call., (Fig. 1424), is from Utah.

FIG. 1424.

31 (24)   Shell small, turreted; spire somewhat elevated; spiral sculpture
           wanting or subobsolete; columella not twisted; inner lip
           usually reflected over the umbilicus.

                                           Subgenus *Galba* Schrank.

> This group of small species has a wide range from the Atlantic to the Pacific.
> The example, *Lymnaea obrussa* Say, (Fig. 1425; × 1½), is a common species in the
> Eastern States.

FIG. 1425.

32 (50)   Shell discoidal, sinistral, or dextral, or spiral with a very low spire.
           Animal sinistral; tentacles cylindrical.

                                           Family PLANORBIDAE . . 33

> The dextral species of this family present the apparent anomaly of a sinistral animal with a
> dextrally-coiled shell. Such shells are not true dextral shells, but represent the condition of
> hypertrophy, so called, in which the spiral growth of the shell, instead of being from the apex
> downward, as is usually the case, is, as it were, from the apex upward, the result being an appar-
> ently dextral shell with a sinistral animal. Such shells are also called ultradextral.   In the
> formation of the key to the subdivisions of the family, the shells are treated with reference to
> their apparent mode of spiral growth.

33 (47)   Shell discoidal. . . . . Subfamily PLANORBINAE . . 34

34 (46)   Aperture edentate. . . . . *Planorbis* Müller . . 35

    Six subgenera: 35, 36, 39, 40, 41, 42.

35 (36)   Shell sinistral, large; whorls rounded above and below, gradually in-
           creasing; aperture but slightly expanded; lip simple and
           sharp. . . . . Subgenus *Planorbis* s.s.

> A single, characteristic species, *P. glabratus* Say, (Fig. 1426; × ⅘), is
> found in Florida.

FIG. 1426.

36 (39)   Shell dextral or sinistral, few whorled; the whorls carinate above and
           rapidly enlarging; base funicular; aperture suddenly ex-
           panded and lip thickened.

                                      Subgenus *Helisoma* Swainson . . 37

37 (38)   Shell dextral, carinated above and below; spire and base funicular.

                                           Section *Helisoma* s.s.

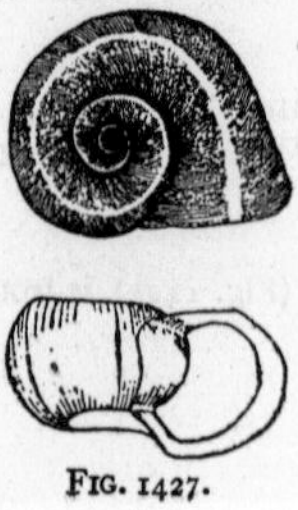

> The typical species, *Planorbis antrosus* Con., (Fig. 1427; × 1½), has a
> general distribution east of the Rocky Mountains and rarely on the
> Pacific coast.

FIG. 1427.

38 (37) Shell sinistral; early whorls flattened and carinate above; base funicular. . . . . Section *Pierosoma* Dall.

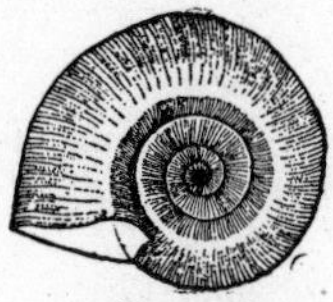

This group includes nearly all the larger North American Planorbes
and is represented by numerous species found in all parts of the country.
Type, *Planorbis trivolvis* Say, (Fig. 1428).

Fig. 1428.

39 (40) Shell sinistral; aperture campanulate; lip thickened.

Subgenus *Planorbella* Haldeman.

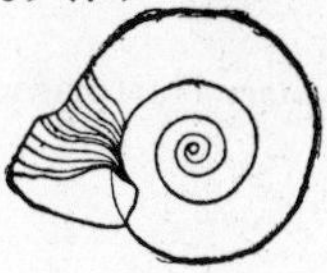

The typical form, *Planorbis campanulatus* Say, (Fig. 1429; × 1½), is of
common occurrence and wide distribution in eastern Canada and the
United States north of Tennessee.

Fig. 1429.

40 (41) Shell dextral, much depressed; upper surface convex, base flattened;
body-whorl carinate; lip simple.

Subgenus *Tropidiscus* Stein.

A single species, *Planorbis cultratus* Orb., (Fig. 1430; × 2), of this (in
America) tropical group has been collected in Texas and Florida.

Fig. 1430.

41 (42) Shell small, dextral; periphery carinated; base convex; aperture
oblique; lip simple. . . . . . Subgenus *Hippuetis* Agassiz.

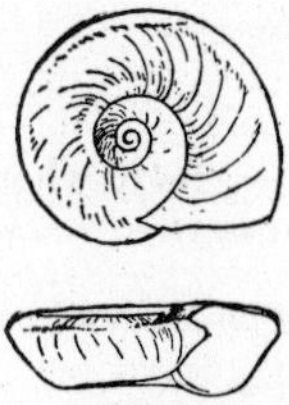

A group of small species of general distribution through the Northern
States and Canada. All of our species belong to the section *Menetus* H.
& A. Adams, of which the type is *Planorbis opercularis* Gld., (Fig. 1431;
× 3), from California.

Fig. 1431.

42 (35) Shell small, depressed; body-whorl rounded or obtusely angulated;
lip simple. . . . . Subgenus *Gyraulus* Agassiz . . 43

43 (44, 45) Surface spirally striate and hispid. . . . Section *Gyraulus* s.s.

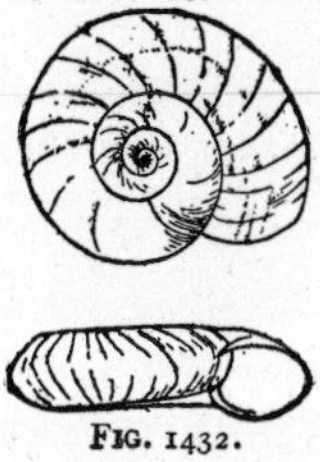

A few, small species, not uncommon in the eastern Northern States
and Canada. The group is not represented on the Pacific coast. Example, *Planorbis hirsutus* Gld., (Fig. 1432; × 3).

Fig. 1432.

44 (43, 45)   Surface smooth or finely striate. . . . . Section *Torquis* Dall.

This group of small species is of general distribution from the Atlantic to the Pacific. Type, *Planorbis parvus* Say, (Fig. 1433; × 4½).

FIG. 1433.

45 (43, 44)   Shell minute; surface costate.   . . Section *Armiger* Hartmann.

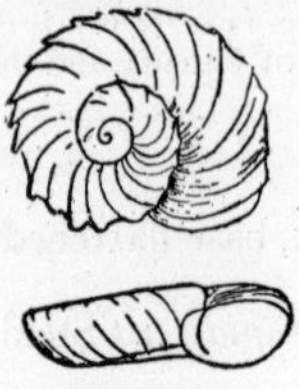

The typical species only, *Planorbis crista* L., (Fig. 1434; × 7), represents this group in our fauna and has been recorded from Maine to Illinois and northward.

FIG. 1434.

46 (34)   Aperture with one or more sets of laminae or teeth behind the margin.
Segmentina Fleming.

The typical Segmentinae are not represented in our fauna.   All of the American species belong to the subgenus *Planorbula* Haldeman.   The type *S. armigera* Say, (Fig. 1435; × 2) is common in the northern Eastern States and Canada.

FIG. 1435.

47 (33)   Shell spiral, dextral, flattened above and convex below; body-whorl very large.   . . . . Subfamily POMPHOLIGINAE . . 48

48 (49)   Shell imperforate. . . . . *Pompholyx* Lea.

Two or three species only are known from California. Type, *P. effusa* Lea., (Fig. 1436; × 2⅔).

FIG. 1436.

49 (48)   Shell deeply umbilicate. . . . . *Carinifex* W. G. Binney.

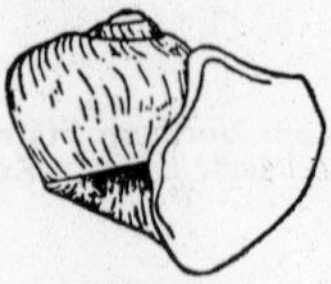

The typical species, *C. newberryi* Lea., (Fig. 1437), is from California.

FIG. 1437.

50 (53)   Shell spiral, sinistral.   Animal sinistral; tentacles slender, cylindrical.
Family PHYSIDAE . . 51

51 (52) Shell with body-whorl usually inflated. Inner edge of mantle digitate or lobed, extending partly over the shell.

Physa Draparnaud.

The species of this genus are very numerous and extremely variable, so that many more species have been described than really exist. The Physae are found in all parts of the country, but the majority of the species are inhabitants of the Northern States and Canada. Example, *P. gyrina* Say, (Fig. 1438; × 1½).

FIG. 1438.

52 (51) Shell slender, elongated. Inner edge of mantle simple, not extending over the shell. . . . . *Aplexa* Fleming.

The typical species, *A. hypnorum* L., (Fig. 1439; × 1½), is circumboreal and has a general distribution through the Northern States and Canada from the Atlantic to the Pacific.

FIG. 1439.

53 (23) Shell patelliform or depressed, dextrally spiral, neritiform or planorbiform. Animal sinistral or dextral; tentacles short, blunt, cylindrical. . . . . Family ANCYLIDAE . . 54

Five genera: 54, 59, 60, 61, 62.

54 (59) Shell patelliform, small, thin; apex posterior, slightly inclined to one side. . . . . *Ancylus* Müller . . 55

55 (58) Apex inclined to the right. . . . . Subgenus *Ancylus* s.s . . 56

56 (57) Apex subacute, radially striate. . . . . . Section *Ferrissia* Walker.

Numerous species and of general distribution, usually found adhering to stones, etc., in running water. Type, *Ancylus rivularis* Say, (Fig. 1440; × 3).

FIG. 1440.

57 (56) Apex depressed, smooth. . . . . Section *Laevapex* Walker.

The species of this group are usually found in quiet water and are, as a rule, larger, thinner, and more depressed than the Ferrissias. Type, *Ancylus diaphanus* Hald., (Fig. 1441; × 2¾).

FIG. 1441.

58 (55) Apex inclined to the left. . . . . Subgenus *Acroloxus* Beck.

Only one American species, *Ancylus nuttallii* Hald., (Fig. 1442; × 2), from Oregon, has been referred to this group, but its anatomy is unknown and its generic position is very doubtful.

FIG. 1442.

59 (60) Shell large, thick and solid; apex smooth. . . . . . *Lanx* Clessin.

This genus is restricted to the Pacific coast and is distinguished by the large size and thick solid shells. Type, *L. newberryi* Lea. (Fig. 1443).

FIG. 1443.

60 (61) Shell ancyliform, small, thin, with a septum across the apical portion of the interior. . . . . *Gundlachia* Pfeiffer.

This very remarkable and peculiar genus has a general but very local distribution from the Atlantic to the Pacific. Example, *G. meekiana* Stimp., (Fig. 1444; × 6), from the Eastern States.

FIG. 1444.

61 (62) Shell small, spiral, dextral, neritoid, or crepidula-like, with a broad, thin, columellar plate projecting across the end of the aperture next to the spire. . . . . *Amphigyra* Pilsbry.

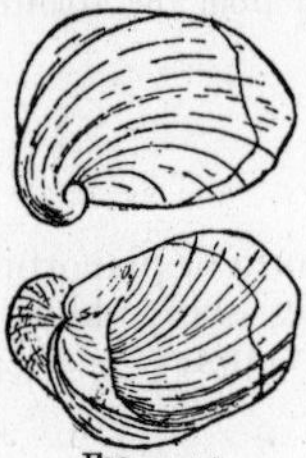

Only a single species, *A. alabamensis* Pils., (Fig. 1445; × 10), from the Coosa River, Alabama, is known.

FIG. 1445.

62 (54) Shell very minute, dextral, spiral, subdiscoidal; columellar margin broadly dilated. . . . . *Neoplanorbis* Pilsbry.

Four species of this genus have been recently described from the Coosa River, Alabama, and are among the smallest mollusks known in our fauna. Type, *N. tantillus* Pils., (Fig. 1446; × 10).

FIG. 1446.

63 (2, 100) Animal operculate, branchiferous (except *Assimenia*). Radula with seven rows of teeth.
    Order **Pectinibranchiata**. . Suborder **Taenioglossa** . . 64
Six families: 64, 65, 66, 71, 72, 90.

64 (65) Shell small, spiral, dextral, conical; operculum spiral. Animal pulmoniferous. . . . . Family ASSIMENIIDAE.
    Only a single genus. . . . . *Assimenia* Leach.

The Assimenias live in brackish water in the upper part of the littoral zone. Two species occur on the Florida keys and two on the coast of California. Example, *A. californica* Tryon, (Fig. 1447; × 4).

FIG. 1447.

65 (66)   Shell large, globose-turbinate; umbilicate; operculum corneus, concentric.   Animal with the respiratory chamber divided into
two parts, one being the lung and the other containing a gill.
Family AMPULLARIIDAE.
Only a single genus. . . . . *Ampullaria* Lamarck.

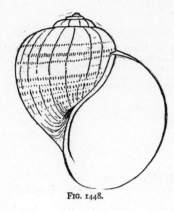

The Ampullarias are the largest of our fresh-
water snails.   Two or three species occur in
Georgia and Florida.   Example, *A. paludosa*
Say, (Fig. 1448).

FIG. 1448.

66 (71)   Shell of moderate size, dextral, turbinate, imperforate, or subperforate;
operculum corneus.   Animal branchiferous.
Family VIVIPARIDAE . .   67

Four genera: 67, 68, 69, 70.

67 (68)   Shell rather thin; operculum concentric, inner margin simple.   Animal
with foot of moderate size, not produced beyond the snout.
Teeth of the radula multicuspid.   . . *Viviparus* Montfort.

Several species are found in the Mississippi Valley and
from Ohio and Indiana south to the Gulf.   They are
usually to be distinguished from the Campelomae by the
thinner and more globose shells and convex whorls.   Example, *V. intertextus* Say, (Fig. 1449; × 1½).

FIG. 1449.

68 (69)   Shell thick and solid; operculum concentric, inner edge simple. Animal
          with the foot very large, much produced beyond the snout.
          Teeth of the radula simple or only minutely crenulate.

Campeloma Rafinesque.

This genus is peculiar to North America and the several
species are usually very abundant, when found. Though normally dextral, sinistral examples are not uncommon. They range
from the Mississippi Valley east to the Atlantic and from the St.
Lawrence Valley south to the Gulf. Example, *C. subsolida* Anth.,
(Fig. 1450).

FIG. 1450.

69 (70)   Shell turreted; operculum with a subspiral nucleus.

Lioplax Troschel.

This genus is also peculiar to this country. The several species are restricted
to the states east of the Mississippi and south of Ohio and New Jersey.   Type,
L. subcarinata Say, (Fig. 1451).

FIG. 1451.

70 (67)   Shell (typically) large, solid, imperforate; spire elevated; operculum
          concentric, with the inner margin reflected, forming an ele-
          vated, marginal fold. . . . .   *Tulotoma* Haldeman.

This genus is peculiar to North America and is restricted to the
Alabama River and its tributaries in Alabama.   The two leading
species are remarkable for their heavy, nodulous, or tuberculated
shell. Type, *T. magnifica* Con., (Fig. 1452).

FIG. 1452.

71 (72)   Shell small, spiral, dextral, turbinate, or subdiscoidal; aperture entire,
          circular; operculum round, multispiral. No basal denticles
          on the central tooth of the radula. . Family VALVATIDAE.
          Only one genus. . . . .   *Valvata* Müller.

The several species of this genus are usually found in great numbers and
are of general distribution. Example, *V. tricarinata* Say, (Fig. 1453; × 4).

FIG. 1453.

72 (90)   Shell small, spiral, dextral.   Central tooth of the radula with one or
                      more basal denticles. . . . Family AMNICOLIDAE . .   73
    Five subfamilies: 73, 74, 82, 88, 89.

73 (74)   Operculum calcareous, concentric. . . . . Subfamily BYTHININAE.
                Only one genus. . . . . *Bythinia* Gray.

A single European species, *B. tentaculata* L., (Fig. 1454; × 2), has been introduced by commerce from the Hudson River, along the line of the Erie Canal,
and into the Great Lakes as far west as Chicago.

FIG. 1454.

74 (82)   Operculum corneus, paucispiral.   Shell thin; columella not thickened.
                Foot simple. . . . . .   Subfamily AMNICOLINAE . .   75
    Six genera: 75, 77, 78, 79, 80, 81.

75 (76)   Shell smooth, usually subglobose.   Central tooth of the radula multi-
                cuspid, with a tongue-shaped process projecting on the ante-
                rior surface and beyond the base and with several basal
                denticles. . . . . *Amnicola* Gould and Haldeman ..   76

Very numerous both in species and individuals.   In shell characters, some of
the more elongate species approach *Paludestrina*, but as a rule the shell is more
globose, with a shorter spire.   Type, *A. limosa* Say, (Fig. 1455; × 4).

FIG. 1455.

76   Radula more minute and the denticulations of the cusps of the teeth
                finer and sharper. . . . . .   Subgenus *Cincinnatia* Pilsbry.

This subdivision is based wholly on the character of the lingual teeth.   The
shell characters are those of *Amnicola*.   Type, *Amnicola cincinnatiensis* Anth.,
(Fig. 1456; × 2½).

FIG. 1456.

77 (78)   Shell similar to *Amnicola*, but more slender and elongated.   Central
                tooth of the radula with but one basal denticle on each side
                and without the tongue-shaped process.
                                        Paludestrina Orbigny.

The species of this genus are numerous and range from the Atlantic to the Pacific.   Example, *P. nickliniana* Lea, (Fig. 1457; × 6).

FIG. 1457.

78 (77)   Shell elongated, turreted, longitudinally ribbed or plicate.
                                        Tryonia Stimpson.

The type and only species, *T. clathrata* Stimp., (Fig. 1458; × 2¾), is found fossil
in southern California and living in Nevada.

FIG. 1458.

79 (80) Shell elongated, strongly carinated on the periphery.

Pyrgulopsis Call and Pilsbry.

The typical species, *P. nevadensis* Stearns (Fig. 1459; × 3), is from Nevada. **Others** have been described from the Mississippi and Tennessee valleys.

FIG. 1459.

80 (81) Shell ovate-conic; whorls shouldered and usually coronated with spines. . . . . *Potamopyrgus* Stimpson.

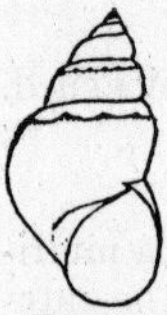

Two species from Florida and Texas, respectively, are represented in our fauna. Typically spinose, all the species are dimorphic, having both an angulate, spinose form and a smooth, ecarinate one. Example, *P. coronatus* Pfr. (Fig. 1460; × 3¾).

FIG. 1460.

81 (75) Shell subpyramidal, rather solid, smooth; body-whorl subangulated at the periphery. . . . *Littoridina* Eydoux and Souleyet.

A South American genus. A single species from Florida, *L. monroensis,* Frfld. (Fig. 1461; × 7), has been doubtfully assigned to it.

FIG. 1461.

82 (88) Shell with a large body-whorl and short spire; columella usually callously thickened; operculum corneus, subspiral. Foot simple. Central tooth of the radula with several basal denticles. . . . . . Subfamily LYTHOGLYPHINAE . . 83

Five genera: 83, 84, 85, 86, 87.

83 (84) Shell depressed-conic; base concave, widely and deeply umbilicated.

Cochliopa Stimpson.

A Central American genus, of which one species, *C. riograndensis* P. and F. (Fig. 1462; × 6), has been found in Texas and another (doubtfully) in California.

FIG. 1462.

84 (85) Shell minute, globose-turbinate, narrowly but deeply umbilicated; columellar lip thin; operculum corneus, paucispiral; nuclear whorls large, slowly and regularly increasing.

Clappia Walker.

Only a single species, *C. clappii* Walker (Fig. 1463; × 6½), from the **Coosa** River, Alabama, is known. It somewhat resembles *Somatogyrus* in shape, but can be easily distinguished by its deep umbilicus and peculiar operculum.

FIG. 1463.

85 (86) Shell obliquely ovate, thick, solid, imperforate; columella flattened
and calloused; lip sinuous, effuse, and projecting anteriorly.
Verge winged. . . . . *Fluminicola* Stimpson.

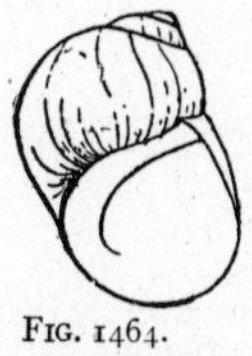

A characteristic west coast genus. In shell characters, it is quite similar to *Somatogyrus*, but differs radically in anatomical details and is widely
separated in range. Type, *F. nuttalliana* Lea (Fig. 1464; × 2).

FIG. 1464.

86 (87) Shell usually thick and solid, imperforate or narrowly perforate;
body-whorl large; columella callously thickened; spire usually short; aperture very oblique, lip projecting above; operculum subspiral, nuclear whorls small, rapidly increasing.
Somatogyrus Gill.

A group of small species found, mainly, south of the Ohio and east of the
Mississippi. The thickened columella is characteristic and enables the species
to be easily separated from the associated genera. Example, *S. subglobosus*
Say (Fig. 1465; × 2).

FIG. 1465.

87 (86) Shell not very thick, imperforate; body-whorl large; spire short;
peritreme continuous in the same plane; columella scarcely
thickened. Verge simple. . . . . *Gillia* Stimpson.

This genus is restricted to the Atlantic coast states, ranging from New Jersey to South Carolina. Type, *G. altilis* Lea (Fig. 1466; × 2).

FIG. 1466.

88 (89) Shell as in Amnicolinae, very small; operculum circular, multispiral.
Foot simple. . . . . Subfamily LYOGYRINAE.
Only one genus. . . . . *Lyogyrus* Gill.

A peculiar genus of minute species restricted to the Atlantic coast states.
Easily distinguished by its operculum. Type, *L. pupoideus* Gld. (Fig. 1467; ×6).

FIG. 1467.

89 (88) Shell elevated, turreted; operculum subspiral. Foot divided by a
transverse sulcus. . . . . . . Subfamily POMATIOPSINAE.
Only one genus. . . . . *Pomatiopsis* Tryon.

The species of this group are terrestrial or rather semiamphibious in habit,
being always found near but not in the water. The divided foot is very peculiar. The animal, aided by its long snout, progresses by a series of steps.
Type, *P. lapidaria* Say (Fig. 1468; × 4).

FIG. 1468.

90 (72) Shell dextral, spiral, thick, solid, globose, or elongated; operculum
corneus, subspiral. Animal without an external verge. Central tooth of the radula without basal denticles.
Family PLEUROCERATIDAE . . 91

Seven genera: 91, 92, 94, 95, 97, 98, 99.

91 (92)   Shell large, fusiform; base of aperture prolonged in a long canal.
Io Lea.

This group of large, striking species is confined to the rivers of eastern Tennessee.   They are found only in very rapidly running water.
Example, *I. spinosa* Lea (Fig. 1469).

FIG. 1469.

92 (94)   Shell globose-conic; columella callously thickened above and below;
aperture shortly channeled below.
Lithasia Haledman . .   93

The Lithasiae form a very distinct group characterized by the columella thickened by deposits of callus above and below and the short canal
at its base.   With the exception of three species, which extend as far
north as the Wabash River, Indiana, the group is restricted to Kentucky, Tennessee, and Alabama.   Type, *L. geniculata* Con. (Fig. 1470).

FIG. 1470.

93   Shell similar to *Lithasia*, but with the basal canal more produced.
Section *Angitrema* Haledman.

This group connects *Lithasia* with *Io*.   Type, *Lithasia armigera* Say
(Fig. 1471).

FIG. 1471.

94 (95)   Shell obovate, thick, solid; spire short; body-whorl large; columella
callously thickened above, incurved below and subtruncate.
Eurycaelon Lea.

This genus, when restricted to the species grouping about the type, is
confined to the rivers of the Tennessee drainage system.   Type, *E. anthonyi*
Budd (Fig. 1472).

FIG. 1472.

95 (97) Shell elongated, conic, or cerithiform; aperture subrhomboidal, prolonged into a short canal below; columella twisted, not
callously thickened. . . . *Pleurocera* Rafinesque . . 96

Exceedingly abundant and of great variety. Numerous species have
been described from the rivers of Kentucky, Tennessee, and Alabama. A
few species extend north to the Great Lakes and west to the Mississippi
Valley. The species vary greatly in contour, ranging from long, slender,
and rather thin to large, heavy, and broadly conic. Example, *P. canalicu-
latum* Say (Fig. 1473).

FIG. 1473.

96 Shell smooth; spire obtusely conical; body-whorl subcylindrical; aperture subquadrate; columella thickened below, twisted and
drawn back, base subcanaliculate; lip very sinuous.
Section *Strephobasis* Lea.

A number of nominal species have been described from Tennessee and
northern Alabama. Type, *Pleurocera plena* Anth. (Fig. 1474).

FIG. 1474.

97 (98) Shell ovate-conic to elongate; smooth, plicate, striate, or tuberculate;
aperture subrhomboidal, subangular at the base, but not
canaliculate; columella simple, smooth. . . *Goniobasis* Lea.

This genus comprises about three-fifths of all the species of the family
and is enormously developed in the rivers of Tennessee and Alabama. A
few species extend north to the St. Lawrence Valley and west to Texas and
the western tributaries of the Mississippi. A small group of species is also
found on the Pacific coast and is the only genus of the family represented in
that region. Example, *G. virginica* Gmel. (Fig. 1475), from the Atlantic
states.

FIG. 1475.

98 (99) Shell conical or globose-ovate; aperture with a slit along the suture,
entire below. . . . . *Gyrotoma* Shuttleworth.

This remarkable genus is confined to the Coosa River, Alabama, where
it is represented by a considerable number of described species. The
sutural slit is characteristic and is either direct, narrow, and deep, or oblique, short, and wide. Example, *G. demissum* Lea (Fig. 1476).

FIG. 1476

99 (91) Shell thick, solid, subglobose, with a very short spire, or thinner and conical; aperture oval or subcircular, entire below; columella callously thickened. . . . . *Anculosa* Say.

This group differs from all of the genera of the family by the entire aperture. The heavy, subglobose species range from the Ohio River south into Alabama and Georgia but are not found in the northern Atlantic States nor in the Mississippi Valley. The thin, conical species are characteristic of the Atlantic drainage from New York southward. Type, *A. praerosa* Say (Fig. 1477).

FIG. 1477.

100 (2, 63) Radula with numerous rows of teeth, consisting of a central tooth, 2–5 laterals, and numerous marginals arranged like the sticks of a fan.
     Order **Aspidobranchia** . . Suborder **Rhipidoglossa**.
     Represented by a single family. . . NERITIDAE . . 101

101 (102) Shell globose, imperforate, very thick and solid; aperture semiovate, columellar region expanded, flattened, and thickened; operculum calcareous, edge with projecting processes (apophyses), articulating with the columella.
     Neritina Lamarck.

A few species of this characteristic tropical genus are found in the fresh and brackish waters of Florida and the Gulf coast. Example, *N. reclivata* Say (Fig. 1478).

FIG. 1478.

102 (101) Shell small, thin, corneus; columella concavely flattened, calloused; operculum corneus, paucispiral, without apophyses.
     Lepyrium Dall.

This genus was created for a single small species, known only from the Coosa and Cahawba rivers in Alabama and is peculiar in the character of the operculum. Type, *L. showalteri* Lea (Fig. 1479; × 3½).

FIG. 1479.

103 (1) Animal acephalous. Shell consisting of two opposing, symmetrical valves united by a ligament. Class **Lamellibranchia** . . 104
     Represented by a single order, **Eulamellibranchia** . . 104
Seven families: 105, 106, 166, 167, 173, 174; in two groups: 104, 165.

104 (165) Shell equivalve; interior nacreous; ligament external; hinge with or without teeth, but never with true cardinal teeth; when present, the modified anterior lateral teeth are known as pseudocardinals and the posterior teeth as laterals. . . 105
Two families: 105, 106.

105 (106) Shell elongated, laterally compressed; hinge with usually only
pseudocardinals; laterals, when present, very obscure. Gills
without water tubes and with scattered interlamellar connections, which in certain places form irregular diagonal rows.
Family MARGARITANIDAE.
Only one genus. . . . . *Margaritana* Schumacher.

The typical species, *M. margaritifera* L. (Fig. 1480; ✕⅔), is circumboreal, but in this country is
found only in the northern Atlantic and Pacific states, being unknown, with one possible exception, from the whole interior portion of the continent. Another species is found in the Tennessee and Ohio drainage systems, and two more have been described from the Gulf drainage.

FIG. 1480.

106 (105) Shell subcircular, oval, subtriangular, or elongated; hinge edentulous
or with pseudocardinals only or with both pseudocardinals
and laterals. Gills with water tubes and distinct, continuous interlamellar septa, running parallel to the filaments.
Family UNIONIDAE . . 107

107 (121, 140) Marsupium formed by all four gills or by the outer gills only;
edge of marsupium always sharp and not distending; water
tubes simple in the gravid female.
Subfamily UNIONINAE . . 108
    Five genera: 108, 113, 114, 115, 117

108 (113) All four gills serving as marsupia. Shell alike in both sexes, triangular, quadrate or rhomboidal, solid, inflated, beaks
usually prominent, sculptured with a few coarse, subparallel
ridges, which are inflated where they cross the posterior
ridge; posterior ridge ordinarily well developed; hinge complete, with strong teeth; hinge plate wide; beak cavities deep
and compressed. . . . . *Quadrula* Rafinesque . . 109
    Four sections: 109, 110, 111, 112.

109 (110)　Surface plicate. . . . . Section *Crenodonta* Schluter.

The species of this group, characterized by the heavy, plicate sculpture of the valves, are among the largest and heaviest of the American Unionidae. They are very abundant throughout the Southern States from Georgia to Texas. Two species range north into the St. Lawrence drainage, the headwaters of the Mississippi, and to Lake Winnipeg. Type, *Quadrula plicata* Say (Fig. 1481; × ⅔).

FIG. 1481.

110 (111)　Surface pustulose, with a radial furrow above the posterior ridge,
　　　　　usually painted with triangular spots or chevron-shaped
　　　　　lines. . . . . Section *Quadrula* s.s.

The typical species, *Q. cylindrica* Say (Fig. 1482; × ½), ranges through the entire Ohio, Cumberland, and Tennessee river systems and west to Arkansas. A few other, less elongated, species are found in Tennessee and Alabama.

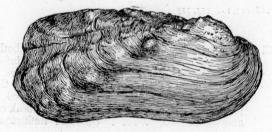

FIG. 1482.

111 (112) Surface pustulose; no radial furrow above the posterior ridge; unicolored or rayed, never painted as in *Quadrula* s.s.

Section *Theliderma* Swainson.

This section comprises three well-marked groups: first, that of the typical species, *Quadrula lachrymosa* Lea (Fig. 1483), having a quadrate or rhomboid shell with a wide, shallow radial furrow in front of the posterior ridge; second, that of *Q. pustulosa* Lea, with a rounded, quadrate shell with no radial furrow; third, two small species from Georgia and Florida, rounded-rhomboid in shape, without the furrow and with the surface covered with zigzag corrugations. Most of the species are found only in the Southern States, but the first two groups have representatives ranging north to Michigan and Minnesota.

FIG. 1483.

112 (109) Surface smooth. . . . . Section *Fusconaia* Simpson.

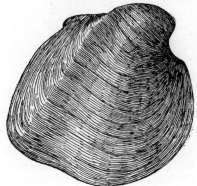

While the majority of the species of this section are found in the Southern States, it is well represented as far north as Michigan and the upper Mississippi. Type, *Quadrula undata* Bar. (Fig. 1484).

FIG. 1484.

113 (114) All four gills serving as marsupia. Shell large, solid, rhomboid,
           truncated posteriorly in the male, elongated, with a strong
           posterior ridge, sexes dissimilar in shape, the posterior region
           being rounded and subcompressed in the female; hinge com-
           plete; surface pustulose, except on the extended portion of
           the female. . . . . *Tritigonia* Agassiz.

   The type, *T. tuberculata* Bar. (Fig. 1485; × ⅔), is very common in the Mississippi drainage and
in the Southern States from Alabama to Texas.

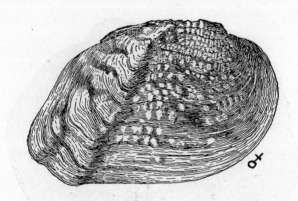

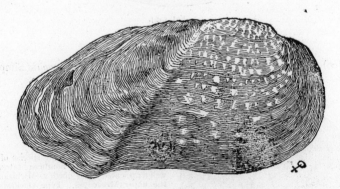

FIG. 1485.

114 (115) Outer gills only serving as marsupia. Shell rounded; beaks sculptured with numerous fine irregular corrugations; hinge complete; nacre violet. . . . . *Rotundaria* Rafinesque.

The type, *R. tuberculata* Raf. (Fig. 1486), ranges from southern Michigan through the Ohio, Tennessee, and Mississippi systems, south to Texas. Another species ranges from Kentucky and Tennessee to Iowa.

Fig. 1486.

115 (117) Outer gills only serving as marsupia. Shell alike in both sexes; triangular to rhomboid, usually with a prominent umbonal region; beaks at or near the anterior end; beak cavities shallow; hinge complete; surface smooth, brown to yellow, usually not very dark, frequently rayed.

Pleurobema Rafinesque . . 116

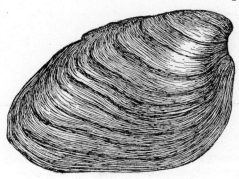

This is a large group, of which more than seventy species are known. With the exception of a few species found in the Ohio and Mississippi drainage, it is confined to the streams of the Southeastern States from Tennessee and Georgia to the Mississippi. The shells of this genus are easily distinguished from the Quadrulae, which they often resemble by the uniformly shallow beak cavities. Type, *P. clava* Lam. (Fig. 1487).

Fig. 1487.

116   Shell large, irregularly oval, inflated; surface with a number of
           large, scattered tubercles. . .   Section *Plethobasus* Simpson.

This section contains only two species, inhabiting the Ohio and Tennessee drainage areas.
The type, *Pleurobema aesophus* Green (Fig. 1488; × ⅔), extends west into Missouri and Minnesota.

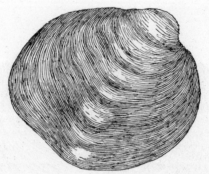

FIG. 1488.

117 (108)   Outer gills only serving as marsupia. Shell alike in both sexes;
            ovate to elongate, rounded in front, pointed or biangulate
            behind; beaks nearer to the middle than to the anterior end;
            hinge complete; surface usually smooth, dark brown to black,
            often indistinctly rayed. . . . .   *Unio* Retzius . .   118

118 (119, 120)   Shell elongated, rhomboid or oval, more or less biangulated
            behind; surface smooth or feebly corrugated; beak sculpture
            consisting of a few rather strong ridges, which are nearly
            parallel to the growth lines or slightly double-looped.
                                 Section *Elliptio* Rafinesque.

The typical section of this genus is restricted to the Old World. The section *Elliptio* is the
largest group of Unionidae represented in our fauna. More than ninety species are recognized.
The metropolis of the genus is in the Southeastern States, but representatives are found in all
of the Eastern, Southern, and Central States. Type, *Unio crassidens* Lam. (Fig. 1489; × ½).

FIG. 1489.

119 (118, 120)   Shell spinose. . . . .   Section *Canthyria* Swainson.

The typical and only species, *Unio spinosus* Lea (Fig. 1490; × ⅔), is confined to the Altamaha River, Georgia, and is one of the most remarkable Unios known. In the extraordinary development of the spines, it is unique.

FIG. 1490.

120 (118, 119)   Shell smooth; beaks sculptured with concentric ridges.
Section *Uniomerus* Conrad.

The typical species, *Unio tetralasmus* Say (Fig. 1491; × ½), has a wide range from Ohio south to Alabama and Texas. A few other species are found in Georgia and Florida.

FIG. 1491.

121 (107, 140)   Marsupium formed by the entire outer gills, distending transversely, when charged; water tubes in the gravid female
divided longitudinally into three tubes, of which only the
center one is used as an ovisac.   Hinge rarely complete, the
laterals or both the pseudocardinals and laterals being often
entirely wanting; sexual differences in the shell very rarely
present. . . . . .   Subfamily ANODONTINAE . .   122
Eleven genera: 122, 123, 124, 125, 126, 127, 128, 129, 130, 134, 139.

122 (123)   Hinge with lateral teeth wanting and only rudimentary pseudocardinals; beak sculpture consisting of a few strong, concentric ridges.   Ovisac of each water tube subdivided into
a number of compartments running crosswise to the gill.
Strophitus Rafinesque.

Only a few species are known, most of them coming from the Southeast-ern States.   The species figured, *S. edentulus* Say (Fig. 1492; × ¾), has a wide range from New England to North Carolina and west to Minne-sota and Tennessee.

FIG. 1492.

123 (124) Shell thin; hinge edentulous; beak sculpture consisting of several more or less doubly-looped parallel ridges, often slightly nodulous on the loops. . . . . *Anodonta* Lamarck.

   This genus is the only one of the North American Naiades that has a general distribution from the Atlantic to the Pacific. Numerous species are recognized. They are easily distinguished by the edentulous hinge and double loop of the beak sculpture. Example, *A. grandis* Say (Fig. 1493; × ½).

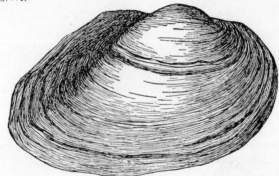

FIG. 1493.

124 (125) Shell smooth, elongated, rather thin, inequilateral, compressed; epidermis shining, often rayed; a single, imperfect pseudocardinal in each valve and sometimes vestiges of laterals.

Lastena Rafinesque.

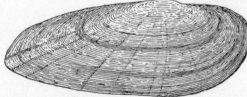

Only a single species is known, *L. lata* Raf. (Fig. 1494; × ⅔), and is found in the Ohio, Cumberland, and Tennessee river systems.

FIG. 1494.

125 (126) Shell smooth, elongated, subtriangular, with usually a high, sharp posterior ridge; hinge with a rudimentary pseudocardinal and lateral in each valve. . . . . *Gonidea* Conrad.

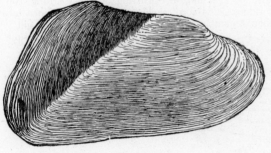

This genus, represented by a single species, *G. angulata* Lea (Fig. 1495; ×¾), as usually found, is remarkable for the sharp posterior ridge and more or less flattened posterior region. It is a characteristic west coast species and ranges from central California north to British Columbia, and east to Idaho.

FIG. 1495.

126 (127) Shell smooth, elliptical; hinge edentulous; beak sculpture consisting of a few fine, concentric ridges. . . *Anodontoides* Simpson.

The type, *A. ferussaciana* Lea (Fig. 1496; × ¾), is of general distribution in the St. Lawrence, Ohio, and Mississippi drainage areas. The concentric undulations of the beaks are characteristic.

FIG 1496.

127 (128) Shell small, solid, thick in front, with two radial ridges extending from the beaks to the biangulated posterior end. Pseudocardinals solid; laterals wanting. . . . . *Pegias* Simpson.

A single species, *P. fabula* Lea (Fig. 1497), from the Cumberland and Tennessee river systems, is the only one known.

FIG. 1497.

128 (129) Shell large, inflated, subrhomboidal, with two radiating rows of knobs; beak sculpture coarse, continuous with that of the surface which consists of oblique folds and wrinkles; pseudocardinals large; laterals short and blurred.

Arcidens Simpson.

The typical and only species, *A. confragosa* Say (Fig. 1498; × ½), is common throughout the Ohio and Mississippi drainage systems and southwest to Texas.

FIG. 1498.

129 (130)   Shell large, solid, inflated, subrotund; beak sculpture weak, not
            continuous with the surface sculpture, which consists of
            oblique folds; hinge strong and complete.

                                              Arkansia Ortmann and Walker.

The type and only species known, *A. wheeleri* O. and W. (Fig. 1499; × ⅔), has recently been
discovered in the Old River, Arkadelphia, Ark.

FIG. 1499.

130 (134)   Shell elliptic-rhomboid, compressed; pseudocardinals well developed;
            laterals more or less imperfect or subobsolete.

                                              Symphynota Lea . .   131

131 (132, 133)   Shell smooth, shining, rayed; teeth delicate; laterals moderately
                 developed. . . . .   Subgenus *Symphynota* s.s.

The type, *S. compressa* Lea (Fig. 1500; × ⅔), is one of the common species of the Northern States,
ranging from New York west to Nebraska and south to Arkansas.   Several other species are
found in the Atlantic drainage from New York to South Carolina and in eastern Tennessee and
northern Alabama.

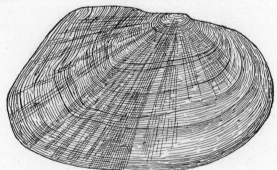

FIG. 1500.

132 (131, 133)   Shell subrhomboid, compressed, posterior slope corrugated;
                 lateral teeth subobsolete.   Subgenus *Lasmigona* Rafinesque.

The type and only species, *Symphynota costata* Raf. (Fig. 1501; × ⅔), is common in the St.
Lawrence and Mississippi drainage systems.

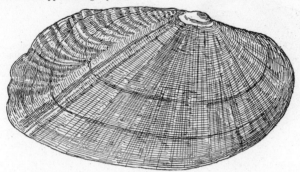

FIG. 1501.

133 (131, 132)   Shell large, ovate-rhomboid, subcompressed, smooth; hinge
                 very heavy; lateral teeth imperfectly developed.
                                          Subgenus *Pterosygna* Rafinesque.

Oniy one species, *Symphynota complanata* Bar. (Fig. 1502; × ⅔), which has a wide range
from the Great Lakes and the upper Mississippi south into Alabama and Arkansas.

FIG. 1502.

134 (139)   Shell rhomboidal, inflated, with a well-developed posterior ridge;
            pseudocardinals well developed; laterals subobsolete or
            wanting. . . . .   *Alasmidonta* Say . .   135

Four subgenera: 135, 136, 137, 138.

135 (136)   Shell ovate-rhomboid, solid, inflated; beak sculpture very coarse
            and heavy; pseudocardinals large, solid; laterals very im-
            perfect or wanting. . . . . .   Subgenus *Alasmidonta* s.s.

The type and only species, *A. undulata*
Say (Fig. 1503; × ⅔), is a characteristic shell
of the Atlantic states south to North Carolina, but is not found west of central New
York.

FIG. 1503.

136 (137)   Shell small, decidedly rhomboid; beak sculpture slightly corrugated;
            teeth compressed. . . . .   Subgenus *Pressodon* Simpson.

The typical species, *Alasmidonta calceola* Lea (Fig. 1504),
has a wide distribution through the Northern States from the
Mississippi eastward.   Several other species occur in the
Atlantic and Southeastern States.   One species, *A. collina*
Con., is remarkable for having one or more small spines
near the center of each valve.

FIG. 1504.

137 (138)   Shell elongated, rhomboid, inflated, posterior slope slightly corru-
            gated; pseudocardinals imperfect; laterals wanting.
                                        Subgenus *Rugifera* Simpson.

The type, *Alasmidonta marginata* Say (Fig. 1505), ranges from New York and South Carolina west to the Mississippi Valley.   Another species is found only in the Tennessee and Cumberland river systems.

FIG. 1505.

138 (135)   Shell thin, triangular, greatly inflated, with a high, sharp posterior
            ridge; pseudocardinals compressed, reflexed; laterals want-
            ing. . . . . Subgenus *Bullella* Simpson.

This group is composed of two very peculiar species found only in South Carolina and Georgia.
Type, *Alasmidonta arcula* Lea (Fig. 1506; × ⅔).

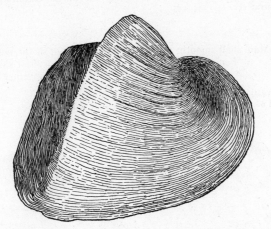

FIG. 1506.

139 (122)   Shell small, thin, elongate-elliptical; beak sculpture consisting of
            fine parallel ridges, looped up in the middle; a high, irregular,
            compressed pseudocardinal in each valve; laterals nearly
            or quite lacking. . . . . *Hemilastena* Agassiz.

The type and only species, *H. ambigua* Say
(Fig. 1507), occurs in the Ohio river system,
ranging north to Michigan, west to Iowa,
south to Arkansas, and east to Tennessee.

FIG. 1507.

140 (107, 121)   Marsupium formed from the outer gill alone and usually from
                the posterior portion only; edge of marsupium, when charged,
                distending and bulging out beyond the original edge of the
                gill; water tubes simple in the gravid female. Hinge com-
                plete; male and female shells usually quite different.
                                Subfamily LAMPSILINAE . . 141

Twelve genera: 141, 146, 151, 152, 153, 156, 159, 160, 161, 162, 163, 164.

141 (146)   Male and female shells different; female shell with a decided inflation in the post-basal region, which is thinner than the rest
of the shell, of different texture, often toothed, and usually
radiately sculptured; hinge complete; marsupium occupying
the posterior part of the gill only.

                              Truncilla Rafinesque . .   142

Four subgenera: 142, 143, 144, 145.

142 (143)   Male shell smooth, no radial groove in front of the posterior ridge.
Female with a high posterior ridge, posterior slope flattened.

                              Subgenus *Truncilla* s.s.

The type, *T. triquetra* Raf. (Fig. 1508), occurs from western New York to Nebraska and south
to Kansas and northern Alabama.   Five other species are found in Tennessee and Alabama.

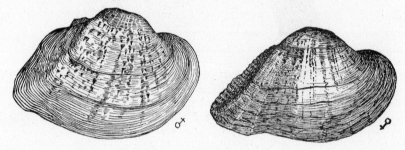

FIG. 1508.

143 (144)   Male shell with a wide, radiating, shallow depression in front of the
posterior ridge.   Female with a small, rounded, well-defined
radial post-basal swelling. . . Subgenus *Scalenaria* Agassiz.

The type, *Truncilla sulcata* Lea (Fig. 1509), ranges from the Tennessee River north to
southern Michigan.   Two other species occur in Tennessee and Georgia.

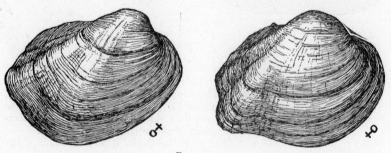

FIG. 1509.

144 (145) Male shell with a posterior and central radiating ridge with a
           furrow between. Female with a greatly produced inflation
           a little behind the center of the base.

                          Subgenus *Dysnomia* Agassiz.

This is one of the most remarkable groups of the genus and is represented by three species
from the Ohio, Cumberland, and Tennessee rivers. Type, *Truncilla foliata* Hild. (Fig. 1510;
× ⅓).

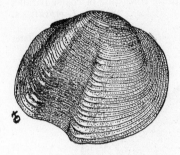

FIG. 1510.

145 (142) Male shell with a wide, shallow, radiating depression in front of
           the posterior ridge. Female with a rounded, foliaceous
           swelling at the posterior base. . . Subgenus *Pilea* Simpson.

Eight species, found mostly in the Tennessee drainage, but ranging north to southern Michigan
and west to Arkansas. Type, *Truncilla personata* Lea (Fig. 1511).

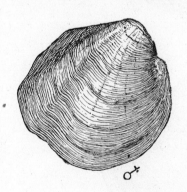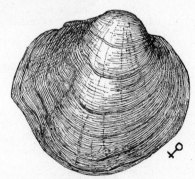

FIG. 1511.

146 (151) Male and female shell different. Shell ovate to elliptical, smooth;
           hinge complete. Female shell more or less expanded in
           the post-basal region, but the expansion does not differ in
           texture from the rest of the shell. Marsupium occupying
           the posterior part of the outer gill.

                          Lampsilis Rafinesque . . 147

147 (150) Beak sculpture consisting of coarse parallel ridges, scarcely looped
           or fine and doubly looped.
                                    Subgenus *Lampsilis* s.s. . . 148

148 (149) Shell often very large, usually rather thin, inflated, shining, fre-
           quently rayed. Beak sculpture consisting of coarse parallel
           ridges, scarcely looped. . . . . . . Section *Lampsilis* s.s.

      This group includes some of the largest of the Unionidae. Found in all of the Eastern States
   from New England to Georgia and west to Arkansas. Type, *L. ovata* Say (Fig. 1512; ✕ ½).

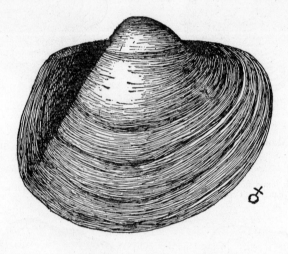

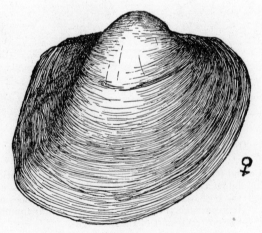

FIG. 1512.

149 (148) Shell oval to oblong; beak sculpture consisting of fine, doubly
looped ridges. . . . . Section *Eurynia* Rafinesque.

This group has many species and is of general distribution from Manitoba to Texas and
eastward. Type, *Lampsilis recta* Lam. (Fig. 1513; × ¾).

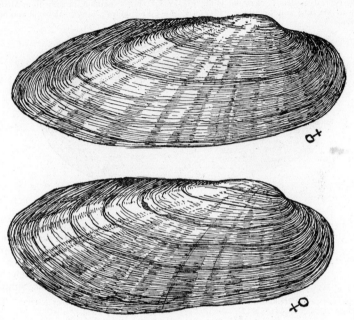

FIG. 1513.

150 (147) Shell small, inflated, oval to obovate; male usually more or less
pointed posteriorly; female truncated obliquely on the post-
base; beak sculpture consisting of rather strong concentric
ridges. . . . . Subgenus *Carunculina* Simpson.

A well-marked group of small, dark-colored species easily distinguished by the peculiar beak
sculpture. Most of the species are confined to the Southern States from Georgia to Texas, but
two or three range north to Illinois and southern Michigan. Type, *Lampsilis texasensis* Lea
(Fig. 1514; × ¾).

FIG. 1514.

151 (152)   Male and female shells alike. Whole outer gill serving as marsu-
            pium, its edge thrown into a number of folds. Shell elon-
            gate-triangular, solid and thick; hinge complete; hinge plate
            wide and flat. . . . .   *Ptychobranchus* Simpson.

   The typical species, *P. phaseolus* Hild. (Fig. 1515; × ½), is common, ranging from Michigan
south to Alabama and Louisiana. Five other species are known, four in Alabama and one in
Arkansas.

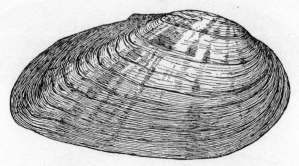

FIG. 1515.

152 (153)   Male and female shells alike. Marsupium occupying nearly the
            whole of the outer gill and, when fully developed, folded.
            Shell solid, round-triangular; hinge complete; hinge plate
            wide and flat; surface sculptured by irregular ridges and
            humps, painted with undulating, radiating, broken hair-
            lines or maculations. . . . .   *Dromus* Simpson.

   Only two species are known, both from the Tennessee and Cumberland river systems. Type,
D. dromas Lea (Fig. 1516; × ½).

FIG. 1516.

153 (156)   Male and female shells different, the latter being slightly inflated
            in the post-basal region. Shell short oval, rounded, or retuse.
            Marsupium occupying the posterior portion of the outer
            gills and projecting far below the rest of the branchiae,
            dolabriform or kidney-shaped. *Obovaria* Rafinesque . . 154

154 (155)   Shell retrorse to short oval; beaks high and central.

Subgenus *Obovaria* s.s.

A small group of species mostly found in the Southern States from Alabama to Arkansas. The type, *O. retusa* Lam. (Fig. 1517), occurs in the Ohio, Tennessee, and Cumberland systems, and another species ranges north to southern Michigan.

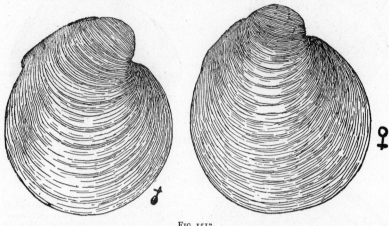

FIG. 1517.

155 (154)   Shell elliptical; beaks anterior. . .   Subgenus *Pseudoon* Simpson.

Two species only.   The type, *Obovaria ellipsis* Lea (Fig. 1518; × ⅔), ranges from the upper Mississippi and lower Great Lakes south to Tennessee and Arkansas.   The other is found from Arkansas to Louisiana and east to Alabama.

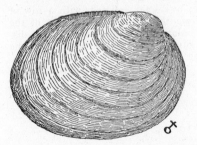 

FIG. 1518.

156 (159)   Male and female shells different, the latter being more or less inflated in the post-basal region.   Shell triangular ovate, with a distinct, often sharp posterior ridge; hinge complete. Marsupium kidney-shaped, occupying the posterior portion of the outer gills, but not extending quite to the hinder end.

Plagiola Agassiz . .   157

157 (158)   Hinge heavy and strong; hinge plate wide and flat.

Subgenus *Plagiola* s.s.

The type and only species, *P. securis* Lea (Fig. 1519; × ½), occurs abundantly in the Ohio and Mississippi systems and south to Alabama.

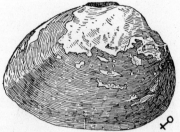

FIG. 1519.

158 (157)   Hinge delicate; hinge plate narrow.

Subgenus *Amygdalonaias* Crosse and Fischer.

A group of only three species character-ized by the sharp posterior ridge and arrow-shaped pattern of the epidermis. Two of them occupy the Mississippi drainage, ex-tending into southern Michigan and south to Alabama and Texas. The third is peculiar to Texas. Example, *Plagiola elegans* Lea (Fig. 1520; × ⅘).

FIG. 1520.

159 (160)   Male and female shells alike; oval-solid, inflated, with a row of large knobs running from the beaks to the center of the base; hinge complete. Marsupium consisting of a few dis-tinctly marked ovisacs situated just behind the center of the outer gill and projecting far below the rest of the branchiae.

Obliquaria Rafinesque.

The typical and only species, *O. reflexa* Raf. (Fig. 1521), ranges from Michigan south to Alabama and Texas.

FIG. 1521.

160 (161)   Male and female shells alike; very thick and solid, inflated, rounded-triangular; surface nodular, radiately wrinkled, or lachrymous; epidermis painted with delicate green mottling on a light ground.   Marsupium consisting of several long purple ovisacs pendent from near the central base of the outer gills and formed into a close coil with the ends turned inward.

Cyprogenia Agassiz.

The typical species, *C. irrorata* Lea (Fig. 1522), is common in the Ohio, Cumberland, and Tennessee river systems.   One other species occurs in the states west of the Mississippi, from Missouri to Oklahoma.

FIG. 1522.

161 (162)   Male and female shells different, that of the latter being slightly swollen behind the middle of the base.   Shell rather small, elongated, dorsal slope plicately or nodulously wrinkled; hinge complete.   Marsupium occupying the central portion of the outer gill. . . . . *Medionidus* Simpson.

A small group of species characterized by their elongate shape and plicate dorsal slope.   It is restricted to the waters of Tennessee, Alabama, Georgia, and Florida.   Type, *M. conradicus* Lea (Fig. 1523).

FIG. 1523.

162 (163) Male and female shells much alike, but the latter is usually somewhat inflated in the post-basal region. Shell large, ovate,
usually rather thin, but in some species quite solid, gaping
at the anterior edge and on the dorsal slope; normally winged
on the dorsal slope, but the wing is often lost in the adult;
hinge complete. Marsupium occupying the posterior portion
of the outer gills. Glochidia celt-shaped, with two spines on
each valve and with gaping margins . . *Proptera* Rafinesque.

This group is well characterized by the large, usually thin shell, which is more or less alate in
the dorsal region. It occurs throughout the St. Lawrence and Mississippi systems and extends
south to Texas and Alabama. Type, *P. alata* Say (Fig. 1524; × ½).

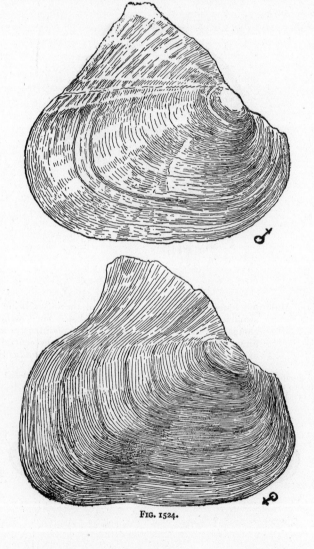

FIG. 1524.

163 (164) Male and female shells not greatly different, the latter being somewhat more inflated and expanded in the post-basal region.
Shell thin, rather compressed, and winged on the dorsal
slope; hinge complete, but the pseudocardinals are reduced
to mere tubercles often nearly wanting. Marsupium as
in *Proptera*. Glochidia semicircular, very small, without
spines. . . . . *Paraptera* Ortmann.

This genus in shell characters is very like the preceding, but has been separated on account
of the great difference in the shape of the glochidia. The type, and only species yet known to
belong to it, *P. gracilis* Bar. (Fig. 1525; × ⅔), has a wide range from the Great Lakes south to
Alabama and west to the Mississippi Valley.

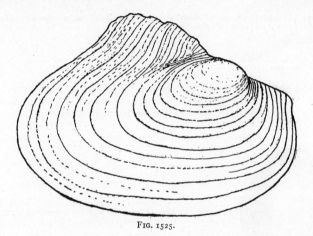

FIG. 1525.

164 (141) Male and female shells different, the latter being swollen in the
post-basal region. Marsupial characters unknown. Shell
short-elliptical, solid, much inflated; pseudocardinals divided
into irregularly radiating, granular laminae; hinge plate
reduced to a mere rounded line behind the pseudocardinals.
Glebula Conrad.

The type and only species, *G. rotundata* Lam. (Fig. 1526; × ½), ranges from Florida to eastern
Texas. Conchologically very distinct by reason of its peculiar hinge, little is known of its
anatomical characters and further information is greatly to be desired, especially in regard to
the gravid female.

FIG. 1526.

165 (104) Interior of shell non-nacreous or porcellanous, or the whole shell of a prevailing prismatic substance. 166

Five families: 166, 167, 168, 173, 174.

166 (167) Shell of a prevailing prismatic substance, mytiliform, very inequilateral; beaks compressed, terminal; ligament subinternal; anterior adductor and pedal protractor muscles inserted on a septum in the beak. Byssiferous.

Family DREISSENSIIDAE.

Only one genus. . . . . *Congeria* Partsch.

Represented in our fauna by two species. Example, *C. leucophaeata* Con. (Fig. 1527; × 2), found on the Atlantic coast from Maryland to Florida.

FIG. 1527.

167 (168) Shell porcellanous, subtrigonal, thick, and solid; ligament external; hinge with true cardinal teeth and with both anterior and posterior laterals; pallial line with a distinct sinus.

Family CYRENIDAE.

Only a single genus. . . . . *Cyrena* Lamarck.

Represented in our fresh-water fauna by a single species, *C. carolinensis* Bosc (Fig. 1528), found in streams and brackish water near the coast from South Carolina to Texas.

FIG. 1528.

168 (173) Shell non-nacreous, usually small and thin; hinge with cardinal and both anterior and posterior lateral teeth; no hinge plate; pallial line simple. . . . Family SPHAERIIDAE . . 169

Four genera: 169, 170, 171, 172.

169 (170) Shell oval, equilateral; beaks nearly subcentral; nepeonic valves not distinctly separated from the subsequent growth of the shell; cardinal teeth two in each valve. . *Sphaerium* Scopoli.

This group contains the largest species of the family and is easily distinguished from *Musculium* by the thicker, striate shell and noncalyculate beaks. The species are numerous and of general distribution. Example, *S. simile* Say (Fig. 1529; × 1⅔).

FIG. 1529.

170 (171)   Shell thin and delicate, suborbicular to oblong; beaks prominent, usually retaining the nepeonic valves; cardinal teeth minute, often obsolete; anterior and posterior laterals present.
Musculium Link.

FIG. 1530.

This group has a general distribution. The prominent beaks with the distinctly marked nepeonic shell are the distinctive feature, but in some species these are lacking. The thin, rounded, polished shell is, however, quite characteristic. Example, *M. partumeium* Say (Fig. 1530; × 2).

171 (172)   Shell subrhomboidal, thin, moderately inflated, with the posterior side longer; cardinal teeth feeble, only one in each valve.
Eupera Bourguignat.

FIG. 1531.

A tropical group, of which two or three species occur in Florida, Alabama, and Texas. The rhomboidal shape is characteristic. The shells appear to be mottled and are usually so described, but according to Dr. W. H. Dall these "spots" are caused by a parasitic infusorian that attacks the interior of the shell. Example, *E. singleyi* Pils. (Fig. 1531; × 3).

172 (169)   Shell small, rounded, oval, or obliquely cuneiform, inequilateral, anterior side longer; beaks subterminal; cardinal teeth double in each valve. . . . . . . *Pisidium* C. Pfeiffer.

FIG. 1532.

The *Pisidia* are of general distribution and a great number of species have been described. They are easily distinguished from the allied genera by the very inequilateral shell, the hinge being on the shorter side. Example, *P. virginicum* Bgt. (Fig. 1532; × 2).

173 (174)   Shell rounded, inflated, thin; beaks forward; surface smooth or slightly concentrically sculptured; cardinal teeth, two in the right and one in the left valve; no lateral teeth.
Family CYRENELLIDAE.
Only one genus. . . . . *Cyrenella* Deshayes.

FIG. 1533.

Represented in our fauna by a single species, *C. floridana* Dall (Fig. 1533; × 1½), from Florida. It is easily distinguished by the lack of lateral teeth.

174 (166)   Shell thick, oval, subtrigonal, ventricose, smooth; beaks prominent; ligament inclosed in a pit and invisible externally; hinge with cardinal and both anterior and posterior lateral teeth; pallial line sinuous. . . . .   Family RANGIIDAE.
Only one genus.   . . . .   *Rangia* Des Moulins.

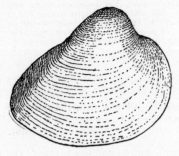

The typical species, *R. cuneata* Gray (Fig. 1534; × ⅓), is found in great abundance in the brackish waters of the Gulf coast from Alabama to Mexico.

FIG. 1534.

IMPORTANT PAPERS ON FRESH–WATER MOLLUSCA.

BAKER, F. C.   1898.   The Mollusca of the Chicago Area.   Part I, Pelecypoda.
   1902.   Part II, Gastropoda.
   1911.   The Lymnaeidae of North and Middle America.

BINNEY, W. G.   1865.   Land and Fresh-water Shells of North America, Part II.   Smithsonian Misc. Coll., v. 7, No. 143, 172 pp.   Part III, No. 144, 128 pp.

HALDEMAN, S. S.   1842.   Monograph of the Fresh-water Univalve Mollusca of the United States.   Continued by G. W. Tyron, Jr., 1870.

ORTMANN, A. E.   1911.   A Monograph of the Najades of Pennsylvania.   Mem. Carnegie Mus., 4 : 279–347.
   1912.   Notes upon the Families and Genera of the Najades.   Ann. Carnegie Mus., 8 : 222–364.

PRIME, TEMPLE.   1865.   Monograph of American Corbiculidae.   Smithsonian Misc. Coll., v. 7, No. 145, 192 pp.

SIMPSON, C. T.   1914.   A Descriptive Catalogue of the Naiades or Pearly Fresh-water Mussels.   Printed by Bryant Walker, Detroit, Mich.   1540 pp.

STIMPSON, WILLIAM.   1865.   Researches upon the Hydrobiinae and Allied Forms.   Smithsonian Misc. Coll., v. 7, No. 201, 64 pp.

TRYON, G. W., JR.   1873.   Land and Fresh-water Shells of North America.   Part IV, Strepomatidae.   Smithsonian Misc. Coll., v. 16, No. 253, 435 pp.

CHAPTER XXX

THE AQUATIC VERTEBRATES

By C. H. EIGENMANN

Professor of Zoology in Indiana University, and Curator of Fishes in the Carnegie Museum, Pittsburgh, Pa.

INTRODUCTORY

THE chief object in the life of any animal is to leave another like it in its place when it dies. To accomplish this object it must find a range in which it may secure its food and itself escape becoming food; it must secure a mate and a home in which its young may be reared to the point of self-dependence. The world contains a great variety of animals adapted to all possible environments. Either the greatly diverse characters of these animals have arisen to adapt them to their different ranges and homes, or the greatly diverse environments have been selected because they were adapted to the otherwise and elsewhere acquired characters of different animals. Certainly when new water or land areas arise the latter will be the origin of its adopted fauna.

The vast territory containing the majority of the innumerable lakes and streams with whose fauna and flora we are concerned, extending from the Arctic regions south to the region of the Ohio River, was a few thousand years ago covered with a continuous sheet of ice. The fauna and flora of this area are composed of immigrants, of animals and plants that moved in as the ice moved out and selected the places adapted to their requirements. While no doubt many of them have become modified since their advent into this area, there can be no doubt that their fundamental adaptations were elsewhere acquired and that in their case it has been a selection of environments to suit these adaptations.

Fresh waters may be and are used first, for ranges; second, for homes; or third, for both purposes by various animals. One finds animals which breed on land but are adapted to utilize fresh waters daily or seasonally for ranges; others that range on land but visit the water during breeding seasons to make therein their homes and to enable their young to grow up in it. Still other animals utilize fresh waters both as a range and a home, — rarely, or never, leave it or even are incapable of leaving it. Roughly speaking, mammals, birds, and reptiles, in so far as they are aquatic, belong to the first of this ecological group. Batrachians belong to the second, a few batrachians and all fishes to the third.

The first of these groups is composed of more or less perfect readaptations of land animals to water. The second is composed of originally aquatic animals as yet imperfectly adapted to the land, while the members of the third group are, and at all times have been, the aquatic animals par excellence. While the visitors or inhabitants of fresh water may be sharply distinguished from the non-aquatic, the relations and adaptations of aquatic animals to the different regions of the water are very diverse.

MAMMALS

The aquatic mammals are but imperfectly adjusted to some part of the aquatic habitat and confine themselves to shallow water and the shore. None of them could live in an enclosed space filled with water. The number of truly aquatic mammals is small. Most mammals only visit the water to drink. Others, as the moose, seek the water to browse on the marginal vegetation or to escape enemies. Others less inclined to enter water secure part of their food from it. The raccoon fishes along the margins of streams for crayfishes. A dexterous tomcat, proverbially wary of wetting his feet, one memorable night neatly cleaned out two aquaria, one stocked with rare blind fishes and one with still rarer axolotls. None of the above dive.

The mink secures most of its food on land but it catches both fishes and muskrats in the water into which it does not hesitate to dive to escape an enemy or to secure food.

The more distinctly aquatic mammals are the star-nosed mole, the muskrat, the beaver, and the otter. All of these use the water as a range, making their homes in very close proximity to the water if not actually in it. Of these the otter is a carnivore, the rest plant feeders, though sometimes eating animal food. They have been so reduced in numbers, — in some places entirely exterminated, — that they have become almost a negligible part of the aquatic vertebrate fauna. Only the muskrat must be considered as an ecological element in all eastern fresh waters.

The muskrat is abundant along most of the eastern streams and lakes. It is a shallow-water animal and affects its environment in a specific way. It builds lodges of sod and cat-tail stalks, twigs and vegetable debris. It gathers lily roots, on which it feeds, but its most specific action is on various mussels. The muskrat lodge is always surrounded by shells of dead bivalves, and at Winona Lake it has been found by Headlee that the muskrat sets a boundary to the shoreward migration of mussels as the soft bottom of the pelagic area sets a limit to their migration toward deep water. The activities of the muskrat are more restricted in winter than in summer, but they do not hibernate.

Beavers have disappeared from thickly-settled regions. They are, in some of their habits, larger editions of the muskrat. They build lodges not unlike those of the muskrat. They cut and gather twigs and stems for food but the action for which beavers are conspicuous, is the building of dams, and creating of ponds. They thus add to the extent of the aquatic environment.

The seal-like otter is no longer a part of the aquatic environment in well settled parts of America. They are the most aquatic of the fresh-water mammals. As swimmers, they are more expert than fishes, which they catch and eat. They also prey upon muskrats and aquatic birds.

Of the star-nosed mole, Stone says: "The star-nosed mole is a creature almost as well fitted for a partially aquatic life as the otter and mink, and, as a matter of fact, does pass most of its time about the water; pushing extensive tunnels through the black, peaty soil of swamps and along the borders of little brooks and ponds. The soft, black loam is thrown up in frequent heaps a foot, more or less, in diameter; the opening of the burrow being under the bank, and as often beneath the water as above. The tunnel itself must frequently be flooded to the great discomfort of its inmates.

"But the old ones show no fear of the water; I have frequently seen them swimming both under water and on the surface, even where the current was pretty strong, and have always observed them to be perfectly confident and unfrightened at such times."

BIRDS

In cold and temperate regions birds are seasonal, robbing, visitors of the water. Only one-fourth to one-fifth of our entire bird fauna is in any sense aquatic.[1]

The passerine birds are dominant now and of this group none are strictly aquatic. One hundred and twenty-nine of the 215 species of birds of Monroe County, Indiana, are passerine. Of these only the red-winged blackbird, the six species of swallows, the water thrushes, and the long-billed marsh wren are, even remotely, related to the water. Taking all the birds that range in or about the water — for none of them can be said to home in the water — one finds a graduated series, from those more to those less aquatic in their habits. More than this, birds show the most complete series of adaptations to different aquatic zones.

The swallows must, by courtesy, be mentioned as forming the first of this series of ecological groups. They are never found upon or in the water, but skim over its surface, occasionally just touching it in their search for food. Mosquitoes and other minute aquatic insects are the attraction for them and they are, therefore, very definitely related to the aquatic fauna. They remain in the latitude of the Ohio River from early April to September.

A second ecological group is formed by the kingfisher, the terns, gulls, and (for fresh waters rarely) the pelicans. The kingfisher, from his perch over a stream, dives into the water beneath him for fishes. He is largely a shore fisher. The terns, gulls, and pelicans dive from an aerial poise into the pelagic region of the lake and secure fishes near the surface. The terns and gulls also alight to pick the refuse floating on the surface for they are scavengers as

---

[1] Out of 99 birds observed during the summer about one of the northern Indiana lakes, 19 are more or less related to the water. Out of 215 birds observed at all seasons of the year about Bloomington, Indiana, 55 are related to the water.

well as robbers. The kingfisher is a poor swimmer, but the terns, gulls, and pelicans rest gracefully on the surface. In the latitude of the Ohio the kingfisher is found between early March and November, rarely even in December. The terns migrate to the northern lakes in summer and the pelicans are but stray visitors. The terns, gulls, and pelicans have certainly acquired the adaptation to the water at the ocean.

The third ecological group is formed by the grebes and loons. They are pelagic birds, swimmers par excellence, both upon the surface and *in* the water. The term diving ought not to be applied to the performance of both kingfisher and loon.

The fourth ecological group is formed by the bottom-feeding ducks, the mudhen, geese, and swans. They are littoral or abysmal forms securing their food in the mud at the bottom, largely about the margins of ponds or lakes in water not too deep to prevent them from reaching the bottom when "tipping." Many of the ducks are good swimmers under water, and the bay and sea ducks are said to reach the bottom at a depth of 100 to 150 feet.

The fifth ecological group is formed by the herons, cranes, and bitterns. These range in much the same zone as most of the ducks, but their food, for the most part, is different. They stalk cautiously, without jerk or sudden motion, or stand in water of a depth not too great for their long legs. Their spearlike bill impales fish or frog.

The sixth and last of the ecological groups of aquatic forms contains the rails and snipes. These are shore birds, wading in the shallowest water or along the wet shores, frequently moving with the advancing and retreating waves, picking the stranded animals from the surface or probing for their prey in the soft beaches.

All of the groups except the first, the swallows, nest as near the water as possible. Less strictly aquatic are the swamp blackbird and long-tailed marsh wren which build their nests in cat tails; likewise the song and marsh sparrows, so abundant along margins of stream or pond. From the nature of the case the waters of northern and temperate zones are a closed book to all the birds in winter. Hence, birds are not perennial elements of the aquatic fauna. Birds derive their food from the water. The few that, as carrion, serve as food for other aquatic animals or that may be captured by fish, otter, or alligator are a negligible quantity.

REPTILES

Reptiles, like mammals, are shallow-water and littoral forms, largely in summer. As with mammals, a gradual gradation is found from species living exclusively on land, — like the turtles and snakes of the Mojave desert or the land tortoise and green snakes of the Mississippi valley, — through those which do not ordinarily go into the water but will enter it without hesitation if circumstances demand, — like the black snake and garter snake, — to such as the water snakes, leather snakes, geographic turtle, painted turtle, and snapping turtle that bask on the margins of lakes and streams but take to the water for food or at the slightest sign of danger; and lastly, to the alligators, musk turtles, and soft-shelled turtles which give the final gradation to adaptations for life in water. Of these, the soft-shelled turtle, which can utilize the oxygen dissolved in the water, has probably reached the highest adjustment to aquatic existence. But no hard and fast line can be drawn. The habits of different species overlap so neatly that one finds a shading from reptiles with a purely aquatic range to those with an entirely terrestrial range. All of them have their homes on land in so far as they have homes at all. Some secure only a part, others all of their food from the water. Of those that obtain it from the water some feed on fishes (purely aquatic food); others like the alligators, which catch water birds, utilize the water to secure terrestrial visitors in part. Others may seek both sorts of food. Snakes take to the margin of water in part for fishes, in part for frogs, etc.

The water snakes give birth to living young. Since the young may be liberated in the water these snakes, in one sense, are the most aquatic of the reptiles. But since they cannot utilize the oxygen in the water the soft-shelled turtles exceed them in adaptation to an aquatic existence in this respect. All the turtles, as well as the alligators, are compelled to make their homes or nests on land. The soft-shelled turtles usually lay their eggs in sandy beaches, sometimes in harder banks near the water. The painted turtles and snapping turtles dig holes more remote from the water's edge. The musk turtles lay their eggs in muck, in decaying stumps or logs, or accumulations of decaying weeds on the margins of lakes.

No one would seriously doubt that the mammalian and reptilian faunas of fresh waters have both been derived from terrestrial ancestors. The adjustment to water conditions consists largely in an adaptation of the limbs and tail to swimming and diving. Both are organs primarily used for land progression. Further adaptations in reptiles, such as the utilization of the oxygen in the water by the turtles, are much more rare, and found only in extreme adaptations to an aquatic sojourn.

The paths of turtles may readily be seen among fields of *Chara* in shallow water. A painted, geographic, or a musk turtle may be seen basking in the sun on the surface, the neck curved up, the nose out of water. If disturbed it dives into the *Chara* and soon disappears in one of its innumerable paths. A curious commensalism is reported between the soft-shelled turtle and the black bass. The bass is said to follow the turtle, which, nosing about under rocks and in crannies scares out some of the crayfishes and other denizens of such places. These are then easily captured by the attending black bass. There is a peculiar correlation between the disposition of turtles and the degree of their armature. The soft-shelled turtle is the least protected by bony plates. Next in order comes the snapping turtle, with only a cross-shaped, ventral plate, most of the ventral surface being open to attack. This is followed by the musk turtle, the painted and the geographic turtle, Blanding's turtle and finally the box turtle. The highest degree of protection is found in the terrestrial box turtle, whose plastron is hinged and can be closed in front and behind. Correlated with the defective armature in the soft-shelled turtle we find the extreme of pugnacity. A soft-shelled turtle will snap and bite on suspicion from the time it is half way out of its shell. The disposition of the snapping turtle, with exposed ventral surface, is proverbial. The musk turtle will bite, as anyone who has collected their eggs can testify. On the other hand, the well-protected painted, geo-

graphic, and Blanding's turtles, and above all, the terrestrial and
perfectly-armored box turtle, are the gentlest of creatures which no
amount of provocation will induce to bite.   Although the correlation between armature and disposition is very striking there may
be no causal relation between the two.   The character of the food
may be the cause of the disposition.

BATRACHIANS

The batrachians, as a group, are aquatic to a much greater
degree than the mammals or reptiles.   In North America they are
summer and especially spring members of the aquatic fauna.
Some of them, with all their ancestry, have been strictly aquatic.
They are autochthons, products of evolution in fresh water.   Such
aquatic forms have gills and a tail throughout life.   The Siren and
the mud puppy, of deadly repute, belong to this group and so does
the blind salamander of Texas.   Whereas in the reptiles and the
mammals gradations from pure terrestrials to less or more aquatics
have been noted, in the batrachians one finds gradations from the
purely aquatic to the more or less terrestrial, and none have reached
the possibility of living in deserts in dry places.   So many of the
batrachians lay their eggs in water that those that do not are
accounted remarkable.   In a small pond near Indiana University,
which has been examined at all seasons of the year, it has been
found that a salamander, *Amblystoma jeffersonianum*, begins to lay
as soon as the ice disappears after December.   Sometimes this
happens early in January or it may not until March.   After the
spawning of *jeffersonianum* comes that of *Amblystoma punctatum*.
Both deposit their eggs in jellylike clumps.   *Hyla pickeringii* and
Acris gryllus spawn in the same pond between early March and late
May.   During late spring and early summer the newt, *Diemictylus
viridescens*, spawns here.   Very frequently this pond dries up in
summer, and then there is an opportunity to see how any of the
aquatic batrachians may become terrestrial.   Late in summer *Amblystoma opacum* spawns in this pond.   Usually the pond is dry at
the time, whereupon the salamander lays its eggs under leaves or
under a board, coiling itself about the eggs.   The hatching of such

eggs may be delayed much beyond the normal time and will then occur at once with the first rain. The young still require a pond for their growth from hatching to the metamorphosis. Toads and frogs have evidently become adapted to range on land without losing their ancestral habit of making their home in water. Whether their webbed toes and swimming legs are in their original condition, or whether they are readaptations to water may be left in abeyance.

The batrachians play an important part in the economy of small pools, a less important one in small streams, and are a negligible quantity in waters of any size. To the rule that their abundance is in inverse proportion to the size of the body of water, the perennibranchs form the only exception. In early spring nearly every puddle contains hundreds or thousands of toad eggs and larvae. The tadpoles act as scavengers for a short time and then pass out of the life of the puddle. Every pond of greater permanence serves the frogs as the puddles and ponds do the toad. Frog tadpoles are scavengers and mud eaters, with elongate, alimentary canal. They remain in the water much longer than young toads and when they become adult may pass out of the life of the puddle or pond as completely as the adult toad, or may remain more or less closely identified with the birthplace. When the adult frogs remain about the water, they bear a different relation to the aquatic life from the young. The alimentary canal has become shortened and the frog is an eater of live food, insects, and fishes. In its turn the frog serves as food for fishes, snakes, and birds.

FISHES

The chief and perennial vertebrate elements of the aquatic fauna are the fishes. They, with a few batrachians and possibly a turtle, are the only members of the fauna that have both their home and their range in the water. They alone of the vertebrates are so adjusted to an aquatic existence that they could be hermetically sealed in a balanced aquarium.

There are fishes, big and little, thick and thin, long and short, deep, and of little elevation, sharp-nosed and blunt-snouted, tooth-

FIG. 1535. Red-Eye or Goggle-Eye, *Ambloplites rupestris* (Rafinesque). Actual size, 32 mm., 115 mm. and 183 mm. long respectively.

less and fanged, naked and scaled, barbeled and not, nocturnal
and diurnal, bottom sitters and top skimmers, riffle inhabitants and
pool dwellers, mud-puddlers and mountaineers, round-bellied and
serrate-edged.   They are adapted, in short, to all conditions of
possible fish environment.   The same gamut of size, shape, and

FIG. 1536.   Long-Eared Sunfish, *Lepomis megalotis* (Rafinesque).   Actual size, 90 mm. long.

habit is found in the fresh waters of South America and North
America though the two continents have no fishes in common.
The members of different families have thus independently become
convergently and divergently adapted.

Fresh-water fishes do not form a group by themselves.   Various

FIG. 1537.   Little Pickerel, *Lucius vermiculatus* (Le Sueur).   Actual size, 119 mm. long.

marine families have contributed to the fauna.   But the larger
per cent of the fresh-water fishes belong to the single superorder
Ostariophysi.   Of the 600 fresh-water species of North America,
307, or over half, belong to this group.

The fresh-water fishes of North America, exclusive of Mexico, are distributed among the following families, of which those of undoubted recent marine origin are printed in italics.

Lamprey[1]	8	Salmon	28	Sunfish	37
Paddlefish	1	Trout perch	1	Perch	72
Sturgeon	7	Blindfish	8	*Bass*	4
Garpike	3	*Killifish*	52	*Drum*	1
Bowfin	1	Mud minnow	2	*Surf fish*	1
Characin[2]	1	Pike	5	Cichlid[2]	2
Carp	230	Alaska Blackfish	1	*Goby*	6
Sucker	51	Eel	1	*Sculpin*	21
Catfish	25	*Stickleback*	7	*Cod*	1
Mooneye	3	*Silverside*	2	*Sole*	1
Herring	5	Pirate perch	2		
Gizzard shad	1	Elassoma	2		

Few localities, even among the most favored, contain more than 50 species of the 600 found in North America. The entire Mississippi basin harbors about 200 species, the Great Lakes with their tributaries, 152,[3] the state of Indiana, 163. Eel River in Indiana (85 miles long), with all of its tributary lakes and streams, harbors 76 species. White River of Arkansas, 84; the Maumee basin, 87. Bean Blossom Creek, about 25 miles long, harbors 44 species in less than two miles near its middle. Lake Ontario with all of its tributaries is inhabited by 73 species; Lake Champlain and its tributaries by 54; Lake Chautauqua with its tributaries by 31; the Winnipeg System, Canada, by 44; the St. Lawrence River, by 63 and 8 marine. Winona Lake of Kosciusko County, Indiana, exclusive of its tributaries, harbors 23 species, Turkey Lake without its tributaries, 29 species. The outlet of Turkey Lake, for a mile of its length, harbors an equal number.

There is a vast difference in the number of species found in equal areas of streams and lakes. Other things equal a given area of surface water or a given cubic quantity of water of a small stream harbors more individuals and greater diversity of species than the same area and bulk of either a large river or lake. The places in America from which the greatest diversity of fish life has been reported are:

[1] These are fully described and many of them figured in Jordan and Evermann's Fishes of North and Middle America, Bull. U. S. Fish Com., and also in Jordan's "Guide to the Study of Fishes," Henry Holt and Co.

[2] Immigrants from South America.

[3] Of these 27 are peculiar to the Great Lakes basin.

Saline and Washita, ½ mile above Arkadelphia, Arkansas............ 47[1]
Fort Smith and neighborhood.................................... 50
Bean Blossom Creek, Indiana................................... 44
Cypress Creek, Alabama.. 42
Obeys River, Tennessee... 39
Tuscaloosa, Alabama... 32
Mammoth Spring, Arkansas..................................... 37
Washita, Arkansas... 36

In contrast with these the following poor faunas are recorded:

Connecticut River.. 18
Clear Lake, California.. 13
Klamath basin, California...................................... 15
The entire Yellowstone Park.................................... 10
San Luis River, California...................................... 4
Kicking Horse River, Canada.................................... 2
Salt Lake basin.. 14
Sevier River, Utah... 7
Columbia River System... 37
Colorado basin.. 33
Pennamaguan Lake, Washington County, Maine.................. 10
Meddybemp Lake and Dennys River, Washington County, Maine..... 9
Western Grand Lake System, Washington County, Maine........... 14
St. Croix River basin, Washington County, Maine................. 8
Perkins Lake, Idaho.. 7
Alturas Lake, Idaho.. 4
San Diego County, California................................... 4

Of these the Connecticut, Klamath, Yellowstone, San Luis, the Maine lakes and streams, and Alturas Lake each have entirely distinct faunas and the Columbia and Colorado have only a few species each in common with the Salt Lake basin. It is quite evident from an inspection of these lists, that a general consideration of the fresh-water fauna of North America applicable to all cases is quite out of the question. There are a number of quite distinct faunas. A few general observations may be supplemented with an analysis of a few typical localities to get at the nature of the fish fauna.

Jordan[2] summarizes a long experience of gathering fishes in many waters of North America as follows:

"Some of the conditions most favorable to the existence in any stream of a large number of species of fishes are the following, the most important of which is the one mentioned first: Connection with a large hydrographic basin; a warm climate; clear water; a moderate current; a bottom of gravel, preferably covered by a

[1] Two localities are included in this and several in the total of 50 in the next.
[2] "A Guide to the Study of Fishes," p. 307.

growth of weeds; little fluctuation during the year in the volume
of the stream or in the character of the water.

"Limestone streams usually yield more species than streams
flowing over sandstone, and either more than the streams of regions
having metamorphic rocks. Sandy bottoms usually are not favorable to fishes. In general, glacial drift makes a suitable river
bottom, but the higher temperature usual in regions beyond the
limits of the drift gives to certain southern streams conditions
still more favorable. These conditions are all well realized in the
Washita River in Arkansas, and in various tributaries of the Tennessee, Cumberland, and Ohio; and in these, among American
streams, the greatest number of species has been recorded.

"The isolation and the low temperature of the rivers of New
England have given to them a very scanty fish fauna as compared
with the rivers of the South and West."

Agassiz says concerning New England: "In this isolated region of
North America, in this zoological island of New England, as we
may call it, we find neither *Lepidosteus*, nor *Amia*, nor *Poliodon*,
nor *Amblodon*, nor *Grystes*, nor *Centrarchus*, nor *Pomoxis*, nor
Ambloplites, nor *Calliurus*, nor *Carpiodes*, nor *Hyodon*, nor indeed
any of the characteristic forms of North American fishes so common everywhere else, with the exception of two *Pomotis*, one
Boleosoma, and a few *Catostomus*."

Continuing, Jordan says:

"Of the six hundred species of fishes found in the rivers of the
United States, about two hundred have been recorded from the
basin of the Mississippi. From fifty to one hundred of these
species can be found in any one of the tributary streams of the
size, say, of the Housatonic River or the Charles. In the Connecticut River there are but eighteen species permanently resident; and
the number found in the streams of Texas is not much larger.**

"The waters of the Great Basin are not rich in fishes, the species
now found being evidently an overflow from the Snake River when
in late glacial times it drained Lake Bonneville. This postglacial
lake once filled the present basin of the Great Salt Lake and Utah
Lake, its outlet flowing northwest from Ogden into Snake River.
The same fishes are now found in the upper Snake River and the

basins of Utah Lake and of Sevier Lake. In the same fashion Lake Lahonton once occupied the basin of Nevada, the Humboldt and Carson sinks, with Pyramid Lake. Its drainage fell also into the Snake [Klamath?] River, and its former limits are shown in the present range of species. These have almost nothing in common with the group of species inhabiting the former drainage of Lake Bonneville. Another postglacial body of water, Lake Idaho, once united the lakes of southeastern Oregon. The fauna of Lake Idaho, and of the lakes Malheur, Warner, Goose, etc., which have replaced it, is also isolated and distinctive. The number of species now known from this region of these ancient lakes is about 125. This list is composed almost entirely of a few genera of suckers, minnows, and trout. None of the catfishes, perch, darters, or sunfishes, moon-eyes, pike, killifishes, and none of the ordinary eastern types of minnows have passed the barrier of the Rocky Mountains.

"West of the Sierra Nevada the fauna is still more scanty, only about seventy species being enumerated. This fauna, except for certain immigrants from the sea, is of the same general character as that of the Great Basin, though most of the species are different. . . . The rivers of Alaska contain but few species, barely a dozen in all, most of these being found also in Siberia and Kamchatka. In the scantiness of its faunal list, the Yukon agrees with the Mackenzie River, and with Arctic rivers generally."

The fauna of the Great Lakes and of the Red River of the north is essentially like that of the Mississippi Valley.

The Origin of the Fresh-water Fishes. — Many of the fresh-water fishes of North America have been more remotely or more recently derived from the sea. Some of them, as the eel, still come from the sea during each generation, to find in fresh water their range; others are but seasonal visitors, entering the fresh waters from the ocean as the salamanders enter them from the land, to find homes. These various anadromous fishes will be considered later.[1] Still

---

[1] The anadromous habit may be of double origin. The various salmons, many of whose relatives live in fresh water, may be fresh-water species contributed to the ocean. The shad and striped perch, on the other hand, whose relatives live in the ocean, have become anadromous through the general habit of many oceanic fishes to seek the shore and shallow water as the breeding season approaches.

others, with both range and home in fresh water, belong to present marine families and have evidently comparatively recently become members of the fresh•water fauna.

A notable example of a fish comparatively recently contributed by the sea to fresh water is *Hysterocarpus traski* Gibbons. It is a viviparous fish of the rivers of central California. All of its relatives live in the Pacific Ocean from which it is an undoubted immigrant.

The sea basses furnish several illustrative examples. The striped bass, *Roccus lineatus*, is an oceanic fish entering rivers to spawn, while its nearest relative, *Roccus chrysops*, the white bass, is confined to the Great Lakes and upper Mississippi Valley. Closely related to these are the yellow bass, *Morone interrupta*, of the lower Mississippi Valley, and the white perch, *Morone americana*, in salt and fresh water from Nova Scotia to South Carolina. The ninety other American members of this family are all marine.

Various species of *Robalos* (*Centropomus*) enter fresh water.

The Mugilidae have added various species to the fresh waters south of the United States. The Atherinidae have contributed the skipjack to our rivers and lakes, and south of us this marine family, whose eggs are provided with threads, has contributed and is contributing to the fresh waters all the way from Mexico to Patagonia.

Fig. 1538. Skipjack, *Labidestes siculus* (Cope). Actual size, 95 mm. long.

The sticklebacks and killifishes help to bridge the gap, if such exists, between the fresh waters and the ocean. Even the pipefishes and flounders have a tendency to colonize fresh waters, and the flounders at least have succeeded in South America.

The Sciaenidae, a marine family, has contributed the thunderpumper or white perch to the Great Lakes and Mississippi Valley, and several other species to the streams of South America. Some of its marine species occasionally run up streams.

The large family of the Cottidae has added the miller's-thumb.

Others of undoubted marine origin have entered fresh water at such remote periods that they have set up distinct fresh-water families, as the sunfishes, the perches, and the Cichlidae.

Finally, we have the dominant fresh-water groups of characins, minnows, carps, suckers, and catfishes whose origin from the sea is so remote that the orders and superorders embracing all of these dominant members of the fresh-water fauna, with the exception of *Arius* and related genera, are peculiar to fresh water.

FIG. 1539. Miller's Thumb, *Cottus ictalops* (Rafinesque).

Dispersal of Fresh-water Fishes. — No fishes have been or are being permanently contributed to the land. The eel is capable of moving over short stretches of land, and *Periophthalmus* may leave the water in search of food. In the South American fresh waters a relative of the catfish is said to be able to move from pond to pond, and in the Congo and in South American rivers live fishes that temporarily fly over the water. But all these species are adapted to the water and can live for longer periods only in connection with it.

The two factors that more than others are responsible for the abundance or paucity of the faunas are accessibility and temperature. The latter will be considered more at length later. Accessibility demands some attention now.

A locality is accessible to fishes if it is connected with an inhabited locality by a permanent or seasonal waterway. There are fishes that apparently defy this general rule and that skip or have skipped in a tantalizing way, from mountain stream to mountain stream, appearing wherever conditions are favorable. Here, as elsewhere, the mystery will probably dissolve when all the facts are in. The catfishes and darters have not been able to cross to the Pacific slope in the United States, but in Mexico they have accomplished this feat. A tilting of the land, or change in relative rainfall, or some other reason has enabled some of the Pacific slope streams to capture some of the former tributaries of the Rio Grande. With the tributary went the darters, the catfishes, and other fishes it contained. A freshet or a cave-stream may sometimes be responsible for an apparently mysterious distribution. Salt water is sometimes a barrier to the migration of fresh-water fishes. Jordan [1] says of the streams of San Luis Obispo County, California, of which the San Luis Creek mentioned before is one:

"The county of San Luis Obispo lies along the coast of California, midway between Monterey and Santa Barbara. It is composed of two or three isolated valleys opening out to the sea, and surrounded on all sides by high and barren mountains. These mountains have served as a barrier, shutting off all access of fishes to the streams of the region from the larger basins of the north and east. The valleys of San Luis Obispo are traversed by clear, swift, cold streams rising in mountain springs. In these streams very few species of fishes are found, and these few, except in one case (*Agosia nubila*), are species which have come into the fresh waters by way of the sea. None of the characteristic types of the San Joaquin and Sacramento valleys are found in San Luis Obispo County. This is evidently not due to any character of the waters, but simply to the fact that these fishes cannot reach San Luis Obispo except by descent to the sea."

But there is also evidence that the ocean is not invariably a barrier. To quote again from Jordan: [2]

"The passage of species from stream to stream along the Atlantic slope deserves a moment's notice. It is under present conditions impossible for any mountain or upland fish, as the trout or the miller's thumb, to cross from the Potomac River to the James, or

---

[1] Bull. U. S. Fish Com. for 1894, p. 141.
[2] "Guide to the Study of Fishes," pp. 312 and 313.

from the Neuse to the Santee, by descending to the lower courses of the rivers, and thence passing along either through the swamps or by way of the sea. The lower courses of these streams, warm and muddy, are uninhabitable by such fishes. Such transfers are, however, possible farther north. From the rivers of Canada and from many rivers of New England the trout does descend to the sea and into the sea, and farther north the white fish does this also. Thus these fishes readily pass from one river basin to another. As this is the case now everywhere in the north, it may have been the case farther south in the time of the glacial cold. We may, I think, imagine a condition of things in which the snow fields of the Allegheny chain might have played some part in aiding the diffusion of cold-loving fishes. A permanent snow field on the Blue Ridge in western North Carolina might render almost any stream in the Carolinas suitable for trout, from its source to its mouth. An increased volume of colder water might carry the trout of the head streams of the Catawba and the Savannah as far down as the sea. We can even imagine that the trout reached these streams in the first place through such agencies, though of this there is no positive evidence. For the presence of trout in the upper Chattahoochee we must account in some other way . . . .

"With the lowland species of the southern rivers it is different. Few of these are confined within narrow limits. The streams of the whole South Atlantic and Gulf Coast flow into shallow bays, mostly bounded by sand pits or sand bars which the rivers themselves have brought down. In these bays the waters are often neither fresh nor salt; or, rather, they are alternately fresh and salt, the former condition being that of the winter and spring. Many species descend into these bays, thus finding every facility for transfer from river to river. There is a continuous inland passage in fresh or brackish waters, traversable by such fishes, from Chesapeake Bay nearly to Cape Fear; and similar conditions exist on the coasts of Louisiana, Texas, and much of Florida."

Adaptations to the Main Object in Life. — Fishes either lay eggs that are fertilized in the water, retain eggs that have been internally fertilized to the time of hatching or in a few species give birth to living young which have been carried far beyond the "hatching" point.

A. *Migration.* As the spawning season approaches, fishes undertake a general migratory movement. The migration may be of great or very limited extent. The movement is in general one of going upstream to small brooks and shoreward to shallow water. In some cases the migration may mean the movement for a few feet only. Some minnows and darters move to a favorably-placed rock or weed. The skipjack in our small lakes moves to the zone of pickerel weeds near shore. The sunfishes, black bass, and many others move shoreward to shallow water. Some minnows move to

Fig. 1540. Sucker, *Catostomus commersoni* (Lacépède). Actual size, 232 mm. long.

riffles from neighboring pools. The upstream movement of suckers is powerful in California, and has become proverbial in Illinois and neighboring waters.

The limit in the extent of migratory movements upstream is reached by the Pacific coast salmons. The quinnat salmon of the Pacific coast is the king of the migrants. It enters the Columbia River at the age of four years, in March and April. The entire summer is taken up, without food, in ascending to its spawning grounds. It spawns a thousand miles and more from the ocean, or in Alaska two thousand miles from the sea, in shallow riffles of small streams at the headwaters of the streams it ascends. Alturas Lake, near one of its spawning places, has an elevation of 7,335 feet. After spawning the adult dies. It never succeeds in regaining the ocean. The Atlantic slope salmon (*Salmo salar*) ascends from the ocean to the headwaters of streams north of Cape Cod. The relative of the salmons, the cisco of Tippecanoe Lake, in December ascends its tributary streams to spawn. The marine lamprey ascends streams from the Atlantic Ocean. The landlocked lamprey (*Petromyzon marinus unicolor*) of central New York migrates eight to ten miles from Cayuga Lake up the streams to spawn. The silver lamprey of the Mississippi Valley ascends small brooks in the spring. On the Pacific slope the Pacific lamprey ascends streams in large numbers. At La Grange, Idaho, I found very many congregated below a milldam which they had not been able to ascend. The sturgeons, for the most part living in the sea, also ascend streams to spawn.

While many species of fishes have the habit of entering fresh water when they approach ripeness, the eel alone, of the fishes of the northern hemisphere, has the reverse habit of taking to salt water when the reproductive period approaches. It has been well known for many years that during winter and early spring the young of the eel enter the mouths of streams in enormous numbers. Redi records the entrance of young eels into the Arno in 1667, and says that at Pisa three million pounds of young eels 30–120 mm. were taken in five hours. They find their way for hundreds of miles from the ocean. "Young individuals three to five inches long ascend rivers in incredible numbers, overcoming all obstacles, ascending vertical walls or floodgates, entering every large and swollen tributary, and making their way even over terra firma to waters shut off from all communications with rivers."

The American eel, which is closely related to the European eel, is found in all fresh waters emptying from the Gulf of St. Lawrence to Mexico. Eels have been seen in Colorado 1500 miles from the Gulf of Mexico, at an elevation of 7200 feet. Only the females ascend such distances, the males remaining near the coast. While in fresh water they feed on everything eatable. When they approach their full size, in about four years, they descend the streams to the ocean in autumn. They are lost sight of beyond a distance of a mile from shore, but about six months after they have entered the sea, eel eggs have been found floating on the surface. They are large eggs, with a very large perivitelline space, and vesicular yolk. They hatch into larvae quite unlike eels. These become gradually greatly modified, but not in the direction of becoming eel-like. It is not until the larvae are about a year old that they are metamorphosed into young eels which ascend streams such as their parents have descended two years previously. Like all fishes, such as the lampreys and salmon, which make very elaborate preparations to produce their young at a great distance from their range, the eels never regain their range, and probably all die after the first reproductive period. It is not improbable that in some landlocked lakes eels mature and reproduce in fresh water, but no eels with ripe eggs, nor eggs, nor larval eels, have been found in fresh water.

Homes of Fishes. — Emphasis has been laid on the fact that the ultimate fate of all fresh water is locomotion, and that usually currents exist between fresh-water lakes and the ocean. All fresh-water fishes are adapted to this condition and make provision to anchor their eggs or give birth to living young. There is but one fresh-water fish known to me that has pelagic eggs, the eel. It has not become adapted to rear its young in fresh water, but enters the sea before the reproductive period. This suggests that the adaptation of fresh-water fishes to resist currents did not arise after they had entered the fresh water, but that such oceanic candidates for fresh-water existence as had eggs adapted to resist the currents gained a permanent lodgment; while, on the contrary, none of those with pelagic eggs have been able to establish permanent homes in fresh waters. All anadromous and fresh-water fishes either have eggs heavier than water which lodge in gravel, or produce attachable eggs. Many marine fishes have pelagic eggs, and none of these have become permanent residents in fresh water. Others have adhesive eggs, that at the moment of being laid will adhere to foreign substances; others have cohesive eggs that will become attached to each other, but not to foreign substances. Of the adhesive eggs some are simply sticky all over and others have mushroom-shaped processes that have sticky heads (stickleback). The eggs of still other fishes have filaments that coil about foreign substances. All of these types are found in fresh waters. The fundamental adaptation, that to flowing water, was acquired by the ancestors of fresh-water fishes before they were able to leave the ocean.

Along with this adaptation against currents, we have in the fresh-water fishes elaborate brooding habits that in part, at least, are an adaptation to another fresh-water condition, i.e., the settling of sediment. A very brief survey of the nature of the eggs and the brooding habits as far as known is instructive.

Amia, the sunfishes, and the black bass build their nests in shallow water with little or no current. The nest is either prepared in weed-covered patches or on the sand. *Amia* prefers weed-covered patches but is not exclusive in its selections. The nest, prepared by the male with the snout and fins, consists simply of an area from which the vegetation has largely been removed, or it may be but a saucer-shaped pit in sand. The eggs of *Amia* are adhesive and are attached to the sides and bottoms of the nest. The male remains over or near the nest until the eggs hatch,

Fig. 1541. Large-mouthed Black Bass, *Micropterus salmoides* (Lacépède).

occasionally fanning away sediment, and always while near the nest ready to drive out intruders. The male accompanies the school of young until they reach a length of 100 mm.

The sunfishes and black bass build their nests preferably in gravel or sand, but not to the entire exclusion of the localities preferred by *Amia*. Their eggs are quite small and also adhesive, and are found at the sides or bottom of a nest.

The male of the small-mouthed black bass builds the nest. There are no secondary sexual characters. " Each [1] male tests the bottom in several places by rooting into it with his snout and fanning away the overlying mud or sand with his tail. If he does not find gravel after going down three or four inches, he seeks another place. Having found a suitable place, he cleans the sand and mud from the gravel by sweeping it with his tail. He then turns over the stones with his snout and continues sweeping until the gravel over a circular spot, some two feet in diameter, is clean. The sand is swept toward the edge of the nest and there forms a few inches

[1] From Lydell, Bull. U. S. Fish Com., 22: 39.

high, leaving the center of the nest concave like a saucer. The nest is usually located near a log or large rock so as to be shielded from one side. If the bank is sheer and the water deep enough, the nest may be built directly against the bank." . . .

After spawning the male drives the female away. "The male, and the male only, now continues to guard the nest, fanning sediment from the eggs and repelling enemies. At 66° F. the eggs hatch in five days and the young fishes swarm up from the bottom in twelve to thirteen days from the day of hatching.

"Shortly after the young small-mouthed bass rise from the nest they scatter out over a space four or five rods across — not in a definite school with all the fish moving together, but as a loose swarm, moving independently or in small groups. The fry may be at the surface or on the bottom, in weeds or clear water, and are attended by the male until they are $1\frac{1}{4}$ inches long. The swarm then gradually disperses and the young fry, which were previously black, take on the color of the old fish."

Other fishes having adhesive eggs attach them to the lower surfaces of rocks and boards. Several of our darters have this habit, as well as several minnows. The eggs of some species of darters are attached to the upper surfaces of rocks. Other fishes suspend their eggs from aquatic plants, with or without nest building. The goldfish, which has adhesive eggs, attaches them singly to aquatic plants, as the fish swims about. The skipjack probably does the same, though in this species, as in the case of its marine relatives, the egg is supplied with long, thread-like filaments. I have seen pairs of these fishes wind in and out near the surface among water plants, and once saw a pair of gar pikes late in June going through the same performance. The yellow perch provides similarly for its eggs. They are laid in long strings which are suspended from aquatic plants. The eggs of the sticklebacks have mushroom-shaped processes that are adhesive.

The lampreys, salmon, trout, some suckers, and some minnows have eggs which are heavier than water. These fishes deposit their eggs among the gravel of swift-flowing water where little sediment falls. Some of our catfishes and the miller's-thumb have cohesive, agglutinating eggs. These are laid under boards or in other protected places and guarded by the male. The male *Noturus* not infrequently proceeds to swallow the eggs he guards when they are uncovered.

"Both [1] parents of the yellow catfish are a pale yellow color, the number of eggs deposited was estimated at two thousand. The incubatory period was five days in a mean water temperature of 77° F., the lowest temperature being 75 degrees and the highest 80 degrees.

"During the entire hatching period both parents were incessant in their efforts to prevent the smothering of the eggs, to keep them clean, and to guard against intruders. The eggs were kept constantly agitated and aerated by a gentle fanning motion of the lower fins, and foreign particles, either on the bottom of the nest or floating near the eggs, were removed in the mouth or by the fins. The most striking act in the care of the eggs was the sucking of the egg masses into the mouth and the blowing of them out, this being repeated several times with each cluster before another lot was treated.

"The male was particularly active in watching for intruders, and savagely attacked the hands of the attendant who brought food; he also rushed at sticks or other objects introduced into the aquarium. Practically the entire work of defence was assumed by the male, although the female occasionally participated.

"During the time the fry were on the bottom the attentions of the parents were unrelaxed, and, in fact, were increased, for the tendency of the different lots to become scattered had to be corrected, and the dense packing of the young in the corners seemed to occasion much concern. The masses of fry were constantly stirred, as the eggs had been, by a flirt of the fins, which often sent dozens of them three or four inches upward, to fall back on the pile.

"The very young fry were also taken into the mouths of the parents and blown out, especially those which became separated from the main lot and were found in the sand and sediment. The old fish would take in a mouthful of fry and foreign particles, retain them for a moment, and expel them with some force. After

[1] From Smith & Harron, Bull. U. S. Fish Com., 22: 151.

the young began to swim and became scattered, the parents continued to suck them in and mouth them, and, as subsequently developed, did not always blow them out.

"An interesting habit of the parents, more especially the male, observed during the first few days after hatching, was the mixing and stirring of the masses of young by means of the barbels. With the chin on the bottom, the old fish approached the corners where the fishes were banked, and with the barbels all directed forward and flexed where they touched the bottom, thoroughly agitated the mass of fry, bringing the deepest individuals to the surface. This act was usually repeated several times in quick succession. The care of the young may be said to have ceased when they began to swim freely, although both parents continued to show solicitude when the attendant approached the aquarium from the rear."

In contrast to the nest-building habits are the habits of those fishes seeking a definite sort of locality where to deposit their eggs. The dace (*Semotilus*), stone roller (*Campostoma*), and rainbow darter (*Ethesostoma caeruleum*) select gravelly bottom on shallow riffles above a pool. The habits of the darter have recently been made the subject of exhaustive study by Miss Cora D. Reeves.[1] These fishes spawn when the temperature reaches about 60° F. The males select holdings which they guard and from which they drive rival males by a display of color and by blows delivered with head and tail. The female buries herself partly in the gravel, the male taking a position over her, other males crowding in. A few eggs and milt are extruded at a time and the spawning act oft repeated. The eggs are adhesive and stick to the gravel.

The adaptation to currents in fresh water thus consists in various devices to anchor the eggs. The adaptation against sediment is found in the guarding and fanning habit of the male, the deposit of eggs to the lower surface of rocks or boards and on riffles, and the suspension of eggs from water weeds. To these groups of more or less adaptive habits we must add the peculiar brooding habits of some catfishes, Cichlids, and the blind fishes, and Cyprinodonts. Some of the South American catfishes have the habit of carrying their eggs in the mouth. Some of them, *Aspredo*, carry

[1] Biol. Bull., 14 : 35.

them attached to the ventral surface. Several African and South American Cichlids carry the eggs and young in their mouths and gill chambers. The so-called myth, that a given fish leads about his brood and guards them in his mouth when danger approaches, is not a myth for some of these species.

The blind fishes of North America carry their eggs in their gill chambers. In these fishes the oviduct has moved forward so that it

FIG. 1542. Rainbow Darter, *Etheostoma caeruleum* Storer, ♂.

opens just behind the isthmus. The young are carried for a month or two until they have reached a length of 10 mm. In a group of Cyprinodonts reaching as far as Indiana, but increasing in diversity of species and numbers of individuals southward, the eggs are retained by the female until the yolk is absorbed by the growing young fish, and sometimes for a much longer period. In the

FIG. 1543. Rainbow Darter, *Etheostoma caeruleum* Storer, ♀. Actual size, 50 mm.

blind fishes of Cuba the young are about an inch in length at the time of birth and in the California surf-perch they may be twice as long.

Secondary Sexual Characters. — Such features consist in size, disposition, color, or structure. Large differences in all of these are found in the killifishes. In some of these species the male is minute and provided with an anal fin modified into a lance-like blade. This is not an intromittent organ but is apparently used as a momentary clasper as the male darts at the female with the lance directed forward and upward, liberating the spermatozoa in spermatophores as the tip of the lance comes in contact with the female. A single impregnation may furnish the female with spermatozoa for several broods of young.

The male of *Amia* has a caudal ocellus. In *Rivulus* it is the female that possesses the caudal ocellus.

The differences in disposition in the black bass, in which no other secondary sexual differences exist, are mentioned elsewhere.

FIG. 1544. Blunt-Nosed Minnow, *Pimephales notatus* (Rafinesque), ♂ . Actual size, 73 mm. long.

The greatest display of secondary sexual colors is seen in the sunfishes and especially in the little darters and in *Chrosomus* whose brilliant coloration is scarcely surpassed by that of the humming birds. The greatest display of secondary sexual color takes place just before the breeding season. It may be used as a sex recognition mark, a battle flag, as in the rainbow darter, or as a lure to the female.

In many males small excrescences appear on the sides, on the fins, or on the head during the breeding season. The anal fin is often provided with hooklets in suckers. The male of *Campostoma* becomes covered with tubercles. *Pimephales* develops short, warty horns on the head and the horned dace (*Semotilus atromaculatus*) large, long ones. Some of these are used as excitants for the female, others undoubtedly to enable the male to cling to the female during the spawning act.

Physical Environment and Adaptations to it. With the exceptions noted, fishes are always found in water. The character of the water, i.e., the per cent of salt and other chemicals in solution, determines the three major ecological divisions of fishes: I, the marine fishes; II, the brackish water fishes; and III, the inland, fresh-water fishes. The first two groups are beyond the scope of this chapter.

The inland fishes, according to the physical character of the environments selected by them, may be divided into the following groups, in part suggested by Cope and Jordan.

1. Lowland fishes: the bowfin, pirate perch, large-mouthed black bass, sunfishes, mud-minnow, and some catfishes.

2. Channel fishes, ranging from lowland to upland: the channel catfish, the moon-eye, gar pike, buffalo fishes, and drum.

3. Upland fishes: many of the darters, shiners, and suckers, and the small-mouthed black bass.

4. Mountain fishes: the brook trout, and many of the darters and minnows.

5. Lake fishes, inhabiting only waters which are deep, clear, and cold: the various species of whitefish and the Great Lake trout.

6. Anadromous fishes, or those which run up from the sea to spawn in the fresh water: the salmon, sturgeon, shad, and striped bass.

7. Catadromous fishes, that descend to the ocean to spawn: the eel.

8. Cave fishes, found exclusively in cave streams: the Amblyopsidae.

Many of the species are found in more than one of the areas mentioned.

Inland waters vary greatly in the amount of the solids in solution or suspension. In the Great Salt Lake and the alkali lakes of the west the amount of solids in solution is prohibitive to fish life. In all other waters, however small, if accessible, fishes are found. Even temporary ponds are colonized by catfishes and sunfishes if they are at all accessible. Sediment is present in variable amounts and some fishes, depending exclusively upon sight to detect their prey, are found only in water free from sediment.

Under given conditions in moving water, the amount of oxygen in solution is tolerably constant. When a body of fresh water freezes over, or after the summer thermocline is formed, the oxygen may become reduced in quantity or disappear altogether in the deeper portions of a lake. Through the reduction in oxygen fishes may be either killed in large numbers or compelled to emigrate. Fishes being exclusive water animals are especially adapted to utilize the oxygen in the water. The gills are the universally present respiratory organs but in special cases the fins and part of the alimentary canal may be forced into service. In the gar-pike the air-bladder serves as a lung, at least for the elimination of CO_2. Various other fishes have cellular air-bladders connected with the alimentary canal that suggest respiration. Tower found that in fishes dying of asphyxiation the ratio of CO_2 to O in the air-bladder increases.

During the breeding season when the gill chambers are full of eggs much of the respiration of the blindfishes is probably forced on the fins and general surface. In the surf-fish, to which the Sacramento *Hysterocarpus* belongs, the young are born fully developed.[1] In their earliest development in the ovary the general surface of the larva must act as a respiratory organ, later the alimentary canal functions as such. A continuous stream of ovarian fluid passes in at the gill-opening and out at the anus at this time. Finally the fins become hypertrophied into enormous sheets superabundantly supplied with blood vessels. In the Cuban blindfishes, in which the young reach a length of an inch at the time of birth, vascular lobes are developed in the ovary, which the young take into their mouths and to which they cling, possibly both for food and oxygen. It is very probable that those fishes that are capable of living out of water for a time carry on respiration through their moist skin.

Temperature and Adjustment to it. — In nearly all fresh waters of the temperate region there is a fluctuation in the water between 32° to 80° F. The extreme fluctuation is found only on the surface of the water. In the bottom of lakes eighty feet deep, the annual fluctuation ranges perhaps between 39° and 60° F. Fishes can always escape the extreme fluctuations by seeking deeper water. That they are adjusted to live through extreme cold is shown by the fact that some species may be frozen in ice and re-

[1] The life history of this species has not been traced, but that of some of its marine relations has.

vive when thawed out. The adjustment in this respect probably increases as one goes northward. Turner says of the Alaskan *Dallia:* "When taken from the traps the fish are immediately put into these baskets and taken to the village, where the baskets of fish are placed on stages out of the way of dogs. The mass of fish in each basket is frozen in a few minutes, and when required to take them out they have to be chopped out with an axe or beaten with a club to divide them into pieces of sufficient size to feed the dogs.

"The vitality of these fish is astonishing. They will remain in those grass baskets for weeks, and when brought into the house and thawed out they will be as lively as ever. The pieces which are thrown to the ravenous dogs are eagerly swallowed, the animal heat of the dog's stomach thaws the fish out, whereupon its movements cause the dog to vomit it up alive."

The lower temperature limit is set to fish life by the freezing point of the medium, 32° F. for fresh water, below this for salt water. The upper observed limit in ponds is somewhere near 100 degrees.[1] If the water is suddenly raised to this point, fishes survive but a few seconds. While the upper limit may be set by the effect of the increased heat on the protoplasm, its effect may be indirect and operate through the reduction in the amount of O held in suspension by the warm as compared with the cold water. That fishes will attempt any temperature is evidenced by the fact that they occasionally enter water in the National Park hot enough to boil them.

The adaptability of fishes to different temperatures is well shown by *Rhinichthys dulcis* which is found in the streams coming from the warm springs at Banff in the Canadian National Park, and also in the icy waters of Vermilion Creek at the same place. The same individuals are adjustable within wide limits, and the same species is sometimes found over a long north and south range. Nevertheless, temperature has doubtless played an important part in setting a northern limit to the migration of species, as they followed the retreating ice of the glacial period. In North

[1] Jordan and Richardson (Proc. U. S. Nat. Mus., 33 : 319–321) record *Lucania browni* from a hot spring with a temperature of 128° F.

America a southward migration has probably not taken place since that time.

Fishes of cold waters are primarily members of the families of salmon and trout, whitefish, miller's-thumb, and blackfishes. The check by cold has not been placed on any individual migration or limits set to the adult. *Rhinichthys dulcis* and the many species adapted to the great range of variation in the temperature in any of our temperate lakes shows this. The temperature factor determining distribution is set rather by the adaptation of the eggs to warm or cold water. Our trout, salmon, and whitefishes breed largely in winter when the temperature is low. The rate of development of their eggs, like that of all cold-water eggs, is slow. The warm-water species are warm-water species not because their individuals are incapable of entering cold water, for many of them do, but because their eggs will not develop in anything but water much warmer than that in which the eggs of cold-water species develop. Their eggs are of rapid development. They are adjusted to fluctuations in temperature and they respond to such fluctuations in temperature by hastening or slowing their rate of development.[1] The point of attack of temperatures is on the eggs and young, not on the adult, and temperature controls distribution through its influence on the eggs.

In all cold waters of the United States accessible to them, trout, salmon, and whitefish are found. Some of them, the brook trout, Rocky mountain whitefish, Coulter's whitefish and salmon, are adjusted to swift currents; others, the lake trout and many white fishes, to the stagnant waters of lakes. Some of the latter are littoral or abysmal or pelagic, depending on the nature of their food. The elevation of a stream has probably primarily nothing to do with the distribution of its inhabitants, but because elevated waters are usually cold (and frequently swift) all accessible mountain waters are inhabited by cold-water species. The number of species adjusted to cold waters is not as great and their affinities

---

[1] The cod eggs which hatch in thirty days at a temperature of from 0.0–2° C. hatch in thirteen days in a temperature of 6–7.9°. Herring eggs which require forty days at a temperature of 2–3.9° C. hatch in eleven at a temperature of 10–11.9°; the shad which hatches in eleven days at a temperature of 13.5° hatches in three to five days in a temperature of from 20–23°.

are not as varied as those adjusted to the warmer, more accessible waters of the central and southern lowlands. The latter are the homes of the black bass, sunfishes, catfishes, gar pikes, and others.

So called warm-water species are capable of a wide range of adjustment to differing climates. Wherever a north and south river connects warmer with colder areas in which the species are otherwise different, the easy route of migration induces some species to extend their range into otherwise shunned areas. The Mississippi has induced a southward migration of several species beyond their normal range, the Nile has extended the equatorial African fauna to its mouth. But the most notable example is offered by the Madeira and Tapajos to Paraguay and La Plata waterway. It extends from the equator south to a latitude equal to that of Memphis. Nearly all of the fishes of Buenos Aires belong to Amazonian genera or even species. Only one or two Amazonian genera have succeeded in reaching the borders of the United States. Fifty Amazonian genera have reached the La Plata basin that have not succeeded in going an equal distance south on the Atlantic coast where they did not have the facilities or inducement of a continuous waterway.

Current and Adjustment to It. — The major adaptation of all fresh-water fishes is to the locomotion of water. Most fishes stand head upstream, a position that makes the respiratory movement easiest in a current. Different fishes, and in some cases the same fishes at different seasons of the year, are adjusted to the entire range of variation in the intensity of the locomotion. Waterfalls only are not inhabited by fishes, but even these are ascended or descended if not too high. Different species of the Salmonidae give us examples of the entire range of adjustment to currents. Some of them live only in the stagnant water of deep lakes. Others live only in swift mountain brooks. The members of the genus *Coregonus* usually live in the stagnant waters of lakes, but *Coregonus coulteri* is found in a mountain torrent, and the Tippecanoe cisco, which lives in the stagnant water of the lake during the greater part of the year, runs up the tributaries in December. Other whitefishes and trout have the same habit. Different fishes are even adjusted to the differences in the same small stream in which quiet pools alternate with swift-flowing ripples. In the Mississippi Valley the riffles are occupied by darters, in Cuba by gobies, in South America by characins, and, although belonging to widely different families, they greatly resemble each other.

Light and Adjustments to It. — In the shallower parts of clear water the fluctuations in light from day to night are but little less than in the air. Various fishes are variously adjusted to the

FIG. 1545. Hog Sucker, *Catostomus nigricans* Le Sueur. Actual size, 305 mm. long.

light. Some are nocturnal, remaining hidden during the day, as the common catfish. Some combine stereotropism with their negative heliotropism, and take shelter in crevices and under rocks. The light-shunning habit on the part of their ancestors doubtless accounts for the cave-inhabiting blindfishes of to-day. Some diurnal fishes habitually stay in the shade of some tree, or log, or pier, while others are found in the open. There seems to be a complete gradation between the blindfishes, which always live in

FIG. 1546. Hog Sucker, *Catostomus nigricans* Le Sueur. Actual size, 81 mm. long.

total darkness, and those fishes, like some sunfishes, that live in total light, as far as this exists.

The eye is not the only light-perceiving organ of aquatic vertebrates. The skin is sensitive to light in many cases. The blindfishes, whose eyes are not functional and may be entirely removed, nevertheless appreciate the difference between light and dark. The young after having their eyes removed are as sensitive to light as those with eyes, and the entire skin seems equally sensitive to light. The sight of the nocturnal fishes is worse than that of owls, and their eyes are but little used. The sight of the positively heliotropic fishes, on the other hand, is good, their eyes are large and they depend on their eyesight for food. They capture living food and are frequently pelagic in habit. Small-mouthed fishes depending on their eyes for food will not take food that is at rest. Small fragments of meat falling through the water will readily be seized but will not be picked up from the bottom. The great variety of artificial flies and gyrating baits are man's adaptations to the fact that some large-mouthed fishes also select their food by sight.

Depth and the Bottom, and Adjustments to Them. — No systematic study of the bottoms of our lakes has been made and it is hence unknown how extensive the abysmal fauna is. In fishes ranging in deep water the adjustment is probably due not so much to the depth itself, as to the things that go with depth. Pressure increases one atmosphere with each thirty feet in depth, plants disappear beyond a few feet, and with the plants necessarily disappear all the animals (fish food for the most part), that are associated with the plants.

The character of the bottom is not a simple element like temperature, light, or current. There is a graduation from mud to gravel and rock and each of these may be weed-covered or bare. But whether the bottom is mud, gravel, or rock depends on current. That certain species are found principally on one bottom or another is certain, but that the adjustment is to the character of the bottom and not to the current and food that go with it is doubtful.

The Biological Environment and Adjustment to It. — Food is the controlling factor in the local distribution of fishes within any unit, as chemical composition and temperature are controlling factors in the geographical distribution among the different units. Food itself is dependent on other food and this ultimately on depth, nature of bottom, current, and the other elements of the physical environment. For the most part the food of the young is essentially different from the food of the adult of the same species, and consists of the organisms composing the plankton, largely Entomostraca. The members of a local fish fauna are distributed in the following ecological groups: pelagic, littoral (bottom fishes, all predacious fishes), and nocturnal.

To these should be added abysmal fishes, but nothing is known of these in America except that *Triglopsis* is found in deeper water of the Great Lakes.

Pelagic, abysmal, littoral, and nocturnal forms are such as find their food in those regions or times. Their adaptations are but secondary adjustments to the region in which their food is found. Everything eatable is food for some fishes though few have such omnivorous tastes as to take the entire bill of fare. The skipjack (*Lapidestes*) is a surface ranger and occupies as definite a position under the surface of the pelagic area of our lakes as the swallows do over it. Insects and all other minute terrestrial organic matters reaching the surface of the water find a lodgment in their stomachs. Frequently the fish darts out of the water as the swallow dips into it to secure its food. Its food is not confined to terrestrial strays, but it also takes Entomostraca and Chironomus larvae. *Zygonectes* and *Fundulus* also range near the surface but nearer the shores. In the mountain lakes in which the skipjack is not found, the half-grown whitefish (*Coregonus williamsoni*) occupies the same ecological niche. In Lake Tahoe on June evenings individuals nine inches long rise to gnats blown into the lake, and they can then be caught with a minute hook baited with a fly.

In the American tropics a killifish with half its eyes adapted to seeing in air and the other half adapted to seeing in water also ranges on the surface. Larger objects reaching the surface of the water are secured by black bass, trout, and other fishes that range and poise in deeper water and "rise" to their prey near the surface as the kingfisher dives for his. All fishes that rise to artificial bait, grasshoppers, etc., belong to this group. Some trout rise more readily to a mouse but for esthetic reasons this cannot be recommended for bait.

Another series of pelagic fishes is formed by the plankton feeders. There are several sorts of these. The young of most fishes, the sunfishes and minnows and some whitefishes, see their minute prey and deliberately pick it from the water. Such are provided with teeth either in their mouths or in their gullets. Another series probably including the spoonbill catfish take in large quantities of water and strain the plankton from it. They have weak teeth or none and specially-adapted gill rakers for straining the water.

The various darters, a peculiar American product, are all littoral. They rest on their pectorals on the bottom in shallow water. With head erect and eyes protruding they are ready for anything that moves within their range of vision. They are found among weeds and gravel, chiefly in flowing water so shallow that

FIG. 1547. Johnny Darter, *Boleosoma nigrum* Rafinesque. Actual size, 55 mm. long.

the surface is rippled. Associated with them, or in places similar to these, in favorable localities, are miller's-thumbs. The pirate perch and trout perch should probably also be placed here.

Other bottom fishes with sucker mouth and elongate alimentary canal are found over mud bottoms. These include *Campostoma*, suckers, carp, and sturgeon in North America. In tropical America their place is taken by peculiar armored relatives of the catfishes, the Loricariidae. Lastly, the large, predacious fishes treat the smaller fishes as they in their turn treat the plankton. Here belong the muscalonge, the pickerels, salmon trout, and the basses. Our nocturnal catfishes and the ubiquitous eel are omnivorous. They take what they can. Everything that tastes or moves and is within reach is food for the nocturnal catfish. Some blindfishes planted in a pool had a way of disappearing that was mysterious, until the pool was drained and the sardonic catfish, lurking under a rock and found in possession of the last blindfish partly digested, solved the mystery.

Fishes are adapted to their food in structure as well as habit.

The dentition varies from none at all to the crushing apparatus of the white perch, the cutting incisors of some of the killifishes and the rasplike patches of the teeth of the muscalonge. The mouth varies in position, shape, and size according to the food, from the ventrally-placed sucker mouth to the upward-pointing mouth of *Zygonectes;* from the small mouth of the cisco to the capacious maw of the muscalonge. The gill-rakers vary from none to the complicated strainers of the spoonbill catfish. The alimentary canal also varies with the food from the short canal of the flesh eaters to the convoluted tube many times as long as the fish in the mud eaters. That fishes are a very adaptable group is shown by the fact that in South America a single family, the characins, have the widest range of adaptation in the alimentary canal to different food. Forbes has pointed out that the minnows of North America are adjusted to a great variety of food. He distinguishes four groups: (1) Intestine two to nine times as long as the fish, pharyngeal teeth not hooked, with grinding surface. (2) Intestine one to one and two-thirds times as long as the fish, pharyngeal teeth hooked, with grinding surface. (3) Intestine somewhat shorter than the fish, teeth hooked, with grinding surface. (4) Intestine usually shorter than the head and body, teeth hooked, without grinding surface.

Concerning the relation of these structures Forbes says:

"It is consequently from a comparison of the ratios of these groups that we shall derive the most interesting facts relating to the correspondence of food and structure. The most conspicuous result is the great preponderance of mud in the intestines of the fishes of the first group, characterized by an extraordinarily elongate intestine, and by pharyngeal teeth destitute of hooks and provided with a broad grinding surface. Here, as already noted, mud, sand, and gravel amount to about three-fourths of the matter ingested, while in the third and fourth groups only trivial and accidental quantities occurred. In the second group, on the other hand, with intestines intermediate in length, mud was still abundant, but much less so than in the first, averaging less than half the whole. If we exclude this indigestible matter, however, we shall find the first group still further distinguished by the predominance of vegetation as compared with animal matter, the latter being only about one-third the former, while in groups three and four, on the other hand, vegetation amounts to about one-third the animal food. The groups last mentioned, distinguished from each other as they are only by the presence of a masticatory surface on the pharyngeal teeth in the first, and its absence in the second, differ scarcely at all in their general food characters, and this structural feature seems therefore to be of little significance. In both the animal ratio amounts to seventy-five per cent, and vegetation stands in each at twenty-five; while insects are respectively fifty and sixty-one."

Recently Pütter has maintained that fishes absorb food in solution in the water. He found that a goldfish lived for forty-one days in tap water which contained no organized food and the oxygen consumed substantially accounted for the loss in weight. When organic substances were dissolved in the tap water, the goldfish survived for seventy-eight days, and the oxygen consumed greatly exceeded the amount that would account for the loss in weight.

Food according to its nature may be detected by sight, perception of vibrations, touch, smell, or taste.

Food is detected by sight in most fishes. Many fishes will seize an object that is in motion without discrimination as to what it is provided it is the right size. If it is suitable for food that fact is discovered by touch or taste, or both, in the mouth and the object is swallowed. If it is not fit for food it is rejected. It is evident that in such cases sight only locates the moving object, other senses distinguish its nature.

Neither friend nor foe of the fishes discloses his presence by sound, but frequently does so by vibrations of lower frequency. It is extremely doubtful whether any sound produced over water is heard by fishes in the water. The sounds of the air are scarcely capable of passing the surface of the water to an extent to be perceived by an ear under water as highly developed as that of man. The ears of fishes are much more simple than those of man. The ability on the part of fishes to hear at all has been disputed, but Parker[1] has recently made experiments that show conclusively that fishes hear sounds produced under water.

[1] Bull. U. S. Fish Com., 22 : 45–64.

In over half of our fresh-water fishes the air bladder is connected by a chain of ossicles with the ear. In some of them the air bladder comes in contact with the skin in an area just behind the head. The intercostal muscles are not developed at this place and a form of tympanum is thus produced. It has been suggested that this Weberian apparatus, as it is called, is in reality an auditory organ; that it is a static apparatus controlling the rising and sinking of the fish in water; that it is a manometer acquainting the fish with the degree of pressure that is exerted by the gases in the air bladder against its walls; that it is a barometer acquainting the fish with the variations in the atmospheric pressure; that it is a sound producer. Judged by its structure alone, in some forms the air bladder is divided into two small lateral parts connected with the ossicles, the rest of the air bladder having disappeared, it seems more than probable that it is an organ for the perception of sound.

Vibrations of lower frequency than those producing sound, such as may be produced by waves or bodies falling into the water, are perceived by the lateral line organs of fishes. The lateral line organs of the head of the blindfishes are greatly exaggerated and their ability to perceive vibrations enables these fishes to secure living prey with precision. The lateral line organs of the head take the place of the eyes of pelagic fishes in detecting food. Fernandus Payne succeeded in getting an *Amblyopsis* to respond to the water dripping into its aquarium. It would rise to the point where the drop of water struck and would try to seize it by snapping at it. Perception of vibrations by the lateral line organs of the head enabled it to locate the point of impact of the water. Touch, taste, or smell could have nothing to do with it. These fishes may touch recently-crushed amphipods on which they feed without paying any attention to them unless a stray leg is still moving. They will readily take meat attached to a string held in the hand to give it motion.

Many fishes are conscious of the presence of food by perceiving it either through the sense of smell, touch, or taste. Parker has demonstrated that the catfish can detect minced earthworms by its sense of smell. The elaborate experiments of Herrick with codfishes have shown that their sense of smell gives them but vague information, while the senses of touch and taste, whose organs are found over the entire body, enable the catfish to detect and secure any food coming in contact with any part of the body. In contrast to the blindfishes (*Amblyopsis*) of the Ohio Valley caves, the Point Loma blindfish secures its food through touch and taste. A hungry Point Loma blindfish with a stroke of the fins brings the mouth in position for operations as soon as any portion of its skin, especially of the head, comes in contact with food.

Fish Enemies. — The enemies of fishes are the mink, otter, an occasional raccoon and cat among the mammals; the kingfisher, herons, ducks, loons, and terns among birds; an occasional bullfrog and possibly *Necturus* among batrachians; several snakes, and many fishes, spawn eaters, fry catchers, lampreys, and adulteating, predacious fishes.

The otter as a fish enemy has been practically eliminated. The occasional fish caught by the mink and raccoon will form but a small annual total. In fact, by the changes incident to advancing civilization, all but the aquatic enemies of the fishes have been reduced to a point where their depredations can have but little selective value.

Fishes evidently could avoid terns and kingfishers by living below the few inches penetrated by these divers. But the advantages of food near the surface evidently outweigh the danger of being caught, as long as a sudden dive or a dart forward will enable the fish to escape.

Herons and ducks are avoided by selecting water too deep for these enemies. Color and swiftness are probably other adaptations to the same enemies. The darter sits with outspread pectorals on the bottom of a stream or lake within easy reach of a heron. A sudden motion of the powerful pectorals and he sits as composedly somewhere else. The dart-like motion which gives the darter its name is an adaptation to secure food and avoid enemies. Swiftness, inconspicuousness, or ability to enter retreats are the means of defense against the loon and his ilk. However, none of the devices are always efficient.

The greatest enemy of fishes is the spawn stealer. At Lake

Tahoe the dead trout eggs from the hatchery were daily thrown into the lake. While no fish might be in evidence a handful of trout eggs was sure to bring a bullhead (*Cottus beldingi*) from under every rock. The same thing happened when the young trout fry were planted in the brooks. The adaptations of the black bass, sunfish, and *Amia* against depredations in their nests have already been given. No doubt many young fishes are eaten by minnows and sunfishes. A half-starved sunfish captured in a cave began to pick out the larval blindfishes in his pail, with neatness and dispatch, as soon as there was light enough for it to see them. The herding or schooling of their young by many fishes, as an adaptation against enemies, has been described before. Against their predacious neighbors strength, agility, endurance, and color are the adjustments. The dispersal of a school and the leap out of the water, reaching its maximum in the flight of the flying fish, are all adaptations to escape specific attacks. Aside from these general adaptations in the habit, structural adaptations against fish-eating enemies are also found.

The stickleback has divergent, erectile spines that can be locked when erected. This arrangement is altruistic rather than egoistic. While it does not prevent a duck or other animal from eating an occasional stickleback the duck is not likely to be tempted by a second stickleback. More effective weapons are the erectile dorsal and pectoral spines of the catfishes. In the stone cats the spine is surrounded by glandular tissue producing poison. The spine in entering an opponent pierces the gland and carries some of the poison into the wound.

Color must be looked upon as an adjustment to light in the presence of enemies. The amount of color on the surface of a fish is proportionate to the intensity of the light in the environment. The arrangement of the color is conditioned by the surroundings. Its presence is an adaptation to the physical environment and its arrangement is an adaptation to the biological environment. All animals living for generations in caves become bleached and finally lose all pigment. Nocturnal fishes are in large measure black. Bottom fishes, like the darters, hog sucker, miller's-thumb, are mottled and crossbarred. Weed-inhabiting species are barred (yellow perch), striped (black bass), or mottled (pickerels, sunfishes, etc.). Large size and strength are the best adaptations against existing fish enemies. Small size and insignificance are advantageous for other reasons. Between these, alertness, with power of quick movement, and protective color are the most efficient means of escaping enemies.

But all of these adaptations are not always sufficient. The most insidious of the fish enemies is the lamprey. So perfect is its means of attachment to its prey, that such a hard-scaled and vigorous. fish as *Amia calva* can rarely prevent the attachment and adhesion, although the most violent efforts be made. If a lamprey is attached to a stone of moderate size, the stone is frequently brought out with the fish if the animal is jerked up suddenly. In letting go its hold all that is necessary is to fill the disc with water from the respiratory bronchus, whereupon suction ceases and the animal is free. In feeding, the sharp teeth pressed against the skin of the animal to which it is attached naturally call the blood to the place. This hyperaemia is caused even more by the suction. At the same time the piston-like tongue with its powerful muscles and the saw-like teeth soon rasp a hole through the skin. The blood is then sucked from the fish and swallowed. The whole operation is something like the extraction of blood by a leech. The lamprey may remain upon a fish so long as the latter supplies sufficient nutriment. Sometimes the fish becomes exceedingly pale and weak so that it floats near the surface. In such a case, the fishermen know immediately that there is a lamprey attached to the fish, and, with a dip net, usually have no great trouble in catching both. The birds of prey also make this their opportunity and frequently carry off the floating fish, the lamprey sometimes remaining attached until it has been carried a considerable distance into the air.

That the injury to the food fishes is very great may be inferred from the fact that sometimes out of fifteen catfish caught on a set line in one night, ten to twelve have great raw sores where lampreys have attacked them. In the spring, too, when the suckers (*Catostomus*) run up to spawn, very many of them carry a lamprey, and naturally by the great drain of blood it causes, the fish must be weakened, so that obstacles on the way to the spawning ground are less liable to be surmounted than if the fish were in full vigor. In South America small catfishes live in the gills of larger catfishes.

Origin of Adapted Faunas. — It has been shown that the major adaptations of fresh-water fishes were acquired by their ancestors before they were eligible to a fresh-water existence.

The origin and modification of the cave fauna gives us a concrete example of the change of location, resulting from predestined adaptation and of subsequent minor adaptations. Caves are at the present time being colonized by the immigration of salamanders of the genus *Spelerpes* and other animals that have become adapted to a cave existence through their habit of living in the dark under rocks, bark, and other similar places. The adaptation to the conditions of cave existence in this case determines the change of location when the opportunity arises.

That minor adaptations will occur in these after they have become exclusively cave forms, is shown by the structure of the permanent cave salamanders of Missouri and Texas. These have in large measure lost their color and have degenerate eyes.

A somewhat more complex example is furnished by the history of the Horse Cave River. At Horse Cave, Kentucky, a wide valley extends north and south. Tributary valleys come from the east and west. The hills bordering these valleys are limestone capped with sandstone. The north and south valley was formed by the Horse Cave River that originally flowed over sandstone like that capping the bordering hills. No doubt it had a fauna as varied as that of any surface stream. The stream cut first through the sandstone, then through the limestone. When it had reached the easily dissolving limestone of the Kentucky caves and Green River had cut some distance below the surface of this, some part of its water, later more and more, found its way to the Green River by underground channels. To-day not a sign is seen on the surface of the streams that are responsible for the valley about Horse Cave. At least one of them rushes through lofty chambers one hundred eighty-five feet beneath the streets of Horse Cave City. With this change in the environment, with the disappearance of Horse

Cave River from the surface, its inhabitants had to migrate. They moved in two directions to adapted environments. The shore fishes and channel fishes moved out to the Green River where their descendants live to the present day. The negatively heliotropic, nocturnal, or stereotropic fishes moved into the holes dissolved in the bottom of the river. Their descendants live, at the present time, in the stream below or within the valley. They are colorless and all but eyeless, and have, no doubt, acquired this exaggerated adaptation to their present abode since their immigration. But the major adaptation to the cave existence they possessed before the formation of the caves, and it was responsible for their migration to their present habitat.

As was pointed out in the opening paragraphs, the fauna of the glaciated region of North America has similarly been derived by immigration from the south and possibly the ocean and Siberia to the north and west. The Great Lake Basin has but twenty-seven of its one hundred fifty-two species peculiar to itself; five are but varieties of more southern species and the remaining twenty-one more than represent the extent to which its fauna has become adapted in this area for some of them (eight Salmonidae and eight Cottidae) are cold-water species that may have been crowded out of the region south of the basin by the encroaching heat after the passing of the glacial epoch.

The selective migration to adapted locations must be added to the factors contributing to the origin of adapted faunas. This factor, "change of location," is as important to the origin of adapted faunas as the "change of function" to the origin of adaptive structures. Innumerable minor adaptations to heat, sediment, light, food, and to the peculiar combinations found in each selected locality have no doubt arisen in such localities.

IMPORTANT WORKS ON AQUATIC VERTEBRATES

GENERAL

Cambridge Natural History, edit. by S. F. Harmer and A. E. Shipley. Volumes: VII, Fishes; VIII, Amphibia; V, Reptilia; IX, Birds; X, Mammals. London.

SCHARFF, R. F. 1912. Distribution and Origin of Life in America. New York.

Bulletin of the U. S. Bureau of Fisheries; Washington, D. C.

(Contains many articles on Fishes, Birds, and Reptiles.)

MAMMALS

INGERSOLL, ERNEST. 1907. The Life of Animals. The Mammals. New York.

SETON, E. T. 1909. Life Histories of Northern Animals. 2 vols. New York.

STONE, WITMER, and CRAM. 1902. American Animals. New York.

BIRDS

CHAPMAN, F. M. 1912. Birds of Eastern North America. New York.

COUES, ELLIOTT. 1903. Key to North American Birds. Boston.

RIDGWAY, ROBERT. Birds of North and Middle America. Bulletin U. S. Nat. Mus., No. 50. Part I, 1901; Part II, 1902; Part III, 1904; Part IV, 1907; Part V, 1911.

REPTILES

COPE, E. D. 1898. Crocodilians, Lizards, and Snakes of North America. Ann. Rep. Smithsonian Inst., pp. 153–1270.

DITMARS, R. L. 1907. Reptile Book. New York.

AMPHIBIA

COPE, E. D. 1889. The Batrachia of North America. Bull. U. S. Nat. Mus., 34: 1–525.

DICKERSON, MARY C. 1906. Frog Book. New York.

FISHES

JORDAN, D. S. 1905. Guide to the Study of Fishes. New York.

JORDAN, D. S., and EVERMANN, B. W. 1896–1900. The Fishes of North and Middle America. Bull. U. S. Nat. Mus., No. 47. 4 Parts.

1902. American Food and Game Fishes. New York.

A number of admirable state lists have been published on Mammals, Birds, and Fishes. Nominally confined to a single state, they are useful over a much wider territory.

CHAPTER XXXI

TECHNICAL AND SANITARY PROBLEMS

By GEORGE C. WHIPPLE

Professor of Sanitary Engineering, Harvard University

THERE are several very practical problems of fresh-water biology which deserve consideration, and which will be treated briefly in this chapter. They relate chiefly to some of the smallest organisms found in fresh water, — the bacteria and the plankton. There are other problems, to be sure, which have to do with larger organisms, but most of these have been referred to in the various chapters which have gone before.

First and foremost is the problem of disease transmission. Pathogenic bacteria are not normally present in natural fresh waters, but rivers and lakes in inhabited regions are subject to pollution with the excrement of animals and human beings and such excrementitious substances are liable to contain the germs of disease. The adoption of the water carriage system of sewerage about the middle of the nineteenth century greatly increased these chances of fresh-water contamination. Water which contains excrementitious matter or bacteria of fecal origin may be said to be contaminated; if bacteria are actually present the water is said to be infected. The most noteworthy diseases which are water-borne are typhoid fever, Asiatic cholera, and dysentery, but there are other water-borne diseases, for contaminated water may contain the spores of other bacteria, molds, and the ova of parasitic worms. Fresh water also may serve as a medium within which mosquito larvae grow and from which mosquitoes emerge. Special kinds of mosquitoes play an important part in the transmission of yellow fever and certain other diseases. Then there may be indirect as well as direct relations between man and the microorganisms found in water.

Microscopic organisms form the basis of the food supply of fishes and thus indirectly contribute to human sustenance. Oysters feed chiefly upon diatoms. The smaller crustacea feed upon bacteria and minute algae and protozoa, and are, in turn, devoured by larger organisms.

In the public water supplies the appearance of algae and protozoa in large numbers is the occasion of complaint by the water consumers, for these organisms make the water unsightly and ill smelling. They also clog filters and increase the cost of water purification.

Water as a Conveyor of Disease Germs. There are few if any bacteria pathogenic to human beings which are naturally found in fresh waters. Trouble comes only when waters become infected with pathogenic bacteria derived from other human beings or from animals. Such bacteria do not thrive and multiply in natural waters so far as is now known but are merely mechanically transported by water. Furthermore, instead of multiplying in water pathogenic bacteria tend to decrease in numbers after the time of infection. This is an important practical matter as it greatly affects the safety of all public water supplies. For example, a rapidly flowing stream may convey infection for long distances in a short time, while, on the other hand, a lake or public reservoir may store the water for so long a time that there is opportunity for dangerous bacteria to die.

The longevity of pathogenic bacteria in water depends upon many things among which may be included the original character of the bacteria themselves, the temperature of the water, the opportunities for sedimentation and destruction by other organisms, the effect of sunlight, etc. Using general figures it may be said that under average conditions about 70 per cent of typhoid fever bacteria will disappear the first week, 90 per cent during the first two weeks, and 99 per cent during six weeks. They will live longer in cold water than in warm water. That is why most of the water-borne typhoid fever epidemics have occurred during the cold months of the year. The spirillum of Asiatic cholera is known to behave in a similar manner but less is known in regard to the rate at which it dies. There is some reason to believe that it has a shorter life in water than the typhoid fever bacillus. There is a group of bacteria presumably of intestinal origin which give rise to dysentery and various diarrhœal disturbances. Presumably these bacteria behave in the same manner as the typhoid fever bacillus.

The routine methods of bacteriology at the present time do not permit of a trustworthy determination of the above-mentioned pathogenic bacteria. It is true that in some instances such have been isolated from water but the process is a difficult one and negative results are of little value. This being the case, modern sanitarians do not attempt to determine the safety of water by searching for these pathogenic organisms. Instead they make tests to determine the presence and abundance of an organism which is commonly found in the intestines of man and warm blooded animals generally known as bacillus coli. This test can be made with a fair degree of reliability and it is much used.

B. Coli as an Index of Contamination. Unpolluted ground waters contain practically no B. coli but in proportion as waters are subject to contamination with excremental substances the numbers of B. coli increase. All surface waters are likely to contain these germs, but in unpolluted sources, such as uninhabited woodland areas, the numbers are very small indeed. Even the broad waters of the Great Lakes contain B. coli in small numbers though very often they are absent from the quantities usually used in the test. Rivers which drain farm lands contain B. coli in larger numbers; streams and fresh waters which receive sewage contain them in still larger numbers. B. coli, therefore, may be fairly regarded as a valuable index of fecal contamination. This is so far true that the U. S. government has established bacteriological standards for drinking water served by interstate carriers which includes a permissible limit for the number of B. coli. As stated by the U. S. Public Health Service, waters in which B. coli are absent from two out of five portions of 10 cc. may be used, but waters in which B. coli is found in three or more out of five 10 cc. portions would be condemned. The dividing line apparently comes at a figure which is about 150 B. coli per liter of water. The whole subject of B. coli in water, the methods of its determination, and the interpretation of its results is one which is now going through a series of evolutionary changes. The reader is therefore referred to current scientific bacteriological literature and especially to the papers which appear in the American Journal of Public Health.

Numbers of Bacteria in Water.　There are two general methods used for determining the numbers of bacteria in water.　By the first method nutrient gelatine is used as the culture medium and the period of incubation is 48 hours at 20° C.　According to the second the media is nutrient agar and the period of incubation is 24 hours at 37° C.　Both of these methods are useful but the gelatine method has been used more than the other.　Neither method gives absolute results; the figures are relative in both cases.

The numbers of bacteria as determined by the gelatine count vary all the way from less than 100 in relatively clean waters to many thousands in waters which are dirty and polluted.　For drinking purposes it is generally considered that the number of bacteria determined by this method should be less than 100 per cc. The numbers of bacteria in streams vary greatly according to the rainfall.　Very heavy rains wash the surface of the ground and increase the numbers of bacteria in the drainage water.　The sewage of cities contains anywhere from a few hundred thousand to several million bacteria per cc.　These bacteria are of many sorts, but most of them are saprophytic in character and in water which contains organic matter, even in small amounts, they are likely to multiply enormously in the course of a day or two.　Hence bacterial counts mean nothing unless the samples are examined immediately after collection.　They also mean little unless the bacteriologist has a knowledge of the character of the waters.

Removal of Bacteria from Water.　The best method of removing bacteria from water is the process of filtration.　There are two general methods in use at the present time, slow sand filtration and mechanical filtration.　In the former process the water is filtered slowly downward through a bed of sand at such a rate that the water above the sand descends ten to twenty feet in the course of a day. By sedimentation within the pores of the sand bed and by the adhesion of the bacteria to the sand grains at or just below the surface of the filter the bacteria are removed from the water.　The process is partly physical, partly biological.　The method is capable of removing upwards of 99 per cent of bacteria from moderately polluted waters and experience has shown that the waters are thereby rendered entirely safe for drinking.

By the mechanical system of filtration the water is first coagulated by the use of chemicals and then filtered rapidly through a small bed of relatively coarse sand at rates which are 20 and 40 times as great as in the case of slow sand filtration. This process is likewise effective in the removal of bacteria. The choice of the two systems depends upon the amount of turbidity and color of the water and upon its hardness and upon various local conditions of an engineering character.

After water has been filtered it must be stored in the dark; otherwise algae and other microscopic organisms are likely to develop and become troublesome.

Bacteria in water may be killed by the use of liquid chlorine, bleaching powder, ozone, and similar substances. These are poisoning processes. The quantities of chemicals used are so small that they may be used with entire safety but it is necessary that the chemicals be thoroughly and quickly mixed with water in order to assure efficient sterilization. These processes are especially valuable in cases of emergency and are not to be regarded as substitutes for filtration. Swimming pools should be disinfected regularly in order to prevent the transfer of pathogenic bacteria from person to person.

Sewage may be treated in various ways to remove bacteria and other objectionable substances. The processes used are screening, sedimentation, chemical precipitation, intermittent sand filtration, contact beds, trickling filters, and disinfection. There are many biological problems involved in these processes and especially in intermittent sand filters and trickling filters. Bacteria play an important part in the disintegration and ultimate absorption of putrescible organic matter while in trickling filters worms and various larvae assist in the process.

Tastes and Odors in Water Supplies. Water supplies derived from surface sources and stored in reservoirs frequently develop tastes and odors that are very unpleasant. These are largely due to the growth of algae and other microscopic organisms. The matter is one of very considerable importance to waterworks superintendents, and much attention has been given to the study of these growths during recent years. This study has resulted in success-ful measures for destroying the organisms by the use of chemicals and for removing the organisms and the odors produced by them by aëration and filtration. Very little success, however, has been achieved in preventing the organisms from growing.

Chemically pure water is free from taste and odor. Water con-taining certain substances, as for example sugar or salt, may have a decided taste but no odor. On the other hand water may con-tain substances, like vanilla, that have a strong odor but no taste. The two senses, though distinct, are closely related to each other. Most of the bad tastes observed in drinking waters are due to organisms that produce odors rather than tastes.

Most surface waters contain some organic matter and have a vegetable or earthy odor. When decomposing organic matter is present the odors may be foul and disagreeable. These odors may be classified in three general groups: — (1) those caused by organic matter other than living organisms; (2) those caused by the de-composition of organic matter; and (3) those caused by living organisms.

Observation of Odor. The odor of cold water is best observed by shaking a partly filled bottle of the water and immediately remov-ing the stopper and applying the nose. The odor of hot water is ob-tained by heating a portion of it in a tall beaker covered with a watch glass to a point just short of boiling. When sufficiently cooled the cover is slipped aside and the observation quickly made. The intensity of odors is commonly indicated by numbers as follows: — 0, no odor; 1, a very faint odor that would not be ordinarily de-tected by a person drinking the water; 2, a faint odor that might be detected by the consumer but that would not attract any spe-cial attention; 3, a distinct odor that would be readily detected; 4, a decided odor, strong enough to make the water unpalatable; 5, a very strong odor that would make the water unfit for use. The character of the odor is usually indicated by a letter which stands for a descriptive adjective. For purposes of record the two are combined. Thus 3f indicates a distinct fishy odor; 2v, a faint vegetable odor; 4m, a decided moldy odor. Heating usually intensifies an odor.   In water analysis it is common to report the odor of both hot and cold water.

Cause of Odors.   The odors are caused by aromatic oils that are produced during the growth of the microscopic organisms.   After disintegration the oily substances are scattered through the water. In many instances the oils are characteristic of the organisms and the presence of organisms in water can sometimes be determined merely by the odor.   They cannot always be thus recognized, however, for the quality of an odor changes with its intensity.   Certain organisms present in small numbers impart to the water an odor that might be termed aromatic, but when the same organisms are present in larger numbers the odor might be more properly described as fishy.   The amount of oily matter required to produce a noticeable odor is very small.   The oily substance that gives *Synura* its odor is recognizable when diluted to the extent of one part in twenty-five million parts of water.   This is not surprising, however, as the oil of peppermint can be recognized in a dilution of one part in fifty million parts of water.   The odors of organisms are intensified by heating, by mechanical agitation, by a change in the density of the water, by pressure, and by any other cause that tends to rupture the cell walls and liberate the oil globules.

The following table gives the natural odor of a number of the common microscopic organisms.   For convenience they may be grouped around three general terms, aromatic, grassy, and fishy. The aromatic odors are due chiefly to diatoms, one of the strongest being that produced by *Asterionella*.   Some of the green algae produce sweetish, grassy odors, and this is even more true of the blue-green algae.   *Anabaena* produce an odor that varies greatly according to its dilution, and various epithets have been applied to it.   The fishy odors are the most disagreeable of any observed in drinking water, and that produced by *Uroglena* is perhaps the worst. The water that contains this organism in large numbers may have an odor resembling that of cod liver oil.   The odor of *Synura* is almost as bad and even more common.   When organisms decay moldy or musty odors may be produced.   But these odors of decomposition are less characteristic than the odors of growth.   Some of the blue-green algae have odors suggestive of the pig pen, doubt-less because of their high nitrogen content.

Group	Organism	Natural Odor
AROMATIC ODOR	DIATOMACEAE	
	Asterionella	Aromatic — geranium — fishy
	Cyclotella	Faintly aromatic
	Diatoma	Faintly aromatic
	Meridion	Aromatic
	Tabellaria	Aromatic.
	PROTOZOA	
	Cryptomonas	Candied violets
	Mallomonas	Aromatic — violets — fishy
GRASSY ODOR	CYANOPHYCEAE	
	Anabaena	Grassy and moldy — green-corn — nas-turtiums, etc.
	Rivularia	Grassy and moldy
	Clathrocystis	Sweet, grassy
	Coelosphaerium	Sweet, grassy
	Aphanizomenon	Grassy
FISHY ODOR	CHLOROPHYCEAE	
	Volvox	Fishy
	Eudorina	Faintly fishy
	Pandorina	Faintly fishy
	Dictyosphaerium	Faintly fishy
	PROTOZOA	
	Uroglena	Fishy and oily
	Synura	Ripe cucumbers — bitter and spicy taste
	Dinobryon	Fishy, like rockweed
	Bursaria	Irish moss — salt marsh — fishy
	Peridinium	Fishy, like clam-shells
	Glenodinium	Fishy

Prevention of Growths of Algae. Various means have been used to prevent the growth of algae in reservoirs and standpipes. Some of these, such as the exclusion of sunlight, are snccessful but most of them afford only a partial remedy.

Soil Stripping of Reservoir Sites. The removal of the vegetation and top-soil from the ground that forms the floor of a reservoir tends to reduce the amount of the organic and mineral matter available for the food supply of the organisms and thus tends to diminish their number. In a number of instances, notably the reservoirs that supply the city of Boston, the soil has been carefully removed from the reservoir sites before the reservoirs were filled. This has tended to reduce the growths of algae during the first few years after construction, but it has been found t at the effect of this "soil stripping" is not always permanently successful and that in the course of a few years heavy growths of organisms have sometimes occurred. Where the reservoir sites are not thus cleaned growths of algae are likely to be heavy during the first few years after construction, diminishing, however, with time. The benefits from soil stripping occur chiefly during the first few years after construction. Whether or not there is economy in removing the soil from the bottom of the reservoir depends upon local conditions. Often it is advisable. In some cases it will be found cheaper not to strip the reservoir bottom but to apply the money that would be thus expended towards a filter plant.

Swamp Drainage. The presence of swamps on a catchment area tends to foster the growth of algae and similar organisms. If these are located above a reservoir they may seed the reservoir and thus increase the number of organisms likely to be found there. The quality of the water may be improved in some instances by draining the swamps, thus diminishing the chances of the reservoir becoming seeded and decreasing the amount of organic food supply in the water. When reservoirs are constructed it not infrequently happens that pools are left with no outlet. Organisms may develop rapidly in such pools and be washed into the reservoir after a rain. So far as possible reservoirs should be self-draining.

Elimination of Shallow Flowage. In the construction of reservoirs efforts should be made to reduce the area over which the water stands with a depth of less than ten feet. For in these areas of shallow flowage aquatic plants are likely to become seated and may serve as a nidus for various organisms that ultimately become scattered through the reservoir and give trouble. Cases occur where it is wise to strip the soil from the areas of shallow flowage without attempting to strip the soil from the entire reservoir bottom.

Prevention of Pollution. Like other plants the algae in water grow best when fertilized. Nitrogen, potash, phosphates, and similar substances stimulate their growth. Polluted waters are, therefore, more likely to develop objectional growths of algae than the same waters unpolluted. The elimination of pollution from a catchment area is desirable not only for sanitary reasons but also for lessening the growths of algae.

Aëration. One of the elements of food supply required by algae is carbonic acid, which is present to some extent in all surface waters but is likely to be especially abundant in swampy and polluted waters, and wherever organic matter is undergoing decay. The stagnant water at the bottom of a reservoir, for example, usually contains large amounts of carbonic acid. The amounts of carbonic acid may be considerably in excess of saturation, so that when the water is exposed to the air the gas escapes. Thus the process of aëration tends to reduce the likelihood of the occurrence of heavy growths of algae. Aëration also tends to reduce the odors of the water as the exposure of the water to the air gives opportunity for the escape or volatilization of the essential oils. Sometimes natural conditions of aëration exist and are very beneficial, when water flows rapidly over the rocky bed of a stream.

Chemical Treatment. With our present knowledge little can be done in the way of treating the water chemically to prevent the growth of algae. It is possible that the application of lime to reduce the free carbonic acid in the water would be of some benefit but this has never been practically used. Chemical treatment has been successful in destroying organisms as referred to below.

Exclusion of Light. The exclusion of light from a reservoir is an effective remedy in preventing the growth of algae. This cannot be done in large reservoirs but in small reservoirs and in standpipes it has proved very successful. In cases where ground water that contained large amounts of plant food has been exposed in open reservoirs algae growths have been very troublesome, and it has been found that covering the reservoir or standpipe in which the water is stored completely prevents the trouble. It has become an axiom, therefore, among waterworks men that ground waters should not be stored in the light.

Methods of Killing Algae. Various methods have been suggested for killing algae in reservoirs, such as copper sulphate, bleaching powder, ozone, and creosote. Of these copper sulphate has proved to be by far the most effective. Quantities as small as one part in one million by weight, and sometimes even smaller quantities, have been found sufficient to destroy the algae. The amount required depends upon the kind of organisms present, and the amount and character of the other organic matter. Copper sulphate is applied to a reservoir by putting crystals of the salt in a gunnysack, or coarse bag, and dragging it around the reservoir after a boat, letting it dissolve in the water as it will. Preferably this should be done while the wind is blowing, and when the water is in a state of some agitation, so as to obtain a rapid dissemination of the solution through the water of the reservoir. Unless care is exercised in this regard there is danger that fish may be killed, and in any case there is always danger that some fish may be killed. The method, therefore, is one that should not be used by one whose experience and judgment is insufficient.

The copper sulphate treatment is not always entirely successful. Sometimes after one kind of an organism has been destroyed by its use some other organism will appear and be more troublesome than the first. A single treatment of a reservoir with copper sulphate therefore does not always suffice, and when a second dose is required it is usually necessary to use larger quantities than the first time.

Purification of Water Containing Algae. Water that contains algae may be purified by filtration, though the ordinary processes may require some modification, depending upon the number and character of the organisms present. One of the essential elements of successful filtration is that the water shall always contain a sufficient quantity of oxygen throughout the process. Aëration, therefore, may be necessary before or after filtration or both. It may be accomplished by spraying the water into the air so that it falls in drops, or by exposing it in thin films as it passes over a weir with a considerable fall through the air. Generally speaking an exposure from one to two seconds is necessary and sufficient.

As an illustration of successful purification of a water heavily laden with algae may be mentioned the old Ludlow supply of Springfield, Massachusetts, which during the summer contained very heavy growths of *Anabaena*. The method employed was intermittent sand filtration, similar to that commonly used for the treatment of sewage. The water was first aërated and allowed to spread over the sand filter, which was built without cover as it was used only during warm weather. After rapid percolation through the sand it was collected in well ventilated under-drains. After the water had passed through the sand the beds were allowed to stand exposed to the air so that they themselves became well aërated. This method almost completely did away with the obnoxious odors that had previously existed in the water supply of the city. In this instance the part played by aëration was very important as experiments had shown that the water could not have been filtered satisfactorily by the ordinary processes of slow sand filtration.

Mechanical filtration is also sometimes employed for the treatment of algae laden water. Used in connection with aëration this method may prove reasonably satisfactory, but special care must be given to maintaining conditions of aëration throughout the process. Sand filters are capable of satisfactorily removing the algae and their accompanying tastes and odors if the growths are not too heavy.

The presence of algae in water tends to clog both sand filters and mechanical filters to an unusual extent and increases the loss of head, and, therefore, shortens the period of service and in general increases the cost of filtration. Where water is stored before filtration, or where it passes through settling basins copper sulphate is sometimes used as an auxiliary process antecedent to filtration.

Self-Purification of Streams. Various microscopic organisms play an important part in the self-purification of streams. It has long been known that rivers polluted by sewage and other waste substances regain their purity to a considerable extent during their subsequent flow. Various influences combine to bring about this result, such as the natural death of pathogenic bacteria in an unfavorable environment, the effect of sunlight, sedimentation of suspended matter, oxidation of organic matter brought about with the assistance of bacteria, and, what is of interest here, by the effect of microscopic organisms. The cycle of changes by which nitrogenous matter is broken down by bacterial action and by which the bacteria are destroyed by protozoa and other larger organisms, the protozoa being devoured by rotifers and crustacea, and these in turn being devoured by fish, is a biological phenomenon of great practical importance. In this way natural streams succeed in cleansing themselves so that waters once foul become clear and attractive in appearance.

An excellent illustration of these biological changes is the Genesee river below the city of Rochester. This river now receives practically all of the sewage of the city at a point about six miles distant from Lake Ontario. Below this point the river receives few accessions. Studies made during the summer of 1912 showed that the effect of the discharge of the sewage into the river was to increase the number of bacteria and reduce the number of green algae. Immediately below the sewer there was a further increase in bacteria and a reduction of the dissolved oxygen in the water. A mile or two down stream the bacteria began to decrease and protozoa increased. At the mouth of the river the rotifers disappeared but crustacea were found in abundance in the lake water around the river mouth. Beyond one-quarter of a mile from the river mouth, however, the crustacea also showed a noticeable decrease. The chemical changes that accompanied these biological conditions were equally interesting. Below the entrance of the sewage the dissolved oxygen in the water almost disappeared but later increased. As the dissolved oxygen decreased the carbonic acid in the water increased. At the river mouth there was an under run of the lake water back into the river due to the lower temperature of the water in the lake.

Algae also assist in self purification of streams and lakes by liberating dissolved oxygen. Sometimes the growth of algae is so rapid and the quantity of oxygen produced is so large that supersaturation occurs. This commonly takes place in lakes in the region of the thermocline, as Birge and Juday have well shown. How great a factor this oxygen production may be is probably not yet realized by sanitarians to its full extent.

Microscopic organisms in streams are also useful in removing the effects of pollution by manufacturing wastes. On the other hand some kinds of trade wastes are of such a character that they tend to destroy microscopic life; such are acid or strongly alkaline wastes, and wastes containing arsenic, copper, and other poisonous substances. Even the wastes containing inert suspended matter may interfere with microscopic life along the shores by smothering the tiny vegetable and animal cells. Oily wastes, such as the wastes from gas works, may produce films upon the surface of a stream; they then interfere with the absorption of oxygen by the water from the air and thus exert a prejudicial influence on the natural agencies of purification. It is for these reasons that the discharge of trade wastes into streams is a matter that is seriously in need of regulation. The wastes from manufacturing establishments are often more objectionable even than domestic sewage. Perhaps the worst conditions arise when streams are polluted both with domestic sewage and with trade wastes.

Identification of the Source of Water. Another practical application of the microscopical examination of water is that of determining the origin of certain waters. One of the studies made in connection with the celebrated Chicago drainage canal case was a series of microscopical examinations of water from Lake Michigan down the Illinois and Mississippi rivers to St. Louis. It was found that certain varieties of organisms were present in the water of Lake Michigan that could not be found in any of the tributary streams, and the argument was made that as these same organisms were found in the water supply of St. Louis taken from the Mississippi river they must have been derived from Lake Michigan, showing that some of the water supplied to St. Louis came from Lake Michigan through the Chicago drainage canal and the rivers mentioned.

The studies made at Rochester in 1912 showed that the water near the surface of Lake Ontario contained various microscopic organisms that could be readily identified but that these were absent from the lower strata. Serial studies made at the shore of the lake sometimes showed the presence of these organisms but at certain times they were absent. The inference was that on these days the water at the shore was that which had been drawn shoreward from the deep strata. This finding corroborated the temperature observations and the wind records, and proved that the effect of a strong off-shore wind was to blow the surface water away from the shore and draw in the cold deep water from the lake.

Ground waters normally do not contain microscopic organisms, and when these are found in ground waters a natural inference is that a ground water has been contaminated with surface water. Thus the microscopical examination of ground water is sometimes useful in determining questions of pollution.

Organisms in Pipes of Water Systems. When surface water which contains algae and other microscopic organisms is allowed to flow through pipes, as in the distribution systems of public water supplies, it frequently happens that the pipes become more or less choked with what is popularly called pipe-moss. Sometimes this pipe-moss acquires a thickness of several inches and forms a mat upon the inside of the pipes which materially reduces their carrying capacity. The organisms which give trouble of this character are chiefly the Polyzoa, *Plumatella*, *Paludicella*, and *Pectinatella*. Fresh-water sponges are also found in pipes and masonry aqueducts. Snails, worms, and various crustacea may be found associated with these moss growths. Dr. Thresh of London has described the occurrence of fresh-water mussels in a thirty-six inch pipe which attained such a growth that the bore was reduced to nine inches.

It is evident that the pipe dwelling organisms depend upon the plankton for their food supply. The above-mentioned growths do not occur in pipes which carry water which has been filtered or ground water, which contains no microscopic organisms.

There is another organism sometimes found in ground waters which contain salts of iron and magnesia, namely *Crenothrix*. There are three distinct varieties of this organism. One of these deposits manganese in its gelatinous sheath, another deposits iron, while the other deposits alumina. All of them grow best in waters somewhat deficient in dissolved oxygen. *Crenothrix* grows on the walls of the pipes in tufts of filaments. The filaments become attached and are found in the water discharged from the faucets. The iron which impregnates the gelatinous sheaths that surround the cells causes trouble in laundries. Clothes washed in such water acquire rusty stains difficult to remove. *Crenothrix* is sometimes found associated with the pipe-moss above mentioned.

Pipe-moss may be removed from a distribution system of a water supply by flushing, but the best practice is to prevent the growths from forming by using filtered water instead of water laden with plankton.

Plankton and Fish Life. The occurrence of plankton in natural waters has a definite and direct bearing upon the occurrence of fish life. Algae and protozoa and such organisms play an important part in the cycle of changes which extend from the decomposition of organic matter by bacteria to the food supply of man. This cycle may be followed through the several elements of organic matter, namely, nitrogen, carbon, sulphur, and phosphorus. The proteid products of metabolism are consumed by bacteria; bacteria are eaten by protozoa and the nitrate formed by bacterial action in the presence of oxygen is utilized as food by algae; algae and protozoa are consumed by rotifers and crustacea and these latter form the basis of the food of many fish. Some fish are provided with special mechanisms for straining the plankton from the water, a notable instance of this being the menhaden, a salt-water fish which swims with its mouth open. The water enters through the mouth and passes out through the gills, while the organisms that are thus removed are carried to the stomach. The late Professor Peck showed by experiments at Woods Hole that the abundance and size of the menhaden are closely related to the abundance of plankton. Similarly oysters have been shown to be dependent upon the occurrence of diatoms in the waters which flow over the oyster beds. Experiments made by the writer in the Great South Bay, Long Island, showed that the best oyster beds were located near mud flats where diatom life abounded.

Intimately connected with the occurrence of the plankton and the bacteria associated with decomposition of organic matter is the presence or absence of dissolved oxygen and carbonic acid in the water of lakes at different depths, and fluctuations in the occurrence of these gases profoundly affect fish life. If the amount of organic matter at the bottom of a lake or pond is large the water below the thermocline may lose most of its oxygen during periods of stagnation. It is impossible for fish to live under such conditions, so that lakes and ponds which undergo stagnation are not likely to contain such fish as naturally seek the colder water found only at great depths during the summer. Thus it is seen that plankton studies and determinations of the amount of oxygen and carbonic acid in stagnation may be a valuable guide to a fish commission in determining the advisability of stocking certain lakes with certain fish. The study of limnology is a matter of great practical importance to the human race.

INDEX

All technical terms and all scientific names are included, but only major references to each are given. Important cross references are grouped together after other entries under a given term. All figures refer to text pages.

Specific names are printed in italics and follow in alphabetic order the name of the genus to which the species belong; the generic name is printed in italics only when it occurs exclusively in a binomial combination and no reference is made to the genus alone.